CHINESE CHARACTER INDEXES
VOLUME 2: Romanization Index

VOLUME 2

Romanization Index

CHINESE CHARACTER INDEXES

By Ching-yi Dougherty

Sydney M. Lamb and Samuel E. Martin

UNIVERSITY OF CALIFORNIA PRESS

Berkeley and Los Angeles 1963

University of California Press
Berkeley and Los Angeles, California

Cambridge University Press
London, England

©1963 by The Regents of the University of California

Library of Congress Catalog Card Number: 63-12210

Printed in the United States of America

ROM	RAD	TEL	TOT	FC	MAT	OSH	TAG	CR	CHAR
A	030,08	0759.0A	11	61020	0002	3047	(INTERJ.),AH		
AR	030,10	084A	13	61047		6424	AH (EXCLAMATORY PART.)		
AA	030,08	0759.0B	11	61020	0002	3047	(INTERJ. FOR SURPRISE)		
AH	167,08	0026	16	81120		3046	ACTINIUM		
AH	170,05	7093.0A	08	71220	0001	3045	PREFIX IN PROPER NAMES		
.A	030,08	0759	11	61020	0002	3047	(INTERJ.),(FINAL PART.)	K7093	
.A	170,05	7093	08	71220	0001	3045	(INTERJ.),(FINAL PART.)	K0759	
AI	030,06	0755	09	00732	0003	5879	LAMENT		
AI	030,06	0740	09	64040	0020	6520	(INTERJ. EXPRE. REGRET),HULLO	A0780.0A	
AI	030,07	0780.0A	10	63034	0004	5176	(INTERJ. OF REGRET)	A0740	
AI	032,07	1002	10	43134	0005	5174	DUST		
AI	064,07	2179	10	53034	0006	5179	SUFFER (HUNGER),NEXT TO		
AI	119,07	473B	13	93934			ANGSTROM UNIT		
AI	167,09	0028	17	80132			EINSTEINIUM		
AIR	030,04	0714.0A	07	60904		5305	STUPID	3738.0A	
AIR	032,07	1002.0A	10	43134	0005		DUST		
AIR	064,07	2179.0A	10	53034	0006	5179	SUFFER (HUNGER),NEXT TO		
AIR	064,08	2209	11	51014	0025	0178	SUFFER,DAWDLE		
AIR	066,10	8491	14	28140			ABLE(IN ADMINISTRATING)		
AIR	094,10	3738.0A	14	23134	5986		STUPID	0714.0A	
AIR	106,10	4114	15	22618	0024	0573	WHITE(OF SNOW/ETC.)		
AE	030,13	0897	16	62047	0010	6484	(INTERJ. OF DISAPPROVAL)		
AE	111,08	4253	13	82444	0008	9047	SHORT(STATURE)		
AE	140,16	5676	20	44627	0015	4383	FRIENDLY		
AE	158,08	4253.1	15	22244	0008		SHORT		
AE	173,15	7224	23	10627	0016	4384	CLOUDY SKY,FRIENDLY		
AE	187,07	7491	17	73334	0022	5180	FOOLISH,TO TROT		
AY	004,01	0034.0A	02	40000	2934		TO REGULATE		
AY	009,13	0307	15	22247		6486	INDISTINCT/HAZY		
AY	029,08	1947.1	10	20407			LOVE/LIKE		
AY	030,13	0897.0A	16	62047	0010	6484	(INTERJ. OF REGRET)		
AY	032,14	8261	17	44117			DUST/MUD		
AY	038,13	8302	16	42447	0011	6488	YOUR DAUGHTER(HON.)		

啊嘠啊鎄阿啊阿哀哎唉埃挨糇鎄杲埃挨捱歔獃噯噯矮藹躾霭駴乂儍愛噯壒嬡

ROM	RAD	TEL	TOT	FC	MAT	OSH	TAG	CR	CHAR
AY	061,09	1947	13	20247	0009	6482	LOVE/LIKE		愛
AY	072,13	8519	17	62047	0012	6485	OBSCURE/CLANDESTINE		曖
AY	096,13	8842	17	12147		6483	JASPER,PRECIOUS STONE		瓈
AY	112,06	8946	11	10682			OBSTRUCT/HINDER	4344	砈
AY	112,06	0032	11	14640			ASTATINE		砹
AY	112,08	4293	13	16641	0023	3224	HINDER/OBSTRUCT	4344	碍
AY	112,14	4344	19	17681	0023	6033	HINDER/OBSTRUCT	4293	礙
AY	140,02	5337	06	44400	0019	6519	ARTEMISIA VULGARIS,(SURNAME)		艾
AY	167,13	699A	21	82147			IONIUM		鑀
AY	170,04	7084.0A	07	71212	4811	7216	DEFILE/PASS,IN DISTRESS	7137	阨
AY	170,10	7137	13	78217	0018	0716	DEFILE/PASS,IN DISTRESS	7084.0A	隘
AY	173,17	7228	25	12747	0013	6487	CLOUDY/SHADY		靉
AY	184,09	7423	17	86727	0014	4389	SOUR FOOD,MOLDY		餲
AY	195,09	765J	20	26327			ZEZERA HILGENDORF		鯣
AN	038,09	1259	12	48446			UNDECIDED,GIRL IN LOVE		嬡
AN	040,03	1344	06	30404	0026	9025	PEACE/QUIET		安
AN	053,08	1658	11	00216	0033	7451	SMALL BUDDHIST TEMPLE	5482	庵
AN	075,06	0043	10	43944			EUCALYPTUS GLOBULUS		桉
AN	084,06	8637	10	80417		7823	AMMONIA		氨
AN	108,11	4152	16	80107			CONTAINER		盫
AN	140,08	5482	12	44716	0033	7453	SMALL BUDDHIST TEMPLE	1658	菴
AN	140,09	5534	13	44446			SMALL BUDDHIST TEMPLE	5482	荨
AN	149,09	6173	16	00661	0037	1520	BE VERSED IN		諳
AN	177,06	9558	15	30506			SADDLE	7254	鞌
AN	177,06	7254	15	43544	0029	9027	SADDLE		鞍
AN	195,06	764A	17	23344			ANGLER		鮟
AN	196,08	7715	19	47727	0034	4656	QUAIL		鵪
AAN	009,08	0219	10	24216	0030	7447	I(NORTHERN DIALECTS)		俺
AAN	112,06	4277	11	13644			AMMONIUM	6941	硋
AAN	167,06	6941	14	83144		9026	AMMONIUM		銨
ANN	046,05	1489	08	22241	0040	2398	BEACH/BANK		岸
ANN	064,06	2174	09	53044	0027	9028	PRESS DOWN,ACCORDING TO		按
ANN	072,09	2542	13	60061	0036	1521	DARK,SECRET		暗

ROM	RAD	TEL	TOT	FC	MAT	OSH	TAG	CR	CHAR
ANN	075,06	2714	10	30904	0028	5419	TABLE,LAW CASE		案
ANN	094,03	3691	06	41240	2029	2386	JAIL	9320	犴
ANN	130,06	5143	10	73244		9029	AMINE		胺
ANN	140,08	5482.0A	12	44716	0033	7458	LUXURIANT		荨
ANN	153,03	9320	10	21240	2029	2385	JAIL	3691	豻
ANN	169,09	7056	16	77601	0038	3472	TO SHUT THE DOOR,UNILLUMINATED		闇
ANN	203,09	7826	21	60361	0039	1524	DEEP BLACK/DARK		黯
ANG	130,04	514A	08	70217			FILTHY	7542	航
ANG	130,08	9131.0A	12	74216	7383	7449	FILTHY	7542	腌
ANG	188,04	7542	14	70217	0041	7865	FILTHY	514A	骯
ARNG	026,02	0600	04	77720	0044	2146	HIGH,RAISE	2491	卬
ARNG	026,03	0601	05	17120	0044	2114	HIGH,RAISE	0600	印
ARNG	072,04	2491	08	60727	0045	2149	HIGH(PRICE),LIFT(HEAD)		昂
ANQ	108,05	4138	10	50107	0042	0707	BOWL/DISH,ABUNDANT		盎
AU	017,03	0425	05	77770	7268	1974	CONCAVE		凹
AU	032,05	0991	08	44127	7271		A HOLLOW,CAVITY		坳
AU	086,11	3581	15	58334	0059	8797	TO BOIL/STEW		熬
AUR	027,11	0629	13	71248		6367	GRANARY	8373	廒
AUR	030,11	0869	14	68040	0056	6364	LOUD CLAMOR		嗷
AUR	053,11	8373	14	00248	0057	6368	GRANARY	0629	廒
AUR	066,07	2407	11	58240	0054	6363	RAMBLE		敖
AUR	086,11	3581.0A	15	58334	0059	8797	TO BOIL,ENDURE		熬
AUR	094,11	3743	15	58430	0060	5100	MASTIFF		獒
AUR	096,11	3870	15	18140			(MUS. INSTR.)		翱
AUR	124,12	5063	18	27420	0067	3391	SOAR		聱
AUR	128,11	9107	17	58401		2739	DIFFICULT TO PRONOUNCE		螯
AUR	142,11	5837	17	58136	0061	8943	NIPPER,ASTACUS FLUVIATILIS		警
AUR	149,11	9296	18	58601	0062	1170	SLANDER,SOUND OF WEEPING,GREATNESS		遨
AUR	162,11	6683	15	38304	0063	6754	RAMBLE,MAKE EXCURSION		麈
AUR	167,11	6971	19	00109	0052	0383	VIOLENT FIGHTING		鏖
AUR	167,11	9495	19	58109	0064	0382	FLAT IRON COOKING PLATE		鼇
AUR	187,11	7514	21	58327	0065	4716	VICIOUS HORSE,UNDISCIPLINED		鰲
AUR	195,11	7663	22	58336	0066	8782	SEA TURTLE	7840	鰲

ROM	RAD	TEL	TOT	FC	MAT	OSH	TAG	CR	CHAR
AUR	205,11	7840	24	58717	0066	7347	(SEA TURTLE)	7663	鰲
AO	038,10	1264	13	46417	0051	0683	OLD WOMAN		媼
AO	145,04	5984.1	09	32234		5129	SHORT AND LINED COAT OR ROBE		袄
AO	145,13	5984	18	37234	0049	5026	SHORT AND LINED COAT OR ROBE		襖
AW	009,11	0277	13	28240	0055	6366	PROUD/ARROGANT		傲
AW	032,05	0991.0A	08	44127	7271		A HOLLOW,CAVITY		坳
AW	032,13	1078	16	47134			BUILDING-PLOT		墺
AW	037,09	1157	12	10223	0053	2751	HAUGHTY,VIGOROUS		奡
AW	037,10	1159	13	27430	0046	5022	OBSCURE/MYSTERIOUS		奥
AW	046,13	8351	16	27773			PLACE NAME		嶴
AW	061,13	2020	16	97034	0047	5025	TO REGRET		懊
AW	085,13	3421	16	37134	0048	5029	DEEP BAY/COVE,AUSTRALIA	K7144	澳
AW	086,13	3603.0A	17	97834	7688	5028	VERY HOT		燠
AW	140,11	552C	15	44240			STELLARIA MEDIA		薁
AW	170,13	7144	16	77234	0050	5027	DEEP BAY/COVE	K3421	隩
BA	009,02	8020	04	28200			(SURNAME)		仈
BA	012,00	0360	02	80000	4845	6509	EIGHT		八
BA	030,02	0665	05	68000	4825	6511	(ONOMAT.)		叭
BA	030,04	0721.0A	07	67017	4841	7282	DUMB,(ONOMAT.)		吧
BA	046,06	8331	09	22601			PLACE NAME		峇
BA	049,01	1572	04	77717	4826	7280	TO HOPE,(SUFF. FOR CERTAIN NOUNS)		巴
BA	064,02	2091	05	58000	4853	6512	PULL(OUT),TO STRIP,CLIMB		扒
BA	064,07	2193	10	52000	4847	2928	EIGHT(FRAUDPROOF),SPLIT		捌
BA	075,04	2618.0A	08	47917	4830		LOQUAT		杷
BA	096,04	378A	08	17117			COPAL		玸
BA	104,04	4002	09	00117	4832	7297	SCAR		疤
BA	118,04	4576	10	88717	4833	7308	FENCE		笆
BA	119,04	4757	10	97917		7292	TSAMBA(FOOD IN TIBET)		粑
BA	123,04	6271.1	10	87517	4834	7284	CORNED BEEF		羓
BA	140,04	5359	08	44717	4836	7307	BANANA		芭
BA	152,04	6271	11	17217		7294	CORNED BEEF,FEMALE PIG		豝
BAR	064,05	2149	08	53047	4848	6053	PULL OUT OR UP		拔
BAR	140,05	5404	09	44447	5330	6057	BETEL		茇

ROM	RAD	TEL	TOT	FC	MAT	OSH	TAG	CR	CHAR
BAR	140,08	547A	12	44547			SMILAX CHINA		菝
BAR	157,05	6405	12	63147	4849	6051	POSTFACE		跋
BAR	167,05	6876	13	83147	4850	6050	CYMBALS		鈸
BAR	194,05	7610	15	23214	4851	7658	DROUGHT DEMON		魃
BAA	064,04	2116	07	57017	4829	7286	TAKE HOLD OF,(PRETRANSITIVE)		把
BAA	167,04	6867	12	87117	4835	7281	PALLADIUM		鈀
BAA	177,04	7249	13	47517	4837	7285	TARGET		靶
BAH	032,07	8218	10	46180	4843	8097	EMBANKMENT,DAM	1100	坝
BAH	032,20	1100	23	41127	4843	3563	EMBANKMENT,DAM	8218	壩
BAH	064,04	2116.0A	07	57017	4827	7286	HANDLE		把
BAH	075,21	294A	25	41927	4838	3564	HANDLE(ESP. SWORD)		欛
BAH	085,21	3496	24	31127	4844	3565	NAME OF A RIVER		灞
BAH	088,04	3640	08	80717	4831	7309	PA		爸
BAH	094,08	8802	11	46240			DOG WITH SHORT SHINBONE		猈
BAH	122,05	5007.1	10	60731		8843	TO FINISH,QUIT		罢
BAH	122,10	5007	15	60211	4841	7188	TO FINISH,QUIT		罷
BAH	146,13	6011	19	10527	4842	3561	USURP,TYRANT,HEGEMON	7218	覇
BAH	173,13	7218	21	10527	4842	3562	USURP,TYRANT/HEGEMON	6011	霸
.BA	030,04	0721	07	67017	4841	7282	(FINAL PART.)	5007.0A	吧
.BA	096,08	3831.0A	12	11717	4858	7298	(MUS. INSTR.)		琶
.BA	122,05	5007.1A	10	60731		8843	(FINAL PART.)		罢
.BA	122,10	5007.0A	15	60211	4841	7188	(FINAL PART.)	0721	罷
BAI	064,08	221A	12	22550	4867	3337	TO BREAK WITH BOTH HANDS		掰
BAIR	106,00	4101	05	26000	4975	1653	WHITE/PURE,GRATUITOUS		白
BAIR	195,05	762F	16	26300			CUTLER		鮊
BAE	009,05	0130.0A	07	26200		1657	FATHER'S ELDER BROTHER,SENIOR		伯
BAE	009,06	0184	08	21260	4976	1684	HUNDRED(FRAUDPROOF)		佰
BAE	064,04	2116.0B	07	57017	4829	7286	PRETRANSITIVE		把
BAE	064,08	2206	11	56040	4861	2324	TO OPEN,SPREAD OUT		捭
BAE	064,10	2369.1	13	56031			TO DISPLAY,TO PLACE/PUT,PENDULUM		摆
BAE	064,15	2369	18	56011	4864	7190	TO DISPLAY,TO PLACE/PUT,PENDULUM		擺
BAE	075,05	2672	09	46900	4980	1661	CEDAR,CYPRESS,(SURNAME)		柏
BAE	075,06	2672.1	10	41960	4980	1691	CEDAR/CYPRESS		栢

ROM	RAD	TEL	TOT	FC	MAT	OSH	TAG	CR	CHAR
BAE	106,01	4102	06	10600	4976	1682	HUNDRED		百
BAE	117,06	454F	11	01160		1683	HECTOLITER		竡
BAE	119,06	473A	12	91960			HECTOMETER		粨
BAE	145,15	9274	20	36211		7189	HEM AT THE BOTTOM OF GARMENT		襬
BAY	030,07	8142	10	66080	4865	8099	TO CHANT		唄
BAY	064,05	2157	09	21550	4860	2601	TO SALUTE/WORSHIP		拜
BAY	066,07	2408	11	68840	4866	6401	BE DEFEATED,TO DEFEAT		敗
BAY	115,08	4458	13	26940	4862	2329	MILLET/PANICUM CRUS		稗
BAY	119,08	4735	14	96940	4864	2328	POLISHED RICE		粺
BAN	064,04	2104	07	51047	4899	6109	PULL UP OR OUT		扳
BAN	064,10	2289	13	57047	4882	6283	TO SHIFT,TRANSPORT		搬
BAN	067,08	2432	12	11114	4890	0321	VARIEGATED		斑
BAN	096,06	3803	10	11114	4889	0319	CLASS/RANK,(SURNAME)		班
BAN	104,10	4057	15	00147	4883	6284	SCAR		瘢
BAN	130,04	8524	08	78227			TO TAX		朌
BAN	137,04	5301	10	27447	4881	6282	SORT,MANNER		般
BAN	181,04	7317	13	81286	4879	8286	PROMULGATE		頒
BAN	196,04	769D	15	87227	4888		WILD PIGEON		鳻
BAAN	032,04	0978	07	42147	1782	6103	HILLSIDE	7090	坂
BAAN	046,04	8323	07	22747			HILLSIDE	0978	岅
BAAN	072,04	8503	08	62047			GREAT/EXPANSIVE		昄
BAAN	075,04	2647	08	41947	4885	6111	BOARD/PLANK,BOSS	D7078	板
BAAN	091,04	3652	08	21047	4886	6108	PRINTING BLOCK,EDITION		版
BAAN	137,04	9153	10	22447			SAMPAN		舨
BAAN	167,04	687B	12	82147		6104	METAL PLATE		鈑
BAAN	169,09	7078	17	77666		3451	BOSS	B2647	闆
BAAN	170,04	7090	07	71247	1786	6107	HILLSIDE	0978	阪
BAAN	195,04	762C	15	22347	4887		SOLE/FLOUNDER		鮁
BANN	009,05	0133	07	29250	4876	2507	COMRADE		伴
BANN	019,02	6586.1	04	33000	4891		DEAL WITH,MANAGE,DO		办
BANN	024,03	0584	05	90500	4875	2504	HALF		半
BANN	038,05	1214	08	49450			MENSTRUATION		姅
BANN	064,04	2101	07	58027	4878	4294	TO DRESS,DISGUISE		扮

6

ROM	RAD	TEL	TOT	FC	MAT	OSH	TAG	CR	CHAR
BANN	064,05	2142	08	59050	4894	2508	MIX (SALAD)		拌
BANN	064,05	8426	08	59050	4894	2508	MIX (SALAD)	52142	拌
BANN	090,00	3645.0A	04	22200	0672		HALF OF A TREE TRUNK		爿
BANN	097,14	3904	19	00441	4892	2465	PETAL,SECTION		瓣
BANN	120,05	4810	11	29950	4877	2510	TRIP UP OR OVER		絆
BANN	160,09	6586	16	00441	4891	2464	DEAL WITH/MANAGE,DO		辦
BANG	009,10	0266.0B	12	20227	4927	4342	NEAR(APPROACHING)		傍
BANG	050,07	1620.1	10	57227	4914	3991	TO HELP		帮
BANG	050,09	1620.2	12	44227	4914	3992	TO HELP		幇
BANG	050,14	1620	17	44227	4914	3970	TO HELP		幫
BANG	064,07	2158	10	57027	4911		PROPEL A BOAT		掤
BANG	075,07	2735	11	47927	4913	2217	WATCHMAN'S RATTLE		梆
BANG	085,07	3203	10	32181	5042	8023	SMALL RIVER,DITCH		浜
BANG	163,04	6721	07	57027	4910	2216	STATE/COUNTRY		邦
BANG	177,13	727A	22	46527	4921		VAMP OF SHOE		鞤
BAANG	075,10	2831	14	40927	4915	4348	PUBLIC ROLL OF SUCCESSFUL EXAMINEES		榜
BAANG	091,10	3659	14	20027	4917	4344	TABLET/REGISTER		牓
BAANG	120,07	4834	13	27927	4913	2218	BIND/TO TIE		綁
BAANG	130,10	5218	14	70227	4931	4346	UPPER ARM,WING		膀
BANQ	009,10	0266.0A	12	20227	4927	4342	NEAR,NESTLE		傍
BANQ	032,10	8244	13	40127			THE EDGE/BORDER OF A FIELD		塝
BANQ	075,08	2788.0A	12	40961	5360	1246	CLUB(WEAPON)	2761	棓
BANQ	075,08	2761	12	45953	4923	2498	CLUB(WEAPON)	2788.0A	棒
BANQ	096,04	3835	08	15100			(GEM)		玤
BANQ	098,12	8853	17	42717	5047	7941	SQUAT JAR FOR WINE		瓺
BANQ	112,10	4319	15	10627	4917	4340	POUND(WEIGHT),WEIGH,SCALE		磅
BANQ	115,08	8993	13	20961			HOE/SPADE		稖
BANQ	130,10	5218.0B	14	70227			TO FLIRT		膀
BANQ	140,10	5538	14	44227			ARCTIUM LAPPA		蒡
BANQ	142,04	5732	10	55100	4924	2592	OYSTER		蚌
BANQ	149,10	6196	17	00627	4919	4341	TO SLANDER		謗
BANQ	167,10	6967	18	80127	4920	4338	POUND(STERLING)		鎊
BAU	018,08	0475	10	22100	5337	2954	PEEL		剝

ROM	RAD	TEL	TOT	FC	MAT	OSH	TAG	CR	CHAR
BAU	020,00	0540	02	27200	4937	4357	WRAP UP,WRAPPER		
BAU	020,03	0545	05	27712	4937	7259	WRAP UP,CONTRACT(TO OR FOR)		
BAU	039,05	132A	08	17417			SPORE		
BAU	130,05	5165	09	77212	4940	7269	WOMB		
BAU	140,05	5383	09	44712	4941	7279	FLOWER CALYX		
BAU	145,09	5988	15	00732	4951	5889	TO PRAISE	5979	
BAU	145,09	5989	15	00732			TO PRAISE	5988	
BAU	145,11	5979	17	00732	4951	5890	TO PRAISE	5988	
BAU	195,05	7637.0A	16	27312	4944		(SURNAME)		
BAUR	118,08	4613.0A	14	88162	5335	1664	LEAF,SHEET,TINSEL		
BAUR	140,13	5631	17	44142	5326	3269	THIN		
BAUR	173,05	7192	13	10712	5338	7278	HAIL		
BAO	009,07	0202	09	26294	4946	5306	PROTECT,GUARANTEE		
BAO	032,09	1027	12	26104	4947	0219	STRONGHOLD		
BAO	038,09	1258	12	46494			GOVERNESS/NURSE		
BAO	039,07	8006	10	10447		3106	BAD		
BAO	040,05	1405.1	08	30103	4956	0350	TREASURE,PRECIOUS		
BAO	040,17	1405	20	30806	4956	8238	TREASURE,PRECIOUS		
BAO	120,09	4892	15	26994	4950	5308	CLOTH FOR CARRYING BABY ON BACK	5965	
BAO	140,09	5508	13	44294	4949	5309	DENSE FOLIAGE,TO COVER		
BAO	145,09	5965	14	36294	4950	5307	CLOTH FOR CARRYING BABY ON BACK	4892	
BAO	184,05	7394	13	87712	4943	7264	SATIATED		
BAO	196,04	7691	15	27427	4953	4623	PROCURESS,CHINESE BUSTARD		
BAW	009,15	0325	17	26232	4958	5680	ON NIGHT DUTY		
BAW	018,05	0442	07	22700	4942	2964	TO PLANE	6888	
BAW	032,09	1032	12	47447	4955	6098	TO REPORT,TO GAIN REVENGE,NEWSPAPER		
BAW	064,04	1032.1	07	57047			TO REPORT,TO GAIN REVENGE,NEWSPAPER		
BAW	064,05	2128	08	57012	4938	7267	CARRY IN THE ARMS,CHERISH		
BAW	072,11	2552	15	60132	4957	5677	CRUEL,VIOLENT	5718	
BAW	085,15	3462.0A	18	36132	4959	5683	SHOWER(RAIN)		
BAW	086,05	3517.0A	09	97812		7272	SAUTE VERY QUICKLY		
BAW	086,09	356A	13	26339	4948	5622	TO COOK WITH LOW FLAME		
BAW	086,15	3615	19	96832	4960	5681	BURST/EXPLODE		

勹包孢苞褒裒褭鮑箔薄雹保堡媬孯宝寶綵葆褓飽鴇儤刨報报抱暴瀑炮煲爆

ROM	RAD	TEL	TOT	FC	MAT	OSH	TAG	CR	CHAR
BAW	140,08	547B	12	44512	4939	7268	HATCH		菢
BAW	141,10	5718	16	11117	4957	7670	CRUEL/VIOLENT	2552	虣
BAW	153,03	6283	10	27220	4954	4363	LEOPARD		豹
BAW	157,03	6399	10	67120	5332	4360	JUMP/LEAP		趵
BAW	167,05	6888	13	87112	4942	7260	TO PLANE, A PLANE		鉋
BAW	167,15	7004	23	86132		5678	TO PLANE, A PLANE	6888	鑤
BAW	195,05	7637	16	27312	4944	7274	ABALONE		鮑
BEI	024,06	0585	08	26400	4993	2314	BASE/HUMBLE		卑
BEI	053,08	1657.0A	11	00246	5070		LOW,SHORT		庳
BEI	061,08	1896	12	11331	4992	8615	SAD		悲
BEI	064,09	2243	12	51027		3654	CARRY ON ONE'S BACK		揹
BEI	075,04	2637	08	41990	4996	7981	CUP	4131	杯
BEI	075,07	2754	11	41969		1443	CUP	2637	桮
BEI	075,08	8572	12	46940			FAGUS SYLVATICA		椑
BEI	108,04	4131	09	10107	4996	0725	CUP	2637	盃
BEI	112,08	4301	13	16640	4995	2317	STONE TABLET		碑
BEI	130,05	5154.0A	09	11227	4989	3653	TO CARRY ON THE BACK		背
BEEI	021,03	0554	05	11110	4974	7147	NORTH		北
BEY	009,08	0223	10	20261	5000	1242	TIMES(MULTIPLIED INSTANCES)		倍
BEY	009,08	0271.1	10	27264	4997	1818	PREPARE/READY		俻
BEY	009,09	8066	11	21227			STAND BACK-TO-BACK,DISOBEY		俏
BEY	009,10	0271	12	24227	4997	3710	PREPARE,READY		備
BEY	009,13	0306.0A	15	20241		2451	SECLUDED		僻
BEY	038,08	1242.0A	11	46440	4994		MAID-SERVANT		婢
BEY	039,04	1319	07	40407	5023	3129	COMET		孛
BEY	061,07	1883	10	94047	5003	3133	PERVERSE,TO REBEL		悖
BEY	061,12	1994	16	24332	4998	8627	EXHAUSTED		憊
BEY	075,08	2788	12	40961	5360	1246	NUT GALL		棓
BEY	086,08	3538	12	90861	5002	1248	DRY OVER FIRE		焙
BEY	094,07	3709	10	46280	5007	8100	DISTRESSED/WRETCHED		狽
BEY	102,03	0271.2	08	27604			PREPARE/READY		备
BEY	112,08	8951	13	10661			PLACE NAME		碚
BEY	130,05	5154	09	11227	4989	3653	THE BACK,LEARN BY HEART		背

ROM	RAD	TEL	TOT	FC	MAT	OSH	TAG	CR	CHAR
BEY	130,13	5242.0A	17	70227	5107	3631	ARM		臂
BEY	140,10	5563	14	44261	5001	1243	BUD		蓓
BEY	145,05	5926	10	34247	4999	6237	GUILT,(EXPRE. PASSIVE)		被
BEY	145,09	5967	14	31227	4990	3655	PAPER OR CLOTH PASTED TOGETHER		褙
BEY	154,00	6296	07	60800	5005	8096	COWRY/SHELL		貝
BEY	159,08	6543	15	11506	4991	2666	GENERATION,CONTEMPORARIES		輩
BEY	162,13	6699.0A	17	30304	5108	6647	AVOID/HIDE		避
BEY	163,05	6731	08	17127	5156	2252	NAME OF A FEUDAL STATE		邶
BEY	167,07	9468	15	86180		8098	BARIUM		鋇
BEY	177,10	7272	19	44527		3711	PISTON		鞲
BEY	182,08	9588	17	76218			TYPHOON,CYCLONE		颮
BEN	009,08	8055	10	24244			NAME OF A YUAN DYNASTY GENERAL		倴
BEN	037,06	1149	09	40444	5028	2820	HURRY,ELOPE	8786	奔
BEN	093,08	8786	12	50550		2515	TO HURRY,ELOPE	1149	犇
BEN	154,05	6321.0A	12	40806	5027	8180	ENERGETIC		賁
BEEN	075,01	2609	05	50230	5025	5420	ORIGIN,OWN,COPY(AN.)		本
BEEN	102,05	3962	10	23603	5032	1796	HOD,BASKET		畚
BEEN	140,05	0058	09	44234		5427	BENZENE		苯
BENN	032,04	0979	07	80104	5033	0209	DUST,BRING TOGETHER		坌
BENN	037,06	1149.0A	09	40444		2820	GO TO,TOWARDS	8786.0A	奔
BENN	093,08	8786.0A	12	50550		2515	GO TO,TOWARDS	1149.0A	犇
BENN	118,05	4570	11	88234	5026	5428	STUPID/CLUMSY		笨
BENG	009,05	0137	07	21249	5037	2422	TO CAUSE		伻
BENG	046,08	1514	11	22227	5038	3570	COLLAPSE		崩
BENG	057,08	1731	11	17220	5039		STRETCH,FULL		弸
BENG	113,04	4366	08	30227			SIDE ALTAR INSIDE ANCESTRAL TEMPLE		祊
BENG	120,08	4855	14	27920	5041	3569	TO TIE,BIND,TO STRETCH TAUT	4890	絣
BENG	120,11	4890	17	22927	5041	3573	TO TIE/BIND,TO STRETCH/TAUT	4855	繃
BENG	142,04	5732.0A	10	55100	4924	2592	OYSTER		蚌
BERNG	101,04	8005	09	10227	5047	3714	NEED NOT		甭
BEENG	096,08	3833	12	15153			GEM ORNAMENT OF SCABBARD	9559	琫
BEENG	120,11	4890.0A	17	22927	5041	3573	TO HAVE A TAUT FACE		繃
BEENG	140,08	9175	12	44503		2500	EXPAND,THICK WEEDS		菶

ROM	RAD	TEL	TOT	FC	MAT	OSH	TAG	CR	CHAR
BEENG	177,08	9559	17	40501			GEM ORNAMENT OF SCABBARD	3833	鞆
BENQ	032,08	8229	11	47120			TO COVER WITH EARTH		堋
BENQ	064,10	2277	13	50027		4345	BOAT,TO WHIP		搒
BENQ	112,10	4319.0A	15	10627	4917	4340	WEIGH,SCALE		磅
BENQ	157,11	6498	18	62127		3571	TO JUMP/BOUNCE		蹦
BENQ	162,06	6618	10	38304	5045	6674	TO CRACK/SPLIT		迸
BI	009,09	0257	11	21268	5134	1753	COMPEL,CLOSE TO	6656	偪
BI	030,04	0070	07	61010			PYRENE		吡
BI	044,05	8317	08	77282	5075	6516	VULVA		屄
BI	162,09	6656	13	31306	5134	6634	COMPEL,CLOSE TO	0257	逼
BYI	140,07	5428	11	44407	5135	3139	WATER CHESTNUT		荸
BYI	207,08	7853	21	44406	5074	2334	WAR DRUM		鼙
BYI	209,00	7865	14	26446	5100	2755	NOSE		鼻
BII	021,00	0552	02	21710	5076	7080	LADLE,DAGGER		匕
BII	032,13	1084.0A	16	70104		0202	NEXT DOOR		壁
BII	038,04	1183	07	41410	5082	7091	DECEASED MOTHER		妣
BII	060,05	1764	08	24247	5093	6236	THAT,HE		彼
BII	081,00	3024	04	21710	5077	7081	COMPARE		比
BII	104,02	8861	07	00114		7156	FACIAL SKIN DISEASE,MANGE		疕
BII	115,04	4431	09	21910		7088	GRAIN NOT FULLY GROWN,HUSKS	4718	秕
BII	118,04	4581.1	10	88714	5130	7395	BRUSH/PEN		笔
BII	118,06	4581	12	88507	5130	2627	BRUSH/PEN		筆
BII	119,04	4718	10	91910	5084	7087	GRAIN NOT FULLY GROWN,HUSKS	4431	粃
BII	163,11	6766.0A	14	67627	5095	2185	LOW/MEAN		鄙
BIH	009,08	0220	10	26240	5069	2319	TO CAUSE,SO THAT		俾
BIH	024,04	3968.1	06	21401			TO FINISH,THE WHOLE OF		毕
BIH	030,11	0874	14	66054	5121	2615	(PHONETIC)		嗶
BIH	032,08	1020.0A	11	46140		2315	LOWLAND		埤
BIH	032,13	1084	16	70104	5113	0202	WALL		壁
BIH	037,15	8271	18	60436			TO HATE/BE INDIGNANT		奰
BIH	038,08	1242	11	46440	4994	2330	MAIO-SERVANT		婢
BIH	038,13	1295	16	70404	5106	9031	FAVORITE		嬖
BIH	050,01	1618.1	04	20227			CURRENCY		币

ROM	RAD	TEL	TOT	FC	MAT	OSH	TAG	CR	CHAR
BIH	050,12	1618	15	98227	5103	3999	CURRENCY		幣
BIH	053,04	1642	07	00211	5083	7092	TO COVER,PROTECT		庇
BIH	053,08	1657	11	00246	5070	2331	LOW-BUILT HOUSE		庳
BIH	055,12	1705	15	98444	5102	2808	FRAUD,DETRIMENT		弊
BIH	057,09	1732	12	17227	5127	4733	ASSIST		弼
BIH	061,01	1801	05	33000	5109	8705	NECESSARILY/MUST		必
BIH	061,05	8391	08	93000			RUDE,FRIVOLOUS		怭
BIH	061,09	1939	12	91066		1752	SINCERE,MELANCHOLY		愊
BIH	061,09	1941	12	98047	5129	6413	OBSTINATE		愎
BIH	066,06	2426.1	10	21212			DIE VIOLENTLY		毖
BIH	066,08	2411	12	98240	5101	6356	POOR,RUINED,MY(POLITE)		敝
BIH	066,14	2426	18	98212	5105	7152	DIE VIOLENTLY	3745	斃
BIH	075,05	8547	09	43900			WEAPON HANDLE OF BAMBOO STRIPS		柲
BIH	075,07	2755	11	41914	5079		STOCKADE		椑
BIH	075,09	2798	13	41966		1757	OX YOKE PLACED ON THE HORNS		楅
BIH	081,00	3024.0A	04	21710	5077	7081	BE NEAR,ASSOCIATE WITH		比
BIH	081,05	3025	09	21331	5086	8714	CAREFUL,PREVENT		毖
BIH	085,05	3125	08	33100	5087	8710	SECRETE/POUR OFF		泌
BIH	085,09	8696	12	31166	5132	1760	PUBLIC BATHHOUSE		湢
BIH	086,09	3567	13	91866	5133		TO DRY BY FIRE		煏
BIH	094,07	3705	10	41214	5080	0235	(TAPIR)		猦
BIH	094,12	3745	16	98430		5099	DIE VIOLENTLY	2426	獘
BIH	096,05	3792	09	13100	5111	8706	GEM ON SCABBARD		琕
BIH	096,13	3880	18	70103	5115	0352	PIECE OF JADE WITH HOLE IN CENTER		璧
BIH	102,03	3952	08	60221	5096	2753	GIVE TO,CONFER ON		畀
BIH	102,06	3968	11	60504	5120	2613	TO FINISH,THE WHOLE OF		畢
BIH	104,08	4036	13	00146	5097	2332	PARALYSIS		痹
BIH	109,08	4211	13	66040	5163	2318	LOOK ASKANCE		睥
BIH	112,09	4310	14	16601	5128	1111	BLUE-GREEN,JADE		碧
BIH	113,05	4365.0A	09	33200	5088	8709	SECRET		祕
BIH	113,08	4386	12	36240			ERRATUM OF 5947		褳
BIH	115,05	4434.0A	10	23900	5088	8708	SECRET		秘
BIH	118,10	4653	16	88711	5090	7130	FINE COMB		篦

ROM	RAD	TEL	TOT	FC	MAT	OSH	TAG	CR	CHAR
BIH	118,11	4656	17	88504	5122	2618	WICKER		篳
BIH	130,13	5242	17	70227	5107	3631	ARM		臂
BIH	140,05	5396	09	44330	5112	8713	FRAGRANT,(PHONETIC)		苾
BIH	140,08	5489	12	44406	5071	2333	CASTOR SEED	5557	蓖
BIH	140,08	5557	12	44711			CASTOR SEED	5489	蓖
BIH	140,11	5598	15	44504	5123	2617	PULSE,BEAN		蓽
BIH	140,12	5599	16	44248	5104	6360	TO SCREEN/CONCEAL		蔽
BIH	140,13	5643	17	44641		2456	FICUS PUMILA		薛
BIH	142,11	583C	17	56154			PSILOMASTAX MACTATOR		蠷
BIH	145,08	5947	13	36240	5072	2320	TO AID,ADVANTAGEOUS		裨
BIH	145,13	9268	19	70732	5118	5815	FOLDS,PLEATS		襞
BIH	148,09	6048	16	53227	5136		FEVER,TARTAR HORN		觱
BIH	149,05	6098	12	04647	5147	6235	FLATTER,A HALF-TRUTH		詖
BIH	154,05	6321	12	40806	5027	8180	BRIGHT		賁
BIH	154,14	6369	21	60886	5168	8101	ABLE TO SUPPORT GREAT WEIGHT		贔
BIH	157,05	6414.0A	12	64147	5317	6232	RECLINE,LEANING TOWARD		跛
BIH	157,11	6462	18	66154	5124	2614	TO CLEAR STREETS WHEN EMPEROR TOURS		蹕
BIH	157,13	6482	20	70801	5119	5984	LAME,BOTH FEET CRIPPLED		躄
BIH	160,06	6582	13	70641	5172	2449	MONARCH,ROYAL		辟
BIH	162,13	6699	17	30304	5108	6647	AVOID/HIDE		避
BIH	163,05	6727	08	37027		2261	ANCIENT PLACE NAME,(SURNAME)		邲
BIH	163,11	6766	14	67627	5095	2185	LOW/MEAN		鄙
BIH	167,05	6940	13	83100		8707	BISMUTH		鉍
BIH	169,03	7028	11	77247	5092	3487	TO CLOSE/STOP UP		閉
BIH	169,05	7038	13	77337	5089	3537	HIDE,HIDDEN		閟
BIH	170,07	7103	10	71214	5081	0232	STEPS(TO THE THRONE)		陛
BIH	177,11	9561	20	46554			LEATHER SHIN GUARD		韠
BIH	178,11	7293	20	46554	5125	2616	KNEEPAD		韠
BIH	184,05	7396	13	83700			FRAGRANCE OF FOOD		飶
BIH	186,05	7452	14	23600			FRAGRANCE		馝
BIH	187,05	7473	15	73300			STRONG HORSE		馝
BIH	188,08	7549	18	76240	5073	2327	BUTTOCKS,THIGH		髀
BIH	195,09	765K	20	21366			LEIOGNATHUS ARGENTEUM		鰏

ROM	RAD	TEL	TOT	FC	MAT	OSH	TAG	CR	CHAR
BIH	196,05	770B	16	37027			WILLOW-WARBLE/PHYLLOSCOPUS		
BIH	196,08	771D	19	27427			BROWN-EARED BULBUL		
BIH	196,12	7749	23	98327		4685	PHASIANUS PICTUS		
BIAN	112,05	4269	10	12637	5236	6592	ACUPUNCTURE		
BIAN	118,09	4629	15	88246	5225		BAMBOO SEDAN CHAIR		
BIAN	118,19	4710	25	88302	5244	6713	BASKET FOR FRUITS		
BIAN	120,09	4882	15	23927	5231	3787	TO PLAIT,COMPILE		
BIAN	142,09	5796	15	53127	5232	3789	BAT		
BIAN	162,02	6708.1	06	34302	5243	6719	SIDE		
BIAN	162,15	6708	19	36302	5243	6712	SIDE		
BIAN	177,09	7267	18	41546	5227	6578	WHIP		
BIAN	195,09	7653	20	23327	5234	3788	BREAM		
BEAN	023,09	0573	11	71712	5229	0810	TABLET		
BEAN	063,05	2078	09	30227	5228	3778	FLAT		
BEAN	116,05	4506	10	30307	5236A	6596	PUT A COFFIN IN GRAVE		
BEAN	140,14	565C	18	44927	5235		FLAT-PODDED BEAN		
BEAN	142,09	5796.0A	15	53127	5232	3789	BAT		
BEAN	145,09	5959	14	33227	5233	3783	NARROW,URGENT		
BEAN	154,05	6312	12	62837	5237	6594	DIMINISH,DISPARAGE		
BIANN	009,07	0189	09	21246	5224	6577	CONVENIENT,THEN,EASE NATURE		
BIANN	025,02	0593	04	00230	5219	1999	HURRIED,(SURNAME)		
BIANN	029,06	6239.1	08	00407	5245		TO CHANGE,REBELLION		
BIANN	055,02	1701	05	23440	5223	2813	CAP		
BIANN	060,09	1786	12	23227	5230	3782	EVERYWHERE	A6664	
BIANN	061,04	1817	07	90030	5220	2000	PLEASED		
BIANN	064,04	8423	07	50030	5221	2002	STRIKE/TAP		
BIANN	085,04	3079	07	30130	5222	2003	NAME OF AN ANCIENT RIVER,HONAN		
BIANN	120,09	4794	15	21946	5226	6584	BRAID		
BIANN	137,09	9158	15	23427	5250		SKIFF		
BIANN	140,04	535A	08	44231			BENZYL(RADICAL)		
BIANN	149,16	6239	23	22407	5245	6475	TO CHANGE,REBELLION		
BIANN	160,09	6587	16	00441	5240	2462	DISTINGUISH		
BIANN	160,14	4947	20	00441			TO PLAIT,CUE		

CHAR column: 鷦 鷝 鷺 砭 籩 邊 緶 蝙 边 邊 鞭 鯿 扁 窆 藊 蝙 褊 疑 便 卞 变 弁 偏 忭 抃 汴 緶 艑 苄 變 辡 辮

ROM	RAD	TEL	TOT	FC	MAT	OSH	TAG	CR	CHAR
BIANN	160,14	6589	21	00441	5242	2457	TO DEBATE		辯
BIANN	162,09	6664	13	33302	5230	6692	EVERYWHERE,A TIME,TURN	A1786	遍
BIANN	165,00	6845	07	20904	5238	5563	TO DISTINGUISH		采
BIAU	009,15	8078	17	20231			WALKING TO AND FRO		儦
BIAU	059,08	1753	11	22212	5181	7679	TIGER-CAT		彪
BIAU	064,11	2315	14	51091	5179	8357	TO SIGNAL,SIGN		摽
BIAU	075,03	2626.0A	07	47920	5831	4364	(STAR)		杓
BIAU	075,05	2871.1	09	41991			MARK/SIGN		标
BIAU	075,11	2871	15	41991	5180	8360	MARK/SIGN		標
BIAU	085,11	3332	14	32112			FLOWING OF WATER		滮
BIAU	085,15	8715	18	30131			COPIOUS(OF RAIN/SNOW)		瀌
BIAU	086,11	3577	15	91891			BLAZE,FLAME FLARING		熛
BIAU	094,08	8803	12	43434	5183	5085	WHIRLWIND	7374	焱
BIAU	104,11	8880	16	00191	5199	8366	WHITLOW		瘭
BIAU	115,15	8992	20	20931			TO WEED		穮
BIAU	130,11	9136	15	71291	5202	8358	FAT		膘
BIAU	130,15	9136.1	19	70231	5185	8800	FAT		臕
BIAU	140,15	567A	19	44231			KIND OF RASPBERRY		藨
BIAU	167,11	6977	19	81191	5204	8354	DARTS	A7009	鏢
BIAU	167,15	7009	23	80131	5186	8799	DARTS,ESCORT,HORSEBIT	A6977	鑣
BIAU	182,05	9587	14	77211	5183		WHIRLWIND	7374	飑
BIAU	182,12	7374.1	21	79218	5183	7844	WHIRLWIND		飚
BIAU	182,12	7374	21	97810		7833	WHIRLWIND		飙
BIAU	187,20	9623	30	71327			A HORDE OF HORSES		驫
BIAU	190,00	7561	10	72722	5182	4187	HAIR/SHAGGY		髟
BIAU	198,04	7777	15	00331	5184	8798	TO WEED		麃
BEAU	009,08	0217	10	25232	5188	5837	DISTRIBUTE		俵
BEAU	038,08	1239	11	45432	5189	5839	PROSTITUTE		婊
BEAU	145,03	5903	08	50732	5187	5835	WATCH,EXTERNAL,CHART	A9473	表
BEAU	145,08	5950	13	35232	5190	5838	HANG(PAPER),MOUNT(PAINTING)		裱
BEAU	153,12	629C	19	21211			MYRMECOPHAGA		貀
BEAU	167,08	9473	16	85132		5836	WATCH	A5903	錶
BIAW	195,11	7674	22	21391	5207	8362	AIR BLADDER OF FISH		鰾

ROM	RAD	TEL	TOT	FC	MAT	OSH	TAG	CR	CHAR
BIE	061,12	198A	16	98334	5209	8673	TO HOLD(BREATH),HOLD IN(URINE)		
BIE	195,12	7667	23	98336	5212	8780	TURTLE	7841	
BIE	205,12	7841	25	98717	5212	7346	TURTLE	7667	
BYE	018,05	0446	07	62400	5208	2927	SEPARATE,ANOTHER,DON,T		
BYE	142,05	573G	11	53147			MIMELA LUCIDULA		
BYE	157,12	9345	19	98801	5211	5987	LIMP		
BIEE	104,14	4085.1	19	00127	5214	3801	SHRIVELLED,DEFLATED,SUNKEN		
BIEE	104,23	4085	28	00127	5214	3801	SHRIVELLED,DEFLATED,SUNKEN		
BIEH	018,05	0446.0A	07	62400	5208		CONTRARY/DIFFICULT	173A	
BIEH	057,12	173A	15	98207		4741	CONTRARY/DIFFICULT/AWKWARD	198A.0A	
BIEH	061,12	198A.0A	16	98334	5209	8673	CONTRARY/DIFFICULT/AWKWARD	173A	
BIEH	142,12	584D	18	98136			STAPHYLINUS INORNATUS		
BIN	009,14	0319	16	23286	5260		ENTERTAIN,BEST MAN		
BIN	040,07	6333.1	10	30801		8024	VISITOR/GUEST		
BIN	059,08	1755	11	42922	5257	4182	REFINED,ORNAMENTAL	2430	
BIN	067,08	2430	12	03440	5257	6892	ORNAMENTAL,REFINED	1755	
BIN	075,07	2919.1A	11	42981	5263	8022	ARECA		
BIN	075,14	2919.0A	18	43986	5263	8195	ARECA		
BIN	085,07	3203.0A	10	32181		8023	BANK/BEACH	3453	
BIN	085,14	3453	17	33186	5265	8199	BANK/BEACH		
BIN	085,16	3464	19	31186	5265	8281	NEAR		
BIN	096,04	3776	08	18127			PORPHYRITES		
BIN	096,14	3888	18	13186			(PEARL)		
BIN	120,14	4952	20	23986	5267	8196	HELTER-SKELTER		
BIN	142,14	9243	20	53186	5269	8197	PEARL-OYSTER		
BIN	152,10	6279	17	22770	5258	1004	NAME OF AN ANCIENT CITY	6724	
BIN	154,07	6333.2	14	30286	5259	8103	VISITOR/GUEST		
BIN	154,07	6333	14	30806	5259	8188	VISITOR/GUEST		
BIN	163,04	6724	07	87227	5258	2219	NAME OF AN ANCIENT CITY	6279	
BIN	167,14	7001	22	83186	5270	8189	FINE STEEL		
BINN	009,14	0319.0A	16	23286	5260	8190	ENTERTAIN,BEST MAN		
BINN	064,14	2363	17	53086	5262	8191	EXPEL,REJECT		
BINN	078,14	3004	18	13286	5264	8194	ENCOFFIN,FUNERAL		

憨鷿鼇別蚊蟞癟癟別弊憨螫儐宾彬斌梹檳浜濱瀕玢璸繽蠙豳賓賓邠鑌儐擯殯

ROM	RAD	TEL	TOT	FC	MAT	OSH	TAG	CR	CHAR
BINN	130,14	9141	18	73286	5268	8192	KNEECAP/PATELLA	755A	臏
BINN	188,14	755A	24	73286	5268	8193	KNEECAP/PATELLA	9141	髕
BINN	190,07	7589.1	17	72801	5271		HAIR ON THE TEMPLE		髩
BINN	190,14	7589	24	72806	5271	8200	HAIR ON THE TEMPLE		鬢
BING	012,05	0365	07	71801	5282	8021	SOLDIER,WEAPON		兵
BING	015,00	0391	02	30100	5283	9069	ICE		冫
BING	015,04	0393	06	32130	5283	5639	ICE	3056	冰
BING	064,08	8437	11	57020			ARROW-QUIVER		掤
BING	075,06	8559	10	48941		2442	TRACHYCARPUS EXCELSA		栟
BING	075,07	2919.1	11	42981	5263	8022	ARECA		梜
BING	075,14	2919	18	43986	5263	8195	ARECA		檳
BING	085,01	3056	05	32230	5283	5650	ICE	0393	氷
BIING	001,04	0014	05	10227	5284	4037	THIRD OF HEAVEN-STEMS		丙
BIING	044,08	1456.0A	11	77241	5298	2445	PUT ASIDE,REJECT		屏
BIING	061,05	8392	08	91027			SAD/MOURNFUL		怲
BIING	072,05	8506	09	60227	5285		BRIGHT/GLORIOUS		昞
BIING	075,05	2671.0A	09	41927	5286	4040	HANDLE,AUTHORITY		柄
BIING	086,05	3521	09	91827	5287	4041	BRIGHT/LUMINOUS		炳
BIING	113,08	4390	13	00901	5272	8351	REPORT TO (A SUPERIOR)	4463	禀
BIING	115,03	4426	08	20907	5291	5566	TO GRASP/HOLD,(SURNAME)		秉
BIING	115,08	4463	13	00904	5273	5548	REPORT TO (A SUPERIOR)	4390	稟
BIING	163,05	6728	08	17227	5290	2215	HAPPY,ANCIENT CITY NAME,(SURNAME)		邴
BIING	167,08	9479	16	88141	5295		THIN PLATE OF GOLD OR SILVER		鉼
BIING	177,08	7260	17	46540			SCABBARD		鞞
BIING	184,08	7399	16	88741	5296	2437	CAKE/COOKIES		餅
BINQ	001,07	0017.1	08	80102		0510	AND/ALSO,TOGETHER WITH		並
BINQ	001,08	0017	09	80107	5292		AND/ALSO,TOGETHER WITH	1629	並
BINQ	009,08	0164	10	28241	5293	2826	COMBINE,AMALGAMATE		併
BINQ	009,08	0233	10	28241	5293	2826	COMBINE,AMALGAMATE	S0164	併
BINQ	009,09	0164.1	11	28217	5293		COMBINE,AMALGAMATE		傡
BINQ	040,09	1388	12	30227			NIGHTMARE,START IN SLEEP		寎
BINQ	051,03	1629.1	06	80441	5292		AND/ALSO,TOGETHER WITH		并
BINQ	051,05	1629	08	80441	5292	2434	AND/ALSO,TOGETHER WITH	0017	幷

ROM	RAD	TEL	TOT	FC	MAT	OSH	TAG	CR	CHAR
BINQ	064,09	2311	12	57041	5294	2446	DRIVE OFF,EXPEL,ARRANGE		摒
BINQ	075,05	2671	09	41927	5286	4040	HANDLE,AUTHORITY		柄
BINQ	104,05	4016	10	00127	5288	4043	DISEASE,DEFECT		病
BINQ	117,05	4543	10	00118	5292	0546	AND/ALSO,TOGETHER WITH	0017	竝
BO	018,08	0475.0A	10	22100	5337	2954	PEEL		剝
BO	030,14	084F	17	64042			OH		嚤
BO	046,12	8348	15	22769	5319	1801	NAME OF A MOUNTAIN		嶓
BO	064,12	2328	15	52047	5339	6290	PUSH ASIDE,TO APPROPRIATE(MONEY)		撥
BO	085,05	3134	08	34147	5314	6247	WAVE		波
BO	096,05	3788	09	14147	5316	6230	GLASS		玻
BO	105,00	4096	05	12232	5321		BACK TO BACK		癶
BO	112,05	8937	10	14630		5423	ALMS BOWL	6886	砵
BO	121,05	9083	11	85730		5422	ALMS BOWL	6886	缽
BO	140,07	543A	11	44227			BORNYLANE		荡
BO	140,08	5474	12	44147	5315	6249	SPINACH		菠
BO	167,05	6886	13	85130	5333	5421	ALMS BOWL	9083	鉢
BO	184,07	7416	15	84747	5328	3134	(CAKE/BISCUIT)		餑
BOR	009,05	0130	07	26200	4977	1657	FATHER'S ELDER BROTHER,SENIOR		伯
BOR	009,12	0316	14	55809		4896	NAME OF AN ETHNIC GROUP		僰
BOR	010,11	0333	13	41216		7558	HECTOGRAM		兡
BOR	019,07	0514	09	44427	4983	4807	SUDDENLY		勃
BOR	024,10	0590	12	43042	5322	3263	EXTENSIVE,TO GAMBLE		博
BOR	039,04	1319.0A	07	40407		3129	CHANGE COLOR IN THE FACE,(SURNAME)		孛
BOR	050,05	1591	08	26227	4979	3966	SILK		帛
BOR	061,10	0590.1	13	93042	5322	3260	EXTENSIVE,TO GAMBLE		愽
BOR	064,10	2276	13	53042	5323	3264	SEIZE		搏
BOR	075,05	2672.0A	09	46900	4980	1661	CEDAR/CYPRESS		柏
BOR	075,06	2672.1A	10	41960	4980	1661	CEDAR/CYPRESS		栢
BOR	075,07	273A	11	44947		3136	QUINCE		桲
BOR	078,08	2996	12	10261			PROSTRATE,CORPSE	6438	殕
BOR	085,05	3124	08	36100	4987	1663	MOOR		泊
BOR	085,07	3202	10	34147	4984	3138	FULL,GUSHING(OF FOUNTAIN)		淳
BOR	085,09	3258	12	34127	4985	4808	GULF OF PECHILI		渤

ROM	RAD	TEL	TOT	FC	MAT	OSH	TAG	CR	CHAR
BOR	106,00	4101.0A	05	26000	4975	1653	WHITE		白
BOR	106,01	4102.0A	06	10600	4976	1682	HUNDRED		百
BOR	118,08	4613	14	88162	5335	1664	LEAF,SHEET,TINSEL		箔
BOR	130,07	9126	11	74247	5327	3135	NECK	7330	脖
BOR	130,10	5225	14	73242	5324	3265	UPPER ARM,SHOULDER		膊
BOR	137,05	5306	11	26400	4981	1660	OCEAN-GOING SHIP		舶
BOR	140,08	5474.0A	12	44147	5315	6249	SPINACH		菠
BOR	140,08	5472.0A	12	44247	2000	6100	TURNIP		菔
BOR	140,09	549D	13	44427			HELEOCHARIS PLANTAGINEA		葧
BOR	140,13	5631.0A	17	44142	5326	3269	MEAN,THIN,SLIGHT		薄
BOR	145,15	9273	20	36232	5341	5682	EXPOSE,EMBROIDERED COLLAR		襮
BOR	157,08	6438	15	60161	2002	1240	PROSTRATE,CORPSE	2996	踣
BOR	159,05	6521	12	53047			TO SACRIFICE TO SPIRITS OF THE ROAD		軷
BOR	167,05	6876.0A	13	83147	4850	6050	CYMBALS		鈸
BOR	167,05	6896	13	86100	5334	1655	PLATINUM		鉑
BOR	167,07	691C	15	84147		3130	BERYLLIUM		鋍
BOR	181,07	7330	16	4148			NECK	9126	顊
BOR	187,04	7463	14	74340	5342	6544	ARGUE,TRANSHIP,PARTI-COLORED	7481	駁
BOR	187,06	7481	16	70348	5342	6534	ARGUE,TRANSHIP,PARTI-COLORED	7463	駮
BOR	195,05	9641	16	22347			BONITO		鮁
BOR	195,05	9641.1	16	23347			BONITO		鮁
BOR	196,07	7712	18	47427	5329	4626	WOOD-PIGEON		鵓
BOO	157,05	6414	12	64147	5317	6232	LAME		跛
BOH	008,08	0082	10	00714	5336	7361	A DISTRICT IN NORTH ANHWEI		亳
BOH	021,03	0554.0A	05	11110	4974	7147	NORTH		北
BOH	064,12	2330	15	52069	5320	1804	SCATTER,SOW,BROADCAST		播
BOH	064,13	2353	17	70502	4985A		THUMB,TO ANALYZE,TO SPLIT		擘
BOH	075,13	290A	17	70904			PHYLLODENDRON AMURENSE		檗
BOH	112,17	4353	22	14642	5326A	3270	FILL,EXTEND		礴
BOH	118,13	4684	19	88847	5318	6246	TOSS(AS WAVES),DUST PAN		簸
BOH	140,13	5631.0B	17	44142	5326	3269	PEPPERMINT		薄
BOH	140,13	5643.0A	17	44641		2456	LIGUSTICUM ACUTILOBUM		薜
BOH	145,12	5995	17	32247	5340	6289	GARMENT OF COARSE CLOTH,RAIN COAT		襏

ROM	RAD	TEL	TOI	FC	MAT	OSH	TAG	CR	CHAR
BOH	149,12	6218	19	02669			TO SPREAD,PROMULGATE		
BOH	167,10	6959	18	83142	5325	3259	LARGE BELL,HOE		
BOH	184,10	9601	18	83742			(CAKE)		
BOH	188,10	7552	20	73242			SHOULDERBLADE		
.BO	025,00	0592.0A	02	23000			TURNIP	5597	
.BO	140,11	5597	15	44627	5331	4448	TURNIP	0592.0A	
BU	072,07	2523	11	63027	5371	3730	3-5 P.M.		
BU	162,07	6628	11	33302	5373	6690	FLEE		
BU	184,07	7409	15	83727	5374	3733	EVENING MEAL		
BWU	164,02	0085.1	09	12603	5382		MOLD ON LIQUIDS		
BWU	164,12	0085	19	12634	5382	5248	MOLD ON LIQUIDS		
BUU	025,00	0592	02	23000	5378	1985	TO DIVINE		
BUU	030,07	0773	10	63027	5367	3728	FEED	7409.0A	
BUU	032,07	1033.0A	10	43127	5369	3726	PORT		
BUU	064,07	2198	10	53027	5370	3735	SEIZE/CATCH		
BUU	145,02	5943.1	07	33200			TO PATCH,SUPPLEMENT		
BUU	145,07	5943	12	33227	5372	3732	TO PATCH,SUPPLEMENT		
BUU	184,07	7409.0A	15	83727	5374	3733	TO FEED	0773	
BUH	001,03	0008	04	10900	5379	7977	NOT		
BUH	009,05	0142	07	24227	5365	3949	DIFFUSE/EXTEND,NOTIFY		
BUH	032,08	1009	11	47147	5377	2276	PORT,QUAI		
BUH	032,08	1009.1	11	47407			PORT,QUAI		
BUH	050,02	1580	05	40227	5364	3946	CLOTH		
BUH	053,11	8374	14	00227			(ELEMENT IN PLACE NAME)		
BUH	061,05	1831	08	94027	5366	3948	TERROR/TERRIFIED		
BUH	077,03	2975	07	21201	5363	4145	STEP		
BUH	118,11	4716	17	88627			SIEVE-LIKE UTENSIL		
BUH	118,13	4689	19	88142	5375	3272	REGISTER/ACCOUNT-BOOK		
BUH	140,11	5561	15	44627		2175	CYCLE OF 76 YEARS,SHADE		
BUH	142,07	5797.0A	13	53127			SOW BUG		
BUH	163,08	6752	11	07627	5376	2174	SECTION/CLASS,MINISTRY		
BUH	167,04	0359	12	81190			PLUTONIUM		
CHA	029,01	0643	03	40000	0096	6559	PITCHFORK		

譜
鐏
餺
髆
卜
葍
晡
逋
餔
酳
醭
卜
哺
捕
捕
袮
補
餔
不
佈
埠
埠
布
廍
怖
步
筄
部
簿
部
蚆
部
鈇
叉

ROM	RAD	TEL	TOT	FC	MAT	OSH	TAG	CR	CHAR
CHA	030,09	081D	12	64016			TWITTER/CHIRP		
CHA	048,07	1567.0A	10	80211	0105	0096	DIFFER BY,TO LACK		
CHA	064,03	2096	06	54000	0097	6562	TO FORK		
CHA	064,09	2252.1	12	52057		2693	INSERT,STICK IN		
CHA	064,09	2252	12	52077	0113	1072	INSERT,STICK IN		
CHA	075,03	2617	07	44900	0098	6563	FORK OF A TREE,PITCHFORK		
CHAR	029,01	0643.0B	03	40000	0096	6559	TO CROSS/BE STUCK		
CHAR	032,06	8208	09	43114			PLACE NAME		
CHAR	040,11	1390	14	30901	0111	8394	OBSERVE/EXAMINE	9288	
CHAR	046,04	1479.0A	07	80772	0109	0997	FAULT,GLASS FRAGMENTS,QUARREL	4329	
CHAR	064,10	2258	13	54094	0102	8494	APPLY (OINTMENT/POWDER)		
CHAR	075,05	2686	09	40106	0103	0049	INVESTIGATE		
CHAR	075,09	8576.0A	13	44916	0106	0055	RAFT,TO HEW,FELL TREES	2848	
CHAR	075,10	2848	14	48911	0106	0104	RAFT,TO HEW,FELL TREES	8576.0A	
CHAR	112,09	4329	14	14616		0053	FAULT,GLASS FRAGMENT,QUARREL	497A	
CHAR	121,09	497A	15	84716	0104	0051	FAULT,GLASS FRAGMENT,QUARREL	4329	
CHAR	137,10	5315	16	28411			SKIFF		
CHAR	140,06	5420	10	44904	0101	8496	TEA		
CHAR	149,06	9288	13	27601			OBSERVE/EXAMINE	1390	
CHAR	167,09	6950	17	82177	0114	1070	SPADE,LONG PINS		
CHAA	029,01	0643.0A	03	40000	0096	6559	TO OPEN(AS LEGS),TO DIVERGE		
CHAA	145,03	5908.0A	08	34200			SHORTS/PANTIES		
CHAH	009,06	8040	08	23214	0107	7365	BOAST,DESPONDENT		
CHAH	018,06	0458	08	42900	0110	2938	BUDDHIST MONASTERY,A BRIEF MOMENT		
CHAH	038,06	1234	09	43414		7366	MAIDEN,GLAMOR		
CHAH	046,04	1479	07	80772	0109	0997	DIVERGE		
CHAH	048,07	1567	10	80211	0105	0096	DIFFER BY,TO LACK		
CHAH	075,03	2617.0A	07	44900	0098	6563	FORK OF A TREE		
CHAH	085,03	3070	06	34100	0099	6564	BRANCHING STREAM		
CHAH	145,03	5908	08	34200	0100	6561	SLIT ON EITHER SIDE OF ROBE		
CHAH	149,06	6109	13	03614	0108	7364	SURPRISED		
CHAI	048,07	1567.0C	10	80211	0105	0096	SEND/TO COMMISSION		
CHAI	064,05	2135	08	52031	0290	2055	TAKE APART/TO OPEN		

ROM	RAD	TEL	TOT	FC	MAT	OSH	TAG	CR	CHAR
CHAI	167,03	6865	11	84100	0119	6560	HAIRPIN		
CHAIR	009,13	0322	15	20223	0120	2760	COMPANION		
CHAIR	009,15	8076	17	24286			COMPANION	0322	
CHAIR	075,05	2693	09	21904	0121	5389	FIREWOOD,(SURNAME)		
CHAIR	094,03	6284.1	06	44200	0122	3302	WOLVES(COLLECT.)		
CHAIR	140,05	5402.0A	09	44111	6978		(HERB)		
CHAIR	153,03	6284	10	24200	0122	3303	WOLVES(COLLECT.)		
CHAE	013,03	0374.0A	05	77440	6756	4101	SAMPLE COPY		
CHAE	013,03	0374.1A	05	77440	6756	3777	SAMPLE COPY		
CHAE	140,07	5436	11	44716			(AROMATIC HERB)		
CHAY	104,10	4059	15	00111	0123	0105	RECOVER FROM DISEASE		
CHAY	142,13	5860	19	44136	0124	8932	(SCORPION)		
CHAN	050,13	8367	16	42261	0166	1182	CURTAIN IN CARRIAGE,SCREEN		
CHAN	064,10	2356.1	13	57033			ASSIST BY THE ARM,MIX		
CHAN	064,11	2296	14	53022	5636	4222	MIX		
CHAN	064,17	2356	20	57016	0159	7767	ASSIST BY THE ARM,MIX		
CHAN	075,07	8564	11	42941		6804	LONG,LENGTH(OF A TREE OR BEAM)		
CHAN	145,13	9267	18	37261	0167	1179	THE FRONT OF CLOTHES		
CHARN	018,17	8107	19	22200		2965	CUT,BORE,POLISH		
CHARN	024,06	0830.1B	08	80506	6030		CHIEFTAIN		
CHARN	030,09	0830.0B	12	66506	6030	2632	CHIEFTAIN		
CHARN	038,12	1292	15	46456	5648	2643	BEAUTIFUL/GRACEFUL		
CHARN	039,09	1329	12	77247	0169	3100	COWARD		
CHARN	046,11	1535.0A	14	22521	0158	2028	CLIFF	1548	
CHARN	046,17	1548	20	27713	0158	7763	CLIFF	1535.0A	
CHARN	053,12	1679	15	00214	0177	0241	MARKET PLACE		
CHARN	075,17	2942	21	47913	0160	7768	COMET,SANTALUM ALBUM		
CHARN	081,13	8632	17	27416	0155	7761	CUNNING/ARTFUL		
CHARN	085,12	3395	15	37147	0171	3102	FLOW/TRICKLE(OF WATER)		
CHARN	085,13	3436	16	30116	5654		STILL WATER,STILL(AS OF WATER)		
CHARN	085,15	3477	18	30114		0245	NAME OF A RIVER		
CHARN	085,17	3486	20	37116			SOUND OF WATER		
CHARN	112,11	8960	16	52601			CLIFF/PEAK	1548	

釵
儕
儨
柴
芘
豺
册
荶
瘥
薑
幨
捖
摻
攙
梴
襜
劖
單
單
嬋
孱
嶄
嶃
巉
塵
橙
毚
潺
潬
灑
瀺
嶄

ROM	RAD	TEL	TOT	FC	MAT	OSH	TAG	CR	CHAR
CHARN	113,12	4407	16	36256	5650	2640	ZEN BUDDHISM		禪
CHARN	120,10	4961.1	16	20914			WIND AROUND,TO BOTHER		纏
CHARN	120,15	4961	21	20914	0178	0244	WIND AROUND,TO BOTHER		纒
CHARN	137,17	9163	23	27416			LARGE SHIP		艬
CHARN	142,12	5848	18	56156	5651	2642	CICADA		蟬
CHARN	142,13	5853	19	57161	5663	1185	STRIPED TOAD,MOON		蟾
CHARN	149,09	6243.1	16	07633			TO SLANDER		諙
CHARN	149,17	6243	24	07613	0161	7764	TO SLANDER		讒
CHARN	157,15	6493	22	60114	0179	0243	COURSE OF STARS,FOLLOW PRECEDENT		躔
CHARN	167,17	7016	25	87116	0162	7762	SHARP INSTRUMENT FOR DIGGING		鑱
CHARN	184,09	7443.1	17	87733			GREEDY(IN EATING)		饞
CHARN	184,17	7443	25	87716	0157	7766	GREEDY(IN EATING)		饞
CHAAN	002,07	8009	08	55006			SKEWER		弗
CHAAN	018,08	0473	10	52500	0164	2961	LEVEL OFF,ROOT UP	0498	剗
CHAAN	018,11	0498	13	02200	0164	2870	LEVEL OFF,ROOT UP	0473	剷
CHAAN	030,19	0912	22	67532		5772	SMILINGLY		囅
CHAAN	046,11	8346	14	20714			WINDING MOUNTAIN PATH		嵼
CHAAN	067,02	3934.1	06	00201			PRODUCE,REPRODUCE		产
CHAAN	086,12	3590	16	96856	5649		MAKE A FIRE		燀
CHAAN	100,06	3934	11	00214	0163	0396	PRODUCE,REPRODUCE		產
CHAAN	140,12	5621	16	44253	0176	7023	COMPLETE,PREPARE		葳
CHAAN	149,08	6149	15	07677	0174	1052	FLATTER		諂
CHAAN	149,18	9303	25	07620			FLATTER	6149	讇
CHAAN	167,11	6980	19	80114	0165	0397	SHOVEL		鏟
CHAAN	169,12	7073	20	77506	0153	3481	OPEN,EXPLAIN		闡
CHANN	009,17	0329	19	27213	0156	7765	MIXED,IRREGULAR		傪
CHANN	018,08	0473.0A	10	52500	0164		TO ATTACK,PACIFY		剗
CHANN	061,03	2039.1	06	92040			FEEL REMORSE		忏
CHANN	061,17	2039	20	93050	0180	6989	FEEL REMORSE		懺
CHANN	123,15	5037	21	77251	0172	2549	SHEEP CROWDING,CONFUSION		羼
CHANN	181,13	7358.0A	12	01186	0136	8243	SHAKE/VIBRATE		顫
CHANG	009,08	0210	10	21232	0214	5795	RASH/RECKLESS,GROPING		倀
CHANG	009,08	0235.0A	10	26260	0207	1533	PROSTITUTE,ENTERTAINER	A1233	倡

ROM	RAD	TEL	TOT	FC	MAT	OSH	TAG	CR	CHAR
CHANG	038,08	1233	11	46460	0209	1535	PROSTITUTE	A0235.0A	
CHANG	072,04	2490	08	60600	0206	1531	PROSPEROUS		
CHANG	094,08	3715	11	46260	0210	1534	MAD/WILD		
CHANG	140,08	5471	12	44606	0211	1536	CALAMUS		
CHANG	142,08	577A	14	56160			UMBONIUM COSTATUM		
CHANG	167,08	9480	16	86160			METAL UTENSIL,MOUNTING/FITTING		
CHANG	169,08	7049	16	77606	0212	3473	GATE OF HEAVEN,GATE OF PALACE		
CHANG	207,08	7855	21	44732			SOUND OF DRUM		
CHARNG	009,09	0326.1	11	29231			RECOMPENSE		
CHARNG	009,15	0326	17	29286	0230	8144	RECOMPENSE		
CHARNG	028,07	0863.1	09	90731			TO TASTE,INDICATOR OF PAST TENSE		
CHARNG	030,11	0863	14	90601	0229	1608	TO TASTE,INDICATOR OF PAST TENSE	3930	
CHARNG	030,14	0916	17	69061		1609	TO TASTE	A0863	
CHARNG	032,09	1034.0A	12	46127	0218	4486	AN. FOR PHENOMENA/AFFAIRS/ETC.		
CHARNG	032,11	1034.1A	14	48127	0218	4500	AN. FOR PHENOMENA/AFFAIRS/ETC.		
CHARNG	038,11	1281	14	49427	0222		THE LADY IN THE MOON		
CHARNG	050,08	1603	11	90227	0221	3965	CONSTANT/OFTEN		
CHARNG	060,08	1782	11	29227	0223	3859	WALK BACK AND FORTH		
CHARNG	099,08	3930	13	90774		1046	TO TASTE,INDICATOR OF PAST TENSE	0863	
CHARNG	130,09	5214	13	76227	0220	4493	INTESTINES		
CHARNG	140,08	5500	12	44732	0216	5802	CARAMBOLA		
CHARNG	145,08	5951.0A	14	90732	5671	5814	LOWER GARMENT		
CHARNG	167,11	9501	19	89127			GRIND,IRON RING IN WHEEL		
CHARNG	168,00	7022.1	06	22732			LONG		
CHARNG	168,00	7022	08	71732	0213	5793	LONG		
CHARNG	195,08	764U	19	21341			STOLEPHORUS JAPONICUS		
CHARNG	195,14	9665	25	29361			(FISH)		
CHAANG	027,00	0617	02	71200			FACTORY	1681	
CHAANG	027,12	1681.1	14	71248	0226	6353	FACTORY		
CHAANG	032,09	1034	12	46127	0218	4486	FIELD,PLACE		
CHAANG	032,11	1034.1	14	48127	0218		FIELD,PLACE		
CHAANG	053,12	1681	15	00248	0226	6354	FACTORY	0617	
CHAANG	061,08	1918	11	99027	0227	3857	DISAPPOINTED		

娼昌猖菖蝟錩闛鼜倘償嘗嚐場塲嫦常徜當腸蓑裳鏘长長鯗鱨厂厰場塲廠惝

ROM	RAD	TEL	TOT	FC	MAT	OSH	TAG	CR	CHAR
CHAANG	066,08	2412	12	98240	0225	6352	UNCOVERED,SPACIOUS		啟
CHAANG	072,05	2512	09	36230	0231	5660	LONG DAY,BRIGHT		昶
CHAANG	082,12	3037	16	98714	0228	7392	OVERCOAT		氅
CHAANG	157,08	9339	15	69127	0224	3856	SIT CROSSLEGGED		踦
CHANQ	009,08	0235	10	26260	0207	1533	INITIATE/INSTIGATE		倡
CHANQ	030,08	0788	11	66060	0208	1532	SING/CHANT		唱
CHANQ	061,08	1898	11	91032	0215	5794	REGRETFUL		悵
CHANQ	072,10	2545	14	56027	0219	4491	HAPPY		暢
CHANQ	086,08	8744	12	96860			VAPOR/HOT AIR		焻
CHANQ	149,08	6252	15	06660			SING/CHANT	0788	誯
CHANQ	178,08	7286	17	41532			BOW BAG		韔
CHANQ	192,00	7598	10	22711	0232	7173	SACRIFICIAL SPIRIT		鬯
CHAU	018,11	0485.0A	13	22900		2939	DESTROY(BANDITS)	0531.0A	劋
CHAU	018,11	0485.1A	13	27920			DESTROY(BANDITS)		勦
CHAU	019,11	0531.0A	13	24927		4821	DESTROY(BANDITS)	0485.0A	勦
CHAU	057,05	1724	08	17262			UNBENT BOW		弨
CHAU	064,04	2113	07	59020	0255	4156	TO COPY		抄
CHAU	156,05	6389	12	47806	0251	5949	SURPASS,SUPER-		超
CHAU	167,04	6872	12	89120	0258	4149	PAPER MONEY		鈔
CHAUR	030,12	0877	15	67020	0249	3558	RIDICULE	6213	嘲
CHAUR	047,08	1560	11	22904	0253	5511	NEST		巢
CHAUR	072,06	2513	10	60113	0233	7705	(SURNAME)		晁
CHAUR	074,08	2600	12	47420	0233	3557	TO FACE,DYNASTY		朝
CHAUR	085,12	3390	15	37120	0250	3559	TIDE		潮
CHAUR	149,12	6213	19	07620			TO RIDICULE	0877	謿
CHAUR	205,05	7839	18	60717	0252		(SURNAME)		鼂
CHAO	030,04	0703	07	69020	0254	4151	TO QUARREL		吵
CHAO	086,04	3509	08	99820	0256	4160	SAUTE/PAN-FRY		炒
CHAO	127,04	0390	10	59920			PULVERIZE SOIL		耖
CHAW	075,14	2921	18	47914	0243	0951	OAR/SCULL		櫂
CHE	112,07	4287	12	15606		2647	TRIDACNA GIGAS		硨
CHE	159,00	6508	07	50006	0280	2646	VEHICLE ON LAND		車
CHEE	030,06	8135.0A	09	67027		4256	OPEN THE MOUTH WIDE		哆

ROM	RAD	TEL	TOT	FC	MAT	OSH	TAG	CR	CHAR
CHEE	044,01	1439.0B	04	77807	1045	4968	CHINESE MUSICAL NOTE		尺
CHEE	064,04	2102	07	51010	0281	0479	TEAR,PULL AT	8465	扯
CHEE	064,12	8465	15	54064	0281	1651	TO TEAR/PULL AT	2102	撦
CHEH	030,05	0723	08	61060	6327	1265	TO TASTE,TO WHISPER		咭
CHEH	032,05	0986	08	42131	0289	2052	TO CRACK/TO CHAP		坼
CHEH	045,00	1469	03	22407	0283		PLANTS SPROUTING		屮
CHEH	060,04	1796.1	07	27220			THOROUGH		彻
CHEH	060,12	1796	15	28240	0285	6348	THOROUGH	A3400	徹
CHEH	064,08	2233	12	22502	0282	3345	HINDER,TO DRAW		掣
CHEH	064,12	2327	15	58040	0286	6350	REMOVE,TAKE AWAY		撤
CHEH	085,12	3400	15	38140	0287	6351	THOROUGH,CLEAR WATER	A1796	澈
CHEH	159,07	6532	14	52010	0284	7062	ABRUPTLY,AT ONCE,SIDES OF CHARIOT	6537	輒
CHEH	159,08	6537	15	57040	0284	6065	ABRUPTLY,AT ONCE,SIDES OF CHARIOT	6532	輙
CHEH	159,12	6568.0A	19	58040	0288	6349	RUT/TRACK		轍
CHEN	030,10	0838	13	64081	0325	8083	ANGRY AT	4217	嗔
CHEN	096,08	3819	12	17194		5391	(GEM)	6338	琛
CHEN	109,10	4217	15	64081	0326	8084	ANGRY AT	0838	瞋
CHEN	154,08	6338	15	67894			(GEM)	3819	賝
CHEN	163,08	6754	11	47927		2236	NAME OF A HSIEN IN HUNAN		郴
CHERN	032,03	1057.1	06	90104			DUST		尘
CHERN	032,11	1057	14	00214	0328	0234	DUST		塵
CHERN	040,07	1368	10	30232	0337	5790	IMPERIAL APARTMENTS		宸
CHERN	061,04	1820	07	94012	0331	7739	SINCERE		忱
CHERN	072,07	2525	11	60232	0338	5780	MORNING		晨
CHERN	075,07	273B	11	42927			FRAXINUS BUNGEANA PUBBINERUS		梣
CHERN	075,12	2892	16	42918	0388	0597	AN ORANGE		橙
CHERN	085,04	3088	07	34112	0332	7743	SINK	3089	沈
CHERN	085,04	3089	07	37117	0332	7876	SINK	3088	沉
CHERN	086,09	8750	13	94818			BRAZIER		煁
CHERN	131,00	5256	06	71717	0327	0846	MINISTER,OFFICIAL		臣
CHERN	149,09	6186	16	04611	5726	0769	SINCERE,FAITHFUL,(SURNAME)		諶
CHERN	161,00	6591	07	71232	0336	5775	5TH EAST'S BRANCH,7-9 A.M.		辰
CHERN	170,08	7115	11	75296	0339	5536	STALE,DISPLAY,(SURNAME)		陳

ROM	RAD	TEL	TOT	FC	MAT	OSH	TAG	CR	CHAR
CHENN	075,16	2932	20	46910	0341	7610	COFFIN,STERCULIA PLANTANIFOLIA		櫬
CHENN	104,04	8864	09	00189	0343	5605	(DISEASE)		疢
CHENN	115,05	4468.1A	10	27992		8436	BALANCED,TO FIT		称
CHENN	115,09	4468.0A	14	22947	0383	4128	TO FIT,WELL OFF		稱
CHENN	145,03	6000.1	08	34200			UNDERWEAR,GIVE ALMS		衬
CHENN	145,16	6000	21	36210	0342	7609	UNDERWEAR,GIVE ALMS		襯
CHENN	149,17	6244	24	03650	0181	6988	FULFIL,PROPHECY		讖
CHENN	156,05	6387.1	12	47809	0345	5971	AVAIL ONESELF OF		趁
CHENN	156,05	6387	12	48802	0345	5959	AVAIL ONESELF OF		趂
CHENN	211,02	7877	17	24710	0344	7141	REPLACE THE MILK TEETH		齔
CHENG	009,09	0248	11	21247	0383		TO CALL	A4468	偁
CHENG	030,12	0886.0A	15	68066		1553	BASS(SOUND)		嘡
CHENG	064,12	2319	15	59041	0391	3331	PROP UP	2300	撑
CHENG	064,12	2300	15	59052	0391	3341	PROP UP	2319	撐
CHENG	075,04	2847.1A	08	48912			COMET		枪
CHENG	075,10	2847.0A	14	48967	0680	1138	COMET		槍
CHENG	075,13	2906	17	46914		0307	TAMARISK		檉
CHENG	096,08	3821	12	12157			TINKLING OF GEMS		琤
CHENG	109,11	4222	16	69014	6170	0189	STARE AT SOMETHING BEYOND REACH		瞠
CHENG	115,05	4468.1	10	27992		8436	STEELYARD		称
CHENG	115,09	4468	14	22947	0383	4128	TO CALL,WEIGH		稱
CHENG	142,13	5855	19	56114	0394	0308	RAZOR CLAM/SOLECURTUS CONSTRICTA		蟶
CHENG	155,09	6380	16	41386	0397	8175	DEEP RED	7337	赬
CHENG	167,13	6997.0A	21	89166	6093	1765	GRIDDLE,FRYING PAN		鐺
CHENG	181,07	7337	16	41386		8317	DEEP RED	6380	頳
CHERNG	001,05	0015	06	17103	0385	0069	DEPUTY		丞
CHERNG	004,09	0042	10	20901	0398	5564	MULTIPLY,RIDE/AVAIL OF		乘
CHERNG	030,04	0701	07	60104	0372	0301	PETITION		呈
CHERNG	032,07	1004	10	43150	0380	7017	CITY,CITY WALL		城
CHERNG	032,07	8224	10	46114	0373	0302	EARTHEN JAR		埕
CHERNG	032,09	1039.1	12	49114	0387		RAISED PATH BETWEEN FIELDS		塍
CHERNG	032,10	1039	13	79214	0387	0217	RAISED PATH BETWEEN FIELDS		塍
CHERNG	040,06	1361	09	30253			STORAGE,LIBRARY STACK		宬

ROM	RAD	TEL	TOT	FC	MAT	OSH	TAG	CR	CHAR
CHERNG	061,08	2033.1	12	21331	0384	8542	PUNISH		惩
CHERNG	061,15	2033	19	28338	0384	8669	PUNISH		懲
CHERNG	062,02	2052	06	53200	0379	7016	TO COMPLETE		成
CHERNG	064,04	2110	07	17232	0386	5707	RECEIVE		承
CHERNG	075,08	2763	12	41932	0396	5800	DOOR POST		棖
CHERNG	075,12	2892.0A	16	42918	0388	0597	AN ORANGE		橙
CHERNG	085,12	3397.0A	15	32118	0389	0599	SETTLE(LIQUID),CLEAR/LIMPID	D3413	澄
CHERNG	085,12	3413	15	38140		6312	CLEAR/LIMPID,NAME OF A RIVER	B3397.0A	瀓
CHERNG	108,06	4141	11	53107	5752	0721	TO HOLD/CONTAIN		盛
CHERNG	115,07	4453	12	26914	0375	0305	JOURNEY,EXTENT,(SURNAME)		程
CHERNG	145,07	5935	12	36214	0376	0304	TAKE OFF CLOTHES		裎
CHERNG	149,06	6134	13	03650	0381	7018	HONEST/SINCERE		誠
CHERNG	163,06	6743	09	57227			NAME OF A FEUDAL STATE		郕
CHERNG	164,07	6805	14	16614	0378	0303	ALCOHOLIC		酲
CHERNG	195,06	764V	17	23312			RICHARDSONIUS HAKUENSIS		鯎
CHEENG	162,07	6642	11	36301	0377	6602	PLEASE ONESELF,PRESUME ON		逞
CHEENG	187,07	7488	17	75327	0395		TO GALLOP,HASTEN ON		騁
CHENQ	004,09	0042.0A	10	20901	0398		TEAM OF HORSES,AN. FOR VEHICLES		乘
CHENQ	115,05	4439	10	21949	0382	2425	STEELYARD	4468.0B	秤
CHENQ	115,05	4468.1B	10	27992		8436	STEELYARD		称
CHENQ	115,09	4468.0B	14	22947	0383	4128	STEELYARD,TO FIT	4439	稱
CHI	001,01	0003	02	40710	0579	7351	SEVEN		七
CHI	015,08	0401	10	35144	0556	8998	INTENSE COLD,MOURNFUL	3246	凄
CHI	030,08	8148.0A	11	60048	6872	2340	(INTERJ. OF CONTEMPT)	0844.0A	啐
CHI	030,10	0844.0A	13	62036			(INTERJ. OF CONTEMPT)	8148.0A	嗤
CHI	030,11	086A	14	63050			WHISPERING SOUND		嘁
CHI	032,11	1068	14	43150	0576		STEPS OF A STAIRWAY		墄
CHI	038,05	1189	08	50404	0555	8995	WIFE		妻
CHI	046,08	1505.0A	11	24721	0515		MOUNTAINOUS		崎
CHI	061,08	1903	11	95044	0557	8996	SORROWFUL		悽
CHI	061,11	1989	15	53330	0577	8681	GRIEF,ASHAMED		慼
CHI	062,07	2058	11	53200	0575	7024	RELATIVE,(SURNAME)		戚
CHI	074,08	2601.0A	12	47820	0526	3579	PERIOD,TO HOPE,A FIXED DATE		期

ROM	RAD	TEL	TOT	FC	MAT	OSH	TAG	CR	CHAR
CHI	075,05	2675	09	34904	0579	5394	SEVEN(FRAUDPROOF)		柒
CHI	075,06	2722	10	41960	2462	1959	TO ROOST	2776	栖
CHI	075,07	3344.1	11	40132	0578	5673	PAINT/LACQUER		泰
CHI	075,08	2776	12	45944	2462	8997	TO ROOST	2722	棲
CHI	076,08	2952	12	47882	0528	4960	TAKE UNFAIR ADVANTAGE OF		欺
CHI	085,04	308A	07	37120		4282	TO STEEP(TEA)		沏
CHI	085,08	3246	11	35144	0556	8999	INTENSE COLD,MOURNFUL	0401	淒
CHI	085,10	3305.0A	13	32134	0510	5060	CREEK	6254.0A	溪
CHI	085,11	3344	14	34132	0578	5675	PAINT/LACQUER		漆
CHI	120,09	4874.0A	15	26941	0571	2733	TO STITCH FINELY		緝
CHI	140,08	5491	12	44404	0558	9000	LUXURIANT,CELOSIA ARGENTEA		萋
CHI	142,11	583A	17	53150			LIMPET/PATELLA LOREUMA		蟛
CHI	149,08	9293	15	04681			DECEIVE/CONTRIVE		諆
CHI	150,10	6254.0A	17	28468	0511	1386	CREEK	3305.0A	谿
CHI	163,08	9394	11	57427			PLACE NAME,NAME OF A RIVER		郪
CHYI	007,02	8016	04	10221			HIS/HER/ITS/THEIR,(SURNAME)	A0366	亓
CHYI	007,06	8018	08	23103			EVEN,TO MAKE EVEN,(SURNAME)	7871	亝
CHYI	012,06	0366	08	44801	0525	8046	HIS/HER/ITS/THEIRS		其
CHYI	032,04	0967	07	42121	0539	2009	BOUNDARY/A BORDER		圻
CHYI	037,05	1142	08	40621	0514	3063	STRANGE,WONDERFUL		奇
CHYI	038,08	8285	11	44481			UGLY,TO RIDICULE		媒
CHYI	046,04	1477	07	24747	0522	6213	DIVERGENT,SIDE ROAD,STEEP	K2978	岐
CHYI	046,08	1505	11	24721		3067	MOUNTAINOUS		崎
CHYI	067,02	7871.2	06	00224			EVEN,TO MAKE EVEN,(SURNAME)		齐
CHYI	067,04	7871.1	08	00224	0560	2757	EVEN,TO MAKE EVEN,(SURNAME)		齊
CHYI	070,06	2461	10	08221	0535	2048	FLAG	2475	斾
CHYI	070,10	2475	14	08281	0535	8055	FLAG	2461	旗
CHYI	074,08	2601	12	47820	0526	3579	PERIOD,TO HOPE,A FIXED DATE		期
CHYI	075,08	2759.1	12	44904	0527		CHESS		幕
CHYI	075,08	2759	12	44981	0527	8049	CHESS	4298	棋
CHYI	077,04	2978	08	24147	0523	6207	DIVERGENT,SIDE ROAD	K1477	歧
CHYI	085,08	3217	11	34181	0529	8054	NAME OF A RIVER		淇
CHYI	096,08	3823	12	14121	0517	3064	VALUABLE STONE,CURIO		琦

ROM	RAD	TEL	TOT	FC	MAT	OSH	TAG	CR	CHAR
CHYI	096,08	3825	12	14181	0530	8047	(WHITE GEM),ANGEL		琪
CHYI	096,11	8836	15	14114			CAP GEMS		璂
CHYI	102,06	3971.0A	11	64014		0165	SMALL PLOT OF FARM LAND		畦
CHYI	112,08	4298	13	44601	0527	1113	CHESS	2759	碁
CHYI	113,03	4359	07	37227	0537	2259	(SURNAME)		祁
CHYI	113,04	4362	08	32221	0540	2046	IMPLORE/PRAY,PLEASE		祈
CHYI	113,04	4361.0A	08	32240	0538	6846	EARTH-SPIRIT,PEACE		祇
CHYI	113,08	4388	12	34281	0531	8052	FELICITY		祺
CHYI	117,04	1142.1	09	00621	0514		STRANGE,WONDERFUL		竒
CHYI	120,08	4847	14	44903	0532	8464	DARK GREY,VARIEGATED,SUPERLATIVE		綦
CHYI	125,04	5075	10	44601	0512	1611	MAN OF SIXTY OR SEVENTY		耆
CHYI	130,04	9111	08	72221			SACRIFICIAL PLATTER		肵
CHYI	130,14	5247	18	70223	0561	2762	NAVEL		臍
CHYI	140,04	5356	08	44742		6847	ASTRAGALUS HENRYI OLIV.		芪
CHYI	140,08	5487	12	44801	0403	8056	STALKS OF PULSE		萁
CHYI	140,09	550F	13	44430			SMILAX CHINA		葜
CHYI	140,14	5654	18	44223	0460	2765	WATER CHESTNUT		薺
CHYI	140,14	5657	18	44903			(FERN)		藄
CHYI	140,16	5682	20	42521	0541	2024	(HERB),PLACE NAME,IMPLORE/PRAY	G4362	蘄
CHYI	142,04	9218	10	52140			GREEN-FROG		蚔
CHYI	142,04	573F	10	54147			CARABUS DEHAANII		蚑
CHYI	142,08	5786	14	54181		8053	GRAPSUS		蜞
CHYI	142,14	9242	20	50123	0562	2763	LARVA,MAGGOT		蠐
CHYI	157,04	6404	11	64147	0524	6208	FOOT WITH SIX TOES		跂
CHYI	159,04	9361	11	52040			END OF AXLE		軝
CHYI	163,16	9415	19	47527			(HERB),PLACE NAME	K5682	鄿
CHYI	167,08	6936	16	84121	0520	3065	CHISEL,CALDRON		錡
CHYI	181,04	7322	13	71286		8262	TALL		頎
CHYI	187,08	7494	18	74321	0521	3076	RIDE(ASTRIDE)		騎
CHYI	187,08	7496	16	74381	0533	8048	PIEBALD HORSE		騏
CHYI	190,10	7580	20	72601	0513		HORSE'S MANE,DORSAL FINS		鬐
CHYI	195,06	764E	17	21367			EPINEPHELUS SEPTEMFASCIATUS		鮨
CHYI	195,10	7662	21	24361		1614	FINS,SUPPORTING SURFACES		鰭

ROM	RAD	TEL	TOT	FC	MAT	OSH	TAG	CR	CHAR
CHYI	198,08	7784	19	04281	0534	8051	MYTHICAL UNICORN		麒
CHYI	210,00	7871	14	00223	0560	2758	EVEN,TO MAKE EVEN,(SURNAME)		齊
CHII	005,02	0047	03	80717	0564	7958	BEG		乞
CHII	030,04	0796.2	07	30267			TO OPEN		启
CHII	030,08	0796.1	11	38604	0542	1427	TO OPEN		啓
CHII	030,08	0796	11	38640	0542	6317	TO OPEN		啟
CHII	046,03	6259.1	06	22717			HOW CAN IT BE THAT		岂
CHII	046,03	1474	06	27717	0546	7247	HILL WITHOUT TREES		屺
CHII	075,03	2630	07	47917	0547	7253	(WILLOW),NAME OF A FEUDAL STATE		杞
CHII	075,08	2790	12	38904		5387	TALLY FOR GOING THROUGH A PASS		棨
CHII	115,10	4472.0A	15	23961	0427	1610	BOW TO THE GROUND		稽
CHII	120,08	4860	14	24921	0518	3078	OPEN-WORK SILK,BEAUTIFUL		綺
CHII	120,08	4851	14	38903	0543	8473	EMBROIDERED BANNER		綮
CHII	137,14	9162	20	20423			HOLE IN A SCULL FOR PIVOT		艤
CHII	140,03	5344	07	44717		7256	PANICUM MILIACEUM		芑
CHII	151,03	6259	10	22108	0544	0569	HOW CAN IT BE THAT		豈
CHII	156,03	6386	10	47801	0548	5968	RISE,RAISE		起
CHIH	007,07	0069.0A	09	10104	0483	0071	REPEATEDLY/FREQUENTLY		亟
CHIH	009,03	0106.0B	05	28217			(ETHNIC GROUP)		仡
CHIH	009,04	0120	06	80101	0545	0482	STAND ON TIPTOE		企
CHIH	030,12	0892.1	15	66661	0549	1075	TOOL		器
CHIH	030,13	0892	15	66663	0549	1077	TOOL		器
CHIH	037,06	1148	09	57430	0551	5046	CONTRACT		契
CHIH	038,05	1189.0A	08	50404	0555	8995	TO MARRY OFF (A DAUGHTER)		妻
CHIH	055,04	2757.1	07	00443		2813	ABANDON,RELINQUISH		弃
CHIH	061,09	1943	12	96027	0807		REST/STOP		愒
CHIH	061,10	2004.1	14	24337	0536		TO REST		憩
CHIH	061,12	2004	16	26330	0536	8578	TO REST		憇
CHIH	075,06	8551	10	57904			CARVE/CUT		契
CHIH	075,08	2757	12	00904	0550	5491	ABANDON,RELINQUISH		棄
CHIH	084,00	3049	04	80107	0552	7794	AIR,ANGER,GAS	3051	气
CHIH	084,06	3051	10	80917	0554	7812	AIR,ANGER,GAS	3049	氣
CHIH	085,03	3072	06	38117			NEAR		汔

31

ROM	RAD	TEL	TOT	FC	MAT	OSH	TAG	CR	CHAR
CHIH	085,04	3086	07	38117	0553	7795	STEAM		汽
CHIH	085,05	3135	08	30118	0563	0555	TO SOB		泣
CHIH	086,04	8735	08	71331	0554		AIR,ANGER	A3051	烾
CHIH	094,03	8794	06	48217			NAME OF A TRIBE		犵
CHIH	109,03	8898	08	68017			(SURNAME)		眣
CHIH	112,04	4265	09	17620	0559	4281	BUILD(BY LAYING BRICKS)		砌
CHIH	112,09	8956	14	17634			BUILD(BY LAYING BRICKS)	4265	磜
CHIH	112,11	4332	16	15686	0573	8113	ROCKS IN SHALLOW WATER,MORAINE		磧
CHIH	120,09	4874	15	26941	0571	2733	ORDER THE ARREST OF		緝
CHIH	140,09	5528	13	44401	0572	2734	TO REPAIR		葺
CHIH	142,13	5857	19	57136			(INSECT),TRYXALIS MASUTA		蠞
CHIH	149,03	6066	10	08617	0567	7964	FINISHED		訖
CHIH	157,04	6404.0A	11	64147	0524	6208	STAND ON TIPTOE		跂
CHIH	162,03	6597	07	38301	0568	6774	UNTIL,AS YET		迄
CHIH	167,11	9502	19	83150			BATTLE-AXE		鏚
CHIH	075,11	286B	15	43950			SUGARWOOD		槭
CH	030,08	8148.0B	11	60048	6872	2340	(INTERJ. OF CONTEMPT)	0844.0B	啐
CH	030,10	0844.0B	13	62036			(INTERJ. OF CONTEMPT)	8148.0B	嗤
CHIA	064,08	2225	11	57077	0618	1055	TO PINCH,PICK (FLOWERS)		掐
CHYA	025,03	0595.0A	05	21231	0616	2007	A CLIP,PUT IN BETWEEN TWO THINGS		拤
CHYA	064,05	2097	08	51031			TO CHOKE/STRANGLE		卡
CHEA	025,03	0595.0B	05	21331	0616	2007	CUSTOMS STATION,TO BE CHOKED		卡
CHIAH	061,06	1874	09	98061	0617	1191	EXACTLY/JUST		恰
CHIAH	085,06	3174	09	38161	2529	1197	ACCORD,MAKE CONTACT		洽
CHIAH	112,06	8942	11	14661			FIRM/SOLID,SUDDEN		硈
CHIAH	140,09	550G	13	44163			KOELERIA		落
CHIAH	188,09	755B	19	73264	0615	1431	ILIUM		髂
CHIAN	009,03	0107	05	22240	0907	2371	THOUSAND		仟
CHIAN	009,11	0286	13	80886	0914	8000	ALL		僉
CHIAN	010,08	8089	10	42214		7560	KILOGRAM		兛
CHIAN	024,01	0578	03	20400	0906	2369	THOUSAND,A SWING	D7276	千
CHIAN	046,04	8325	07	21740			NAME OF A MOUNTAIN		岍
CHIAN	046,09	1523	12	22782	3249	4912	INLAY,DEEP VALLEY		嵌
CHIAN	061,09	1936	13	21332	0889	8623	FAULT,TRANSGRESSION		愆

ROM	RAD	TEL	TOT	FC	MAT	OSH	TAG	CR	CHAR
CHIAN	061,11	1984	14	97014	0826		STINGY		慳
CHIAN	064,03	8422	06	52040	0910	2373	STICK IN,GRAFT(TREE)		扦
CHIAN	064,08	8451	12	77501	0886		SUBSTANTIAL,LEAD ALONG	D3677	掔
CHIAN	064,10	2291	14	30502	0890	3349	SEIZE		搴
CHIAN	085,06	3162	09	31140			PLACE NAME		汧
CHIAN	093,05	3677.1	09	40502			LEAD ALONG		牵
CHIAN	093,07	3677	11	00503	0881	2538	LEAD ALONG	B8451	牽
CHIAN	098,03	3926	08	12714		7951	KILOWATT,KILOGRAM		瓩
CHIAN	117,03	9003	08	02140		2370	KILOLITER		竏
CHIAN	118,07	4687.1	13	88109			SIGN ONE'S NAME	C4706	签
CHIAN	118,13	4687	19	88886	0915	8012	SIGN ONE'S NAME	C4706	簽
CHIAN	118,17	4706	23	88153	0917	6992	A STICK,A NOTE,SIGN ONE'S NAME	G4687	籤
CHIAN	119,03	9032	09	91940			KILOMETER		粁
CHIAN	140,03	5340	07	44401	0908	2375	LUXURIANT GROWTH,GREEN		芊
CHIAN	140,06	9172	10	44441			IRIS ENSATA		茾
CHIAN	142,06	5746	12	54141			TELEPHORUS SUTURELLUS		蚈
CHIAN	145,10	5973	16	30732	0891	5825	LIFT UP THE SKIRTS,LOWER GARMENTS		褰
CHIAN	149,08	6160	15	26601			FAULT,TRANSGRESSION	1936	諐
CHIAN	149,10	6197	17	08637	0885	5571	MODEST		謙
CHIAN	162,03	6692.1	07	32304	0911	6644	TO MOVE/TO SHIFT		迁
CHIAN	162,12	6692	16	31301	0911	6761	TO MOVE/TO SHIFT		遷
CHIAN	167,03	7244	11	82140			ROCK DRILL		釬
CHIAN	167,05	6884	13	87161	0900	1437	LEAD(METAL)		鉛
CHIAN	167,07	6913	15	87147	0913	6186	ENGRAVE		鋟
CHIAN	170,03	7082	06	72240	0909	2372	ROAD LEADING NORTH AND SOUTH		阡
CHIAN	172,06	9541	14	10414			WAGTAIL		雃
CHIAN	177,15	7276	24	41531	0912	6763	A SWING	B0578	韆
CHIAN	179,08	7297	17	83150	0916	6987	WILD ONIONS OR LEEKS		韱
CHIAN	187,10	7505	20	30327	0892	4711	DEFECTIVE,RAISE		騫
CHYAN	005,10	0051.0A	11	48417	3233	7966	STRONG,MALE,(SURNAME)		乾
CHYAN	018,07	0467	09	80221	0919	2901	FRONT,FORMERLY,BEFORE		前
CHYAN	032,11	8246	14	48117			BRINK/SHORE(OF WATER)		墘
CHYAN	038,09	8290	12	48420			PLANET VENUS IN THE MORNING		媊

ROM	RAD	TEL	TOT	FC	MAT	OSH	TAG	CR	CHAR
CHYAN	064,05	8425	08	54070	0897	1039	PLIERS/PINCERS,TO CLAMP	6883	拑
CHYAN	064,08	8438	11	53027	0893	3581	CARRY ON SHOULDERS		掮
CHYAN	085,12	3383	15	31161	0918	1620	SUBMERGE,HIDE	3480	潛
CHYAN	085,16	3480	19	35161	0918	1620	SUBMERGE,HIDE	3383	灊
CHYAN	086,12	8760	16	91846	6064	2294	TO HEAT/TO SCORCH		燂
CHYAN	118,08	4617	14	88575	0898	1040	PLIERS/PINCERS,TO CLAMP	6883	箝
CHYAN	140,09	550H	13	44221			RUBUS PALMATUS		葥
CHYAN	141,04	5709	10	21240	0894	6553	DEVOUT		虔
CHYAN	167,04	6870	12	88127	0895	2843	SEAL,LATCH OF DOOR		鈐
CHYAN	167,05	6883	13	84170	0899	1036	PLIERS/PINCERS,TO CLAMP		鉗
CHYAN	167,08	6929	16	83153	0921	6949	MONEY,COIN,(SURNAME)		錢
CHYAN	203,04	7816	16	68327	0896	2847	KWEICHOW		黔
CHEAN	030,10	0840	13	68037	0883	5570	POUCH OF A MONKEY,DEFICIENT		嗛
CHEAN	085,08	3239	11	33153	0920	6959	SHALLOW		淺
CHEAN	120,14	4953	20	25937	0902	6621	ATTACHED TO,LOVING		繾
CHEAN	130,07	9122	11	74238			PELVIC CAVITY/LOWER ABDOMEN		脥
CHEAN	149,14	6232	21	05637	0903	6620	SCOLD,PUNISHMENT		譴
CHEAN	162,10	6680	14	35307	0901	6619	DISPATCH		遣
CHIANN	009,08	0241	10	25227	0922	3689	WINSOME,NIECE,PLAGIARIZE		倩
CHIANN	032,11	1058	14	52104	0926	0201	MOAT AROUND A CITY		塹
CHIANN	046,09	1523.0A	12	22782		4912	INLAY,DEEP VALLEY		嵌
CHIANN	061,10	1965	13	98037	0806	5573	DISSATISFIED		慊
CHIANN	075,11	2858	15	52904	0927	5341	TABLETS,PRINTING BLOCKS		槧
CHIANN	076,00	2944	04	27802	0904	4898	OWE,DEFICIENT		欠
CHIANN	076,10	2959	14	87382	0884	4952	DEFICIENT,TO REGRET,APOLOGIZE		歉
CHIANN	118,08	4621	14	88227	0923		DRAW A BAMBOO BOW/BIG BAMBOO GROVE		箐
CHIANN	118,10	9017	16	88227			LUXURIANT GROWTH OF BAMBOO		篟
CHIANN	120,03	4928.1	09	22940			BOATMAN'S TOW-ROPE		纤
CHIANN	120,08	9063	14	25927			DARK RED COLOR(OF SILK PRODUCT)		綪
CHIANN	120,11	4928	17	20953		2540	BOATMAN'S TOW-ROPE		縴
CHIANN	140,04	5349	08	44802	0905	4967	EURYALE FEROX		芡
CHIANN	140,06	5409	10	44601	0929	1962	RUBIA CORDIOLIA		茜
CHIANN	140,10	5541	14	44227	0925	3690	LUXURIANT GROWTH		蒨

ROM	RAD	TEL	TOT	FC	MAT	OSH	TAG	CR	CHAR
CHIANG	030,10	0850.0A	13	68067		1133	AGAINST WIND	2293.0A	嗆
CHIANG	064,10	2293.0A	13	58067	0679	1136	AGAINST WIND	0850.0A	搶
CHIANG	075,04	2847.1	08	48912			SPEAR,RIFLE		枪
CHIANG	075,08	8570	12	43911			(WOODEN MUS. INSTR.)		椌
CHIANG	075,10	2847	14	48967	0680	1138	SPEAR,RIFLE	6957	槍
CHIANG	090,04	2446	08	22221			HOLE FOR HANDLE IN AXE		斨
CHIANG	096,08	8826	12	18111			(PERSON)		瑲
CHIANG	096,10	3856	14	18167	6712		TINKLING OF GEMS		瑲
CHIANG	123,02	5018	08	80211	0666	7525	NAME OF A TRIBE,EDUCATED,STRONG		羌
CHIANG	123,04	5018.1	10	80213	0666	7527	NAME OF A TRIBE,EDUCATED,STRONG		羗
CHIANG	130,08	5204	12	73211	0665	0119	CAVITY OF BODY,TUNE		腔
CHIANG	142,08	5780	14	58111	0667	7526	DUNG BEETLE		蜣
CHIANG	157,10	6461	17	68167	0682	1132	WALK RAPIDLY		蹌
CHIANG	157,11	6476	18	67140		3275	MANNER OF WALKING		蹡
CHIANG	167,10	6957	18	88167	0683	1131	SPEAR/RIFLE	2847	鎗
CHIANG	167,11	6973	19	87142	0671	3274	TINKLING OF SMALL BELLS		鏘
CHIANG	167,12	6987.0A	20	86136			SULFURIC ACID		鏹
CHYANG	032,11	3649.1	14	44161			WALL		墙
CHYANG	032,13	8259	16	44161	0674		WALL	3649	墻
CHYANG	038,13	1297	16	44461	0675	1862	FEMALE COURT OFFICIALS		嬙
CHYANG	053,13	8376	16	00261	0674	1864	WALL	3649	廧
CHYANG	057,08	1730	11	13236	0668	8951	STRONG,SUPERIOR	1735	强
CHYANG	057,09	1730.1	12	16236	0668	8922	STRONG,SUPERIOR		強
CHYANG	057,13	1735	16	11216	0668	0063	STRONG,SUPERIOR	1730	彊
CHYANG	062,04	2056	08	23250	0673		SPEAR,KILL		戕
CHYANG	075,13	2915	17	44961	0676	1860	MAST,BOOM		檣
CHYANG	090,00	3645	04	22200	0672	2081	HALF OF A TREE TRUNK		爿
CHYANG	090,13	3649	17	25261	0674	1857	WALL	8259	牆
CHYANG	137,13	2915.1	17	24461	0676	1859	MAST,BOOM		艢
CHYANG	140,11	5638.1	15	44601			WILD ROSE		薔
CHYANG	140,13	5638	17	44601	0677	1865	WILD ROSE		薔
CHYANG	167,08	9478	16	85127		3683	RUST,TARNISH		錆
CHEANG	057,08	1730.0A	11	13236	0668	8951	COMPEL	1735.0A	強

35

ROM	RAD	TEL	TOT	FC	MAT	OSH	TAG	CR	CHAR
CHEANG	057,09	1730.1A	12	16230	0668	8922	COMPEL		强
CHEANG	057,13	1735.0A	16	11216	0668	0063	COMPEL	1730.0A	彊
CHEANG	064,10	2293	13	58067	0679	1136	FIGHT OVER		搶
CHEANG	120,12	4929	18	26936	0647	8954	CLOTH FOR CARRYING BABY ON BACK	5982	繈
CHEANG	123,07	7278	13	81511			HYDROXYL(RADICAL)		羥
CHEANG	145,11	5982	16	33236	0647	8953	CLOTH FOR CARRYING BABY ON BACK	4929	襁
CHEANG	167,12	6987	20	86136	0648	8952	MONEY,STRING OF COINS		鏹
CHIANQ	030,10	0850	13	68067	0678	1133	CHOKE,PUNGENT		嗆
CHIANQ	086,10	7294	14	98867		1139	COOK IN SOY		熗
CHIANQ	157,10	6461.0A	17	68167	0682	1132	STAGGER/SWAY FROM SIDE TO SIDE	6476.0A	蹌
CHIANQ	157,11	6476.0A	18	67140		3275	STAGGER/SWAY FROM SIDE TO SIDE	6461.0A	蹡
CHIAU	032,12	8252	15	44111	0738	7485	STONY SOIL	4338	墝
CHIAU	044,16	8320	19	77227		3853	CANVAS SHOES,STRAW SANDALS		屩
CHIAU	064,12	2334	15	52014	0736	7382	PRY OPEN		撬
CHIAU	066,10	2418	14	01247	0735	6201	KNOCK/TO STRIKE,EXTORT		敲
CHIAU	112,12	4338	17	14611	0738	7490	STONY SOIL		磽
CHIAU	157,12	9348	19	62127	0750	3843	RAISE ONE'S FOOT	6475	蹻
CHIAU	157,12	6475	19	64111	0750	7487	RAISE ONE'S FOOT	9348	蹺
CHIAU	167,09	9483	17	29109	0755	0379	SHOVEL,TO DIG	6942	鍫
CHIAU	167,09	6942	17	89180		5593	SHOVEL,TO DIG	9483	鍬
CHIAU	172,03	7158.0B	11	90214	1185	0962	LENTIGO		雀
CHYAU	009,12	0294	14	22227	0745	3846	RESIDE ABROAD,EMIGRANT		僑
CHYAU	030,09	0829	12	20227	0744	3842	TALL		喬
CHYAU	037,03	0829.1	06	20223		2750	TALL		乔
CHYAU	061,12	1997	15	90031	0756	8759	HAGGARD	7356	憔
CHYAU	075,12	2884	16	40931	0757	8760	GATHER WOOD,FIREWOOD		樵
CHYAU	075,12	8587	16	42914	0737	7383	SLEDGE FOR MUD OR SNOW		橇
CHYAU	075,12	2890	16	42927	0747	3851	BRIDGE	8965	橋
CHYAU	109,12	4225	17	60031	0741	8755	LOOK AT		瞧
CHYAU	112,12	8965	17	12627			BRIDGE	2890	礄
CHYAU	124,12	5062	18	47212	0739	7503	TO RAISE,OUTSTANDING		翹
CHYAU	140,06	5431	10	44748	0748	6325	BUCKWHEAT	5606	荍

ROM	RAD	TEL	TOT	FC	MAT	OSH	TAG	CR	CHAR
CHYAU	140,12	5606	16	44227	0748	3854	BUCKWHEAT	5431	蕎
CHYAU	149,12	6222	19	00631	0758	8754	DRUM TOWER,(SURNAME)		譙
CHYAU	156,12	9326	19	42802	0749	5957	NIMBLE,WALK ON STILTS		趫
CHYAU	181,12	7356	21	21386	0756		HAGGARD	1997	顦
CHEAU	048,02	1564	05	11127	0743	4535	SKILLFUL,TIMELY		巧
CHEAU	061,07	1877	10	98027	0761	3663	QUIET,SAD		悄
CHEAU	061,09	1934	12	99080	0753	5596	WORRY,CHANGE COUNTENANCE		愀
CHEAU	172,03	7158.0A	11	90214	1185	0962	BIRD		雀
CHEAU	196,08	7717.0A	19	47627	1184	4618	MAGPIE		鵲
CHIAW	009,07	0195	09	29227	0759	3664	SMART		俏
CHIAW	033,04	8199.0A	07	40217	3406	7877	SHELL	3011.0A	壳
CHIAW	046,07	1495	10	29727	0760	3659	STEEP HILL		峭
CHIAW	064,12	2334.0A	15	52014	0736	7382	TO LIFT		撬
CHIAW	079,08	3011.0A	12	47247		6299	SHELL	8199.0A	殼
CHIAW	116,05	4534.1	10	30127			OPENING,INTELLIGENCE		窃
CHIAW	116,13	4534	18	30248	0751	6378	OPENING,INTELLIGENCE		竅
CHIAW	149,07	6132	14	09627	0762	3662	TO BLAME,RIDICULE	6222.0A	誚
CHIAW	149,12	6222.0A	19	00631	0758	8754	TO BLAME,RIDICULE	6132	譙
CHIAW	170,07	1495.1	10	79227	0760		STEEP HILL		陗
CHIAW	177,07	7258	16	49527	2613	3665	SCABBARD	7285	鞘
CHIAW	178,07	7285	16	49527			SCABBARD	7258	韒
CHIE	018,02	0434	04	47720	0811	4280	TO CUT		切
CHYE	009,05	8026	07	26200	0581		(PHONETIC)		伽
CHYE	140,05	5401	09	44460	0802	1089	EGGPLANT		茄
CHIEE	001,04	0011	05	77100	0803	0603	MOREOVER		且
CHIEH	018,02	0434.0A	04	47720	0811	4280	CLOSE TO		切
CHIEH	030,08	8147	11	60044	0815	8990	SPEAK EVIL,GOBBLING SOUND		喋
CHIEH	037,06	1148.0A	09	57430	0551	5046	TO BE SEPARATED FROM		契
CHIEH	038,05	1190	08	00400	0814	8989	CONCUBINE		妾
CHIEH	061,05	1845	08	94031	0810	8836	AFRAID,RUSTIC		怯
CHIEH	061,09	1948	12	91013	0805		SATISFIED,CHEERFUL		愜
CHIEH	061,10	1965.0A	13	98037	0806	5573	CONTENTED		慊
CHIEH	064,06	2173	10	57502	0808	3347	PULL OUT,TAKE FAMILY ALONG		挈

ROM	RAD	TEL	TOT	FC	MAT	OSH	TAG	CR	CHAR
CHIEH	073,10	2586	14	46727		4394	TO LEAVE/ABANDON		蝎
CHIEH	116,04	4537.1	09	30727	0813	4283	STEAL,I BEG TO PRESUME		窃
CHIEH	116,17	4537	22	30927	0813	4079	STEAL,I BEG TO PRESUME		竊
CHIEH	118,09	4640	15	88713	0804	0818	TRUNK,PORTFOLIO		篋
CHIEH	156,05	6388.0A	12	47801	1579	5946	RECLINE		趄
CHIEH	167,09	6951	17	87134	0809	5047	TO CARVE,CUT		鍥
CHIN	009,07	0187	09	27247	1108	6187	INVADE		侵
CHIN	046,12	1538	15	22182		4907	LOFTINESS (OF MOUNTAIN)		嶔
CHIN	075,05	6024.1	09	00904	0291		CLOSELY RELATED		亲
CHIN	075,07	273C	11	47947			CINNAMOMUM CASSIA		梫
CHIN	120,07	9062	13	27947			RED SILK CREST OF HELMET		綅
CHIN	145,04	5911	10	80732	1105	5818	COVERLET/QUILT		衾
CHIN	147,09	6024	16	06910	1107	7608	CLOSELY RELATED		親
CHIN	167,04	2953	12	87182	1095	4905	ROYAL		欽
CHIN	187,07	7485	17	77347	1111	6190	FLEET HORSE		駸
CHIN	195,07	764J	18	27347			DACTYLOPTERA ORIENTALIS		鰻
CHYN	019,11	0530	13	44127	1097	4786	DILIGENT		勤
CHYN	030,10	084E	13	65094			(PHONETIC)/-Z + INE(CHEM.)		嗪
CHYN	030,13	8168	15	68027		4075	HOLD IN THE MOUTH		噙
CHYN	053,04	8370	07	00227			(PERSON)		庈
CHYN	061,13	2014	17	44332	1098	8645	SOLICITOUS/THOUGHTFUL		懃
CHYN	064,08	2350.1	11	58019	1102		CAPTURE		捦
CHYN	064,12	2350	15	58027	1102	4076	CAPTURE		擒
CHYN	075,13	8589	17	48927		4077	(FRUIT)		檎
CHYN	096,08	3830	12	11207	1103	2849	(MUS. INSTR.)		琴
CHYN	114,08	4419	13	80227	1100	4074	BIRDS		禽
CHYN	115,05	4440	10	50904	1112	5554	NAME OF A DYNASTY,(SURNAME)		秦
CHYN	140,04	5355	08	44207	1104	2852	PHRAGMITES JAPONICA		芩
CHYN	140,04	5367	08	44221	1096	2049	CHINESE CELERY		芹
CHYN	140,10	5550.0A	14	44904	0294	5559	CHILI PEPPER		蓁
CHYN	142,10	9231	16	55194	1113	5557	SMALL CICADA WITH A SQUARE HEAD		螓
CHYN	142,13	586D	19	58127			REDUVIOLUS REUTERI		螼

ROM	RAD	TEL	TOT	FC	MAT	OSH	TAG	CR	CHAR
CHYN	145,04	5911.0A	10	80732	1105	5818	BURIAL GARMENTS		袞
CHYN	172,04	9540	12	80214			(BIRD)		雛
CHIIN	040,09	1392.1	12	30247			LIE DOWN		寢
CHIIN	040,11	1392	14	30247	1110	6189	LIE DOWN		寢
CHINN	064,12	8471	15	57082			TO PRESS(BELL)		摮
CHINN	085,04	3084	07	33100	1114	8530	NAME OF A RIVER		沁
CHINN	085,07	3190.0A	10	37147	1092		SOAK,IMMERSE		浸
CHINN	140,08	548A	12	44747			ARTEMISIA APIACEA		蔮
CHING	009,11	0282	13	21286	1161	8300	INCLINE,OVERTHROW,POUR OUT		傾
CHING	026,08	0615.1	10	77720			MINISTER,THOU(POET.)		卿
CHING	026,10	0615	12	77720	1155	2127	MINISTER,THOU(POET.)		卿
CHING	031,08	8191	11	60227			1884	REST-ROOM,PIGSTY		圊
CHING	084,07	8641	11	80117			7796	HYDROGEN	B6535	氫
CHING	084,08	8642	12	80217			7806	CYANOGEN		氰
CHING	085,08	3237	11	35127	1171	3697	CLEAR/PURE		清
CHING	120,08	4851.0A	14	38903	0543	8473	ARTICULATION OF JOINTS		綮
CHING	142,08	5808	14	55127	1151	3695	DRAGONFLY		蜻
CHING	159,07	6535	14	51011	1156	0127	LIGHT,HYDROGEN	D8641	輕
CHING	174,00	7230	08	50227	1168	3682	BLUE-GREEN,9TH OF MONTH(TELE.)		青
CHING	195,08	7645	19	25327	1173	3694	MACKEREL,MULLET		鯖
CHING	196,08	772A	19	57227			4634	MYCTOCORAX PRASINOSCEUS		鶄
CHYNG	009,11	0282.0A	13	21286			8300	INCLINE,OVERTHROW,POUR OUT		傾
CHYNG	018,08	0486	10	02900			2976	TATTOO CRIMINALS ON FACE	A7823	剠
CHYNG	019,08	0518	10	04927	1128	4832	VIOLENT/STRONG		勍
CHYNG	061,08	1906	11	95027	1170	3688	EMOTION		情
CHYNG	064,13	2348	17	48502	1157	3359	TO RAISE(HAND)		擎
CHYNG	072,08	2532	12	65027	1170A	3686	CLEAR(OF WEATHER)		晴
CHYNG	075,13	2913	17	48904			5388	INSTRUMENT FOR STRAIGHTENING BOWS		檠
CHYNG	094,04	8796	09	42214			(PERSON)		狂
CHYNG	140,09	551A	13	44170			SALVIA JAPONICA		勤
CHYNG	149,08	6153.0A	15	05627	1172	3685	RECEIVE,SALARY		請
CHYNG	195,08	7650.0A	19	20396	1158	8403	WHALE		鯨
CHYNG	203,08	7823	20	60396	1159	8402	TATTOO CRIMINALS ON FACE,(SURNAME)	A0486	黥
CHIING	053,11	8375	14	00286			SMALL HALL,ROOM		廎

ROM	RAD	TEL	TOT	FC	MAT	OSH	TAG	CR	CHAR
CHIING	140,05	7305	09	44227			(FIBER GRASS)		苟
CHIING	149,08	6153	15	05627	1172	3685	ASK/INVITE,PLEASE		請
CHIING	181,02	7308	11	21786	1160	8299	A SHORT WHILE AGO,100 MOU		頃
CHINQ	009,08	0241.0A	10	25227	0922		NIECE,PLAGIARIZE		倩
CHINQ	053,03	1987.1	06	00234			CELEBRATE		庆
CHINQ	061,11	1987	15	00247	1167	6477	CELEBRATE		慶
CHINQ	075,05	6024.1A	09	00904	0291		PARENTS-IN-LAW OF ONE'S OFFSPRING		亲
CHINQ	112,08	8972	13	15627			(STONE)		碃
CHINQ	112,11	4334	16	47601	1164	1116	MUSICAL STONE		磬
CHINQ	121,11	4977	17	47772	1165	1018	EXHAUSTED,ENTIRELY,STERN		腈
CHINQ	130,08	520A	12	75227			NITRILE		親
CHINQ	147,09	6024.0A	16	06910	1107	7608	PARENTS-IN-LAW OF ONE'S OFFSPRING		謦
CHINQ	149,11	6205	18	47601	1166	1169	SPEAK SOFTLY		俥
CHIO	009,07	8046	09	25206			TURN AROUND(FOOCHOW DIAL.)		穹
CHIONG	116,03	4498	08	30207	1246	4742	ARCHED,LOFTY/VAST		芎
CHIONG	140,03	5343	07	44207		4738	CONIOSELINUM UNIVITTATUM		蝥
CHIONG	167,06	9454	14	17109		0384	EYE OF AN AXE		嫒
CHYONG	038,13	1298.0A	16	46432	2877		ALONE,DESOLATE,FINE IN TEXTURE	K3560	悍
CHYONG	061,09	1930	12	97047	1249	3126	ALONE,DESOLATE	3560	煢
CHYONG	086,09	3560	13	99217	1250	7792	ALONE,DESOLATE	K1298.0A	琼
CHYONG	096,08	8825	12	10196			(RED STONE),BEAUTIFUL	3890	璃
CHYONG	096,12	8839.0A	16	17127			(RED STONE)	B3890	瓊
CHYONG	096,15	3890	19	17147	1245	6422	(RED STONE),BEAUTIFUL	8825	璚
CHYONG	096,18	8846	22	12127			(RED STONE)	B3890	衆
CHYONG	109,08	4215	13	60732	1248	5867	GAZE IN TERROR,LONELY	8917	窮
CHYONG	109,10	8917	15	60732			GAZE IN TERROR,LONELY	4215	穹
CHYONG	116,02	4522.1	07	30427			POOR,EXHAUSTED		窮
CHYONG	116,03	4498.0A	08	30207	1246	4742	ARCHED,LOFTY/VAST		竆
CHYONG	116,10	4522	15	30227	1247	4735	POOR,EXHAUSTED		笻
CHYONG	116,14	4522.2	19	30266	1247	1470	POOR,EXHAUSTED		藭
CHYONG	118,06	4582	12	88127	1252	2156	SPECIES OF BAMBOO		蛩
CHYONG	140,15	567B	19	44227		4736	ANGELICA POLYMORPHA		
CHYONG	142,06	5757	12	17136	1253	8947	GRASSHOPPER/A CRICKET,ANXIOUS		

ROM	RAD	TEL	TOT	FC	MAT	OSH	TAG	CR	CHAR
CHYONG	157,06	6417	13	17801		5990	SOUND OF TRAMPLING		琹
CHYONG	163,03	6713	06	17127	1251	2155	PLACE NAME,MOUND		邛
CHYONG	196,06	770G	17	17327			STERNA LONGIPENNIS		鴛
CHEONG	086,06	8737.0A	10	94814			THREE-CORNERED STOVE		娃
CHIOU	001,04	8002	05	72101	1213	0498	MOUND,CONFUCIUS' GIVEN NAME	A8202	丘
CHIOU	032,05	8202	08	42111	1213	0499	MOUND	A8002	坵
CHIOU	075,09	2825	13	49980	1229	5599	CATALPA/MALLOTUS JAPONICUS		楸
CHIOU	115,04	4428	09	29980	1227	5592	AUTUMN,A SWING	D7264	秋
CHIOU	140,09	5498	13	44989		5602	LESPEDEZA BICOLOR		萩
CHIOU	142,05	5739	11	52111	1214	0501	EARTHWORM		蚯
CHIOU	163,05	6726	08	77127	1215	2162	MOUND,(SURNAME)	A8002	邱
CHIOU	177,09	7264	18	49580	1231	5597	A SWING	B4428	鞦
CHIOU	195,09	7656	20	28361	1232	1972	LOACH	7655	鰌
CHIOU	195,09	7655	20	29380	1232	5600	LOACH	7656	鰍
CHIOU	196,09	7723	20	29327	1233	4681	CRANE		鶖
CHYOU	009,02	0092.0A	04	24217	1332	7904	MATCH/MATE,(SURNAME)		仇
CHYOU	009,07	8045	09	23232	1218		ORNAMENTAL CAP		俅
CHYOU	028,02	0636	04	40731			SPEAR		厹
CHYOU	031,02	0933	05	60800	1234	1889	PRISONER		囚
CHYOU	048,11	156A	14	10113			HYDROSULFURYL		巰
CHYOU	082,07	3033	11	23713	1220	7402	BALL		毬
CHYOU	085,02	3061	07	43132	1217	5688	BESEECH		求
CHYOU	085,05	3120	08	36100	2799	1890	SUBMERGE,SWIM UNDER WATER		泅
CHYOU	094,02	369A	05	44217			ARMADILLO		犰
CHYOU	096,07	3808	11	13132	1221	5689	BALL,SPHERE		球
CHYOU	096,11	3868	15	17122		4204	(GEM),TO TINKLE		璆
CHYOU	108,07	8896	12	43107			(SURNAME)		盓
CHYOU	120,07	4833	13	23932			URGENT/PRESSING		絿
CHYOU	140,02	5336	06	44417		7910	STEPPES		艽
CHYOU	142,01	5876	07	52110	1216	7072	YOUNG DRAGON WITH HORNS	9217	虬
CHYOU	142,02	9217	08	54100	1216	2715	YOUNG DRAGON WITH HORNS	5876	虯
CHYOU	142,09	9230	15	58161		1973	LARVA/GRUB		蝤
CHYOU	145,07	5941	13	43732	1222	5827	FUR/FUR COAT,(SURNAME)		裘

ROM	RAD	TEL	TOT	FC	MAT	OSH	TAG	CR	CHAR
CHYOU	148,07	6045	14	23232		5691	BENT UPWARDS,TAUT		觓
CHYOU	154,07	6334	14	63832	1223	5692	TO BRIBE		賕
CHYOU	162,07	6633	11	33303	1224	6731	COLLECT,TO MATCH		逑
CHYOU	162,09	6669	13	38306	1236	6639	END,CONSOLIDATE,STRONG		遒
CHYOU	164,02	6790	09	80601	1235	1967	TRIBAL CHIEF		酋
CHYOU	167,07	9460	15	83132			SINGLE-HEADED PICK,STONE CHISEL		銶
CHYOU	181,02	9575	11	41086			CHEEKBONE		頄
CHYOU	195,07	764K	18	23332			LEPIDOTRIGLA STRAUCHI		鯄
CHYOU	209,02	7866	16	24417		7906	CONGESTED NOSE		齨
CHEOU	119,10	4744	16	96934	1225	5095	DRY PROVISIONS,(SURNAME)		糗
CHIU	009,05	8027	07	24232		8837	(SURNAME)		佉
CHIU	017,00	0422	02	22770	3241	0968	RECEPTACLE		凵
CHIU	023,02	0575.1	04	71714			DISTRICT,DISTINGUISH,SMALL		区
CHIU	023,09	0575	11	71716	1599	0787	DISTRICT,DISTINGUISH,SMALL		區
CHIU	030,09	0831	12	69080	1206	5594	WAILING OF A CHILD		啾
CHIU	044,05	1448	08	77272	1621	1027	BENT,FEEL WRONGED		屈
CHIU	046,05	8327.0A	08	27710	1574		ROCKY HILL	8933.0A	岨
CHIU	046,11	1536	14	21716	1600	0788	RUGGED		嶇
CHIU	066,11	2423	15	71747	1602	6198	EXPEL,URGE ON	7517	敺
CHIU	073,02	2575	06	55600	1623	1846	BENT/CROOKED		曲
CHIU	109,13	4234	18	66214	1608	0941	(SURNAME)		瞿
CHIU	112,05	8933.0A	10	17610	1574		ROCKY HILL	8327.0A	砠
CHIU	113,05	4374	09	34231	1596	8840	TO EXERCISE		祛
CHIU	119,06	7363	12	95960			LEAVEN/YEAST		粬
CHIU	130,05	5167	09	74231	1597	8839	OPEN,FLANK OF ANIMAL		胠
CHIU	140,08	547F	12	44272			CHRYSENE		菣
CHIU	140,11	556A	15	44716			MISEANTHUS SACCHARIFLORUS		藘
CHIU	142,05	5747	11	57110	1619	0619	MAGGOT		蛆
CHIU	142,06	5792	12	55160	1625	1847	CRICKET		蛐
CHIU	145,05	5925	10	34231		8838	SLEEVE OPENING		祛
CHIU	149,05	6099	12	02672	1622	1022	TO BEND,YIELD		詘
CHIU	156,05	6395.1	12	47807	1618	5947	WALK FAST		趍
CHIU	156,10	6395	17	47802	1618	5962	WALK FAST		趨

ROM	RAD	TEL	TOT	FC	MAT	OSH	TAG	CR	CHAR
CHIU	158,11	6504	18	21216	1601	0796	HUMAN BODY		軀
CHIU	187,11	7517	21	71316	1602	0798	EXPEL,URGE ON	2423	驅
CHYU	019,05	0507	07	24627	1604	4815	LABOR		劬
CHYU	073,02	2575.0A	06	55600			YEAST	D7798	麯
CHYU	074,05	2593	09	77220			(SURNAME)		胊
CHYU	082,18	3042	22	62214	1609	7371	WOOLEN RUG		氍
CHYU	085,05	8667	08	37120			NAME OF A RIVER IN HOPEI		洵
CHYU	085,09	3255	12	31904	1603	5283	STREAM OR CANAL,BIG		渠
CHYU	096,13	8840	17	11132			(SURNAME),(JADE RING)		璩
CHYU	104,18	4091	23	00114	1610	9060	WORN,LEAN/THIN		癯
CHYU	109,13	4234.0A	18	66214	1608		(SURNAME)		瞿
CHYU	112,12	4336	17	11694			TRIDACNA GIGAS		磲
CHYU	118,17	4709	23	88303		6746	CRUDE BAMBOO MAT		籧
CHYU	140,12	5608	16	44904		5284	LOTUS		蕖
CHYU	140,17	5698	21	44303	1613	6745	DIANTHUS SUPERBUS,(SURNAME)		蘧
CHYU	142,06	5792.0A	12	55160	1625	1847	EARTHWORM		蛐
CHYU	144,18	5900	24	21221	1611	3018	THOROUGHFARE		衢
CHYU	159,05	9362	12	57020			ENDS OF YOKE		輈
CHYU	196,05	7702	16	27627	1606	4641	(MYNAH)		鴝
CHYU	196,18	7702.1	29	67227	1606	4607	(MYNAH)		鸜
CHYU	199,06	7798	17	45406	1626	6430	YEAST	2575.0A	麹
CHYU	199,08	7800	19	47402	1626	6432	YEAST	2575.0A	麴
CHEU	029,06	0648	08	17140	1615	6062	TAKE/FETCH		取
CHEU	038,08	1235	11	17404	1616	9051	TAKE A WIFE		娶
CHEU	073,02	2575.0B	06	55600	1623	1846	TUNE/SONG		曲
CHEU	211,09	7889	24	22727		4083	DECAYED TEETH,DENTAL CARIES		齲
CHIUH	028,03	0637	05	40731	1594	8832	GO,REMOVE		去
CHIUH	075,07	3344.1A	11	40132	0578		PITCH-DARK		桼
CHIUH	085,11	3344.0A	14	34132	0578	5675	PITCH-DARK		漆
CHIUH	147,11	6028.1	18	26210	1620	7584	TO SPY,WATCH FOR		覷
CHIUH	147,12	6028	19	26210	1620	7588	TO SPY,WATCH FOR		覰
CHIUH	156,08	6393	15	47804	1617	5964	INTEREST		趣
CHIUH	169,09	7055	17	77430	1627	3500	LIVE ALONE,QUIET		闃

ROM	RAD	TEL	TOT	FC	MAT	OSH	TAG	CR	CHAR
CHIUAN	031,08	0946.0A	11	60712	1655	1923	CIRCLE/RING/LOOP		圈
CHIUAN	061,07	1886	10	93047	1676	6465	TO REFORM		悛
CHIUAN	167,12	9504	20	87181			HALF-RING TO HELP DOOR PIVOT		鐉
CHYUAN	009,06	0158	08	28214	1667		IMMORTAL		佺
CHYUAN	011,04	0356	06	80104	1666	0337	COMPLETE(LY)		全
CHYUAN	026,06	0608·0B	08	90712	1640	7234	CURLY/CURLED		卷
CHYUAN	031,09	8192	12	60227		1887	RING,ROUND		圂
CHYUAN	061,08	1911	11	99012	1656	7236	EARNEST		惓
CHYUAN	064,06	2164	10	90502	1654	3355	FIST		拳
CHYUAN	075,02	2938.1	06	47940			POWER,AUTHORITY		权
CHYUAN	075,18	2938	22	44914	1663	0938	POWER,AUTHORITY		權
CHYUAN	085,05	3123	08	26232	1674	5645	SPRING,FOUNTAIN	8672	泉
CHYUAN	085,06	8672	09	38114	1674		SPRING,FOUNTAIN	3123	洤
CHYUAN	093,06	3675	10	28514	1668	0340	ONE-COLOR BULLOCK		牷
CHYUAN	096,09	8832	13	16132			(JADE/SHELL)		瑓
CHYUAN	104,06	4019	11	00114	1669	0344	RECOVER(FROM ILLNESS)		痊
CHYUAN	118,06	4586	12	88104	1670	0346	BAMBOO FISH-TRAP		筌
CHYUAN	140,06	5425	10	44104	1671	0345	(FRAGRANT PLANT)		荃
CHYUAN	142,08	5806	14	59112	1659	7241	WRIGGLE(AS A WORM),MELANIA LIBERTINA		蜷
CHYUAN	142,18	5880	24	54114			AULACOPHORA FEMORALIS		蠸
CHYUAN	149,06	6112	13	08614	1672	0339	EXPLAIN/COMMENT		詮
CHYUAN	157,06	9335	13	68114			TO CURL UP/CROUCH		跧
CHYUAN	157,08	6441	15	69112	1660	7235	CRUMPED,TO CURL UP		踡
CHYUAN	159,06	6530	13	58014		0341	WHEEL WITHOUT SPOKES,SMALL		輇
CHYUAN	164,10	7379	17	14614			ALDEHYDE		醛
CHYUAN	167,06	6898	14	88114	1673	0338	ESTIMATE,SELECT		銓
CHYUAN	181,18	7362	27	41286	1664	8253	CHEEK BONES		顴
CHYUAN	190,08	7576	18	72712	1661	7242	TO CURL/CURLED		鬈
CHYUAN	195,09	765L	20	26332			SARCOCHEILICHTHYS VARIEGATUS		鰁
CHEUAN	094,00	3689	04	43030	1650	5066	DOG		犬
CHEUAN	102,03	3950	08	62000	1651		FIELD DRAINS	3955	甽
CHEUAN	102,04	3955	09	63034	1651	5072	FIELD DRAINS	3950	畎
CHEUAN	120,08	4870	14	29912	1658	7240	BOUND IN A LEAGUE		綣

ROM	RAD	TEL	TOT	FC	MAT	OSH	TAG	CR	CHAR
CHIUANN	018,06	0457	08	90227	1652	4302	TICKET,DEED/BOND/CONTRACT		券
CHIUANN	019,02	0538.1	04	74427	1662	4825	PERSUADE		劝
CHIUANN	019,18	0538	20	44227	1662	4798	PERSUADE		勸
CHIUANN	046,13	7606.0A	16	22227		4141	FAT,(SURNAME)	7165.0A	巂
CHIUANN	172,05	7165.0A	13	20227	1677	4136	FAT,(SURNAME)	7606.0A	雋
CHIUE	086,04	7448	08	95830			ALKYNE		炔
CHIUE	121,04	4972	10	85730	1708	5206	LACK,VACANT POST,SCARCE		缺
CHIUE	169,10	7067.0A	18	77482	1712	3499	DEFICIENCY		闕
CHYUE	104,11	4063	16	00127	1710	1094	LAME		瘸
CHIUEH	026,05	0606	07	47720	1183	2141	DECLINE,NEVERTHELESS	0611	却
CHIUEH	026,07	0611	09	87620	1183	2122	DECLINE,NEVERTHELESS	0606	卻
CHIUEH	061,11	1952	15	47334		8668	HONEST		愨
CHIUEH	064,10	2274	13	54014	1713	0966	KNOCK/BEAT,CONSULT		搉
CHIUEH	112,05	8939	10	11660			CLASHING SOUND OF STONES		砳
CHIUEH	112,07	4292	12	17627		3701	AUTHENTICATED,SOLID/FIRM	4315	确
CHIUEH	112,08	8950	13	14661			(GEMS)		碏
CHIUEH	112,10	8959	15	10627			SOLID/FIRM	B4315	碻
CHIUEH	112,10	4315	15	14614	1181	0964	AUTHENTICATED,SOLID/FIRM	4292	確
CHIUEH	112,14	8939.1	19	77601			CLASHING SOUND OF STONES		礐
CHIUEH	169,09	7060	17	77430	1711	3501	SHUT,SECTION OF A SONG		闋
CHIUEH	169,10	7067	18	77482	1712	3499	IMPERIAL CITY,(SURNAME)		闕
CHIUEH	172,03	7158	11	90214	1185	0962	BIRD		雀
CHIUEH	196,08	7717	19	47627	1184	4618	MAGPIE		鵲
CHIUN	162,07	6645	11	33304	1733	6756	SHRINK FROM		逡
CHYUN	050,07	5942.1	10	17227	1738	3964	SKIRT		帬
CHYUN	123,07	5028	13	17501	1737	2559	CROWD,FLOCK		羣
CHYUN	123,07	5028.1	13	18651	1737	2543	CROWD,FLOCK		群
CHYUN	145,07	5942	12	37267	1738	1146	SKIRT		裙
CHONG	010,04	0339	06	00213	1520	7685	FILL		充
CHONG	015,04	0394	06	35106	1523		DASH AGAINST,WASH OUT	A5897	冲
CHONG	061,04	1814	07	95006	1522	2671	UNEASY		忡
CHONG	061,11	8403	15	50337	1526	8558	STUPID/DULL		憃
CHONG	061,12	2002	15	90014	1529	0452	UNSETTLED		憧

ROM	RAD	TEL	TOT	FC	MAT	OSH	TAG	CR	CHAR
CHONG	064,11	2295	14	55077	1527		TO POUND,RUN AGAINST		搏
CHONG	085,04	3095	07	35106	1523	2674	DASH AGAINST,WASH OUT	0394	沖
CHONG	124,04	5039	10	15100			SOAR		翀
CHONG	134,05	5277	11	50777	1525	1059	TO POUND(GRAIN)		舂
CHONG	140,06	540B	10	44213			LEONURUS SIBIRICUS		茺
CHONG	144,09	5897	15	21221	1532	3017	DASH AGAINST	A0394	衝
CHORNG	046,08	1504	11	22901	1528	8376	TO HONOR,LOFTY		崇
CHORNG	142,00	5722	06	50136	1518	8899	INSECT,WORM	5849	虫
CHORNG	142,12	5849	18	50136	1519	8916	INSECT,WORM	5722	蟲
CHORNG	166,02	6850.0A	09	20104	1509	0462	DOUBLE,TO REPEAT		重
CHOONG	014,17	1404.1	19	37211	1534	7334	TO FAVOR		寵
CHOONG	032,08	1069	11	49127			UNEASY		埫
CHOONG	040,17	1404	20	30211	1534	7335	TO FAVOR		寵
CHONQ	015,04	0394.0A	06	35106	1523	2673	TOWARDS,OF GREAT FORCE	5897.0A	冲
CHONQ	043,09	1433	12	42011	1512		SWOLLEN		尰
CHONQ	064,09	8443	12	52014	1531	0466	PUSH INTO,POKE OUT,PUNCH		撞
CHONQ	144,09	5897.0A	15	21221	1532	3017	TOWARDS,OF GREAT FORCE	0394.0A	衝
CHONQ	167,06	6893	14	80113	1521	7686	PISTOL		銃
CHOU	064,05	2132	08	55060	1314	1835	DRAW OUT	A2294	抽
CHOU	064,10	2294	13	50063	1413	1821	DRAW OUT,SPASM	A2132	搐
CHOU	064,10	8454	13	57027	1329	4453	PLUCK(STRINGED INSTRUMENT)		搊
CHOU	093,23	8790	27	20501			(SURNAME),BREATHING OF BOVINE		犨
CHOU	104,11	4065	16	00122	1328	4216	HEAL		瘳
CHOU	118,10	4641	16	88427			BASKET FOR STRAINING,TO STRAIN		篘
CHOU	120,05	4795.0A	11	25960	1315	1839	CLUE,INVESTIGATE,UNWIND		紬
CHOUR	009,02	0092	04	24217	1332	7904	ENMITY,FEUD	6241	仇
CHOUR	009,14	0321	16	24241	1321	3181	COMRADE/COMPANION		儔
CHOUR	032,03	1101.0A	06	42100			DITCH		圳
CHOUR	050,14	1621.0A	17	44241	6128	5722	CANOPY/CURTAIN		幬
CHOUR	061,08	1907	11	97020	1316	3886	FORLORN		惆
CHOUR	061,09	1935	13	29338	1325	8659	WORRY ABOUT		愁
CHOUR	093,16	3687	20	20501	1334		GRUNTING OF OX		犨
CHOUR	102,14	3985	19	64041	1322	3179	ARABLE FIELDS		疇

ROM	RAD	TEL	TOT	FC	MAT	OSH	TAG	CR	CHAR
CHOUR	115,08	4464	13	27920	1317	3889	THICK(OF SOUP),MANY		稠
CHOUR	118,14	4693	20	88641	1323	3187	MANAGE/PLAN		籌
CHOUR	118,14	4693.1	20	88641			MANAGE/PLAN		籌
CHOUR	120,05	4795	11	25960	1315	1839	SILK	4846	紬
CHOUR	120,08	4846	14	27920	1318	3891	SILK	C4795	綢
CHOUR	142,07	575E	13	53132			MELANTUS LEGATUS		蛛
CHOUR	145,08	5948	13	37220	1319	3888	COVERLET,BED CURTAIN		裯
CHOUR	149,16	6241	23	20214	1333	0873	ENMITY,FEUD	0092	儔
CHOUR	149,16	6241.1	23	20601	1333	1159	ENMITY,FEUD		讐
CHOUR	157,14	6486	21	64141	1324	3177	HESITATE		躊
CHOUR	164,06	6804	13	12600	1320	2839	REWARD/COMPENSATE	9431	酬
CHOUR	164,06	6804.1	13	13642	1320	3256	REWARD/COMPENSATE		酧
CHOUR	164,14	9431	21	14641			REWARD/COMPENSATE	6804	醻
CHOUR	195,07	9644	18	27236		8781	LEUCISCUS MACROPUS		鯈
CHOOU	001,03	0010	04	17105	1330	0533	1-3 A.M.,CLOWN,UGLY	G6823	丑
CHOOU	009,07	8051	09	80121			(SURNAME)		刅
CHOOU	075,04	8537.0A	08	47910		0539	HANDCUFFS		杻
CHOOU	109,09	4197	14	69080	1326	5595	TAKE A LOOK AT		瞅
CHOOU	109,13	4197.1	17	69038	1326	8660	TAKE A LOOK AT		瞉
CHOOU	164,10	6823	17	16613	1327	7638	UGLY	C0010	醜
CHOOU	194,14	9637	24	46613			REJECT,DISAGREEABLE		魗
CHOW	132,04	5263	10	26430	1331	5093	SMELL BAD		臭
CHU	017,03	0427	05	22772	1409	1020	GO OUT,AN. FOR PLAYS	D7892	出
CHU	018,05	0443	07	37220	1390	4277	AT THE BEGINNING		初
CHU	075,11	2880.0A	15	41927	5863	4558	SIMARUBACEAE		樗
CHU	195,05	762G	16	22372			TYLOSURUS ANASTOMELLA		魖
CHU	203,05	7819	17	62372	1410	1026	DEGRADE,DISMISS		黜
CHU	211,05	7892	20	27720	4945	4417	AN. FOR PLAYS	B0427	齣
CHWU	009,16	0328.0A	18	24260	1399	1630	SAVINGS,TO SAVE		儲
CHWU	027,10	1676.1	12	71240	1400	3167	KITCHEN		厨
CHWU	053,12	1676	15	00240	1400	3170	KITCHEN		廚
CHWU	058,02	5368.1	05	27177			CUT GRASS,HAY,(SURNAME)		刍
CHWU	075,14	8599	18	41940		3172	WARDROBE,CABINET		櫥

ROM	RAD	TEL	TOT	FC	MAT	OSH	TAG	CR	CHAR
CHWU	085,10	3315	13	38194	1392	8504	NAME OF A RIVER		滁
CHWU	118,10	4651	16	88294		8505	CRUDE BAMBOO MAT		籇
CHWU	127,05	5092	11	57910			HOE	5094	耝
CHWU	127,07	5094	13	54927	1404	4792	HOE	6915	耡
CHWU	140,04	5368	08	27427	1405	4451	CUT GRASS,HAY,(SURNAME)	5542	芻
CHWU	140,10	9184	14	44294			HEDYSARUM		除
CHWU	140,10	5542	14	44427	1405	4456	CUT GRASS,HAY	5368	蒭
CHWU	142,07	5773	13	58194	5872	8507	TOAD,BUFO VULGARIS		蜍
CHWU	157,13	6484	20	64164	1398	1649	HESITATE		躇
CHWU	157,14	6480	21	61140			UNDECIDED,IRRESOLUTE		躕
CHWU	157,15	6480.1	22	60140	1402	3171	UNDECIDED,IRRESOLUTE		躊
CHWU	167,05	6882	13	87110	1403	0604	HOE	6915	鉏
CHWU	167,07	6915	15	84127	1403	4791	HOE	6882	鋤
CHWU	170,07	7110	10	78294	1391	8503	EXCEPT,DIVIDE		除
CHWU	172,10	7176	18	20414	1406	0892	CHICK/YOUNG BIRD	7730	雛
CHWU	196,10	7730	21	27427	1406		CHICK/YOUNG BIRD	7176	鶵
CHUU	009,16	0328	18	24260			SAVINGS,TO SAVE		儲
CHUU	066,02	5710.1A	05	23400			GET ALONG WITH,DEAL WITH		处
CHUU	075,04	2643	08	48940	1389	2433	PESTLE,TO POKE		杵
CHUU	075,09	2806	13	44801	1393	6030	ANCIENT PLACE NAME,(SURNAME)		楚
CHUU	075,09	2816	13	44960	1396	1635	BROUSSONETIA KASINOKI		楮
CHUU	112,05	4342.1	10	12672			FOUNDATION		础
CHUU	112,13	4342	18	14681	1395	6031	FOUNDATION		礎
CHUU	141,05	5710.0A	11	21241	1407	6491	GET ALONG WITH,DEAL WITH		處
CHUU	142,10	582D	16	57127			HISTER JEKELI		蝺
CHUU	145,09	5969	14	34260	1397	1633	(SURNAME)		褚
CHUH	007,01	8015	03	10201	1408	3014	STEP WITH THE RIGHT FOOT		亍
CHUH	009,08	0209	10	27240	5882	6088	BEGIN		俶
CHUH	061,05	1847	08	93094	1411	7078	FEARFUL/TIMID		怵
CHUH	064,10	2294.0A	13	50063	1413	1821	LEAD/PULL		搐
CHUH	066,02	5710.1	05	23400			A PLACE,RESPECT		处
CHUH	076,13	8621	17	67182			ANGRY,(PERSON)		歜
CHUH	102,05	3964	10	00603	1412	1820	LIVESTOCK		畜

ROM	RAD	TEL	TOT	FC	MAT	OSH	TAG	CR	CHAR
CHUH	109,19	4238	24	40117	1415	0751	LOFTY,UPRIGHT		矗
CHUH	120,05	4806	11	22972	1274	1025	DEFICIENCY,CRIMSON SILK,TO STITCH		絀
CHUH	141,05	5710	11	21241	1407	6491	A PLACE,RESPECT		處
CHUH	148,06	6051.1	13	25236			TOUCH,KNOCK AGAINST		觕
CHUH	148,13	6051	20	26227	1416	4471	TOUCH,KNOCK AGAINST		觸
CHUH	149,05	6099.0A	12	02672	1622	1022	DEGRADE,DISMISS	7819	詘
CHUH	163,10	9406	13	07627			(SURNAME)		鄐
.CHU	050,05	1590.0B	08	17227			BROOM		帚
CHUA	076,08	2964.0A	12	97882	2857	4954	(ONOMAT.)/A CRASHING SOUND		欻
CHUA	086,04	8733	08	20331			ACCOMPANY/TAKE(AMOY DIAL.)		炰
CHOAI	064,09	2260	12	52027	1422	3760	SURMISE		揣
CHUAY	030,12	0872.0A	15	66047	1427	6071	TO GNAW/EAT RAVENOUSLY		嘬
CHUAY	157,09	6447	16	62127	1423	3756	TRAMPLE,KICK		踹
CHUAN	047,00	1556	03	22000	1439	8981	STREAMS		巛
CHUAN	047,00	1557	03	22000	1439	2833	RIVER		川
CHUAN	064,10	2268.0A	13	57032			DRIVE AWAY		搋
CHUAN	084,03	305C	07	80217			TRITIUM		氚
CHUAN	116,04	4502	09	30241	1442	3334	PIERCE,TO THREAD,WEAR		穿
CHUAN	167,09	696B	17	83141			HAMMER		鐩
CHWAN	009,11	0278	13	25243	1446	3292	PASS ON		傳
CHWAN	075,08	2772	12	49912	1657	7239	WOODEN BOWL		棬
CHWAN	075,10	2796	14	47932	1448	5739	BEAM,RAFTERS		椽
CHWAN	137,04	5303	10	28432			SHIP/BOAT	5307	舩
CHWAN	137,05	5307	11	27461	1447	1438	SHIP/BOAT		船
CHWAN	162,09	6660	13	32302	1444	6691	HURRY/GO TO AND FRO		遄
CHOAN	030,09	0820	12	62027	1443	3758	TO PANT		喘
CHOAN	136,00	5292	06	25200	1441	2560	ERRONEOUS		舛
CHOAN	140,06	540A	10	44252		2565	THEA SINENSIS		荈
CHUANN	002,06	0025	07	50006	1445	2676	STRING		串
CHUANN	096,03	3772	07	12100			JADE RING		玔
CHUANN	167,03	6861	11	82100	1440	2834	BRACELET		釧
CHUANG	018,10	0482.0A	12	82600	1462	2872	TO WOUND/A WOUND		創
CHUANG	031,04	0935.0A	07	26000		1933	WINDOW,SHUTTER	4514	囱

ROM	RAD	TEL	TOT	FC	MAT	OSH	TAG	CR	CHAR
CHUANG	062,10	0482.1A	14	83250	1462	6904	TO WOUND/A WOUND		戧
CHUANG	091,11	3656	15	26030	1461	8602	WINDOW/SHUTTER	4514	牕
CHUANG	104,04	4056.1	09	00112			SORE/SKIN ULCER		疕
CHUANG	104,10	4056	15	00167	1463	1143	SORE/SKIN ULCER		瘡
CHUANG	116,07	4514	12	30602	1461	1934	WINDOW,SHUTTER	3656	窗
CHWANG	050,12	1617	15	40214	1464	0456	AN. FOR HOUSES/TENTS		幢
CHWANG	053,04	1643	07	00294	1459	5281	BED	3646	床
CHWANG	090,04	3646	08	24290	1459	5269	BED	1643	牀
CHWANG	104,00	3994	05	00100	4675	4232	DISEASE		疒
CHOANG	169,10	7068	18	77327	1465	3496	RUSH INTO		闖
CHUANQ	018,06	8103	09	87420		4314	CREATE	0482	剙
CHUANQ	018,10	0482	12	82600	1462	2872	CREATE		創
CHUANQ	061,10	1955	13	98067	6710	1134	SAD/SORRY		愴
CHUANQ	062,10	0482.1	14	83250	1462		CREATE		戧
CHUANQ	064,12	2326.0A	15	50014			BUMP INTO		撞
CHUANQ	169,10	7068.0A	18	77327	1465	3496	TO CAUSE TROUBLE		闖
CHUEI	030,04	0706	07	67082	1476	4915	TO BLOW		吹
CHUEI	086,04	3507	08	97882	1477	4953	DRESS FOOD,TO STEAM		炊
CHUEI	214,04	9699	21	87282	1476	4931	TO BLOW	0706	龡
CHWEI	031,09	8192.0A	12	60227		1887	NAME OF A MOUNTAIN		圌
CHWEI	032,05	0987	08	20104	1478	0409	HANG DOWN		垂
CHWEI	064,08	2211	11	52014	1479	0415	TO HAMMER,BEAT WITH THE FIST	2285	捶
CHWEI	064,10	2285	13	57037	1483	6625	TO HAMMER,BEAT WITH THE FIST	2211	椎
CHWEI	075,08	2785.0A	12	40914	1484	0902	A HAMMER	2846	棰
CHWEI	075,08	2774	12	42914			FLOG,WHIP	4618	棰
CHWEI	075,10	2846	14	47937	1484	6626	A HAMMER	2785.0A	槌
CHWEI	118,09	4618	15	88104	1480	0416	FLOG,WHIP	2774	箠
CHWEI	167,08	6925	16	82114	1482	0410	WEIGHT OF STEEL YARD,HAMMER		錘
CHWEI	167,10	6958	18	87137	1485	6624	A HAMMER		鎚
CHWEI	170,08	7114	11	72214	1481	0414	FRONTIER		陲
CHUEN	072,05	2504	09	50603	1493	1578	SPRING		春
CHUEN	075,04	8535	08	45917	1495	7410	(TREE)		杶
CHUEN	075,09	2797	13	45963	1494	1579	CEDRELA CHINENSIS,FATHER		椿

ROM	RAD	TEL	TOT	FC	MAT	OSH	TAG	CR	CHAR
CHUEN	075,12	2902	16	48927			(TREE)		楢
CHUEN	159,09	6556	16	52064		1717	HEARSE		轀
CHUEN	195,09	765E	20	25363			SCOMBEROMORUS SINENSIS		鰆
CHWEN	030,07	0782	10	71263	1491	1399	LIP	5188	唇
CHWEN	045,01	1470.0B	04	50717	6592	7405	NAME OF A HSIEN IN SHENSI		屯
CHWEN	085,08	3196	11	30147	5932	3124	PURE,GENUINE	4783	淳
CHWEN	085,09	3196.1	12	30166	5932	1529	PURE,GENUINE		滰
CHWEN	085,11	3349	14	31127	1492	3639	SHORE		漘
CHWEN	112,08	6815.1	13	10647			STEROLS		碻
CHWEN	120,04	4783	10	25917	5930	7412	PURE,GENUINE	3196	純
CHWEN	130,07	5188	11	71227	1491	3638	LIP	0782	脣
CHWEN	140,10	5573	14	44917	5931	7413	BRASENIA PURPUREA	5574	蒓
CHWEN	140,11	5574	15	44403	5931	3300	BRASENIA PURPUREA	5573	蓴
CHWEN	164,08	6815	15	10647	5933	3120	STEROLS		醇
CHWEN	167,08	6935	16	80147		3117	COPPER DRUM		錞
CHWEN	195,08	764W	19	20347			SCOMBEROMORUS SINENSIS		鰆
CHWEN	196,08	7718	19	06427	1497	4625	QUAIL		鶉
CHOEN	061,09	8401	13	50336		8571	BLUNT,STUPID,TO WIGGLE(OF WORMS)	5868	惷
CHOEN	142,15	5868	21	50136	1496	8907	BLUNT,STUPID,WIGGLE(OF WORMS)	8401	蠢
CHUO	062,14	2067	18	13250	1283	6903	TO PRICK,WOODEN OR RUBBER STAMP		戳
CHUO	120,08	4862.0A	14	21946	1284	2307	SPACIOUS,WELL-OFF		綽
CHUOH	030,08	0799	11	67047	1277	6079	SIP,SUCK	2969	啜
CHUOH	037,10	8270	13	27430			(RABBIT)		奊
CHUOH	038,08	8289	11	41446		2308	WEAK/DELICATE		婥
CHUOH	038,09	1249	12	44464			RECALCITRANT		婼
CHUOH	061,08	1914	11	97047	1278		MOURNFUL,UNCERTAIN		惙
CHUOH	076,08	8616	12	77482	1277	4956	SIP,SUCK	0799	歠
CHUOH	076,15	2969	19	77682	1277	4920	SIP,SUCK	0799	歠
CHUOH	120,08	4862	14	21946	1284	2307	SPACIOUS,WELL-OFF		綽
CHUOH	159,08	6541	15	57047	1280	6082	TO STOP/CEASE		輟
CHUOH	162,00	6595	07	20801	1282	5991	WALKING		辵
CHUOH	162,08	9376	12	31304		6648	DISTANT,HIGHLY,APPARENT		逴
CHUOH	164,08	6817	15	17647	1281	6080	POUR LIBATION ON GROUND		醊

ROM	RAD	TEL	TOT	FC	MAT	OSH	TAG	CR	CHAR
CHUOH	211,07	7887	22	26781	1287	5978	SMALL-MINDED,DIRTY		嶷
CHY	030,03	0676	06	68017	1047	7962	EAT	0848	吃
CHY	030,09	0848	12	67034	1047	5048	EAT	0676	喫
CHY	030,10	0844	13	62036	1019	8920	SCOFF AT/SNEER AT		嗤
CHY	038,10	1263	13	42436	1020	8921	UGLY WOMAN		媸
CHY	059,20	1759	23	12222			HORNLESS DRAGON	5835	彲
CHY	064,10	2312	13	50027			WIELD(PEN),TO SPREAD(FAME)		摛
CHY	098,07	3912	12	41217		7935	LARGE WINE JAR		瓻
CHY	104,08	4035	13	00160	1025	1094	IMBECILE,SENTIMENTAL	4082	痴
CHY	104,14	4082	19	00181	1025	6037	IMBECILE,SENTIMENTAL	4035	癡
CHY	109,06	4184	11	67027	1039	4257	GRITTY SECRETION IN EYES		眵
CHY	118,05	4565	11	88603	1022	1465	TO WHIP WITH BAMBOO STRIPS		笞
CHY	120,07	4832	13	24927	1015	3957	FINE FIBERS OF HEMP,LINEN		絺
CHY	142,04	5736	10	22136	1018	8918	WORM,IGNORANT,(SURNAME)		蚩
CHY	142,11	5835	17	50127		4072	HORNLESS DRAGON	1759	螭
CHY	163,07	6741	10	47227	1014	2214	NAME OF AN ANCIENT CITY,(SURNAME)		郗
CHY	194,11	7620	21	20212	1017	7656	MOUNTAIN ELF		魑
CHY	196,05	7689	16	77727	1031	4653	SCOPS OWL		鴟
CHY	202,11	7813	23	20127			BIRDLIME		黐
CHYR	021,09	0555	11	61801	5796	6014	SPOON		匙
CHYR	032,05	8201	08	42140	1029	6849	ISLET/ROCK IN RIVER		坻
CHYR	032,11	1062	14	47153	1023	2518	COURTYARD		墀
CHYR	044,01	1439.0A	04	77807	1045	4968	SIZE/MEASUREMENT		尺
CHYR	057,03	1716.0A	06	14212	5767	7424	RELAX		弛
CHYR	060,05	8386	08	22240			GO TO AND FRO		彽
CHYR	064,06	2170	09	54041	1035	3238	TO HOLD,SUPPORT		持
CHYR	085,03	3069	06	34112	1032	7427	POND		池
CHYR	118,03	9006	09	88712		7437	BAMBOO FLUTE WITH 8 HOLES		篪
CHYR	118,08	4609	14	88217	1027		BAMBOO FLUTE WITH 8 HOLES	4654	箎
CHYR	118,10	4654	16	88217	1027	7678	BAMBOO FLUTE WITH 8 HOLES	9006	麗
CHYR	140,05	0421	09	44214			NAME OF A HSIEN IN SHANTUNG		茌
CHYR	140,06	9173	10	44214		0158	PLACE NAME		茬
CHYR	142,05	9220	11	52140	1030	6862	ANT EGGS		蚳

ROM	RAD	TEL	TOT	FC	MAT	OSH	TAG	CR	CHAR
CHYR	157,08	6442	15	66100	1026	1092	HESITATING		踟
CHYR	162,04	6688.1	08	37308			LATE		迡
CHYR	162,11	6688	15	37305	1024	6649	LATE		遲
CHYR	187,03	7459	13	74312	1034	7424	GALLOP		馳
CHYY	009,06	0172	08	27227	1038	4258	EXTRAVAGANT		侈
CHYY	030,04	8125	07	67037		4969	FOOT(ENGLISH)		呎
CHYY	044,01	1439	04	77807	1045	4968	A CHINESE FOOT,A RULER (MEASURE)		尺
CHYY	061,06	1866	10	13100	1036	8528	SHAME	5103	恥
CHYY	077,04	7876.1	08	21772			TOOTH		齿
CHYY	128,04	5103	10	11110	1036	0478	SHAME	1866	耻
CHYY	145,10	5972	15	32217	1028	7676	DEPRIVE OF,UNDRESS		褫
CHYY	149,06	9291	13	07627			TO SEPARATE		誃
CHYY	151,04	6262	11	14147	5805	6209	SALTED FERMENTED BEANS		豉
CHYY	211,00	7876	15	21772	1037	0983	TOOTH		齒
CHYH	009,11	8069	13	22291	1040	8390	HINDER,DETAIN		傺
CHYH	019,07	0515	09	54927	1050	4823	IMPERIAL ORDERS	2406	勅
CHYH	019,08	8111	10	44927	3769	4822	IMPERIAL ORDERS	0515	敕
CHYH	030,02	0667	05	64010	1046	7352	HOOT AT		叱
CHYH	030,09	0804	12	00602		1356	(NOT)JUST/(NOT)ONLY		啻
CHYH	060,00	1761	03	20202	1044	2004	STEP WITH LEFT FOOT		彳
CHYH	061,11	2028	14	92091			INSECURE,PERTURBED		憏
CHYH	064,05	8424	08	54030	1051	5199	BEAT/FLOG		抶
CHYH	066,07	2406	11	58940	1050	6387	IMPERIAL ORDERS	0515	敕
CHYH	068,01	2444	05	72231	1052	2051	REPRIMAND		斥
CHYH	109,05	4182	10	63060	2965	1450	GAZE AT		眙
CHYH	119,12	9045	18	94965			FOOD,TO COOK	7434	糦
CHYH	124,04	5041	10	47402	1042	6225	WING		翅
CHYH	124,09	504C	15	78701			CONTOUR FEATHERS		翨
CHYH	1⁵⁵,00	6375	07	40331	1048	8513	SCARLET,BARE		赤
CHYH	157,07	643A	14	52801		5983	TO HOP ON ONE FOOT		踀
CHYH	184,04	7389	12	88727	1049	4841	TO ORDER/DIRECT,STERN		飭
CHYH	184,12	7434	20	84765			FOOD,TO COOK	9045	饎
CHYH	196,13	9683	24	3⁷127			BIRD-LIKE MANDARIN DUCK		鶒

ROM	RAD	TEL	TOT	FC	MAT	OSH	TAG	CR	CHAR
DA	030,13	8174	16	64035	5957	6654	COMMAND TO A HORSE,(PHONETIC)		
DA	032,12	8256	15	48161			ROUND HILL		
DA	064,10	2290	13	54061	5953	1202	BUILD(SCAFFOLDING),TAKE(BOAT/TRAIN)		
DA	118,06	4594.0A	12	88601	5951	1203	TO ANSWER,AGREE	9171.0A	
DA	140,06	9171.0A	10	4460	5952	1198	TO ANSWER/AGREE	4594.0A	
DA	145,10	5968	15	34261	5955	1201	CUMMERBUND		
DAR	038,05	1199	08	46410	5946		CONCUBINE OF LAST SHANG EMPEROR		
DAR	061,05	1834	08	96010	5947	0014	GRIEVED,TO ALARM		
DAR	064,02	2092.0A	05	51020	5945	2992	DOZEN		
DAR	096,13	387A	17	14134			DAMMAR		
DAR	104,10	4079.1	15	00161			SORE/BOIL/SCAB		
DAR	104,12	4079	17	00161	5954	1205	SORE/BOIL/SCAB		
DAR	118,05	4572	11	88106	5948	0058	(SURNAME),ROUGH BAMBOO MAT		
DAR	118,06	4594	12	88601	5951	1203	ANSWER	9171	
DAR	140,06	9171	10	44601	5952	1198	ANSWER	4594	
DAR	162,03	6671.1	07	34303			ATTAIN/REACH		
DAR	162,09	6671	13	34304	5956	6651	ATTAIN/REACH		
DAR	177,05	9557	14	46510	5949	0017	DRESSED LEATHER,(PHONETIC)		
DAR	177,13	7275	22	44534	5960	6655	NOMADIC TRIBE		
DAA	064,02	2092	05	51020	5945	2992	TO STRIKE		
DAH	037,00	1129	03	40030	5943	5001	BIG/GREAT		
DAI	030,04	0714	07	60904	5986	5305	STUPID	3738	
DAI	060,06	1769.0A	09	24241		3236	TO STAY		
DAI	094,10	3738	14	23134	5986	5067	STUPID,STAY	0714	
DAE	078,00	2983	04	10207	5988	4266	EVIL		
DAE	162,08	6649.0A	12	35303	5992	6732	CATCH/SEIZE,UNTIL		
DAY	009,03	0108	05	23240	5996	6874	SUBSTITUTE,GENERATION,DYNASTY		
DAY	009,06	8037	08	21247			TO WEAR(HAT/GLASSES ETC.)	2071	
DAY	032,08	1011	11	45132	5994	5694	DAM		
DAY	037,00	1129.0A	03	40030	5943	5001	DOCTOR		
DAY	046,05	1486	08	23772	5997	0999	NAME OF A MOUNTAIN IN SHANTUNG		
DAY	050,06	1601.1	09	44227			BELT,CARRY		
DAY	050,08	1601	11	44227	6005	3979	BELT,CARRY		

ROM	RAD	TEL	TOT	FC	MAT	OSH	TAG	CR	CHAR
DAY	060,06	1769	09	24241	6002	3236	WAIT,TREAT		待
DAY	061,05	1836	09	23336	5989	8564	NEGLIGENT		怠
DAY	062,14	2071	18	43850	6003	6985	WEAR(GLASSES/HAT/GLOVES)		戴
DAY	078,05	2990	09	13263	5990	1455	PERILOUS,ALMOST		殆
DAY	096,05	3782	09	13140	5998	6875	TORTOISE-SHELL	3848	玳
DAY	096,09	3848	13	15157	5998	4888	TORTOISE-SHELL	3782	瑇
DAY	099,03	393A	08	43700			GLYCOSIDE		甙
DAY	120,05	4805	11	23960	5991	1459	TO FOOL,PRETEND,BIND		紿
DAY	145,05	5915	11	23732	5999	5828	BAG/SACK		袋
DAY	145,18	6004	23	33250	6004	6986	UNTIDY(IN DRESS)		襪
DAY	154,05	6313	12	23806	6000	8222	LEND/LOAN		貸
DAY	162,05	6610	09	33306	5992	6618	UNTIL CATCH/SEIZE	A6649	迨
DAY	162,08	6649	12	35303	5992	6732	UNTIL,CATCH/SEIZE	A6610	逮
DAY	171,00	7152.0A	08	50132	5993	5693	UNTIL,ABBR. OF 7153	A6649	隶
DAY	173,16	7226	24	15733	5995	6733	CLOUDY SKY		靆
DAY	203,05	7818	17	23331	6001	8732	BLACK,EYEBROW INK		黛
DAN	003,03	0030	04	77440	6026	4106	RED,CINNABAR		丹
DAN	009,13	0317	15	27261	6042	1178	CARRY	D2137	儋
DAN	024,06	0830.1	08	80506	6030		SINGLE,A BILL		单
DAN	030,09	0830	12	66506	6030	2632	SINGLE,A BILL		單
DAN	064,05	2137	08	56010	6039	0018	TAKE RESPONSIBILITY,CARRY	2351	担
DAN	064,13	2351	16	57061	6044	1180	TAKE RESPONSIBILITY,CARRY	2137	擔
DAN	078,12	3000	16	16259	6032	2638	TO EXHAUST,ENTIRELY		殫
DAN	104,12	8883.0A	17	00156	6033	2644	(DISEASE)		癉
DAN	109,04	4167	09	64012	6029	7737	GAZE INTENTLY		眈
DAN	112,04	8929	09	17640			WHITE STONE		研
DAN	118,12	4673	18	88506	6034	2645	ROUND BASKET FOR COOKED RICE		簞
DAN	128,04	5104	10	14112	6028	7740	INDULGE,PROCRASTINATE	6502	耽
DAN	128,04	5106.1	10	17150	6027	4131	EARS WITHOUT RIM		聃
DAN	128,05	5106	11	15147	6027		EARS WITHOUT RIM		耼
DAN	145,12	5986	17	36256	6035	2635	GARMENT WITHOUT A LINING		襌
DAN	158,04	6502	11	24212	6029	7741	INDULGE,PROCRASTINATE	5104	躭
DAN	163,12	6779	15	67527	6036	2193	NAME OF A HSIEN IN HOPEI		鄲

ROM	RAD	TEL	TOT	FC	MAT	OSH	TAG	CR	CHAR
DAN	164,04	6795.0A	11	14612	0309	7738	ADDICTED TO LIQUOR		酖
DAN	187,12	7521	22	71346			BLACK HORSE WITH WHITE STOCKINGS		驔
DAAN	008,11	0083	13	00106	6048	0040	SINCERE,(SURNAME)		亶
DAAN	064,05	2137.0B	08	56010	6039		TO DUST	8473.0B	担
DAAN	064,12	232A	15	51046	6062	2293	TO DUST	2137.0B	撣
DAAN	064,12	8473	15	56056	6073	2637	TO DUST	2137.0B	撢
DAAN	104,05	4010	10	00116	6040	0020	JAUNDICE	8883.0A	疸
DAAN	120,04	4778	10	24912			SILK FRINGE OF A CORONET		紞
DAAN	130,05	9116	09	76210	6047	0019	GALL BLADDER,COURAGE	5237	胆
DAAN	130,13	5237	17	77261	6047	1181	GALL BLADDER,COURAGE	9116	膽
DANN	009,05	0141	07	26210	6038	0015	BUT		但
DANN	009,12	8074	14	26256			SEVERE,GREAT		儃
DANN	030,08	8145	11	67077	6052	1051	EAT,ENTICE	0797	啗
DANN	030,08	0797	11	69089	6052	5626	EAT,ENTICE		啖
DANN	030,12	0885	15	68040	6052	6327	EAT,ENTICE	0797	噉
DANN	057,12	1734	15	16256	6072	2639	BULLET		彈
DANN	061,12	1998	15	96056	6031	2634	TO DREAD		憚
DANN	064,05	2137.0A	08	56010	6039	0018	LOAD,A PICUL (133.33 LBS.)	2351.0A	担
DANN	064,13	2351.0A	16	57061	6044	1180	LOAD,A PICUL(133.33 LBS.)	2137.0A	擔
DANN	072,01	2481	05	60100	6037	0011	MORNING		旦
DANN	084,08	8644	12	80817		7816	NITROGEN		氮
DANN	085,08	3225	11	39189	6053	5630	INSIPID,LIGHT,NITROGEN		淡
DANN	085,13	3422	16	37161	6045	1186	TRANQUIL/PLACID		澹
DANN	098,13	3924	18	21217			LARGE EARTHEN JAR		甔
DANN	104,12	8883	17	00156	6033	2644	TO HATE		癉
DANN	112,00	4258.0A	05	10600	5813	1101	10 PECKS		石
DANN	116,08	4513	13	30777		1058	PIT/CAVE		窞
DANN	117,05	454H	10	01160			HECTOLITER		竑
DANN	140,08	5564	12	44777		1057	LOTUS		萏
DANN	142,05	5751	11	17136	6050	8936	EGG		蛋
DANN	142,07	9222	13	12136	6050	8945	NAME OF AN ETHNIC GROUP		蜑
DANN	149,07	6130	14	02641	6051	6803	BIRTHDAY,TO INCREASE,BRAG		誕
DANN	167,05	7843	13	86110		0013	TANTALUM		鉭

ROM	RAD	TEL	TOT	FC	MAT	OSH	TAG	CR	CHAR
DANN	173,12	7220	20	10111			DENSENESS OF CLOUDS		霳
DANN	184,08	9596	16	89789	6080		EAT,CAKE	A0797	餤
DANG	030,13	8173	16	69066		1766	DONG(ONOMAT. FOR BELL)	3981.1	噹
DANG	042,03	3981.1	06	90177			RIGHT AT/JUST AT/ABBR.OF 8173	8173	当
DANG	094,13	373C	16	49266			WOMBAT		獡
DANG	096,13	3885	17	19166	6090	1764	PENDANT ORNAMENTS		璫
DANG	102,08	3981	13	90606	6087	1763	RIGHT AT/JUST AT,OUGHT/SHOULD		當
DANG	118,13	9022	19	88606			(BAMBOO)		簹
DANG	145,13	5991	18	39266	6091	1767	CROTCH		襠
DANG	167,13	6997	21	89166	6093	1765	SOUND OF METAL		鐺
DAANG	010,08	8093	10	90216	6094	7554	PARTY	7825	党
DAANG	042,03	3981.1B	06	90177			THINK(MISTAKENLY)THAT...		当
DAANG	064,10	2386.1	13	59016	6088		RESIST,HINDER		搅
DAANG	064,13	2346	16	59066	6088	1768	RESIST,HINDER	2386	擋
DAANG	064,20	2386	23	59031	6088	8729	RESIST,HINDER	2346	攩
DAANG	075,06	2909.1	10	49977			FILES/RECORDS		档
DAANG	075,13	2909	17	49966		1769	FILES/RECORDS,SHELVES		檔
DAANG	102,08	3981.0B	13	90606	6087	1763	THINK(MISTAKENLY)THAT...		當
DAANG	149,20	6249	27	09631	6096	8727	COUNSELS,ADVICE		讜
DAANG	203,08	7825	20	90331	6095	8726	PARTY	8093	黨
DANQ	032,13	8255	16	49166			SMALL DAM OF A WATER FIELD		壋
DANQ	040,05	1349	08	30601	6100	1112	PUT OFF,DISSIPATED		宕
DANQ	042,03	3981.1A	06	90177			AT OR IN THE VERY SAME...,TO PAWN		当
DANQ	075,06	2909.1A	10	49977			FILES/RECORDS		档
DANQ	075,13	2909.0A	17	49966	6089	1769	FILES/RECORDS,SHELVES		檔
DANQ	102,08	3981.0A	13	90606	6087	1763	AT OR IN THE VERY SAME...,TO PAWN		當
DANQ	108,12	4155.0A	17	36107	6097	0698	AGITATE		盪
DANQ	112,09	4307	14	16627	6099	4487	STONE WITH COLOR VEINS		碭
DANQ	118,12	4671	18	88127			(BAMBOO)		蕩
DANQ	140,08	0429	12	44601			HENBANE		莨
DANQ	140,12	5616	16	44127	6098	4498	DISSOLUTE		蕩
DAU	018,00	0430	02	17220	6124	4274	KNIFE		刀
DAU	030,02	0660	05	67020	6141	4275	GRUMBLE/GARRULOUS		叨

ROM	RAD	TEL	TOT	FC	MAT	OSH	TAG	CR	CHAR
DAU	061,02	1802	05	97020	6125	4276	GRIEVED		
DAU	084,02	305B	06	80217			DEUTERIUM		
DAU	137,02	5298	08	27420		4278	KAYAK		
DAUR	009,08	0227.0B	10	22200			REWIND		
DAUR	018,00	0430.0A	02	17220			DOLL UP		
DAO	009,08	0227	10	22200	6134	2865	TOPPLE/COLLAPSE		
DAO	032,14	109A	17	44141	6127	3175	COLUMN,CYLINDER		
DAO	041,03	1418.1	06	77341			TO LEAD		
DAO	041,13	1418	16	38343	6137	3285	TO LEAD		
DAO	046,07	1497	10	27727	6131	4597	ISLAND		
DAO	064,10	2281	13	57027	6132	4598	STIR,TO POUND	2360	
DAO	064,14	2360	17	54041	6132	3182	STIR,TO POUND	2281	
DAO	113,14	4411	18	34241	6130	3185	PRAY		
DAO	113,14	4411.1	18	35241			PRAY		
DAW	009,08	0227.0A	10	22200	6134	2865	POUR,INVERTED		
DAW	018,06	0451	08	12100	6133	2864	ARRIVE		
DAW	041,03	1418.1A	06	77341			TO LEAD		
DAW	041,13	1418.0A	16	38343	6137	3285	TO LEAD		
DAW	050,14	1621	17	44241	6128	3183	CANOPY		
DAW	061,08	1902	11	92046	6135	2302	MOURN		
DAW	086,14	3614.0A	18	40334		8789	COVER OVER,TO ENVELOPE		
DAW	108,07	4142	12	37107	6138	0703	ROB/A ROBBER		
DAW	115,10	4470	15	22977	6139	1067	RICE(PLANT)		
DAW	120,19	4966	25	50993	6511	8493	FEATHER BANNER OR FAN,BIG BANNER	A5068	
DAW	124,14	5068	20	47620			FEATHER BANNER OR FAN	A4966	
DAW	144,09	5901	15	21221			ROAD	B6670	
DAW	157,10	6457	17	62177	6140	1062	TREAD ON		
DAW	162,09	6670	13	38306	6136	6632	PRINCIPLE,ROAD,SAY	D5901	
DER	060,08	1779	11	26241	6161	3225	GET		
DER	060,12	1795	15	24231	6162	8531	VIRTUE,GERMANY		
DER	061,08	1895	12	40331	6162	8545	VIRTUE	A1795	
DER	167,08	0539	16	86141			TECHNETIUM		

ROM	RAD	TEL	TOT	FC	MAT	OSH	TAG	CR	CHAR
.DE	032,03	0966.0A	06	44112	6198	7419	(SUBOR. PART. ADVERBIAL),-LY	B4104	
.DE	053,05	1646.0A	08	00242	6190	6864	(SUBOR.PART.),(POSSESSIVE PART.) A	4104	
.DE	060,08	1779.0A	11	26241		3225	-ABLE		
.DE	106,03	4104	08	27620	6213	4361	SUBOR. PART.-,S,-LY,-ER(NOM.),'IC	A1646.0A	
.DE	145,18	6004.0A	23	33250	6004	6986	UNTIDY(IN DRESS)		
DEEI	060,08	1779.0B	11	26241	6161	3225	MUST		
DENN	064,13	2336	16	51086			PULL WITH A JERK	7319.0A	
DENN	181,04	7319.0A	13	51786	6584	8301	PULL WITH A JERK		
DENG	086,02	3597.1	06	91820	6169	2994	LAMP		
DENG	086,12	3597	16	92818	6169	0598	LAMP		
DENG	105,07	4098	12	12108	6167	0590	ASCENT,PUBLISH(IN NEWSPAPER)		
DENG	118,12	4678	18	88108	6173		LARGE UMBRELLA FOR STALLS		
DENG	140,12	556E	16	44108			THEA SINENSIS		
DENG	151,06	6260	13	27108		0589	CEREMONIAL VESSEL		
DEENG	062,09	2062	13	63150	6179	6896	SMALL STEELYARD FOR WEIGHING MONEY		
DEENG	118,06	4583	12	88341	6178	3240	WAIT,GRADE,ETC.		
DEENG	140,06	4583.1	10	44341			WAIT,GRADE,ETC.		
DENQ	016,12	0419	14	12217	6177	7872	STOOL	2923	
DENQ	046,12	4347.1	15	22718	6171	0593	CLIFF-LEDGE,STONESTEP		
DENQ	075,14	2923	18	42911	6177	7873	STOOL	0419	
DENQ	085,12	3397	15	32118	0389	0599	SETTLE(LIQUID)		
DENQ	109,12	4223	17	62018	6170	0596	STARE		
DENQ	112,12	4347	17	12618	6171	0594	CLIFF-LEDGE,STONESTEP		
DENQ	157,12	6478	19	62118	6174	0592	STEP INTO(AS TIGHT SHOE)		
DENQ	163,02	6772.1	05	77427			(SURNAME)		
DENQ	163,12	6772	15	17127	6175	2164	(SURNAME)		
DENQ	167,12	6989	20	82118	3982	0591	STIRRUP		
DI	009,05	0144	07	22240	6188	6852	LOW,LOWER THE HEAD,BENEATH		
DI	032,09	1029.0A	12	46181	6231	6003	DIKE	7125.0A	
DI	064,09	2251.0A	12	56081		6008	CARRY (SUSPENDED)		
DI	083,01	3045.0A	05	72740	6187	6848	NAME OF AN ANCIENT TRIBE		
DI	085,11	3336	14	30127	6222	3881	A DROP,TO DRIP		
DI	104,05	8865	10	00142			DISEASE,SICKNESS		

地
底
得
的
襪
得
擷
頓
灯
燈
登
簦
登
戥
等
莛
凳
燈
橙
澄
瞪
磴
蹬
邓
鄧
鐙
低
堤
提
氏
滴
疷

ROM	RAD	TEL	TOT	FC	MAT	OSH	TAG	CR	CHAR
DI	123,05	5025	11	82540	6195	6855	RAM,BILLY GOAT		羝
DI	167,11	6970	19	80127	6224	3876	DYSPROSIUM		鏑
DI	170,09	7125.0A	12	76281	6210	6007	DIKE	1029.0A	隄
DI	177,09	7268	18	46581			LEATHER SHOES,(SURNAME)		鞮
DYI	038,11	1279	14	40427	6220	3880	FIRST WIFE,SON OF FIRST WIFE		嫡
DYI	054,05	6611.1	08	15406	6218	6809	FOLLOW,DIRECT		迪
DYI	064,05	2107.0A	08	5204	6192	6865	RESIST,REPAY		抵
DYI	066,06	2420.1	10	28640			MATCH,ENEMY		敌
DYI	066,11	2420	15	08240	6221	6355	MATCH,ENEMY		敵
DYI	085,11	3321	14	38194	6229	5384	WASH/CLEANSE		滌
DYI	094,04	3695	07	49280	6215	5590	NAME OF A TRIBE,BARBARIANS,(SURNAME)		狄
DYI	106,03	4104.0A	08	27620	6213	4361	REALLY AND TRULY		的
DYI	118,05	4564	11	88603	6217	1845	FLUTE		笛
DYI	118,11	4658	17	88303			FLUTE	4564	邃
DYI	119,02	4756.1	08	80904		5453	BUY UP(GRAIN)		籴
DYI	119,16	4756	22	87914	6227	0953	BUY UP(GRAIN)		糴
DYI	124,08	5049.0A	14	17214	6225	0946	LONG-TAIL PHEASANT		翟
DYI	140,07	5441	11	44289	6216	5591	ANAPHALIS YEDOENSIS		荻
DYI	140,11	9192	15	44147			DRY/SCORCHED		薓
DYI	147,15	6032	22	46810	6230	7613	FACE TO FACE		覿
DYI	157,11	6477	18	60127		3877	HOOF		蹄
DYI	162,05	6611	09	35306	6218	6636	FOLLOW,DIRECT		迪
DYI	177,03	9554	12	47520	6214		REINS/BRIDLE		靮
DII	027,05	0619	07	71242	0951	6863	WHETSTONE,BAFFLE (PIER)	A4272	厎
DII	030,05	0718	08	62040	6189		VEX		呧
DII	032,05	8201.0A	08	42140	1029	6849	PLACE NAME		坁
DII	053,05	1646	08	00242	6190	6864	BOTTOM,BACKGROUND		底
DII	057,05	1723	08	12240	6191	6859	CARVED BOW		弤
DII	064,05	2107	08	52040	6192	6865	PUSH AGAINST,HOLD UP,ON THE WHOLE		抵
DII	075,05	2685	09	42940	6193	6860	FOUNDATION,ROOT		柢
DII	083,01	3045	05	72740	6187	6848	FOUNDATION,ON THE WHOLE	F2107	氐
DII	093,05	3669	09	22540	6194	6854	TO BUTT,RESIST	6041	牴
DII	112,05	4272	10	12640	0951	6850	WHETSTONE,BAFFLE (PIER)	A0619	砥

ROM	RAD	TEL	TOT	FC	MAT	OSH	TAG	CR	CHAR
DII	140,08	562A	12	44242			STILBENE		蓝
DII	148,05	6041	12	22240	6194	6858	TO BUTT/RESIST	3669	觚
DII	149,05	6090	12	02640	6196	6851	TO SLANDER,DEFAME		詆
DII	163,05	6732	08	77727	6197	2249	LODGING-HOUSE,(SURNAME)		邸
DII	188,05	754A	15	72240			SACRUM		骶
DIH	032,03	0966	06	44112	6198	7419	GROUND		地
DIH	032,11	8262	14	40127			STAIRS/STEPS		墒
DIH	038,07	1229	10	48427	6202	4765	WIFE OF A YOUNGER BROTHER		娣
DIH	050,06	1593	09	00227	6204	3983	EMPEROR		帝
DIH	057,04	1717	07	80227	6201	4758	YOUNGER BROTHER		弟
DIH	075,03	8529	07	44930	6199	5003	LONE-STANDING TREE		杕
DIH	075,08	2769	12	45932	6200	5695	KERRIA JAPONICA		棣
DIH	085,05	8668	08	32140			NAME OF RIVERS IN HOPEI		泜
DIH	096,07	3813	11	18127			WHITE JADE WORN ON BELT		瑅
DIH	096,09	385A	13	10127			MASTIC		瑅
DIH	106,03	4104.0B	08	27620	6213	4361	AIM,CLEAR		的
DIH	109,07	4195	12	68027	6251	4760	LOOK DOWN UPON		睇
DIH	112,09	0556	14	10627		3986	TELLURIUM		碲
DIH	113,09	4396	13	30227	6206		IMPERIAL ANCESTRAL SACRIFICE		禘
DIH	118,05	4574	11	88227	6203	4769	PREFIX FOR ORDINAL NUMBERS	9168	第
DIH	120,09	4877	15	20927	6243	3988	KNOT,CLOSELY JOINED,CONNECTION		締
DIH	140,05	9168	09	44227		4768	PREFIX FOR ORDINAL NUMBERS	4574	苐
DIH	140,09	5530	13	44227	6207	3990	STEM(OF FRUIT)	5586.0A	蒂
DIH	140,11	5586	15	44227	6007	3982	STEM(OF FRUIT)		蔕
DIH	142,08	9225	14	57147	6211	6085	RAINBOW	5836	蝃
DIH	142,11	5836	17	54127	6212	3980	RAINBOW	9225	蟀
DIH	149,09	6167	16	00627	6208	3987	EXAMINE,TRUTH(BUDDHIST)		諦
DIH	157,09	9341	16	66181	6236	6004	TREAD ON,KICK		踶
DIH	162,07	6677.1	11	38302		6718	HAND OVER/TO PASS		逓
DIH	162,10	6677	14	32301	6209	6770	HAND OVER/TO PASS		遞
DIH	162,11	9378	15	34302	6261	6702	GO AWAY,MIGRATE		迣
DIAN	046,19	1553	22	22886	6338	8311	SUMMIT		巔
DIAN	064,08	2195	11	50061	6343	1282	WEIGH IN THE HAND		掂

ROM	RAD	TEL	TOT	FC	MAT	OSH	TAG	CR	CHAR
DIAN	066,05	2195.1	09	21647	6343	6200	WEIGH IN THE HAND		战
DIAN	085,10	3329	13	34181	6334	8090	YUNNAN		滇
DIAN	090,10	0261	12	24234		8086	INVERSION,MISTAKE		慎
DIAN	104,10	8878	15	00134			CRAZY,CONVULSIONS	4094	瘨
DIAN	104,19	4094	24	00186	6335	8310	CRAZY,CONVULSIONS	8878	癫
DIAN	140,19	570A	23	44886			BELLADONNA		蘵
DIAN	157,05	6411	12	61160	6306		TIPTOE	6443	跕
DIAN	157,08	6443	15	60161			TIPTOE	6411	踮
DIAN	181,10	7351	19	21886	6337	8308	TOP,JOLT,INVERTED		顛
DEAN	012,06	0368	08	55801	6347	8072	CANON/DICTIONARY		典
DEAN	086,05	7820.1	09	21336		8770	A POINT/TO DOT,TO LIGHT		点
DEAN	112,08	4290	13	15681	6348	8073	IODINE		碘
DEAN	154,08	6349	15	65881			MAKE RICH,GIFT/PRESENT		奠
DEAN	203,05	7820	17	61360	6346	1275	A POINT/TO DOT,TO LIGHT		點
DIANN	005,04	7193.1	05	50716			ELECTRICITY/ELECTRIC		电
DIANN	009,05	0140	07	26200	6349	1747	FARMER		佃
DIANN	032,05	0989	08	41160	6339	1262	STAND FOR GOBLETS		坫
DIANN	032,06	1067.1	09	54104			CUSHION		垫
DIANN	032,11	1067	14	44104	6359	0247	CUSHION		墊
DIANN	037,09	1156	12	80430	6357	5021	LIBATION		奠
DIANN	053,05	1648	08	00261	6341	1280	INN/SHOP		店
DIANN	061,08	1855	11	90061	6342		FEEL CONCERNED ABOUT		惦
DIANN	079,09	3013	13	77247	6354	6300	PALACE HALL		殿
DIANN	085,08	3244	11	33181	6352	6023	SHALLOW WATER,PRECIPITATE	D3434	淀
DIANN	085,13	3434	16	37147	6355	6301	SEDIMENT/PRECIPITATE	B3244	澱
DIANN	096,05	3783	09	11160	6344	1263	FLAW IN JADE,BLEMISH,DISGRACE		玷
DIANN	102,02	3949	07	27620	6350	4446	SUBURB,IMPERIAL DOMAIN		甸
DIANN	104,05	8867	10	00161	6345	1283	MALARIAL FEVER		店
DIANN	104,13	4080	18	00147	6356		ERYTHEMA,LEUCODERM		癜
DIANN	112,12	8967	17	11646			STONE WEDGE		磹
DIANN	118,12	4672	18	88406	6360	2299	FINE WOVEN GRASS MAT		簟
DIANN	167,05	6879	13	86100	6364	1741	GOLD INLAID WORK		鈿
DIANN	170,05	9532.0A	08	71260		1269	DANGEROUS		阽

ROM	RAD	TEL	TOT	FC	MAT	OSH	TAG	CR	CHAR
DIANN	173,05	7193	13	10716	6358	7441	ELECTRICITY/ELECTRIC		電
DIANN	174,08	7233	16	53281	6353	6020	INDIGO PIGMENT		靛
DIAU	015,08	0406	10	37120	6270	3893	WITHERED		凋
DIAU	018,00	0431	02	17120	6268	4272	WICKED,ARTFUL		刁
DIAU	018,08	1754.1	10	72200	6273		ENGRAVE		剮
DIAU	059,08	1754	11	72222	6273	4179	ENGRAVE	A7171	彫
DIAU	096,08	8824	12	17120	6271		ENGRAVE GEMS		琱
DIAU	112,08	4306	13	17620	6272	3884	TIBETAN STONE HOUSE		碉
DIAU	142,05	5748	11	57162			POMPONIA MACULATIOCOLLIS		蜩
DIAU	153,05	6285	12	27262	6275	1370	SABLE/MARTEN		貂
DIAU	172,08	7171	16	70214	6273	0882	ENGRAVE,SHREWD,EAGLE	A1754	雕
DIAU	195,08	9648	19	27320	6299		PAGRUS MAJOR		鯛
DIAU	196,08	7716	19	77227	6274	4636	GOLDEN EAGLE		鵰
DEAU	044,06	145A	09	77227		3963	PENIS		屌
DIAW	030,03	0680	06	60227	6276	3962	CONDOLE WITH,HANG	1713	吊
DIAW	032,06	8212	09	42113			BANK AROUND GRAVE,BOUNDARY OF GRAVE		垗
DIAW	057,01	1713	04	17527	6276	4757	CONDOLE WITH,HANG	0680	弔
DIAW	064,08	2220	11	51046	6278	2304	TO DROP,TO FALL		掉
DIAW	116,11	4525	16	30327	6280	4689	DEEP,DISTANT,PROFOUND		窵
DIAW	140,07	5371	11	44240	6301		BAMBOO BASKET	5568	莜
DIAW	140,11	5568	15	44294	6301	5385	BAMBOO BASKET	5371	篠
DIAW	140,14	565B	18	44214			SAMBUCU JAVINICA		蓧
DIAW	149,08	6148	15	07620	6298	3885	TUNE,MODE(MUSIC),TO MOVE(TROOPS)		調
DIAW	167,03	6860	11	87120	6279	4359	TO FISH		釣
DIAW	167,06	6903.0A	14	82113	6289	7691	PAN WITH A LONG HANDLE		銚
DIE	009,07	8050	09	28227			WHICH/WHAT/WHOSE/WHO(FOOCHOW DIAL.)		俤
DIE	088,06	3638	10	80207	6304	4263	DAD		爹
DYE	017,03	0424.0A	05	77777		1975	CONVEX		凸
DYE	029,11	0655	13	77107	6325	0628	FOLD UP,REPEAT	3986	叠
DYE	030,06	8134.0A	09	61014	2456	0257	GNAW/BITE		哑
DYE	030,09	0818	12	64094	6316	5288	TO CHATTER,FLOWING FLOOD		喋
DYE	032,06	8209	09	41114	6312	0256	MOUND,ANTHILL		垤
DYE	032,09	1026	12	44194	6317	5286	BATTLEMENTS		堞

ROM	RAD	TEL	TOT	FC	MAT	OSH	TAG	CR	CHAR
DYE	072,15	2567	19	60107	6325	0626	FOLD UP,REPEAT	3986	疊
DYE	075,09	276C	13	44994			DAPHNIPHYLLUM MACROPODUM		楪
DYE	091,09	3655	13	24094	6319	5292	DOCUMENT/DISPATCH		牒
DYE	097,05	3901	10	75233	6308	4997	YOUNG MELON		瓞
DYE	102,17	3986	22	60107	6325	0627	FOLD UP,REPEAT	0655	疊
DYE	112,09	4308	14	14694	6320	5289	PLATE/DISH		碟
DYE	120,06	4826	12	21914	6313	0261	HEMPEN CLOTH WORN BY MOURNER		絰
DYE	142,08	9226	14	55181		6045	BUTTERFLY	5805	蜨
DYE	142,09	5805	15	54194	6321	5294	BUTTERFLY	9226	蝶
DYE	145,11	5977	16	37262	6324	1669	LINED COAT		褶
DYE	149,09	6183	16	04694	6322	5290	TO SPY		諜
DYE	157,05	6407	12	65130	6310	5195	STUMBLE/FALL DOWN		跌
DYE	157,09	6454	16	64194	6323	5287	TREAD ON		蹀
DYE	162,05	6613	09	35303	6311	6723	ALTERNATELY,REPEATEDLY,ABBR. 0655		迭
DIEH	195,09	7654	20	24394			FLOUNDER/PLEURONECTES		鰈
DING	001,01	0002	02	10200	6381	2981	FOURTH HEAVEN'S STEM, (SURNAME)		丁
DING	009,02	0089	04	21220	6382	2990	ALONE		仃
DING	030,02	0666	05	61020	6383	2984	STING(OF MOSQUITO),TO ASK		叮
DING	096,02	3770	06	11120	6384	2982	JINGLING,TINKLING		玎
DING	104,02	3995	07	00121	6385	2996	BOIL/CARBUNCLE		疔
DING	109,02	4169	07	61020		2987	STARE/GAZE		盯
DING	167,02	6857	10	81120	6388	2983	NAIL		釘
DING	181,02	7307.0A	11	11286	6390	8271	WITHSTOOD		頂
DING	184,02	7383	10	81720	6391	2991	ARRANGE FOOD IN PLATES FOR A SHOW		飣
DIING	075,13	8600	17	42927			STAFF/STICK		橖
DIING	164,02	6789	09	11620	6387	2989	INTOXICATED		酊
DIING	181,02	7307	11	11286	6390	8271	TOP,MOST,GO AGAINST		頂
DIING	206,00	7844	13	22221	6392	2854	TRIPOD		鼎
DINQ	030,08	0570	11	63081			-D + INE(CHEM.)		啶
DINQ	040,05	1353	08	30801	6393	6016	DEFINITE,TO ORDER		定
DINQ	075,08	2642	12	43981		6021	ANCHOR,(PLANT)	A4299	椗
DINQ	112,02	4259	07	11620		2985	ANCHOR	4290	矴
DINQ	112,08	4299	13	13681	6394	6018	ANCHOR	A2642	碇

ROM	RAD	TEL	TOT	FC	MAT	OSH	TAG	CR	CHAR
DINQ	149,02	6057	09	01620	6386	2986	TO ORDER,CONCLUDE,SUBSCRIBE		訂
DINQ	167,07	6910.0A	15	82141	6413	6790	INGOT	6928	鋌
DINQ	167,08	6928	16	83181	6395	6017	INGOT	6910.0A	錠
DIOU	001,05	0016	06	20731	6115	8844	LOSE		丢
DIOU	167,07	0576	15	82131			THULIUM		铥
DONG	015,03	0392	05	27303	6603	9071	WINTER,BOOM(OF A DRUM)	D7850	冬
DONG	030,05	8131	08	67033			BOOM(OF A DRUM)		咚
DONG	075,02	2639.1	06	40904	6605		EAST		东
DONG	075,04	2639	08	50906	6605	5535	EAST		東
DONG	084,05	0598	09	80317			RADON		氡
DONG	140,05	537B	09	44303			PETASITES JAPONICUS		苳
DONG	142,08	5787	14	55196	6608	5538	RAINBOW		蝀
DONG	196,08	772B	19	57927			THRUSH/TARDUS FUSCATUS		鶇
DONG	207,05	7850	18	44303	6604	9075	BOOM(OF A DRUM)	B0392	鼕
DOONG	061,13	2016	16	94014	6613	0471	UNDERSTAND		懂
DOONG	140,09	5516	13	44104	6614	0470	(SURNAME),SUPERVISE		董
DONQ	009,08	0179.0A	08	27220			(ETHNIC GROUP)		侗
DONQ	009,11	0211	13	24227	6612	4789	MOTOR,AUTOMATIC(JAPAN.)		働
DONQ	015,08	0408	10	53196	6606	5539	FREEZE		凍
DONQ	019,04	0520.1	06	14727			MOVE		动
DONQ	019,09	0520	11	24127	6611	4787	MOVE		動
DONQ	046,06	8333	09	22227		3871	SETTLEMENT OF MIAO OR OTHER TRIBES		峝
DONQ	061,06	1871.0A	09	97020	6618	3866	FRIGHTEN		恫
DONQ	075,08	2767	12	45996	6607	5537	ROOF BEAM		棟
DONQ	085,06	3159	09	37120	6609	3870	CAVE,HOLE		洞
DONQ	085,09	8690	12	32114	1510	0469	MILK OF COWS OR MARES,SOUND OF DRUM		湩
DONQ	086,06	7906.0A	10	97820			FLAMING/FIERY		烔
DONQ	130,06	0634	10	77220	6610	3868	TORSO,LARGE INTESTINE		胴
DOU	010,10	0351	12	77217	6469	7528	POCKET		兜
DOU	163,09	6757	12	47627	6500	2181	ALL,ALREADY		都
DOOU	064,04	2122	07	54000	6473	2698	TREMBLE,SHAKE OUT		抖
DOOU	068,00	2435	04	34000	6472	2694	CHINESE PECK		斗
DOOU	075,04	8539	08	44900	6474	2702	SQUARE BASE FOR CHINESE FLAGSTAFF		枓

ROM	RAD	TEL	TOT	FC	MAT	OSH	TAG	CR	CHAR
DOOU	117,04	454J	09	04100			DECALITER		蚪
DOOU	142,04	5737	10	54100	6475	2707	TADPOLE		蝌
DOOU	167,04	9445	12	84100	6476		WINE FLAGON,(SURNAME)		斜
DOOU	170,04	7107.1	07	74200	6477	2697	STEEP		阧
DOOU	170,07	7107	10	74281	6477	5944	STEEP		陡
DOW	018,07	0499	09	12100			PLACE NAME		刣
DOW	068,00	2435.0A	04	34000			FIGHT,INCITE	7591	斗
DOW	104,07	4026	12	00118	6479	0568	SMALL POX		痘
DOW	116,15	4535	20	30806	6485	8161	(SURNAME),SINUS (ANATOM.)		竇
DOW	130,07	9125	11	71218	6480	0566	THROAT,NECK		脰
DOW	140,07	5439	11	44108	6481	0588	BEAN,PEAS	A6258	荳
DOW	149,09	6236.1A	16	04634			COMMA,PHRASE MARKED BY PAUSE		讀
DOW	149,15	6236.0A	22	04686	6521	8149	COMMA,PHRASE MARKED BY PAUSE		讀
DOW	151,00	6258	07	10108	6478	0563	BEAN,SACRIFICIAL VESSEL	A5439	豆
DOW	162,07	6637	11	31301	6482	6604	LINGER		逗
DOW	184,07	7405	15	81718	6483	0565	SET OUT FOOD		餖
DOW	191,00	7591	10	77114	6484	3424	FIGHT,INCITE	K2435.0A	鬥
DOW	191,10	7595.1	20	77141	6484	3428	FIGHT,INCITE		鬪
DOW	191,14	7595	24	77121	6484	3426	FIGHT,INCITE	7591	鬬
DOU	064,08	2218.0A	11	57047			TIDY UP		掇
DU	030,12	088E	15	67027	6501		TOOT		嘟
DU	109,08	4206	13	27604	6508	1728	SUPERVISE		督
DU	163,09	6757.0A	12	47627	6500	2181	METROPOLIS,(SURNAME)		都
DU	169,09	7062	17	77604	6502	3475	TOWER OVER A CITY GATE		闍
DWU	022,15	0569	17	71718	6516	0823	CABINET/CASE	A2927	匵
DWU	075,15	2927	19	44986	6516	8154	CABINET/CASE,CASKET	A0569	櫝
DWU	080,04	3021	08	50507	6509	4887	POISON		毒
DWU	085,15	3460	18	34186	6518	8159	DITCH,TROUBLE(SOME ONE TO DO)		瀆
DWU	091,15	3658	19	24086	6520	8151	DOCUMENTS		牘
DWU	093,15	3685	19	24586	6519	8150	CALF,SACRIFICIAL VICTIM		犢
DWU	094,06	3747.1	09	45236		8902	ALONE,INDEPENDENT		独
DWU	094,13	3747	16	46227	6512	4472	ALONE,INDEPENDENT		獨
DWU	112,09	4304	14	15657	6510	4889	STONE ROLLER		碡

ROM	RAD	TEL	TOT	FC	MAT	OSH	TAG	CR	CHAR
DWU	123,13	502C	19	86527			CAPRA CYLINDERICORNIS		觕
DWU	149,09	6236.1	16	04634			READ ALOUD,STUDY		讀
DWU	149,15	6236	22	04686	6521	8149	READ ALOUD,STUDY		讀
DWU	149,22	6251	29	0066[1]	6522	1158	TO SLANDER,TO MURMUR		讟
DWU	150,15	6256	22	84686			DITCH,SLUICE	3460	瀆
DWU	178,13	9571	22	46527			BOW CASE		韇
DWU	188,13	7553	23	76227	6513	4470	SKULL		髑
DWU	203,15	7830	27	64386	6523	8157	BLACKEN,TO INSULT,CONSTANTLY		黷
DUU	032,09	1035	12	44160	6497	1627	STOP UP		堵
DUU	109,09	4212	14	64060	6498	1632	OBSERVE/SEE	6023	睹
DUU	118,10	4648	16	88327	6514	4718	SINCERE/TRUE,SERIOUS(ILLNESS)		篤
DUU	130,03	5137.0A	07	74210	6496	0149	TRIPE		肚
DUU	140,03	533A	07	44104			CYPERUS MALACCENSIS		芏
DUU	147,09	6023	16	46610	6498	7596	OBSERVE,SEE	4212	覩
DUU	154,09	6350	16	64860	6499	1638	GAMBLE,BET		賭
DUH	038,04	1176	07	43477	6503	4237	JEALOUS		妒
DUH	038,05	1176.1	08	41460	6503	1107	JEALOUS		妬
DUH	053,06	1653	09	00247	6504	6168	CAPACITY,STANDARD,DEGREE		度
DUH	066,13	2424.0A	17	68440	3062	6321	TO RUIN/DESTROY		斁
DUH	075,03	2629	07	44910	6495	0150	(SURNAME),RESTRICT,FABRICATE		杜
DUH	085,09	3256	12	30147	6505	6171	CROSS(RIVER)		渡
DUH	130,03	5137	07	74210	6496	0149	BELLY		肚
DUH	140,09	547E	13	44430			FOLLICLE		蔤
DUH	142,18	5871	24	50136	6507	8906	BOOKWORM/LEPISMA SACCHARINA		蠹
DUH	167,08	9471	16	27109			BRIDLE LINK		鍍
DUH	167,09	6947	17	80147	6506	6169	-PLATED,TO PLATE		鍍
DUAN	117,09	4551	14	02127	6541	3757	ONE END,REGULAR,CARRY		端
DOAN	111,07	4252	12	81418	6542	0567	SHORT,LACK		短
DUANN	032,09	0641	12	47147			(PLACE NAME ELEMENT)		塅
DUANN	069,07	2451.1	11	22721	6547	2012	BREAK,JUDGE		断
DUANN	069,14	2451	18	22721	6547	2013	BREAK,TO JUDGE		斷
DUANN	075,09	1110	13	47947			HIBISCUS SYRIACUS		椴
DUANN	079,05	3008	09	77447	6543	6270	PARAGRAPH,SECTION,(SURNAME)		段
DUANN	079,12	8628	16	77747	6546	6272	INFERTILE EGG		毈

ROM	RAD	TEL	TOT	FC	MAT	OSH	TAG	CR	CHAR
DUANN	086,09	3548	13	97847	6544	6273	TO FORGE,WROUGHT,TO DISCIPLINE	6939	煅
DUANN	112,09	4312	14	17647			COARSE STONE (USED FOR WHETSTONE)		碫
DUANN	118,14	1113	20	88721			BAMBOO FISH TRAP		籪
DUANN	118,18	1113.1	24	88721	6548		BAMBOO FISH TRAP		籪
DUANN	120,09	4876	15	27947	6545	6274	SATIN		緞
DUANN	130,09	9133	13	77247			DRIED MEAT		腶
DUANN	167,09	6939	17	87147	6544	6271	FORGE/WROUGHT,TO DISCIPLINE	3548	鍛
DUEI	032,08	1018	11	40114	6557	0867	A PILE/A MASS		堆
DUEI	112,10	4324	15	17637			TO CONSTRUCT WITH ROCKS/BOULDERS		碓
DOEI	041,02	1417.1A	05	74400			EXCHANGE		对
DOEI	041,11	1417.0A	14	34100			EXCHANGE		對
DUEY	010,05	0345	07	80216	6560	7565	TO CASH		兑
DUEY	041,02	1417.1	05	74400	6562	3220	OPPOSITE/CORRECT		对
DUEY	041,11	1417	14	34100	6562	3165	OPPOSITE,CORRECT		對
DUEY	061,12	2000	16	08334	6563	8672	DISLIKE/HATE	2029	憝
DUEY	061,14	2029	18	34330	6563	8624	DISLIKE/HATE	2000	懟
DUEY	112,08	4302	13	10614	6558	0871	PESTLE,POUND WITH A PESTLE		碓
DUEY	149,12	9297	19	08640	6563		DISLIKE/HATE	2000	譈
DUEY	170,02	7130.1	05	78200			SQUADRON		队
DUEY	170,09	7130	12	78232	6561	5746	SQUADRON		隊
DUEN	030,04	0903.1A	07	65017			TON		吨
DUEN	030,13	0903.0A	16	61086			TON		噸
DUEN	032,12	1076	15	48140	6572	6339	BLOCK,GATE PILLAR,PIER		墩
DUEN	061,08	1908	11	90047	6571	3121	KIND-HEARTED	A2415	惇
DUEN	066,08	2415	12	08440	6571	6338	KIND-HEARTED,PLACE NAME	A1908	敦
DUEN	086,12	3625.0A	16	98840			PLACE NAME		燉
DUEN	112,12	434A	17	18640			STONE BLOCK		礅
DUEN	157,12	6472	19	68146	6576	3250	CROUCH/SQUAT		蹲
DUEN	167,12	9503	20	88140		6340	UPSETTING(FORGED PIECES)		鐓
DOEN	109,04	8901	09	65017	6582	7407	DOZE/NAP		盹
DOEN	157,13	6485	20	44801	6580	5985	WHOLESALE		躉
DUENN	030,04	0903.1	07	65017			TON		吨
DUENN	030,13	0903	16	61086	6585	8302	TON		噸

ROM	RAD	TEL	TOT	FC	MAT	OSH	TAG	CR	CHAR
DUENN	031,04	0937	07	60717	6593	1924	BIN FOR GRAIN		囤
DUENN	085,04	3090	07	35117	6595	7415	TURBID,CONFUSED		沌
DUENN	086,04	351A	08	95817		7411	STEW SLOWLY	3625	炖
DUENN	086,12	3625	16	98840	6575	6342	STEW SLOWLY		燉
DUENN	109,04	4163	09	72264	6578	1715	A SHIELD		盾
DUENN	112,04	1116	09	15617			SOIL PULVERIZER		砘
DUENN	162,09	6658	13	32306	6579	6631	TO ESCAPE,DISAPPEAR	6687	遁
DUENN	162,11	6687	15	31303	6586	6735	TO ESCAPE,DISAPPEAR	6658	遯
DUENN	167,04	6868	12	85117	6583	7406	BLUNT,STUPID		鈍
DUENN	181,04	7319	13	51786	6584	8301	A TIME,JERK,STOP		頓
DUO	030,06	8135	09	67027	6417	4256	WOOLEN CLOTH,QUIVER		哆
DUO	036,03	1122	06	27207	6416	4255	MUCH/MANY,HOW (ADV. OF DEGREE)		多
DWO	036,03	1122.0A	06	27207	6416	4255	HOW (ADV. OF DEGREE)		多
DWO	037,03	1161.1	06	40343			ROB/SNATCH		夺
DWO	037,11	1161	14	40341	6433	3241	ROB/SNATCH		奪
DWO	064,08	2218	11	57047			PICK UP,TIDY UP		掇
DWO	145,08	5949	13	37247	6438	6081	MEND CLOTHES		裰
DWO	167,13	6995	21	86141	6431	2480	LARGE ANCIENT BELL		鐸
DUOO	030,17	8184	20	06456		2636	HANG DOWN		嚲
DUOO	032,06	1000.0A	09	47194		5370	TARGET,BATTLEMENT		垛
DUOO	032,06	1000.1A	09	47194			TARGET,BATTLEMENT		垜
DUOO	032,08	1022	11	42114			SOLID EARTH		埵
DUOO	075,02	2614.1	06	17904	6419	5369	AN. FOR FLOWERS		朶
DUOO	075,02	2614	06	77904	6419	5369	AN. FOR FLOWERS		朵
DUOO	158,06	6503	13	27294	6424	5373	HIDE,AVOID,GET OUT OF WAY		躲
DUOH	018,06	0449	08	12900	6420	2937	CHOP(MEAT)		剁
DUOH	030,05	0732	08	62072	6432	1021	CRY OUT		咄
DUOH	030,06	075A	09	67094			(PHONETIC)/-D + OLE (CHEM.)		哚
DUOH	032,06	1000	09	47194		5370	PILE		垛
DUOH	032,06	1000.1	09	47194	6421		PILE		垜
DUOH	032,08	1022.0A	11	42114			SOLID EARTH		埵
DUOH	032,09	1077.1	12	74104		0207	FALL,DEGENERATE		堕
DUOH	032,12	1077	15	74104	6427	0208	FALL,DEGENERATE		墮

ROM	RAD	TEL	TOT	FC	MAT	OSH	TAG	CR	CHAR
DUOH	046,12	8341	15	74772			MOUNTAIN PEAK		隨
DUOH	053,06	1653.0A	09	00247	6504	6168	ESTIMATE		度
DUOH	061,09	1924	12	94027	6425	3596	LAZY		惰
DUOH	075,05	2689	09	42972			WOOD SCRAPS		杝
DUOH	137,05	5305	11	23411	6418	7179	RUDDER,HELM		舵
DUOH	157,06	1118	13	67194	6423	5371	STAMP THE FEET		跺
DUOH	157,09	6453	16	60147	6429	6170	WALK SLOWLY		踱
DUOH	187,03	7461.0A	13	74330	6452	5002	CARRY ON BACK		馱
E	038,05	8275	08	41420	4804	3048	GRACEFUL/WILLOWY,UNSTABLE	1128	妸
E	038,08	1128	11	41420	4804	3048	GRACEFUL/WILLOWY,UNSTABLE	8275	婀
E	044,08	145B	11	77221	4805	3050	DEFECATE		屙
E	104,05	4008	10	00121	4806	3056	MALADY	4038	疴
E	104,08	4038	13	00121	4806	3049	MALADY	4008	痾
E	170,05	7093.0B	08	71220	0001	3045	FLATTER		阿
ER	009,07	0192	09	23250	4779	6928	RUSSIA,SUDDENLY		俄
ER	030,04	8122	07	64010		7143	MOVE		吪
ER	030,07	0768.0B	10	63050	47806	926	TO CHANT	6127	哦
ER	031,04	0952	07	60214	4788	1922	DECOY		囮
ER	038,07	1230	10	43450	4781	6931	GOOD/BEAUTIFUL		娥
ER	046,07	1494·1	10	22553	4782	6932	LOFTY,NAME OF A MOUNTAIN		峩
ER	046,07	1494	10	23750	4782	6925	LOFTY,NAME OF A MOUNTAIN		峨
ER	112,07	8948	12	13650		6927	CLIFF		硪
ER	140,07	5458	11	44553	4783	6933	ZEDOARY		莪
ER	142,07	5760	13	53150	4784	6930	MOTH		蛾
ER	149,04	6073	11	04610	4789	7144	ERROR,EXHORT,FALSE	6215	訛
ER	149,07	6127	14	03650			TO CHANT	0768.0B	誐
ER	149,12	6215	19	04627	4789	4524	ERROR,EXHORT,FALSE	6073	譌
ER	167,07	1154	15	83150			OSMIUM		鋨
ER	181,06	9578	15	21686	1742		FOREHEAD,AMOUNT,QUOTA	7345	頟
ER	181,09	7345	18	31686	1742	8261	FOREHEAD,AMOUNT,QUOTA	9578	額
ER	196,07	7709.1	18	23327		4687	GOOSE		鵞
ER	196,07	7709	18	27527	4786	4655	GOOSE		鵝
EE	038,08	8283	11	46494	7157		DELICATE,BEAUTIFUL		婐

ROM	RAD	TEL	TOT	FC	MAT	OSH	TAG	CR	CHAR
EE	061,06	1921.1A	10	10331			NAUSEATED		
EE	061,08	1921.0A	12	10331		8544	NAUSEATED		
EE	094,08	3716.0B	11	44221	2956		PLIANT		
EH	009,07	0192.0A	09	23250			RUSSIA		
EH	027,02	0618	04	71212	1739	7214	DISTRESSED	8415	
EH	030,04	0713	07	61012	1740	7215	HICCOUGH		
EH	030,06	8133	09	66207	4790	4549	BEAT A DRUM,STARTLE		
EH	030,12	088C	15	61031	7419A		(PHONETIC)	B1921.1	
EH	030,13	0893	16	10106	4799	0354	STARTLING		
EH	032,08	1019	11	10104	4808	0183	TO WHITEWASH/TO PLASTER		
EH	032,09	8238	12	46127			DAM,TO STOP/CHECK	D6666	
EH	046,09	8340	12	26727			CLIFF/PRECIPICE		
EH	061,06	1921.1	10	10331			EVIL,(PHONETIC)	D088C	
EH	061,08	1921	12	10331	4809	8544	EVIL		
EH	061,09	1945	12	96027	4792	4553	STARTLED		
EH	063,01	8415	05	30217	1739	7957	DISTRESSED	0618	
EH	064,04	2108	07	51012	4810	7218	HOLD(STRATEGIC POSITION)	8458	
EH	064,10	8458	13	58017	4810	0717	HOLD(STRATEGIC POSITION)	2108	
EH	075,04	2652	08	41912			TREE KNOT		
EH	076,14	2971	18	67382			BLANK,FOOLISH		
EH	130,09	7890.1	13	76227	4793		PALATE		
EH	140,04	535E	08	44212			ACENAPHTHYLENE		
EH	140,09	5501	13	44207	4794	4555	STEM AND CALYX OF FLOWER		
EH	140,21	5702	25	44227			PHALARIS		
EH	149,06	9289	13	07664			HARSH/FORBIDDING		
EH	149,09	6166	16	06627	4795	4552	HONEST SPEECH		
EH	149,16	6166.1	23	01616	4795	0355	HONEST SPEECH		
EH	159,04	6515	11	51012	1741	7217	YOKE,RESTRAIN		
EH	162,09	6666	13	36302	4812	6714	TO STOP/CHECK	B8238	
EH	163,09	6759	12	67227	4796	2223	HUPEH		
EH	167,09	6948	17	86127		4550	SHARP,BLADE EDGE		
EH	169,08	7052	16	77233	4814	3541	SHUT,STOP		
EH	170,04	7084	07	71212	4811	7216	DEFILE/PASS,IN DISTRESS	7137.0A	

CHAR column characters:
惡 惡 猗 俄 厄 呝 咢 噁 靈 堊 堨 崿 惡 惡 愕 厄 扼 搕 柀 歑 腭 芐 蕚 蘁 詻 譌 讍 軶 遏 鄂 鍔 閼 阨

ROM	RAD	TEL	TOT	FC	MAT	OSH	TAG	CR	CHAR
EH	170,10	7137.0A	13	78217	0018	0716	DEFILE/PASS,IN DISTRESS	7084	隘
EH	181,06	7326	15	31486	4813	8323	JUNCTION OF NOSE AND FOREHEAD		頞
EH	181,09	7329	18	61286	4797	8287	PALATE	7890	齶
EH	184,07	7408	15	83750	4785	6929	HUNGRY		餓
EH	195,09	9653	20	26327	4800	4554	CROCODILE/ALLIGATOR	7677	鰐
EH	195,16	7677	27	21316	4800	0356	CROCODILE/ALLIGATOR	9653	鱷
EH	196,08	7722	19	27317	4787	7537	CACKLING OF GEESE		鵝
EH	196,09	7725	20	67227	4798	4643	OSPREY/FISH-EAGLE/FISH-HAWK		鶚
EH	211,09	7890	24	26727	4793	4551	PALATE	7329	齶
ERL	010,00	0334	02	22010			SON	0348	儿
ERL	010,06	0348	08	77217	1759	7532	SON	0334	兒
ERL	038,09	1249.0A	12	44464			RECALCITRANT		娨
ERL	075,06	8555	10	41927		3752	TREE MUSHROOM		栭
ERL	085,06	8670	09	31127			TO FLOW(AS WATER/TEARS)		洏
ERL	126,00	5079	06	10227	1756	3750	AND/AND YET		而
ERL	126,03	9100	09	12222	4616		(SURNAME),BEARD		耏
ERL	130,06	9118	10	71227			OVER-COOKED/SOFT		胹
ERL	140,14	9196	18	44227		4036	BLOOMING,SHINING		蕭
ERL	159,06	6529	13	51027	1757	3751	HEARSE		輀
ERL	170,06	9533	09	71227			PLACE NAME		陑
ERL	195,06	9642	17	21327		3753	CAVIAR,FISH ROE		鮞
ERL	196,06	770D	17	17227			EMU		鴯
ERL	208,08	785F	21	77711			DIDELPHYS DECHIANA		貾
EEL	042,02	1422	05	27900	1754	8434	THOU	3643	尔
EEL	042,02	1422.1	05	80900	1754	8439	THOU		尓
EEL	085,06	3167	09	31140	1747	2728	NAME OF A RIVER		洱
EEL	089,10	3643	14	10227	1754	4028	THOU	1422	爾
EEL	096,06	3799	10	11140	1748	2718	PEARL OR JADE EARRING		珥
EEL	128,00	5101	06	10400	1744	2717	EAR		耳
EEL	162,05	6705.1	09	37309	1755	6781	NEAR		迩
EEL	162,14	6705	18	31302	1755	6704	NEAR		邇
EEL	167,06	1436	14	81140			ERBIUM		鉺
EEL	184,06	7403	14	81740	1750	2720	CAKES,BAIT		餌

ROM	RAD	TEL	TOT	FC	MAT	OSH	TAG	CR	CHAR
EEL	187,06	7479	16	71340			(HORSE)		駬
EEL	208,06	785C	19	71711			PHASCOLOGALE		[illegible]
ELL	007,00	0059	02	10100	1751	0002	TWO		二
ELL	009,06	8034	08	21240	1745	2719	ASSISTANT		佴
ELL	018,06	0454	08	12100	1746	2886	CUT OFF THE EARS AS PUNISHMENT		刵
ELL	030,06	8132	09	61040			SPACE BETWEEN MOUTH AND EARS		咡
ELL	056,02	1708	05	43100	1751	6878	TWO (FRAUD PROOF)		弍
ELL	075,12	8582	16	43940	1753	6887	ACID VARIETY OF JUJUBE PLUM		樲
ELL	154,05	6310	12	43800	1752	6885	TWO(FRAUDPROOF)		貳
-L	010,00	0334.0A	02	22010			NON-SYLLABIC DIMI. SUFF.	0348.0A	儿
-L	010,06	0348.0A	08	77217	1759	7532	NON-SYLLABIC DIMI. SUFF.	0334.0A	兒
EN	061,06	1869	10	60330	1743	8597	KIND ACT (FROM ABOVE)		恩
EN	140,10	1419	14	44336			ANTHRACENE		蒽
FA	009,04	0127	06	23250	1765	6914	TO ATTACK,PUNITIVE EXPEDITION		伐
FA	029,03	4099.1	05	23447			SEND OUT,DEVELOP		发
FA	085,05	3127.0B	08	34131		8841	METHOD/WAY(WITH-L)		法
FA	105,07	4099	12	12247	1768	6287	SEND OUT,DEVELOP		發
FA	164,12	683A	19	12647		6288	FERMENT		醱
FAR	004,04	0040	05	20307	1761	6591	TIRED,SHORT OF		乏
FAR	032,06	1012	09	23104		0231	TO PLOUGH		垡
FAR	075,06	4589.1	10	43950	1766	6915	RAFT OF LOGS		栰
FAR	085,05	3127.0A	08	34131	1762	8841	METHOD/WAY(WITH-TZ)		法
FAR	112,05	8935	10	14632	1764	8835	STEELYARD WEIGHT		砝
FAR	118,06	4589	12	88253	1766	6916	RAFT OF LOGS		筏
FAR	122,09	5000	14	60620	1769	2873	PUNISH(MENT)		罰
FAR	122,10	5000.1	15	60640		3189	PUNISH(MENT)		罸
FAR	140,06	5421	10	44253			DENSENESS OF GRASS-FOLIAGE		茷
FAR	169,06	7042	14	77253	1767	3525	CLIQUE,VALVE		閥
FAA	029,03	4099.1A	05	23447			HAIR	7569.0A	发
FAA	085,05	3127	08	34131	1762	8841	METHOD/WAY,LAW	8719	法
FAA	085,18	8719	21	30132			METHOD/WAY,LAW	3127	灋
FAA	190,05	7569.0A	15	72447	1770	6058	HAIR	4099.1A	髮
FAH	029,03	4099.1B	05	23447			HAIR	7569	发

ROM	RAD	TEL	TOT	FC	MAT	OSH	TAG	CR	CHAR
FAH	085,05	3127.0C	08	34131	1762	8841	FRANCE,DHARMA		法
FAH	096,08	8828	12	14131	1763	8842	ENAMEL WARE/CLOISONNE WARE		琺
FAH	167,08	693A	16	84131			FRANCIUM		鍅
FAH	190,05	7569	15	72447	1770	6058	HAIR	4099.1B	髮
FAN	050,03	1581.0A	06	47210		7893	SAIL		帆
FAN	050,12	1616	15	42269	1792	1806	BANNER		幡
FAN	064,05	2155.0C	08	52043	4898	2814	TURN OVER	B5064	拚
FAN	070,14	2473	18	08269	1793	1812	PENNANT		旛
FAN	102,07	3972	12	20609	1790	1797	AN. FOR ACTS/DEEDS,FOREIGN		番
FAN	118,15	4698	21	88169			BIG WINNOW BASKET		籓
FAN	120,12	4932	18	22969	1795	1808	TRANSLATE	A5064	繙
FAN	124,12	5064	18	27620	1796	3388	TRANSLATE,TURN OVER,FLIT ABOUT	A4932	翻
FAN	183,12	9592	21	22613		7851	TRANSLATE,TURN OVER,FLIT ABOUT	5064	飜
FARN	016,01	0416.1	03	20217	1771	7887	WHATEVER,WORLDLY		凣
FARN	016,01	0416	03	77210	1771	7888	WHATEVER,WORLDLY		凡
FARN	022,03	055A	05	71711			VAT		匜
FARN	032,12	1082	15	42169	1791	1798	A GRAVE		墦
FARN	050,03	1581	06	47210		7893	SAIL		帆
FARN	075,11	2868	15	44430	1775	5051	(SURNAME),FENCE,CAGE		樊
FARN	086,09	3565	13	91886	1789	8294	TO BOTHER,FEEL VEXED		煩
FARN	086,12	3600	16	92869	1794	1807	TO ROAST MEAT FOR SACRIFICE,BURN		燔
FARN	096,12	3879	16	12169		1799	(GEM)		璠
FARN	112,03	4345.1	08	17610		7891	ALUM		矾
FARN	112,15	4345	20	44261	1776	1114	ALUM		礬
FARN	118,05	9008	11	88443			OSIER BASKET OF BRIDES		笲
FARN	120,11	4907	17	88903	1788	8474	COMPLICATED		繁
FARN	130,12	5233	16	72269	1797	1805	COOKED MEAT USED IN SACRIFICE		膰
FARN	140,12	5603	16	44609	1798	1817	FLOURISHING,TO REPRODUCE		蕃
FARN	140,15	5672	19	44169	1800	1811	FRONTIER,TO PROTECT		藩
FARN	140,17	5694	21	44903		8475	ARTEMISIA STELLARIANA		蘩
FARN	142,15	5865	21	44136		8933	CYRTOPHYLLUS SP.		蠜
FARN	145,05	5983	10	39250			PLAIN GARMENTS		袢
FARN	157,12	6471	19	62169	1799	1800	PAWS OF ANIMAL		蹯

ROM	RAD	TEL	TOT	FC	MAT	OSH	TAG	CR	CHAR
FARN	167,03	9440	11	87110		7890	VANADIUM		釩
FARN	182,10	7369	19	77310			TO GALLOP(OF HORSE)		飆
FARN	196,12	775B	23	27627			WATER-HEN/GALLINULA		鷭
FAAN	029,02	0646	04	71247	1781	6102	WRONG SIDE OUT OR UP		反
FAAN	162,04	6604	08	31304	1785	6752	RETURN TO		返
FANN	075,07	2753	11	44217	1774	7902	BRAHMA,SANSKRIT		梵
FANN	085,02	3058	05	37112	1777	7211	TO OVERFLOW,EXTENSIVE		氾
FANN	085,03	3062	06	37110	1773	7901	FLOAT,BROAD/VAST,PAN-	A3131	汎
FANN	085,05	3131	08	32137	1773	6595	FLOAT,GENERAL/VAGUE	A3062	泛
FANN	094,02	3690	05	47212	1779	7194	OFFEND,VIOLATE		犯
FANN	102,04	8858	09	62047			FIELD/FARM		畈
FANN	118,05	9009	11	88112		7213	BAMBOO MOLD		笵
FANN	118,09	4636	15	88512	1780	7193	MODEL	B5400	範
FANN	140,05	5400	09	44112	1778	7212	(SURNAME),MODEL	D4636	范
FANN	154,04	6305	11	61847	1784	6112	DEAL IN/TRADE IN		販
FANN	184,04	7391	12	81747	1787	6106	COOKED RICE,MEAL		飯
FANG	022,00	0557	02	71710	1801	0775	A BOX		匚
FANG	032,04	0972	07	40127	1803	4322	SUBDIVISION OF A CITY		坊
FANG	038,04	1186.0A	07	40427	1804	4333	HINDER/HARM		妨
FANG	070,00	2455	04	00227	1802	4321	SQUARE,DIRECTION,JUST		方
FANG	075,04	2658	08	40927	1810	4330	SANTALUM ALBUM		枋
FANG	085,08	8684	11	34127			NAME OF A RIVER		淓
FANG	140,04	5364	08	44227	1815	4354	FRAGRANT		芳
FANG	142,04	573C	10	50127			NARAGA DIFFUSA		蚄
FANG	163,04	6720	07	07227		2220	NAME OF A HSIEN IN SZECHUAN		邡
FANG	167,04	9443	12	80127			FRANCIUM		鈁
FARNG	038,04	1186	07	40427	1804	4333	HINDER/HARM		妨
FARNG	063,04	2075	08	30227	1806	4334	HOUSE		房
FARNG	130,04	9112	08	70227	1813	4328	ANIMAL FAT		肪
FARNG	170,04	7089	07	70227	1817	4327	GUARD AGAINST		防
FARNG	195,04	7629	15	20327	1818	4332	BREAM/ZEUS JAPANICUS		魴
FAANG	009,04	0119	06	20227	1808	4325	IMITATE	0236	仿
FAANG	009,08	0236	10	28240	1808		IMITATE	0119	倣

ROM	RAD	TEL	TOT	FC	MAT	OSH	TAG	CR	CHAR
FAANG	060,04	1762	07	20227	1805	4326	SEEMINGLY	7564	彷
FAANG	072,04	2499	08	60027	1809	4324	DAWN,TO BEGIN		昉
FAANG	120,04	4791	10	20927	1812	4331	SPIN		紡
FAANG	137,04	5302	10	20427	1814	4329	LARGE BOAT,2 BOATS LASHED TOGETHER		舫
FAANG	149,04	6078	11	00627	1816	4323	INQUIRE,SEEK,VISIT		訪
FAANG	190,04	7564	14	72227	1805	4356	SEEMINGLY	1762	髣
FANQ	066,04	2397	08	08240	1807	6361	LET GO,LET OUT,TO PLACE		放
FEI	005,02	7378.1	03	12013			TO FLY		飞
FEI	030,08	0803	11	61011	1821	2773	COFFEE		啡
FEI	037,08	8269	11	11430			(SURNAME)	8805	斐
FEI	038,03	1173	06	47417	1838	7251	IMPERIAL CONCUBINE		妃
FEI	063,08	2084	12	30211	1823	2782	DOOR WITH ONLY ONE LEAF		扉
FEI	094,08	8805	12	11430			(SURNAME)	8269	棐
FEI	120,08	4869	14	21911	1828	2781	DARK RED,PURPLE SILK		緋
FEI	140,08	5481	12	44111	1831	2786	PHENANTHRENE,PHILIPPINE		菲
FEI	173,08	7204	16	10111	1834	2787	FALL OF SNOW		霏
FEI	175,00	7236	08	11111	1819	2772	IS NOT,NON- IN-		非
FEI	183,00	7378	09	12413	1850	7850	TO FLY		飛
FEI	186,08	7453	17	21611	1835		FRAGRANT		馞
FEI	187,08	7493	18	71311	1836	2780	HORSE WITH YELLOW BACK		騑
FEIR	085,08	3224	11	37117	1840	7289	NAME OF A RIVER		淝
FEIR	130,04	5142	08	77217	1839	7288	FAT,FERTILE		肥
FEIR	130,08	5203	12	71211	1830	2779	CALF OF LEG,DECAY,PROTECT		腓
FEEI	022,08	0564	10	71711	1820	0807	BANDIT		匪
FEEI	061,08	1894	11	91011	1822	2775	WANT BUT CANNOT SPEAK		悱
FEEI	067,08	2431	12	11400	1824	6555	ELEGANT,(PHONETIC),(SURNAME)		斐
FEEI	074,05	2595	09	72272	1841	1024	CRESCENT MOON		朏
FEEI	075,08	2787	12	11904	1825	5350	TORREYA NUCIFERA,STRENGTHEN	A2833	棐
FEEI	075,10	2833	14	41911	1825	0808	TORREYA NUCIFERA	A2787	榧
FEEI	096,08	3836	12	11111	5017		STRING OF PEARLS(500)		琲
FEEI	118,10	4644	16	88711	1827	0809	ROUND COVERED BASKET		篚
FEEI	124,08	5051	14	11127	1829	3413	KINGFISHER,GREEN JADE		翡
FEEI	142,08	5777	14	11136	1832	8931	GAD-FLY		蜚

ROM	RAD	TEL	TOT	FC	MAT	OSH	TAG	CR	CHAR
FEEI	149,08	6145	15	01611	1833	2774	SLANDER	7236.0A	誹
FEEI	175,00	7236.0A	08	11111	1819	2772	SLANDER	6145	非
FEY	030,04	0693	07	63034	1837	5068	TO BARK		吠
FEY	044,08	1457	11	77211			COARSE,SANDALS		屝
FEY	053,12	1683	15	00247	1848	6292	CRIPPLED,ABOLISH,USELESS		廢
FEY	061,05	1844.0A	08	95027	1985	4772	ANGER		怫
FEY	085,05	3110	08	35127	1845	4778	BOIL		沸
FEY	094,05	369B	08	45227		4776	HAMADRYAD BABOON		狒
FEY	104,05	4015	10	00127	1846	4779	PRICKLY HEAT	4032	痱
FEY	104,08	4032	13	00111	1826	2783	PRICKLY HEAT	4015	痮
FEY	104,12	1683.1	17	00147	1849	6293	CRIPPLED,ABOLISH		癈
FEY	112,05	1468	10	15627			DAM UP WATER WITH ROCKS		砩
FEY	130,04	5151	08	70227	1843	4012	LUNG		肺
FEY	140,05	5372.0A	09	44227			SMALL		芾
FEY	154,05	6316	12	55806	1847	8213	EXPENSES,TO WASTE,(SURNAME)		費
FEY	167,12	1561	20	85186			FERMIUM		鐨
FEY	195,08	765F	19	21311			HERRING/MENHADEN		鯡
FEN	010,09	8091	11	48212		7563	DECIGRAM		兝
FEN	018,02	0433	04	80227	1851	4289	DIVIDE		分
FEN	030,04	0695	07	68027	1853	4290	TO ORDER,LEAVE INSTRUCTIONS		吩
FEN	084,04	3050	08	80217	1856	7808	VAPOR,MIASMA		氛
FEN	098,04	391A	09	18712		7952	DECIGRAM		甐
FEN	117,04	454C	09	08127			DECILITER		竕
FEN	120,04	4788	10	28927	1859	4297	CONFUSED		紛
FEN	140,04	5358	08	44227	1861	4300	FRAGRANT		芬
FEN	140,07	544B	11	44227			FENCHENE		芬
FEN	140,08	2780	12	44904			(TREE)		棻
FEN	164,04	1568	11	18627		4292	PHENOL		酚
FEN	173,04	7187	12	10227		4301	MISTY/FOGGY		雰
FERN	032,04	0970	07	40140	1868	6546	A GRAVE	1079	坟
FERN	032,12	1079	15	44186	1868	8181	A GRAVE	0970	墳
FERN	050,13	8365	16	44286	1869		ORNAMENTAL TASSEL ON BRIDLE		幩
FERN	075,04	2659	08	48927	1855	4295	(TREE)		枌

ROM	RAD	TEL	TOT	FC	MAT	OSH	TAG	CR	CHAR
FERN	075,08	2781	12	44227	1865	4303	BEAMS IN ROOF,CONFUSED		
FERN	085,04	3083	07	38127	1857	4298	NAME OF A RIVER		
FERN	085,12	3409	15	34186		8185	EDGE OF WATER		
FERN	086,08	3539	12	44809	1866	5621	BURN		
FERN	123,13	5033	19	84586	1871		SEXLESS GOAT		
FERN	140,12	5613	16	44806	1872	8186	HEMP SEEDS,LUXURIOUS/ABUNDANT		
FERN	142,04	5728	10	58127			(MOLE)	7858	
FERN	142,04	9219	10	80136			(MOLE)	7858	
FERN	152,13	9317	20	14286	1873		GELDED PIG		
FERN	159,12	6571	19	54086			WAR CHARIOT		
FERN	207,06	7852	19	40147			LARGE BRASS DRUM		
FERN	208,04	7858	17	78712	1863	6830	(MOLE)	5728	
FEEN	119,04	4720	10	98927	1858	4296	POWDER		
FENN	009,04	0118	06	28227	1852	4293	PORTION		
FENN	009,12	0292	14	24286	1867	8184	RUIN/DESTROY,INSTIGATE		
FENN	018,02	0433.0A	04	80227	1851	4289	PART		
FENN	030,05	0899.1A	08	64030			SNEEZE		
FENN	030,12	0899.0A	15	64086		8182	SNEEZE		
FENN	037,05	1164.1	08	40603			EXERT ONESELF		
FENN	037,13	1164	16	40601	1874	1750	EXERT ONESELF		
FENN	061,04	1825	08	80332	1854	8635	VEHEMENT		
FENN	061,12	2001	15	94086	1870	8183	INDIGNANT		
FENN	064,05	2155.0B	08	52043	4898	2814	SWEEP		
FENN	085,17	8717	20	39181			VALLEY VAPOR,NAME OF A RIVER		
FENN	119,06	4747.1	12	90801			MANURE/DUNG		
FENN	119,11	4747	17	90801	1875	8036	MANURE/DUNG		
FENG	002,03	0023	04	50000	1876	2591	GRACEFULNESS,ABUNDANT	D6265	
FENG	009,13	8075	15	25218			IMMORTAL		
FENG	041,06	1409	09	44100	1887	3163	TO SEAL,(AN. FOR LETTERS)		
FENG	046,07	1496	10	22504	1878	2599	PEAK		
FENG	046,07	1496.1	10	27754		2596	PEAK		
FENG	046,09	1524	12	22147			NAME OF A LEGENDARY HILL		
FENG	075,09	2800	13	47910	1891	7834	MAPLE		

梦汾濆焚蕡蕢蚡瓫瀆轒鼖韇粉份債分呠噴奮奮忿憤拚漢糞糞半僼封峯峰封楓

ROM	RAD	TEL	TOI	FC	MAT	OSH	TAG	CR	CHAR
FENG	085,18	3488	21	32118	1898		NAME OF A RIVER		灃
FENG	086,07	3536	11	97854	1879	2597	BEACON FIRE		烽
FENG	104,09	4045	14	00117	1892	7837	INSANE,MAD/WILD		瘋
FENG	112,09	431A	14	17610			SULFONE		砜
FENG	140,09	5531	13	44140	1889	3164	(TURNIP)		葑
FENG	142,07	5762	13	57154	1880	2598	BEE,WASP		蜂
FENG	142,17	9244	23	37136	1880	8913	BEE,WASP	5762	蠭
FENG	149,09	6174.0A	16	07610	1893	7832	SATIRIZE		諷
FENG	151,11	6265	18	22108	1897	0576	ABUNDANT,(SURNAME)	B0023	豐
FENG	163,18	6785	21	27127	1900	2163	NAME OF AN ANCIENT CITY,(SURNAME)		酆
FENG	167,07	6912	15	87154	1883	2595	POINT OR EDGE OF A TOOL		鋒
FENG	182,00	7364.1	04	77210			WIND,CUSTOM		风
FENG	182,00	7364	09	77210	1890	7829	WIND,CUSTOM		風
FENG	187,02	7458	12	31127	1895	4705	(SURNAME)		馮
FERNG	034,04	1112	07	27504	1877	2593	TO BUTT (AS HORNED ANIMALS)		夆
FERNG	085,09	8688	12	37110			BUOYANT/FLOATING		渢
FERNG	120,11	4911	17	27934	1882	6662	SEW		縫
FERNG	162,07	6646	11	37304	1881	6661	MEET BY CHANCE,EVERYTIME		逢
FEENG	030,08	8146	11	65053	1886	2495	RECITE/CHANT		哗
FENQ	009,08	0218	10	25253	1885	2496	SALARY		俸
FENQ	029,02	7685.1	04	77210			PHOENIX		凤
FENQ	037,05	1144	08	50503	1884	2494	TO OFFER,RECEIVE (FROM SUPERIOR)		奉
FENQ	120,11	4911.0A	17	27934	1882	6662	SEAM,CRACK		縫
FENQ	149,09	6174	16	07610	1893	7832	SATIRIZE		諷
FENQ	154,09	6352	16	66860		1721	GIFT TO THE DEAD		賵
FENQ	196,03	7685	14	77210	1894	7828	PHOENIX		鳳
FOR	009,05	0154	07	25227	1982	4773	BUDDHA		佛
FOR	030,05	8129	08	65027	1983	4771	OPPOSE,CONTRARY TO		咈
FOR	195,05	762H	16	27327			SILLAGO SIHAMA		鮄
FOH	120,10	4902.0A	16	23942	1901	3267	BIND/TIE WITH ROPE		縛
FOUR	085,07	3187.0A	10	32147	1906		FLOAT		浮
FOUR	120,04	9054	10	21990	1903		BRIGHT/GLOSSY(OF SILK)		紑
FOUR	140,04	5350	08	44901		7983	PLANTAGO MAJOR		芣

ROM	RAD	TEL	TOT	FC	MAT	OSH	TAG	CR	CHAR
FOOU	030,04	0694	07	10609	1902	1442	NOT		
FOOU	121,00	4970	06	80772	1905	1006	POTTERY		
FOOU	167,07	691B	15	81169			VIRGINIUM		
FU	009,04	0183	06	25230		5187	PORTER		
FU	030,04	069A	07	65030			(PHONETIC)/AS IN FURAN/PHORONE		
FU	035,08	9690.1	11	55230			BRAN		
FU	037,01	1133	04	50030	1908	5182	MAN,HUSBAND		
FU	039,10	1335	13	72747	1938	3153	HATCH		
FU	041,07	2421.1	10	53342	1950	3258	APPLY,ANNOUNCE		
FU	066,11	2421	15	58240	1950	6379	APPLY,ANNOUNCE		
FU	075,05	2668	09	44900		3199	CALYX OF FLOWER		
FU	075,05	2696	09	47917	1962	7271	QUERCUS GLANDULIFERA		
FU	112,04	4261	09	15630		5186	INFERIOR GEM,AGATE		
FU	130,04	5227.1	08	75230			SKIN		
FU	130,11	5227	15	21227	1958	3621	SKIN		
FU	157,04	6402	11	65130	1913	5185	INSTEP,TARSUS	6416	
FU	157,05	6416	12	64100	1923	3194	INSTEP,TARSUS	6402	
FU	163,11	6771	14	07227		2250	NAME OF A HSIEN IN SHENSI		
FU	164,04	679C	11	15630			PHTHALIC ACID		
FU	167,04	6866	12	85130	1914	5184	AXE		
FU	199,04	9690	15	45403	1916	6434	BRAN	9691	
FU	199,07	9691	18	43402			BRAN	9690	
FWU	009,04	0126	06	23234	1964	5074	SUBMIT,PROSTRATE,CONCEAL(AMBUSH)		
FWU	009,07	0199	09	22247	1937	3152	PRISONER OF WAR		
FWU	018,05	8102	07	52000			TO CHOP/STRIKE		
FWU	020,09	0550	11	27620	1976	4447	FALL PROSTRATE		
FWU	029,03	8119	05	20447	1968		JAB A DOG TO MAKE IT GO		
FWU	029,03	8119.1	05	43047	1968		JAB A DOG TO MAKE IT GO		
FWU	039,04	1318	07	20407	1936	3151	TRUST		
FWU	040,05	1348.0A	08	30332	4463	8712	TAME,(SURNAME)		
FWU	050,05	1587	08	43247			OBJECT HELD BY DANCER		
FWU	050,09	1607	12	41266	1977	1756	AN. FOR TEXTILE OR PICTURE		
FWU	057,02	1715	05	55027	1981	4770	NOT		

否缶銛佮呋麱夫孵尃敷柎枹砆肤膚跌跗廍酜鈇麩麲伏俘制匍夋友孚宓帗幅弗

ROM	RAD	TEL	TOT	FC	MAT	OSH	TAG	CR	CHAR
FWU	060,05	1765	08	25227	1984	4774	SEEMINGLY	7572	佛
FWU	061,05	1844	08	95027	1985		ANXIOUS		怫
FWU	064,04	2105	07	55030	1909	5189	TO SUPPORT		扶
FWU	064,05	2133	08	55027	1986	4775	BRUSH AWAY		拂
FWU	074,04	2591	08	77247	1999	6099	GARMENT,SUBMIT,TAKE(MEDICINE)		服
FWU	075,07	2727	11	42947	1939	3156	RAFTER,BEAM		桴
FWU	084,05	8636	09	80517		7810	FLUORINE		氟
FWU	085,06	3339	09	33134	1965	5076	UNDERCURRENT EDDY		洑
FWU	085,07	3187	10	32147	1906	3158	FLOAT		浮
FWU	085,08	3242	11	30161	1961	1250	NAME OF A RIVER		涪
FWU	112,05	1468.0A	10	15627			NAME OF A STONE		砩
FWU	113,05	4369	09	33247	1970	6055	REMOVE EVIL,CLEANSE		祓
FWU	113,09	4395	13	31266	1978	1758	GOOD FORTUNE		福
FWU	118,05	4569	11	88243	1922	3206	COINCIDE,SYMBOL,WRITTEN CHARM		符
FWU	118,05	9007	11	88527			DUSTER		箁
FWU	118,08	9015	14	88247			QUIVER		箙
FWU	120,05	4811	11	23947	1971	6056	SASH,RIBBON FOR A SEAL		綍
FWU	120,05	4803	11	25927	1987	4777	ROPE OF A BIER,HEAVY ROPE	4839	紼
FWU	120,07	4839	13	24947	2001	3137	ROPES OF A BIER,HEAVY ROPE	4803	綍
FWU	120,10	4902	16	23942	1901	3267	BIND/TIE WITH ROPE		縛
FWU	122,04	4989	09	60901	1904	7982	PLACE NAME		罘
FWU	122,07	9086	12	60407			NET FOR CATCHING BIRDS		罦
FWU	139,05	5332	11	57017	1988	7314	ANGRY		艴
FWU	140,04	5346	08	44530	1911	5192	LOTUS		芙
FWU	140,05	5372	09	44227			LUXURIANCE OF VEGETATION		芾
FWU	140,05	5394	09	44240		3205	ANGELICA ANOMALA		苻
FWU	140,05	5397	09	44527	1989	4780	LUXURIANT GROWTH		茀
FWU	140,06	5415	10	44234	1966	5077	PACHYMA COCOS/CHINA ROOT		茯
FWU	140,07	5457	11	44407	1940	3159	PELLICLE OF CULMS		莩
FWU	140,08	5472	12	44247	2000	6100	(TURNIP)		菔
FWU	140,09	9179	13	44606			WEEDS		菖
FWU	142,04	5738	10	55130	1912	5191	(WATER-BEETLE),MONEY		蚨
FWU	142,07	5772	13	52147	1907	3157	(WASP),(LARGE ANT),(DRAGON FLY)		蜉

ROM	RAD	TEL	TOT	FC	MAT	OSH	TAG	CR	CHAR
FWU	142,09	5799	15	51166	1979	1759	BAT		蝠
FWU	145,05	5921	10	33247	1972		KNEE-PADS/BUSKINS		袯
FWU	145,06	5931	11	33234	1967	5075	BUNDLE WRAPPED IN CLOTH		袱
FWU	153,12	629B	19	22234			GENETIA		貚
FWU	159,09	6553	16	51066	1980	1754	SPOKE OF A WHEEL		輻
FWU	163,07	6744	10	27427	1941	2206	SUBURBS		郭
FWU	178,05	7280	14	43547	1973	6052	KNEEPAD		鞁
FWU	186,09	7450	18	28647	1998	6412	FRAGRANCE		馥
FWU	190,05	7572	15	72527	1990	4781	SEEMINGLY	1765	髴
FWU	196,02	7683	13	27217	1959	7883	MALLARD/ANAS PLATYRHYNCHA		鳧
FWU	196,08	7719	19	77227		4651	OWL		鵩
FWU	204,05	7833	17	33247	1974	6054	(EMBROIDERY)		黻
FUU	009,07	8047	09	23227			AUXILIARY,ASSIST	6534	俌
FUU	009,08	0214	10	20240	1929	3203	STOOP,LOOK DOWN		俯
FUU	053,05	1650	08	00240	1928	3202	PREFECTURE/MANSION		府
FUU	057,05	1719	08	14200			HANDLE OF BOW		弣
FUU	064,05	2140	08	54000	1919	3197	PAT		拊
FUU	064,08	8435	11	50040	1932		TOUCH GENTLY WITH HAND,TO COMFORT	2329	捬
FUU	064,12	2329	15	58031	1932	8744	TOUCH GENTLY WITH HAND,TO COMFORT	8435	撫
FUU	069,04	2445	08	80221	1934	2050	HATCHET		斧
FUU	085,10	8702	13	38119		0388	NAME OF A RIVER IN HOPEI		滏
FUU	101,02	3940	07	53227	1942	3725	JUST/JUST NOW		甫
FUU	118,12	4674	18	88107	1943	0695	BASKET USED IN STATE WORSHIP		簠
FUU	130,07	5194	11	73227	1944	3737	CANDIED FRUIT		脯
FUU	130,08	5201	14	00227	1930	4060	DECAY,ROTTEN		腐
FUU	130,08	5202	12	70240	1931	3204	INTERNAL ORGANS		腑
FUU	142,07	5797	13	53127			CRAB		蚹
FUU	142,08	577B	14	58121			LEMA FLAVIPES		蝜
FUU	159,07	6534	14	53027	1945	3734	AUXILIARY,ASSIST		輔
FUU	163,07	6749	10	57227			ANCIENT PLACE NAME		鄜
FUU	167,02	6858	10	80109		0387	KETTLE/CALDRON		釜
FUU	181,06	7332	15	31186	1929	8305	STOOP,LOOK DOWN	0214	頫
FUU	193,07	7602	17	13227	1946	3738	LARGE GRAIN MEASURE,CALDRON		鬴

ROM	RAD	TEL	TOT	FC	MAT	OSH	TAG	CR	CHAR
FUU	204,07	7834	19	33227	1947	3739	(EMBROIDERY)		蕭
FUH	009,02	0091.0B	04	23200	1953	1993	FALL PROSTRATE		仆
FUH	009,03	0102	05	24200	1917	3192	PAY		付
FUH	009,09	8065	11	27286			TO RESEMBLE,RELY ON		傅
FUH	009,10	0265	12	23242	1948	3261	TUTOR,(SURNAME)		傅
FUH	014,09	8099	11	37606			RICH	1381	富
FUH	018,09	0479	11	12600	1951	2880	AN. FOR A PAIR,ASSISTANT		副
FUH	030,05	0696	08	64000	1918	3195	TO ORDER		咐
FUH	032,05	8205	08	44100		3193	TO BE ATTACHED	7096	坿
FUH	032,08	1009.0A	11	47147		2276	PORT,QUAI		埠
FUH	032,08	1009.1A	11	47407			PORT,QUAI		埠
FUH	035,06	1788.1	09	80407	1991	6411	ABBR. OF 1788/6010/5958		夏
FUH	038,03	1244.1	06	47470			WOMAN		妇
FUH	038,08	1244	11	47427	1963	3977	WOMAN		婦
FUH	040,09	1381	12	30606	1952	1761	RICH		富
FUH	060,09	1788	12	28247	1992	6414	REPLY TO A LETTER,RECOVER,AGAIN	A6010	復
FUH	085,06	3339.0A	09	33134	1965	5076	TO SWIM		洑
FUH	085,07	3187.0B	10	32147	1906	3158	SWIM		浮
FUH	088,00	3637	04	80400	1933	6521	FATHER		父
FUH	113,05	4370	09	34200	1921	3200	WORSHIP ANCESTORS		祔
FUH	130,09	5215	13	78247	1994	6418	ABDOMEN		腹
FUH	142,05	573E	11	54100			EULOTA PELIOMPHALA		蚹
FUH	142,09	5803	15	58147	1995	6420	VENOMOUS SNAKE		蝮
FUH	142,12	587B	18	27136			LOCUST LARVAE		蟲
FUH	145,09	5958	14	38247	1996	6417	COMPLEX,DOUBLE	1788.1	複
FUH	146,12	6010	18	10247	1993	6416	TO REPLY TO A LETTER,OVERFLOW,COVER	1788.1	覆
FUH	149,02	6058	09	03600	1954	1992	OBITUARY NOTICE		訃
FUH	154,02	6298	09	27806	1956	8202	TO BEAR,LOSE,NEGATIVE(MATH. ETC.)		負
FUH	154,08	6346	15	63840	1957	6893	POETIC ESSAY,TAXATION		賦
FUH	154,10	6355	17	63842	1949	3266	CONTRIBUTE TO FUNERAL EXPENSES		賻
FUH	156,02	6384	09	43800	1955	5951	GO,ATTEND		赴
FUH	159,09	6552	16	58047	1997		PARTS OF CART HOLDING THE AXLE		輹
FUH	170,00	7079	08	27407	1960	2275	MOUND,ABUNDANT	7080	阜

ROM	RAD	TEL	TOT	FC	MAT	OSH	TAG	CR	CHAR
FUH	170,00	7080	03	77227	1960	2153	MOUND,ABUNDANT	7079	
FUH	170,05	7096	08	74200	1924	3196	TO BE ATTACHED	8205	
FUH	187,05	7470	15	74300	1926	3198	PRINCE CONSORT		
FUH	195,05	7631	16	24300	1927	3201	SILVER CARP		
FUH	195,09	9652	20	28347		6419	HALIOTIS GIGANTEA/SEA EAR		
FUH	208,10	785G	23	73711			WALLABY		
GA	030,11	0867.1	14	61053		6945	CACKLING SOUND		
GA	030,12	0867	15	61053	0609		(ONOMAT.)		
GAR	030,11	0867.1A	14	61053		6945	CACKLING SOUND		
GAR	030,12	0867.0A	15	61053			(ONOMAT.)		
GAR	030,13	0900.0A	16	64027	3367		(PHONETIC)		
GAR	167,01	1576.1	09	82110		7058	GADOLINIUM		
GAR	167,08	1576	16	82110		7058	GADOLINIUM		
GAA	042,02	1427	05	17902		8438	(PHONETIC)		
GAH	009,02	0094.0A	04	80220	0629	2742	LIKE THIS/IN THIS MANNER(DIAL)		
GAH	043,04	1435	07	48012	3187	7710	IN AN EMBARRASSING SITUATION		
.GAH	194,04	7616	14	28212			IN AN EMBARRASSING SITUATION	1435	
GAI	032,06	0993	09	40182	3188	7990	BOUNDARY		
GAI	140,06	5437	10	44280	3190	7999	ROOTS OF PLANT		
GAI	142,06	574H	12	50182			TENEBRIO VENTIALIS		
GAI	149,06	6115	13	00682	3191	7992	OUGHT TO,OWE		
GAI	154,06	6326	13	60882	3192	7998	INCLUDE IN,PREPARE,(SURNAME)		
GAI	170,06	7101	09	70282	3193	7993	STEP,TERRACE		
GAE	066,03	2395	07	18140	3196	6393	ALTER,TO CORRECT		
GAY	001,03	0009	04	10207	3194	4529	BEGGAR,BEG FOR ALMS		
GAY	020,03	0544	05	27720	3194	4377	BEG FOR ALMS,BEGGAR	0009	
GAY	062,09	2072	13	13150	3198	6901	INFRINGE UPON A TRADE MARK		
GAY	075,11	8581	15	21904	3201	5395	IN GENERAL	2861	
GAY	075,11	2861	15	41914	3201	7731	IN GENERAL		
GAY	085,11	3346	14	31114	3202	7732	IRRIGATE		
GAY	108,06	5556.1	11	80107	3199		COVER,BUILD		
GAY	140,09	4146	13	44107	3199		COVER,BUILD	5556	
GAY	140,10	5556	14	44107	3199	0743	COVER,BUILD	4146	

阝附駙鮄鰒鼥嘎嘎嘎嘎噶釓鍸乃介尬魆垓荄峐該賅陔改丐匃戱槩槪溉盖葢蓋

ROM	RAD	TEL.	TOT	FC	MAT	OSH	TAG	CR	CHAR
GAY	167,04	6862	12	81127	3195	4530	CALCIUM		鈣
GAN	005,10	0051	11	48417	3233	7966	DRY	B1626	乾
GAN	005,11	0049	12	48417			DRY	0051	乹
GAN	032,05	0984	08	44170	3243	1035	CRUCIBLE		坩
GAN	043,10	1434	13	48013	0831	7713	IN AN EMBARRASSING SITUATION		尲
GAN	043,15	1434.1	18	48011	0831	7709	IN AN EMBARRASSING SITUATION		尷
GAN	051,00	1626	03	10400	3211	2376	TO CONCERN,DRY	D0051	干
GAN	075,03	2616	07	41940	3214	2394	POLE		杆
GAN	075,05	2674	09	44970	3224	1041	LARGE TANGERINE		柑
GAN	085,01	0053	05	12713			POOL(CANTONESE)		氹
GAN	085,05	3121	08	34172	3225	1044	SLOP FROM RINSING RICE		泔
GAN	096,03	3771	07	11140	3215		(INFERIOR GEM)		玕
GAN	099,00	3927	05	44770	3223	1034	SWEET,(SURNAME)		甘
GAN	104,05	4007	10	00175	3226	1045	RICKETS		疳
GAN	109,03	8899	08	61040			(SURNAME)		盰
GAN	118,03	4557	09	88401	3216	2416	POLE		竿
GAN	130,03	5139	07	71240	3217	2383	LIVER		肝
GAN	140,05	537D	09	44774	3228		GLYCOSIDE		苷
GAN	164,03	1638	10	17640			ANHYDRIDE		酐
GAN	194,10	7615	20	28213			IN AN EMBARRASSING SITUATION	1434	魐
GAAN	061,09	1949	13	53330	3232	8677	AFFECTED,FEEL		感
GAAN	064,13	234A	16	58041	3236	2412	TO ROLL(DOUGH)		擀
GAAN	066,08	2413	12	18140	3229	6326	DARE		敢
GAAN	075,03	2616.0A	07	41940	3214	2394	AN. FOR GUNS		杆
GAAN	075,07	2731	11	46941	3219	2405	STICK/POLE		桿
GAAN	075,12	2888	16	48940	3230	6329	OLIVE		橄
GAAN	085,12	8709	15	38140	3231		WASH,PLACE NAME		澉
GAAN	115,03	4427	08	21940	3220	2395	STALKS OF GRAIN	4452	秆
GAAN	115,07	4452	12	26941	3220	2406	STALKS OF GRAIN	4427	稈
GAAN	118,03	4557.0A	09	88401	3216	2416	SHAFT OF ARROW		笴
GAAN	118,10	9021.0A	16	88806			CASE/TRUNK		簳
GAAN	156,03	6385	10	41804	3222	5952	HURRY,DRIVE AWAY,CATCH UP	6391	赶
GAAN	156,07	6391	14	46804	3222	5953	HURRY,DRIVE AWAY,CATCH UP	6385	趕

ROM	RAD	TEL	TOT	FC	MAT	OSH	TAG	CR	CHAR
GANN	051,00	1626.0A	03	10400			MANAGE	1631	千
GANN	051,10	1631	13	48441	3235	2411	MANAGE	1626.0A	幹
GANN	072,03	2486	07	61040	3213	2379	SUNSET/EVENING		旰
GANN	075,10	2832	14	48494	3237	5374	TRUNK OF TREE		榦
GANN	085,08	3227	11	38119	3238	0372	NAME OF A RIVER		淦
GANN	120,05	4802	11	24970	3227	1042	VIOLET OR PURPLE		紺
GANN	154,14	6371	21	01486		8105	KIANGSI	6373	贑
GANN	154,17	6373	23	07486	3239	8107	KIANGSI	6371	贛
GANN	167,02	685A	10	38119			METALLIC ELEMENT		淦
GANN	188,03	7541	13	71240	3218	2384	SHINBONE		骭
GANN	196,05	9674	16	67027			CHIRPING OF BIRDS		鴨
GANG	018,08	0474	10	72200	3268	2909	HARD,JUST/EXACTLY		剛
GANG	032,10	8245	13	46111		0495	MOUND	1481	堈
GANG	046,05	1481	08	77220	3269	3814	MOUND	1511	岡
GANG	046,08	1511	11	22227	3269	3817	MOUND	1481	崗
GANG	064,03	2095.0A	06	51010	3261	0089	LIFT OVERHEAD WITH BOTH HANDS		扛
GANG	075,03	8530.0A	07	41910	3262	0092	FOOTBRIDGE		杠
GANG	093,04	366B	08	20517			TRUE BUFFALO		牨
GANG	104,03	8862	08	00111			ANUS	5138	疘
GANG	120,08	4854	14	27920	3271	3816	MAIN HEADINGS		綱
GANG	121,03	4971	09	81710	3264	0086	VAT	4976	缸
GANG	121,08	4976	14	87720	3264		VAT	4971	鋼
GANG	122,05	4993	10	60101	3266	0494	(STARS)		罡
GANG	130,03	5138	07	71210	3265	0090	ANUS	8862	肛
GANG	140,09	551B	13	44917			CAMPYLOTROPIS		菕
GANG	167,03	6864	11	81110	3700	0084	HANGING BOWL FOR LAMP OR FISH		釭
GANG	167,08	6921	16	87120	3272	3815	STEEL		鋼
GAANG	046,05	1481.0A	08	77220	3269	3814	MOUND,POLICEMAN'S BEAT	1511.0A	岡
GAANG	046,08	1511.0A	11	22227	3269	3817	MOUND,POLICEMAN'S BEAT	1481.0A	崗
GAANG	085,09	3263	12	34117	3267	7258	HARBOR		港
GANQ	075,03	8530	07	41910	3262	0092	HORIZONTAL BAR,CARRYING POLE	2850	杠
GANQ	075,10	2850	14	41986	3716	8106	HORIZONTAL BAR,CARRYING POLE	8530	槓
GANQ	142,03	5725	09	51110	2384	0094	RAINBOW		虹

ROM	RAD	TEL	TOT	FC	MAT	OSH	TAG	CR	CHAR
GAU	075,12	2863	16	46943	3286	2367	WATER PULLEY		楻
GAU	075,15	2926	19	50904		5322	WEAPON CASE		橐
GAU	106,05	4108.1	10	26403	3285		MARSH,BANK		皋
GAU	106,06	4108	11	26403	3285	2363	MARSH,BACK	5264	皐
GAU	109,09	5264.1	14	26401	3285	2493	MARSH,BANK,TESTICLES		睪
GAU	118,10	4643	16	88227	3294	3841	POLE FOR PUNTING BOATS		篙
GAU	119,10	4741	16	98931	3283	8721	CAKE	9602	糕
GAU	123,04	5021	10	80331	3282	8719	LAMB		羔
GAU	130,10	5221	14	00227	3296	3614	OINTMENT		膏
GAU	132,06	5264	12	26401	3285	2363	MARSH,BANK	4108	皋
GAU	184,10	9602	18	88731	3283	8720	CAKE	4741	餻
GAU	189,00	7559	10	00227	3290	3827	HIGH/TALL		高
GAU	189,00	7559.1	11	00227			HIGH/TALL		髙
GAU	196,12	7750	23	27427			ARA MACAW		鷎
GAU	207,08	7854	21	44604		1435	LARGE DRUM		鼛
GAO	064,10	2269	13	50027		3832	DO,TAKE CARE OF		搞
GAO	064,20	2383.0A	23	57016		7624	TO DO/ACT		攬
GAO	075,04	2640	08	60904	3284	5324	SUN SHINES BRIGHTLY,HIGH		景
GAO	075,10	2842	14	40927	3291	3833	ROTTEN(AS WOOD),DRY		槁
GAO	115,10	4473.1	15	00904	3293	5546	MANUSCRIPT/DRAFT,STALK OF GRAIN		槀
GAO	115,10	4473	15	20927	3293	3834	MANUSCRIPT/DRAFT,STALK OF GRAIN		稿
GAO	120,10	4908	16	20927	3295	3836	PLAIN WHITE SILK		縞
GAO	140,14	5664	18	44904	3297	5362	MANUSCRIPT/DRAFT,STALK OF GRAIN	4473	藁
GAO	167,10	6964.0A	18	80127	2084	3828	A PICK		鎬
GAW	030,04	0707	07	24601	3287	1330	TELL		告
GAW	149,07	6138	14	04661	3288	1332	GRANT(A TITLE),ENJOIN		誥
GAW	163,07	6750	10	27627	3289	2177	NAME OF A FEUDAL STATE,(SURNAME)		郜
GAW	167,07	1691	15	84161		1331	ZIRCONIUM		鋯
GE	018,10	0480	12	32600	3380	2877	CUT OFF		割
GE	030,06	0748.0B	09	67064	4120	1409	(PHONETIC)		咯
GE	030,07	0766	10	10621	3363	3061	ELDER BROTHER		哥
GE	032,03	8198	06	48117		7959	(PHONETIC)		圪
GE	062,00	2047	04	53000	3358	6895	SPEAR,(SURNAME)		戈

ROM	RAD	TEL	TOT	FC	MAT	OSH	TAG	CR	CHAR
GE	064,14	2364	17	57020	3370	3457	TO PLACE		擱
GE	076,10	2960	14	17682	3364	4927	SONG	9295	歌
GE	085,09	3235	12	34121	3362		PLACE NAME		涽
GE	090,05	3648	09	21220	3359		PLACE NAME		牁
GE	104,03	4095	08	00117	3311	7971	PIMPLE,WART		疙
GE	120,03	4769.0A	09	28917	2086	7969	KNOT		紇
GE	130,06	5163	10	77264	3310	1416	ARMPIT		胳
GE	149,10	9295	17	01621	3364	3062	SONG	2960	謌
GE	196,05	770A	16	21320			LEUCOBCEPHAPON CANADENSIS HUTCHINSI		駒
GE	196,06	7704	17	87627	3376	4613	PIGEON/DOVE		鴿
GER	009,03	0106.0A	05	28217			(ETHNIC GROUP)		仡
GER	030,03	0677.0A	06	27604		1401	EACH		各
GER	030,03	0678.0B	06	80601			SIDE DOOR	A7040	合
GER	030,10	084C	13	61027	3316		HICCUP/BELCH		嗝
GER	030,13	0900	16	64027	3367	4398	(PHONETIC)		噶
GER	032,10	8247	13	41127			DRY CLAY LUMP		塥
GER	064,10	8466	14	22550		3336	TO HUG		搿
GER	075,06	2706	10	47964	3309	1420	RULE,FRAME		格
GER	075,10	2843	14	41927		3914	YOKE		楁
GER	124,10	5058.0A	16	17220	3317	3394	QUILL		翮
GER	130,10	5224	14	71227	3318	3913	DIAPHRAGM		膈
GER	140,09	5514	13	44727	3377	4397	COARSE GRASS LINEN		葛
GER	142,06	5756	12	58161	3373	1196	CLAM		蛤
GER	148,06	9279	13	27264			HORNS/ANTLERS		觡
GER	159,13	6566	20	54027	3379	4399	CONFUSED/DISORDERLY		轕
GER	163,06	6740.0A	09	87627		2172	NAME OF A HSIEN IN SHENSI		郃
GER	167,10	9493	18	81127		3910	CADMIUM		鎘
GER	169,06	7040	14	77601	3374	3453	COUNCIL-CHAMBER,SHELF,SIDE DOOR	K7041	閤
GER	169,06	7041	14	77604	3369	3456	COUNCIL-CHAMBER,SHELF	7040	閣
GER	170,10	7133	13	71227	3319	3912	PARTITION,SEPARATED BY		隔
GER	177,00	7245	09	44506	3314	2629	REMOVE,LEATHER		革
GER	188,06	7547	16	77264	3371	1417	SKELETON		骼
GER	193,00	7601	10	10227	3315	3909	EARTHEN POT,IRON CALDRON,(SURNAME)		鬲

ROM	RAD	TEL	TOT	FC	MAT	OSH	TAG	CR	CHAR
GEE	030,03	0677.0B	06	27604			EACH		各
GEE	030,03	0678.0A	06	80601		1188	1/10 OF A PECK		合
GEE	030,07	0776	10	46621	3361	3058	EXCELLENT,HAPPY/WELL-BEING		哿
GEE	108,06	5556.1A	11	80107	3199		(SURNAME)		盇
GEE	137,05	5308	11	21420	3360	3053	BARGE		舸
GEE	140,09	5514.0A	13	44727	3377	4397	(SURNAME)		葛
GEE	140,10	5556.0A	14	44107	3199	0743	(SURNAME)		蓋
GEH	002,02	0020	03	80200	3366	1983	GENERAL CLASSIFIER	0222	个
GEH	009,08	0222	10	26200	3366	1870	GENERAL CLASSIFIER	0020	個
GEH	030,03	0677	06	27604	3368	1401	EACH		各
GEH	064,13	8475	16	54027	3378		SCRAPE/GRATE		搨
GEH	118,08	4612	14	88603	3366	1873	GENERAL CLASSIFIER	0020	箇
GEH	142,03	573D	09	58117	3312	7970	FLEA		虼
GEH	167,06	9459	14	87164		1403	CHROMIUM		鉻
.GE	009,08	0222.0A	10	26200	3366	1870	GENERAL CLASSIFIER		個
GEEI	120,06	4822	12	28961	0482	1195	GIVE,TO.FOR PASSIVE PART.		給
GEN	075,06	2704	10	47932	3328	5911	ROOT,RADICAL(CHEM.)		根
GEN	157,06	6418	13	67132	3330	5900	FOLLOW,WITH,AND		跟
GENN	007,04	0065.0A	06	10107	3344	0525	EXTEND ACROSS/THROUGH		互
GENN	138,00	5327	06	77732	3327	5897	A SIGN IN TRIGRAM		艮
GENN	140,06	1706	11	44732	3815	5926	RANUNCULUS		茛
GENG	053,05	1649	08	00237	3339	5228	AGE,7TH HEAVEN'S STEM		庚
GENG	073,03	2577.0A	07	10506	3346	6573	TO CHANGE		更
GENG	085,07	8676	10	31146		6587	NAME OF A RIVER IN HOPEI		浭
GENG	102,04	3958	09	65000	3343	2748	TO PLOUGH/TILL	5087	畊
GENG	115,04	4433	09	20917	3350	7869	NON-GLUTINOUS RICE	4734	秔
GENG	115,07	4734.1	12	21946	3350	6583	NON-GLUTINOUS RICE		稉
GENG	119,07	4734	13	91946	3350	6582	NON-GLUTINOUS RICE	4433	粳
GENG	123,13	5036	19	80430	3342	5008	SOUP		羹
GENG	127,04	5087	10	54900	3343	2831	TO PLOUGH/TILL	3958	耕
GENG	154,08	6342	15	00286	3340	8218	CONTINUE(AS A SONG)		賡
GENG	196,08	7733	19	07227	3341	4648	ORIOLE		鶊
GERNG	075,09	2656	13	46914			FLAG STAFF		桿

ROM	RAD	TEL	TOT	FC	MAT	OSH	TAG	CR	CHAR
GEENG	030,07	0775	10	61046	3347	6575	CHOKING		哽
GEENG	032,07	8217	10	41146	3348	6574	CHANNEL FOR IRRIGATION		埂
GEENG	075,07	2739	11	41946	3349	6581	STEM		梗
GEENG	094,07	370C	10	41246			TERRIER		猄
GEENG	120,07	4837	13	21946	3351	6584	WELL-ROPE,ROPE		綆
GEENG	128,04	5105	10	19180	3353	5589	(SURNAME),BRIGHT		耿
GEENG	163,07	9393	10	17527			PLACE NAME		鄆
GEENG	188,07	7550	17	71246	3352	6580	FISH BONES,UNYIELDING,BLUNT	7643	骾
GEENG	195,07	7643	18	21346	3352	6585	FISH BONES,UNYIELDING,BLUNT	7550	鯁
GENQ	007,04	8017.0A	06	10106	2889	0021	EXTEND ACROSS/THROUGH	0065	亘
GENQ	007,04	0065	06	10107	3344	0525	EXTEND ACROSS/THROUGH	8017.0A	亙
GENQ	073,03	2577	07	10506	3346	6573	STILL MORE		更
GIE	195,08	7652	19	24321			SALTED SEA FISH(AMOY DIAL.)		鯦
GONG	009,06	0180.0A	08	24281	3710	8029	SUPPLY,OFFER(INFORMATION ETC)		供
GONG	012,02	0361	04	80732	3701	8846	PUBLIC/JUST,HONORABLE(DESIGNATION)		公
GONG	019,03	0501	05	14127	3698	4784	ACCOMPLISHMENT		功
GONG	040,07	1362	10	30606	3705	1474	PALACE		宮
GONG	048,00	1562	03	10100	3697	0083	WORK/LABOR		工
GONG	057,00	1712	03	17207	3703	4732	A BOW (WEAPON)		弓
GONG	061,06	1872	10	44338	3711	8519	RESPECTFUL		恭
GONG	066,03	2396	07	18140	3699	6306	ATTACK		攻
GONG	118,10	9021	16	88806			BAMBOO HAT		簀
GONG	130,04	5147	08	74232	3706	8826	BRACHIUM,HUMERUS		肱
GONG	142,04	5733	10	58132	3702	8854	SCOLOPENDRA CENTIPEDE		蚣
GONG	148,06	6044	13	29211	3587	7508	CUP MADE OF HORN,BIG		觥
GONG	158,03	6501	10	27227	3704	4734	BODY,ONESELF,PERSONALLY		躬
GONG	158,07	6501.1	14	26260	3704	1469	BODY,ONESELF,PERSONALLY		躳
GONG	167,03	6864.0A	11	81110	3700	0084	HANGING BOWL FOR LAMP OR FISH		釭
GONG	195,03	762A	14	21310	7293		RAY (FISH)		魟
GONG	196,04	769A	15	87727			MUSICAPA SIBIRICA		鴻
GONG	196,06	770H	17	47827			RUFOUS TINAMOU		鵊
GONG	212,06	7895	22	01801	3714	8045	(SURNAME)		龔
GORNG	124,03	9095	09	11110			FLY TO,TO REACH(HEAVEN)		羾
									工

ROM	RAD	TEL	TOT	FC	MAT	OSH	TAG	CR	CHAR
GOONG	048,03	7255.1	06	17110			SECURE/SOLID		巩
GOONG	055,00	1699	03	44000	3707	1033	HANDS JOINED		廾
GOONG	064,06	2162	09	54081	3712	8030	FOLD HANDS IN SALUTE,TO ARCH		拱
GOONG	075,06	2703	10	44981	3713	8032	POST		栱
GOONG	085,03	3074	07	10232	2382	5642	MERCURY	6955	汞
GOONG	096,06	3797	10	14181		8027	(GEM)		珙
GOONG	112,03	4349.1A	08	10600			ORE		矿
GOONG	112,15	4349.0A	20	10686	3607	8334	ORE	7006.0A	礦
GOONG	167,07	6955	15	81132			MERCURY	3074	錄
GOONG	167,15	7006.0A	23	80186	3607	8333	AN ORE	4349.0A	鑛
GOONG	177,06	7255	15	17506	3718	2631	SECURE/SOLID		鞏
GONQ	009,06	0180	08	24281	3710	8029	OFFER,SACRIFICIAL OFFERING		供
GONQ	012,04	0364	06	44801	3709	8026	TOGETHER		共
GONQ	154,03	6300	10	10806	3715	8104	TRIBUTE/GIFTS		貢
GOU	020,02	0551	04	27720	3409	4462	HOOK		勾
GOU	075,05	2667.0B	09	47920	3412		ACGLE SEPIARIA		枸
GOU	085,04	3297.1	07	37120			DITCH/GUTTER		沟
GOU	085,10	3297	13	35147	3429	4124	DITCH/GUTTER		溝
GOU	118,10	4645	16	88447		4125	BAMBOO FRAME FOR DRYING CLOTHES		篝
GOU	120,09	9071	15	27934	3424		(SURNAME)		緱
GOU	167,04	6869	12	87120	3417	4463	HOOK,ENTICE	6887	钩
GOU	167,05	6887	13	87120	3417	4414	HOOK,ENTICE	6869	鉤
GOU	177,10	7271	19	45547	3433	4119	PISTON		鞲
GOU	178,10	7287	19	45547	3433		ARCHER'S ARM GUARD		韝
GOOU	046,05	1490	08	27720	3410	4416	NAME OF A HILL IN HUNAN		岣
GOOU	075,05	2667	09	47920	3412		LYCIUM CHINENSE		枸
GOOU	094,05	3699	08	47220	3413	4421	DOG		狗
GOOU	118,05	4578	11	88627	3414	4429	BASKET FOR TRAPPING FISH		笱
GOOU	125,05	5076	11	44627			WIZENED FACE OF AGE,OLD		耇
GOOU	140,05	5384	09	44627	3416	4425	IF INDEED,THOUGHTLESS,(SURNAME)		苟
GOW	013,08	0377	10	55447	3425	4117	TEN BILLIONS,INNER ROOMS OF PALACE		冓
GOW	020,02	0551.0A	04	27720	3409	4462	AFFAIR,TO REACH FOR(WITH HAND)		勾
GOW	032,06	0996	09	42161	3421	1151	DIRT,DISGRACE		垢

ROM	RAD	TEL	TOT	FC	MAT	OSH	TAG	CR	CHAR
GOW	036,08	1124	11	27220	3419	4424	ENOUGH	1733	夠
GOW	036,08	1124.1	11	27627	3419	4259	ENOUGH		够
GOW	038,06	1208	09	42461	3422	1153	COPULATE,GOOD		姤
GOW	038,10	1266	13	45447	3426	4123	COPULATE,MARRIAGE		媾
GOW	057,10	1733	13	47247	3420	6294	ENOUGH	1124	彀
GOW	064,10	2273	13	55047	3427	4120	REACH TO,IMPLICATE		搆
GOW	075,04	2845.1	08	47920			CONSTRUCT,BROUSSONETIA PAPYRIFERA		构
GOW	075,10	2845	14	45947	3428	4121	CONSTRUCT,BROUSSONETIA PAPYRIFERA		構
GOW	147,10	6026	17	56410	3430	7604	MEET UNEXPECTEDLY,SEE,COMPLETE	A6673	覯
GOW	149,05	9284	12	07620	3423		SENSE OF SHAME,TO ABUSE	6110	訽
GOW	149,06	6110	13	02661	3423	1152	SENSE OF SHAME,TO ABUSE		詬
GOW	154,04	6356.1	11	67820			TO PURCHASE		购
GOW	154,10	6356	17	65847	3431	5576	TO PURCHASE		購
GOW	162,06	6626.0A	10	32306	2145	6610	MEET UNEXPECTEDLY	6673	遘
GOW	162,10	6673	14	35304	3432	6707	MEET UNEXPECTEDLY	6626.0A	遘
GOW	172,05	7169	13	20614	3418	0891	CROWING OF PHEASANT		雊
GU	009,05	0131	07	24260	3448	1293	ESTIMATE		估
GU	030,05	0722.0A	08	62030	5995	4984	CRYING SOUND OF CHILD		呱
GU	030,05	0734	08	64060	3449	1289	MUTTER		咕
GU	038,05	1196	08	44460	3453	1300	PATERNAL AUNT		姑
GU	039,05	1324	08	12430	3470	4985	LONE/LONELY		孤
GU	085,05	8666	08	32130			NAME OF A RIVER		泒
GU	085,05	3114	08	34160	3456	1302	BUY/SELL		沽
GU	118,08	4616	14	88432	3471		(BAMBOO),TRUMPET FOR CHARIOTS		箛
GU	118,08	4611	14	88512	3474	0814	HOOP/BIND WITH HOOPS		箍
GU	122,05	4990	10	60232	3472		LARGE FISHING NET		罟
GU	140,05	5395	09	44232			ZIZANIA LATIFOLIA	A5479	苽
GU	140,08	5479	12	44432		4986	ZIZANIA LATIFOLIA,MUSHROOM	D5466	菰
GU	140,08	5466	12	44464	3454	1301	MUSHROOM		菇
GU	142,05	5745	11	54160	3460	1299	MOLE-CRICKET		蛄
GU	148,05	6040	12	22230	3473	4987	GOBLET,RULE/LAW		觚
GU	159,05	652A	12	54060	3462	1295	WHEEL		轱
GU	159,10	6560.0A	17	47547	3491	6275	WHEEL		轂

ROM	RAD	TEL	TOT	FC	MAT	OSH	TAG	CR	CHAR
GU	160,05	6581	12	40401	3463	2471	CRIME/SIN,(SURNAME)		韋
GU	164,05	6800	12	14660	3464	1291	TO DEAL IN LIQUORS		酤
GU	196,05	7698	16	47627	3466	4614	PARTRIDGE/FRANCOLINUS CHINENSIS		鴣
GU	140,10	554E	14	44227	3488	3630	FOLLICLE		菩
GWU	188,00	7539.0A	10	77227	3486	3625	BONE		骨
GUU	009,05	0131.0A	07	24260	3448	1293	ESTIMATE		估
GUU	017,03	0424.0B	05	77777	6305	1975	CONVEX	G7849	凸
GUU	030,02	0657	05	40600	3447	1286	ANCIENT		古
GUU	030,11	0858	14	47647		6128	GOOD FORTUNE,LONGEVITY		嘏
GUU	064,03	8419	06	58017			TO RUB,CLEAN		抾
GUU	075,10	2841	14	47927	3487	3628	SCRAPS OF WOOD		榾
GUU	075,10	2828	14	47947			PAPER MULBERRY TREE		穀
GUU	085,04	3102	07	36100	7695	1498	CONFUSED,EXTINGUISHED		汩
GUU	085,10	3323.0A	13	37127	2227	3629	COMICAL		滑
GUU	085,13	1711	16	37147			NAME OF A RIVER IN HUNAN		灤
GUU	093,05	3672	09	24560	3457	1294	BULLOCK,COW		牯
GUU	096,05	379A	09	14160			COPAL		珓
GUU	107,09	4124	14	44147	3479	6233	DRUM	A7849	鼓
GUU	108,13	4156	18	78107		0651	COVERED POT		鹽
GUU	109,13	4233	18	44604	3481	1176	BLIND		瞽
GUU	115,10	4474	15	47947	3490	6296	GRAIN/CORN	B6253	穀
GUU	119,10	9042	16	47947	3490		GRAIN/CORN	4474	穀
GUU	122,05	4992	10	60604	3458	1311	NET FOR BIRDS OR FISH,IMPLICATE		罟
GUU	123,04	9091	10	87547	3459	6276	BLACK EWE		羖
GUU	123,05	9091.1	11	84560	3459		BLACK EWE		羧
GUU	123,10	502B	16	87527			CAPRA FALCONERI		羭
GUU	130,04	5140	08	77247	3467	6278	THIGH,SHARE/PORTION,WHIFF		股
GUU	130,13	1746	17	74247	3480	6211	SWOLLEN,DROPSICAL		臌
GUU	142,17	5872	23	50107	3475	0744	INSANITY,POISON		蠱
GUU	149,05	6089	12	04660	3461	1290	EXPLAIN,COMMENT		詁
GUU	150,00	6253	07	80608	3483	1379	VALLEY,GRAIN/CORN	D4474	谷
GUU	154,06	6328.0A	13	10806	3476	8162	MERCHANT,TO BUY		賈
GUU	159,10	6560	17	47547	3491	6275	HUB OF WHEEL		轂

ROM	RAD	TEL	TOT	FC	MAT	OSH	TAG	CR	CHAR
GUU	167,05	6895	13	84160	3465	1287	COBALT		鈷
GUU	188,00	7539	10	77227	3486	3625	BONE		骨
GUU	196,07	77¹1	18	27627	3485	4616	SWAN,WHITE-HAIRED		鵠
GUU	207,00	7849	13	44147	3479	6210	DRUM,TO ROUSE,CONVEX	A4124	鼓
GUH	009,05	0131.0B	07	24260	3448	1293	OLD/SECOND-HAND(CLOTHES)		估
GUH	009,12	0289	14	23214	3477	0925	HIRE	7163	僱
GUH	031,05	0942	08	60604	3450	1868	SOLID,BE SURE		固
GUH	032,08	8233	11	46100			PLACE NAME		堌
GUH	046,08	8339	11	22607			(ELEMENT IN MOUNTAIN NAMES)		崮
GUH	046,08	8339.1	11	26700			(ELEMENT IN MOUNTAIN NAMES)		岣
GUH	066,05	2399	09	48640	3455	6315	OLD,DECEASED,CAUSE		故
GUH	075,07	2736	11	44961	3484	1338	MANACLES,FETTERS,BRACES (MED.)		梏
GUH	093,07	3678	11	24561		1337	SHED OR PEN FOR CATTLE		牿
GUH	104,08	4037	13	00160	3451	1872	OBSTINATE DISEASE	C6933	痼
GUH	167,08	6933	16	86100	3452	1869	TO STOP,RESTRAIN,OBSTINATE DISEASE	G4037	錮
GUH	172,04	7163	12	30214	3477	0924	HIRE	0289	雇
GUH	181,05	7357.1	14	71286			LOOK AFTER,TAKE INTO CONSIDERATION		頋
GUH	181,12	7357	21	31286	3478	8252	LOOK AFTER,TAKE INTO CONSIDERATION		顧
GUH	196,10	7737	21	76227	3489	4633	FALCON/FALCO PEREGRINUS		鶻
GUA	018,06	0450	08	22600	3518	2876	SCRAPE,BLOW(OF THE WIND)	D7377	刮
GUA	064,05	2161	08	52064	3519	1321	INCLUDE,ENCLOSE		括
GUA	075,06	8552	10	42964	3520	1322	MEASURING-FRAME,JUNIPERUS CHINENSIS		栝
GUA	097,00	3900	05	72230	3504	4982	MELON		瓜
GUA	128,06	5109	12	12164	3521	1320	CLAMOR		聒
GUA	130,05	5157	09	72230			GUANIDINE		胍
GUA	142,09	5815	15	57127	3509	3939	SNAIL		蝸
GUA	162,06	6624.0A	10	32306	3522	6616	HASTEN/QUICKLY		适
GUA	182,06	7377	15	72216	3523	7839	BLOW(OF THE WIND)	B0450	颳
GUA	187,09	7504	19	77327	3510	3937	PIEBALD HORSE		騧
GOA	018,09	0478	11	72200	3508	2910	CUT OFF THE FLESH AS PUNISHMENT		剮
GOA	040,11	1391	14	30227	3517	4288	FEW,WIDOWED		寡
GUAH	025,06	0597	08	43100	3514	1987	DIVINATORY TRIGRAM		卦
GUAH	064,06	2229	09	53000	3515	1989	HANG/SUSPEND	2171	掛

ROM	RAD	TEL	TOT	FC	MAT	OSH	TAG	CR	CHAR
GUAH	064,06	2171	09	54014	3515	0169	HANG,SUSPEND	2229	挂
GUAH	120,06	9058	12	24914	3512		COARSE SILK,FASTEN,ANXIOUS		絓
GUAH	122,06	4994	11	60104	3511	0181	ANXIOUS ABOUT		罣
GUAH	122,08	5004.0A	13	60130		1990	SQUARES OF A CHESS BOARD		罫
GUAH	145,08	5962	13	33200	3516	1988	COAT		褂
GUAH	149,06	6118	13	04614	3513	0164	DECEIVE,DISTURB		詿
GUAI	004,07	0041	08	20111	3532	7154	CLEVER		乖
GOAI	075,05	8542	09	46927	3534	4844	OLD MAN'S STAFF		枴
GUAY	037,01	1134	04	50030		5203	DECISIVE		夬
GUAY	061,05	1843	08	97014	3536	0223	QUEER,TO BLAME		怪
GUAN	009,08	0212	10	23277	3553	1482	A GROOM		倌
GUAN	014,07	0385	09	37214	3564	7481	CAP		冠
GUAN	037,03	7070.2	06	80430			SHUT,MOUNTAIN PASS,(SURNAME)		关
GUAN	040,05	1351	08	30777	3552	1479	AN OFFICIAL		官
GUAN	075,08	2778	12	43977	3554	1485	COFFIN		棺
GUAN	104,10	4048	15	00132	3560	5000	INEFFICIENT,INCAPACITATED		瘰
GUAN	104,13	8886	18	00132			INEFFICIENT,INCAPACITATED	4048	癏
GUAN	140,07	5451.0A	11	44211	2247	7478	SKIMMIA JAPONICA		莞
GUAN	147,02	6034.1	09	76410	3575	7611	BEHOLD,OBSERVE		观
GUAN	147,18	6034	25	46210	3575	7592	BEHOLD,OBSERVE		觀
GUAN	169,06	7070.1	14	77430	3571	3502	SHUT,MOUNTAIN PASS,(SURNAME)		関
GUAN	169,10	7070.3	18	77333	3571	3538	SHUT,MOUNTAIN PASS,(SURNAME)		閞
GUAN	169,11	7070	19	77772	3571	3538	SHUT,MOUNTAIN PASS,(SURNAME)		關
GUAN	195,10	7659	21	26332	3561	4999	WIDOWER		鰥
GOAN	087,07	4619.1	11	20777	3557	1489	TUBE/PIPE,TO CONTROL,TAKE CARE		爯
GOAN	096,08	3828	12	13177	3555	1480	MUS·INSTR.,TO POLISH JADE OR GOLD	D8841	琯
GOAN	096,13	8841	17	17134			TO POLISH JADE OR GOLD	B3828	瓘
GOAN	104,08	8872	13	00177	3556		ILL-LOOKING		痯
GOAN	118,07	9012	13	88211	3557	7479	TUBE/PIPE,TO CONTROL,(SURNAME)	K4619	筦
GOAN	118,08	4619	14	88777	3557	1488	TUBE/PIPE,TO CONTROL,TAKE CARE		管
GOAN	130,07	5184	11	73211	3558	7475	INNER LAYER OF STOMACH		脘
GOAN	135,10	5290	16	83677	3559	1481	HOUSE/ESTABLISHMENT	7419	舘
GOAN	140,07	5451.0B	11	44211	2247	7478	(DISTRICT)		莞

95

ROM	RAD	TEL	TOT	FC	MAT	OSH	TAG	CR	CHAR
GOAN	184,08	7419	16	83777	3559	1483	HOUSE/ESTABLISHMENT	5290	館
GUANN	002,04	0024	05	22770	3562	2790	TUFTS OF HAIR		艸
GUANN	014,07	0385.0A	09	37214	3564	7481	TO HEAD		冠
GUANN	061,12	1977	15	96086	3567	8166	ACCUSTOMED		慣
GUANN	064,11	2335	14	56086	3568	8167	FLING,SMASH		摜
GUANN	085,18	3487	21	34114	3573	0940	POUR,IRRIGATE		灌
GUANN	086,18	3623	22	94814	3573A	0939	LIGHT A FIRE		爟
GUANN	096,18	3898	22	14114			JADE USED FOR MAKING GOBLETS		瓘
GUANN	108,11	4150	16	77107	3569	0647	WASH(ESPECIALLY HANDS)		盥
GUANN	109,18	8920	23	64014			BRILLIANT(OF EYES)		矔
GUANN	113,08	4387	12	36294	3565		POUR OUT LIBATION		祼
GUANN	121,11	4985	17	87786			COLOR-GLAZED SMOKING POT		礶
GUANN	121,18	4984	24	84714	3574	0933	A JAR,A CAN	7014	罐
GUANN	147,02	6034.1A	09	76410	3575	7611	TAOIST MONASTERY		覩
GUANN	147,18	6034.0A	25	46210	3575	7592	TAOIST MONASTERY		觀
GUANN	154,04	6306	11	77806	3566	8165	PIERCE,TO STRING		貫
GUANN	167,18	7014	26	84114	3576	0932	JAR/CAN	4984	鑵
GUANN	196,18	7764	29	47227	3577	4606	CRANE/STORK		鸛
GUANG	010,04	0342	06	90211	3583	7504	LIGHT		光
GUANG	075,06	2725	10	49911	3584	7509	ARENGA SACCHARIFERA		桄
GUANG	085,06	3171	09	39111	3585	7511	SPARKLING WATER		洸
GUANG	096,06	3798	10	19111			(JADE)		珖
GUANG	130,06	5180	10	79211	3586	7507	BLADDER		胱
GUANG	130,12	2454	16	74286			FAT/PORTLY		膭
GOANG	053,00	1639	03	00200			WIDE	1684	广
GOANG	053,12	16⁸⁴	15	00286	3590	8331	WIDE	1639	廣
GUANQ	054,07	6640.1	10	11401			TO STROLL,TO VISIT		逛
GUANQ	075,06	2725.0A	10	4991	3584	7509	RUNG OF LADDER		桄
GUANQ	162,07	6640	11	31301	3589	6601	TO STROLL,TO VISIT		逛
GUEI	009,10	0264.0A	12	26213	3653	7640	GRAND,STRANGE/EXOTIC		傀
GUEI	032,03	0964	06	40104	3609	0159	JADE TABLET	3802	圭
GUEI	038,12	1289	15	42427	3619	4527	NAME OF A RIVER,(SURNAME)		嬀
GUEI	058,02	2981.1	05	37070	3617		TO RETURN		归

ROM	RAD	TEL	TOT	FC	MAT	OSH	TAG	CR	CHAR
GUEI	075,11	8584	15	56904			ELAEOCARPUS JAPONICA		椝
GUEI	077,14	2981	18	27127	3617	3974	TO RETURN		歸
GUEI	085,12	3415	15	32127	3620	4528	NAME OF A RIVER		潙
GUEI	096,06	3802	10	14114	3609	0160	JADE TABLET,SILICON	0964	珪
GUEI	096,10	3855.0A	14	16113	3635	7636	EXTRAORDINARY,(SEMI-PRECIOUS STONE)	8843	瑰
GUEI	096,16	8843	20	10132		5832	EXTRAORDINARY,(SEMI-PRECIOUS STONES	3855.0A	瓌
GUEI	102,02	7898.1	07	27716			TORTOISE/TURTLE		龟
GUEI	106,04	4107	09	21647	3616	6105	FOLLOW,COMPLY WITH		皈
GUEI	112,06	8944	11	14614	3611	0163	SILICON	4264	硅
GUEI	112,06	4264	11	40601			SILICON	8944	砉
GUEI	140,06	540C	10	44104			RUBUS TOKKURA		茥
GUEI	145,06	9257	11	34214		0167	WOMAN'S BLOUSE		袿
GUEI	147,04	6016	11	56010	3618	7605	COMPASS,RULE		規
GUEI	163,06	6734	09	47127	3612	2157	ANCIENT PLACE NAME,(SURNAME)		邽
GUEI	167,06	9458	14	84114			SILICON		銈
GUEI	169,06	7043	14	77104	3613	3440	WOMEN'S APARTMENT		閨
GUEI	195,06	7634	17	24314	3614	0171	SALMON		鮭
GUEI	195,11	766M	22	27316			LOGOCEPHALUS VERMICULARIS		鰌
GUEI	198,06	779A	17	00214			TRAGULUS		麂
GUEI	213,00	7898	16	27117	3621	7349	TORTOISE/TURTLE		龜
GOEI	009,06	8033	08	27212	3622	7223	CRAFTY,ALMOST SUCCEED,SUDDENLY	A6111	佹
GOEI	022,09	0567	11	71711	3632	0822	SMALL BOX		匦
GOEI	032,06	0994	09	47112	3623	7220	DILAPIDATED		垝
GOEI	038,06	8278	09	47412	3624	7228	QUIET AND NICE		姽
GOEI	040,02	1339	05	30417	3630	7909	TRAITOR		宄
GOEI	064,05	2145	08	56027	3533	4843	TO TURN,KIDNAP		拐
GOEI	072,08	2534	12	60604	3629	1434	SUNDIAL		晷
GOEI	085,02	8659	05	34117			MOUNTAIN SPRING		氿
GOEI	105,04	4097	09	12430	3628	5141	10TH HEAVEN'S STEM		癸
GOEI	118,11	4663	17	88107	3633	0709	ROUND BASKET OF BAMBOO		簋
GOEI	149,06	6111	13	07612	3626	7222	SLY/CRAFTY		詭
GOEI	159,02	6510	09	54017	3631	7905	TRACK		軌
GOEI	194,00	7607	10	26213	3634	7634	GHOST,SLY/CRAFTY	D6111	鬼

ROM	RAD	TEL	TOT	FC	MAT	OSH	TAG	CR	CHAR
GUEY	009,04	2585.1C	06	80731	2345		PLACE NAME		
GUEY	018,13	8106	15	22200	3640	2962	CUT/INJURE		
GUEY	022,12	0566	14	71718	3638	0823	CUPBOARD/CABINET/WARDROBE	2922	
GUEY	046,12	8347	15	21782			PRECIPITOUS/MOUNTAINOUS		
GUEY	073,09	2585.0C	13	80606	2345	1537	PLACE NAME		
GUEY	075,05	2681	09	41917		0841	CUPBOARD/CABINET/WARDROBE	2922	
GUEY	075,06	2710	10	44914	3610	0170	CINNAMONUM CASSIA		
GUEY	075,13	2910.0A	17	48966	3538	1542	JUNIPERUS CHINENSIS		
GUEY	075,14	2922	18	41918	3638	0825	CUPBOARD/CABINET/WARDROBE	2681	
GUEY	085,10	3370	13	34114			NAME OF A RIVER		
GUEY	086,04	8732	08	60809			(SURNAME)		
GUEY	096,10	3855	14	16113	3635		ROSE		
GUEY	109,12	4231	17	65086	3663		DIM SIGHT FROM SENILITY		
GUEY	154,05	6311	12	50806	3636	8120	NOBLE,EXPENSIVE,YOUR(NAME)		
GUEY	157,06	6422	13	67112	3627	7221	KNEEL		
GUEY	195,12	7675	23	21382	3641	4940	HELICOLENUS		
GUEY	195,13	767A	24	21353			LEUCISCUS HAKUENSIS		
GOEN	002,00	0019	01	20000	3671	1978	DOWNSTROKE		
GOEN	085,09	3268.0B	12	37156	2366	2662	FLOWING(AS OF WATER)		
GOEN	085,11	3340	14	30132	3676	5884	TO ROLL,TO BOIL		
GOEN	120,08	9064	14	26911	3673	7122	EMBROIDERED SASH,SEW,CORD		
GOEN	140,10	9187	14	44732			TO BANK UP THE ROOTS OF PLANTS		
GOEN	145,04	5981	10	00732	3675	5887	IMPERIAL ROBE	5922	
GOEN	145,05	5922	11	00732	3675	5883	IMPERIAL ROBE	5981	
GOEN	159,08	6547	15	56011	3674	7119	REVOLVE,STONE ROLLER		
GOEN	195,07	7641	18	22393	3677	8495	FATHER OF GREAT YEU		
GUENN	075,08	2760	12	46911	3672	7120	STICK		
GUO	030,06	8139.0A	09	77227			(SURNAME)		
GUO	030,11	8165	14	66000	3739	1918	LOUD SWALLOWING SOUND		
GUO	032,09	8241	12	47127	3729	3933	CRUCIBLE		
GUO	046,08	8338	11	20747	3745	3118	NAME OF A MOUNTAIN		
GUO	085,09	3260.0A	12	37127	7154	3941	NAME OF A RIVER		
GUO	130,11	5226	15	76200			POPLITEAL SPACE		

ROM	RAD	TEL	TOT	FC	MAT	OSH	TAG	CR	CHAR
GUO	142,11	5841	17	56100	3742	1921	CYRTOPHYLLUS SP.		蟈
GUO	163,08	6753	11	07427	3746	2201	(SURNAME),OUTER CITY WALL		郭
GUO	167,09	6938	17	87127	3731	3934	POT		鍋
GWO	031,04	0948.3	07	60104		1849	COUNTRY/STATE		囯
GWO	031,05	0948.1	08	60103			COUNTRY/STATE		囗
GWO	031,05	0948.2	08	60747		1916	COUNTRY/STATE		囻
GWO	031,08	0948	11	60153	3738	1917	COUNTRY/STATE		國
GWO	050,11	1613	14	46200	3740	1920	CAP WORN BY WOMEN,FEMININE		幗
GWO	064,11	2310	14	56000	3741	1919	TO SLAP		摑
GWO	128,08	9106	14	13150	3743		CUT OFF THE LEFT EAR OF THE SLAIN	7446	聝
GWO	141,09	5716	15	21317	3744	7668	NAME OF AN ANCIENT STATE		虢
GWO	185,08	7446	17	83650	3743	6963	CUT OFF THE LEFT EAR OF THE SLAIN	9106	馘
GUOO	075,04	2654	08	60904	3732	5492	FRUIT,RESULT	A5470	果
GUOO	075,08	2779	12	40947	3747	3123	OUTER COFFIN	2859	椁
GUOO	075,11	2859	15	47927	3747	2204	OUTER COFFIN	2779	槨
GUOO	119,08	9039	14	96994			COOKED RICE FOR MAKING CAKE		粿
GUOO	140,08	5470	12	44904	3733	5509	FRUIT	A2654	菓
GUOO	142,08	5811	14	56194		5507	EUMENES POMIFORMIS		蜾
GUOO	145,08	5955	14	00732	3735	5891	WRAP AROUND		裹
GUOO	159,08	6546	15	56094	3736	5500	GREASE-POT UNDER A CART		輠
GUOO	184,08	9606	16	86794	3737	5499	CAKE/PASTRY		餜
GUOH	130,08	9128	12	76294			RED AND SWOLLEN		腜
GUOH	162,03	6665.1	07	34300	3730	6679	TO PASS,DID ONCE,(SURNAME)		过
GUOH	162,09	6665	13	37302	3730	6698	TO PASS,DID ONCE,(SURNAME)		過
HA	030,05	0725.0A	08	61020	2110	3040	LAUGHTER,YAWN,EXPEL BREATH	K0761	呵
HA	030,06	0761	09	68061	2003	1190	LAUGHTER,YAWN	K0725	哈
HA	167,06	1760	14	88161		1189	HAFNIUM		鉿
HAR	142,03	5802.1A	09	51130			TOAD,FROG		虾
HAR	142,06	5756.0A	12	58161	3373	1196	TOAD,FROG		蛤
HAR	142,09	5802.0A	15	57147	2516	6134	TOAD,FROG		蝦
HAA	030,06	0761.0A	09	68061	2003	1190	A PEKINESE,A PUG		哈
HAI	030,05	8130	08	63060	2013	1448	SOUND OF LAUGHTER,HAPPY,(INTERJ.)		咍
HAI	030,06	0750.0A	09	60082			SOUND OF SIGHING	0780	咳

ROM	RAD	TEL	TOT	FC	MAT	OSH	TAG	CR	CHAR
HAI	030,07	0780	10	63034	0004	5176	SOUND OF SIGHING	0750.0A	唉
HAI	030,10	084G	13	68057			OH ALAS		嗨
HAIR	039,06	1326	09	10482	2005	7994	CHILD		孩
HAIR	162,04	6703.1	08	31309	2261	6778	STILL/YET		还
HAIR	162,13	6703	17	36303	2261	6748	STILL/YET		還
HAIR	181,06	7331.0A	15	01286	2008	8307	CHIN		頦
HAIR	188,06	7546	16	70282	2010	7995	BONES OF THE BODY		骸
HAE	085,07	3189	10	38157	2014	4881	SEA		海
HAE	130,06	518C	10	70282			HYDROXYLAMINE		胲
HAE	164,07	681A	14	10613			MINCED MEAT,PICKLED MEAT	6826	酼
HAE	164,10	6826	17	14617	2012	0649	MINCED MEAT,PICKLED MEAT		醢
HAY	008,04	0075	06	00280	2004	7989	9-11 P.M.,12TH EARTH'S BRANCH		亥
HAY	030,10	084B	13	63061	2534		EXCLAMATION OF REGRET		嗐
HAY	040,07	1364	10	30601	2015	1341	TO HARM,SUFFER FROM		害
HAY	084,06	8640	10	80217		7822	HELIUM		氦
HAY	187,06	7480	16	70382	2009	7996	ASTONISH,STARTLE		駭
HAN	061,12	2003	16	18334	2053	8671	SILLY/SIMPLE-MINDED		憨
HAN	142,05	5743	11	54170		1043	SMALL CLAM/ARCA INFLATA		蚶
HAN	142,11	583B	17	44136			EXARTEMANORI		[illegible]
HAN	164,05	6799	12	14670	2037	1038	INTOXICATED		酣
HAN	181,03	7310	12	11486	2034	8265	DAWDLING		頇
HAN	209,03	7867	17	21440	2035	2381	SNORE		鼾
HARN	017,06	0428	08	10772	2049	0974	LETTER	0949	函
HARN	017,07	0428.1	09	10772	2049	0978	A LETTER		凾
HARN	030,04	0698	07	80607	2017	1355	CONTAIN		含
HARN	031,07	0949	10	17603	2049		CONTAIN,LETTER	0428	圅
HARN	040,09	1383	12	30303	2048	9070	COLD		寒
HARN	086,07	1799	11	98862			CYCLOHEXANTHRENE		焓
HARN	072,07	2498	11	68062			DAWN		晗
HARN	085,08	3211	11	31172	2050	0976	CONTAIN		涵
HARN	163,03	6714	06	17427	2032	2190	NAME OF AN ANCIENT RIVER		邗
HARN	163,05	6725	08	47727	2036	2168	NAME OF A HSIEN IN HOPEI		邯
HARN	178,08	7281	17	44456	2041	2580	(SURNAME)		韓
HAAN	027,00	0617.0A	02	71200	2016	4230	CLIFF		厂

ROM	RAD	TEL	TOT	FC	MAT	OSH	TAG	CR	CHAR
HAAN	030,09	0815	12	63050	2045	7001	CRY/CALL		喊
HAAN	122,03	4988	07	37401	2031	2415	RARE		罕
HAAN	140,11	557B	15	44841			NASTURTIUM MONTANUM		蔊
HANN	030,05	0735.0C	08	26900	2115	1095	WITH/AND		和
HANN	061,07	1880	10	96041	2024	2402	VIOLENT		悍
HANN	061,13	2013	16	93035	2046	8678	REGRET		憾
HANN	064,03	2098	06	51040	2027	2382	WARD OFF(A BLOW)	2194	扞
HANN	064,07	2194	10	56041	2025	2403	WARD OFF (A BLOW)	2098	捍
HANN	064,13	2338	16	53050	2047	8680	TO INCITE,SHAKE		撼
HANN	072,03	2487	07	60401	2023	2399	DROUGHT		旱
HANN	072,11	2553	15	64034	2038	5259	HOT,DRY		暵
HANN	085,02	3352.1	05	37140			CHINESE,NAME OF A DYNASTY		汉
HANN	085,03	3063	06	31140	2028	2397	PERSPIRATION		汗
HANN	085,11	3352	14	34134	2039	5261	CHINESE,NAME OF A DYNASTY		漢
HANN	085,16	3466	19	38127	2043	3417	VASTNESS,OCEAN		瀚
HANN	086,07	3549	11	96841		2407	WELDING		焊
HANN	086,11	3582	15	94834	2040	5260	TO DRY WITH FIRE		熯
HANN	094,03	3691.0A	06	41240	2029		(CANINE)	9320.0A	犴
HANN	109,07	8911	12	66041	2237	2401	PROTUBERANT EYES		睅
HANN	124,10	5060	16	48427	2042	3416	PEN		翰
HANN	140,08	5496	12	44772		0977	LOTUS BLOSSOM		菡
HANN	142,10	582E	16	44136			AULACOPHORA FEMORALIS		蛿
HANN	153,03	9320.0A	10	21240	2029	2385	(CANINE)	3691.0A	豻
HANN	167,03	9439	11	81140	2026	2377	TO SOLDER,WELD BY HEAT	6919	釬
HANN	167,07	6919	15	86141	2026	2400	TO SOLDER,WELD BY HEAT	9439	銲
HANN	169,03	7029	11	77401	2033	3477	GATE OF VILLAGE,VILLAGE		閈
HANN	181,07	7318	16	81686	2022	8260	CHIN,NOD ASSENT		頷
HANG	037,02	1137	05	40427		4862	DRIVE PILES		夯
HANG	085,04	3100.0A	07	30117	2057	7870	BIG EXPANSE OF WATER		沆
HANG	112,06	1137.1	11	17654	2061		DRIVE PILES		硆
HARNG	030,04	0699	07	60017	2055	7860	THROAT	514A	吭
HARNG	075,04	2635	08	40917	2056	7867	HANGCHOW,(SURNAME)		杭
HARNG	075,06	2709.0A	10	41921	2102	3022	WOODEN COLLAR FOR PUNISHMENT		桁

ROM	RAD	TEL	TOT	FC	MAT	OSH	TAG	CR	CHAR
HARNG	085,04	3100	07	30117	2057	7870	CROSS(A RIVER)		沆
HARNG	130,04	514A.0A	08	70217			THROAT	0699	肮
HARNG	137,04	5300	10	20417	2059	7866	TO SAIL		航
HARNG	144,00	5887.0B	06	21221	2754	3020	A ROW,PROFESSION/PROFESSIONAL		行
HARNG	181,04	7314	13	01286	2060	8306	FLY DOWN		頏
HARNG	196,06	770J	17	27127			KENTISH SAND-PLOVER		鴴
HANQ	075,06	2709.0B	10	41921	2102	3022	CLOTHES-HORSE		桁
HAU	030,14	8178	17	64027	2082	3840	SOUND/NOISE		嚆
HAU	064,06	5632.1	09	54090	2085	5265	PULL OUT(WEED)		揪
HAU	140,10	5548	14	44227	2081	3839	WORMWOOD		蒿
HAU	140,13	5632	17	44443	2085	3282	PULL OUT(WEED)		薅
HAUR	010,09	8092	11	42211		7564	MILLIGRAM		毻
HAUR	030,02	5714.1A	05	60207	2064	4537	ROAR/CRY		号
HAUR	030,10	0881.1	13	66043	2073		HOWL/BAWL,TO BARK/ROAR		噑
HAUR	030,12	0881	15	66043	2073	2364	HOWL/BAWL,TO BARK/ROAR	A0866	嗥
HAUR	030,14	0866	17	60032	2073	5728	HOWL/BAWL	A0881	嚎
HAUR	032,14	1091	17	40132	2068	5727	TRENCH,AIR-RAID SHELTER	A3445	壕
HAUR	082,07	3032	11	00714	2066	7389	1/10,000(AN.),FINE HAIR		毫
HAUR	085,14	3445	17	30132	2070	5730	TRENCH	A1091	濠
HAUR	094,06	3713.0A	09	47264			BADGER		狢
HAUR	094,10	8808	13	46243			TO BARK	B0881	獋
HAUR	094,12	8808.1	15	46243			TO BARK		犿
HAUR	117,04	454D	09	02114		7370	MILLILITER		竓
HAUR	140,07	5714.0A	13	61217	2064	7669	ROAR/CRY		號
HAUR	142,14	5823	20	50132	2071	5729	OYSTER		蠔
HAUR	152,07	6275	14	00232	2067	5726	GRAND/HEROIC		豪
HAUR	153,06	6288.0A	13	27264	2127	1418	BADGER-LIKE ANIMAL		貉
HAUR	196,10	7729	21	47227	2131	4608	CRANE		鶴
HAO	038,03	1170	06	47447	2062	3105	GOOD		好
HAO	163,07	6787	10	47327	2129	2260	(SURNAME),ANCIENT PLACE NAME		郝
HAW	030,02	5714.1	05	60207	2064	4537	(ORDINAL)NUMBER		号
HAW	038,03	1170.0A	06	47447	2062	3105	BE FOND OF		好
HAW	072,04	8504	08	60430	2072	5153	VAST,CLEAR SUMMER SKY		昊

ROM	RAD	TEL	TOT	FC	MAT	OSH	TAG	CR	CHAR
HAW	072,07	8510	11	64061	2076	1333	BRIGHT,WHITE	4110	晧
HAW	085,07	3185	10	34161	2077	1339	VAST(WATER),GRAND	3401	浩
HAW	085,08	3212.0A	11	36100	2133	1871	TO DRY UP		涸
HAW	085,12	3401	15	34161		1335	VAST(OF WATER),GRAND	3185	澔
HAW	085,21	3493	24	31186	2079	8313	VAST(OF WATER)		灝
HAW	106,07	4110	12	24661	2078	1334	BRIGHT,WHITE,D(19TH)		皓
HAW	106,10	4113	15	20627	2080	3830	CLEAR,WHITE		暭
HAW	106,12	4116	17	26643	2075	2366	BRIGHT,BRILLIANT		皞
HAW	119,04	9033	10	92914		7379	MILLIMETER		粍
HAW	127,04	5088	10	52914	2065	7378	TO WASTE,MOUSE,NEW		耗
HAW	140,07	5714	13	61217	2064	7669	(ORDINAL)NUMBER		號
HAW	140,13	557D	17	44127			CYPERUS AMURICUS		薅
HAW	163,10	6764	13	07227	2083		ANCIENT PLACE NAME		鄗
HAW	167,10	6964	18	80127	2084	3828	STOVE,BRIGHT,PLACE NAME		鎬
HAW	181,12	7355	21	61986	2078	8312	BRIGHT,WHITE	4110	顥
HE	030,05	0725	08	61020	2110	3040	MY GOODNESS,EXPEL BREATH	B0824.0A	呵
HE	030,09	0824	12	66027	2123	4380	TO DRINK,MY GOODNESS	D0725	喝
HE	030,11	086D	14	64021			(EXCLAMATION)		嗬
HE	149,05	6084	12	01620	2112	3041	TO BLAME/RIDICULE IN LOUD VOICE		訶
HE	195,05	7679	16	21320			SEA BLUBBER		魺
HER	009,05	0149	07	21220	2109	3043	WHAT/HOW/WHY/WHICH,CARRY		何
HER	019,06	0511	08	04227	2088	4828	IMPEACH		劾
HER	030,03	0678	06	80601	2117	1188	FIT,CHINESE MUSICAL NOTE		合
HER	030,05	0735	08	26900	2115	1095	HARMONIOUS		和
HER	030,10	0836	13	64017	2120	0737	LOQUACIOUS,SOUND OF VOICES		嗑
HER	038,06	8276	09	48461			BEAUTIFUL/CHARMING(OF WOMAN)		姶
HER	073,05	2578	09	60727	2122	4378	WHY/HOW/WHEN/WHAT/WHERE		曷
HER	075,06	2702	10	40982	2089	7997	STONE(OF FRUIT)		核
HER	085,05	3109	08	31120	2111	3055	RIVER		河
HER	085,08	3212	11	36100	2133	1871	TO DRY,TO DRY UP		涸
HER	092,06	366A	10	78261			BITE		硌
HER	093,10	5295	14	40503			GIB/CHOCK		犗
HER	094,06	3713	09	47264			BADGER		狢

ROM	RAD	TEL	TOT	FC	MAT	OSH	TAG	CR	CHAR
HER	108,04	4137.1	09	40107	2119	0704	WHY NOT		
HER	108,05	4137	10	40107	2119	0734	WHY NOT		
HER	108,06	4139	11	80107	2118	0650	SMALL BOX		
HER	115,00	4421	05	20904	2114	5540	GRAIN,CEREAL		
HER	115,06	8986	11	28961			TO PLOUGH/CULTIVATE		
HER	120,03	4769	09	28917	2086	7969	TASSELS		
HER	124,10	5058	16	17220	3317	3394	QUILL		
HER	140,07	5440	11	44221	2113	3044	LOTUS		
HER	145,09	5964	14	36227	2125	4388	ROUGH CLOTHING,DULL,DARK BROWN		
HER	146,13	6012	19	10248	2093	6377	EXAMINE THOROUGHLY		
HER	153,06	6288	13	27264	2127	1418	BADGER-LIKE ANIMAL		
HER	163,06	6740	09	87627		2172	NAME OF A PERSON		
HER	167,05	9447	13	82194			SMALL BELL		
HER	169,06	7039	14	77280	0017	3532	OBSTRUCT		
HER	169,10	7066	18	77107	2121	3445	ENTIRE(FAMILY)		
HER	177,09	9560	18	46527			TURBAN,BUSKIN,NAME OF A TRIBE		
HER	181,06	9577	15	81686			MAXILLA AND MANDIBLE		
HER	196,09	9679	20	67727	2126	4640	LONG-TAILED PHEASANT,CROSSBILL		
HER	211,03	7878	18	28717	2087	7960	GNAW		
HER	214,05	7901	22	82294	2115	5542	HARMONIOUS	0735	
HEH	009,06	8035	08	27264			(SURNAME)		
HEH	030,02	0687.0A	05	61030		2006	FRIGHTEN	0907.0A	
HEH	030,05	0735.0A	08	26900		1095	CAP(A POEM),RESPOND IN SINGING		
HEH	030,09	0824.0A	12	66027		4380	SHOUT APPLAUSE		
HEH	030,10	0832	13	60027	2134	3829	SCOLD WITH SEVERITY		
HEH	030,14	0907.0A	17	64031	2092	8515	FRIGHTEN	0687.0A	
HEH	032,14	1089	17	27104	2128	0228	GULLY		
HEH	062,04	2057.0A	08	53100	2402		OR		
HEH	072,09	2539.0A	13	66027	7323		HOT		
HEH	094,09	8806.0A	12	46227			FRIGHTENED/TERRIFIED		
HEH	124,10	5059	16	17227	2783		GLISTENING PLUMAGE OF BIRDS		
HEH	140,07	5440.0A	11	44221	2113	3044	TO CARRY BURDEN,PEPPERMINT		
HEH	149,08	0907.1A	15	01617			FRIGHTEN		

盍 盉 盒 禾 秙 紀 翮 荷 褐 毇 貉 郃 鉌 闔 闍 鞨 領 鷊 齕 龢 佫 吓 和 喝 嗃 嚇 瞉 或 暍 獦 翯 翯 葀 何 覟 誮

104

ROM	RAD	TEL	TOT	FC	MAT	OSH	TAG	CR	CHAR
HEH	150,10	6255.0B	17	38668	2404	1383	SPACIOUS AND LIGHT(AS OF ROOM)		寙
HEH	154,05	6320	12	46806	2116	8142	CONGRATULATE		賀
HEH	155,07	6378	14	44331	2091	8514	AWE-INSPIRING,(SURNAME)		赫
HEH	163,07	6787.0A	10	47327	2129	2260	(SURNAME),ANCIENT PLACE NAME		郝
HEH	196,10	7729.0A	21	47227	2131	4608	CRANE		鶴
HEH	208,06	7850	19	77716			LAGOSTOMUS TRICHODACTYLUS/VISCACHA		鼺
HEI	030,12	0884	15	66031		8724	HEY		嘿
HEI	203,00	7815	12	60331	2090	8723	BLACK,DARK		黑
HERN	030,04	0698.0A	07	80607		1355	HOLD IN MOUTH		含
HERN	104,06	4024	11	00132	2098	5912	SCAR,TRACES		痕
HEEN	060,06	1771	09	27232	2094	5906	VERY	B3703	很
HEEN	094,06	3703	09	47232	2097	5909	FIERCE,VERY	D1771	狠
HENN	061,06	1868	09	97032	2095	5905	HATE		恨
HENG	008,05	0077	07	00207	2099	3093	PROSPEROUS		亨
HENG	030,07	0774	10	60027	2100	3094	HUM		哼
HENG	130,07	9124	11	70227	2101	3095	FAT/BLOATED		脝
HERNG	038,06	1220	09	41416	2106A		THE LADY IN THE MOON		姮
HERNG	061,06	1854.1	09	91016	2107	0024	PERMANENT		恒
HERNG	061,06	1854	09	91017	2107	0526	PERMANENT		恆
HERNG	075,06	2709	10	41921	2102	3022	RIDGEPOLE,PURLIN,POLE PLATE		桁
HERNG	075,12	2897	16	44986	2106	8328	HORIZONTAL		橫
HERNG	096,06	3801	10	11121	2103	3021	TOP GEM OF PENDANT FROM GIRDLE		珩
HERNG	140,16	5683	20	44221	2105	3030	ASARUM BLUMEI		蘅
HERNG	144,10	5899	16	21221	2104	3029	WEIGHTS		衡
HENQ	075,12	2897.0A	16	44986	2106	8328	UNRULY		橫
HM	030,07	0774.0B	10	60027		3094	(INTERJ. OF CONTEMPT)		哼
HNG	030,07	0774.0A	10	60027		3094	(INTERJ. OF CONTEMPT)		哼
HONG	029,06	6575.2	08	40441			RUMBLE,STRIKE (BY THUNDER/BOMB)		叕
HONG	030,04	8124	07	65000	2376	2513	(PHONETIC)		吽
HONG	030,06	0758.0A	09	64081		8028	RESOUND WITH LAUGHTER		哄
HONG	086,06	3530	10	94881	2389	8031	BAKE,HEAT BY FIRE		烘
HONG	140,13	5645	17	44212	2393	7151	DEATH OF A PRINCE,SWARMING		薨
HONG	149,02	6059	09	27620	2391	4430	SOUND OF A CRASH,(SURNAME)		訇

ROM	RAD	TEL	TOT	FC	MAT	OSH	TAG	CR	CHAR
HONG	156,06	639A	13	44808			CHASE/SHOO AWAY		
HONG	159,04	6575.1	11	50441			RUMBLE,STRIKE(BY THUNDER/BOMB)		
HONG	159,14	6575	21	50556	2394	2649	RUMBLE,STRIKE(BY THUNDER/BOMB)		
HONG	195,03	762A.0A	14	21310			RAY (FISH)		
HORNG	030,04	8127	07	64032			CLANG OF BELLS		
HORNG	040,04	1347	07	30432	2377	8828	SPACIOUS		
HORNG	057,02	1738	05	13202	2380	8818	GREAT,LIBERAL		
HORNG	085,05	3126	08	33100	2381	8819	CLEAR,VAST AND DEEP		
HORNG	085,06	3163	09	34181	2388	8033	FLOOD		
HORNG	085,07	8677	10	33132			SOUND OF WATER SURGING		
HORNG	117,04	4540	09	04132			TO ESTIMATE,LARGE		
HORNG	120,03	4767	09	21910	2383	0093	RED,BONUS,POPULAR		
HORNG	120,04	4785	10	24932	2378	8827	CORD FOR HAT,VAST		
HORNG	124,04	9096	10	47020			TO SWARM(OF INSECTS)		
HORNG	140,09	9183	13	44181			POLYGONUM ORIENTALE		
HORNG	140,09	551C	13	44912			POLYGONUM ORIENTALE		
HORNG	142,03	5725.0A	09	51110	2384	0094	RAINBOW		
HORNG	149,03	6069	10	01610	2385	0088	TO SLANDER,DISCORD,REVOLUTION		
HORNG	167,06	9457	14	84181			PROJECTILE MECHANISM OF CATAPULT		
HORNG	167,07	9464	15	8³132			UTENSIL/IMPLEMENT		
HORNG	169,04	7031	12	77432	2379	3539	GATE,BIG,(SURNAME)		
HORNG	177,05	9556	14	42530			A LEANING BOARD ON CARRIAGE		
HORNG	196,06	7703	17	37127	2386	4601	GREAT/LARGE,EASTERN BEAN GOOSE		
HOONG	030,06	0758	09	64081	2387	8028	DECEIVE/COAX		
HOONG	030,10	8156	13	61086			SING		
HONQ	085,12	3414	15	31186			VAST/INFINITE		
HONQ	140,13	5584	17	44781			BUDDING,FLOURISHING		
HONQ	169,06	9528	14	77801			RIOT,HAVE A HILARIOUS TIME	7592	
HONQ	191,06	7592	16	77801	2390	3433	RIOT/HAVE A HILARIOUS TIME	9528	
HOU	209,05	7868	19	27420	2150	4419	SNORE,THIRSTY FROM SALTY FOOD		
HOUR	009,07	0186	09	27234	2135	5165	MARQUIS		
HOUR	030,09	0814	12	67034	2137	5167	THROAT		
HOUR	094,09	3729	12	47234	2139	5169	MONKEY		

ROM	RAD	TEL	TOT	FC	MAT	OSH	TAG	CR	CHAR
HOUR	104,09	406A	14	00134	2140	5171	WART		瘊
HOUR	111,04	0186.1	09	27234		5158	MARQUIS		矦
HOUR	118,09	4667	15	88234	2141	5172	(MUS. INSTR.)		篌
HOUR	119,09	4742	15	97934	2142	5170	DRY PROVISIONS	7422	糇
HOUR	167,09	6952	17	87134			METAL ARROWHEAD		鍭
HOUR	184,09	7422	17	87734	2142	5168	DRY PROVISIONS	4742	餱
HOOU	030,04	0709	07	62010	2148	7064	ROAR(OF A LION)		吼
HOW	009,08	0230	10	27234	2136	5164	WAIT		候
HOW	027,07	0624	09	71247	2147	3125	THICK,GENEROUS		厚
HOW	030,03	0683	06	72261	2144	1150	AFTER,LATER QUEEN	K1775	后
HOW	032,06	8214	09	72214			THICK	0624	垕
HOW	032,09	1028	12	47134	2138	5166	MOUNDS FOR BEACONS		堠
HOW	060,06	1775	09	22247	2143	6489	AFTER,LATER	K0683	後
HOW	162,06	6626	10	32306	2145	6610	MEET UNEXPECTEDLY		逅
HOW	163,06	9390	09	77227	2146	2171	PLACE NAME,(SURNAME)		郈
HOW	163,09	9399	12	27227			PLACE NAME		鄇
HOW	188,06	754D	16	72261			EPIPHYSIS		骺
HOW	195,13	7670	24	77336	2151	8776	KING CRAB		鱟
HU	004,04	0039	05	20409	2154	3316	(INTERROG. PART.)		乎
HU	030,05	0729	08	62049	2155	3317	CALL/EXHALE		呼
HU	030,11	8162.0A	14	61047	2157	3320	CALL,(SURNAME)	A0729	嘑
HU	050,12	8364	15	48231			TO COVER,ARROGANT/RUDE		幠
HU	061,04	1824	08	27332	2194	8638	SUDDENLY		忽
HU	061,08	1915	11	97032	2196	8639	INDISTINCT		惚
HU	076,08	2964	12	97882	2857	4954	SUDDENLY		欻
HU	085,11	3367	14	31149	2158	3322	NAME OF A RIVER,(SURNAME)		滹
HU	130,12	5236	16	78231		8745	DRIED MEAT,BIG PIECE OF MEAT		膴
HU	141,00	5705	06	21214	2160	7353	STRIPES OF TIGER		虍
HU	141,05	9214	11	21249	2156	3318	SCREAM OF TIGER,TO CALL,EXHALE	D0729	虖
HWU	030,05	0735.0E	08	26900			TERM USED IN MAHJONG		和
HWU	031,04	0939	07	60227	2191	1888	WHOLE/IN ONE LUMP		囫
HWU	033,07	1106.1	10	40102			POT		壶
HWU	033,09	1106	12	40107	2187	0524	POT		壺

ROM	RAD	TEL	TOT	FC	MAT	OSH	TAG	CR	CHAR
HWU	057,05	1721	08	12230	2184	4990	ARC		弧
HWU	064,10	2284	13	57027	2226	3626	DIG,MIX		搰
HWU	068,07	2437	11	24200	2200	2699	(MEASURE)/5 PECKS		斛
HWU	075,06	2702.0A	10	40982	2089	7997	STONE(OF FRUIT)		核
HWU	075,11	2086	15	44900	2201	2700	OAK/QUERCUS DENTATA		槲
HWU	085,09	3275	12	37120	2168	3551	LAKE		湖
HWU	086,09	355A	13	97820	2169	3549	SCORCH		煳
HWU	094,05	3698	08	42230	2185	4988	FOX		狐
HWU	094,09	3724	12	47220	2170	3547	(MONKEY)		猢
HWU	096,09	3840	13	17120	2171	3544	CORAL		瑚
HWU	119,09	4739	15	97920	2172	3548	PASTE,MUDDLED,SCORCHED		糊
HWU	120,10	4909	16	47947	2203	6302	FINE SILK GAUZE		縠
HWU	130,05	5170	09	47620	2167	3543	WHAT WHY HOW (SURNAME),BEARD	G7579	胡
HWU	140,09	5519	13	44627	2173	3552	BOTTLE GOURD,ALLIUM SCORODOPRASUM		葫
HWU	142,09	5814	15	57120	2174	3550	BUTTERFLY		蝴
HWU	144,09	5896	15	21221	2175	3026	LANE		衚
HWU	148,10	6049	17	47247	2204	6281	(MEASURE),FRIGHTENED		觳
HWU	164,09	6820	16	17620	2176	3545	ESSENTIAL OIL OF BUTTER		醐
HWU	180,14	7304	23	04647			PROTECT,MUSIC OF EMPEROR TANG		護
HWU	184,09	7420	17	87720	2177	3546	MAKING A LIVING,CONGEE		餬
HWU	190,09	7579	19	72627	2178	3553	BEARD/MUSTACHE	C5170	鬍
HᵂU	196,09	7724	20	47627	2179	4630	PELICAN		鶘
HWU	196,10	7737.0A	21	76227	3489	4633	MIGRATORY BIRD,FALCON		鶦
HWU	208,05	785A	18	72712			CHRYSOTHRIX SOTHRIX		鸌
HUU	030,08	0801	11	61017	2163	7666	TO FOOL,INTIMIDATE,TIGER'S ROAR		唬
HUU	085,11	3338	14	38140	2188	2430	BANK OF A RIVER		滸
HUU	096,08	3822	12	11117	2162	7665	AMBER		琥
HUU	141,02	5706	08	21217	2161	7885	TIGER		虎
HUU	149,04	6079.0A	11	08640	2825	2429	SOUND OF MANY PEOPLE IN ONE JOB		許
HUU	195,08	765B	19	21317			GREY MULLET/GRAMPUS SAKAMATA		鯱
HUH	007,02	0062	04	10107	2152	0529	MUTUALLY		互
HUH	015,04	0395	06	31117	2153	0530	FROZEN,CONGEALED	3091	冱
HUH	030,11	8162	14	61049	2157	3320	TO MENACE,BAWL		嚄

ROM	RAD	TEL	TOT	FC	MAT	OSH	TAG	CR	CHAR
HUH	046,05	1487	08	24760	2164	1288	WOODED HILL		岵
HUH	061,05	1833	08	94060	2165	1292	PRESUME		怙
HUH	063,00	2073	04	30277	2180	4234	DOOR,A HOUSEHOLD		户
HUH	063,04	2077	08	30247	2181	2708	WATER BUCKET FOR IRRIGATION		戽
HUH	063,07	2083	11	30217	2182	7303	RETINUE		扈
HUH	064,04	6233.1	07	53077			PROTECT		护
HUH	075,09	2822	13	44964			(TREE)		楛
HUH	085,04	3091	07	31117	2153		FROZEN,CONGEALED	0395	沍
HUH	085,04	3337.1	07	33177		4238	SHANGHAI		沪
HUH	085,11	3337	14	33117	2183	7304	SHANGHAI		滬
HUH	086,10	3573	14	90827		3835	HOT		熇
HUH	094,04	370A	07	41217			GALAGO/BUSH BABY		狐
HUH	096,06	3902	11	42230	2186	4989	GOURD		瓠
HUH	113,05	4375	09	34260	2166	1298	CELESTIAL BLESSING		祜
HUH	115,14	4490.0A	19	24947	2207	6155	REAP/HARVEST	3752.1B	穫
HUH	118,04	4561	10	88227	2193	4484	TABLET HELD AT AN AUDIENCE		笏
HUH	127,14	9102.0A	20	54947			REAP/HARVEST	3752.1B	穫
HUH	140,07	3752.1B	11	44234			REAP/HARVEST	4490.0A	获
HUH	149,14	6233	21	04647	2190	6150	PROTECT		護
HUH	163,11	6770	14	17227	2189	2224	NAME OF A HSIEN IN SHENSI		鄠
HUH	196,04	7695	15	30227			(BIRD)		鳸
HUA	024,04	5478.1A	06	24401			FLOWER		华
HUA	030,12	0873.0A	15	64054	2218	2606	CRASHING SOUND		嘩
HUA	106,16	9200.1A	21	24627			FLOWER/BLOSSOM		皣
HUA	140,04	5363	08	44214	2212	7146	FLOWER,FANCY PATTERN,SPEND		花
HUA	140,08	5478.0A	12	44504	2217	2604	FLOWER	A5363	華
HUA	140,17	9200.0A	21	44627			FLOWER/BLOSSOM	5363	蘤
HWA	018,04	0439	06	52000	2213	2960	TO ROW		划
HWA	024,04	5478.1	06	24401			CHINA,FLOWERY		华
HWA	030,12	0873	15	64054	2218	2606	CLAMOR/NOISE,CAT-CALLING SOUND	A6212	嘩
HWA	064,12	8470	15	54054			STRIKE (A MATCH)		撶
HWA	085,10	3323	13	37127	2227	3629	SLIPPERY,CUNNING,COMICAL		滑
HWA	094,10	3736	13	47227	2228	3627	SLY		猾

ROM	RAD	TEL	TOT	FC	MAT	OSH	TAG	CR	CHAR
HWA	140,08	5478	12	44504	2217	2604	CHINA,FLOWERY		華
HWA	149,12	6212	19	04654	2218	2607	CLAMOR/NOISE	A0873	譁
HWA	150,10	6255.0C	17	38668	2404	1383	PLAY CHINESE FINGER GAME		豁
HWA	167,12	6985	20	84154	2220	2605	PLOUGHSHARE,SPADE		鏵
HWA	187,12	7520	22	74354	222I	2610	CHESTNUT HORSE		驊
HUAH	018,04	0439.0A	06	52000	2213		TO MARK OFF/DRAW(A LINE)	0487	划
HUAH	018,12	0487	14	52100	2223	2861	TO MARK OFF/DRAW(A LINE)	0439.0A	劃
HUAH	021,02	0553	04	24210	2211	7142	TRANSFORM,-IZE		化
HUAH	024,04	5478.1B	06	24401			NAME OF A MOUNTAIN,(SURNAME)		华
HUAH	038,12	8299	15	45016		0068	TRANQUIL		嬅
HUAH	064,11	8462	14	52030			WIDE/BROAD		㩊
HUAH	075,12	2901	14	44954	2219	2611	BETULA JAPONICA		樺
HUAH	102,03	3973.1	08	10772	2222	0971	PICTURE/PAINTING,DRAW		画
HUAH	102,07	3973	12	50106	2222	0067	PICTURE/PAINTING,DRAW		畫
HUAH	122,08	5004	13	60130		1990	OBSTACLE		罭
HUAH	130,08	9128.0A	12	76294			(MEDICINAL HERB)		腂
HUAH	140,08	5478.0B	12	44504	2217	2604	NAME OF A MOUNTAIN,(SURNAME)		華
HUAH	149,06	6114	13	02664	2215	1316	SPOKEN WORDS,DIALECT/LANGUAGE		話
HUAH	157,08	6435.0A	15	66194	2214	5495	ANKLE BONE		踝
HWAI	060,06	1773.0A	09	26200			MOVE BACK AND FORTH,IRRESOLUTE		徊
HWAI	061,04	2037.1	07	91090	2233		BOSOM,CHERISH		怀
HWAI	061,16	2037	19	90032	2233	5833	BOSOM,CHERISH		懷
HWAI	075,10	2849	14	46913	2230	7643	SOPHORA JAPONICA		槐
HWAI	085,08	3232	11	30114	2229	0923	NAME OF A RIVER		淮
HWAI	094,14	3752.0A	17	44247			PLACE NAME		獲
HWAI	140,07	3752.1A	11	44234			PLACE NAME		荻
HWAI	157,08	6435	15	66194	2214	5495	ANKLE BONE		踝
HOAI	075,16	293B	20	40932			SOPHORA JAPONICA		檓
HUAY	032,04	0975	07	41190	5008	7978	BAD,SPOILED	1095	坏
HUAY	032,16	1095	19	40132	2232	5831	BAD	0975	壞
HUAN	061,18	2041	21	94014	2265	0935	PLEASED		懽
HUAN	076,02	2970.1	06	77482		4955	JOYOUS/HAPPY		欢
HUAN	076,18	2970	22	47282	2266	4911	JOYOUS/HAPPY		歡

ROM	RAD	TEL	TOT	FC	MAT	OSH	TAG	CR	CHAR
HUAN	094,18	8814	21	44214	2267		BADGER	6294	
HUAN	149,18	6246	25	04614	2268	0934	ACCLAMATION		
HUAN	153,18	6294	25	24214	2267	0936	BADGER	8814	
HUAN	187,18	7536	28	74314	2269	0937	DOCILE HORSE		
HWAN	031,13	0958	16	60732	2255	1914	CIRCLE/ENCIRCLE		
HWAN	038,13	1298.0B	16	46432	2877	5876	PLACE WHERE SUPREME BESTOWS BOOKS		
HWAN	040,13	1403	16	30732	2256	5877	LARGE DOMAIN		
HWAN	075,06	2719	10	41916	2236	0027	(SURNAME),SAPINDUS MUKUROSI		
HWAN	085,06	3180	09	31116		0029	NAME OF A RIVER		
HWAN	085,13	3433	16	36132			TO RETURN(OF WAVES)		
HWAN	096,04	3883.1	08	11190			RING(NOT FOR FINGER),BRACELET		
HWAN	096,13	3883	17	16132	2258	5868	RING(NOT FOR FINGER),BRACELET		
HWAN	120,13	4944	19	26932	2259	5875	BIND/TIE,NOOSE		
HWAN	140,06	9170	10	44106			(VEGETABLE)/VIOLA VAGINATA		
HWAN	140,08	5495	12	44214	7031	0945	(REEDS)		
HWAN	153,06	6286	13	21216	2868	0026	BADGER		
HWAN	162,04	6703.1A	08	31309	2261	6778	RETURN,PAY BACK,(SURNAME)		
HWAN	162,13	6703.0A	17	36303	2261	6748	RETURN,PAY BACK,(SURNAME)		
HWAN	167,09	6953	17	82147	2262	6115	(ANCIENT MEASURE),MONEY	6994	
HWAN	167,13	6994	21	86132	2262	5869	METAL RING,(ANCIENT WEIGHT)		
HWAN	169,13	7076	21	77732	2263	3515	WALL AROUND A MARKET PLACE		
HWAN	190,13	7587	23	72732	2264	5878	A KNOT OF HAIR ON TOP OF HEAD		
HWAN	196,13	775F	24	67227			JAPANESE CRESTED IBIS		
HWAN	198,06	779B	17	00216			EUROPEAN ROE DEER		
HOAN	085,07	3183	10	33111	2244	7477	CLEANSE/BATHE	3418	
HOAN	085,13	3418	16	38141	2244	2413	CLEANSE/BATHE	3183	
HOAN	109,07	4196	12	63011	2246	7473	GOOD-LOOKING/CUTE		
HOAN	120,09	4883	15	22947	2242	6122	SLOW,GO SLOW		
HUANN	030,09	0822	12	67034	2249	5031	TO CALL		
HUANN	037,06	1147	09	27430	2248	5030	EXCELLENT,(SURNAME)		
HUANN	040,06	1360	09	30717	2238	0847	AN OFFICIAL		
HUANN	052,01	1634	04	27720	2235	4267	FANTASY		
HUANN	061,07	1891	11	50336	2240	8611	MISFORTUNE,SUFFER (FROM ILLNESS)		

獾
讙
貛
驩
圜
嬛
寰
桓
洹
澴
环
環
繯
萈
萑
貆
还
還
鍰
鐶
闤
鬟
鸛
嚾
浣
澣
睆
緩
喚
奂
宦
幻
患

ROM	RAD	TEL	TOT	FC	MAT	OSH	TAG	CR	CHAR
HUANN	064,09	2255	12	57034	2250	5032	TO EXCHANGE		
HUANN	064,13	8474	16	56032	2257	5873	PASS THROUGH,TO GET INTO(ARMOR)		
HUANN	085,09	3251	12	37134	2252	5034	DISPERSE EXPANSIVE (OF RIVER)		
HUANN	085,11	3376	14	35136	2241	8613	INDECIPHERABLE		
HUANN	086,09	3562	13	97834	2253	5033	BRILLIANT/LUSTROUS		
HUANN	104,09	4050	14	00134	2254	5035	ILLNESS,NUMBNESS OF THE LIMBS		
HUANN	152,06	6273	13	90232	2243	5744	FEED PIGS AND DOGS,TO REAR		
HUANN	159,13	6573	20	56032	2260	5872	TO TEAR BETWEEN CHARIOTS(PUNISHMENT		
HUANN	162,08	6648	12	33307	2239	6622	ESCAPE FROM		
HUANG	032,10	2390	13	44111			UNPROCESSED ORE		
HUANG	061,10	1967	13	94011	2272	7777	NERVOUS		
HUANG	130,03	5134	07	00227	2274	3603	REGION BETWEEN HEART AND DIAPHRAGM		
HUANG	140,06	5435	10	44211	2271	7775	UNCULTIVATED,OUT OF PRACTICE		
HUANG	143,03	5879	09	00107	2275		BLOOD		
HUANG	167,10	9491	18	86111			SOUND OF BELL		
HWANG	016,09	0420	11	77210	2285	7824	PHOENIX		
HWANG	030,09	8151	12	66014	2286	0326	SOUND OF BELL,SOBBING		
HWANG	060,09	1787	12	26214	2287	0329	IRRESOLUTE		
HWANG	061,09	1929	12	96014	2288	0327	FRIGHTENED		
HWANG	085,09	3207	12	36114	2289	0335	NAME OF A RIVER		
HWANG	085,12	3385	15	34186	2298		LAKE/POND,DYE PAPER,MOUNT SCROLL		
HWANG	086,09	3552	13	96814	2290	0332	BRILLIANT		
HWANG	086,12	8757	16	94886			BRILLIANT	3552	
HWANG	094,12	3738	15	44286			SPANIEL		
HWANG	096,12	3874	16	14186	2299	8326	SEMI-CIRCULAR JADE ORNAMENT		
HWANG	106,04	4106	09	26104	2283	0324	EMPEROR,(SURNAME)		
HWANG	112,12	4337	17	14686	2301	8327	SULFUR	C7806	
HWANG	118,09	4635	15	88104	2291	0336	BAMBOO GROVE,(BAMBOO)		
HWANG	118,12	4679	18	88806	2302	8342	METALLICREED,SPRING OF LOCK		
HWANG	130,12	2454.0A	16	74286			(DISEASE)		
HWANG	137,09	5317	15	26414	2292	0331	FAST-SAILING BOAT		
HWANG	142,09	5794	15	56114	2293	0334	LOCUST		
HWANG	142,12	2434	18	54186	2303	8329	HORSE-LEECH		

ROM	RAD	TEL	TOT	FC	MAT	OSH	TAG	CR	CHAR
HWANG	162,09	6668	13	36301	2294	6603	LEISURE		遑
HWANG	167,09	6949	17	86114		0325	TRIDENT,SOUND OF DRUMS AND BELLS		鍠
HWANG	167,12	9499	20	84186			SOUND OF BELL		鐄
HWANG	170,09	7124	12	76214	2295	0330	GOD OF CITY,DRY MOAT		隍
HWANG	180,09	9573	18	06614			MUSIC OF BELL AND DRUM		韹
HWANG	195,09	9650	20	26314	2296	0333	STURGEON		鰉
HWANG	201,00	7806	12	44806	2297	8325	YELLOW,(SURNAME),SULFUR	G4337	黃
HWANG	201,13	7808	25	77806	2392	8341	SCHOOL		黌
HOANG	050,10	1610	13	46211	2278	7515	ADVERTISING SIGN		幌
HOANG	061,05	8390	08	96010	2276	7547	FLURRIED,INDISTINCT,DISAPPOINTED	1857	恍
HOANG	061,06	1857	09	99011	2276	7500	FLURRIED,INDISTINCT,DISAPPOINTED	8390	怳
HOANG	072,06	2515.0A	10	60211	2277	7512	DAZZLE	3570	晃
HOANG	075,10	2853	14	46911	2280	7516	SCREEN		榥
HOANG	085,10	8701	13	36111			BRIGHT EXPANSE OF WATER		潢
HOANG	086,10	3570	14	96811	2281		DAZZLE	2515.0A	熀
HOANG	149,06	6106	13	08611	2273	7774	LIES/TO LIE	6192	詤
HOANG	149,10	6192	17	04611	2273	7776	LIES/TO LIE	6106	謊
HUANQ	064,10	227A	13	56011		7514	SHAKE		撓
HUANQ	072,06	2515	10	60211	2277	7512	SWAY,TO SHADE		晃
HUEI	032,09	1077.1A	12	74104		0207	DESTROY,OVERTHROW		墮
HUEI	032,12	1077.0A	15	74104		0208	DESTROY,OVERTHROW	7149	隳
HUEI	060,14	1798.1	17	22248	2354	6402	INSIGNIA		嶶
HUEI	060,14	1798	17	28240	2354	6402	INSIGNIA		徽
HUEI	061,06	1863	09	94089	2307	5608	RECOVER		恢
HUEI	064,09	2264	12	57056	2318	2659	WIELD,SCATTER,WIPE AWAY		揮
HUEI	064,12	2325	15	52027	2356	4526	TO DIRECT,UNASSUMING		撝
HUEI	072,09	2547	13	67056	2319	2655	BRIGHT/RADIANT		暉
HUEI	075,11	2877	15	45977	2334		SMALL COFFIN		槥
HUEI	086,02	3500	06	40089	2306	5606	ASHES,GRAY		灰
HUEI	086,09	8748	13	97856	2321	2660	BRIGHT/GLORIOUS	6540	輝
HUEI	124,09	5057	15	17506	2322	2665	VARIEGATED PHEASANT,TO FLY		翬
HUEI	142,03	5726.0A	09	15213	2316	7462	SICK,WITH NO AMBITION		虺
HUEI	145,09	5966	14	34256	7092		SACRIFICIAL ROBE OF THE EMPRESS		褘

113

ROM	RAD	TEL	TOT	FC	MAT	OSH	TAG	CR	CHAR
HUEI	149,06	6117	13	04689	2308	5607	WHIMSICAL/HUMOROUS		詼
HUEI	152,03	9315	10	11213	2317	7461	GRUNTING OF PIGS,CLASH		豗
HUEI	159,08	6540	15	97256	2323	2661	BRIGHT,GLORIOUS	8748	輝
HUEI	170,15	7149	18	74338	2355	8517	DESTROY,OVERTHROW	1077.0A	隳
HUEI	200,04	7804	15	00214	2325	7393	SIGNAL FLAG,TO SIGNAL		麾
HWEI	009,06	0161	08	26200			MOVE BACK AND FORTH,IRRESOLUTE	1773	佪
HWEI	031,03	0932	06	60600	2309	1850	TO REVOLVE/TO RETURN,A TIME	K6616	回
HWEI	054,06	1697	09	16400	2315	6810	REVOLVE,RETURN	6616	廻
HWEI	060,06	1773	09	26200	2310	1851	MOVE BACK AND FORTH,IRRESOLUTE	0161	徊
HWEI	085,06	3150	09	36100	2312	1853	EDDY/WHIRLPOOL		洄
HWEI	104,06	8869	11	00160			ROUND WORM/ASCARIS LUMBRICOIDES	5784	痐
HWEI	140,06	5418	10	44600	2313	1866	FENNEL		茴
HWEI	142,04	5784.1	10	53111	2314	7721	ROUNDWORM/ASCARIS LUMBRICOIDES		蚘
HWEI	142,06	5784	12	56100	2314	1852	ROUNDWORM/ASCARIS LUMBRICOIDES	8869	蛔
HWEI	162,06	6616	10	36300	2315	6637	REVOLVE,RETURN,TO CURVE	K0932	迴
HWEI	195,06	764F	17	26300	7055		CATFISH/AMIURUS SP.		鮰
HOEI	009,04	2585.1A	06	80731	2345		MOMENT		会
HOEI	061,07	1882	10	98057	2336	4878	REGRET		悔
HOEI	073,09	2585.0A	13	80606	2345		MOMENT		會
HOEI	079,09	3014	13	77147	2327	6261	DESTROY/RUIN		毀
HOEI	086,13	3607	17	97847	2328	6263	DESTROY BY FIRE,BLAZE		燬
HOEI	142,03	5726	09	15213	2316	7462	POISONUOUS SNAKES		虺
HOEI	149,07	6140.0A	14	08657	2338	4876	INSTRUCT,ADMONISH		誨
HOEI	149,09	6191.1	16	07614	2329	0186	TO SLANDER,DEFAME		𧩊
HOEI	149,13	6191	20	07647	2329	6262	TO SLANDER,DEFAME		譭
HOEI	154,06	6325.0A	13	64827	2330	3586	BRIBE(RY)		賄
HUEY	009,04	2585.1	06	80731	2345		MEETING,ASSOCIATION,CAN(BE ABLE)		会
HUEY	022,11	0565	13	71711	2353	0784	REMIT,TO CONVERGE(OF RIVERS)		匯
HUEY	024,03	0583	05	40440	2326	2819	PLANTS		卉
HUEY	024,04	0583.1	06	40440	2326		PLANTS		𠦄
HUEY	030,09	0821	12	67032	2348	5737	BEAK,TO PANT		喙
HUEY	030,11	0861	14	65077	2332	0861	SHRILL SOUND,TWINKLING		嘒
HUEY	058,08	1741	11	55177	2331	0860	COMET		彗

ROM	RAD	TEL	TOT	FC	MAT	OSH	TAG	CR	CHAR
HUEY	058,11	1743	14	27904	2349	5508	CLASS,COLLECTION	K0565.1	彙
HUEY	061,06	1861	10	40331	7121	8539	RAGE		恚
HUEY	061,06	8396	10	50336			FAVOR/KINDNESS	1920	惠
HUEY	061,08	1920	12	50331	2339	8698	KIND ACT (FROM ABOVE),FAVOR		惠
HUEY	061,11	1979	15	55337	2333	8552	INTELLIGENT		慧
HUEY	072,07	2526	11	68057	2337	4877	DARK,NIGHT,UNLUCKY		晦
HUEY	073,09	2585	13	80606	2345	1537	MEETING,ASSOCIATION,CAN(BE ABLE)		會
HUEY	085,02	0565.1	05	31110			CLASS,COLLECTION,REMIT	K1743	汇
HUEY	085,06	311A	09	34140			OXONIUM(ION)HYDRONIUM(ION)		泙
HUEY	085,12	3391.0A	15	35186	2343	8129	BREAK DOWN,BE DISPERSED		潰
HUEY	085,13	3442	16	31153	2350	7014	VAST/EXPANSIVE(AS OF WATER)		濊
HUEY	086,13	2476	17	98866		1543	COOKED IN SOY AND VINEGAR		燴
HUEY	096,13	3882	17	18166			JADE ORNAMENT IN THE SEAMS OF CAP		璯
HUEY	115,06	4486.1	11	22927			DIRT/FILTH		秽
HUEY	115,13	4486	18	21953	2351	7013	DIRT/FILTH		穢
HUEY	118,11	4655	17	88174		0863	BROOM		篲
HUEY	120,12	4936	18	25986	3665	8128	TO DRAW,MULTI-COLOR		繢
HUEY	120,13	4940	19	28966	2346	1544	TO DRAW		繪
HUEY	124,13	5066	19	27220	2352	3397	NOISE OF BIRD'S WINGS		翽
HUEY	140,12	5610	16	44333	2340	8702	COUMAROUNA ODORATA		蕙
HUEY	140,13	5634	17	44606	2347	1548	FLOURISH		薈
HUEY	142,12	5844	18	55133	2341	8701	(CICADA)/PLATYPLEURA KAEMPFERI		蟪
HUEY	149,07	6140	14	08657	2338	4876	INSTRUCT,ADMONISH		誨
HUEY	149,09	6172	16	04656	2357	2578	AVOID MENTIONING/TO TABOO		諱
HUEY	154,06	6325	13	64827	2330	3586	BRIBE(RY)		賄
HUEY	167,05	690B	13	84140			OXONIUM		鉌
HUEY	169,12	7072	20	77806	3668	3534	GATE OF MARKET		闠
HUEY	176,12	7242	21	15686	2344	8122	WASH THE FACE	7334	靧
HUEY	181,07	7334	16	11486	2344	8269	WASH THE FACE	7242	頮
HUEN	038,08	1241	11	42464	2360	1597	MARRIAGE,TAKE A WIFE		婚
HUEN	061,08	1916	11	92064	2361	1596	SILLY,FORGETFUL,CONFUSED	8398	惛
HUEN	061,09	8398	12	97064		1599	SILLY,FORGETFUL,CONFUSED	1916	惽
HUEN	072,04	2495	08	72604	2359	1595	TWILIGHT,MUDDLE-HEADED		昏

ROM	RAD	TEL	TOT	FC	MAT	OSH	TAG	CR	CHAR
HUEN	072,05	2495.1	09	77604	2359	1598	TWILIGHT,MUDDLE-HEADED		
HUEN	109,09	4216	14	78604			TO BE AGONIZED,WORRIED		
HUEN	140,09	5526	13	44506	2368	2664	MEAT DISH		
HUEN	140,11	9189	15	44336			MEAT DISH	5526	
HUEN	169,08	7053	16	77604	2364	3474	DOOR-KEEPER		
HWEN	075,09	8578	13	47956	2320		CLOTHESHORSE		
HWEN	085,08	3236.0A	11	36111	2371	7124	CONFUSED,DIRTY		
HWEN	085,09	3268	12	37156	2366	2662	MUDDY		
HWEN	096,09	8829	13	17156	2367	2653	(FINE JADE)		
HWEN	184,08	7412	16	86711	2370	7118	CHINESE RAVIOLI	9599	
HWEN	184,09	9599	17	87756	2370	2658	CHINESE RAVIOLI	7412	
HWEN	194,04	7609	14	16713	2365	7644	SOUL		
HOEN	085,08	3236.0B	11	36111	2371	7124	MIXED UP/UNDIFFERENTIATED		
HUENN	031,07	0951	10	60232	2373	1911	PIG-STY,GRAIN-FED ANIMALS		
HUENN	061,10	1968	14	60330	2374	8599	DISHONOR,CONFUSED		
HUENN	061,10	1968.1	13	96000	2374	1912	DISHONOR,CONFUSED		
HUENN	085,08	3236	11	36111		7124	CONFUSED,MIX		
HUENN	085,09	3268.0A	12	37156	2366	2662	CONFUSED,TALL,BIG		
HUENN	085,10	3311	13	36100	2375	1913	DISORDERED,PRIVY		
HUENN	149,09	9294	16	07656	2369	2654	NICKNAME,JEST		
HUO	127,06	2605	12	58961			(PLOUGH)		
HUO	150,10	6255.0A	17	38668	2404	1383	OPENING,STAKE ALL		
HWO	030,05	0735.0D	08	26900		1095	WARM,SOFT		
HWO	085,06	3172	09	32164	2401	1324	TO LIVE,WORK/WORKMANSHIP		
HUOO	009,04	0129	06	29280	2396	5588	PARTNER,ASSISTANT,FURNITURE	K1127	
HUOO	036,11	1127	14	67927	2397	4260	PARTNER,ASSISTANT	K0129	
HUOO	086,00	3499	04	90800	2395	5586	FIRE		
HUOO	167,04	2982	12	89180		5587	HOLMIUM		
HUOO	173,08	7202	16	10214	2405	0957	CHOLERA		
HUOH	009,06	0166	08	22264	2400		UNITE		
HUOH	030,05	0735.0B	08	26900	2115	1095	MIX TOGETHER		
HUOH	030,06	8137	09	61060			TO SHOUT/CRY		
HUOH	030,12	8137.1	15	65016			TO SHOUT/CRY		

ROM	RAD	TEL	TOT	FC	MAT	OSH	TAG	CR	CHAR
HUOH	030,14	8179	17	64047	2205	6149	STUNNED AND SPEECHLESS		嚄
HUOH	032,14	1089.0A	17	27104	2128	0228	GULLY		壑
HUOH	058,23	1745	26	14347			STANDARD/NORM	4256	彟
HUOH	061,08	1910	12	53330	2403	8676	CONFUSE		惑
HUOH	062,04	2057	08	53100	2402	6961	OR		或
HUOH	064,14	2366	17	54047	2206		TRAP		擭
HUOH	075,14	8596	18	44947			(TREE)		檴
HUOH	079,09	8159	13	47647			TO VOMIT		嗀
HUOH	085,09	3284	12	35161	2199		DASHING OF WAVES		湱
HUOH	085,14	3455	17	34147	2411		COOK,DASHING OF WATER		濩
HUOH	094,14	3752	17	44247	2412	6153	TO CATCH/OBTAIN		獲
HUOH	111,14	4256	19	84447		6154	STANDARD/NORM	1745	矆
HUOH	113,09	4393	13	37227	2399	3938	DISASTER		禍
HUOH	115,14	4490	19	24947	2207	6155	REAP/HARVEST	B3752.1	穫
HUOH	127,14	9102	20	54947			REAP/HARVEST	B3752.1	䆶
HUOH	130,16	9143	20	71214	2132		MEAT BROTH		臛
HUOH	140,07	3752.1	11	44234		5591	TO CATCH/OBTAIN,REAP/HARVEST	D4490	获
HUOH	140,16	5681	20	44214	2408		BEANS,LOPHANTHUS RUGOSUS		藿
HUOH	142,14	5863	20	54147	2208	6156	LOOPER CATERPILLAR		蠖
HUOH	150,10	6255	17	38668	2404	1383	EXEMPT FROM,OPEN,LIBERAL-MINDED		豁
HUOH	154,04	6303	11	24806	2398	8224	GOODS/COMMODITY		货
HUOH	167,14	7000	22	84147	2209	6148	BOILER OR CALDRON		鑊
HUOH	172,10	7174	18	74447	2210	6152	RED EARTH USED FOR PAINTS		雘
HUOH	173,08	7202.0A	16	10214	2405	0957	(SURNAME),CHOLERA		霍
HUOH	195,14	9664	25	24347			SHAD		鱯
HUOH	196,14	775C	25	24347			PUFFIN		鸌
I	001,00	0001	01	10000	3016	0001	ONE		一
I	009,04	0122	06	27257	2936	4244	HE/SHE		伊
I	009,06	0181	08	20232	2990	5811	ACCORDING TO,DEPEND ON,NEAR TO		依
I	023,05	6829.1	07	71713	2978		MEDICINE,TO TREAT		医
I	030,04	0764.1	07	67057	2937	4243	(ONOMAT.)		吚
I	030,06	0764	09	67057	2937	4245	(ONOMAT.)		咿
I	030,13	0895	16	60036	2961	8566	BELCH,(INTERJ. OF APPROVAL)		噫

ROM	RAD	TEL	TOT	FC	MAT	OSH	TAG	CR	CHAR
I	033,09	1105	12	40108	3016	0583	ONE (FRAUD PROOF FORM)		
I	056,01	8382	04	43100	3016	6877	ONE	A0001	
I	064,09	2253	12	56041	3030	2731	GREET (BY RAISING THE JOINED HANDS)		
I	076,08	2951	12	47682	2956	4928	INTERJECTION	3716	
I	085,11	3354	14	34121	2957	3075	RIPPLE		
I	094,08	3716	11	44221	2956	3074	(INTERJ.)	2951	
I	113,09	4400	13	34256	2971	2584	RARE,EXCELLENT,PRECIOUS		
I	120,11	4922	17	77903	2976	8469	SIGHING SOUND,INTERJ.		
I	142,06	575A	12	57170			WOOD-LOUSE		
I	142,11	583D	22	77136			TRIGONOTYLUS RUFICORNIS		
I	145,00	5902	06	00732	2989	5809	CLOTHES		
I	164,11	6829	18	77601	2978	1966	MEDICINE,TO TREAT		
I	167,06	7917	14	80132		5810	IRIDIUM		
I	196,11	7746	22	77327	2979	4682	WIDGEON		
I	203,06	9694	18	67327	2981	4262	BLACK AND SHINING EBONY		
YI	009,13	0308	15	28253	3003	6936	RITES,APPARATUS		
YI	022,03	0558	05	71711	2942	0820	WASHBASIN WITH A TUBULAR HANDLE		
YI	037,03	1138	06	50032	2982	5235	A BARBARIAN		
YI	038,06	1210	09	45432	2985	5239	AUNT (MATERNAL)		
YI	040,05	13⁵⁵	08	30107	2992	0629	PROPER,SUITABLE,SHOULD		
YI	040,07	1406	10	30716			NORTHEASTERN CORNER OF A ROOM		
YI	046,06	1500	09	25732			PLACE NAME		
YI	046,14	1544	17	22481	4671	6038	NAME OF A MOUNTAIN IN HUNAN		
YI	058,16	1744	19	27449	3001	2811	RULE,NORMAL NATURE OF MAN		
YI	061,05	1837	08	93060	2964	1451	HARMONY,PLEASED		
YI	061,18	2034.0A	22	47138	2999	8648	VIRTUOUS,RESTRAIN		
YI	063,06	2080	10	30227	7337		UPRIGHT BAR FOR FASTENING A DOOR		
YI	075,03	8532	07	44912			(TREE)	8543	
YI	075,05	8543	09	48912			(TREE)	8532	
YI	075,06	8557	10	45932			(TREE)		
YI	075,09	2821	13	48912	2948	7432	CLOTHES-HORSE		
YI	085,04	3085	07	32121	2941	2047	NAME OF A RIVER		
YI	085,06	3158	09	35132	2986		SNIVEL		

壹 弍 揖 欹 漪 猗 禪 繄 蜉 醫 衣 醫 酉 鈠 鷖 黟 儀 迆 夷 姨 宜 宧 崺 嶷 彛 怡 懿 廙 杝 椸 橫 杝 沂 澫

ROM	RAD	TEL	TOI	FC	MAT	OSH	TAG	CR	CHAR
YI	103,09	3992	14	27481	2940	6032	DOUBT/SUSPECT		疑
YI	104,06	4021	11	00132	2987	5241	SORES,BRUISE		瘗
YI	108,05	4135.0A	10	80107	3052	0712	BENEFIT,INCREASE		益
YI	109,05	4182.0A	10	63060	2965	1450	PLACE NAME		眙
YI	115,06	4448	11	27927	2980	4261	CHANGE POSITION,REMOVE		移
YI	118,11	4669	17	88927			SMALL HOUSE CONNECTED TO LARGE ONE		篪
YI	130,06	5166	10	75232	2988	5238	SOAP		胰
YI	140,06	542A	10	44277			IDRYL		荑
YI	140,06	5434.0A	10	44532	6245	5242	TO WEED		薐
YI	140,11	556D	15	44927			POLYGONATUM OFFICINALE		蓤
YI	145,06	9254	12	00732			PLACE NAME		褱
YI	149,03	6071	10	04612	2943	7420	ARROGANT,MEAN		訑
YI	149,05	6095	12	03660	2966	1449	BEQUEATH,A PRESENT IN WRITING	A6318	詒
YI	149,08	6146.0A	15	03617	2994	0630	FRIENDSHIP		誼
YI	154,03	6301	10	64812	2944	7425	PROMOTE,REWARD		貤
YI	154,05	6318	12	63860	2967	1458	BEQUEATH	A6095	貽
YI	162,05	6607.1A	09	38301	2947	6766	WINDING		迤
YI	162,06	4448.1	10	37302	2980	6711	CHANGE POSITION,REMOVE		迻
YI	162,12	6695	16	35308	2995	6776	LEAVE BEHIND		遺
YI	164,03	9426	10	14612			SWEET WINE,ELIXIRS		酏
YI	181,06	7328	15	71786	2969	8250	CHEEKS,NOURISH		頤
YI	184,05	7392	13	83760	2968	1452	SYRUP		飴
YII	005,00	0044	01	17710	3017	7954	2ND IN ORDER,2ND HEAVEN'S STEM		乙
YII	009,03	0110	05	28100	2932	7984	TO USE,BECAUSE,IN ORDER TO		以
YII	009,08	0231	10	24221	2953	3069	LEAN ON		倚
YII	009,09	8063	11	20232			TO SOB/WAIL		俒
YII	032,03	8197	06	47117	2931	7244	BRIDGE,BANK		圯
YII	044,04	1442.0A	07	77214	7109	7386	TAIL		尾
YII	049,00	1571	03	17717	2930	7243	ALREADY		已
YII	063,06	2081	10	30232	2991	5812	SCREEN,(SURNAME)		扆
YII	070,08	2470	12	04221			FLUTTERING OF FLAG		旖
YII	075,07	2783	11	44921	2954	3077	CHAIR		椅
YII	094,08	3716.0A	11	44221	2956		PLIANT,LUXURIANT GROWTH		猗

ROM	RAD	TEL	TOT	FC	MAT	OSH	TAG	CR	CHAR
YII	111,02	4248	07	23430	2938	5173	FINAL PART.		
YII	137,13	5320	19	28453	3004	6937	MOOR A BOAT TO THE BANK		
YII	140,05	5405	09	44777	2933	1490	PLANTAGO MAJOR L. VAR. ASIATICA	5386	
YII	140,05	5386	09	44780	2933	7988	PLANTAGO MAJOR L. VAR. ASIATICA	5405	
YII	142,10	5819	16	52118		0575	ANT	5852	
YII	142,13	5852	19	58153	3005	6938	ANT	5819	
YII	162,05	6607	09	38301	2947	6766	EXTENDING TO		
YII	167,01	7918	09	87110			YTTRIUM		
YII	181,10	9582	19	21186	2970	8248	PLEASING/RESPECTFUL MANNER		
YII	196,01	7681	12	27310		7956	A SWALLOW(BIRD)		
YII	211,08	7888	23	24721	2958	3066	BITE,(SURNAME)		
YIH	004,01	0034	02	40000	2934	6518	MOW	0435	
YIH	004,02	5030.1	03	40000			RIGHTEOUSNESS,PUBLIC,MEANING		
YIH	005,12	8013	13	42110			COVETOUS/GREEDY		
YIH	008,04	0076	06	00330	3021	8511	ALSO		
YIH	009,01	0310.1	03	27210			A HUNDRED MILLION,CALCULATE		
YIH	009,03	0106	05	28217	0565	7965	STRONG/BRAVE		
YIH	009,05	0153	07	25230	3025	5197	IDLE,(SURNAME)		
YIH	009,06	0168	08	28227	3024	3651	ROW OF DANCERS AT SACRIFICES		
YIH	009,13	0310	15	20236	3042	8568	A HUNDRED MILLION,CALCULATE		
YIH	018,02	0435	04	42000	2935	2956	MOW	0034	
YIH	018,14	0496	16	22400	3013	2887	CUT OFF THE NOSE		
YIH	019,12	0532	14	44827	2951	4830	TOIL		
YIH	030,05	8128	08	64017			TALKATIVE/LOQUACIOUS		
YIH	030,07	0779	10	66017	3038		SHORT BREATHING,PALPITATION		
YIH	030,19	0927	22	64031	3015	8875	TALK IN SLEEP		
YIH	031,13	8193	16	60401			MIST ROLLING UPWARDS		
YIH	032,08	8226	11	44117	3014	7916	SKILL/ART	5669	
YIH	032,08	1023	11	46127	3035	4506	BORDER		
YIH	037,06	1150	09	00430	3022	5053	ABUNDANT,GRACEFUL		
YIH	046,03	1473	06	28717	0566	7961	HIGH AND STEEP		
YIH	046,13	1542	16	26741	3060	2481	NAME OF HILLS IN SHANTUNG		
YIH	050,06	1595	09	00227			CANOPY		

ROM	RAD	TEL	TOT	FC	MAT	OSH	TAG	CR	CHAR
YIH	055,03	8381	06	17441			(INTERJ.),TO STOP,RAISE		异
YIH	055,06	1704	09	00443	3023	2812	CHINESE CHESS GAME		弈
YIH	056,00	1707	03	43000	3018	6873	TO SHOOT		弋
YIH	060,04	1763	07	27247	3028	6268	SERVICE		役
YIH	061,05	8389	08	94017			IMITATE/EMULATE		忕
YIH	061,06	8389.1	09	95006			IMITATE/EMULATE		悗
YIH	061,07	1881	10	96017	3039	7300	ANXIETY/WORRY		悒
YIH	061,09	1942	13	00336	2960	8565	IDEA/MEANING		意
YIH	061,13	2011	16	90036	3043	8567	REMEMBER		憶
YIH	061,13	2022	16	96041	3061	2483	REJOICE,PLEASED		懌
YIH	061,18	2034	22	47138	2999	8648	VIRTUOUS,RESTRAIN		懿
YIH	064,04	2117	07	57020	3031	2148	REPRESS,OR,(PART.)		抑
YIH	064,07	2184	10	56017	3040	7301	LADLE OUT,POUR OUT,GIVE UP		挹
YIH	064,08	2227.0A	11	50047	3032	6493	ASSIST BY THE ARM		掖
YIH	064,11	8467	14	54017			RUB PIECES OF WOOD TOGETHER		撎
YIH	066,13	2424	17	68440	3062	6321	BE WEARY OF	2967	斁
YIH	072,04	2496	08	60227	2952	4505	EASY,CHANGE,(SURNAME)		易
YIH	072,12	2558	16	64018	2996	0585	SUN HIDDEN BY CLOUDS,OBSCURE		曀
YIH	073,02	2576	06	50006	3008	7052	DRAG		曳
YIH	075,03	8534	04	43940	3019	6876	POST FOR TETHERING ANIMALS		杙
YIH	075,05	2669	09	44917	2949	0852	OAR,STAND FOR CORRECTING A BOW		枻
YIH	075,13	2918	17	40936			QUERCUS. GLAUCA		檍
YIH	076,13	2967	17	67482			BE WEARY OF	2424	歝
YIH	078,12	3002	16	14218	2997	0587	EXTERMINATE		殪
YIH	079,11	3015	15	07247	3010	6297	PERSEVERENCE		毅
YIH	084,08	8643	12	80217			EMULSIN		氥
YIH	085,05	3122	08	35130	3026	5202	OVERFLOW,DISSIPATE		泆
YIH	085,07	3204	10	36117	3041	7302	DAMP/MOIST		浥
YIH	085,08	3210.0A	11	30147	3033	6495	LIQUID		液
YIH	085,10	3300	13	38117	3054	0719	OVERFLOW		溢
YIH	086,11	8758	15	97818			(PERSON)		熤
YIH	086,11	3584	15	97862	3049	1671	TO GLOW/FLASH		熠
YIH	086,13	8765	17	96841			RADIANT,BLAZING		燡
YIH	102,06	3976	11	60801	3009	8034	DIFFERENT/STRANGE		異

ROM	RAD	TEL	TOT	FC	MAT	OSH	TAG	CR	CHAR
YIH	104,04	4004	09	00147	3029	6303	EPIDEMIC		
YIH	104,10	4053	15	00114	3012	0216	BURY,SACRIFICE		
YIH	104,13	407A	18	00137			HYSTERIA		
YIH	108,05	4135	10	80107	3052	0712	BENEFIT,INCREASE		
YIH	109,08	4203	13	60401	3059	2479	TO SPY,LEAD ON		
YIH	109,11	422A	16	77604		1730	CATARACT		
YIH	115,03	5669.2	08	24917	3014		SKILL/ART		
YIH	120,10	4898	16	28917	3055	0718	STRANGLE ONESELF,HANG		
YIH	120,13	4946	19	26941	3063	2489	UNRAVEL,EXPLAIN,CONTINUOUS		
YIH	123,07	5030	13	80553	3002	6934	RIGHTEOUSNESS,PUBLIC,MEANING		
YIH	124,03	5056	09	17442	3000	2805	NAME OF A FAMOUS ARCHER		
YIH	124,05	5042	11	07120	3047	3386	ASSIST,RESPECT,READY TO FLY		
YIH	124,05	5043	11	17108	3048	0560	TOMORROW,BRIGHT		
YIH	124,11	5065	17	17801	3051	8035	WING		
YIH	124,11	5061	17	77127	2977	3418	FEATHER SCREEN,TO SCREEN,TO SHADE		
YIH	129,07	5125	13	25407	2939	2622	PRACTICE,DISTRESS,DESCENDANTS		
YIH	130,08	5199	12	70247	3034	6494	ARMPIT		
YIH	130,13	5244	17	70236	3044	8569	THOUGHTS,FEELINGS,OPINION		
YIH	137,10	5316	16	28417	3056		BOW OF A CHINESE BOAT		
YIH	140,01	5669.1	05	44717			SKILL/ART		
YIH	140,11	9188	15	44117	3014	7917	SKILL/ART	5669	
YIH	140,13	5650	17	44336	2962	8570	COIX LACRYMA		
YIH	140,15	9198	19	44247			ZANTHOXYLUM AILANTHOIDES		
YIH	140,15	5669	19	44731	3014	8874	SKILL/ART	8226	
YIH	142,08	5785	14	56127	3036	4514	CHAMELEON/EUMECES LATISCUTATUS		
YIH	142,10	582C	16	58117			ECHIURUS UNICIUCTUS		
YIH	145,00	5902.0A	06	00732	2989	5809	TO DRESS/TO WEAR		
YIH	145,07	5939	13	00227	2992	3907	FRONTIER,DESCENDENTS		
YIH	145,19	6003	24	34231		8876	SLEEVE OF DRESS		
YIH	149,06	6105	13	01661	3011	1605	GO		
YIH	149,08	6146	15	03617	2994	0630	FRIENDSHIP		
YIH	149,13	6230	20	06641	3064	2482	TRANSLATE		
YIH	149,13	6231	20	08653	3006	6935	DISCUSS,CRITICIZE		

疫瘞癔益罭醫 秧縊繹義羿翊翌翼翳肄腋臆艦艺蓺薏薿藝蜴蝪螠 衣裔襒詣誼譯議

ROM	RAD	TEL	TOT	FC	MAT	OSH	TAG	CR	CHAR
YIH	149,19	6248	26	04631			TALK IN SLEEP	0927	讛
YIH	152,12	9318	19	14218			BREATHING OF PIGS		豲
YIH	159,05	6522	12	55030	3027	5198	SURPASS,DISPERSE,PUT IN ORDER		軼
YIH	162,08	6654	12	37301	3045	6772	LEISURELY,ESCAPE,OUTSTANDING		逸
YIH	163,00	6712	07	60717	3037	7299	CITY		邑
YIH	167,10	6965	18	88117	3057	0713	GOLD-20 TAELS IN WEIGHT,ABRASION		鎰
YIH	167,13	7919	21	80136			YTTERBIUM		鐿
YIH	184,12	7435	20	84718	2998	0586	RANCID		饐
YIH	187,13	7531	23	76341	3065	2487	REMOUNT STATIONS		驛
YIH	187,16	7535	26	71381	0444	8038	THOROUGHBRED HORSE		驐
YIH	196,10	9680	21	17227		4638	MELEAGRIS GALLOPARO		鷁
YIH	196,10	7739	21	86127	3058	4604	FISH HAWK		鷁
IA	002,02	0021	03	80207	7213	1984	SLAVE GIRL		丫
IA	027,04	1090.1	06	71213		0290	PRESS DOWN		压
IA	030,03	067A	06	68020			(PHONETIC)/ACR- AS IN ACRIDINE		吖
IA	030,06	0800.1A	09	61012			(ONOMAT.)		哑
IA	030,08	0800.0A	11	61017	7226	0518	(ONOMAT.)		啞
IA	032,14	1090	17	71214	7231	0215	PRESS DOWN		壓
IA	064,05	2131	08	56050	7234	2681	DETAIN IN CUSTODY		押
IA	075,08	8571	12	41917	7228	0520	FORKING BRANCH		椏
IA	128,03	5102.0B	09	17127	7307	2195	(FINAL PART.)		耶
IA	196,04	7693	15	77227	7223	4627	CROW		鴉
IA	196,05	7700	16	67527	7235	4624	DUCK		鴨
YA	064,05	2131.0A	08	56050	7234	2681	MAKE A CROSS (AS SIGNATURE)		押
YA	075,04	8541	08	41940	7217	3327	FELLOE OF A WHEEL		枒
YA	085,08	3209	11	31114	7237	0179	BORDER,SHORE,HORIZON		涯
YA	092,00	3660	04	10240	7214	3323	TOOTH		牙
YA	140,04	5370	08	44241	7219	3333	SPROUT		芽
YA	142,04	5742	10	51140		3328	APHIS		蚜
YA	144,07	5895	13	21221	7224	3019	OFFICE,YAMEN,(SURNAME)		衙
YEA	007,04	0068.1	06	10102			ASIA,SECONDARY		亚
YEA	007,06	0068.2	08	10106			ASIA,SECONDARY		亜
YEA	007,06	0068	08	10107		0516	ASIA,SECONDARY		亞

ROM	RAD	TEL	TOT	FC	MAT	OSH	TAG	CR	CHAR
YEA	030,06	0800.1	09	61012			DUMB/MUTE		哑
YEA	030,08	0800	11	61017	7226	0518	DUMB/MUTE		啞
YEA	084,08	8645	12	80117		7798	ARGON		氬
YEA	104,08	4042	13	00117	7229	0522	DUMB,HOARSE	0800	瘂
YEA	172,04	7161	12	70214	7222	0879	ELEGANT		雅
YAH	007,04	0068.1A	06	10102			ASIA,SECONDARY		亚
YAH	007,06	0068.2A	08	10106		0515	ASIA,SECONDARY		亜
YAH	007,06	0068.0A	08	10107	7225	0516	ASIA,SECONDARY		亞
YAH	027,04	1090.1A	06	71213			TO CRUSH,IN THE FIRST PLACE		压
YAH	032,14	1090.0A	17	71214			TO CRUSH,IN THE FIRST PLACE	6509	壓
YAH	038,08	1246	11	41417	7227	0521	ADDRESS TERM BETWEEN SONS-IN-LAW		婭
YAH	064,08	8436	11	51017		0519	ATTACH,BRANDISH,HOLD		揠
YAH	064,09	2257	12	51014	7232	0831	PULL UP,ERADICATE		擭
YAH	112,04	4267	09	11640	7218	3325	TO CALENDER		研
YAH	149,04	6074	11	01640	7220	3326	ASTOUNDED		訝
YAH	159,01	6509	08	52010	7233	7060	CRUSH,IN THE FIRST PLACE	1090.0A	軋
YAH	162,04	6603	08	31304	7221	6682	RECEIVE(AS A GUEST)		迓
YAH	167,08	9472	16	81117	7230		AMMONIUM		錏
.IA	030,04	0711	07	61040	7215	3324	(FINAL PART.)		呀
YAI	027,06	0620	08	71214	7236	0176	PRECIPICE	1509	厓
YAI	046,08	1509	11	22214	7236	0180	PRECIPICE	0620	崖
YAI	109,08	4199	13	61014	7238	0177	CANTHUS,STARE		睚
IAN	030,06	0754	09	66000	7396	1893	THROAT,NARROW PASS		咽
IAN	032,11	8250	14	41127		4583	HILL WITH PLATEAU		塓
IAN	037,05	1141	08	40716	7378	7442	CASTRATE,TO DELAY		奄
IAN	038,11	1280	14	41427	7331	4584	CAPTIVATING		嫣
IAN	046,08	1517	11	24716	7379	7444	NAME OF A MOUNTAIN IN KANSU		崦
IAN	061,14	2044.1	18	71333	7388		PEACEFUL,CONTENTED		懕
IAN	061,14	2044	17	91034		5080	PEACEFUL,CONTENTED		懨
IAN	079,06	3009.0A	10	27247	7423	6285	DARK RED		殷
IAN	085,08	3238	11	34116	7381	7450	SUBMERGE,DROWN	3264	淹
IAN	085,09	3281.0A	12	31114	7415	0199	SUBMERGED,OBSCURED		湮
IAN	085,09	3264	12	38146	7381	2803	SUBMERGE,DROWN	3238	渰

ROM	RAD	TEL	TOT	FC	MAT	OSH	TAG	CR	CHAR
IAN	086,06	3533	10	96800	7397	1897	SMOKE,CIGARETTE	3591	烟
IAN	086,07	3547	11	10327	7330	4582	WHERE/HOW		馬
IAN	086,09	3591	13	91814	7397	0197	SMOKE,CIGARETTE/TOBACCO	3533	煙
IAN	086,12	3601.0A	16	44331	7399	8801	(SURNAME),PLACE NAME		燕
IAN	130,06	5168	10	76200	7398	1895	ROUGE	5249	胭
IAN	130,08	9131	12	74216	7383	7449	TO SALT/PICKLE	6812	腌
IAN	130,16	5249	20	74231	7398	8804	ROUGE	5168	臙
IAN	140,08	5510	12	44233	7397	8959	CIGARETTE/TOBACCO	B3533	菸
IAN	163,11	6768	14	17327	7333	2225	NAME OF A FEUDAL STATE,(SURNAME)		鄢
IAN	164,08	6812	15	14616	7384	7446	TO SALT/PICKLE	9131	醃
IAN	169,08	7052.0A	16	77233	4814	3541	FIRST WIVES OF HSIONG-NU CHIEFS		閼
IAN	169,08	7050	16	77716	7385	3527	CASTRATE		閹
IAN	186,08	7454	17	24616			SAVORY		馣
YAN	027,05	0917.1	07	10201			STERN,(AIR OR WATER)TIGHT		严
YAN	030,17	0917	20	66248	7347	6330	STERN,(AIR OR WATER)TIGHT		嚴
YAN	032,07	1007	10	42141	7343	6802	BOUNDARY		埏
YAN	038,06	1177	09	41440	7340	2392	BEAUTIFUL		妍
YAN	046,05	1484	08	22601	7349	1108	CLIFF	1554	岩
YAN	046,09	1527	12	60772		0995	CLIFF	1554	嵒
YAN	046,20	1554	23	22248	7349	6334	CLIFF		巖
YAN	054,04	1693	07	12401	7342	6801	TO DELAY		延
YAN	064,09	8441	13	11502	7341		GRIND FINE,STUDY/RESEARCH	4282	孹
YAN	075,13	2908	17	47961	7351	1183	EAVES	4683	檐
YAN	085,05	3116	08	37161	7354	1439	ALONG		沿
YAN	086,04	3508	08	90809	7335	5623	FLAME/INFLAMMATION/-ITIS		炎
YAN	086,08	3543.0A	12	97877	7394	1056	FLAME	3596.0A	焰
YAN	086,12	3596.0A	16	29789	7394	5625	FLAME	3543.0A	燄
YAN	104,12	4074	17	00172	7346A	0996	CANCER,CARCINOMA		癌
YAN	108,05	7770.1	10	43107			SALT		盐
YAN	108,08	7770.2	13	48107	7352		SALT		塩
YAN	112,06	4282	11	11640	7341	2390	GRIND FINE,STUDY/RESEARCH	8441	研
YAN	112,09	8954	14	60601		1110	CLIFF	1554	嵒
YAN	118,07	4605	13	88401	7344	6808	BAMBOO MAT FOR SITTING		筵

ROM	RAD	TEL	TOT	FC	MAT	OSH	TAG	CR	CHAR
YAN	118,13	4683	19	88261	7351	1187	EAVES	2908	簷
YAN	120,07	9060	13	22941		6805	CAP TASSELS		綖
YAN	142,07	5783	13	52141	7346	6806	SLUG		蜒
YAN	149,00	6056	07	00601	7334	1154	SPEECH,SPEAK		言
YAN	163,07	9391	10	17427			PLACE NAME		郔
YAN	169,03	7027	11	77101	7395	3439	(SURNAME),ABBR. OF 7051	A7051	閆
YAN	169,08	7051	16	77777	7395	3448	(SURNAME),GATE OF VILLAGE	7027	閻
YAN	170,05	9532	08	71260		1269	DANGEROUS		阽
YAN	181,09	7346	18	01286	7375	8285	COUNTENANCE,COLOR,(SURNAME)		顏
YAN	194,14	7623	24	71213	7392	7650	NIGHTMARE		魘
YAN	195,09	765R	20	20361			UPENCOIDES JAPONICUS		鰋
YAN	197,13	7770	24	78107	7352	0686	SALT		鹽
YEAN	009,09	0249	11	21214	7357	0829	TO LIE SUPINE,(SURNAME)		偃
YEAN	009,20	0332	22	26248	7348	6332	MAJESTIC		儼
YEAN	010,07	0350	09	00216	7355	7574	PLACE NAME		兗
YEAN	018,08	0470	10	92800		2952	SHARP		剡
YEAN	027,17	063A	19	71716			OPERCULUM		厴
YEAN	037,01	1130.0A	04	20430	7277	5126	DIE PREMATURELY	2986	夭
YEAN	037,05	1141.0A	08	40716	7378	7442	SUDDENLY,TO EMBRACE		奄
YEAN	038,09	1259.0A	12	48446			GIRL IN LOVE		媕
YEAN	046,20	1552	23	23734	7368	5082	PEAK OF MOUNTAIN		巘
YEAN	053,00	1639.0A	03	00200	7371	4231	COVERING		广
YEAN	055,06	1703	09	80446	7377	2801	TO COVER,TRAP		弇
YEAN	063,08	2085	12	30289	7337	5631	UPRIGHT BAR FOR FASTENING A DOOR		扊
YEAN	064,08	2237	11	54016	7380	7448	COVER UP,TO SURPRISE		掩
YEAN	064,09	2256	12	58046	7380	2802	COVER UP,TO SURPRISE	2237	揜
YEAN	075,08	8568	12	49989			(TREE)		棪
YEAN	075,14	8598	18	71904	7389	5377	WILD MULBERRY TREE		檿
YEAN	085,04	8662	07	33110		7684	(SURNAME)		沇
YEAN	085,11	3348	14	33186	7403	8344	PERFORM		演
YEAN	096,08	8827	12	19189	7339		GEM,GLITTER OF GEMS,D(28TH)		琰
YEAN	098,16	3923	21	21217	7369	7934	EARTHENWARE VESSEL		甗
YEAN	109,06	4190	11	67032	7400	5904	EYE		眼

ROM	RAD	TEL	TOT	FC	MAT	OSH	TAG	CR	CHAR
YEAN	122,08	5001	13	60716	7382	7452	VALVE,FOMENT		罨
YEAN	142,08	577F	14	54116			DRASPIS PATELLIFORMIS		蜓
YEAN	142,09	5795	15	51114	7359	0833	HEMIDACTYLUS BOWRINGII		蝘
YEAN	144,03	5888	09	21221	7402	3035	TO SPREAD OUT/AMPLIFY,GLOSS		衍
YEAN	163,09	9401	12	77727	7360	2167	PLACE NAME		鄢
YEAN	186,08	7454.0A	17	24616			FRAGRANT ODOR		馦
YEAN	195,09	9651	20	21314	7361	0832	MUDFISH		鰋
YEAN	203,14	7829	26	71331	7393	8741	BLACK SPOTS ON BODY		黶
YEAN	208,09	9697	22	71711	7362	6825	MOLE		鼴
YEAN	208,10	7862	23	76714		6833	MOGERA WOGURA WOGURA		鼹
YANN	027,04	0630.1	06	71234			LOATHE		厌
YANN	027,12	0630	14	71234	7387	5079	LOATHE		厭
YANN	030,06	0754.0A	09	66000	7396	1893	TO SWALLOW	0913	咽
YANN	030,07	0777	10	60061	7373	1155	CONDOLE WITH	0849	唁
YANN	030,09	0849	12	60022	7373	4189	CONDOLE WITH	0777	喭
YANN	030,16	0913	19	64031	7396	8802	TO SWALLOW	0754.0A	嚥
YANN	032,09	1037	12	41114	7358	0828	WEIR		堰
YANN	040,07	1365	10	30404	7364	9023	FEAST,REPOSE	6240	宴
YANN	059,06	1750	09	00222	7372	4188	ELEGANT,ACCOMPLISHED		彦
YANN	072,06	2518	10	60404	7363	9030	LATE,QUIET,(SURNAME)		晏
YANN	085,05	3116.0A	08	37161		1439	RIVERSIDE(WITH-L)		沿
YANN	085,07	3241.0A	10	32141	2714	6807	SALIVA		涎
YANN	085,28	3495	31	34112	7	0736	TOSSING OF BILLOWS		灩
YANN	086,08	8746	12	90889	7338	5603	FLAMES	3543	焱
YANN	086,08	3543	12	97877	7394	1056	FLAME	3596	焰
YANN	086,12	3596	16	29789	7394	5625	FLAME	3543	燄
YANN	086,12	3601	16	44331	7399	8801	SWALLOW(BIRD)		燕
YANN	086,16	3618	20	97820		3449	FLAME	3543	爛
YANN	112,07	4291	12	16610	7401	7594	INK-STONE		硯
YANN	139,04	5333.1	10	57017			GLAMOROUS		艳
YANN	139,13	5333	19	57117	7406	7311	GLAMOROUS	6267	艷
YANN	149,09	6176	16	00622	7374	4190	PROVERB		諺
YANN	149,16	6240	23	04631	7364	8803	FEAST,REPOSE	1365	讌

ROM	RAD	TEL	TOT	FC	MAT	OSH	TAG	CR	CHAR
YANN	149,20	6250	27	03634	7370	5083	DECIDE JUDICIALLY		讞
YANN	151,20	6267.1	27	24117	7406	0705	GLAMOROUS		豔
YANN	151,21	6267	28	24117	7406	0735	GLAMOROUS	5333	艷
YANN	154,12	6372.1	19	71806	7405	8133	FALSE		贗
YANN	154,15	6372	22	71806	7405	8212	FALSE		贗
YANN	164,16	6839	23	14631			STRONG(OF TEA)	9433	醶
YANN	164,20	9433	27	16648	7350	6331	STRONG(OF TEA)	6839	釅
YANN	172,04	7159	12	71214	7404	0878	WILD GOOSE	7692	雁
YANN	184,14	7441	23	71732	7391	5938	EAT TO THE FULL		饜
YANN	187,13	7526	23	78386	7367	8010	EXAMINE		驗
YANN	196,04	7692	15	71227	7404	4620	WILD GOOSE	7159	鴈
YANN	196,10	7742	21	67427	7365	4667	QUAIL-LIKE BIRD		鷃
IANG	032,05	8203	08	45130			FINE DUST,BOUNDLESS(SPACE)		块
IANG	037,02	1135	05	50030	7239	5217	CENTER,BEG		央
IANG	078,05	2988	09	15230	7242	5221	CALAMITY		殃
IANG	085,05	3142	08	35130	7243	5223	BOUNDLESS,AGITATED(WIND/CLOUD)		泱
IANG	109,05	8907	10	65030			OBSCURE/DARK		映
IANG	115,05	4441	10	25930	7244	5222	SHOOTS/SPROUTS		秧
IANG	196,05	7699	16	50327	7246	4680	MANDARIN DUCK		鴦
YANG	009,06	0162	08	28251	7248	2545	PRETEND		佯
YANG	032,06	8213	09	48151			CLAY SHEEP BURIED WITH THE DEAD		垟
YANG	060,06	1772	09	28251	7249	2546	WALK BACK AND FORTH		徉
YANG	064,09	2254	12	56027	7259	4492	HURL,TO RAISE		揚
YANG	066,09	2428	13	68240			HURL,RAISE,TO EXPERIENCE	K2254	敭
YANG	072,09	2543	13	66027	7260	4488	RISING SUN/SUNSHINE		暘
YANG	075,09	2799	13	46927	7261	4494	POPLAR,(SURNAME)		楊
YANG	085,06	3152	09	38151	7252	2556	OCEAN,FOREIGN		洋
YANG	086,06	352A	10	98851	7262	2551	SMELT,MOLTEN		烊
YANG	086,09	3568.0A	13	96827	7262	4495	SMELT,MOLTEN	352A	煬
YANG	104,09	4046	14	00127	7263	4499	ULCERS/SORES		瘍
YANG	123,00	5017	06	80501	7247	2541	SHEEP,(SURNAME)		羊
YANG	167,09	9486	17	86127			ORNAMENTS ON HEADSTALL OF HORSE		鍚
YANG	170,04	7122.1	07	76200		1495	SUN,POSITIVE(ELECTRIC.)		阳

ROM	RAD	TEL	TOT	FC	MAT	OSH	TAG	CR	CHAR
YANG	170,09	7122	12	76227	7265	4490	SUN,POSITIVE(ELECTRIC.)		陽
YANG	182,09	7370	18	76212	7266	7843	TOSSED BY WIND OR WAVE,SOAR		颺
YANG	196,06	7766	17	86527			(BIRD)		鴹
YEANG	009,04	0111	06	27220	7267	2147	LOOK UP		仰
YEANG	084,06	8638	10	80517	7251	7803	OXYGEN		氧
YEANG	104,06	4022	11	00151	7255	2558	ITCH	4083	痒
YEANG	104,15	4083	20	00132	7255	5934	ITCH	4022	癢
YEANG	123,04	7402.1	10	80223			TO SUPPORT,KEEP(PETS),GIVE BIRTH		养
YEANG	177,05	7248	14	45530	7245	5220	MARTINGALE		鞅
YEANG	184,06	7402	15	80732	7254	5932	TO SUPPORT,KEEP(PETS),GIVE BIRTH		養
YANQ	061,05	1828	08	95034	7241	5219	DISCONTENTED		怏
YANQ	061,06	1860	10	80331	7250	8541	SICKNESS		恙
YANQ	075,06	2876.1	10	48951			MANNER,SHAPE		样
YANQ	075,11	2876	15	48932	7256	5658	MANNER,SHAPE		樣
YANQ	085,11	3363	14	38132	7257	5659	RIPPLES,D(23RD)	3463	漾
YANQ	085,15	3463	18	38132	7257	5933	RIPPLES	3363	瀁
YANQ	086,09	3568	13	96827	7262	4495	TO ROAST,TO BURN		煬
IAU	017,03	0425.0B	05	77770	7268	1974	CONCAVE		凹
IAU	030,03	0697	06	62032		8822	SHOUT		吆
IAU	030,03	0697.1	06	62032	7283	8879	SHOUT		吢
IAU	030,09	0817	12	61044	7301	9033	GRASSHOPPER CHIRP,MOSQUITO BUZZ		喓
IAU	030,09	0847	12	67020	7494	4367	(INTERJ. OF DOUBT/FRIGHT/OR REGRET)		喲
IAU	037,01	1130	04	20430	7277	5126	DIE PREMATURELY		夭
IAU	038,04	1179	07	42434	7279	5132	MONSTER/PHANTOM		妖
IAU	052,00	1633	03	22730	7282	8878	ONE ON DICE,SMALL	8010.0D	幺
IAU	052,00	8010.0D	03	22730	7282	8821	ONE ON DICE,SMALL	1633	么
IAU	060,13	1797.0C	16	28240	0686	6373	PRAY,INTERCEPT		徼
IAU	113,04	4360	08	32234	7281	5131	CALAMITY FROM TERRESTRIAL DISORDER		祅
IAU	120,03	4766.0A	09	27920	7493	4366	WEIGH		約
IAU	130,09	5212	13	71244	7302	9034	WAIST		腰
IAU	140,09	5529	13	44404		9035	POLYGALA JAPONICA,LUSH(GRASS)		葽
IAU	146,03	6008.0A	09	10404	7300	9032	COERCE,DEMAND		要

ROM	RAD	TEL	TOT	FC	MAT	OSH	TAG	CR	CHAR
IAU	162,13	6700	17	38304	7276	6755	INVITE TO COME		邀
YAU	009,10	0274	12	27274	7285	1012	YAO TRIBE		傜
YAU	032,06	8210	09	40114		0145	EMBANKMENT		垚
YAU	032,09	1031	12	40211	7295	7484	EMPEROR YAO,(SURNAME)		堯
YAU	038,06	1202	09	42413	7269	7702	(SURNAME)		姚
YAU	043,03	1031.1	06	50211			EMPEROR YAO,(SURNAME)		尧
YAU	046,08	1541	11	24727	2585	3593	NAME OF A MOUNTAIN IN HONAN		崤
YAU	046,12	8344	15	24711		7488	STEEP,TO TOWER,HIGH		嶢
YAU	060,10	1791	13	27272	7285	1013	COMPULSORY SERVICE		徭
YAU	064,10	2280	13	52072	7286	1014	SHAKE,TO ROCK		搖
YAU	079,08	3012	12	47247	2586	6279	VIANDS,MIXED		殽
YAU	085,06	3165.0A	09	32113	6149	7703	NAME OF A LAKE		洮
YAU	085,08	3216	11	34127	2587	3595	MISCELLANEOUS/MIXED		淆
YAU	089,00	3641	04	40400	2583	6543	LINES ON A TRIGRAM		爻
YAU	094,10	3734	13	47272	7287	1015	YAO TRIBE	0274	猺
YAU	096,06	3804	10	12113	7270	7690	MOTHER-OF-PEARL	B3852	珧
YAU	096,10	3852	14	17172	7288	1010	(JADE),MOTHER-OF-PEARL,YAO	D3804	瑤
YAU	116,10	4523	15	30772	7289	1017	KILN		窯
YAU	120,11	4925.0A	17	22793	7548	8485	FORCED LABOR,FOLK-SONG		繇
YAU	130,04	5149	08	40227	2584	3592	MEAT DISHES	7413	肴
YAU	149,10	6202	17	07672	7290	1011	RUMOR,POPULAR BALLAD		謠
YAU	159,05	6523	12	57062		1368	LIGHT CARRIAGE		軺
YAU	162,10	6674	14	37307	7291	6608	FAR/FAR AWAY		遙
YAU	167,06	6903	14	82113	6289	7691	WEEDING TOOL,(SURNAME)		銚
YAU	182,10	7371	19	27710	7292	7831	FLOATING IN THE AIR		颻
YAU	184,08	7413	16	84727	2588	3594	MEAT DISHES	5149	餚
YAU	195,10	766B	21	22372	7293	1016	RAY(FISH)		鰩
YEAU	030,06	0747	09	60048	7298	6526	TO BITE	7885	咬
YEAU	038,12	1290.0B	15	44411	3086		TENDER AND WEAK		嬈
YEAU	075,04	2641	08	40609	7297	1580	DARK AND QUIET,DISAPPEAR		杳
YEAU	078,04	2986	08	12234	7280	5130	DIE PREMATURELY	1130.0A	殀
YEAU	116,05	4505	10	30608	7296	1735	DEEP		窅
YEAU	116,05	4507	10	30727	7274	4840	QUIET AND ELEGANT,DEEP		窈

ROM	RAD	TEL	TOT	FC	MAT	OSH	TAG	CR	CHAR
YEAU	116,06	9000	11	30408			DARK,DEEP,SOUTHEAST CORNER OF ROOM		突
YEAU	134,04	5276	10	20777	7299	1061	TO SCOOP		舀
YEAU	196,11	7745	22	63327			CRY OF HEN PHEASANT		鷂
YEAU	211,06	7885	21	20748	7298	6525	BITE	0747	齩
YAW	072,14	2565	18	67014	7305	0948	GLORIOUS,DAZZLE		曜
YAW	086,14	3613	18	97814	5693		GLORIOUS,BRILLIANT	5069	燿
YAW	104,03	4061.1A	08	00114			MALARIA		疟
YAW	104,09	4061.0A	14	00114	4735	0858	MALARIA		瘧
YAW	124,14	5069	20	97214	7306	0955	GLORIOUS/BRILLIANT	3613	耀
YAW	140,09	5522	13	44927	7501	4368	MEDICINE/DRUG	5673	葯
YAW	140,15	5673	19	44904	7501	5418	MEDICINE/DRUG	5522	藥
YAW	146,03	6008	09	10404	7300	9032	TO WANT,WILL,IMPORTANT		要
YAW	149,17	9302	24	08627			TO ERR IN SPEECH		論
YAW	167,04	7011.1	12	87120			KEY		鉥
YAW	167,17	7011	25	88127	7500	3803	KEY		鑰
YAW	196,10	7740	21	26727	7294	4609	SPARROW HAWK/ACCIPITER NISUS		鷂
IE	030,12	0888	15	64⁰18	3066	0584	CHOKE		噎
IE	064,08	2227	11	50047	3032	6493	TUCK (IN)		掖
IE	128,03	5102	09	17127	7307	2195	(FINAL PART.),(PHONETIC)		耶
IE	142,17	9245	23	57127			AMMOPHILA INFESTA		蠮
YE	046,07	1483	10	27727			PLACE NAME	3815	嶁
YE	064,07	8434	10	57027	7308	2211	GESTICULATE,PLAY ANTICS	8448	揶
YE	064,09	8448	12	57027	7308	2197	GESTICULATE,PLAY ANTICS	8434	挪
YE	075,04	8541.0A	08	41940	7217	3327	COCONUT PALM	2794	枒
YE	075,07	2794.1	11	47927	7309		COCONUT PALM		椰
YE	075,09	2794	13	47927	7309	2198	COCONUT PALM		楲
YE	088,02	3639.1	06	80202			OLD GENTLEMAN,GRANDPA/ETC.		爷
YE	088,09	3639	13	80127	7310	2199	OLD GENTLEMAN,GRANDPA/ETC.		爺
YE	096,07	3815	11	17127	7311	2210	PLACE NAME	1483	瑘
YE	128,03	5102.0A	09	17127	7307	2195	(PHONETIC)		耶
YEE	005,02	0048	03	44712	7312	7418	ALSO		也
YEE	015,05	0396	07	33160	7313	1462	SMELT		冶
YEE	030,03	8121	06	64⁰12					吧

ROM	RAD	TEL	TOT	FC	MAT	OSH	TAG	CR	CHAR
YEE	166,04	6851	11	67122	7314	3082	WILD		野
YEH	001,04	2814.1	05	32100			BUSINESS/OCCUPATION		业
YEH	030,02	0673	05	64000			ABBR. OF 5509 AND 2814	5509	叶
YEH	030,06	0754.0B	09	66000	7396	1893	TO CHOKE(IN CRYING)		咽
YEH	036,05	1123	08	00247	7315	6492	NIGHT		夜
YEH	064,06	2167.0A	09	55006	1419	7054	DRAG		拽
YEH	064,14	8476	17	51034			TO PRESS DOWN		擪
YEH	072,09	2539	13	66027	7323	4385	HOT		曷
YEH	072,12	8518	16	64054		2608	BRIGHT LIGHT,TO SPARKLE		曄
YEH	073,02	2576.0A	06	50006	3008		DRAG		曳
YEH	075,09	2814	13	32904	7321	5488	BUSINESS/OCCUPATION		業
YEH	085,08	3210	11	30147	3033	6495	LIQUID		液
YEH	086,12	8763	16	94854	7329		BLAZE OF FIRE,GLORIOUS		燁
YEH	130,08	5199.0A	12	70247	3034	6494	ARMPIT		腋
YEH	140,09	5509	13	44904	7319	5297	LEAF,PAGE,(SURNAME)	0673	葉
YEH	149,09	6181	16	06627	7324	4382	TO VISIT(A SUPERIOR)		謁
YEH	163,13	6777	16	37927	7322	2238	(SURNAME),NAME OF ANCIENT DISTRICT		鄴
YEH	176,14	7243	23	71601	7328		DIMPLE		靨
YEH	181,00	7306	09	10800	7316	8242	PAGE		頁
YEH	184,10	7428	18	84717	7326	0740	CARRY FOOD TO LABORERS IN THE FIELD		饁
IN	030,09	0819	12	60061	7419	1519	DUMB		喑
IN	031,03	0936	06	60430	7407	1891	BECAUSE,REASON		因
IN	032,06	1025.1	09	10104	7414	0194	TO DAM/CLOSE,MOUND,BURY		垔
IN	032,09	1025	12	41114	7414	0195	TO DAM/CLOSE,MOUND,BURY	7123	堙
IN	038,06	1215	09	46400	7408	1899	MARRIAGE CONNECTIONS		姻
IN	038,08	1243	11	42400	7408	2083	MARRIAGE CONNECTIONS	1215	婣
IN	061,09	1944	12	90061	7420	1522	PEACEFUL,SOLEMN		愔
IN	061,10	1963	14	27334	7424	8667	SOLICITOUS		慇
IN	079,06	3009	10	27247	7423	6285	(SURNAME),DYNASTY,FLOURISHING		殷
IN	084,06	3052	10	80617	7409		GENERATIVE FORCES,MAGIC EMANATION	4824	氤
IN	085,09	3281	12	31114	7415	0199	SUBMERGED,OBSCURED		湮
IN	104,09	4052	14	00161	7421	1525	DUMB	0819	瘖
IN	113,09	4392	13	31214	7416	0198	SACRIFICE		禋

ROM	RAD	TEL	TOT	FC	MAT	OSH	TAG	CR	CHAR
IN	120,06	4824	12	26900	7410	1898	GENERATIVE FORCE,MAGIC EMANATION	3052	絪
IN	140,06	5419	10	44600	7411	1900	CUSHION,SKIMMIA JAPONICA		茵
IN	145,06	5936	11	36200	7412	1894	MAT,UNDERCLOTHING		裀
IN	167,06	7920	14	86100		1892	INDIUM		銦
IN	169,09	7058	17	77146		3441	INNER GATES,(SURNAME)		闉
IN	170,04	7113.1	07	77220			CLOUDY,SHADY,NEGATIVE(ELECTRIC.)		阴
IN	170,08	7113	11	78231	7444	8865	CLOUDY,SHADY,NEGATIVE(ELECTRIC.)		陰
IN	170,09	7123	12	71214	7414	0196	TO DAM/CLOSE,MOUND,BURY	1025	陻
IN	170,09	7113.2	12	78231	7444	8830	CLOUDY,SHADY,NEGATIVE(ELECTRIC.)		陰
IN	180,00	7299	09	00601	7418	1518	SOUND		音
IN	187,06	7484	16	76300	7413		IRON-GREY(AS A HORSE)		駰
YN	030,04	0692	07	68027	7425	2844	TO HUM,MOAN		吟
YN	030,15	0910	18	66661	7443	1076	INSINCERE,STUPID		嚚
YN	032,06	0995	09	47132	7431	5898	BANK		垠
YN	036,10	1126	13	27806	7427	8345	LATE AT NIGHT		夤
YN	040,08	1377	11	30806	7426	8343	3-5 A.M.,3RD EARTH'S BRANCH		寅
YN	046,08	8337	11	22109		0373	HIGH,RUGGED MOUNTAINS,STEEP		崟
YN	085,08	3230	11	32114	7434	0312	OBSCENE		淫
YN	094,07	3711	10	40261	7436	1157	SNARLING OF DOGS		狺
YN	149,08	6147	15	77601	7437	3452	SPEAK GENTLY,RESPECTFUL,(SURNAME)		誾
YN	163,11	6769	14	47127	7442	2161	NAME OF A HSIEN IN CHEKIANG		鄞
YN	167,06	6892	14	87132	7432	5899	SILVER		銀
YN	173,11	7214	19	10114	7435	0313	HEAVY RAIN		霪
YN	211,04	7879	19	22721	7453	2015	GUMS		齗
YN	211,06	7883	21	27732	3333	5901	GUMS	8186	齦
YIIN	030,04	067B	07	62000	5728		(PHONETIC)/IND- AS IN INDOLE		吲
YIIN	044,01	1438	04	17507	7439	4242	(SURNAME),TO RULE		尹
YIIN	054,00	1692	03	10400	7441	6788	MOVE ON		廴
YIIN	057,01	1714	04	12200	7429	1979	TO LEAD		引
YIIN	062,11	8414	15	33850			LONG SPEAR		戭
YIIN	075,17	2935	21	72904	7449	5410	BEVEL,CORRECTING		檃
YIIN	079,06	3009.0B	10	2724	7423	6285	ROLL OF THUNDER		殷
YIIN	104,12	4090.1	17	00137			ADDICTION,CRAVING		癮

ROM	RAD	TEL	TOT	FC	MAT	OSH	TAG	CR	CHAR
YIIN	104,17	4090	22	00137	7450	8550	ADDICTION,CRAVING		癮
YIIN	142,04	5727	10	52100	7430	1982	EARTHWORM		蚓
YIIN	170,09	7148.1	12	77237		8554	CONCEAL/CONCEALED		隱
YIIN	170,14	7148	17	72237	7448	8549	CONCEAL/CONCEALED		隱
YIIN	177,04	7250	13	42500		1980	TRACES(OF A CARRIAGE)		靷
YIIN	184,04	7390	12	87782	7454	4924	DRINK		飲
YINN	026,04	0603	06	77720	7451	2124	TO PRINT		印
YINN	053,11	1677	14	00232	7446	8866	SHADE	5593	廕
YINN	061,12	2026	16	43333	7455	8652	INJURED,MOREOVER,PREFERABLY		憖
YINN	116,09	4518	14	30601	7422	1527	CELLAR		窨
YINN	130,05	5255	09	22010	7452	7067	HEIR,INHERIT		胤
YINN	140,06	537E	10	44727			INDENE		茚
YINN	140,11	5593	15	44231	7446	8867	SHADE	1677	蔭
ING	030,17	0919	20	66044	7458	9056	CALLING OF BIRDS		嚶
ING	038,09	1260	12	44434			BEAUTY		媖
ING	038,10	8294	13	99404		9024	ATTENTIVELY/CAREFULLY		嫈
ING	038,14	1305	17	66404	7457	9054	INFANT		嬰
ING	053,04	2019.1	07	00219			OUGHT		应
ING	061,13	2019	17	00231	7477	8555	OUGHT		應
ING	064,17	2375	20	56044	7459	9057	OPPOSE,TO ATTACK		攖
ING	075,17	2937	21	46944	7460	9058	CHERRY		櫻
ING	086,09	8751	13	94834			(PERSON)		煐
ING	096,09	3841	13	14134	7490	5225	(CRYSTAL),LUSTROUS		瑛
ING	096,17	3892	21	16144	7461	9055	NECKLACE		瓔
ING	098,10	3915	15	99717			EARTHEN JAR WITH LONG NECK	4975	甇
ING	098,14	3925	19	66717	7470	7945	EARTHEN JAR WITH SMALL MOUTH	4981	甖
ING	120,09	9069	15	24934			TASSEL OF HAT	4964	縈
ING	120,17	4964	23	26944	7463	9059	TASSEL OF HAT		纓
ING	121,10	4975	16	99772	7470	1008	EARTHEN JAR WITH LONG NECK	3915	罃
ING	121,14	4981	20	66772	7470	1019	EARTHEN JAR WITH SMALL MOUTH	3925	罌
ING	130,13	5235	17	00227	7478	3604	BREAST,RECEIVE		膺
ING	140,05	5391	09	44530	7489	5224	BRAVE,ENGLISH,(SURNAME)		英
ING	167,09	9487	17	84134			JINGLING OF BELLS		鍈

ROM	RAD	TEL	TOT	FC	MAT	OSH	TAG	CR	CHAR
ING	173,09	9545	17	10430		5227	SLEET,SNOWFLAKES		
ING	180,09	7303	18	04634			MUSIC OF LEGENDARY EMPEROR KUH		
ING	196,10	7727	21	99327	7472	4674	GOLDEN ORIOLE		
ING	196,13	7751	24	00327	7479	4670	EAGLE		
ING	196,17	7761	28	67427	7464	4668	PARROT		
YNG	032,10	1041	13	99104	7466	0200	A GRAVE		
YNG	038,13	1299	16	00217	7480	7899	PROFIT,WIN,FULL/OVERPLUS	K6366	
YNG	075,09	2819	13	47917	7475	0702	PILLAR		
YNG	085,15	8714	18	39113			CLEAR/LIMPID(OF WATER)		
YNG	085,16	3467	19	30117	7481	7900	OCEAN		
YNG	085,16	3470	19	39193			EDDY,SMALL RIVER		
YNG	086,10	3576	14	99809	7468	5613	GLIMMER,POLYEONATUM OFFICINALE		
YNG	086,13	3602	17	99606	7467	1473	CAMP,NOURISHMENT,TO MANAGE		
YNG	096,10	3853	14	99103	7469	0351	LUSTER OF GEMS		
YNG	108,04	4134	09	77107	7474	0701	FULL/FILLED		
YNG	118,16	9024	22	88217	7482		TUBE TO HOLD CHOPSTICKS	4714	
YNG	118,20	4714	26	88217		7897	SLENDER BASKET FOR CHOPSTICKS	9024	
YNG	120,10	4896	16	99903	7587	8461	WIND AROUND		
YNG	142,08	5859.1	14	56116			FLY/MUSCA		
YNG	142,10	5821	16	99136	7471	8926	FIREFLY		
YNG	142,13	5859	19	57117	7476	7340	FLY/MUSCA		
YNG	149,10	619A	17	99601			HUMMING SOUND		
YNG	154,13	6366	20	00217	7483	7896	PROFIT,WIN	K1299	
YNG	162,04	6601	08	37302	7473	6643	TO WELCOME		
YNG	167,10	9496	18	99109			(METAL UTENSIL)		
YIING	059,12	1758	15	62922	7484	4185	IMAGE,SHADOW		
YIING	085,11	3379	15	21286		8295	NAME OF A RIVER		
YIING	094,07	371B	10	41211			HUNTING/CHASE		
YIING	104,17	4086	22	00144	7462	9060	GOITRE,KNOB ON TREE		
YIING	115,11	4481	16	21986	7486	8293	CLEVER/GIFTED	7336	
YIING	163,07	6747	10	67127	7486	2159	NAME OF AN ANCIENT CITY		
YIING	181,07	7336	16	21986	7485		CLEVER/GIFTED	4481	
YINQ	038,10	1262	13	79244	7492	9039	MAID ESCORTING BRIDE TO NEW HOME		

ROM	RAD	TEL	TOT	FC	MAT	OSH	TAG	CR	CHAR
YINQ	053,04	2019.1A	07	00219			TO ANSWER,(SURNAME)		应
YINQ	061,13	2019.0A	17	00231	7477	8555	TO ANSWER,(SURNAME)	A6224	應
YINQ	072,05	2503	09	65034	7488	5218	SHINE,REFLECT		映
YINQ	072,09	2527	13	64034	7488	5226	SHINE,REFLECT	2503	暎
YINQ	085,07	8678	10	36114			MUD/MIRE		涅
YINQ	109,05	8907.0A	10	65030			LOOK		暎
YINQ	112,07	4289	12	11646	7487	6576	HARD		硬
YINQ	149,13	6224	20	00261		1160	TO ANSWER	A2019.0A	譍
YINQ	162,04	6601.0A	08	37302	7473	6643	TO CALL FOR		迎
YINQ	195,06	764D	17	27327			SUCKER/ECHENEIA NOUCRATES		鰤
IONG	009,05	0096.0A	07	27220			HIRE,SERVANT	0276	佣
IONG	009,11	0276	13	20227	7577	3749	HIRE,SERVANT	0096.0A	傭
IONG	030,10	8157	13	62017			TO CHOKE		喠
IONG	032,11	1066	14	40127	7578	3746	FORTIFIED WALL		墉
IONG	032,13	1085	16	00104	7555		STOP UP,OBSTRUCT		壅
IONG	053,08	1661	11	00227	7576	3745	ORDINARY,TO USE		庸
IONG	053,18	1688	21	00214		0909	HARMONIOUS	A7167	龎
IONG	061,11	1986	14	90027	7579	3748	CARELESS		慵
IONG	064,05	2340.1	08	57020			CROWDED,TO SUPPORT		拥
IONG	064,13	2340	16	50014		0888	CROWDED,TO SUPPORT		擁
IONG	085,18	3489	21	30114	7552	0908	SLUICE,NAME OF A RIVER		澭
IONG	104,05	4092.1	10	00127			CARBUNCLE		疿
IONG	104,18	4092	23	00114	7553	0910	CARBUNCLE		癰
IONG	140,13	557E	17	44714	7558		IPOMAEA AQUATICA		蕹
IONG	163,03	6716	10	22717	7554	7305	HARMONIOUS	A7167	邕
IONG	163,11	6767	14	07227		2213	NAME OF A FEUDAL STATE,(SURNAME)		鄘
IONG	167,11	6978	19	80127	7580	3747	LARGE BELL		鏞
IONG	172,05	7167	13	00714	7554	0886	HARMONIOUS,(SURNAME)	A6716	雍
IONG	172,10	7178	18	20714	7551	0907	HARMONIOUS	A7167	雝
IONG	184,13	7438	22	00732	7559	5935	FIRST MEAL OF THE DAY,DRESSED FOOD		饔
YONG	030,09	0806	12	66027	7565	4088	BREATHING(OF FISH)		喁
YONG	053,08	1661.0A	11	00227	7576	3745	ORDINARY,TO USE		庸
YONG	061,11	1986.0A	14	90027	7579	3748	CARELESS		慵

ROM	RAD	TEL	TOT	FC	MAT	OSH	TAG	CR	CHAR
YONG	085,14	8713	17	39189	7588		REVOLVE,CURL IN EDDIES		濴
YONG	167,11	6978.0A	19	80127	7580	3747	LARGE BELL		鏞
YONG	167,14	9513	22	89194			SOUND OF BELLS		鑅
YONG	181,09	9581	18	61286		8278	STERN,JUST,GREAT		顒
YONG	195,11	766T	22	20327			BIGHEAD/ARISTICHTHYS NOBILIS		鱅
YEONG	009,07	0197	09	27227	7569	3718	WOODEN FIGURES BURIED WITH THE DEAD		俑
YEONG	019,07	0516	09	17427	7571	4858	BRAVE		勇
YEONG	030,05	0737	08	63032	7591	5653	SING	6102	咏
YEONG	032,07	8223	10	47127	7570		RAISED PATH		埇
YEONG	032,13	1085.0A	16	00104	7555	0184	STOP UP,OBSTRUCT		壅
YEONG	061,07	1960.1	11	17332	7573	8628	URGE/INCITE		恿
YEONG	061,10	1960	14	37332	7573	8629	URGE/INCITE	5274.0A	慂
YEONG	064,05	2340.1A	08	57020		3709	TO SUPPORT,EMBRACE		拥
YEONG	064,13	2340.0A	16	50014	7556	0888	TO SUPPORT,TO EMBRACE		擁
YEONG	085,01	3057	05	30232	7589	5652	PERPETUAL(LY)		永
YEONG	085,05	3144	08	33132	7590	5656	SWIMMING		泳
YEONG	085,07	8673	10	37127	7572	3722	BUBBLE UP/RUSH FORTH	3279	涌
YEONG	085,09	3279	12	37127	7572	4860	BUBBLE UP,RUSH FORTH	8673	湧
YEONG	101,02	3941	07	17227	7568	3715	(MEASURE) 5 PECKS,NINGPO		甬
YEONG	130,13	5250	17	70214		0889	TUMOR		臃
YEONG	134,02	5274.0A	09	77437	7609	5229	URGE,INCITE	1960	臾
YEONG	142,07	5769	13	57127	7574	3721	CHRYSALIS/PUPA		蛹
YEONG	149,05	6102	12	03632	7591	5654	SING	0737	詠
YEONG	157,07	6429	14	67127	7575	3716	LEAP	6445	踊
YEONG	157,09	6445	16	67127	7575	4859	LEAP	6429	踴
YEONG	195,07	764T	18	27327			DUSKY FLATHEAD/PLATYCEPHALUS SP.		鯒
YONQ	009,05	0096	07	27220		3708	COMMISSION(FOR MIDDLEMAN)		佣
YONQ	032,10	1055	13	43168			UNEASY		塎
YONQ	101,00	3938	05	77220	7567	3707	TO USE		用
YONQ	113,11	8982	16	99901			(SACRIFICE)		禜
YONQ	172,05	7167.0A	13	00714	7554	0886	NAME OF AN ANCIENT DISTRICT		雍
IO	030,08	079A	11	60027		3680	(EXCLAMATORY PART.)		唷
IOU	009,04	0327.1	06	23214			SUPERIOR		优

ROM	RAD	TEL	TOT	FC	MAT	OSH	TAG	CR	CHAR
IOU	009,15	0327	17	21247	7509	6479	SUPERIOR		優
IOU	030,05	0717	08	64027	7545	4836	BLEATING OF THE DEER		呦
IOU	052,06	1636	09	22770	7505	1005	QUIET/SECLUDED		幽
IOU	061,04	1992.1	07	93014			WORRIED		忱
IOU	061,07	1890	11	28334	7520	8670	AT EASE,SAD,LONG (IN TIME)		悠
IOU	061,11	1992	15	11407	7508	6478	WORRIED		憂
IOU	075,15	8602	19	41947	7510		HARROW	5099	檀
IOU	085,11	8703	14	38134			FLOWING		滺
IOU	127,15	5099	21	51947	7510	6481	HARROW	8602	耰
IOU	163,15	9416	18	17427			PLACE NAME		鄾
IOU	198,02	7776	13	00711	7506	7191	FEMALE DEER		麀
YOU	031,04	0952.0A	07	60214	4788	1922	DECOY		囮
YOU	043,01	1429	04	43010	7511	7714	ESPECIALLY		尤
YOU	064,09	2246.0A	12	58021	7633	8974	SCOOP OUT (GRAIN)		揄
YOU	066,03	2394	07	28240	7519	6319	PLACE,(EXPLETIVE),WALK FAST		攸
YOU	070,05	2458	09	08247	7521	3113	SCALLOPS ALONG LOWER EDGE OF FLAG		斿
YOU	075,09	2811	13	48961			QUERCUS GLANDULIFERA		梄
YOU	085,05	3111	08	35160	7515	1842	OIL,SLY		油
YOU	085,09	3266	12	38147	7522	3115	SWIM,ROAM/TRAVEL	D6662	游
YOU	094,04	3730.1	07	43214		7717	AS IF/STILL,JEW,TO SCHEME		犹
YOU	094,09	3730	12	48261	7528	1970	AS IF/STILL,JEW,TO SCHEME	G3731	猶
YOU	094,09	3731	12	83634	7530	5073	TO SCHEME,CONSULT WITH	C3730	猷
YOU	102,00	3945	05	50600	7513	1830	FROM,IT IS FOR...TO,FOLLOW		由
YOU	104,04	4001	09	00114	7512	7722	WART,NODULE		疣
YOU	120,11	4925	17	22793	7548	8485	CAUSE,MEANS		繇
YOU	130,04	4001.1	08	73214	7512	7716	WART,NODULE		肬
YOU	140,12	5607	16	44261		1971	CARYOPTERIS DIVARICATA		蕕
YOU	140,17	5696	21	44793			LUXURIANT,DENSE		蕤
YOU	142,05	5740	11	55160	7516	1840	HOUSE CENTIPEDE		蚰
YOU	142,09	5812	15	58147	7523	3114	EPHEMERA STRIGATA		蝣
YOU	149,04	9283	11	03614		7715	MISTAKE,FAULT		訧
YOU	159,09	6557	16	58061	7531	1969	LIGHT CARRIAGE,TRIFLING		輶
YOU	162,08	9375	12	31306			JOYOUS,SATISFIED,DISTANT		迪

ROM	RAD	TEL	TOT	FC	MAT	OSH	TAG		CR	CHAR
YOU	162,09	6662	13	38304	7524	6677	TO TRAVEL/ROAM		B3266	遊
YOU	163,05	6755.1	08	57627			TO POST/MAIL			邮
YOU	163,08	6755	11	27127	7525	2160	TO POST/MAIL			郵
YOU	163,09	6755.2	12	27727			TO POST/MAIL			鈾
YOU	167,05	6914	13	85160		1831	URANIUM			魷
YOU	195,04	7626	15	23314			CUTTLEFISH			鮋
YOU	195,05	763C	16	25360			HELICOLENUS MARMORATUS			鼬
YOU	208,05	7860	18	75716	7518	6829	SIBERIAN WEASEL,POLECAT			卣
YEOU	025,05	0596	07	21600		1949	WINE CONTAINER			友
YEOU	029,02	0645	04	40047	7540	6113	FRIEND			懮
YEOU	061,15	8407	18	91047			RELAXED,GRIEVOUS			有
YEOU	074,02	2589	06	40227	7533	3582	HAVE,THERE IS			櫾
YEOU	075,11	2881	15	41936			RITUAL BONFIRE			牖
YEOU	091,11	3657	15	20027			LATTICE WINDOW,ENLIGHTEN			牗
YEOU	091,11	3657.1	15	23027	7507	3742	LATTICE WINDOW,ENLIGHTEN			羑
YEOU	123,03	5020	09	80407	7532	4971	TO LEAD			莠
YEOU	140,07	5452	11	44227	7537	4731	SETARIA VIRIDIS,VICIOUS			酉
YEOU	164,00	6788	07	10600	7526	1963	10TH EARTH'S BRANCH,5-7 P.M.			銪
YEOU	167,06	7921	14	84127		3583	EUROPIUM			黝
YEOU	203,05	7821	17	64327	7547	4839	BLACK,DARK GREEN			佑
YOW	009,05	0147	07	24260	7542	1123	BLESS,PROTECT			侑
YOW	009,06	0176	08	24227	7534	3584	URGE TO EAT			又
YOW	029,00	0642	02	77400	7539	6059	AGAIN			右
YOW	030,02	0671	05	40600	7541	1122	RIGHT(-HAND)			囿
YOW	031,06	0943	09	60227	7535	1883	TO LIMIT,PARK			宥
YOW	040,06	1359	09	30227	7536	3591	FORGIVE,HELP,PROFOUND			幼
YOW	052,02	1635	05	24727	7544	4835	YOUNG			柚
YOW	075,05	2680	09	45960	7514	1837	POMELO			祐
YOW	113,05	4368	09	34260	7543	1124	PROTECT			蚴
YOW	142,05	574F	11	54127			LARVA			褏
YOW	145,09	5946	15	00732	2802	5892	ELABORATELY DRESSED			誘
YOW	149,07	6131	14	02627	7538	4729	ENTICE,TEMPT			釉
YOW	165,05	6848	12	25960	7517	1838	GLAZE(OF PORCELAIN)			

ROM	RAD	TEL	TOT	FC	MAT	OSH	TAG	CR	CHAR
YOW	196,05	769C	16	27727			(DUCK)		
IU	076,09	8617	13	87282		4965	SING		
IU	085,08	3226	11	38133	7645	8957	SILT		
IU	118,08	4626	14	88233			BAMBOO WITH THIN/WIDE LEAVES		
IU	120,03	4768	09	21940	7597	3311	TWIST,CORD,(SURNAME)		
IU	162,03	6596	07	31304	7599	6681	LITERAL-MINDED		
IU	195,07	764L	18	28391			LABRACOGLOSSA ARGENTIVENTRIS		
YU	001,03	5280.1B	04	21127			(INTERROG. PART.)		
YU	006,03	0056	04	17202	7601	3081	I		
YU	007,01	2456.2	03	10207	7643	4548	AT/IN,IN REGARD TO		
YU	007,01	0060	03	10400	7592	3306	AT/IN,(SURMANE)	A2456	
YU	009,04	8024	06	27222	7602		HANDSOME AND FAIR	1184	
YU	009,05	0151	07	80904	7605	8499	I/ME,REMAINDER	D7411	
YU	009,07	0205	09	80221	7628	2900	(SURNAME),ACCEDE	0358	
YU	011,07	0358	09	80232	7628	8963	(SURNAME),ACCEDE	0205	
YU	030,09	0806.0A	12	66027	7565	4088	WHISPER		
YU	032,03	0962	06	41140	7593	3307	DIKE		
YU	032,06	8216	09	43141			DIKE	0962	
YU	038,04	1184	07	47422	7602		HANDSOME/FAIR	8024	
YU	038,07	1225	10	46434	7647	5107	AMUSE		
YU	038,09	8295	12	48421	7630	8977	TO SLIGHT,ENJOY		
YU	046,09	1549	12	22221			NAME OF A MOUNTAIN		
YU	046,09	1525	12	26727	7623	4087	MOUNTAIN RANGE		
YU	061,09	1946	13	60332	7624	8633	STUPID		
YU	061,09	1938	12	98021	7631	8968	PLEASED		
YU	064,04	2456.1	07	58033	7643	8955	AT/IN,IN REGARD TO		
YU	064,09	2246	12	58021	7633	8974	LET HANGING,DRAW OUT		
YU	070,04	2456	08	08233	7643	8956	AT/IN,IN REGARD TO	A006D	
YU	070,15	2474	19	08281	7619	8063	BANNER WITH FALCONS,MUSSED UP HAIR		
YU	075,03	8533	07	41940			TUB,BOWL		
YU	075,09	8573	13	47937			(TREE)		
YU	075,09	2810	13	48921	7634	8975	ELM		
YU	076,14	2968	18	77882	7616	4961	(INTERROG. PART.)	5280.0B	

鷞 歈 淤 篎 紆 迃 鵌 与 予 亏 于 伃 余 俞 兪 唹 圩 埠 妤 娛 媮 萮 崳 嵎 愚 愉 捈 揄 於 旟 杅 楈 榆 歟

ROM	RAD	TEL	TOT	FC	MAT	OSH	TAG	CR	CHAR
YU	085,09	3254	12	38121	7635	8978	CHUNGKING		渝
YU	085,11	3342	14	37136	7669	8775	TO FISH,FISHERMAN		漁
YU	091,09	8778.0A	13	28021		8973	SHORT BOARD/PLANK		牏
YU	094,07	371A	10	48294			ARMADILLO		狳
YU	096,03	8818	07	11140			STONE WHICH RESEMBLES JADE		玗
YU	096,09	3842	13	18121	7636	8964	LUSTER OF GEMS,EXCELLENCE		瑜
YU	096,14	3889	18	17181			(GEM)		璵
YU	102,07	3974	12	80609	7606	1819	CULTIVATED FIELD		畬
YU	108,03	4130	08	10107	7595	0693	CONTAINER,CUP		盂
YU	114,04	4417	09	60227	7621	4086	DISTRICT,(PLACE)		禺
YU	116,09	4521	14	30221		8980	HOLE IN A WALL		窬
YU	118,03	4556	09	88401	7596	3315	(MUS. INSTR.)		竽
YU	123,09	9092	15	88521			BLACK RAM		羭
YU	130,09	5208	13	77237	7612	5231	FAT ON BELLY,RICH,FERTILE		腴
YU	134,02	5274	09	77437	7609	5229	A MOMENT/LITTLE WHILE,(SURNAME)		臾
YU	134,03	5275	09	77447	7614	2800	TO LIFT/RAISE		舁
YU	134,07	5280.0B	14	77801	7615	8059	(INTERROG. PART.)	2968	與
YU	140,07	5713	13	21234	7648	5108	FOREWARNED,WORRY,PEACE		虞
YU	140,08	5510.0A	12	44233	7397	8959	FADE(AS OF PEOPLE)		菸
YU	140,09	550D	13	44221			MOINGA OLIFERA		萮
YU	140,09	5505	13	44437		5234	CORNELIAN CHERRY		萸
YU	140,12	556J	16	44123			ALISMA PLANTAGS		蕍
YU	142,09	9227	15	58121	7638A	8975	SNAIL		蝓
YU	145,09	9259	14	38221	7639	8971	LOOSE GARMENT		褕
YU	147,09	6022	16	86210		7616	PASSIONATELY DESIRE		覦
YU	149,09	6161	16	07637	7613	5230	FLATTER		諛
YU	157,09	6444	16	68121	7642	8965	JUMP OVER,EXCEED	6661	踰
YU	159,10	6559	17	77801	7168	8058	SEDAN CHAIR,WORLD,CARRIAGE	A9367	輿
YU	159,14	9367	21	77506	7168		SEDAN CHAIR	A6559	轝
YU	162,09	6661	13	38302	7642	6785	JUMP OVER,EXCEED		逾
YU	163,03	9386	06	17427		2208	(SURNAME),PLACE NAME		邘
YU	167,07	6918	15	81161	7652	1227	HOE		鋙
YU	170,09	7126	12	76227	7626	4090	CORNER		隅

ROM	RAD	TEL	TOT	FC	MAT	OSH	TAG	CR	CHAR
YU	170,09	9535	12	78221		8969	JUMP OVER,EXCEED	6661	踰
YU	173,03	7184	11	10207	7663	4556	SUMMER SACRIFICE FOR RAIN		雩
YU	184,07	7411	15	88794	7608	8502	REMAINDER	B0151	餘
YU	195,00	7625	11	27336	7668	8773	FISH		魚
YU	195,04	762E	15	24322			BARRACUDAS/SPHYRAENA SP.		魣
YU	198,14	779D	25	00281			WAPITI		麌
YEU	001,03	5280.1	04	21127			WITH,AND,GIVE		与
YEU	006,03	0056.0A	04	17202	7601	3081	TO GIVE	C5280	予
YEU	009,07	8049	09	26234		5105	BIG		俣
YEU	009,11	0279	13	21216	7654	0793	HUNCHBACKED		傴
YEU	030,13	8175	16	61034			STAG/BUCK,HERD	7781	嘆
YEU	030,13	0889	16	67034	7657	5024	MOAN		噢
YEU	031,07	0945	10	60601	7649	1867	IMPRISON		圄
YEU	031,08	0947	11	60401	7659	1877	FRONTIER,STABLE,GROOM,		圉
YEU	032,14	8260	17	47181			ISLET	1546	塸
YEU	040,03	1342	06	30401	7594	3313	UNIVERSE,ROOM		宇
YEU	040,10	1398	13	30232			USELESS,WEAK,BAD		寙
YEU	046,03	1546.1	06	21727			ISLET		屿
YEU	046,14	1546	17	27781	2853	8061	ISLET		嶼
YEU	053,09	1662	12	00237	7610	5232	(SURNAME),NAME OF A MOUNTAIN		庾
YEU	066,07	2409	11	18640		6314	(ANCIENT MUS. INSTR.)		敔
YEU	075,09	8575	13	42927			(SURNAME),(TREE)		楀
YEU	096,09	3846	13	12127		4089	(CHALCEDONY)		瑀
YEU	104,09	4049	14	00137	7611	5233	MALTREAT(AS PRISONERS)		瘐
YEU	114,04	4416	09	20227	7620	4080	NAME OF AN EMPEROR		禹
YEU	116,10	4524	15	30232	7660	4992	USELESS,WEAK,BAD		窳
YEU	124,00	5038	06	17120	7658	3385	FEATHER		羽
YEU	134,07	5280	14	77801	7615	8059	WITH,AND,GIVE		與
YEU	149,07	6133	14	01661	7651	1230	SPEECH,DIALECT/LANGUAGE		語
YEU	173,00	7183	08	10227	7662	4019	RAIN		雨
YEU	198,07	7781	18	00430		5109	STAG/BUCK,HERD	8175	麌
YEU	211,07	7886	22	21761	7653	1228	IRREGULAR TEETH		齵
YUH	001,03	5280.1A	04	21127			TAKE PART IN		与

ROM	RAD	TEL	TOT	FC	MAT	OSH	TAG	CR	CHAR
YUH	030,03	0675	06	61040			IMPLORE	4715	呼
YUH	030,09	0827	12	68021	7629	8966	ALLEGORY		喻
YUH	032,08	8230	11	40127			FERTILE SOIL		堉
YUH	032,08	1008	11	43150	7676	6962	REGION		域
YUH	038,11	1277	14	41416	7655	0801	OLD WOMAN,BROOD OVER,PROTECT		嫗
YUH	040,09	1384	12	30227	7622	4094	RESIDE,RESIDENCE		寓
YUH	041,08	1414.0A	11	74200	7111	3222	(SURNAME)		尉
YUH	046,07	1502	10	28768	7670	1381	VALLEY		峪
YUH	053,09	1384.1	12	00227		4093	RESIDE,RESIDENCE		厲
YUH	059,07	1751	10	53100	7677	7056	ELEGANT,ACCOMPLISHED		或
YUH	060,08	1785	11	27220	7664	2117	IMPERIAL,DEFEND,TO DRIVE	D4403	御
YUH	061,09	1937	13	80332	7632	8703	HEAL,THE MORE...THE MORE	A4044	愈
YUH	061,11	1990	15	87338	7672	8650	DESIRE		慾
YUH	072,05	2509	09	60108	7682	0557	BRIGHT LIGHT		昱
YUH	075,08	2771	12	43950	7678	6965	THORNY SHRUB,(OAK)		棫
YUH	075,08	8567	12	48933	7644		TRAY FOR CARRYING SACRIFICIAL MEATS		槆
YUH	075,22	2939	26	44746	7692	3207	MELANCHOLY,DENSE(GROWTH)		鬱
YUH	076,07	2948	11	87682	7671	4917	DESIRE/WISH		欲
YUH	080,09	3022	14	80513	7687	7784	NOURISH/REAR		毓
YUH	085,04	3102.0A	07	36100	7695	1498	RUSHING,FLOW FAST,BRIGHT		汩
YUH	085,07	3188	10	38168	7673	1388	BATH		浴
YUH	085,08	8686	11	33150			SWIFT CURRENT,MOAT		減
YUH	085,13	3429	16	31186	7604		PLACE NAME IN SZECHWAN		澦
YUH	085,13	3421.0A	16	37134	0048	5029	BAY/COVE	7144.0A	澳
YUH	086,08	8747	12	90827			BRILLIANT/GLORIOUS	3558	焴
YUH	086,09	3558	13	96818	7683	0558	BRILLIANT,GLORIOUS		煜
YUH	086,11	3580.0A	15	74809	7661	5615	SMOOTH,RECONCILED		尉
YUH	086,12	8762	16	97827			RADIANCE OF FIRE		炎
YUH	086,13	3603	17	97834	7688	5028	WARM		燏
YUH	094,11	3739	14	43234	7685	5069	PRISON		燠
YUH	096,00	3768	05	10103	7666	0347	JADE		獄
YUH	102,08	1008.1	13	63050	7676	6964	REGION		玉
									畷

ROM	RAD	TEL	TOT	FC	MAT	OSH	TAG	CR	CHAR
YUH	104,08	4040	13	00133	7646	8958	EXTRAVASATED BLOOD		
YUH	104,09	4044	14	00121	7637	8979	HEAL	A1937	
YUH	104,13	8884	18	00132		8704	HEAL	1937	
YUH	110,07	4245	12	17227	7689	3902	PROPITIOUS,GRAND/ELEGANT		
YUH	113,11	4403	16	27901	7665	8373	RESIST/DEFEND	B1785	
YUH	114,04	4417.0A	09	60227	7621	4086	FEMALE MONKEY		
YUH	118,26	4715	32	88286	7693	8276	IMPLORE	0675.0A	
YUH	120,08	4865	14	23950			SEAM		
YUH	120,12	9074	18	27927			A WELL-ROPE		
YUH	122,08	4998	13	60153	7679	6967	DRAG-NET		
YUH	129,00	5124	06	50007	7684	2619	INTRODUCTORY PART.,PEN		
YUH	130,04	5148	08	00227	7687	3679	NOURISH/TO REAR		
YUH	134,07	5280.0A	14	77801	7615	8059	TAKE PART IN		
YUH	140,03	5341	07	44401	7598	3314	COLOCASIA ANTIQUORUM		
YUH	140,11	5588.0A	15	44240	7113	3223	PLACE NAME,(SURNAME)		
YUH	140,13	5626	17	44286			DIOSCOREACEAE		
YUH	140,13	5625	17	44430			PRUNUS JAPONICA		
YUH	140,14	5658.0A	18	44801			DIOSCOREA JAPONICA		
YUH	142,08	5790	14	53150	7680	6966	MYTHICAL CREATURE,TOAD,WORM		
YUH	145,07	5940	12	38268	7667	1385	ABUNDANT		
YUH	149,06	6235.1	13	90601			REPUTATION		
YUH	149,07	6133.0A	14	01661	7651	1230	TELL TO		
YUH	149,09	6170	16	08621	7641	8967	ORDER(FROM ABOVE)		
YUH	149,14	6235	21	77601	7617	1167	REPUTATION		
YUH	150,00	6253.0A	07	80608	3483	1379	(SURNAME)		
YUH	152,09	6276	16	17232	7603	5759	BEFOREHAND,PREPARE,HONAN	K7315	
YUH	162,09	6657	13	36302	7625	6705	MEET WITH		
YUH	162,12	6694	16	37302		6700	FOLLOW,IN ACCORDANCE WITH,(SURNAME)		
YUH	163,06	6735	09	47227	7686	2212	(SURNAME),MELANCHOLY,ELEGANT	D7599	
YUH	167,05	6877	13	81113		0348	HARD METALS		
YUH	169,08	7054	16	77153	7681	3526	THRESHOLD		
YUH	170,13	7144.0A	16	77234	0050	5027	BAY/COVE	3421.0A	
YUH	173,00	7183.0A	08	10227	7662	4019	TO RAIN		

瘀瘉癒喬禦禺籲絨繘罭聿育與芋蔚蕷蕷蝛裕譽語諭譽谷豫遇遹郁鈺閾隩雨

ROM	RAD	TEL	TOT	FC	MAT	OSH	TAG	CR	CHAR
YUH	173,03	7184.0A	11	10207	7663	4556	RAINBOW		雴
YUH	173,12	7215	20	10227			TRI-COLORED CLOUDS		霭
YUH	181,04	7315	13	11286	7603	8272	BEFOREHAND,PREPARE	K6276	預
YUH	184,04	7388	12	82734	7656	5128	FULL(AS OF EATING)		飫
YUH	184,11	7388.1	19	81716	7656	0794	FULL(AS OF EATING)		饇
YUH	187,02	7457	12	77340	7664	6558	TO DRIVE,MANAGE	G1785	馭
YUH	187,12	7518	22	77327		3905	BLACK HORSE WITH WHITE LEGS		驈
YUH	192,19	7599	29	44722	7692	4184	MELANCHOLY,DENSE(GROWTH)	B6735	欝
YUH	193,12	7605	22	17227	7691	3915	VEND		鬻
YUH	194,08	7612	18	23215			GHOST OF A CHILD		魆
YUH	196,05	9675	16	23382			FALCE AESALON		鴥
YUH	196,07	7714	18	87627	7675	4617	MYNAH		鴝
YUH	196,12	7756	23	17227	7690	4637	COMMON SNIPE		鷸
YUH	214,09	7902	26	81286	7693		IMPLORE	0675.0A	龥
IUAN	014,08	0387	10	37413	7719	7758	TO WRONG,INJUSTICE	1375	冤
IUAN	040,08	1375	11	30413	7719	7759	TO WRONG,INJUSTICE	0387	寃
IUAN	085,08	3220	11	32100	7723	2084	ABYSS		淵
IUAN	085,08	3220.1	11	32100			ABYSS		渊
IUAN	109,05	8905	10	27601	7715	1734	INFLAMED EYELIDS,PARCHED		眢
IUAN	142,07	5775	13	56127	1637	3611	LARVA OF MOSQUITO,(SURNAME)		蜎
IUAN	196,03	7687	14	43327	7744	4686	KITE		鳶
IUAN	196,05	7696	16	27327	7717	4688	MANDARIN DUCK		鴛
IUAN	196,08	9677	19	37227		4659	FIREBIRD		鵷
YUAN	010,02	0337	04	10211	7707	7463	DOLLAR,PRIMARY,(DYNASTY)	A0955	元
YUAN	027,08	0626	10	71296	7725	8428	SOURCE,CAUSE		原
YUAN	030,07	0765	10	60806	7721	8135	MEMBER	9322	員
YUAN	031,04	0954.1	07	60211	7007		GARDEN		园
YUAN	031,10	0955	13	60806	7722	1928	DOLLAR,CIRCLE/ROUND	A0337	圓
YUAN	031,11	0954	14	60232	7731	1915	GARDEN		園
YUAN	031,13	0958.0A	16	60732	2255	1914	CIRCLE/ROUND	B0955	圜
YUAN	032,06	0997	09	41116	7724	0022	WALL		垣
YUAN	032,10	8242	13	41196			PLATEAU		塬
YUAN	038,09	1254.0A	12	42447	7736	6123	A BEAUTY		媛

145

ROM	RAD	TEL	TOT	FC	MAT	OSH	TAG	CR	CHAR
YUAN	038,10	1270	13	41496	7726	8432	NAME OF AN EMPRESS		嫄
YUAN	064,09	2266	12	52047	7737	6119	AID		援
YUAN	075,15	2928	19	47932	7742	5741	CITRUS MEDICA		櫞
YUAN	085,04	3104	07	31111	7708	7469	NAME OF A RIVER		沅
YUAN	085,06	3180.0A	09	31116			NAME OF A RIVER		洹
YUAN	085,09	3283	12	32147		6124	RUSHING(WATER)		湲
YUAN	085,10	3293	13	31196	7728	8433	SOURCE/ORIGIN		源
YUAN	087,05	3633	09	20447	7735	6114	TO LEAD ON TO,THEREFORE		爰
YUAN	094,09	8804	12	42247	7732		APE	3737	猨
YUAN	094,10	3737	13	44232	7732	5882	APE	8804	猿
YUAN	118,04	4577	10	88211			BAMBOO WITH BLACK PATCHES		笎
YUAN	120,09	4878	15	27932	7741	5740	ALONG,PREDESTINED AFFINITY		緣
YUAN	123,10	9093	16	81596		8429	OVIS AMMON		羱
YUAN	140,04	5357	08	44211	7709	7480	DAPHNE GENKWA		芫
YUAN	142,09	9232	15	52147	7732		APE	3737	蝯
YUAN	142,09	9233	15	57132	7743	5742	YOUNG LOCUST WITHOUT WINGS		蝝
YUAN	142,10	582A	16	51196		8431	DIEMYELIUS PYROGASTER		螈
YUAN	145,04	5913	10	40732	7730	5885	(SURNAME)		袁
YUAN	149,00	6056.0A	07	00601	7334	1.154	SAY A WORD		言
YUAN	154,02	9322	09	23806		8241	MEMBER	0765	貟
YUAN	159,10	6562	17	54032	7733	5881	SHAFTS OF CART,YAMEN		轅
YUAN	163,04	9387	07	17227			PLACE NAME		邧
YUAN	187,09	7508	19	71396		8430	CHESTNUT HORSE WITH WHITE BELLY		騵
YUAN	196,10	774C	21	67827			JAPANESE LONGTAILED TIT		鶢
YUAN	205,04	7837	17	10717	7711	7348	(SEA TURTLE)		黿
YEUAN	162,04	6678.1	08	31301		6767	FAR		远
YEUAN	162,10	6678	14	34303	7734	6747	FAR		遠
YUANN	038,09	1254	12	42447	7736	6123	A BEAUTY		媛
YUANN	061,05	1841	09	27331	7714	8683	COMPLAIN,BLAME		怨
YUANN	061,10	1959	14	71339	7727	8690	SINCERE,WILLING	D7349	愿
YUANN	064,09	2268	12	57032			OFFICIAL		掾
YUANN	096,09	3850	13	12147	7738		LARGE JADE RING		瑗
YUANN	120,09	4878.0A	15	27932	7741	5740	PUT PIPING ON GARMENT		縁

ROM	RAD	TEL	TOT	FC	MAT	OSH	TAG	CR	CHAR
YUANN	140,05	5373	09	44212	7716	7210	PARK,(SURNAME)		苑
YUANN	170,07	7108	10	73211	7712	7474	COURTYARD,INSTITUTION		院
YUANN	181,10	7349	19	71286	7729	8315	WILLING,A WISH	B1959	願
IUE	030,13	0902	16	61053	7706	7012	BELCH,VOMIT		噦
IUE	073,00	2574	04	60000	7694	1491	SAY		曰
IUE	120,03	4766	09	27920	7493	4366	APPROXIMATELY,MAKE APPOINTMENT		約
YUEH	018,04	0440	06	72200	7697	2898	CUT OFF THE FEET AS PUNISHMENT		刖
YUEH	046,05	1471	08	72772	7495	0994	MOUNTAIN,WIFE'S FATHER,(SURNAME)	A1547	岳
YUEH	046,14	1547	17	22234	7445	5070	MOUNTAIN	A1471	嶽
YUEH	061,07	1878	10	98016	7702	7568	PLEASED		悅
YUEH	062,01	6885.1	05	53700	7701	7050	BATTLE-AXE		戉
YUEH	072,14	2565.0A	18	67014	7305	0948	GLORIOUS,DAZZLE		曜
YUEH	074,00	2588	04	77220	7696	3542	MOON,MONTH		月
YUEH	075,02	2867.1A	06	72904			MUSIC,(SURNAME)		乐
YUEH	075,11	2867.0A	15	22904	4129	5411	MUSIC,(SURNAME)		樂
YUEH	075,12	2887	16	43985	7700	5967	SHADE OF TREES		樾
YUEH	085,17	3485	20	38127	7497	3805	TO BOIL,CLEANSE		瀹
YUEH	086,14	3613.0A	18	97814	5693		GLORIOUS,BRILLIANT	5069.0A	耀
YUEH	086,17	3621	21	98827		3804	BRIGHT/FIERY		爚
YUEH	096,04	8819	08	17120			PEARL USED IN SACRIFICE		玥
YUEH	113,03	4364	07	37227	7498		SPRING IMPERIAL ANCESTRAL SACRIFICE	8984	礿
YUEH	113,17	8984	21	38227	7498		SPRING IMPERIAL ANCESTRAL SACRIFICE	4364	禴
YUEH	118,17	4707	23	88226	7499	3807	(FLUTE),KEY	D7011.0A	籥
YUEH	119,06	4727	12	26207	7704	4545	KWANGTUNG,CANTONESE		粤
YUEH	119,06	4727.1	12	27207			KWANGTUNG,CANTONESE		粵
YUEH	124,14	5069.0A	20	97214	7306	0955	GLORIOUS,BRILLIANT	3613.0A	耀
YUEH	140,09	5522.0A	13	44927	7501	4368	MEDICINE/DRUG	5673.0A	葯
YUEH	140,15	5673.0A	19	44904	7501	5418	MEDICINE/DRUG	5522.0A	藥
YUEH	156,05	6390	12	43805	7698	5966	EXCEED,THE MORE...THE MORE		越
YUEH	156,14	9327.0A	21	47801	7504	5945	TO JUMP	6460	趯
YUEH	157,04	6460.1	11	62134			TO JUMP		跃
YUEH	157,14	6460	21	67114	7504	0947	TO JUMP	9327.0A	躍
YUEH	159,03	6512	10	51010	7705	7457	CROSSBAR FOR YOKING HORSES		軏

ROM	RAD	TEL	TOT	FC	MAT	OSH	TAG	CR	CHAR
YUEH	167,04	7011.1A	12	87120			KEY		
YUEH	167,05	6885	13	83150	7701	7051	BATTLE-AXE		
YUEH	167,17	7011.0A	25	88127	7500	3803	KEY	B4707	
YUEH	169,07	7048	15	77216	7703	3529	PERUSE/REVIEW		
YUEH	196,14	7758	25	43327	7503	4678	YOUNG PHOENIX		
YUEH	214,00	7900	17	80227	7496	3802	FLUTE,ANCIENT MEASURE		
IUN	072,04	8502	08	67020			SUNLIGHT,SUNRISE		
IUN	072,09	2546.0A	13	60506	7762	2663	FAINT AWAY,CONFUSED		
IUN	084,09	3053	13	80117	7767	7800	HEAVY ATMOSPHERE		
IUN	085,07	8675.0A	10	37167	6591		TORTUOUS(OF WATERWAY)		
IUN	120,10	4888.0A	16	26917	7769	0681	GENERATIVE FORCE,ORANGE COLOR		
IUN	154,12	6364	19	03806	7758		GOOD APPEARANCE		
YUN	007,02	0061	04	10731	7745	8856	SAY,CLOUD	D7189	
YUN	020,02	0542	04	27120	7751	4371	UNIFORM/EVEN		
YUN	075,12	8592	16	41931			(TREE)		
YUN	085,04	8661	07	31131	7746		RUSHING OF A TORRENT		
YUN	085,12	8710	15	31131		8869	RIVER WAVES		
YUN	086,10	8756	14	96886			(YELLOW COLOR)		
YUN	102,04	3960	09	67020	7752	4376	RECLAIMED LAND		
YUN	115,04	5089.1	09	21931	7748	8859	TO WEED		
YUN	118,07	4596	13	88127	7753	4373	SKIN OF BAMBOO		
YUN	118,10	4642	16	88806		8146	(BAMBOO)		
YUN	120,04	4789	10	21931	7747	8861	CONFUSED,NUMEROUS		
YUN	127,04	5089	10	51931	7748	8860	TO WEED		
YUN	140,04	5366	08	44731	7749	8863	RUTA GRAVEOLENS		
YUN	140,12	557A	16	44731		8873	CELZA		
YUN	163,10	6765	13	67827		2256	NAME OF A FEUDAL STATE		
YUN	167,07	9462	15	47109		0377	GOLD		
YUN	173,04	7189	12	10731	7750	8868	CLOUD	B0061	
YEUN	010,02	0336	04	23210	7759	7681	TO PERMIT		
YEUN	078,10	2998	14	16286	7755	8141	PERISH/DIE		
YEUN	094,04	3696	07	43210	7760	7683	NAME OF A TRIBE		
YEUN	112,10	8958	15	16686	7756	8137	PERISH,FALL,METEOR	7134	

鑰鉞鑰閱獻龠昀暈氳涒緼贇云勻橒沄澐煩昀耘鈞箟紜耘芸蕓鄆蝝雲允殞狁碩

ROM	RAD	TEL	TOT	FC	MAT	OSH	TAG	CR	CHAR
YEUN	170,10	7134	13	76286	7756	8139	PERISH,FALL,METEOR	8958	隕
YEUN	173,10	9546	18	10806		8145	TO FALL,RAIN STORM		霣
YUNN	039,02	1314	05	17407	7765	3144	PREGNANT		孕
YUNN	061,09	1950	12	96017	7766	0673	INDIGNANT/FEEL HURT		慍
YUNN	061,09	1926	12	97056	7761	2656	(SURNAME)		惲
YUNN	072,09	2546	13	60506	7762	2663	DIZZY,RING AROUND MOON OR SUN		暈
YUNN	086,10	3572	14	96817	7768	0679	TO IRON	3580	熅
YUNN	086,11	3580	15	74809	7661	5615	TO IRON,AN IRON	3572	熨
YUNN	120,10	4888	16	26917	7769	0681	HEMP,VAGUE/MYSTERIOUS		緼
YUNN	140,13	5619	17	44117	7126		HIPPURIS OR MARE'S TAIL		薀
YUNN	140,16	5686	20	44917	7770	0682	COLLECT,BRING TOGETHER		蘊
YUNN	162,04	6663.1	08	31303			MOVE ABOUT,TRANSPORT,LUCK		运
YUNN	162,09	6663	13	37304	7763	6671	MOVE ABOUT,TRANSPORT,LUCK		運
YUNN	163,09	9398	12	37527	7764	2194	PLACE NAME		鄆
YUNN	164,04	6824.1	11	11631			TO BREW		酝
YUNN	164,10	6824	17	16617		0672	TO BREW		醞
YUNN	178,10	7291	19	46517	7772	0674	CONTAIN		韞
YUNN	180,04	7301.1	13	07620	7757	4375	RHYME		韵
YUNN	180,10	7301	19	06686	7757	8138	RHYME		韻
JA	037,06	1151	09	40207	0074		EXTEND OUT/OPEN		奓
JA	064,01	2089	04	52010	0086	7066	PRICK		扎
JA	064,09	8439	12	54016	0071	0054	TO PICK UP WITH FINGERS		揸
JA	075,05	2686.0A	09	4010	0103	0049	(SURNAME)		查
JA	075,05	8546	09	47910			(HAWTHORN),CHAENOMELES JAPONICA	8576	柤
JA	075,09	8576	13	44916	0106	0055	HAWTHORN,CHINESE QUINCE	8546	楂
JA	075,11	8546.1	15	41916	0072	0636	(HAWTHORN),CHAENOMELES JAPONICA		樝
JA	085,09	3257	12	34116	0069	0056	DREGS		渣
JA	120,04	4796.1A	10	52903		8477	BIND WITH ROPE OR CORD,TO STOP		紥
JA	120,05	4796.0A	11	42903	6647	8478	BIND WITH ROPES OR CORD,TO STOP		紮
JAR	018,12	0488	14	82600			WRITE DOWN		劄
JAR	064,01	2089.0A	04	52010	0086	7066	STRUGGLE,PENETRATING(AS OF COLD)		扎
JAR	075,01	2610	05	42910	0087	7069	SHORT NOTE		札

ROM	RAD	TEL	TOT	FC	MAT	OSH	TAG	CR	CHAR
JAR	086,01	3498.1	05	92810	0089	7070	FRY		灼
JAR	086,05	3498	09	98811	0089	2071	FRY	3558	炸
JAR	086,09	3558	13	94894		5293	FRY	3498	煠
JAR	091,09	7037.1	13	22077	0095	1071	WATERGATE,GEAR		紮
JAR	120,04	4796.1	10	52903		8477	BIND WITH ROPE OR CORD,TO STOP		紫
JAR	120,05	4796	11	42903	6647	8478	BIND WITH ROPES OR CORD,TO STOP		蟄
JAR	142,05	574D	11	41136	0088		APHROPHORA MARTIMA		鍘
JAR	167,09	9484	17	82100	0091	2969	LEVER-KNIFE		閘
JAR	169,05	7037	13	77506	0094	3482	WATERGATE,GEAR		霅
JAR	173,07	7196	15	10601		1164	RAIN,(SURNAME)		扎
JAA	064,01	2089.0B	04	52010	0086	7066	STOP		扱
JAA	064,03	2096.0A	06	54000	0097	6562	FINGER SPAN	2387	拃
JAA	064,05	2387	08	58011			A SPAN	2096.0A	渣
JAA	085,09	3257.0A	12	34116	0069	0056	FRAGMENTS	4270.0A	眨
JAA	109,05	4172	10	62037	0092	6593	WINK		砟
JAA	112,05	4270.0A	10	18611		2060	FRAGMENTS	3257.0A	詐
JAA	149,05	6094.0A	12	08611		2061	TO SOUND OUT		鮓
JAA	195,05	7633	16	28311	0084	2073	PRESERVED FISH		乍
JAH	004,04	0038	05	80211	0080	2058	FOR THE FIRST TIME,SUDDENLY		吒
JAH	030,03	0688	05	62014	0075	7557	UPBRAID	0741	咋
JAH	030,05	0738.0A	08	68011	6743	2059	SHOUT,LOUD NOISE,SUDDENLY		咤
JAH	030,06	0741	09	63014	0075	7363	UPBRAID	0688	喳
JAH	030,08	8150	11	64061	0078		SIGH,GROAN,CRY OF BIRDS		搾
JAH	064,10	2265	13	53011		2078	TO EXTRACT,OPPRESS	A2834	栅
JAH	075,05	2694	09	47940	0093	4104	FENCE		榨
JAH	075,10	2834	14	43911	0083	2079	TO EXTRACT,SALTED VEGETABLE	A2265	溠
JAH	085,10	3299	13	38111			NAME OF A RIVER		灺
JAH	086,01	3498.1A	05	92810	0089	7070	EXPLODE		炸
JAH	086,05	3498.0A	09	98811	0089	2071	EXPLODE		煠
JAH	091,09	8779	13	22077	0095	1071	SLUICE GATE,TO BLOCK A DOOR		疟
JAH	104,05	401A	10	00111	0081	2075	MUMPS		砟
JAH	112,05	4270	10	18611		2060	STONE,HEADSTONE(OF A GRAVE)		筜
JAH	118,05	4575.0A	11	88211		2080	WINE VESSEL,TO SQUEEZE		

150

ROM	RAD	TEL	TOT	FC	MAT	OSH	TAG	CR	CHAR
JAH	142,05	5741	11	58111	6745	2074	GRASSHOPPER		
JAH	149,05	6094	12	08611	0082	2061	DISHONEST,CRAFTY		
JAH	164,10	6825	17	13611	0083		PRESS FOR EXTRACTING WINE		
JAI	009,09	0258.0A	11	22200	6757	2971	LEAN ON ONE SIDE		
JAI	064,11	2298	14	50027	0278	3879	PICK (FLOWERS/FRUIT),BORROW		
JAI	067,06	7872.1	10	00227	0115	3776	STUDIO,A FAST		
JAI	210,03	7872	17	00223	0115	2770	STUDIO,A FAST		
JAIR	040,03	1341	06	30714	0275	7362	RESIDENCE		
JAIR	064,13	2344.0A	16	56041	0276	2484	PICK OVER		
JAIR	124,08	5049	14	17214	6225	0946	(SURNAME)		
JAE	116,05	4504	10	30211	6744	2076	NARROW		
JAY	009,11	0280	13	25286	0118	8114	DEBT		
JAY	040,11	1396	14	30904	0116	5376	STRONGHOLD/STOCKADE		
JAY	104,11	4067	16	00191	0117	8393	FOCI OF TUBERCULAR INFECTION		
JAY	112,05	4274	10	21601	0116	1120	STRONGHOLD/STOCKADE	1396	
JAY	113,06	4385.0A	11	27901	0465	8389	(SURNAME)		
JAN	025,03	0594	05	21600	0125	1261	TO DIVINE		
JAN	070,06	2462	10	08247	0133	4109	SILKEN BANNER,FELT	D3041	
JAN	070,15	2472	19	08216	0134		SILKEN BANNER	A2462	
JAN	082,05	3030	09	21716	0135	7397	FELT	3041	
JAN	082,13	3041	17	02114	0135	7368	FELT	3030	
JAN	082,13	3041.1	17	20711	0135	7396	FELT		
JAN	085,05	3115	08	31160	0127	1278	MOISTEN,RECEIVE FAVORS,INFECTED BY	A7205	
JAN	109,13	4232	18	47061	0151	1176	GAZE/VIEW		
JAN	119,05	4724.0A	11	91960	0129	1272	TO STICK/PASTE		
JAN	147,05	6019	12	26610	0130	7595	TO SPY,KEEP AT		
JAN	149,06	6124	13	27261	0150	1174	VERBOSE,EXCELLENT,(SURNAME)		
JAN	149,13	6228	20	07661	0152	1175	TALKATIVE,INCOHERENT TALK		
JAN	162,13	6704	17	30301		6598	NOT MAKING PROGRESS		
JAN	173,08	7205	16	10161	0132	1279	MOISTEN	A3115	
JAN	184,03	7384	11	81740	0137		THICK CONGEE	9604	
JAN	184,13	9604	21	80716	0137	0043	THICK CONGEE	7384	
JAN	187,13	7530	23	70316			(HORSE)		

虾
詐
醡
側
摘
斋
齋
宅
擇
翟
窄
債
寨
瘵
砦
祭
占
旃
旝
毡
氈
邅
沾
瞻
粘
覘
詹
譫
邅
霑
飦
饘
驙

ROM	RAD	TEL	TOT	FC	MAT	OSH	TAG	CR	CHAR
JAN	195,13	7672	21	20316		0047	ACIPENSER MICADOI/STURGEON		
JAN	196,13	7757	24	06127	0138	4600	SPARROW-HAWK,SWIFT		
JAAN	044,07	1455	10	77232	0139	5770	UNFOLD,POSTPONE		
JAAN	046,11	1535	14	22521	0158	2028	PRECIPITOUS PEAK		
JAAN	064,10	8457	13	57032	0140	5774	WIPE,BIND		
JAAN	069,07	2447	11	52021	0142	2025	CHOP,BEHEAD		
JAAN	075,12	8586	16	46956			(WOOD)		
JAAN	096,08	3817	12	13153		6948	WINE CUP		
JAAN	107,13	4127	18	04147		6228	SCAB		
JAAN	108,08	4144	13	53107	0149	0720	AN. FOR LAMP		
JAAN	159,10	6558	17	57032	0141	5773	TURN HALF OVER,ROLL OVER ON SIDE		
JAAN	164,08	6814	15	13653			WINE WHICH IS SETTLING,GOBLET		
JAAN	182,05	7365	14	71216		7838	SWAY		
JANN	009,05	0148	07	21260	0126	1268	OCCUPY		
JANN	062,05	2069.1	09	23650		6905	WAR		
JANN	062,12	2069	16	63550	0147	6919	WAR		
JANN	072,09	2548	13	52602	6683	1568	TEMPORARILY,UNEXPECTEDLY	6463	
JANN	075,08	2770	12	43953	0148	6955	WAREHOUSE		
JANN	085,09	3277	12	34118	0146	0772	DEEP/CLEAR(WATER)		
JANN	117,05	4541	10	01160	0128	1264	TO STAND,STATION		
JANN	120,08	4861	14	23981	0143	6022	RIPPED SEAM		
JANN	140,19	5699	23	44331	0145	8756	DIP INTO		
JANN	141,10	5717	16	23253			STRIPED WILD CAT		
JANN	157,11	6463	18	52801		5982	TEMPORARILY,UNEXPECTEDLY	2548	
JANN	159,12	6570	19	57047			CHARIOT FOR SLEEPING AND CONVEYANCE		
JANN	181,13	7358	22	01186	0136	8243	SHAKE/VIBRATE		
JANG	038,11	1286	14	40446		2285	LADY IN THE MOON,HUSBAND'S PARENT		
JANG	057,08	1728	11	11232	0195	5798	OPEN UP,(SURNAME)		
JANG	059,11	1757	14	02422	0185	4176	MANIFEST		
JANG	072,11	8517	15	60046			TO RISE(OF SUN),BRIGHT		
JANG	075,03	2627	07	44940	0202	6568	CANE		
JANG	075,11	2874	15	40946	0187	2284	CAMPHOR/CINNAMONUM CAMPHARA		
JANG	085,11	3361	14	30146	0188	2286	NAME OF A RIVER		

鱣鸇展靳振斬戔醆盞輾醼颭佔战戰暫棧湛站綻蘸戲薝轞顫嫜張彰暲杖樟漳

RÒM	RAD	TEL	TOT	FC	MAT	OSH	TAG	CR	CHAR
JANG	094,11	3742	14	40246	0189	2283	ROEBUCK,RIVER DEER	7791	獐
JANG	096,11	3864	15	10146	0190	2279	ANCIENT STONE ORNAMENT		璋
JANG	117,06	4545	11	00406	0182	2278	CHAPTER,SEAL,(SURNAME)		章
JANG	119,08	9038	14	91932			WHITE COOKED RICE,FOOD		粻
JANG	142,11	7924	17	50146			COCKROACH		蟑
JANG	163,11	9410	14	07427	0193	2188	PLACE NAME		鄣
JANG	195,11	766L	22	20346			POULPE		鱆
JANG	198,11	7791	21	00406	0189	2288	ROEBUCK,RIVER DEER,MUSK	3742	麞
JAANG	009,02	8022	04	27210	0204		SURNAME OF MENCIUS' MOTHER		仉
JAANG	064,08	2222	12	90502	0203	3340	PALM OF HAND,IN CHARGE OF		掌
JAANG	085,11	3360	14	31132	0196	5799	TO RISE(OF PRICES/RIVERS)		漲
JAANG	112,12	7925	17	19652			COAL FACE		礃
JAANG	168,00	7022.1A	06	22732			GROW,ELDER,CHIEF/HEAD		长
JAANG	168,00	7022.0A	08	71732	0213	5793	GROW,ELDER,CHIEF/HEAD		長
JAANG	177,08	726A	17	49527	0205		PATCH OF LEATHER		鞝
JANQ	001,02	0004	03	50000	0200	6566	TEN FEET		丈
JANQ	009,03	0101	05	25200	0201	6567	BATTLE		仗
JANQ	046,11	1534	14	20746	0184	2280	CLIFF,RANGE OF PEAKS		嶂
JANQ	050,08	1600	11	41232	0197	5797	TENT,MOSQUITO NET,ACCOUNT	G6348	帳
JANQ	050,11	1625	14	40246		2282	HANGING SCROLL		幛
JANQ	085,11	3360.0A	14	31132	0196	5799	TO SWELL/DISTEND		涨
JANQ	104,11	8879	16	00132			DROPSICAL	B5195	癥
JANQ	104,11	4066	16	00146	0191	2287	MIASMA,MALARIA		瘴
JANQ	130,08	5195	12	71232	0198	5796	SWOLLEN,DROPSICAL	D8879	脹
JANQ	154,08	6348	15	61832	0199	5801	ACCOUNT	C1600	賬
JANQ	170,11	7140	14	70246	0194	2281	OBSTACLE		障
JAU	030,12	0877.0A	15	67020	0249	3558	TO RIDICULE	6213.0A	嘲
JAU	064,05	2156	08	57062	0235	1369	TO RECRUIT,PROVOKE		招
JAU	072,05	2507	09	67062	0236	1365	MANIFEST,ILLUSTRIOUS		昭
JAU	074,08	2600.0A	12	47420	0233	3557	MORNING		朝
JAU	109,07	4192.0A	12	80601	1258		CATCH,RECEIVE,SUFFER		著
JAU	140,09	5511.0B	13	44604		1648	CATCH/RECEIVE,SUFFER		著
JAU	149,12	6213.0A	19	07620			TO RIDICULE	0877.0A	謿

ROM	RAD	TEL	TOT	FC	MAT	OSH	TAG	CR	CHAR
JAU	167,02	6856	10	82100		2867	TO CUT,TO STRAIN,ENCOURAGE		剴
JAU	187,05	7472	15	77362			(HORSE)		駔
JAUR	109,07	4192	12	80601	1258	1704	TOUCH,RESULTAT. COMPL.,IGNITED	5511.0A	着
JAUR	140,09	5511.0A	13	44604	1361	1648	TO TOUCH,(RESULTAT. COMPL.),IGNITED	4192	著
JAO	064,04	2109	07	53050	2042	6923	LOOK FOR		找
JAO	085,05	3113	08	37162	0237	1373	POND/POOL		沼
JAO	087,00	3629.0B	04	72230	0240	4978	CLAW		爪
JAW	010,04	0340	06	32113	0247	7689	OMEN,TRILLION		兆
JAW	030,02	0664	05	17602	0234	1362	SUMMON		召
JAW	070,08	2466	12	08213		7704	BANNER		旐
JAW	085,08	8681.0A	11	31146	4645		PEACE		淖
JAW	086,05	8734	09	97862	0238	1371	SHINE ON,(SURNAME)	A3564	焯
JAW	086,09	3564	13	67336	0238	8771	SHINE ON,ACCORDING TO		照
JAW	118,04	4560	10	88232	0241	4980	LOOSELY WOVEN BAMBOO LADLE		笊
JAW	122,08	4996	13	60406	0246	2311	COVER,SHADE,FISH TRAP(BASKET)		罩
JAW	129,08	5128.1	14	33507	0245	2626	DEVISE,ORIGINATE,AT FIRST		肇
JAW	129,08	5128	14	38507	0245	2625	DEVISE,ORIGINATE,AT FIRST		肈
JAW	149,05	6096	12	07602	0239	1364	IMPERIAL ORDER		詔
JAW	156,02	6392.1	09	44800			(SURNAME)		赵
JAW	156,07	6392	14	49802	0244	5956	(SURNAME)		趙
JE	140,07	5764.0A	13	52136	0270	8927	TO STING	5826	蜇
JE	142,11	5826	17	48136	5826	8944	TO STING	5764.0A	螫
JE	162,11	6686	15	30303	0260	6784	SCREEN OFF,COVER UP(A SHORTCOMING)		遮
JER	030,07	0772	10	52602	0268	1285	WISE,PHILOSOPHY		哲
JER	030,09	0811	12	44661		1208	WISE,PHILOSOPHY	0772	喆
JER	061,11	1985	14	97062	2500	1668	TERRIFIED		慴
JER	061,18	2042	21	91041	0272	2725	AFRAID,BE FEARED		懾
JER	064,04	2124	07	52021	0267	2029	TO BREAK,TENTH (IN PRICE),TO FOLD	G2309	折
JER	064,11	2298.0A	14	50027	0278		PICK OUT		摘
JER	064,11	2309	14	57062	0271	1670	TO FOLD,FOLDED DOCUMENT	C2124	摺
JER	072,07	2520	11	52602		1569	BRIGHT		晢
JER	112,10	4325	15	15694		5347	TEARING OFF LIMBS AS PUNISHMENT		磔
JER	140,07	5764	13	52136	0270	8927	JELLYFISH		蜇

ROM	RAD	TEL	TOT	FC	MAT	OSH	TAG	CR	CHAR
JER	142,11	5832.0A	17	44136	0998	8948	HIBERNATE		蟄
JER	145,11	5977.0B	16	37262	6324	1669	PLEATS		褶
JER	149,11	6207	18	00627	0279	3878	FIND FAULT,DISGRACE(AN OFFICIAL)	6238	謫
JER	149,15	6238	22	00632	0279	6695	FIND FAULT,DISGRACE(AN OFFICIAL)	6207	讁
JER	149,16	6242	23	01601		1173	BE FRIGHTENED		讋
JER	159,12	6568	19	58040	0288	6349	RUT/TRACK		轍
JER	195,07	9645	18	22310			(FRESH-WATER FISH)		鮙
JEE	125,04	5074	09	44600	0263	1626	HE WHO,-ER/-OR		者
JEE	155,09	6379	16	44360	0264	1640	OCHER		赭
JEE	167,09	7926	17	84160		1628	GERMANIUM		鍺
JEH	040,03	1341.0A	06	30714	0275	7362	RESIDENCE,GRAVE		宅
JEH	075,05	2678	09	41960	0266	1105	CUDRANIA TRILOBA		柘
JEH	085,07	3181	10	32121	0269	2031	CHEKIANG		浙
JEH	140,11	5587	15	44237	0261	8767	SUGAR CANE		蔗
JEH	157,05	6412.0A	12	61160	1003	1102	SOLE OF FOOT		跖
JEH	162,03	6638.2	07	34300	0265	6678	THIS/THESE		迠
JEH	162,04	6638.1	08	30304	0265	6757	THIS/THESE		这
JEH	162,07	6638	11	30306	0265	6611	THIS/THESE		這
JEH	196,11	7744	22	06237	0262	4665	PARTRIDGE/FRANCOLINUS CHINENSIS		鷓
.JE	109,07	4192.0B	12	80601	1258	1704	PART. INDICATES ACCOMPANYING ACTION		着
.JE	140,09	5511.0C	13	44604		1648	PART.INDICATES ACCOMPANYING ACTION		著
JEY	162,03	6638.2A	07	34300	0265	6678	THIS/THESE		迠
JEY	162,04	6638.1A	08	30304	0265	6757	THIS/THESE		这
JEY	162,07	6638.0A	11	30306	0265	6611	THIS/THESE		這
JE(MM)	162,03	6638.2C	07	34300	0265	6678	SO/THUS/(IN)THIS WAY		迠
JE(MM)	162,04	6638.1C	08	30304	0265	6757	SO/THUS/(IN)THIS WAY		这
JE(MM)	162,07	6638.0C	11	30306	0265	6611	SO/THUS/(IN)THIS WAY		這
JEN	009,09	0259	11	21286	0347	8172	TO SPY,TO SCOUT		偵
JEN	064,10	8450	13	55094			TO GATHER/COLLECT		搸
JEN	068,09	2440	13	44700	0319	2695	POUR,TO DELIBERATE		斟
JEN	075,07	8561	11	41932			SPACE BETWEEN TWO PILLARS,EAVES		桭
JEN	075,09	2823	13	42986	0349		(EVERGREEN SHRUB)		楨
JEN	075,10	2830	14	45994	0291	5556	HAZEL TREE/CORYLUS HETEROPHYLLA		榛

ROM	RAD	TEL	TOT	FC	MAT	OSH	TAG	CR	CHAR
JEN	085,10	3308	13	35194	0292	5558	NAME OF A RIVER		溱
JEN	096,05	3791.1	09	17192	0301		TREASURE		琛
JEN	096,05	3791	09	18122	0301	4192	TREASURE		珍
JEN	098,09	3914	14	11117	0295	7926	TO MOLD,(SURNAME)		甄
JEN	109,05	4176	10	40801	0297	8078	TRUE,REAL		真
JEN	112,05	4278	10	11660	0321	1266	ANVIL	4305	砧
JEN	112,09	4305	14	14618	0321	0768	ANVIL	4278	碪
JEN	113,09	4394	13	31286	0350	8174	LUCKY,AUSPICIOUS		禎
JEN	118,09	4631	15	88253	0310	7010	WARN		箴
JEN	130,05	5155	09	78222	0303	4198	GIZZARD		胗
JEN	133,10	5271	16	15194	0293	5555	UTMOST,TO REACH		臻
JEN	140,09	551D	13	44212			PHYSALIS ALKEKENGI		蒇
JEN	140,10	5550	14	44904	0294	5559	LUXURIANT		蓁
JEN	140,13	5655	17	44117	0296		(ORCHID),(GRASS)		蕽
JEN	149,05	6085.0A	12	08622	0306	4194	EXAMINE OR TREAT MEDICALLY		診
JEN	154,02	6297	09	21806	0346	8171	CHASTE		貞
JEN	167,02	6859	08	84100	0311	2265	NEEDLE	6944	針
JEN	167,05	6878	13	88122			TREASURE	3791	鉁
JEN	167,09	6944	17	83150	0311	7000	NEEDLE	6859	鍼
JEN	187,05	7538	15	78322			CHATTER MARK		駗
JEN	195,15	767C	26	28353			HYPORHAMPUS SAJURI		鱵
JEEN	009,03	7581.1	05	80202	0300	4191	BUSHY BLACK HAIR		今
JEEN	075,04	2650	08	44912	0308	7742	PILLOW		枕
JEEN	102,05	3963	10	68022	0302	4195	FIELD-PATH,BORDER/BOUNDARY		畛
JEEN	104,05	4011	10	00122	0303	4202	MEASLES,RASH	5155.0A	疹
JEEN	109,05	8908	10	68022			RESTRAIN ANGER		眕
JEEN	109,06	4193	11	68034	0317	5149	PUPIL OF THE EYE,FOREBODING		眹
JEEN	115,10	4466	15	21981		8087	ACCUMULATE,FINE AND CLOSE	D4903	稹
JEEN	120,05	4804	11	28922	0304	4200	TWIST A CORD,CROOKED,OBSTINATE		紾
JEEN	120,10	4903	16	24981		8088	FINE AND CLOSE	B4466	縝
JEEN	130,05	5155.0A	09	78222	0303	4198	MEASLES,RASH	4011	胗
JEEN	145,05	5919	10	38222	0305	4196	UNLINED GARMENT		袗
JEEN	149,05	6085	12	08622	0306	4194	EXAMINE OR TREAT MEDICALLY		診

ROM	RAD	TEL	TOT	FC	MAT	OSH	TAG	CR	CHAR
JEEN	159,05	6518	12	58022	0307	4197	D(11TH),STRONGLY(AS OF EMOTION)		輱
JEEN	190,10	7581	20	72801	0300	8092	BUSHY BLACK HAIR	9695	鬒
JEEN	203,10	9695	22	61381		8089	BUSHY BLACK HAIR	7581	黰
JENN	038,07	1228.0A	10	41432	0312	5779	PREGNANT		娠
JENN	038,07	1228.1A	10	47440	0312	4135	PREGNANT		娠
JENN	064,07	2182	10	51032	0313	5776	ROUSE		振
JENN	064,09	8446	12	54018		0770	TO HIT,TO THRUST		揕
JENN	074,06	2596	10	78234	0316	5150	I/WE(IMPERIAL USE),SUBTLE		朕
JENN	075,04	2650.0A	08	44912	0308	7742	PUT HEAD ON		枕
JENN	096,10	3859.0A	14	14134		8081	JADE EAR-PLUG		瑱
JENN	120,04	9053	10	22900	0335		ROPE FOR LEADING CATTLE		紖
JENN	154,07	6331	14	61832	0314	5778	TO RELIEVE(THE DISTRESSED)		賑
JENN	164,04	6795	11	14612	0309	7738	POISONOUS,TO POISON	7690	酖
JENN	167,10	6966	18	81181	0299	8082	SMALL TOWN,COMPOSED,SUPPRESS		鎮
JENN	170,07	7109	10	75206	0322	2648	DISPOSITION OF TROOPS,SHORT PERIOD		陣
JENN	173,07	7201	15	10232	0315	5791	SHAKE,SIGN IN TRIGRAM		震
JENN	196,04	7690	15	47027	0309	4660	POISONOUS,TO POISON	6795	鴆
JENG	006,05	3630.1	06	27507	0365	3364	FIGHT OVER		争
JENG	038,09	8291	12	41486			(FEMININE NAME)		嫃
JENG	046,08	1513	11	22757	0366	3368	EXCEL,LOFTY		崝
JENG	060,05	1767	08	21211	0352	0492	ATTACK,LEVY (TROOPS OR TAXES)	D1794	征
JENG	060,12	1794	15	28240	0358	6310	LEVY (TROOPS OR TAXES)	B1767	徵
JENG	061,05	1850.0A	08	91011		0491	BE STARTLED		忪
JENG	064,08	2197	11	52057	0390	3371	STRUGGLE		掙
JENG	066,05	2398	09	18140	0355	6313	GOVERNMENT,POLITICAL		政
JENG	077,01	2973.0A	05	10101	0351	0488	CHINESE 1ST MONTH OF YEAR		正
JENG	086,06	3532	10	17331	0361	8717	STEAM,MANY,ADVANCE		烝
JENG	087,04	3630	08	20507	0365	3365	FIGHT OVER		爭
JENG	094,08	3717	11	42257	0367	3373	HIDEOUS/FIERCE-LOOKING		猙
JENG	104,05	4017.0A	10	00111	0353	0493	OBSTRUCTION OF BOWELS	4084	症
JENG	104,15	4084	20	00148	0359	6311	OBSTRUCTION OF BOWELS	4017.0A	癥
JENG	109,08	4201	13	62057	0368	3370	TO OPEN(EYE)		睜
JENG	118,08	4620	14	88507	0369	3376	(MUS. INSTR.)		箏

ROM	RAD	TEL	TOT	FC	MAT	OSH	TAG	CR	CHAR
JENG	118,10	9016	16	88331			BAMBOO		篆
JENG	140,10	5544	14	44331	0362	8718	TO STEAM		蒸
JENG	149,08	6154	15	02657	0370	3369	EXPOSTULATE		諍
JENG	167,05	6891	13	81111	0354	0489	CENTURIUM		鉦
JENG	167,08	6927	16	82157	0371	3366	SMALL GONG,CLANG OF METALS		鎁
JEENG	064,06	2163	09	57013	0360	0070	TO AID/SUPPORT,RAISE		拯
JEENG	066,12	2419	16	58101	0356	0496	IN GOOD ORDER,WHOLE,EXACTLY	G2973.0B	整
JEENG	077,01	2973.0B	05	10101	0351	0488	EXACTLY	C2419	正
JEENG	181,07	7338.0A	16	11186	1126	8245	NECK		頸
JENQ	009,05	8029	07	21211			BE STARTLED	1850.0A	佂
JENQ	050,09	1608	12	41286	0348	8173	PICTURE,ONE OF A PAIR (SCROLLS)		幀
JENQ	064,08	2197.0A	11	52057	0390	3371	EARN (MONEY)		掙
JENQ	077,01	2973	05	10101	0351	0488	UPRIGHT,MAIN,JUST(RIGHT)		正
JENQ	104,05	4017	10	00111	0353	0493	DISEASE		症
JENQ	149,05	6086	12	01611	0357	0490	PROOF,CERTIFICATE	6214	証
JENQ	149,12	6214	19	02618	0357	0595	PROOF,CERTIFICATE	6086	證
JENQ	163,06	6774.1	09	87427			(SURNAME)		郑
JENQ	163,12	6774	15	87427	0363	2232	(SURNAME)		鄭
JI	001,02	8000	03	10220			(SURNAME)		丌
JI	005,05	8012	06	22610	0406		TO DIVINE		乩
JI	016,00	0415	02	77210	0404	7853	SMALL TABLE,ALMOST	D1637.0A	几
JI	018,08	8104	10	42600	0418	2895	CURVED WOOD GRAVER		剞
JI	019,11	0529	13	54827	0499	4829	MERIT/ACCOMPLISHMENT	4921	勣
JI	030,06	0875.1	09	64061			GRUMBLE		咭
JI	030,07	0825.1A	10	67020			TO PUMP(WATER),(ONOMAT.)		唧
JI	030,09	0825.0A	12	67020	0496	2126	TO PUMP(WATER),(ONOMAT.)		喞
JI	030,12	0875	15	62053	0410	7040	GRUMBLE		嘰
JI	030,14	8177	17	60023			-ISH/WITH ADJ. OF TASTE/COLOR		嚌
JI	032,08	1015	11	44104	0399	0211	FOUNDATION,RADICAL(CHEM.)		基
JI	037,05	1142.0A	08	40621	0514	3063	ODD (NUMBER)		奇
JI	038,06	1213	09	41417	0408	0849	WOMEN,(SURNAME)		姬
JI	044,04	1453.1	07	77247			CLOGS		屐
JI	044,07	1453	10	77247			CLOGS		屐

ROM	RAD	TEL	TOT	FC	MAT	OSH	TAG	CR	CHAR
JI	046,09	1518	12	23772			(SURNAME),NAME OF A MOUNTAIN		嵇
JI	046,09	1518.1	12	23972	0426	1000	(SURNAME),NAME OF A MOUNTAIN		嵆
JI	052,09	1637.0A	12	22453	0409	7038	ALMOST	B0415	幾
JI	066,08	2389	12	41647	0420		PICK UP WITH CHOPSTICKS,CROOKED		敧
JI	074,08	2599	12	44227	0401	3656	A FULL YEAR		朞
JI	075,02	2623	06	47910	0411	7857	MACHINE,OPPORTUNITY,SECRET	2894	机
JI	075,12	2894	16	44953	0411	7044	MACHINE,OPPORTUNITY,SECRET	2623	機
JI	085,13	3423	16	38140	0479	6376	INCITE/STIMULATE,VIOLENT		激
JI	093,08	8787	12	24521	2955	3070	OX-HORNS/WING OF AN ARMY		犄
JI	096,12	3875	16	12153	0413	7039	IRREGULAR PEARL		璣
JI	102,08	3982	13	64021	0422	3068	ODD,FRACTIONAL REMAINS		畸
JI	102,10	3983	15	22653	0412	6993	TERRITORY AROUND THE CAPITAL		畿
JI	112,12	4335	17	12653	0414	7041	JETTY,BREAKWATER		磯
JI	113,12	4408	16	32253			OMEN,PRAY		禨
JI	115,05	4480.1	10	26980			ACCUMULATE		积
JI	115,08	2599.1	12	24981	0401	8050	A FULL YEAR		稘
JI	115,10	4472	15	23961	0427	1610	INSPECT/CHECK		稽
JI	115,11	4480	16	26986	0500	8116	ACCUMULATE		積
JI	117,04	1142.1A	09	00621	0514		ODD (NUMBER)		奇
JI	118,04	4558	10	88441		2393	HAIR-PIN FOR BUN,15 YEARS OLD	4593	笄
JI	118,06	4593	12	88441	0407	2393	HAIRPIN FOR BUN,15 YEARS OLD	4558	筓
JI	118,08	4614	14	88801	0402	8057	WINNOW BASKET		箕
JI	120,11	4921	17	25986	0501	8117	MERIT/ACCOMPLISHMENT	0529	績
JI	122,17	5014	22	60521	0424	3071	INN,TO LODGE		羇
JI	122,19	5015	24	60527	0425	4700	HALTER,RESTRAIN	6013	羈
JI	130,02	5133	06	77210	0405	7856	FLESH,MUSCLE		肌
JI	140,19	5697	23	44101	0463	0505	FRAGMENT,SPICES,SALTED VEGETABLES	K7874	虀
JI	142,08	5776.0A	14	56100	0934	1093	CICADA		蜘
JI	146,19	6013	25	10527	0425	4701	HALTER,RESTRAIN	5015	羁
JI	148,08	6047	15	24221	0423	3073	ONE HORN UP AND ONE HORN DOWN,ODD		觭
JI	149,12	6217	19	02653	0416	7042	RIDICULE		譏
JI	154,08	6340	15	40806	0464	8170	TO PRESENT IN BOTH HANDS,SEND	7873	賫
JI	157,06	6419	13	60130	0502	8512	FOOTPRINT,TRACE	6619	跡

ROM	RAD	TEL	TOT	FC	MAT	OSH	TAG	CR	CHAR
JI	157,11	6465	18	65186	0502	8110	FOOTPRINT,TRACE	6419	
JI	157,14	6487	21	60123	0461	2759	GO UP	A7146	
JI	162,06	6619	10	30303	0502	6783	FOOTPRINT,TRACE	6465	
JI	170,14	7146	17	70223	0461		GO UP,RAINBOW		
JI	172,10	7179	18	20414	0428	0894	CHICKEN	7741	
JI	184,02	7382	10	87710	0417	7855	HUNGRY	7436	
JI	184,12	7436	20	82753	0417	7043	HUNGRY	7382	
JI	190,06	7573	16	72601	0451	1218	DRESSED HAIR OF A CHINESE WOMAN		
JI	196,02	7741.1	13	77427			CHICKEN		
JI	196,10	7741	21	26427	0428	4645	CHICKEN	7179	
JI	210,07	7873	21	00223	0464	2769	TO PRESENT IN BOTH HANDS,SEND	6340	
JI	210,09	7874	23	00223	0464	2767	FRAGMENT,SPICES	K5697	
JYI	007,07	0069	09	10104	0483	0071	URGENT		
JYI	009,01	7162.1	03	80100	0508	4897	COLLECT/COLLECTED WORKS		
JYI	009,04	0123	06	27247	0469	6501	UNREAL		
JYI	009,06	0165	08	24261		1209	DIFFICULT TO PRONOUNCE		
JYI	026,05	0613.1	07	77720		2143	NAMELY,RIGHT AWAY		
JYI	026,07	0613	09	27720	0495	2125	NAMELY,RIGHT AWAY		
JYI	029,02	0644	04	17247	0468	6496	REACH,AND		
JYI	030,03	0679	06	40601	0476	1206	LUCKY		
JYI	030,03	0676.0A	06	68017		7962	STAMMER		
JYI	030,07	0825.1	10	67020			A SQUEAK/FAINT SOUND		
JYI	030,09	0825	12	67020	0496	2126	A SQUEAK/FAINT SOUND		
JYI	032,04	0969	07	47147	0470	6497	PERILOUS,LOFTY PEAK	1476	
JYI	038,06	1205	09	44461	0477	1217	(SURNAME)		
JYI	046,02	2345.1	05	50772			TO STRIKE		
JYI	046,04	1476	07	22247	0471	6506	PERILOUS,LOFTY PEAK	0969	
JYI	053,08	1664	11	00261			PLACE NAME		
JYI	061,05	1838	09	27337	0480	8553	HURRIED,WORRIED		
JYI	062,09	2061	13	63150	0506	6921	PUT AWAY,COLLECT ONESELF		
JYI	064,13	2345	17	57502	0481	3358	TO STRIKE		
JYI	075,04	2817.1	08	47947			EXTREMELY,POLE(GEOG./PHYSICS)		
JYI	075,08	2817	12	47914	0484	0073	EXTREMELY,POLE(GEOG./PHYSICS)		

CHAR column (read top to bottom): 蹟 蹟 迹 隮 雞 飢 饑 髻 鳮 鷄 齎 齏 丞 亼 仮 佶 即 卽 及 吉 吃 唧 喞 圾 姞 击 炭 唐 急 戢 擊 极 極

ROM	RAD	TEL	TOT	FC	MAT	OSH	TAG	CR	CHAR
JYI	075,08	2765.0A	12	55992	0486	5516	THORNS		棘
JYI	075,09	2813	13	46941	0799	2732	OAR,TO ROW	2912	楫
JYI	075,13	2912	17	43950	0799	6922	OAR,TO ROW	2813	檝
JYI	078,08	2997	12	11214	0485	0072	PUT TO DEATH		殛
JYI	085,04	3078	07	37147	0472	6505	DRAW WATER FROM WELL		汲
JYI	085,12	3441	15	33150			HARMONIOUS,FRIENDLY		濈
JYI	104,05	4014	10	00134	0492	5155	DISEASE		疾
JYI	104,10	4055	15	00127	0490	3636	LEAN,BARREN		瘠
JYI	118,04	4559	10	88247	0473	6508	TRUNKS(FOR BOOKS)		笈
JYI	118,14	4694	20	88961	0507	1516	RECORD/REGISTER,(SURNAME)		籍
JYI	120,04	4787	10	27947	0474	6504	A STEP/A GRADE		級
JYI	130,06	5182.0A	10	11227	0489	3634	SPINE RIDGE		脊
JYI	137,13	9160	19	23450	0799		OAR/TO ROW	2813	艥
JYI	140,04	5353	08	44247	0475	6507	SAMBUCUS JAVANICA		芨
JYI	140,10	5546	14	44134	0494	5157	TRIBULUS TERRESTRIS		蒺
JYI	140,13	5601	17	44153			HOUTTUYNIA CORDATA		蕺
JYI	140,14	5659.0A	18	44961	0767	1515	IN DISORDER		藉
JYI	145,12	9271	17	35296			COAT COLLAR		襋
JYI	157,08	6434	15	64161	0569	1508	TO STEP,WALK REVERENTLY		踖
JYI	157,10	6455	17	61127		3635	WALK WITH SHORT STEPS		蹐
JYI	167,04	9442	12	87147		6498	GERMANIUM		鈒
JYI	172,04	7162	12	20904	0508	5298	COLLECT/COLLECTED WORKS		集
JYI	196,09	772E	20	27327			GRASSHOPPER WARBLER		鶝
JYI	196,10	7731	21	17227	0491	4635	PIED WAGTAIL		鶺
JII	016,00	0415.0A	02	77210	0404	7853	HOW MANY,A FEW	1637	几
JII	049,00	1569	03	17717	0429	7245	SELF,6TH HEAVEN'S STEM		己
JII	052,09	1637	12	22453	0409	7038	HOW MANY,A FEW	0415.0A	幾
JII	053,04	1644	07	00247	0440	6223	CUPBOARD,TO STORE		庋
JII	062,08	2060	12	23450	0487	6918	A LANCE WITH TWO POINTS		戟
JII	064,08	2224	11	54021	0421	3072	DRAG		掎
JII	064,14	2357	17	50023	0458	2761	SQUEEZE,TO CROWD		擠
JII	075,05	2663.0A	09	46980	0948	8095	HOVENIA DULCIS		枳
JII	085,05	3143	08	35127			CLEAR WINE,NAME OF A RIVER		泲

ROM	RAD	TEL	TOT	FC	MAT	OSH	TAG	CR	CHAR
JII	120,03	4764.0A	09	27917	0430	7250	ORDER/DISCIPLINE		紀
JII	120,06	4822.0A	12	28961	0482	1195	TO SUPPLY/PROVIDE		給
JII	130,06	5182	10	11227	0489	3634	SPINE,RIDGE		脊
JII	142,12	5843	18	52153	0415	7045	NYMPH OF LOUSE		蟣
JII	157,08	9337	15	64121	0519		SHIN		踦
JII	198,02	7774	13	00211		7886	MOSCHUS CHINENSIS		麂
JIH	009,04	0125	06	24247	0438	6216	CRAFT		伎
JIH	009,09	8060	11	24241			TO STORE UP		偫
JIH	009,09	0245.0A	11	26227	0775	4387	BUDDHIST HYMN		偈
JIH	012,14	0370	16	11801	0443	8037	TO HOPE,(HOPEI)		冀
JIH	018,14	0495	16	02200	0457	2888	DOSE		劑
JIH	032,09	8235	12	27104			TO BRICK A GRAVE,TO SNUFF OUT		聖
JIH	032,11	8251	14	21104	0454	0246	PLASTER A WALL,COLLECT,REST		墍
JIH	038,04	1178	07	44447	0439	6222	PROSTITUTE		妓
JIH	038,10	1271	13	40434	0493	5156	JEALOUS		嫉
JIH	039,05	1323	08	20407	0435	3146	SEASON		季
JIH	040,08	1376	11	30621	0419	3080	TO MAIL,LODGE AT		寄
JIH	040,08	1374	11	30947	0505	6091	LONESOME		寂
JIH	058,00	1739	03	17100	0450	0859	PIG'S HEAD		彐
JIH	061,03	1803	07	17331	0432	8684	AVOID AS TABOO,JEALOUS		忌
JIH	061,08	1909	12	44338		8646	INJURE,VILIFY		惎
JIH	061,08	1900	11	92047	0436	3147	AFRAID		悸
JIH	061,14	8405	17	90023			ANGRY/SUSPICIOUS		懠
JIH	064,04	2111	07	54047	0442	6219	SKILL		技
JIH	071,07	2478	11	21714	0453	7728	ALREADY,SINCE		既
JIH	072,12	2555	16	21106	0455	0057	REACH TO,THE END,AND		暨
JIH	075,08	2765	12	55992			THORNS		棘
JIH	085,06	3154	09	36100	0446	1738	TO REACH,WHEN		洎
JIH	085,10	3365	13	38117			NAME OF A RIVER		濟
JIH	085,11	3368	14	37191			RIVER BANK		溰
JIH	085,14	3444	17	30123	0459	2764	AID,FERRY,FRUGAL		濟
JIH	104,08	4062	13	00147	0437		NERVOUS START IN SLEEP		瘈
JIH	104,09	8876	14	00134		5050	HYDROPHOBIA,MADNESS,FURIOUS		瘈

ROM	RAD	TEL	TOT	FC	MAT	OSH	TAG	CR	CHAR
JIH	104,14	8887	19	00123			SICK/DISEASED		瘠
JIH	113,06	4385	11	27901	0465	8389	OFFER SACRIFICE		祭
JIH	113,10	4402	14	36247			(NAME)		禨
JIH	115,10	4469	15	26947	0504	6456	(MILLET)		稷
JIH	115,11	4475	16	27991	0466	8392	(MILLET)		穄
JIH	115,14	8991	19	20923			STACK GRAIN STALKS EVENLY		穧
JIH	120,03	4764	09	27917	0430	7250	ORDER/DISCIPLINE,RECORD		紀
JIH	120,07	4949.1	13	29919			INHERIT,CONTINUE		継
JIH	120,13	4941.0A	19	57903	2458	8470	TO TIE		繋
JIH	120,14	4949	20	22913	0452	0758	INHERIT,CONTINUE		繼
JIH	122,12	5010	17	60211	0448	2953	(FISHING NET),WOOLEN RUG		罽
JIH	140,04	5362	08	44407		6224	TRAPANATANS		芰
JIH	140,11	5580	15	44714			DENSENESS(OF GRASS)		薿
JIH	140,13	5636	17	44320	0447	2978	CIRSIUM		薊
JIH	140,14	5654.0A	18	44223	0460	2765	CAPSELLA BURSA PASTORIS		薺
JIH	147,10	6025	17	26110	0449	7589	COVET,LONG FOR		覬
JIH	149,02	6060	09	04600	0456	2268	RECKON,TO PLAN,RUSE		計
JIH	149,03	6068	10	07617	0431	7248	TO RECORD,REMEMBER		記
JIH	157,07	6427	14	67131	0434		KNEEL		跽
JIH	159,09	6549	16	56041	0503	2730	EDIT,FRIENDLY		輯
JIH	170,05	7139.1	08	71291			INTERVAL,BOUNDARY,WHILE		际
JIH	170,11	7139	14	77291	0467	8391	INTERVAL,BOUNDARY,WHILE		際
JIH	173,14	7221	22	10223	0462	2766	SKY CLEARING UP		霽
JIH	195,05	7636	16	21336			(FISH)		鲚
JIH	195,09	7651	18	27320	0498	2128	BASTARD CARP,SAND PERCH		鯽
JIH	195,09	7651.1	20	27320	0498	2128	BASTARD CARP,SAND PERCH		鲫
JIH	195,11	766P	22	27391			KONOSIRUS PUNCTATUS		鰶
JIH	195,14	9662	25	20323			COILIA NASUS		鱭
JIA	009,06	0163	08	24214	0593	0166	EXCELLENT		佳
JIA	009,10	0159	12	23232	0595	5732	TOOL,FURNITURE	C1367	傢
JIA	019,03	0502	05	46000	0580	1083	ADD		加
JIA	030,05	0739.0A	08	66000	0582	1085	COFFEE		咖
JIA	030,11	0857	14	40465	0592	1088	EXCELLENT		嘉

ROM	RAD	TEL	TOT	FC	MAT	OSH	TAG	CR	CHAR
JIA	037,03	1140.1	06	50030			FOLDER,CLIP,HOLD BETWEEN		
JIA	037,04	1140	07	40038	0611	5112	FOLDER,CLIP,HOLD BETWEEN	G2188.0B	
JIA	040,07	1367	10	30232	0594	5731	HOME/FAMILY,-IST/-ER/-IAN,TOOL	G0159	
JIA	064,07	2188.0B	10	54038		5118	HOLD BETWEEN	C1140	
JIA	075,05	2666	09	46900	0584	1086	CANGUE		
JIA	096,05	3786	09	16100			GAMMA,JEWELRY		
JIA	104,05	4018	10	00160	0585	1087	SCAB		
JIA	118,05	4579	11	88463	0586	1090	WHISTLE MADE OF REED		
JIA	127,05	5093	11	56900	0587		FLAIL		
JIA	140,09	5521	13	44247	0601	6136	REED/PHRAGMITES COMMUNIS		
JIA	145,05	5914	11	46732	0588		BUDDHIST MONK'S ROBE		
JIA	152,09	6278	16	17247		6132	MALE PIG,BOAR		
JIA	157,05	6409	12	66100	0589		SIT CROSS-LEGGED		
JIA	162,05	6609	09	36300	0590	6609	SHAKYAMUNI,BUDDHA		
JIA	167,10	3006	18	83132			GALLIUM		
JIA	178,06	7284	15	48561			LEATHER KNEEPAD		
JIA	198,09	7788	20	00247			BUCK/STAG		
JYA	037,03	1140.1A	06	50030			NARROW LANE,LINED,HOLD BETWEEN		
JYA	037,04	1140.0A	07	40038	0611	5112	NARROW LANE,LINED,HOLD BETWEEN	D6005	
JYA	061,06	1862	10	57332	0605	8634	INDIFFERENT		
JYA	062,08	2059	12	10503		6944	LANCE,STANDING ALONE		
JYA	062,08	2059.1	12	10503	0608	6946	A LANCE,STANDING ALONE		
JYA	085,07	3191	10	34138	0787	5122	SOAKED,DAMP		
JYA	115,06	4447	11	24961	0624	1213	STALKS OF CORN OR SORGHUM		
JYA	140,07	5453	11	44438	0768	5123	POD		
JYA	142,07	5758	13	54138	0769	5121	BUTTERFLY		
JYA	145,06	5930	11	38261	0606	1192	LINED	6005	
JYA	145,07	6005	12	34238	0606	5116	LINED	5930	
JYA	157,06	9334	13	68161	0785		STUMBLE		
JYA	163,07	6751	10	47027	0613	2235	NAME OF A HSIEN IN HONAN		
JYA	167,07	6911	15	84138	0770	5113	PINCERS FOR USE AT A FIRE,SWORD		
JYA	181,07	7335	16	41086	0614	8289	CHEEKS		
JEA	009,09	0250	11	27247	0599	6130	FALSE		

夾夾家挾枷珈痂笝勑葭袈褹跏迦鎵豁夾夾忿戛戞浹秸莢蛺袷裌跲郟鋏頰假

ROM	RAD	TEL	TOT	FC	MAT	OSH	TAG	CR	CHAR
JEA	030,11	0858.0A	14	47647		6128	GRAND,FAR		嘏
JEA	046,05	8328	08	26750		2679	CAPE(GEOG.)		岬
JEA	068,06	8496	10	23402	0602	2709	JADE CUP WITH EARS	2439	斚
JEA	068,08	2439	12	66402	0602	2709	JADE CUP WITH EARS	8496	斝
JEA	075,09	3017	13	27247			(GRAPEFRUIT)		椵
JEA	075,10	2851	14	41947	0604	6425	(EVERGREEN SHRUB),CELTIS SINENSIS		榎
JEA	075,13	2911	17	41986	0604	8164	THEA SINENSIS		檟
JEA	102,00	3946	05	60500	0610	2677	ARMOR,1ST IN ORDER		甲
JEA	104,09	4051	14	00147	0600	6135	OBSTRUCTION IN THE INTESTINE		瘕
JEA	130,05	9113	09	76250		2682	SHOULDER BLADE		胛
JEA	154,06	6328	13	10806	3476	8162	(SURNAME)		賈
JEA	167,05	6905	13	86150		2678	POTASSIUM		鉀
JIAH	009,04	0116	06	28220		2745	PRICE	0305	价
JIAH	009,09	0250.0A	11	27247	0599	6130	VACATION		假
JIAH	009,13	0305	15	21286	0603	8163	PRICE	0116	價
JIAH	038,10	1268	13	43432	0596	5734	MARRY (A HUSBAND)		嫁
JIAH	075,05	2665	09	46904	0584	5319	FRAMEWORK		架
JIAH	115,10	4471	15	23932	0597	5733	SOW GRAIN		稼
JIAH	187,05	7468	15	46327	0591	4707	TO MOUNT,DRIVE(VEHICLE)		駕
JIAN	012,08	0369	10	80337	0830	5567	TAKE TWO(JOBS)SIMULTANEOUSLY		兼
JIAN	032,08	1017	11	77104	0825	0225	SOLID/FIRM		堅
JIAN	038,03	1169	06	41440	0818	2395	TRAITOR		奸
JIAN	038,06	1211	09	40444	0817	8984	ADULTERY		姦
JIAN	042,03	1423	06	90430	0865	5052	SHARP,SHREWD,POINT (OF NEEDLE)		尖
JIAN	043,10	1434.0A	13	48013	0831		IN AN EMBARRASSING SITUATION		尲
JIAN	043,15	1434.1A	18	48011	0831		IN AN EMBARRASSING SITUATION		尷
JIAN	046,10	152A	13	21727			RIDGE		嵴
JIAN	062,04	2055	08	53503	0866	6947	NARROW,SMALL		戔
JIAN	075,09	2793	13	43950	0827	7006	A BOX,LETTERS		椷
JIAN	075,12	2804	16	47920			INTERSTICE	7035	橺
JIAN	078,03	3005.1	07	12240			ANNIHILATE		歼
JIAN	078,17	3005	21	13250	0864	6990	ANNIHILATE		殲
JIAN	085,09	3289	12	38121		2903	CLEANSE,NAME OF A RIVER		湔

ROM	RAD	TEL	TOT	FC	MAT	OSH	TAG	CR	CHAR
JIAN	085,11	3362.0A	14	32121	0878	2027	IMBUE		
JIAN	086,09	3553	13	80332	0874	8786	PAN-FRY		
JIAN	086,12	3586	16	91861			EXTINGUISH(OF FIRE)		
JIAN	091,08	3653	12	23053	0867	6953	NOTE-PAPER,LETTER	4608	
JIAN	093,09	3682	13	25540	0858	6815	BULLOCK		
JIAN	108,05	4148.1	10	28107			SUPERVISE,PRISON		
JIAN	108,09	4148	14	78107	0839	0638	SUPERVISE,PRISON		
JIAN	118,08	4608	14	88503	0867	6960	NOTE-PAPER,LETTER	3653	
JIAN	118,16	4702	22	88153		6950	(SURNAME)		
JIAN	120,09	4873	15	23950	0829	7007	TO CLOSE/SEAL,LETTERS		
JIAN	120,10	4906	16	28937	0832	5577	THICK WATERPROOF SILK		
JIAN	130,04	5144	08	30227	0824	3580	SHOULDER		
JIAN	138,02	5329.1	08	77432			HARDSHIP		
JIAN	138,11	5329	17	47532	0834	5910	HARDSHIP		
JIAN	140,08	548C	12	44227			ALTHAEA ROSEA		
JIAN	140,08	5465	12	44777	0816	1487	(GRASS)/THEMEDA FORSBALI		
JIAN	140,10	5545	14	44237		5584	REED		
JIAN	140,12	5623	16	44227		3469	(SURNAME),EUPATORIUM CHINENSE		
JIAN	140,13	563A	17	44886			SEIGESBECKIA ORIENTALIS		
JIAN	152,06	9316	13	11240	0821		BIG PIG		
JIAN	164,10	682A	17	18637			BASE ALKALINE		
JIAN	167,17	9516	25	83150			AWL,SHARP IRON POINT		
JIAN	169,04	7034.0A	12	77227	2672	3489	INTERSTICE	7035	
JIAN	169,04	7035	12	77607	0835	3460	INTERSTICE		
JIAN	177,17	7277	26	40527		4588	SADDLE BLANKET		
JIAN	190,09	7578	19	72221		2904	TO HANG DOWN(HAIR)		
JIAN	195,10	7660	21	28337		5578	FLATFISH,A FLOUNDER		
JIAN	195,12	3028	23	27314			BONITO		
JIAN	196,10	7738	21	86327	0833	4650	MYTHICAL BIRD WITH 1 EYE AND 1 WING		
JEAN	009,13	0313	15	28286	0848	8003	FRUGAL,TO BE IN NEED		
JEAN	015,09	8096	11	33150	0828	7008	DIMINISH,SUBTRACT	3253	
JEAN	018,09	0477	11	80227	0876	4287	SCISSORS,CUT WITH SCISSORS		
JEAN	031,03	8188	06	60407	0823	1880	CHILD		

漸煎熸燖健監箋錢緘練肩艱菺菅蒹蕑薟豜醶鐗間鬋鰊鰹鶼儉減剪刅囝

ROM	RAD	TEL	TOT	FC	MAT	OSH	TAG	CR	CHAR
JEAN	032,09	1072	12	43150			SODA,ALKALI	A7769	墄
JEAN	062,10	2065	14	13650		6913	CARRY TO THE UTMOST,TO CUT	E0477	戬
JEAN	064,05	2245.1	08	54094			PICK UP,CHOOSE		拣
JEAN	064,09	2245	12	55096	0846	5531	PICK UP,CHOOSE		揀
JEAN	075,05	2687	09	50906	0845	5528	CARD,LETTER		柬
JEAN	075,07	8565	11	46910			SODA		梘
JEAN	075,13	2914	17	48986	0851	8011	INSPECT		檢
JEAN	085,09	3253	12	33150	0828	7009	DIMINISH,SUBTRACT	8096	減
JEAN	109,13	3636	18	68086		8001	EYELID		瞼
JEAN	112,03	1632	08	12640	2030		ALKALI/SODA	A7769	矸
JEAN	112,07	7769.1	12	18619			SODA/ALKALI,BASE(CHEM.)		硷
JEAN	112,09	4354	14	13650		7002	ALKALI/SODA	A7769	碱
JEAN	118,07	4600	13	88216		7629	BAMBOO WATER PIPE		筧
JEAN	118,12	4675	18	88227	0837	3470	SIMPLE		簡
JEAN	120,13	4942	19	44227		4018	COCOON		繭
JEAN	124,09	5054	15	80127	0876	3414	SCISSORS,CUT WITH SCISSORS	0477	翦
JEAN	140,06	4942.1	10	44136			COCOON		茧
JEAN	149,10	6190	17	30601	0842	1166	SPEAK OUT BOLDLY		謇
JEAN	149,15	6237	22	08627	0877	3415	STUPID,SHALLOW		謭
JEAN	157,06	3644	13	61140	0822	2389	CALLOUS	9336	趼
JEAN	157,06	9336	13	61140	0822	2389	CALLOUS	3644	趼
JEAN	157,10	6456	17	30801	0843	5986	LAME,DIFFICULTY,(SURNAME)		蹇
JEAN	159,14	6574	21	58017			CAGE-CART(FOR PRISONERS)		轞
JEAN	167,12	9505	20	87120		3461	WHIP(WEAPON)		鐧
JEAN	197,10	7769.2	21	28637	0852	5572	SODA/ALKALI,BASE(CHEM.)		鹻
JEAN	197,13	7769	24	28686	0852	8002	SODA/ALKALI,BASE(CHEM.)	A4354	鹼
JIANN	009,04	0115	06	25200	0862	2514	AN. FOR THING/CLOTHES,ITEM		件
JIANN	009,08	8057	10	23253			SHORT/SHALLOW,THIN PLATE		俴
JIANN	009,09	0256	11	25240	0854	6814	HEALTHY		健
JIANN	009,10	8068	12	28237		5574	TO ESCORT/FOLLOW		傔
JIANN	009,12	0301	14	21261	0879	1619	USURP		僭
JIANN	018,13	0494	15	82800	0849	2967	DOUBLE-EDGED SWORD		劍
JIANN	018,14	0494.1	16	87840	0849		DOUBLE-EDGED SWORD		劔

ROM	RAD	TEL	TOT	FC	MAT	OSH	TAG	CR	CHAR
JIANN	054,06	1696	09	15400	0853	6812	BUILD		建
JIANN	064,09	8449	12	55040	0855		TO BLOCK UP/FIX BOUNDARY		揵
JIANN	075,06	8554	10	44947			FENCE,PALISADE		梐
JIANN	075,09	2803	13	45944	0856		DOOR LOCK	A6943	楗
JIANN	075,14	2920.0A	18	48917	2690	0642	RAILING,BAR		槛
JIANN	082,09	7266.1	13	25714	0857	7403	SHUTTLECOCK		毽
JIANN	085,06	3151	09	34147	0880	3111	SUCCESSIVE,FLOWING WATER		洊
JIANN	085,11	3362	14	32121	0878	2027	GRADUAL(LY)		漸
JIANN	085,12	3386	15	37120	0836	3467	MOUNTAIN STREAM	8966	澗
JIANN	085,15	3457	18	33153	0869	6957	SPLASH		濺
JIANN	085,17	8718	20	34127			TO ARRIVE(OF WATER)		瀳
JIANN	093,04	8781	08	23504		2532	PROP UP		牮
JIANN	093,09	367A	13	26527			BOS GAURUS		犍
JIANN	096,06	8822	10	14147			(JADE)		珔
JIANN	108,05	4148.1A	10	28107			SUPERVISOR		监
JIANN	108,09	4148.0A	14	78107	0839	0638	SUPERVISOR		監
JIANN	109,12	4228	17	67020	2678	3490	TO SPY	6029	瞷
JIANN	112,12	8966	17	17620	0836	3462	MOUNTAIN STREAM	3386	磵
JIANN	118,09	4628	15	88221	0875	2905	ARROW		箭
JIANN	130,09	5213	13	75240		6816	GRISTLE		腱
JIANN	133,06	5269	12	14147			REPEAT,RETURN		荐
JIANN	137,07	5324.1	13	26410			WARSHIP		舰
JIANN	137,14	5324	20	26417	0840	0641	WARSHIP		艦
JIANN	140,06	5433	10	44247	0928	3112	RECOMMEND(A PERSON)	5644	荐
JIANN	140,13	5644	17	44227	0872	4587	RECOMMEND(A PERSON)	5433	薦
JIANN	147,00	6015	07	60210	0860	7583	SEE,INTERVIEW		見
JIANN	147,12	6029	19	76210	0838	7600	TO SPY	4228	覵
JIANN	149,09	6169	16	05696	0847	5530	ADMONISH		諫
JIANN	154,08	6345	15	63653	0868	6956	INEXPENSIVE,LOWLY		賤
JIANN	157,08	6432	15	63153	0870	6951	TREAD,WALK,FULFILL(A PROMISE)		踐
JIANN	167,05	7003.1	13	28109			MIRROR,TO VIEW,EXAMPLE		鉴
JIANN	167,09	6943	17	85140	0859	6813	DOOR LOCK KEY		鍵
JIANN	167,12	9505.0A	20	87120		3461	IRON AXLE TIP		鐧

ROM	RAD	TEL	TOT	FC	MAT	OSH	TAG	CR	CHAR
JIANN	167,14	7003	22	78109	0841	0375	MIRROR,TO VIEW,EXAMPLE	7002	
JIANN	167,14	7002	22	88117	0841	0639	MIRROR,TO VIEW,EXAMPLE	7003	
JIANN	169,04	7034.0B	12	77227	2672	3489	INTERSTICE,SEPARATE	7035.0A	
JIANN	169,04	7035.0A	12	77607	0835	3460	INTERSTICE,SEPARATE	7034.0B	
JIANN	177,11	7266	20	45540		6817	SHUTTLECOCK,SADDLE-QUIVER		
JIANN	184,08	7415	16	83753	0871	6952	FAREWELL DINNER,PRESERVES		
JIANG	009,13	0304	15	21216	0639	0060	RIGID/DEADLOCK,STIFF(CORPSE)	D8626	
JIANG	038,06	1203	09	90404	0637	8988	(SURNAME),GINGER	D5637	
JIANG	041,07	1412.1	10	32142			TAKE,(PRE-TRANSITIVE)		
JIANG	041,08	1412	11	27240	0656	3273	TAKE,(PRE-TRANSITIVE)		
JIANG	075,13	291A	17	41916			QUERCUS GLAUCA		
JIANG	078,13	8626	17	11216	0640	0062	STIFF(CORPSE)	B0304	
JIANG	085,03	3068	06	31110	0638	0095	LARGE RIVER		
JIANG	085,06	3364.1	10	37232			TO STARCH,SERUM,BROTH		
JIANG	085,11	3364	15	22232	0659	5649	TO STARCH,SERUM,BROTH		
JIANG	102,08	3984.1	13	10106	0643	0059	BORDER/BOUNDARY		
JIANG	102,14	3984	19	11116	0643	0064	BORDER/BOUNDARY		
JIANG	112,03	4260	08	11610	3263	0087	STONE BRIDGE		
JIANG	120,13	4943	19	21916	0641	0065	REINS,BRIDLE	7274	
JIANG	140,06	541A	10	44111			CYPERUS MALACCENSIS		
JIANG	140,13	5637	17	44106	0642	0066	GINGER	B1203	
JIANG	142,11	5831	17	27136			COSMOPSALTRIA OPALIFERA		
JIANG	151,03	6263	10	11110	0653	0085	COWPEAS/BLACK-EYED BEANS		
JIANG	151,06	6263.1	13	17154	0653		COWPEAS/BLACK-EYED BEANS		
JIANG	177,13	7274	22	41516	0641	0061	REINS,BRIDLE	4943	
JIANG	195,11	766N	22	22343			ORYZIAS LATIPES		
JEANG	037,06	1162.1	09	37430			A PRIZE,ENCOURAGE		
JEANG	037,11	1162	14	27430	0657	5036	A PRIZE,ENCOURAGE		
JEANG	075,06	2862.1	10	37904			OAR		
JEANG	075,11	2862	15	22904	0658	5359	OAR		
JEANG	127,10	5095	16	55947	0644		TO PLOUGH,TO SOW		
JEANG	130,12	523A	16	76236	0646		CALLOUS		
JEANG	140,11	5592	15	44242	0660	3276	(SURNAME)		

鑒
鑑
閒
間
鞬
餞
僵
姜
將
將
橿
殭
江
浆
漿
畺
疆
矼
繮
汪
薑
螿
缸
踔
韁
鱂
奖
獎
浆
桨
耩
膙
蔣

ROM	RAD	TEL	TOT	FC	MAT	OSH	TAG	CR	CHAR
JEANG	149,04	6199.1	11	05600			TO TALK,EXPLAIN		講
JEANG	149,08	6199.2	15	00647			TO TALK,EXPLAIN		講
JEANG	149,10	6199	17	05647	0645	4118	TO TALK,EXPLAIN		講
JEANG	181,10	7353	19	51486			HONEST/UPRIGHT		顜
JIANQ	022,04	0561	06	71712	0662	0805	CRAFTSMAN		匠
JIANQ	034,03	7100.1	06	27504	0654		DESCEND		夅
JIANQ	041,07	1412.1A	10	32142			A GENERAL		將
JIANQ	041,08	1412.0A	11	27240	0656	3273	A GENERAL		將
JIANQ	057,08	1730.0B	11	13236		8951	WILLFUL	1735.0A	強
JIANQ	057,09	1730.1B	12	16236		8922	WILLFUL		强
JIANQ	057,13	1735.0B	16	11216			WILLFUL	1730.0B	彊
JIANQ	085,06	3179	09	37154	0651	2589	FLOOD		洚
JIANQ	085,06	3364.1A	10	37232			STARCH PASTE		浆
JIANQ	085,11	3364.0A	15	22232			STARCH PASTE		漿
JIANQ	120,06	4829	12	27954	0652	2588	PURPLE-RED		絳
JIANQ	142,03	5725.0B	09	51110	2384	0094	RAINBOW		虹
JIANQ	164,06	6830.1	13	37601			THICK SAUCE,JAM		醬
JIANQ	164,11	6830	18	22601	0661	1965	THICK SAUCE,JAM		醬
JIANQ	170,06	7100	09	77254	0654	2587	DESCEND		降
JIAU	008,04	0074	06	00408	0702	6522	JOIN,PAY,DELIVER		交
JIAU	009,12	8072	14	20231	07²²	8758	CLEVER,PIGMIES		僬
JIAU	009,13	0315.0A	15	28240	0684	6372	BY MERE LUCK		傲
JIAU	030,13	8176	16	68040	0685	6370	WAIL,CALL,NEIGH		噭
JIAU	038,06	1207	09	40448	0704	6540	PRETTY,CUNNING,(SURNAME)		姣
JIAU	038,12	1293	15	42427	0690	3852	PAMPERED,LOVABLE		嬌
JIAU	060,13	1797.0A	16	28240	0686	6373	TO DESIRE		徼
JIAU	061,12	2010	15	92027		3845	ARROGANT	7524	憍
JIAU	066,07	2403	11	48440	0737	6337	TEACH		教
JIAU	075,08	2786	12	47940	0729	6067	PEPPER		椒
JIAU	085,12	3398	15	34111	0696	7501	TO WATER		澆
JIAU	086,08	3542	12	20331	0721	8751	SCORCHED		焦
JIAU	086,12	8761	16	90831	0724		CAUTERIZE/SCORCH		燋
JIAU	112,12	4339	17	10631	0725	8753	SHOAL ROCK,REEF		礁

ROM	RAD	TEL	TOT	FC	MAT	OSH	TAG	CR	CHAR
JIAU	118,12	4677	18	88227			LARGE PIPE		簥
JIAU	130,06	5231.1	10	70248			GLUE		胶
JIAU	130,11	5231	15	77222	0697	4211	GLUE		膠
JIAU	140,06	5414	10	44408	0710	6542	ZIZANIA AQUATICA		茭
JIAU	140,12	5604	16	44331	0726	8762	BANANA		蕉
JIAU	142,06	5754	12	50148	0711	6539	SCALY DRAGON		蛟
JIAU	142,12	5850	18	50131			EGGS OF MANTIS		螓
JIAU	157,06	9332	13	60148	0712	6524	BONES OF LEG,WRESTLE		胶
JIAU	159,11	6565	18	57022	0698	7097	CONFUSED/DISORDERLY		轇
JIAU	163,06	6738	09	07427	0714	2248	SUBURB		郊
JIAU	187,12	7524	21	72327	0694	3849	ARROGANT	2010	驕
JIAU	195,06	7640	17	20348	0717	6538	SHARK		鮫
JIAU	196,06	770C	17	07427		4652	MYCTICORAX PRASINOSCELES		鵁
JIAU	196,12	775E	23	27227			PHOENIX COCK		鶋
JIAU	196,12	7753	23	27327	0728	4664	EASTERN WREN		鷦
JYAU	030,18	0920	21	62046	1180	3209	CHEW		嚼
JEAU	009,06	8032	08	20248	0703	6529	HANDSOME		佼
JEAU	009,12	0299	14	24211	0695	7493	BY MERE LUCK	0315	僥
JEAU	009,13	0315	15	28240	0684		BY MERE LUCK	0299	傲
JEAU	018,11	0485	13	22900	0731	2939	DESTROY(BANDITS)	0531	剿
JEAU	018,11	0485.1	13	27920	0731		DESTROY(BANDITS)		勦
JEAU	019,11	0531	13	24927	0732	4821	DESTROY(BANDITS)	0485	勦
JEAU	038,06	1207.0A	09	40448	0704	6540	PRETTY,CUNNING		姣
JEAU	060,13	1797.0B	16	28240	0686	6373	BY MERE LUCK	0299	徼
JEAU	064,11	8464	14	52094			TO KNOCK/STRIKE		摤
JEAU	064,20	2383	23	57016	0699	7624	STIR,DISTURB		攪
JEAU	066,12	8493	16	28240			TIE UP(LACES)		敫
JEAU	085,09	3280.0A	12	39180	1230	5601	MARSH		湫
JEAU	094,06	3701	09	40248	0707	6533	SLY		狡
JEAU	104,04	400A	09	00127	0701	2716	COLIC WITH GRIPING		疞
JEAU	106,06	4109	11	20648	0708	6527	BRIGHT,WHITE		皎
JEAU	106,13	4117	18	28640	0687	6371	SPARKLING/BRIGHT,(SURNAME)		皦
JEAU	111,12	4255	17	82427	0692	3850	RECTIFY,DISSEMBLE		矯

ROM	RAD	TEL	TOT	FC	MAT	OSH	TAG	CR	CHAR
JEAU	118,06	4584	12	88408			BAMBOO ROPE		
JEAU	120,06	4819	12	20948	0709	6537	TO TURN/TWIST,HANG(A CRIMINAL)		
JEAU	120,13	4945	19	28940	0688	6375	HAND IN/HAND OVER		
JEAU	130,07	5183	11	77220	1177	2142	FOOT,A KICK,ROLE	5223	
JEAU	130,09	5223	13	77220	1177	2123	FOOT,A KICK,ROLE	5183	
JEAU	142,12	9239	18	52127			(SURNAME),(INSECT)		
JEAU	148,00	6037	07	27227	1174	3699	HORN,ANGLE		
JEAU	159,06	6525	13	50048	0713	6531	COMPARE,THAN		
JEAU	167,06	6890	14	80148	0715	6523	TO CUT(WITH SCISSORS),SCISSORS		
JEAU	184,06	7398	14	80748	0716	6530	DUMPLINGS WITH MEAT FILLING		
JEAU	195,12	9657	23	22327			(FISH)		
JEAU	197,10	777A	21	28637	0852	5572	ALKALOID		
JIAW	030,02	0663	05	64000	0700	2713	TO CALL		
JIAW	030,04	0663.1	07	64000	0700	2696	TO CALL		
JIAW	030,11	8164	14	66660			LOUD		
JIAW	030,12	0887	15	60031	0723	8752	CHEW		
JIAW	046,12	1540	15	22727	0746	3844	HIGHEST PEAK		
JIAW	060,13	1797	16	28240	0686	6373	GO AROUND,BOUNDARY		
JIAW	064,06	2175	09	50048	0705	6532	COMPARE,CRITICISE		
JIAW	066,07	2403.0A	11	48440	0719	6337	TEACHING,RELIGION		
JIAW	066,09	8490	13	28240	0478	6369	SONG		
JIAW	068,10	8497	14	54400		2701	TO MEASURE		
JIAW	075,06	2699.0A	10	40948	0706	6536	TO CHECK,PROOFREAD		
JIAW	085,10	3330	13	37161			PLACE NAME IN KWANGTUNG		
JIAW	096,06	3795	10	10148			(DIVINATION DEVICE)		
JIAW	106,18	4118	23	22646	0733	3210	PURE		
JIAW	116,05	4509	10	30727	0718		CELLAR	4512	
JIAW	116,07	4512	12	30601	0718	1340	CELLAR		
JIAW	147,04	6030.1A	11	00216		7627	A NAP/A SLEEP		
JIAW	147,05	6030.2A	12	90216			NAP/SLEEP		
JIAW	147,13	6030.0A	20	77216	1178	7623	NAP/SLEEP		
JIAW	149,02	9282	09	84600			TO CALL	0663	
JIAW	159,06	6525.0A	13	50048	0713	6531	COMPARE,CLEAR/DISTINCT		

笑絞繳腳腳蟜角較鉸餃鱎鹻叫髐噍嶠徼挍教敽斠校滘玌爵節窖竟覺矕訧較

ROM	RAD	TEL	TOT	FC	MAT	OSH	TAG	CR	CHAR
JIAW	159,12	6569	19	52027	0693	3847	SEDAN CHAIR		轎
JIAW	164,07	6806	14	14647	0720	3109	YEAST		酵
JIAW	164,12	6831	19	10631	0727	8756	PERFORM SACRIFICE		醮
JIAW	164,18	6842	25	12646	0734	3211	DRAIN A GOBLET		釂
JIE	009,09	0253	11	21262	0621	1676	IN COMPANY WITH		偕
JIE	030,09	0813	12	61062	0622	1674	HARMONIOUS(OF MUSIC)		喈
JIE	030,10	0842	13	68011	0763	0099	SIGH		嗟
JIE	032,09	1038	12	41161	0625	1673	STAIRS,RANK OR STEP	7132	堦
JIE	064,08	2234	11	50044	0800	8991	JOIN,RECEIVE		接
JIE	064,09	2263	12	56027	0776	4392	LIFT OFF (A COVER)		揭
JIE	085,09	3278	12	31162			FLOWING(OF WATER)		湝
JIE	106,01	8895	06	27610			(SURNAME)		皀
JIE	106,04	4105	09	21602	0620	1672	IN ALL CASES		皆
JIE	115,09	4465	14	21962	0624	1681	SORGHUM OR CORN STALKS		稭
JIE	120,06	4814.0A	12	24961	0782	1214	TO BEAR(FRUIT),STURDY,KNOT		結
JIE	144,06	5894	12	21221	0619	3015	STREET		街
JIE	145,09	5961	14	37234			SHORT GARMENT		褉
JIE	170,04	7132.1	07	78220			STAIRS,RANK OR STEP		阶
JIE	170,09	7132	12	71262	0625	1677	STAIRS,RANK OR STEP	1038	階
JIE	170,10	7133.0B	13	71227	3319	3912	SEPARATED BY		隔
JYE	009,08	8053	10	25281		6043	HANDSOME	1240	健
JYE	009,09	0245	11	26227	0775	4387	FORCEFUL/MARTIAL		偈
JYE	009,10	0267	12	25294	0774	5348	HERO,HEROIC	2638	傑
JYE	018,05	0447	07	42700	0771	2979	PLUNDER	0506	刧
JYE	018,05	0506.1	07	47720	0771	4284	PLUNDER		刦
JYE	018,06	0506.2	08	47720	0771	4318	PLUNDER		刼
JYE	019,05	0506	07	44727	0771	4834	PLUNDER		劫
JYE	019,06	0512	08	44627		4799	CAREFUL,FIRM,DILIGENT		劼
JYE	026,00	0599	02	77220	0798	2113	JOINT		卩
JYE	026,00	0599-1	02	77712	0798	7192	A JOINT		卪
JYE	038,08	1240	11	45481	0788	6046	HANDSOME	8053	婕
JYE	039,00	1312	03	17407	0784	3161	ALONE,SMALL,MOSQUITO LARVAE		孑
JYE	046,04	8326	07	77772			MOUNTAIN PEAK		岊

ROM	RAD	TEL	TOT	FC	MAT	OSH	TAG	CR	CHAR
JYE	050,13	1623	16	48227			WIPE		櫩
JYE	062,10	2066	14	43250	0793	6977	CUT OFF (A LENGTH),A SECTION		截
JYE	064,06	2159	09	54061	0780	1211	LABORING HARD,PRESSED,ANTAGONISTIC		拮
JYE	064,08	2212	11	55081	0789	6044	RAPID VICTORY		捷
JYE	075,04	2638	08	40339	0774	8794	HERO/HEROIC	0267	杰
JYE	075,06	2708	10	25904	0773	5346	(EMPEROR OF HSIA DYNASTY),CRUEL		桀
JYE	075,06	2720	10	44961	0781	1212	PLATYCODON GRANDIFLORUS		桔
JYE	075,07	2741	11	44938	0612	5120	CHOPSTICKS		楬
JYE	075,09	8579	13	46927		4393	A PEG,TALLY/SCORE		榤
JYE	075,10	2852	14	45994		5349	A STUMP ON WHICH CHICKENS ROOST		橤
JYE	075,15	2802	19	48927	0796	2131	COMB		櫛
JYE	085,06	3381.1	09	34161			CLEAN		洁
JYE	085,12	3381	15	37193	0772	8463	CLEAN	4817.0A	潔
JYE	104,02	4081.1	07	00127			FURUNCLE/BOIL		疖
JYE	104,15	4081	20	00127	0797	2132	FURUNCLE/BOIL		癤
JYE	109,08	4208	13	65081	0790	6042	EYELASHES		睫
JYE	112,09	4309	14	16627	0777	4381	STONE TABLET		碣
JYE	117,09	4550	14	06127	0778	4379	EXHAUST		竭
JYE	118,08	4623.0A	14	88801	0791	6048	FAN		箑
JYE	118,09	4634	15	88727	0795	2130	SECTION,FESTIVAL,TEMPERATE		節
JYE	120,06	4814	12	24961	0782	1214	TO KNOT,A BOND,TO BEAR		結
JYE	120,06	4817.0A	12	57903	2634	8462	CLEAN	3381	絜
JYE	123,09	5031	15	86527	0779	4390	CASTRATE A RAM,DEER'S SKIN		羯
JYE	125,06	5077	12	44104	6314	0272	SENILE		耋
JYE	140,02	4634.1	06	44227			SECTION,FESTIVAL,TEMPERATE		节
JYE	142,06	5755	12	54161			BEETLE		蛣
JYE	142,14	586C	20	53150			CRAB/NEPTUNUS PELAGICUS		蟹
JYE	145,06	9255	11	34261		1210	LIFT UP A DRESS		袺
JYE	145,06	5930.0A	11	38261	0606	1192	(COLLAR)		袷
JYE	149,03	6063	10	01640	0786	2378	ACCUSE,PRY		訐
JYE	149,06	6113	13	04661	0783	1207	SCOLD,INVESTIGATE,RESTRAIN		詰
JYE	170,10	7133.0A	13	71227	3319	3912	PARTITION		隔
JYE	195,06	9643	17	24361		1216	OYSTER		鮚

ROM	RAD	TEL	TOT	FC	MAT	OSH	TAG	CR	CHAR
JYE	195,15	767D	26	28327			ACHEILOGNATHUS LIMBATUM		鱊
JIEE	038,05	1192.0A	08	45427	6948	4755	OLDER SISTER	1195	姊
JIEE	038,05	1195	08	47410	0766	0620	OLDER SISTER		姐
JIEE	075,12	290B	15	47952			QUERC- IN CHEM. COMPOUNDS		槲
JIEE	120,06	4814.0B	12	24961	0782	1214	A KNOT		結
JIEE	148,06	6043	13	27252	0626	2525	UNTIE,EMANCIPATE,EXPLAIN		解
JIEE	148,06	6043.1	13	28251	0626	2550	UNTIE,EMANCIPATE,EXPLAIN		鮮
JIEH	009,02	0094	04	80220	0629	2742	LIE BETWEEN,INTRODUCE		介
JIEH	009,04	0116.0A	06	28220	0630	2745	SERVANT,MIDDLEMAN,GREAT/GOOD		价
JIEH	009,08	0234	10	24261	0765	1511	BORROW,LEND,BY MEANS OF	G5659	借
JIEH	043,04	1435.0A	07	48012	3187		IN AN EMBARRASSING SITUATION		尬
JIEH	044,05	1447.1	08	77267	0636	1843	PERIOD,ARRIVE AT (PLACE OR TIME)		届
JIEH	044,05	1447	08	77272	0636	0970	PERIOD,ARRIVE AT (PLACE OR TIME)		屆
JIEH	053,13	1685.0A	16	00241		2530	OFFICE		廨
JIEH	062,03	2054	07	53400	0627	6972	SWEAR OFF,WARN AGAINST		戒
JIEH	096,04	3775	08	18120	0631	2743	JADE TABLET INDICATING RANK		玠
JIEH	102,04	3954	09	60228	0632	2748	BOUNDARY		界
JIEH	104,04	4003	09	00128	0633	2747	SCABIES		疥
JIEH	127,08	9101	14	54961	0767	1514	BY MEANS OF	5659	藉
JIEH	140,04	5354	00	44228	0634	2749	MUSTARD		芥
JIEH	140,14	5659	18	44961	0767	1515	BY MEANS OF	C0234	藉
JIEH	142,04	5735	10	58120	0635	2746	HORNED TOAD		蚧
JIEH	145,10	596A	15	30227	0764	3960	DIAPER		褯
JIEH	148,06	6043.0A	13	27252	0626	2525	TRANSPORT UNDER GUARD		解
JIEH	148,06	6043.1A	13	28251	0626	2550	TRANSPORT UNDER GUARD		鮮
JIEH	149,07	6135	14	03650	0628	6973	COMMANDMENT,PROHIBIT		誡
JIEH	170,10	7133.0C	13	71227	3319	3912	NEIGHBOR/NEIGHBORING		隔
JIEH	203,06	7822.0A	18	64361	2537	1215	CRAFTY,(PHONETIC)		黠
JIN	009,02	0093	04	80207	1053	2842	NOW		今
JIN	050,00	1577	03	40227	1056	3944	TOWEL		巾
JIN	069,00	2443	04	72221	1059	2008	CATTY	6038	斤
JIN	085,06	3160	09	35107	1081	2624	FERRY,TIENTSIN		津
JIN	096,12	3871	16	10131			(GEM)		璡

ROM	RAD	TEL	TOT	FC	MAT	OSH	TAG	CR	CHAR
JIN	110,04	4244	09	18227	1115	2846	SYMPATHIZE,BOAST,ESTEEM		矜
JIN	113,07	4381	11	37247	1094	6191	EVIL FORCE		祲
JIN	113,08	4391.0A	13	44901	1077	8386	ENDURE		禁
JIN	118,06	4585	12	88227	1058	4810	MUSCLE		筋
JIN	145,04	5912	09	38227	1080	2845	OVERLAPPING PART OF CHINESE GOWN	5992	衿
JIN	145,13	5992	18	34291	1080	8388	OVERLAPPING PART OF CHINESE GOWN	5912	襟
JIN	148,02	6038	09	24227	1059	4811	CATTY	2443	觔
JIN	167,00	6855	08	80109	1057	0369	MONEY/GOLD,METAL		金
JIIN	009,02	0284.1	04	27240			MERELY		仅
JIIN	009,11	0284	13	24214	1066	0422	MERELY		僅
JIIN	009,14	0324	16	25217	1083	0729	TO THE UTMOST	4147.1A	儘
JIIN	026,06	0610	08	17712	1076	7230	NUPTIAL WINECUP		巹
JIIN	027,11	1668.1	13	71214	1068		HUT,CAREFUL		厪
JIIN	032,11	1070	14	44114	1067	0419	PLASTER WITH MUD,BURY		墐
JIIN	044,03	4147.1A	06	77303			TO THE UTMOST	0324	尽
JIIN	053,11	1668	14	00214	1068	0426	HUT,CAREFUL		厪
JIIN	075,11	2865	15	44914	1070	0425	TRANSIENT,HIBISCUS SYRIACUS		槿
JIIN	096,11	3866	15	14114	1072	0420	BRILLIANCY(OF GEMS)		瑾
JIIN	120,04	4868.1	10	27903			TIGHT,STRICT		紧
JIIN	120,08	4868	14	77903	1064	8468	TIGHT,STRICT		緊
JIIN	140,08	5477	12	44104	1065	0417	VIOLA VERECUNDA		堇
JIIN	147,11	6027	18	46110	1073	7587	VISIT A SUPERIOR		覲
JIIN	149,11	6210	18	04614	1074	0421	CAUTIOUS		謹
JIIN	167,08	6930	16	86127	1063	3967	BROCADE,EMBROIDERED WORK		錦
JINN	019,07	0513.0A	09	14127	1119	4785	STRENGTH		劲
JINN	030,13	0891	16	64091	1079	8337	UNABLE TO SPEAK/SILENT		噤
JINN	038,04	1180	07	48427	1054	2848	WIFE OF MOTHER'S BROTHER		妗
JINN	040,10	1386	13	30147	1093	6193	SOAK,IMMERSE	3190	寖
JINN	044,03	4147.1	06	77303	1082	8960	EXHAUST		尽
JINN	064,10	8452	13	51061	1089	1500	STICK INTO,SHAKE,STRIKE		搢
JINN	072,06	2516	10	10601	1088	1499	CHIN DYNASTY		晋
JINN	072,06	2516.1	10	10601	1088	1503	CHIN DYNASTY		晉
JINN	078,11	8625	15	14214	1071	0424	DIE OF HUNGER		殣

ROM	RAD	TEL	TOT	FC	MAT	OSH	TAG	CR	CHAR
JINN	085,07	3190	10	37147	1092	6192	SOAK,IMMERSE		浸
JINN	086,06	3612.1	10	97833			ASHES/EMBERS		烬
JINN	086,14	3612	18	95817	1085	0731	ASHES/EMBERS		燼
JINN	108,09	4147	14	50107	1082	0728	EXHAUST		盡
JINN	113,08	4391	13	44901	1077	8386	PROHIBIT		禁
JINN	120,10	4897	16	21961	1090	1501	RED SILK		縉
JINN	140,13	563C	17	44521			SANICULA		薪
JINN	140,14	5660	18	44107	1086	0733	LOYAL,ARTHRAXON CILIARE		藎
JINN	154,09	6353	16	50806	1087	8240	FAREWELL PRESENTS	6367	賮
JINN	154,14	6367	21	65817	1087	0732	FAREWELL PRESENTS	6353	贐
JINN	162,04	6602	08	32302	1061	6640	NEAR		近
JINN	162,04	6651.1	08	35300			ADVANCE,ENTER		进
JINN	162,08	6651	12	30301	1091	6605	ADVANCE,ENTER		進
JINN	177,04	7246	13	42521	1062	2023	MARTINGALE,STINGY,(SURNAME)		靳
JINN	184,11	7431	19	84714	1075	0423	FAMINE/NO CROPS		饉
JING	008,06	0079	08	00906	1127	8398	CAPITAL		京
JING	010,12	0352	14	44216	1132	7556	TO BE FEARFUL/APPREHENSIVE		兢
JING	061,08	7528.1	11	90096			ALARM		惊
JING	070,07	2468	11	08214	1142	0399	BANNER,MAKE MANIFEST		旌
JING	072,08	2533	12	60660	1141	1493	CRYSTAL		晶
JING	085,07	3193	10	31111	1121	0130	NAME OF A RIVER		涇
JING	109,08	4200	13	65027	1147	3687	EYE		睛
JING	118,08	4621.0A	14	88227	0923		LITTLE BASKETS		箐
JING	119,08	4737	14	95927	1149	3692	FINE,PROFICIENT,ESSENCE		精
JING	120,07	4842	13	21911	1123	0129	PASS THROUGH,CLASSICS/SACRED BOOK		經
JING	140,06	5427	10	42400	1116	2894	THORNS/BRAMBLES,(SURNAME)		荆
JING	140,07	5449	11	44101	2761	0132	STEM		莖
JING	140,08	5464	12	44227	1150	3698	FLOWER OF LEEK		菁
JING	187,13	7528	23	48327	1140	4717	ALARM		驚
JING	195,08	7650	19	20396	1158	8403	WHALE		鯨
JING	198,08	779C	19	00296			SAMBUR		麖
JIING	007,02	0064	04	55000	1143	2828	WELL,WARN	D6226	井
JIING	009,13	0311	15	28240	1139	6382	WARN,	6226	儆

ROM	RAD	TEL	TOT	FC	MAT	OSH	TAG	CR	CHAR
JIING	018,07	0462	09	12100	1118	2862	CUT THE THROAT		剄
JIING	061,12	2005	15	96096	1130	8408	AWAKEN		憬
JIING	072,08	2529	12	60906	1129	8406	SCENERY,CIRCUMSTANCE,BRIGHT		景
JIING	096,12	3878	16	16196	1131	8407	LUSTER OF GEM		璟
JIING	096,13	3899	17	18140			(GEM)		璥
JIING	116,04	4501	09	30558	1144	2832	PITFALL,HOLE	7088	穽
JIING	149,13	6226	20	48601	1139	1171	WARN		警
JIING	167,04	687C	12	85100			HYDRAZONIUM		鉙
JIING	170,04	7088	07	75200	1144	2830	PITFALL,HOLE	4501	阱
JIING	181,07	7338	16	11186	1126	8245	NECK		頸
JINQ	015,08	0403	10	32157	1153	3374	CLEAN	3228	净
JINQ	015,08	8095	10	35121	1169	3696	COOL/FRESH,TO COOL		凊
JINQ	019,07	0513	09	14127	1119	4785	STALWART/STURDY		勁
JINQ	032,11	1064	14	40116	1136	7576	BOUNDARY,TERRITORY,CIRCUMSTANCES		境
JINQ	060,06	1777.1	09	21214	1120		PATH		徑
JINQ	060,07	1777	10	21211	1120	0124	PATH		徑
JINQ	066,09	2417	13	48640	1138	6381	RESPECTFUL,TO OFFER		敬
JINQ	085,08	3228	11	32157	1153	3375	CLEAN	0403	淨
JINQ	085,16	8716	19	32157			CLEAN	3228	瀞
JINQ	094,11	3741	14	40216		7578	AN ANIMAL WHICH EATS ITS MOTHER		獍
JINQ	104,07	3997	12	00111	1122	0131	SPASM		痙
JINQ	117,05	4552.1	10	00216			COMPETE		竟
JINQ	117,06	4544	11	00216	1135	7575	INDEED/ACTUALLY		竟
JINQ	117,15	4552	20	00216	1133	7553	COMPETE		競
JINQ	130,04	3661	08	75200			HYDRAZINE		肼
JINQ	130,07	5185	11	71211	1124	0128	LOWER PART OF LEG		脛
JINQ	162,07	6635	11	31301	1125	6599	DIRECTLY		逕
JINQ	167,11	6975	19	80116	1137	7577	MIRROR		鏡
JINQ	174,05	7231	13	05127	1148	3684	PACIFY,QUIET		靖
JINQ	174,07	7232	15	56210	1152	7601	MAKE UP(FACE)		靚
JINQ	174,08	7234	16	52257	1154	3372	QUIET/NOT MOVING		靜
JIONG	013,00	0372	02	77220	1238	3808	ENVIRONS,WILDERNESS	0990	冂
JIONG	013,03	0372.1	05	77220	1238	3819	ENVIRONS,WILDERNESS		冏

ROM	RAD	TEL	TOT	FC	MAT	OSH	TAG	CR	CHAR
JIONG	032,05	0990	08	47120	1238	3820	ENVIRONS,WILDERNESS	0372	坰
JIONG	063,05	2079	09	30227	1239	3826	SHUT		扃
JEONG	013,05	0376	07	77220		3894	ABUTILON AVICENNAE(PLANT)		冏
JEONG	063,05	2079.0A	09	30227	1239	3826	SHUT,CLEAR AND LUCID		扄
JEONG	085,05	8664	08	37120	1240	3825	VAST		洞
JEONG	086,05	3518	09	97820	1241	3823	BRIGHT,CLEAR	8741	炯
JEONG	086,07	8741	11	97820	1241	3895	BRIGHT/CLEAR	3518	焗
JEONG	086,09	8753	12	61809			FIRE		煛
JEONG	086,11	3585	15	21886	3719		BLAZE		熲
JEONG	116,07	4515	12	30567	1716	1149	EMBARRASSED,DISTRESSED		窘
JEONG	120,05	4812	11	27920	1242	3824	MONOTONE GARMENT WITH NO LINING	5971	絅
JEONG	145,10	5971	16	19732	1242	5826	MONOTONE GARMENT WITH NO LINING	4812	褧
JEONG	162,05	6608	09	37302	1243	6693	DISTANT		迥
JEONG	187,05	7477	15	77320	1244	3822	IN GOOD CONDITION(AS A HORSE)		駉
JIOU	064,09	8444	13	29502	1207	3356	GATHER/COLLECT		揫
JIOU	064,09	2262	12	59080	1212	5598	TO CLUTCH		揪
JIOU	075,11	2872	15	47922		4212	HANG DOWN,(SURNAME)		樛
JIOU	085,09	3280	12	39180	1230	5601	POOL		湫
JIOU	116,02	4496	07	30417	1199	7911	INVESTIGATE,AFTER ALL		究
JIOU	120,02	4763	08	24900	1195	2714	GATHER TOGETHER,TO INVESTIGATE	4776.0A	糾
JIOU	120,04	4776.0A	10	24900			GATHER TOGETHER,TO INVESTIGATE	4763	紏
JIOU	191,16	7596	26	77117	1186	3431	(DRAW)LOTS		鬮
JIOU	196,02	7682	13	47027	1200	4661	TURTLEDOVE/TURTUR ORIENTALIS		鳩
JYOU	195,11	766E	22	25366			(FISH)		鰽
JEOU	004,02	0036	03	27800	1188	4972	LONG (TIME)		久
JEOU	005,01	0046	02	40017	1198	7903	NINE		九
JEOU	061,09	1934.0A	12	99080			WORRY,CHANGE COUNTENANCE		愀
JEOU	086,03	3502	07	27809	1189	5619	CAUTERIZE		灸
JEOU	096,03	3773	07	17130	1198	4973	NINE(FRAUDPROOF),(BLACK STONE)		玖
JEOU	156,02	6383	09	42800	1196	5954	VALIANT		赳
JEOU	164,03	6794	10	31160	1208	1964	WINE/LIQUOR		酒
JEOU	179,00	7295	09	11101	1197	0502	LEEK	7296	韭
JEOU	179,04	7296	13	44101	1197	0503	LEEK	7295	韮

ROM	RAD	TEL	TOT	FC	MAT	OSH	TAG	CR	CHAR
JIOW	009,12	0291	14	23214	1211	7720	TO RENT,HIRE		
JIOW	030,05	0736	08	28604	1192	1432	BLAME		
JIOW	043,09	1432	12	03914	1210	7718	AT ONCE,THEN		
JIOW	053,11	1673	14	00214	1201	7733	A STABLE		
JIOW	064,07	2189	10	53032			TO RESCUE	2405	
JIOW	066,07	2405	11	48140	1193	6390	RESCUE		
JIOW	072,01	5283.1	05	26000	1205	1494	OLD(OPPOSITE OF NEW)		
JIOW	075,05	2943	09	41918	1191	0815	BIER		
JIOW	075,06	2721	10	47970	1203	1048	SAPIUM SEBIFERUM,TALLOW TREE		
JIOW	104,03	3998	08	00187	1190	4976	CHRONIC DISEASE		
JIOW	116,02	4496.0A	07	30417	1199	7911	INVESTIGATE,AFTER ALL		
JIOW	134,00	5273	06	77770	1202	1047	MORTAR		
JIOW	134,07	5279	13	77427	1204	4848	MATERNAL UNCLE		
JIOW	134,12	5283	18	44777	1205	1049	OLD(OPPOSITE OF NEW)		
JIOW	195,06	764G	17	27312			SPHYRAENA SCHLEGELI		
JIOW	196,12	7750	23	03327	1237	4690	BLACK EAGLE,CONDOR,CRUEL		
JIU	009,08	0215	10	27281	1557	8068	ENTIRELY/WITHOUT EXCEPTION		
JIU	038,08	8282	11	47440			(FEMININE NAME),(STAR)		
JIU	044,05	1446.1	08	77218	1535	0556	RESIDE		
JIU	044,05	1446	08	77264	1535	1303	RESIDE		
JIU	046,05	8327	08	27710	1574		ROCKY HILL	8933	
JIU	064,05	2153	08	57020	1542	4420	CAPTURE,RESTRAIN,ADHERE		
JIU	064,08	2207.0A	11	57064	1537	1309	SICKNESS OF HAND		
JIU	075,08	2791	12	47964		1310	ZELKOWA ACUMINATA		
JIU	085,05	3107.0A	08	37110	1575	0621	(SURNAME),NAME OF A RIVER		
JIU	094,05	3700	08	47210	1576	0610	TO SPY/LIE IN AMBUSH,(APE)		
JIU	096,08	3818	12	17164			ORNAMENTAL GEMS FOR BELT		
JIU	104,05	4013	10	00117	1577	0623	GANGRENE		
JIU	112,05	8933	10	17610	1574		ROCKY HILL	8327	
JIU	122,05	4991	10	60107		0624	NET FOR CATCHING RABBITS		
JIU	130,08	9130	12	77264			DRIED POULTRY		
JIU	140,05	5392	09	44107	1578	0632	SACK CLOTH,(HEMP),(SURNAME)		
JIU	140,08	5484	12	44117	6821	0622	PICKLED FRUIT OR VEGETABLE,MARSH		

傲咎就廐捄救旧枢柏疚究臼舅舊鮨鷲俱嫗屄居岨拘据椐沮狙琚疽砠置腒苴萐

ROM	RAD	TEL	TOT	FC	MAT	OSH	TAG	CR	CHAR
JIU	142,05	5747.0A	11	57110	1619	0619	CENTIPEDE		蛆
JIU	142,08	577C	14	57164			HYDROPHILUS COGNATUS		蛷
JIU	145,08	5957	13	37264	1538	1308	GARMENT		裾
JIU	156,05	6388	12	47801	1579	5946	MARK TIME,HESITATE		趄
JIU	159,00	6508.0A	07	50006	0280	2646	VEHICLE ON LAND		車
JIU	167,07	3767.0A	15	87127			MEND CHINAWARE WITH STAPLES	6920.0A	鋦
JIU	167,08	6920.0A	16	87164	1540	1305	TO MEND(CHINA)WITH STAPLES	3767.0A	鋸
JIU	172,05	7168	13	70114	1580	0869	OSPREY,(FISH-HAWK)		雎
JIU	187,05	7467	15	77320	1543	4422	COLT		駒
JYU	009,07	0182	09	27227	1585	4270	NARROW		侷
JYU	020,06	0547	08	27920	1587	4457	RECEIVE WITH BOTH HANDS	2239	匊
JYU	044,04	1444	07	77227	1584	4268	OFFICE		局
JYU	064,07	2183	10	57027			STRUCTURE FOR CARRYING DIRT	4271	挶
JYU	064,08	2239	11	57020	1587	4460	RECEIVE WITH BOTH HANDS	0547	掬
JYU	075,06	2720.0A	10	44961	0781	1212	TANGERINE	2904	桔
JYU	075,08	276B	12	47920			FAGUS SYLVATICA		椈
JYU	075,12	2904	16	47927	1592	3906	TANGERINE	2720.0A	橘
JYU	093,08	3674	12	27581			(BOVINE)		犋
JYU	140,08	5468	12	44927	1589	4461	CHRYSANTHEMUM		菊
JYU	157,07	6430	14	67127	1586	4269	NARROW/CRAMPED		跼
JYU	157,08	6440	15	67120			4458	LEATHER BALL		踘
JYU	163,09	9402	12	27427			PLACE NAME		鄐
JYU	163,09	9402.1	12	77427			PLACE NAME		郰
JYU	167,07	3767	15	87127			CURIUM		鋦
JYU	177,08	7263	17	47520	1590		TO BOW,(SURNAME)		鞠
JYU	177,09	7265	18	47520	1591	4431	MAKE JUDICIAL INVESTIGATION		鞫
JYU	195,07	764P	18	27327			COTTUS POLLUX		鮈
JYU	196,04	7694	15	25330	1582	5213	SHRIKE		鴃
JYU	208,08	785E	21	76718			TREE KANGAROO		鼰
JEU	002,08	5282.1	09	90503			TO LIFT(UP HIGH),ELECT		舉
JEU	030,05	0731	08	67010	1573	0606	CHEW		咀
JEU	075,05	2681.0A	09	41917	1546	0841	SALIX MULTINERVIS		柜

ROM	RAD	TEL	TOT	FC	MAT	OSH	TAG	CR	CHAR
JEU	075,05	2667.0A	09	47920	3412		CITRUS MEDICA		枸
JEU	075,10	2829	14	81904			CARPENTER'S SQUARE,RULE	4251	榘
JEU	075,17	8603	21	47953	1568	2502	ZEIKOWA ACUMINATA		櫸
JEU	085,05	3107	08	37110	1575	0621	TO STOP;DESTROY		沮
JEU	111,05	4251	10	81417	1548	0840	CARPENTER'S SQUARE,RULE		矩
JEU	118,07	4598	13	88606		1476	ROUND BAMBOO BASKET		筥
JEU	118,17	4709.0A	23	88303		6746	FRAME FOR RAISING SILKWORMS		簴
JEU	134,10	5282	17	77503	1567	2501	TO LIFT(UP HIGH),ELECT		舉
JEU	140,05	5392.0A	09	44107	1578	0632	STRAW PAD IN THE SHOE		苴
JEU	140,07	5447	11	44606	1569	1475	(FIBROUS PLANT)		莒
JEU	140,10	5540	14	44127		4415	BETEL		蒟
JEU	157,09	6449	16	62127	1570	4082	WALK ALONE,HUNCHBACKED		踽
JEU	211,05	7880	20	27710	6820	0605	UNEVEN TEETH,IRREGULAR		齟
JIUH	009,08	0240	10	27264	1536	1307	STUBBORN		倨
JIUH	009,08	0215.0A	10	27281	1557		A SOCIAL CLUB		俱
JIUH	012,06	0367	08	77801	1556	8065	INSTRUMENT		具
JIUH	018,08	0489.1	10	72200			SEVERE,DRAMA		劇
JIUH	018,13	0489	15	22200	1593	2955	SEVERE,DRAMA		劇
JIUH	030,02	0658	05	27620	1541	4413	SENTENCE		句
JIUH	032,08	1056	11	46134	1558	8066	DIKED POND		埧
JIUH	040,11	1397	14	30404	1571	9020	POOR,RUSTIC	4526	寠
JIUH	044,14	1464	17	77244	1572	9009	SANDALS		屨
JIUH	048,02	1565	05	71717	1544	0834	HUGE		巨
JIUH	061,08	2040.1	11	96034	1560		TO FEAR		懼
JIUH	061,18	2040	21	96014	1560	0942	TO FEAR		懼
JIUH	064,05	2147	08	51017	1545	0839	REFUSE		拒
JIUH	064,08	2207	11	57064	1537	1309	SEIZE,ACT IN ACCORDANCE WITH	2354	据
JIUH	064,13	2354	16	51032	1563	5714	SEIZE,ACT IN ACCORDANCE	2207	據
JIUH	086,05	3515	09	91817	1547	0844	TORCH		炬
JIUH	109,13	4234.0B	18	66214			STARTLED		瞿
JIUH	115,05	4445	10	21917	1549	0843	BLACK MILLET		秬
JIUH	116,11	4526	16	30404	1571		POOR/RUSTIC	1397	窶
JIUH	118,12	4690	18	88217			UPRIGHT POSTS OF A DRUM FRAME		簴

ROM	RAD	TEL	TOT	FC	MAT	OSH	TAG	CR	CHAR
JIUH	128,08	5112	14	17232	1581	5705	GATHER,FORM GATHERING		聚
JIUH	140,05	5385	09	44717	1551	0845	(LETTUCE)		苣
JIUH	141,07	571A	13	21232			INVUS SILENUS		豦
JIUH	141,08	5715	14	21281		8025	BELL PENDANT STAND		虡
JIUH	149,05	6093	12	01617	1552	0838	HOW (INTERJ. OF SURPRISE)		詎
JIUH	157,04	6400.0A	11	61110			ASTRUGALUS		趾
JIUH	157,05	6415	12	61117	1553	0837	AT A DISTANCE OF		距
JIUH	157,08	6436	15	67164	1539	1306	SQUAT,BE BASED UPON		踞
JIUH	162,13	6698	17	31303	1565	6744	HURRY/FAST/SUDDENLY		遽
JIUH	164,13	6835	20	11632	1566	5713	CONTRIBUTE TO A FEAST		醵
JIUH	167,05	6880	13	81117	1554	0835	GREAT,HARD IRON		鉅
JIUH	167,08	6920	16	87164	1540	1305	A SAW,TO SAW		鋸
JIUH	167,13	6998	21	81132	1564	5711	(MUS. INSTR.)		鐻
JIUH	182,08	7367	17	77218	1559	7847	HURRICANE		颶
JIUH	196,05	770E	16	27327			JAPANESE ROBIN		駒
JIUAN	031,08	0946.0B	11	60712	1655	1923	TO CONFINE/ENCLOSE		圈
JIUAN	038,07	1227	10	46427	1628	3612	BEAUTIFUL/GRACEFUL		娟
JIUAN	061,07	1893.0A	10	96027	1629	3607	ANGRY,SAD		悁
JIUAN	064,07	2196	10	56027	1630	3608	CONTRIBUTE		捐
JIUAN	085,07	3197	10	36127	1631	3613	BROOK,TO SELECT,(SURNAME)		涓
JIUAN	093,06	8782	10	90503	1647		RING THRU THE NOSE OF ANIMAL		牮
JIUAN	130,07	5189	11	73247		6468	FLEECE/EXTORT,REDUCE		朘
JIUAN	142,17	5873	23	86127	1649	4468	GLOW-WORM,BRIGHT,REMIT TAXES		蠲
JIUAN	164,07	681B	14	16627			LACTAM OR LACTAN		酮
JIUAN	167,13	6990	21	80127	0863	4137	ENGRAVE(WOOD OR STONE),DEGRADE		鐫
JIUAN	177,07	7259	16	46527	1638		SCABBARD,REINS,JADE-LIKE		鞙
JIUAN	187,07	9617	17	76386			GREY HORSE		駽
JIUAN	196,07	7710	18	67227	1639	4632	CUCKOO		鵑
JEUAN	026,06	0608.0A	08	90712	1640	7234	TO ROLL	2208	卷
JEUAN	064,08	2208	11	59012	1642	7238	TO ROLL	0608.0A	捲
JIUANN	009,08	0239	10	29212	1641	7237	TIRED		倦
JIUANN	026,06	0608	08	90712	1640	7234	EXAMINATION PAPER,CHAPTER		卷
JIUANN	031,08	0946	11	60712	1655	1923	PEN(PIG)/A FOLD		圈

ROM	RAD	TEL	TOT	FC	MAT	OSH	TAG	CR	CHAR
JIUANN	050,06	8361	09	90227	1646		A BAG WHICH HOLDS 30 PECKS		
JIUANN	061,07	1893	10	96027	1629	3607	IMPATIENT		
JIUANN	094,07	3712	10	46227	1632	3609	TIMID/CAUTIOUS	3746	
JIUANN	094,13	3746	16	46232	1632	5874	TIMID/CAUTIOUS	3712	
JIUANN	109,06	4187	11	90603	1648	1727	WIFE AND CHILDREN,CONCERN		
JIUANN	109,07	8910	12	66027	1633	3606	LOOK		
JIUANN	109,08	8912	13	69012	1643		LOOK FONDLY		
JIUANN	112,11	7444	16	16600			STOPE		
JIUANN	120,07	4831	13	26927	1635	3610	THICK BUT LOOSELY WOVEN SILK		
JIUANN	122,06	4995	11	60227			NET		
JIUANN	163,09	6761	12	17127			NAME OF A HSIEN IN SHANTUNG		
JIUE	030,10	0842.0A	13	68011	0763	0099	SIGH		
JIUE	030,12	088G	15	61082			POUT		
JIUE	064,12	2313	15	51082	1684	4937	STICK UP(AS A TAIL),BREAK OFF		
JIUE	075,11	2854	15	44914	1176	0967	FOOT BRIDGE		
JYUE	006,00	0054	01	20000	3408	2859	MARK OFF		
JYUE	009,08	8056	10	27272	1693	1029	CRABBY/TOUGH		
JYUE	015,04	0414	06	35134	1697	5215	DECIDE,BREACH(A DIKE)	3082	
JYUE	018,12	8105	14	72200	1681	2934	CHISEL,ENGRAVE		
JYUE	027,10	0628	12	71282	1680	3934	HIS/ITS		
JYUE	030,13	0904	16	61032		5712	LOUD LAUGHTER		
JYUE	030,18	0920.0A	21	62046	1180	3209	TO CHEW		
JYUE	032,07	8221	10	47127	1707	3700	STONY SOIL		
JYUE	039,00	1315	03	17407	3708	3096	LARVAE OF MOSQUITO		
JYUE	044,15	1465	18	77227		3853	HEMP SANDALS	8320.0A	
JYUE	044,16	8320.0A	19	77227		3853	HEMP SANDALS	1465	
JYUE	046,08	1512	11	27772	1694	1028	TOWERING AS A PEAK		
JYUE	046,12	8347.0A	15	21782			SACRIFICIAL VESSEL		
JYUE	061,20	8409	23	96047	2784	6145	FEAR/BE IN AWE,SUDDEN GLANCE		
JYUE	064,04	2115	07	55030	1696	5211	PICK,DIG		
JYUE	064,08	2228	11	57072	1695	1030	DIG		
JYUE	064,20	2384	23	56047	1705	6146	SEIZE(BIRD OR ANIMAL)		
JYUE	075,12	2893	16	41982		4939	LOW POST,A PEG		

ROM	RAD	TEL	TOT	FC	MAT	OSH	TAG	CR	CHAR
JYUE	075,12	2893.1	16	71904	1685		LOW POST,A PEG		厤
JYUE	085,04	3082	07	35130	1697	5216	DECIDE,BREACH(A DYKE)	0414	决
JYUE	085,12	3404	15	37127			BUBBLE UP		潏
JYUE	086,18	3622	22	92846		3212	TORCH		爝
JYUE	087,13	3635	17	20746	1179	3208	NOBILITY		爵
JYUE	094,12	3744	15	41282	1686	4938	UNRULY/RUDE		獗
JYUE	096,04	3777	08	15134	1698	5204	HALF-CIRCLE JADE RING		玦
JYUE	096,05	3778	09	11113		0315	GEMS MOUNTED TOGETHER	3861	玨
JYUE	096,10	3861	14	47147		6264	GEMS MOUNTED TOGETHER	3778	瑴
JYUE	096,12	8839	16	17127			HALF-CIRCLE JADE RING	3777	璚
JYUE	109,15	4236	20	66407	1704	6142	GLANCE FEARFULLY,(SURNAME)		矍
JYUE	120,06	4815	12	27917	1703	7315	CUT SHORT,ABSOLUTELY,EXTINCT		絕
JYUE	130,07	5183.0A	11	77220	1177	2142	ROLE	5223.0A	脚
JYUE	130,09	5223.0A	13	77220	1177	2123	ROLE	5183.1A	腳
JYUE	130,13	5243	17	71232		5715	PALATE,SAUSAGE		膹
JYUE	140,12	5615	16	44282	1687	4941	PTERIDIUM AQUILINUM		蕨
JYUE	140,12	5611	16	44917			COARSE GRASS USED TO SHOW RANK		蕝
JYUE	147,04	6030.1	11	00216		7627	TO FEEL,FIND THAT		覚
JYUE	147,05	6030.2	12	90216			FEEL,FIND THAT		覺
JYUE	147,13	6030	20	77216	1178	7623	FEEL,FIND THAT		覺
JYUE	148,00	6037.0A	07	27227	1174	3699	HORN,ANGLE,CHINESE MUSICAL NOTE		角
JYUE	148,04	6039	11	25230	1699	5212	DISSATISFIED		觖
JYUE	148,15	6053	22	27247			RING,CLASP,BUCKLE		觼
JYUE	149,04	6076	11	05630	1700	5207	SECRETS(OF AN ART),FAREWELL		訣
JYUE	149,12	6216	19	07627	1702	3904	DECEITFUL		譎
JYUE	153,20	9321	27	26247			(APE)		貜
JYUE	157,04	6403	11	65130			TO GALLOP		趹
JYUE	157,12	6474	19	61182	1690	4935	TRAMPLE,STUMBLE	9347	蹶
JYUE	157,12	9348.0A	19	62127	0750	3843	SANDALS,TO WALK RAPIDLY		蹻
JYUE	157,12	9347	19	71801			TRAMPLE,STUMBLE	6474	蹷
JYUE	157,20	6496	27	66147	1714	6144	LEAP,BEND		躍
JYUE	167,12	9510	20	81127			HOE		鐝
JYUE	196,04	7694.0A	15	25330	1582	5213	SHRIKE	771A	鴃

ROM	RAD	TEL	TOT	FC	MAT	OSH	TAG	CR	CHAR
JYUE	196,07	771A	18	67827	1582	4662	SHRIKE	7694.0A	
JEUE	075,07	2730	11	47927	1175	3703	MALUS OR PIRUS TORINGO		
JEUE	157,12	6474.0A	19	61182	1690	4935	TO KICK(AS A HORSE)	9347.0A	
JEUE	157,12	9347.0A	19	71801			TO KICK(AS A HORSE)	6474.0A	
JIUN	030,04	0689	07	17607	1715	1145	RULER/GENTLEMAN		
JIUN	031,05	0940	08	60904	1719	1907	GRANARY		
JIUN	032,04	0971	07	47120	1724	4372	UNIFORM,ALL		
JIUN	107,09	4125	14	34547	1723	6239	TO CHAP		
JIUN	159,02	6511	09	37506	1722	2652	ARMY		
JIUN	167,04	6874	12	87127	1725	4374	GREAT,YOUR(HON.),30 CATTIES		
JIUN	195,07	764M	18	27361			SEBASTODES GUNTHERI		
JIUN	198,05	7778	16	00904	1721	5561	HORNLESS DEER	7786	
JIUN	198,08	7786	19	80601	1721	1909	HORNLESS DEER	7778	
JEUN	116,07	4515.0A	12	30567	1716	1149	EMBARRASSED,DISTRESSED		
JIUNN	009,07	0193	09	23247	1727	6466	EMINENT,TALENTED,HANDSOME	K0303	
JIUNN	009,13	0303	15	20227	1726	4138	EMINENT,TALENTED	K0193	
JIUNN	032,03	1101	06	42100			DITCH		
JIUNN	046,07	1498	10	23747	1728	6460	STEEP		
JIUNN	046,13	7606	16	22227		4141	EMINENT,TALENTED	7165	
JIUNN	064,07	8433	10	53047			TO PINCH,LAY HAND ON		
JIUNN	064,07	8432	10	57067		1147	GATHER,TO SORT	8478	
JIUNN	064,19	8478	22	50061		1910	GATHER,TO SORT	8432	
JIUNN	085,07	3182	10	33147	1729	6472	PROFOUND,ENLIGHTEN,DEEPEN	3449	
JIUNN	085,14	3449	17	31163	1729	1726	PROFOUND,ENLIGHTEN,DEEPEN	3182	
JIUNN	086,07	3537	11	93847			SET FIRE		
JIUNN	096,07	8823	11	17167			(GOOD JADE)		
JIUNN	102,07	3975	12	63047	1730	6463	OVERSEER,STEPPE		
JIUNN	117,07	4546	12	03147	1731	6459	COMPLETE/FINISH		
JIUNN	118,08	4624	14	88603			BAMBOO SHOOTS		
JIUNN	140,07	5483	11	44607	1717	1148	HIPPURIS/BETA VULGARIS		
JIUNN	140,08	5497	12	44600	1720	1908	BACTERIA,MUSHROOM,MOLD		
JIUNN	163,07	6746	10	17627	1718	2170	REGION		
JIUNN	172,05	7165	13	20227	1677	4136	EMINENT,TALENTED	7606	

ROM	RAD	TEL	TOT	FC	MAT	OSH	TAG	CR	CHAR
JIUNN	184,07	7410	15	83747	1734	6467	REMAINS OF A SACRIFICE OR A MEAL		餕
JIUNN	187,07	7486	17	73347	1735	6470	SPIRITED HORSE		駿
JONG	002,03	0022	04	50006	1504	2669	MIDDLE,CHINA		中
JONG	009,04	8025	06	28232	1498		RESTLESS/AGITATED	8388	伀
JONG	061,03	1813	07	50336	1506	8610	LOYAL		忠
JONG	061,04	8388	07	98032	1499	8848	RESTLESS/AGITATED	8025	忪
JONG	085,11	3408	14	36132	6913		JUNCTION OF STREAMS	8706	潨
JONG	085,11	8706	14	38181	6913		JUNCTION OF STREAMS	3408	滧
JONG	108,04	4132	09	50107	1507	0687	CUP		盅
JONG	120,05	4807	11	27933	1500	9073	FINISH		終
JONG	142,11	5830	17	27136	1501	8917	(GRASSHOPPER)/GOMPSOCLEIS MIKADO		螽
JONG	145,04	5907	10	00732	1508	5885	INNER FEELINGS		衷
JONG	167,04	6988.1	12	85106			CLOCK,BELL,(SURNAME)	G6945	鈡
JONG	167,09	6945	17	82114	1514	0463	(SURNAME),(ANCIENT MEASURE)	C6988.1	鍾
JONG	167,12	6988	20	80114	1503	0449	CLOCK,BELL		鐘
JOONG	014,08	0386	10	37232	1515	5755	MOUND,GREAT		冢
JOONG	032,10	1046	13	47132	1516	5756	MOUND		塚
JOONG	104,09	4043	14	00114			SWELLING OF THE FEET		瘇
JOONG	115,04	4429	09	25906	1524		SEED,KIND,RACE	4467	种
JOONG	115,09	4467	14	22914	1511	0468	SEED,KIND,RACE(OF PEOPLE)	4429	種
JOONG	130,04	5209.1	08	75206			SWOLLEN		肿
JOONG	130,09	5209	13	72214	1512	0467	SWOLLEN		腫
JOONG	157,09	6446	16	62114	1513	0464	HEEL,FOLLOW,ARRIVE		踵
JONQ	002,03	0022.0A	04	50006	1504	2669	HIT(THE MARK)		中
JONQ	004,05	5883.2	06	20503	1517	2675	MULTITUDE		柬
JONQ	009,04	0112	06	25206	1505	2672	2ND IN SENIORITY		仲
JONQ	009,04	5883.1	06	80880			MULTITUDE		众
JONQ	094,04	370B	07	45206			PEKINGESE		狆
JONQ	109,06	4191	11	60232	1517	5703	MULTITUDE	5883	眾
JONQ	115,04	4429.0A	09	25906	1524		TO PLANT	4467.0A	种
JONQ	115,09	4467.0A	14	22914	1511	0468	TO PLANT	4429.0A	種
JONQ	119,08	9040.0A	14	93991	6900	8373	RICE DUMPLINGS WRAPPED IN LEAVES	4740.0A	粽
JONQ	119,09	4740.0A	15	92947	6900	6452	RICE DUMPLINGS WRAPPED IN LEAVES	9040.0A	糭

ROM	RAD	TEL	TOT	FC	MAT	OSH	TAG	CR	CHAR
JONQ	119,13	4740.1A	19	92947			RICE DUMPLINGS WRAPPED IN LEAVES		
JONQ	143,06	5883	12	27232	1517	5704	MULTITUDE	4191	
JONQ	166,02	6850	09	20104	1509	0462	HEAVY,SERIOUS		
JOU	009,06	8038	08	27240	1292	4112	TO COVER,CONCEAL		
JOU	030,05	0719	08	77220	1293	3882	(SURNAME),ENCIRCLE,COMPLETE		
JOU	030,08	0791	11	67020	0248	3883	TWITTERING OF BIRDS		
JOU	038,08	8287	11	47420			(FEMININE NAME)		
JOU	047,03	1558	06	32000	1289	2837	SUB PREFECTURE		
JOU	085,06	3166	09	32100	1290	2840	CONTINENT,ISLAND		
JOU	108,12	4154	17	48107		0711	NAME OF A HSIEN IN SHENSI		
JOU	119,06	4728	12	17227	1384	4737	CONGEE		
JOU	137,00	5297	06	27440	1291	4111	BOAT		
JOU	149,14	6234	21	04641		3178	DECEIVE,TO LIE		
JOU	154,08	6335	15	67820	1294	3890	BESTOW ALMS		
JOU	159,06	6527	13	57040		4113	SHAFT,POLE,BEAM		
JOU	162,08	6650	12	37302	1295	6697	CYCLE,WEEK		
JOU	187,08	9619	18	77320			DIVINE HORSE		
JOUR	038,05	1187	08	45460	1377	1841	WIVES OF BROTHERS		
JOUR	137,05	5310.0A	11	25460		1836	STERN OF BOAT,POOPDECK		
JOUR	159,05	6519	12	55060	1378	1834	AXIS/AXLE		
JOOU	050,05	1590	08	17227	1299	3972	BROOM	4622	
JOOU	118,08	4622	14	88227	1299	3978	A BROOM	1590	
JOOU	130,03	5136	07	74200	1301	3213	ELBOW,PORK SHOULDER		
JOW	013,07	0378	09	50227	1297	3622	HELMET		
JOW	030,05	0720.1	08	66010	1303	7546	PUT A CURSE ON		
JOW	030,05	0720	08	66217	1303	7874	PUT A CURSE ON	6092	
JOW	030,06	8138	09	65090	1304	5478	PECK AT,BEAK OF BIRD		
JOW	040,05	1352	08	30602	1298	1844	UNIVERSE		
JOW	072,05	2521.1	09	77106			DAYTIME		
JOW	072,07	2521	11	50106	1302	0039	DAYTIME		
JOW	098,09	3913	14	29717	1305	7943	BRICKWORK OF WELL		
JOW	107,10	4126	15	24447	1306	6244	TO WRINKLE/WRINKLED		
JOW	118,13	4699	19	88562		1788	DEVELOP,(WRITING),(SURNAME)		

椶豪重俏周喌娟州洲蓥粥舟禱賙輈週騆妯舳軸尋篲肘胄呪咒哜宙昼書梵皴籀

ROM	RAD	TEL	TOT	FC	MAT	OSH	TAG	CR	CHAR
JOW	120,03	4765	09	24900	1300	3221	SADDLE CRUPPER,NAME OF AN EMPEROR		
JOW	120,10	4900	16	27927	1307	4455	CREPE,WRINKLE		
JOW	120,11	4925.0B	17	22793	7548	8485	INTERPRETATIONS OF THE TRIGRAMS		
JOW	130,05	5153	09	50227	1296	3622	DESCENDANTS		
JOW	149,05	6092	12	06610	1303		PUT A CURSE ON	0720	
JOW	164,03	6793	10	14600		3190	STRONG WINE		
.JOU	050,05	1590.0A	08	17227			BROOM		
JU	009,06	0175	08	25290	1347	5481	DWARF		
JU	030,09	8155	12	66320			TO CALL FOWLS		
JU	075,02	2612	06	25900	1346	5474	VERMILION(SURNAME)	A4281	
JU	075,06	2701	10	45990	1348	5483	TRUNK OF TREE,(AN. FOR TREES)		
JU	075,16	8601	20	14904		5327	ZELKOVA ACUMINATA		
JU	075,16	293A	20	44960	1363		QUERCUS GLANCA		
JU	085,06	3178.0A	09	35190	5852	5486	NAME OF A RIVER,(SURNAME)		
JU	085,12	3393	15	34160			POOL/POND	3479	
JU	085,16	3479	19	34160	1358	1584	POOL/POND	3393	
JU	094,09	3727	12	44260	1357	1634	PIG/HOG	6277	
JU	096,06	3796	10	15194	1349	5475	PEARL,BEAD		
JU	112,06	4281	11	15690	1350	5479	VERMILION	A2612	
JU	140,06	5416	10	44904	5853	5487	CORNELIAN CHERRY		
JU	140,16	5675	20	44664	5869	1631	SUGAR CANE		
JU	142,06	5753	12	55190	1351	5484	SPIDER		
JU	149,06	6121	13	05690	1352	5480	PUNISH,EXECUTE		
JU	149,09	6175	16	04660	1362	1629	ALL/MANY,(SURNAME)		
JU	152,09	6277	16	14260	1357	1636	PIG/HOG	3727	
JU	157,06	9333	13	65190		5477	TO WALK,PACE BACK AND FORTH		
JU	163,06	6739	09	27927	1353	2237	NAME OF A FEUDAL STATE,(SURNAME)		
JU	167,06	6899	14	85194	1354	5476	FORTY-EIGHTH PART OF A TAEL		
JWU	069,21	2453	25	72221			HOE-LIKE INSTRUMENT		
JWU	075,01	2611.0A	05	43900	5886	7077	ATRACTYLIS LANCEA VAR. OVATA		
JWU	086,06	3608.1	10	94830	1385	8903	CANDLE		
JWU	086,13	3608	17	96827	1385	4473	CANDLE		
JWU	086,21	8767	25	97827		4479	CANDLE	3608	

紂
綯
繇
胄
說
酎
帚
侏
咒
朱
株
櫧
樗
洙
渚
瀦
猪
珠
硃
茱
藸
蛛
誅
諸
豬
跦
邾
銖
斸
木
烛
燭
爥

ROM	RAD	TEL	TOT	FC	MAT	OSH	TAG	CR	CHAR
JWU	104,08	8873	13	00132	1382	5754	CHILBLAIN		
JWU	116,05	4508	10	30772			IN A HOLE		
JWU	118,00	4554	06	88220	1373	3036	BAMBOO		
JWU	118,02	4555	08	88101	1374	0007	(SURNAME)		
JWU	118,06	4591	12	88117	1375	7889	BUILD,FIVE-STRING LUTE	A4639	
JWU	118,10	4639	16	88904	1376	5397	BUILD	A4591	
JWU	137,05	5310	11	25460		1836	STERN OF BOAT,POOPDECK		
JWU	140,11	5569	15	44303			(WEED)/PHYTOLACCA ACINOSA		
JWU	142,06	5753.0A	12	55190	1351	5484	SPIDER		
JWU	159,05	6519.0A	12	55060	1378	1834	AXIS/AXLE		
JWU	162,07	6632	11	31303	1383	6734	CHASE AWAY		
JUU	003,00	0027	01	30000	1335	7974	A POINT		
JUU	003,04	0031	05	00104	1336	0357	MASTER		
JUU	018,21	8108	23	72200		2929	A SPADE/A SHOVEL		
JUU	030,12	0928.1	15	67027	1386	4085	ENJOIN		
JUU	030,21	0928	24	67027	1386	4477	ENJOIN	1466.0A	
JUU	044,05	1466.2A	08	77227	5896		ENJOIN		
JUU	044,09	1466.1A	12	77227	5896		ENJOIN		
JUU	044,18	1466.0A	21	77227	5896	4476	ENJOIN	0928	
JUU	064,05	2134	08	53014	1338	0361	PROP,POST		
JUU	085,09	3252	12	34160	1355	1641	ISLET,BANK	7121	
JUU	086,09	3554.1	13	44336		8772	TO BOIL		
JUU	086,09	3554	13	44809	1356		TO BOIL		
JUU	109,21	4241	26	67027	1387	4478	GAZE		
JUU	112,05	8936	10	10614			ANCESTRAL TABLET		
JUU	154,05	6308	12	63821	1368	3011	TO STORE		
JUU	170,09	7121	12	74260	1355		ISLET/BANK	3252	
JUU	198,05	7779	16	00104	1345	0368	STAG,LEADER OF HERD		
JUH	009,05	0145	07	20214	1337	0359	RESIDE,STOP		
JUH	009,05	8028	07	23221	1365	3010	STAND AND WAIT,HOPE FOR	4542	
JUH	019,05	0504	07	74127	1370	4790	TO HELP		
JUH	040,02	1337.0B	05	30201	1364	3008	SPACE BEHIND THE THRONE		
JUH	075,04	2645	08	47922	1369	3085	SHUTTLE OF A LOOM		

瘃窀竹竺筑築舳遂蛛軸逐、主劚囑屚屬屬挂渚煑煮矖硅貯陼廛住佇助宁杼

ROM	RAD	TEL	TOT	FC	MAT	OSH	TAG	CR	CHAR
JUH	075,05	2691	09	43914	1339	0363	PILLAR		柱
JUH	075,05	8540	09	46910	1379	7549	(MUS. INSTR.)		柷
JUH	085,05	3137	08	33114	1340	0366	POUR INTO,TO NOTICE,ANNOTATE	G6087	注
JUH	086,05	3522	09	90814	1341	0364	CANDLEWICK,INCENSE STICK		炷
JUH	113,05	4376	09	36210	1380	7548	INVOKE,PRAY TO		祝
JUH	117,05	4542	10	03121	1365	3009	STAND AND WAIT,HOPE FOR	8028	竚
JUH	118,07	4606	13	88127	1360	4794	CHOPSTICKS	4632	筋
JUH	118,09	4632	15	88604	1360	1652	CHOPSTICKS	4606	箸
JUH	120,05	4774	11	23921	1366	3012	BOEHMERIA NIVEA	5389	紵
JUH	123,05	5023	11	83521			FIVE-MONTH-OLD LAMB		羜
JUH	124,09	5053	15	44127	1359	3412	SOAR		翥
JUH	140,04	5352.0A	08	44202	2852	3088	BOEHMERIA NIVEA	5389	苧
JUH	140,05	5389	09	44201	1367	3013	BOEHMERIA NIVEA	4774	苎
JUH	140,09	5511	13	44604	1361	1648	MAKE KNOWN,WRITE		著
JUH	142,05	5746	11	50114	1342	0365	TO BORE(OF INSECTS),TERMITE		蛀
JUH	149,05	6087	12	00614	1343	0358	ANNOTATE	C3137	註
JUH	157,13	6483	20	66127	1388	4467	HESITATING		躇
JUH	167,14	6999	22	84141	1372	3176	TO COIN(MONEY),CAST METALS		鑄
JUH	183,09	5053.1	18	44413	1359	7852	SOAR		翥
JUH	187,03	9613	13	71442	1371		(HORSE)		馵
JUH	187,05	7465	15	70314	1344	0362	BE STATIONED		駐
JUH	195,05	762J	16	23321			LETHRINUS HAEMATOPTERUS		鯺
JUA	064,04	2119	07	52030	1417	4979	TO SCRATCH,SNATCH/GRASP	3629.0A	抓
JUA	064,13	2339	16	57032	1418	6699	BEAT		摳
JUA	087,00	3629.0A	04	72230	0240		SCRATCH,SNATCH	2119	爪
JUA	190,07	9632	17	72104	0077	0289	DRESS THE HAIR		髻
JOA	087,00	3629	04	72230	0240	4978	CLAW		爪
JUAI	064,06	2167.0B	09	55006	1419	7054	THROW		拽
JOAI	157,06	642A	13	65106	1420	7053	WADDLE/SWAGGER		跩
JOAI	159,11	6567.0B	18	55043	1431	3293	SHOW OFF WITH LITERARY EXPRESSIONS		轉
JUAY	064,06	2167	09	55006	1419	7054	DRAG		拽
JUAN	007,03	1413.1	05	50307			CONCENTRATED,SPECIALIZED		专
JUAN	032,11	1059	14	45143		3290	BRICK	3919	塼

ROM	RAD	TEL	TOT	FC	MAT	OSH	TAG	CR	CHAR
JUAN	041,08	1413	11	50343	1428	3289	CONCENTRATED,SPECIALIZED	5083	專
JUAN	098,11	3919	16	51317	1429	7932	BRICK	1059	甎
JUAN	112,11	4331	16	13643	1429	3291	BRICK	1059	磚
JUAN	126,03	5083	09	22227	1428	3754	CONCENTRATED,SPECIALIZED	1413	耑
JUAN	181,09	7348	18	21286	1433	8274	GOOD,SIMPLE,(SURNAME)		顓
JUAN	195,11	9656	22	25343			(SURNAME),(FISH)		鱄
JOAN	030,18	0921	21	65043	1432	3294	WARBLE LIKE A BIRD		囀
JOAN	159,11	6567	18	55043	1431	3293	TO TURN,TO FORWARD(MAIL),CONVEY		轉
JUANN	009,11	0278.0A	13	25243	1446	3292	BIOGRAPHY		傳
JUANN	018,11	0483.0A	13	52300		2896	SLASH		劐
JUANN	030,08	8152	11	69012			COIL		啳
JUANN	064,12	2332	15	57081	1434	8044	COMPOSE,COMPILE	B6219	撰
JUANN	096,09	3849	13	17132		5736	ENGRAVED LINES		瑑
JUANN	118,09	4637	15	88232	1438	5743	SEAL CHARACTERS		篆
JUANN	118,11	9019	17	88107			FOOD/DELICACIES,COMPOSE/COMPILE	D2332	籑
JUANN	120,11	4914	17	25943	1430		TIE UP		縳
JUANN	149,12	6219	19	07681	1435	8041	DISCOURSE IN PRAISE,COMPOSE/COMPILE	D2332	譔
JUANN	154,10	6354	17	68837	1437	5576	EARN,MAKE A PROFIT		賺
JUANN	154,11	6354.1	18	65836	1437	8612	EARN,MAKE A PROFIT		賺
JUANN	159,11	6567.0A	18	55043	1431	3293	REVOLVE		轉
JUANN	184,12	7433	20	87781	1436	8043	FOOD/DELICACIES	A9019	饌
JUANG	038,03	1182.1	06	34140			ADORNMENT/ADORN		妆
JUANG	038,04	1182	07	24240	1451	8983	ADORNMENT/ADORN	4730	妝
JUANG	053,03	8369	06	00214	1450	0153	FARM/VILLAGE	5445	庄
JUANG	075,06	2866.1	10	45914			STUMP,ITEM		桩
JUANG	075,11	2866	15	45977	1457	1060	STUMP,ITEM		椿
JUANG	094,03	3692.1	07	33134			STATE/CONDITION,ACCUSATION/SUIT		状
JUANG	119,06	4730	12	90914	1451	0154	ADORNMENT/ADORN	1182	粧
JUANG	140,07	5445	11	44214	1454	0143	FARM,VILLAGE	8369	莊
JUANG	145,06	5944.1	12	34732			COSTUME,ADORNMENT/ADORN		装
JUANG	145,07	5944	13	24732	1455	5813	COSTUME,ADORNMENT/ADORN	D1182	裝
JOANG	037,07	1155	10	24430	6700	5004	FAT/STOUT		奘
JUANQ	009,12	0302.0A	14	20214	6627	0453	NAME OF AN ETHNIC GROUP IN KWANGSI		僮

ROM	RAD	TEL	TOT	FC	MAT	OSH	TAG	CR	CHAR
JUANQ	033,03	1104.1	06	34110			STRONG/ROBUST		壯
JUANQ	033,04	1104	07	24210	1453	0142	STRONG/ROBUST		壯
JUANQ	061,24	2045	28	07338	1458	8688	SIMPLE/STUPID		戆
JUANQ	064,12	2326	15	50014	1456	0454	BUMP INTO		撞
JUANQ	094,04	3692	07	23234	1452	5078	STATE/CONDITION,ACCUSATION/SUIT		狀
JUEI	075,08	2785	12	40914		0902	SPINE		椎
JUEI	162,06	6620	10	37307	1469	6623	TO CHASE/PURSUE(A PROBLEM)		追
JUEI	167,08	6923	16	80114	1467	0868	AWL,TO BORE		錐
JUEI	172,00	7155	08	20214	1466	0866	SHORT-TAILED BIRD		佳
JUEI	187,08	7489	18	10314	1468		PIEBALD,(SURNAME)		騅
JUEI	196,08	9678	19	20314			TURTLEDOVE,SNIPE		鵻
JUEY	032,12	1071	15	78104	1471	0220	FALL		墜
JUEY	061,09	1928	12	92027	1473	3759	ANXIOUS/WORRIED		惴
JUEY	098,08	8850	13	21117			VASE WITH A SMALL MOUTH		甄
JUEY	112,08	4303	13	12614	1474		TO WEIGHT,IODIDE		硾
JUEY	120,08	4856	14	27947	1475	6084	APPEND		綴
JUEY	120,10	4899	16	27937	1470	6628	LET DOWN WITH A ROPE		縋
JUEY	130,10	9134	14	77237			SWELLING OF FOOT		腄
JUEY	154,11	6361	18	58806	1472	8221	SUPERFLUOUS		贅
JUEY	184,08	7417	16	87747	1281		CIRCLE SHRINES AND MAKE SACRIFICES		餕
JUEN	045,01	1470.0A	04	50717	6592	7405	DIFFICULT,STINGY		屯
JUEN	116,04	4503	09	30717	6596	7416	GRAVE		窀
JUEN	130,04	5145	08	75217	1489	7409	GIZZARD		肫
JUEN	149,08	6150	15	00647	1490	3119	REPEATEDLY(IN GIVING ADVICE)		諄
JOEN	015,08	0402	10	30114	1486	0922	ACCURATE,STANDARD,TO PERMIT	K3294	准
JOEN	085,10	3294	13	30401	1488	2274	ACCURATE,STANDARD	K0402	準
JOEN	172,02	7157	10	20401	1487	2271	FALCON		隼
JUO	064,07	2191	10	56081	1276	5980	TO CATCH		捉
JUO	075,06	2715	10	21904	1262	5325	TABLE	2777	桌
JUO	075,08	2777	12	41946	1262	2305	TABLE	2715	棹
JUO	085,08	3214	11	31132	1268	5753	PLACE NAME		涿
JUO	102,08	3978	13	67047			RAISED PATHS BETWEEN PADDY-FIELDS		畷
JWO	009,08	0213	10	21246	1261	2303	DISTINCT/MANIFESTED		倬

ROM	RAD	TEL	TOT	FC	MAT	OSH	TAG	CR	CHAR
JWO	024,06	0587	08	21406	1260	2300	OUTSTANDING,(SURNAME)		卓
JWO	030,08	0793	11	61032	1266	5750	TO PECK		啄
JWO	064,05	2154	08	52072	1542	1023	STUPID		拙
JWO	064,14	2359	17	57014	1264	0950	PULL OUT,SELECT		擢
JWO	068,08	8498	12	42621	1255		CUT IN TWO		斲
JWO	069,10	2452	14	72121	1263	2011	CHOP/CARVE WOOD		斵
JWO	069,13	2452.1	17	72121	1263	2010	CHOP/CARVE WOOD		斷
JWO	075,07	2751	11	48916	1279	7571	SMALL PILLAR,CLUB(WEAPON)		棁
JWO	075,08	2792	12	41932	1267	5752	BEAT		椓
JWO	085,06	3424.1	09	35136			IMPURE,MUDDY		浊
JWO	085,13	3424	16	36127	1271	4475	IMPURE,MUDDY		濁
JWO	085,14	3451	17	37114	1265	0956	RINSE,TO CLEANSE		濯
JWO	086,03	3504	07	97820	1256	4365	BRILLIANT,CAUTERIZE		灼
JWO	086,08	8743	12	91846		2306	BRIGHT,CLEAR		焯
JWO	096,08	3820	12	11132	1269	5749	TO CUT (GEMS)		琢
JWO	109,07	4192.0C	12	80601	1258	1704	READING PRON.OF 4192,4192.0A		着
JWO	112,04	4273	09	12621		2017	TO CHOP		斫
JWO	113,10	8981	14	38231			PLACE NAME		禚
JWO	118,10	4650	16	88214			CREEL FOR TRAPPING FISH		籗
JWO	140,05	5398	09	44772	1275	1032	SPROUT,INCREASE		茁
JWO	140,09	5511.0D	13	44604	1361	1648	TO WEAR,PLAN,SETTLEMENT		著
JWO	142,14	5868	20	57114			(APE),(SHELL)		蠗
JWO	149,08	6157	15	01632		5751	COMPLAIN		諑
JWO	157,08	6433	15	61146	1285	2301	STRIDE,EXCEL		踔
JWO	164,03	6791	10	17620	1257	4362	POUR WINE,CONSIDER		酌
JWO	167,07	6992.1	15	86181			BRACELET		鋜
JWO	167,13	6992	21	86127	1272	4466	BRACELET		鐲
JWO	196,11	7763	22	08327		4679	PHOENIX,RIVER GULL		鷟
JY	004,03	0037	04	30307	0935	6589	(SUBOR. PART.),HIM/HER/IT		之
JY	026,03	0612	05	72212		7229	GOBLET	1573	卮
JY	030,02	0662.0A	05	60800		8093	AN. FOR ONE OF A PAIR	7156	只
JY	030,04	8123.0A	07	64047	6922	6214	(PHONETIC)		吱
JY	049,04	1573	07	72217	0930	7295	GOBLET	0612	巵

ROM	RAD	TEL	TOT	FC	MAT	OSH	TAG	CR	CHAR
JY	064,10	8455	13	54061	0961	1613	PROP UP		揩
JY	065,00	2388	04	40407	0937	6206	DIVISION,DRAW MONEY,BRANCH		支
JY	075,04	2655	08	44947	0938	6221	BRANCH		枝
JY	075,07	2738	11	42917	0931	7296	GARDENIA		梔
JY	085,02	3059	05	34100	0999	2270	JUICE		汁
JY	111,03	4249	08	86400	0932	1091	KNOW		知
JY	113,05	4372	09	32240	0952	6861	RESPECTFUL(LY)		祇
JY	120,12	4930	18	23950	0989	6912	WEAVE		織
JY	130,04	5141	08	74247	0949	6220	LIMB		肢
JY	130,05	5164	09	72240		6857	CALLOUS		胝
JY	130,06	5176	10	71261	0960	1607	FAT		脂
JY	140,04	5347	08	44307	0936	6590	ZOYSIA PUNGENS		芝
JY	142,08	5776	14	56100	0934	1093	SPIDER		蜘
JY	172,02	7156	10	20407	0967	6138	AN. FOR ONE OF A PAIR	0662.0A	隻
JY	196,04	9673	15	47427			GARRULUS LIDTHI		鵤
JYR	009,06	1212.1	08	21214	0991		NEPHEW (OF THE SAME SURNAME)		侄
JYR	009,08	0237	10	24217	0975	0752	BE WORTH		值
JYR	032,08	1021	11	44117		0750	CLAYEY SOIL		填
JYR	032,08	1013	11	44417	0996	7918	GRASP,EXECUTE(A PLAN)		執
JYR	038,06	1212	09	41414	0992	0263	NEPHEW (OF THE SAME SURNAME)		姪
JYR	040,10	1387	13	30801	0976	8091	PUT ASIDE,ARRANGE	4999	寘
JYR	064,03	1013.1	06	54017		7920	GRASP,EXECUTE(A PLAN)		执
JYR	064,11	2303	14	50037	1001	8766	PICK UP,TO SELECT		摭
JYR	064,15	2367	18	57027	1012	2234	THROW		擲
JYR	075,05	8545	09	45930			THRESHOLD		柣
JYR	075,08	2784	12	44917	1007	0754	TO PLANT		植
JYR	075,12	8606	16	43950			STAKE/PICKET		樴
JYR	078,08	2994	12	14217	1008	0753	GROW,REPRODUCE		殖
JYR	109,03	4160	08	40107	1006	0749	STRAIGHT		直
JYR	115,06	4446	11	21914			SOUND OF REAPING		桎
JYR	115,08	8987	13	24917			EARLY-PLANTED CROP		稙
JYR	120,11	4916	17	44903	0997	8481	TIE UP,CONNECT		繄
JYR	122,08	4999	13	60107	0976	0755	PUT ASIDE,ARRANGE	1387	置

ROM	RAD	TEL	TOT	FC	MAT	OSH	TAG	CR	CHAR
JYR	128,05	5120.1	11	16180			OFFICE/DUTY		职
JYR	128,12	5120	18	13150	0990	6908	OFFICE/DUTY		職
JYR	140,18	569D	22	44150			PHYSALIS ANGULATA		蕺
JYR	142,11	5832	17	44136	0998	8948	HIBERNATE		蛰
JYR	154,04	6347.1	11	72806	1009		MATTER,QUALITY,TO QUESTION		顶
JYR	154,08	6347	15	72806	1009	8176	MATTER,QUALIFY,TO QUESTION		質
JYR	157,05	6412	12	61160	1003	1102	SOLE OF FOOT	A6470	跖
JYR	157,11	6477.0A	18	60127		3877	TO STOP,HESITATING	6490	蹢
JYR	157,11	6470	18	60131	1002	8764	SOLE OF FOOT,TREAD ON,METATARSUS	A6412	蹠
JYR	157,15	6490	22	67127	1013	2233	TO STOP,HESITATING		蹰
JYY	027,05	0619.0A	07	71242	0951	6863	WHETSTONE	4272.0A	厎
JYY	030,02	0662	05	60800	0946	8093	ONLY,BUT	4372.0A	只
JYY	030,06	0746	09	76808	0947	4971	8 IN. LENGTH UNIT OF CHOW DYNASTY		咫
JYY	032,04	0968	07	41110	0940	0473	LOCATION		址
JYY	034,00	1111	03	27400	0962	6409	FOLLOW		夂
JYY	050,04	1582	07	72227	0953	4000	PAPER	4786	帋
JYY	053,06	8371	09	00241			KEEP IN STOCK/IN READINESS		庤
JYY	060,12	1794.0A	15	28240	0358	6310	NOTE IN CHINESE MUSICAL SCALE		徵
JYY	061,06	1876	09	91061	0958		PURPORT	A2482	恉
JYY	064,06	2172	09	51061	0959	1606	FINGER,TO POINT		指
JYY	072,02	2482	06	21601	0957	1604	PURPORT,IMPERIAL DECREE	A1876	旨
JYY	075,05	2663	09	46980	0948	8095	HEDGE THORN,(ORANGE)		枳
JYY	077,00	2972	04	21100	0939	0472	TO STOP		止
JYY	085,04	3098	07	31110	0941	0481	ISLET		沚
JYY	112,05	4272.0A	10	12640	0951	6850	WHETSTONE	0619.0A	砥
JYY	113,04	4363	08	31210	0942	0480	FELICITY		祉
JYY	113,04	4361	08	32240	0538		BUT,ONLY	0662	祇
JYY	113,05	4372.0A	09	32240	0952	6861	BUT,ONLY	0662	衹
JYY	115,05	4435	10	22940			BUT/ONLY	0662	秖
JYY	120,04	4786	10	22940	0953	6845	PAPER	1582	紙
JYY	140,04	5365	08	44101	0943		(PLANT ROOT USED FOR MEDICINE)		芷
JYY	140,05	538A	09	44711			ASTRAGALUS REFLEXISTIPULUS		茋
JYY	157,04	6400	11	61110	0944	0476	TOE		

ROM	RAD	TEL	TOT	FC	MAT	OSH	TAG	CR	CHAR
JYY	159,05	6520	12	56080	0950	8094	END OF AXLE OUTSIDE OF HUB		軑
JYY	164,06	7927	13	11661			ESTER		酯
JYY	170,04	7087	07	71210	0945	0477	FOUNDATION		阯
JYY	204,00	7832	12	32227	0956	4017	EMBROIDERY		黹
JYH	018,06	0455	08	22200	0986	2913	SYSTEM,MANUFACTURE,REGULATE	D5956	制
JYH	027,06	0621	08	71214			RIVER BENT		屄
JYH	046,06	1492	09	24741	0954	3227	PEAK,TO STORE		峙
JYH	050,05	1589	08	45230	1010	5200	BOOK COVER,(SURNAME)	5923	帙
JYH	050,12	1615	15	43250	0977	6906	FLAG		幟
JYH	053,10	1667	13	00227	1043	4586	(MYTHICAL ANIMAL),DISCRIMINATE	A6282	廌
JYH	058,10	1742	13	27711	0963	7153	SWINE		彘
JYH	061,03	1807	07	40331	0971	8536	THE WILL		志
JYH	061,04	1818	07	94047	0441	6215	AGGRESSIVE		忮
JYH	061,14	2031	17	94081	0965	6000	ENRAGED		懥
JYH	064,11	2304	15	44502	0979	3361	SINCERE,(SURNAME)		摯
JYH	072,08	2535	12	86600	0933	1530	WISE/WISDOM		智
JYH	075,06	2716	10	41914	0993	0260	FETTERS		桎
JYH	085,05	3112	08	33160	1021	1463	MANAGE,HEAL		治
JYH	085,09	3333.1	12	34127			SLUGGISH		滞
JYH	085,11	8705	14	33114			OBSTRUCT,STOP UP	4510	窒
JYH	085,11	3333	14	34127	0974	3981	SLUGGISH		滯
JYH	086,04	3511	08	27809	1000	5616	BROIL		炙
JYH	086,12	3589	16	93850	0978	6911	ILLUSTRIOUS,BURN		熾
JYH	094,08	3723	11	42200		2914	MAD DOG		猘
JYH	102,06	3969	11	64041		3233	ANCIENT SACRIFICE		畤
JYH	103,09	3991	14	40801	0964	5998	PROSTRATE		寷
JYH	104,06	4023	11	00141	0955	3239	PILES/HEMORRHOID		痔
JYH	104,07	4029	12	00131	0972	8538	MOLE,BIRTHMARK		痣
JYH	115,05	4442	10	25930	1011	5201	ORDER(LINESS)		秩
JYH	115,08	4460	13	20914	0969	0904	INFANTILE,YOUNG	4477	稚
JYH	115,10	8989	15	27941		2470	INFANTILE,YOUNG	4477	稺
JYH	115,12	4477	17	27953	0969	2520	INFANTILE,YOUNG	4460	穉
JYH	116,06	4510	11	30104	0994	0279	OBSTRUCT/STOP UP		窒

ROM	RAD	TEL	TOT	FC	MAT	OSH	TAG	CR	CHAR
JYH	120,05	9056	11	25930			TO STITCH/MEND		紩
JYH	120,10	4887	16	28940	0985	6308	FINE AND CLOSE	C5268	緻
JYH	133,00	5267	06	10104	0982	0255	ARRIVE,MOST		至
JYH	133,03	5268	09	18140	0984	6307	TO CAUSE,CONVEY,FINE AND CLOSE	G4887	致
JYH	142,06	5759	12	51114	0994A	0262	LEECH/HIRUDINEA,FLUKE		蛭
JYH	145,05	5923	11	00732	1010	5888	BOOK COVER,(SURNAME)	1589	袠
JYH	145,08	5956	14	22732	0987	5820	MANUFACTURE	B0455	製
JYH	148,12	6052	19	26256	0970		GOBLET		觶
JYH	149,07	6125	14	04631	0973	8537	TO RECORD,WRITE A FOOTNOTE		誌
JYH	149,12	6221.0B	19	03650	5825	6907	TO RECORD,WRITE A FOOTNOTE	6125	識
JYH	151,11	6266.1	18	55130			FEUDAL NOBLE RANKS		豑
JYH	151,18	6266	25	28127			FEUDAL NOBLE RANKS		豒
JYH	153,00	6282	07	20222	1043	4144	(MYTHICAL ANIMAL)	A1667	豸
JYH	154,04	6347.1A	11	72806	1009		HOSTAGE		貭
JYH	154,08	6347.0A	15	72806	1009	8176	HOSTAGE		質
JYH	154,11	6360	18	44806	0980	8233	GIFTS TO SUPERIORS		贄
JYH	157,06	9331	13	64141			TO STOP,TO SQUAT		跱
JYH	157,15	6492	22	62186	0966	8178	STUMBLE		躓
JYH	159,06	6531	13	51014	0983A	0259	BACK AND LOWER OF CHARIOT,SHORT/LOW		輊
JYH	163,06	6736	09	17127	0995	2158	EXTREMELY,(SURNAME)		郅
JYH	167,06	9455	14	81114			SICKLE		銍
JYH	167,07	9463	15	84131			TO RECORD,ENGRAVE		鋕
JYH	167,15	9514	23	82186		8177	(EXECUTIONER S) BLOCK		鑕
JYH	170,07	7106	10	71221	1004	4146	ASCEND,ADVANCE		陟
JYH	172,05	7164	13	80414	0968	0895	RINGED PHEASANT		雉
JYH	187,07	7492	17	79227	1005	4709	STALLION,DETERMINE,PROMOTE		騭
JYH	187,10	7492.1	20	71327	1005	4710	STALLION,DETERMINE,PROMOTE		騺
JYH	195,07	764N	18	24331			ERYTHRICHTHYS SCHLEGELI		鯄
JYH	195,08	765A	19	22336			SARDINELLA ZUNASI		鯯
JYH	195,10	765S	21	28340			AMIA LINCATA		鰶
JYH	196,11	7747	22	44327	0981	4691	BIRDS OF PREY		鷙
KA	009,05	3906	07	21231			KAWA(ETHNIC GROUP)		佧
KA	030,05	3931	08	61031			CARBAZOLE,PHONETIC		咔

ROM	RAD	TEL	TOT	FC	MAT	OSH	TAG	CR	CHAR
KA	030,05	0739	08	66000	0582	1085	COFFEE		咖
KA	030,09	0807.0A	12	63064			(ONOMAT.)		喀
KAA	025,03	0595	05	21231	0616	2007	CARD		卡
KAA	030,06	0750.0B	09	60082		7991	TO BE CHOKED/TO COUGH(BLOOD)		咳
KAA	096,05	3798	09	11131			CARAT		珓
KAA	130,05	518A	09	71231			ISONITRITE OR CARBYLAMINE		胩
KAA	167,05	6888	13	81131			(PHONETIC)		鈝
KAH	030,09	0807	12	63064	3325	1430	(PHONETIC)		喀
KAI	007,02	7030.1	04	10440			OPEN,START,OPERATE(VEHICLE)		开
KAI	064,09	2261	12	51062	3203	1678	WIPE		揩
KAI	167,12	3987	20	87120			CALIFORNIUM		鐦
KAI	169,04	7030	12	77441	3204	3485	OPEN,START,OPERATE(VEHICLE)		開
KAE	016,10	0418	12	27110	3205	7854	TRIUMPHANT/VICTORIOUS		凱
KAE	018,10	0481	12	22100	3197	2871	CAREFULLY/MODERATELY		剴
KAE	030,11	0854	14	61014	3209	7729	TO SIGH/TO REGRET		嘅
KAE	032,10	1052	13	42118		0570	DRY TERRAIN		塏
KAE	061,10	1956	13	92018	3206	0574	JOYFUL,KIND		愷
KAE	061,12	1980	15	91014	3210	7730	GENEROUS,SAD		慨
KAE	075,09	2818	13	41962	0623	1680	NORM/MODEL/(WRITING)		楷
KAE	140,09	550B	13	44601			CARANE		菩
KAE	167,09	6946	17	81162			HIGH QUALITY IRON		鍇
KAE	167,10	6963	18	82118	3207	8919	ARMOR		鎧
KAE	169,10	7065	18	77108	3208	3444	LOOSEN,OPEN		闓
KAE	182,10	9589	19	27110			BALMY,GENIAL AS WIND		颽
KAE	182,10	9589.1	19	72211			BALMY,GENIAL AS WIND		颶
KAY	061,09	1943.0A	12	96027	0807	4386	TO DESIRE		愒
KAY	061,10	1958	13	98017	2454	7813	ANGER		愾
KAN	018,03	0436	05	12400	3242	2881	TO PRINT/PUBLISH		刊
KAN	019,09	0522.0A	11	44727	3253		INVESTIGATE,COLLATE		勘
KAN	032,09	1030	12	44111	3254	0767	ENDURE		堪
KAN	062,09	2063	13	43750	3256	6902	SUPPRESS,KILL		戡
KAN	075,06	8553	10	11904		5342	TO PRINT/PUBLISH	0436	栞
KAN	109,04	4170.0A	09	20604	3251	1710	TO WATCH/TO GUARD		看

ROM	RAD	TEL	TOT	FC	MAT	OSH	TAG	CR	CHAR
KAN	109,05	4170.1A	10	20604			TO WATCH/TO GUARD		看
KAN	212,06	7896	22	80211	3258	7333	NICHE,SHRINE		龕
KAAN	009,06	0170	08	26210	3250	7778	BOLD		侃
KAAN	009,09	8061	11	26260			BOLD	0170	侃
KAAN	032,04	0974	07	47182	3245	4904	PIT,THRESHOLD		坎
KAAN	075,14	2920	18	48917	2690	0642	DOOR SILL/THRESHOLD		檻
KAAN	076,08	2954	12	27782	3248	4913	DISCONTENTED WITH ONESELF		欿
KAAN	076,09	8618	13	47782			UNSATISFIED(OF EATING)		歁
KAAN	112,04	4266	09	17682	3247	4916	TO CHOP		砍
KAAN	140,07	544C	11	44182			CAMPHANE		莰
KAAN	159,13	9366	20	53035	3257	8679	UNABLE TO REACH ONE'S AIM		轗
KANN	019,09	0522	11	44727	3253	4795	INVESTIGATE,COLLATE		勘
KANN	032,11	8962.1	14	44127	3255	4796	DANGEROUS SEA-CLIFF		墈
KANN	109,04	4170	09	20604	3251	1710	LOOK AT,THINK,IT DEPENDS		看
KANN	109,05	4170.1	10	20604			LOOK AT,THINK,IT DEPENDS		看
KANN	109,12	4230	17	68040	3260	6328	GLANCE,BIRD S-EYE VIEW	4239	瞰
KANN	109,20	4239	25	67020	3260	3519	GLANCE,BIRD S-EYE VIEW	4230	矙
KANN	112,11	8962	16	14627	3255		DANGEROUS SEA-CLIFF		磡
KANN	144,03	5889	09	21221	3252	3024	PLEASED		衎
KANN	169,12	7074	20	77448	3259	3517	PEEP,(SURNAME)		闞
KANG	053,08	1660	11	00232	3278	5698	PEACEFUL,SPONGY (OF RADISHES)		康
KANG	061,11	1988	14	90032	3279	5700	GENEROUS/MAGNANIMOUS		慷
KANG	115,11	4749.1	16	20932	3280	5702	HUSK		棟
KANG	118,08	4625	14	88101	3727		ANCIENT KIND OF LUTE		箜
KANG	119,11	4749	17	90932	3280	5701	HUSK		糠
KANG	195,11	766D	22	20332			LOPHIOMUS STETIGERUS		鱇
KARNG	064,03	2095	06	51010	3261	0089	CARRY ON ONE'S SHOULDER		扛
KAANG	061,11	1988.0A	14	90032	3279	5700	GENEROUS/MAGNANIMOUS		慷
KANQ	008,02	0073	04	00217	3273	7858	OVERBEARING		亢
KANQ	009,04	0121	06	20217	3274	7862	HUSBAND/WIFE		伉
KANQ	022,04	0560	06	71711	3275	0821	COUCH FOR TWO		匠
KANQ	031,04	8190	07	60217			TO HIDE/STORE		园
KANQ	064,04	2123	07	50017	3276	7864	RESIST		抗

ROM	RAD	TEL	TOT	FC	MAT	OSH	TAG	CR	CHAR
KANQ	086,04	3510	08	90817	3277	7868	HEATED BRICK BED		炕
KANQ	094,04	8795	07	40217			FIERCE DOG		犹
KANQ	167,04	3993	12	80117			SCANDIUM		鈧
KAU	044,02	1440	05	77217	3298	7907	END OF SPINE		尻
KAO	064,06	2166	09	54027	3300	4578	EXAMINE BY TORTURE		拷
KAO	066,02	2393	06	18240	3299	6383	EXAMINE	5072	攷
KAO	075,06	2723	10	44927	3301	4579	MANGROVE		栲
KAO	086,06	3628	10	94827	3302	4580	TO ROAST/BAKE		烤
KAO	086,10	3573.0A	14	90827	3305	3835	DRY		熇
KAO	125,00	5072	06	44207	3299	4576	EXAMINE	2393	考
KAO	167,06	9456	14	84127	3304	4517	HANDCUFFS		銬
KAW	093,10	3683	14	20527	3306	3831	GIVE A BONUS TO		犒
KAW	175,07	7237	15	24111	3308	2784	LEAN ON,DEPEND UPON		靠
KE	018,06	0466	08	02200	3322	2966	CARVE		刻
KE	030,07	077C	10	64016			PHONETIC FOR CLICKING		唠
KE	064,10	2270	13	54017	3402	0741	SMASH,TO STRIKE		搕
KE	075,05	2688	09	41920	3384	3054	(SURNAME),STEM,HANDLE OF AXE		柯
KE	075,08	2644	12	46994	3391	5505	AN. FOR PLANTS		棵
KE	096,05	3784	09	11120	3385	3039	JADE-LIKE STONE		珂
KE	104,05	4008.0A	10	00121			MALADY	4038	疴
KE	112,10	4326	15	14617	3405	0738	TO TAP/KNOCK		磕
KE	115,04	4430	09	24900	3389	2704	SUBJECT,BRANCH OF MEDICINE		科
KE	115,08	4459	13	26994	3392	5506	(WHEAT)		稞
KE	116,08	4517	13	30904	3393	5510	NEST		窠
KE	118,13	4686	19	88302			BIG,HUNGER		簻
KE	140,05	5381	09	44621	3386	3059	SEVERE/EXACTING		苛
KE	140,13	5639	17	44302	3399		BIG,HUNGRY-LOOKING		薖
KE	142,09	5809	15	54100	3390	2705	TADPOLE		蝌
KE	159,05	9363	12	51020	3387	3051	GIVEN NAME OF MENCIUS		軻
KE	167,05	4100	13	81120			COLUMBIUM		鈳
KE	181,06	7331	15	01286	2008	8307	CHIN		頦
KE	181,08	7341	17	61986	3396	8291	AN. FOR BEADS/PEARLS/STARS		顆
KE	188,08	9629	18	76294	3398	5501	CONDYLES		髁

ROM	RAD	TEL	TOT	FC	MAT	OSH	TAG	CR	CHAR
KER	030,06	0750	09	60082	3323	7991	COUGH	2947	
KER	033,04	8199	07	40217	3406	7877	SHELL	3011	
KER	076,06	2947	10	07282	3323	4958	TO COUGH	0750	
KER	079,08	3011	12	47247	3406	6299	SHELL	8199	
KER	109,10	4209	15	64017	3404	0739	BE DROWZY/DOZE		
KER	181,06	7331.0B	15	01286	2008	8307	CHIN		
KEE	030,02	0668	05	10620	3381	3037	CAN/MAY		
KEE	032,05	0985	08	41120	3382	3038	UNEVEN(PATH),UNFORTUNATE(IN LIFE)		
KEE	046,05	1482	08	22621		3057	NAME OF A MOUNTAIN		
KEE	085,09	3265	12	36127	3401	4396	THIRSTY		
KEH	010,05	0344	07	40216	3320	7555	SUBDUE,GRAM	A0460	
KEH	010,08	8090	10	44210	3321		SUBDUE	1411	
KEH	018,06	0466.0A	08	02200	3322	2966	QUARTER OF AN HOUR,OPPRESSIVE		
KEH	018,07	0460	09	42210	3321	7561	SUBDUE	A0344	
KEH	030,10	0836.0A	13	64017	2120	0737	TO CRACK(SEEDS) WITH FRONT TEETH		
KEH	040,06	1356	09	30604	3324	1429	GUEST		
KEH	041,07	1411	10	44210	3321	7562	SUBDUE	0460	
KEH	061,06	1870	09	97064	3400	1413	RESPECTFUL,(SURNAME)		
KEH	075,10	2855	14	44917			PUSAETHA SCANDENS		
KEH	084,07	4121	11	80217		7821	KRYPTON		
KEH	085,10	3328	13	34117	3403	0742	SUDDENLY		
KEH	120,09	9065	15	24956			TO WOOF		
KEH	149,08	6143	15	06694	3394	5496	LESSON		
KEH	167,08	9481	16	86194	3395	5494	GREASE-POT FOR CART,INGOT		
KEI	064,11	2305.0A	14	51016		0795	TO ASSAULT		
KEEN	030,08	8186	11	61027		3600	GNAW/BITE	7883.0A	
KEEN	032,06	1083.1	09	77104			RECLAIM(LAND)		
KEEN	032,13	1083	16	27104	3337	0221	RECLAIM(LAND)		
KEEN	061,06	2017.1	10	77333			EARNEST		
KEEN	061,13	2017	17	27333	3338	8662	EARNEST		
KEEN	130,04	5146	08	21227	3334	3599	WILLING		
KEEN	211,06	7883.0A	21	27732	3333	5901	GNAW/BITE	8186	
KENN	064,08	2240	11	51027	3336	3602	TAKE BY FORCE		

咳壳欬殼瞌頦可坷岢渴克尅刻剋嗑客尅恪樫氪溘緙課錁摳啃垦墾恳懇肯齦揹

ROM	RAD	TEL	TOT	FC	MAT	OSH	TAG	CR	CHAR
KENN	112,06	8941	11	17632	3331		RUMBLING OF ROLLING STONES		硍
KENG	009,11	0282.0B	13	21286	1161	8300	BANKRUPT		傾
KENG	032,04	0977	07	40117	3354	7859	PIT,DEFRAUD	7085	坑
KENG	093,07	8783	11	21511	3355	0126	SHANK BONE OF OX		牼
KENG	112,07	4284	12	11611	3356	0123	OBSTINATE	8957	硍
KENG	112,08	8957	13	77601			OBSTINATE	4284	磬
KENG	167,11	6972	19	87114	3357	0226	JINGLING OF METALS,TO STRIKE		鏗
KENG	170,04	7085	07	70217	3354	7863	PIT,TO DEFRAUD	0977	阬
KONG	009,08	0238	10	23211	3723	0116	IGNORANT/BLANK-MINDED		倥
KONG	030,08	079B	11	63011			-K + ONE AS IN CHALKONE		喀
KONG	046,08	1519	11	23711	3724	0114	NAME OF A MOUNTAIN		崆
KONG	061,08	1904	11	93011	3725	0115	SINCERE,SIMPLE-MINDED		悾
KONG	116,03	4500	08	30101	3722	0113	EMPTY,IN VAIN		空
KONG	196,08	772C	19	37127			TOCO TOUCAN		鵼
KOONG	009,08	0238.0A	10	23211	3723	0116	URGENT/PRESSED		倥
KOONG	039,01	1313	04	12410	3720	7063	HOLE,(SURNAME)		孔
KOONG	061,06	1858	10	17331	3721	8687	AFRAID/FRIGHTENED		恐
KONQ	064,08	2235	11	53011	3726	0118	TO CONTROL,SUE		控
KONQ	116,03	4500.0A	08	30101	3722	0113	EMPTIED,LEISURE		空
KONQ	177,08	7261	17	43511`	3728		BRIDLE/REINS		鞚
KOU	064,11	2305	14	51016	3442	0795	DIG OUT(WITH FINGER),STINGY		摳
KOU	140,04	5351	08	44412			SCALLION STALK,HOLLOW		芤
KOU	140,11	5575	15	44214		7483	AMOMUM COSTATUM		蔻
KOOU	030,00	0656	03	60000	3434	1073	MOUTH		口
KOW	009,05	013A	07	27220		4418	HUNCH BACK		佝
KOW	030,02	0661	05	67020	3435	2119	KNOCK		叩
KOW	040,08	1379	11	30214	3444	7482	BANDIT		寇
KOW	057,11	1729	14	11216	3441	0799	END OF BOW,(SURNAME)		彄
KOW	064,03	2099	06	56000	3436	1082	DETAIN,BUTTON,10 PERCENT	D6863	扣
KOW	066,05	2410	09	28640		6380	KNOCK	0661	敂
KOW	118,06	9010	12	88560			(A MEASURE OF WIDTH OF CLOTH)		筘
KOW	118,11	4661	17	88214			HEALDS OF A LOOM		簆
KOW	167,03	6863	11	86100	3439	1074	BUTTON	B2099	釦

203

ROM	RAD	TEL	TOT	FC	MAT	OSH	TAG	CR	CHAR
KOW	196,10	7734	21	47347	3446	6286	FLEDGLINGS		鷇
KU	018,06	0453	08	42200	3495	2932	TO CUT OPEN/RIP UP/SCOOP OUT		刳
KU	030,07	0770	10	66430	3500	5092	CRY/WEEP		哭
KU	032,08	8232	11	47172			CAVE/HOLE	4516	堀
KU	075,05	2661	09	44960	3492	1297	DRIED UP		枯
KU	116,08	4516	13	30272	3503	1031	CAVE/HOLE	8232	窟
KU	188,05	7545	15	74260	3494	1296	SKELETON		骷
KUU	075,09	2822.0A	13	44964		1313	BROKEN UTENSIL		楛
KUU	140,05	5388	09	44604	3493	1312	BITTER,MISERABLE,INTENSELY		苦
KUH	030,17	8185	20	77601	3502		NAME OF AN EMPEROR		嚳
KUH	053,07	1655	10	00256	3496	2650	WAREHOUSE		庫
KUH	112,03	4262	08	18617	3498	7963	TO TOIL		矻
KUH	120,06	4818	12	24927	3497		TROUSERS,DRAWERS	5928	絝
KUH	142,06	575C	12	54127			PLUSIA FESTUCAE		蛒
KUH	145,06	5928	11	34227	3497	4565	TROUSERS,DRAWERS	5974	袴
KUH	145,10	5974	15	30256	3497	2651	TROUSERS,DRAWERS	5928	褲
KUH	164,07	6807	14	14661	3501	1336	RUTHLESS,STRONG(AS OF WINE)		酷
KUA	037,03	1139	06	40207	3526	4559	TO BOAST	6122	夸
KUA	038,06	1221	09	44427	3528	4569	FASCINATING,PRETTY		姱
KUA	149,06	6122	13	04627	3530	4563	TO BOAST	1139	誇
KOA	032,06	1006	09	44127		4560	COLLAPSE		垮
KUAH	130,06	5169	10	74227	3529	4567	THIGH/LEG		胯
KUAH	157,06	6421	13	64127	3531	4561	STEP ASTRIDE,STEP ACROSS		跨
KUAI	030,06	8139	09	77227	3507	3932	WRY MOUTH		咼
KOAI	064,13	232B	16	51011	3545	0785	SCRATCH AN ITCHY PLACE		搲
KOAI	134,04	5276.0B	10	20777	7299	1061	TO SCOOP		舀
KOAI	140,10	5566	14	42200	3551	2899	A RUSH/SCIRPUS CYPERINUS		蒯
KUAY	009,04	2585.1B	06	80731	2345	1537	ACCOUNTING		会
KUAY	009,13	0312	15	28266	3546	1539	BROKER		儈
KUAY	017,03	0426	05	22770		0969	LUMP/PIECE	1040	凷
KUAY	018,13	0492	15	82600	3639	2879	AMPUTATE		劊
KUAY	030,13	0898	16	68066	3537	1538	THROAT,TO SWALLOW,(SURNAME)		噲
KUAY	032,04	1040.1	07	45134			LUMP/PIECE		块

ROM	RAD	TEL	TOT	FC	MAT	OSH	TAG	CR	CHAR
KUAY	032,10	1040	13	46113	3550	7635	LUMP/PIECE	0426	塊
KUAY	061,04	1816	07	95034	3547	5208	QUICK,SHARP		快
KUAY	070,15	8499	19	08266	3543	1547	SIGNAL FLAG/BANNER		旝
KUAY	073,09	2585.0B	13	80606	2345	1537	ACCOUNTING		會
KUAY	075,13	2910	17	48966	3538	1542	JUNIPERUS CHINENSIS		檜
KUAY	085,13	3420	16	38166	3539	1546	STREAM,DRAIN		澮
KUAY	094,13	3748	16	48266			CRAFTY/CUNNING		獪
KUAY	118,07	4599	13	88934	3548	5209	CHOPSTICK		筷
KUAY	130,13	5239	17	78266	3541	1540	CHOPPED MEAT OR FISH	7671	膾
KUAY	163,13	6778	16	87627	3542		NAME OF A FEUDAL STATE,(SURNAME)		鄶
KUAY	187,04	7464	14	75334	3549	5214	FAST(HORSE)		駃
KUAY	195,13	7671	24	28366	3541	1545	CHOPPED MEAT OR FISH	5239	鱠
KUAN	040,12	1401	15	30213	3578	7631	WIDE,LENIENT		寬
KUAN	120,08	4858.0A	14	28927	4252	3798	SILK KERCHIEF		綸
KUAN	188,15	7556	25	73213		7633	PELVIS/PELVIC		髖
KOAN	075,07	8562	11	43911	3582		STAND FOR SACRIFICE,(TREE)		梡
KOAN	076,07	2949.1	11	27482	3579	4945	FUNDS		欵
KOAN	076,08	2949	12	47982	3579	4963	FUNDS		款
KOAN	116,11	4530	16	30432			HOLLOW,IGNORANT		窾
KUANG	019,06	0510	08	74727	3594	4797	ZEALOUS		劻
KUANG	022,04	0562	06	71711	3593	0776	CORRECT		匡
KUANG	061,06	8393	09	91011	3595		TO FEAR/APPREHENSIVE		恇
KUANG	112,15	4349	20	10686			A MINE,ORE	7006	礦
KUANG	118,06	4590	12	88711	3598	0782	BASKET		筐
KUANG	149,06	6119	13	01611	3599	0777	TO SWINDLE,MISLEAD		誆
KWANG	094,04	3693	07	41214	3601	0317	MAD,CONCEITED		狂
KWANG	149,07	6128	14	01614	3602	0318	LIES,DECEIVE		誑
KOANG	094,15	3755	18	40286	3591	8337	FIERCE/RUDE/BARBARIC		獷
KUANQ	015,05	0066	07	36110		7551	MOREOVER,SITUATION	S0400	况
KUANQ	015,05	0400	07	36110		7551	MOREOVER,SITUATION	8665	况
KUANQ	032,15	1094	18	40186	3605	8332	TOMB		壙
KUANQ	037,03	8268	06	40223			(USED IN PLACE NAMES)		夼
KUANQ	072,15	2568	19	60086	3606	8335	WASTE,WILDERNESS		曠

ROM	RAD	TEL	TOT	FC	MAT	OSH	TAG	CR	CHAR
KUANQ	075,06	2713	10	41911	3596	0781	FRAME/DOOR FRAME		
KUANQ	085,05	8665	08	36110	3603	7552	MOREOVER,SITUATION	0400	
KUANQ	109,06	4186	11	61011	3597	0778	EYE SOCKET		
KUANQ	112,03	4349.1	08	10600			A MINE,ORE		
KUANQ	120,06	4830	12	29911	3608	7510	FINE FLOSS-SILK OR COTTON	4962	
KUANQ	120,15	4962	21	20986	3608	8340	FINE FLOSS-SILK OR COTTON	4830	
KUANQ	154,05	6315	12	66810	3604	7550	BESTOW,CONFER		
KUANQ	163,15	6782	18	07227	3592	2257	(SURNAME)		
KUANQ	167,15	7006	23	80186	3607	8333	A MINE,ORE	4349	
KUEI	007,01	5719.1	03	10207		4571	DEFICIENCY,DEFICIT		
KUEI	018,06	0452	08	42100	3642	2863	CUT OPEN AND CLEAN		
KUEI	046,18	8354	21	22127		3975	HILLY,HIGH AND MIGHTY(OF MOUNTAIN)		
KUEI	061,07	1887	10	96014	3645	0432	LAUGH AT		
KUEI	108,06	4140	11	40107	3647	0708	HELMET		
KUEI	116,11	4529	16	30516	3648	7607	PRY INTO,PEEP	7071	
KUEI	141,11	5719	17	21227	3650	4573	DEFICIENCY,DEFICIT		
KUEI	169,11	7071	19	77516	3649	3530	PRY INTO,PEEP	4529	
KWEI	030,09	081A	12	64014			(PHONETIC)/QUIN- AS IN QUINOLINE		
KWEI	035,20	1117	23	44407	3662	6474	RESPECTFUL,ONE-LEGGED MONSTER	S5688	
KWEI	035,20	5688	23	44407	3662	6474	ONE-LEGGED MONSTER,RESPECTFUL	S1117	
KWEI	037,06	1145	09	40104	3643	0182	NAME OF CONSTELLATION,STRIDE		
KWEI	062,09	2064	13	13450	3657	6943	A LANCE		
KWEI	064,09	2247	12	52034	3658	5144	CONSIDER,ESTIMATE		
KWEI	072,09	8514	13	62034	3659	5142	SEPARATED FROM,IN OPPOSITION TO		
KWEI	109,09	8915	14	62034	3660	5143	SEPARATED,STARE		
KWEI	140,09	5525	13	44430	3661	5146	SUNFLOWER		
KWEI	142,09	579A	15	54114			VIPER		
KWEI	162,08	6652	12	34301	3651	6600	CROSS-ROADS,THOROUGHFARE		
KWEI	163,09	9408	12	17427			PLACE NAME		
KWEI	181,07	9580	16	21486		8268	CHEEKBONE,PROTRUDE		
KWEI	185,02	7447	11	48016	3652	7913	CROSSROADS,CHEEKBONE,HIGH		
KWEI	187,09	7503	19	72334		5145	STRONG,POWERFUL		
KWEI	194,04	7608	14	24210	3655	7653	CHIEF/HEAD		

ROM	RAD	TEL	TOT	FC	MAT	OSH	TAG	CR	CHAR
KOEI	009,10	0264	12	26213	3653	7640	PUPPET		傀
KOEI	064,09	2247.0A	12	52034	3658	5144	CONSIDER,ESTIMATE		揆
KOEI	086,09	8749	13	94814			FIERY/BLAZING		煃
KOEI	157,06	6423	13	64114	3644	0161	SHORT STEP,BRIEF		跬
KOEI	181,04	7321	13	41486		8296	RAISE ONE'S HEAD		頍
KUEY	022,12	0566.0A	14	71718	3638	0823	LACKING/EMPTY/EXHAUSTED,(SURNAME)		匱
KUEY	030,09	0846	12	66027	3646	3616	TO SIGH		喟
KUEY	038,10	1267	13	46413	3654	7645	ASHAMED	1951	媿
KUEY	061,10	1951	13	96013	3654	7639	ASHAMED	1267	愧
KUEY	061,12	2025	15	95086	3637	8123	TROUBLED,CONFUSED		憒
KUEY	085,12	3391	15	35186	2343	8129	BREAK DOWN,BE DISPERSED		潰
KUEY	118,12	4676	18	88806	3664	8131	BASKET FOR CARRYING SOIL	4695	簣
KUEY	118,14	4695	20	88718	3664	0826	BASKET FOR CARRYING SOIL	4676	籄
KUEY	128,12	5118	18	15186	3666	8126	DEAF,BORN DEAF		聵
KUEY	140,12	5614	16	44806	3667	8130	AMARANTHUS MANGOSTANUS,(SURNAME)		蕢
KUEY	184,10	7427	18	86713	3656	7641	MAKE A PRESENT	B7432	餽
KUEY	184,12	7432	20	85786	3669	8125	FOOD,MAKE A PRESENT	D7427	饋
KUEN	032,05	0981	08	45106	3684	2686	THE EARTH-/FEMALE-PRINCIPLE	1024	坤
KUEN	032,08	1024	11	00104	3684	0210	THE EARTH-/FEMALE-PRINCIPLE	0981	堃
KUEN	046,08	1507	11	22711	3679	7125	KOULKUN MOUNTAINS	1506	崑
KUEN	046,08	1506	11	26711	3679	7117	KOULKUN MOUNTAINS	1507	崐
KUEN	072,04	2492	08	60711	3678	7114	ELDER BROTHER,DESCENDANT	8511	昆
KUEN	072,07	8511	11	60227		4767	ELDER BROTHER,DESCENDANT	2492	晜
KUEN	086,08	3540	12	96811	2372	7121	BRILLIANT		焜
KUEN	096,08	3824	12	16111	3680	7115	(JADE)		琨
KUEN	145,09	5960	14	37256	3686	2657	DRAWERS,LOOSE-FITTING TROUSERS		裩
KUEN	164,08	4128	15	16611			QUINONE		醌
KUEN	167,08	6924	16	86111		7116	STEEL SWORD		錕
KUEN	190,02	7562	12	72217	3685	7881	MAKE THE HEAD BALD		髡
KUEN	195,08	7649	19	26311	3682	7123	SEA-MONSTER,YOUNG OF FISHES		鯤
KUEN	196,08	7721	19	67727	3683	4658	JUNGLE-FOWL		鶤
KOEN	033,12	1109	15	40102	3687	0523	CORRIDOR IN PALACE		壼
KOEN	061,07	1875	10	96000	3689	1903	SINCERE		悃

ROM	RAD	TEL	TOT	FC	MAT	OSH	TAG	CR	CHAR
KOEN	064,07	2190	10	56000	3690	1904	TIE TOGETHER,A BUNCH		
KOEN	075,07	2749	11	46900	3691	1905	MOVEABLE DOOR SILL		
KOEN	115,08	4461	13	26900			FULL		
KOEN	120,07	4841	13	26900	3694	1906	TIE TOGETHER,A BUNCH	2190	
KOEN	169,07	7045	15	77607	3696	3476	THRESHOLD,DOOR TO WOMEN'S ROOM		
KUENN	031,04	0938	07	60904	3688	1901	DISTRESS,SLEEPY/DOZE OFF	D419A	
KUENN	109,07	419A	12	66000	3692	1902	SLEEPY/DOZE OFF	B0938	
KUO	142,06	4157	12	52164	3749	1323	GARDEN-SLUG		
KUOH	053,11	1674	14	00227	3753	2205	BIG,EMPTY,OPEN		
KUOH	064,03	2368.1	06	50000			ENLARGE		
KUOH	064,05	2161.0A	08	52064	3519	1321	INCLUDE,ENCLOSE		
KUOH	064,15	2368	18	50086	3752	8336	ENLARGE		
KUOH	085,11	8708	14	37127			CLASHING OF TWO CURRENTS		
KUOH	085,14	7059.1	17	37120	3750	3454	WIDE,RICH		
KUOH	162,06	6624.0B	10	32306	3522	6616	HASTEN/QUICKLY		
KUOH	169,09	7059	17	77164	3750	3455	WIDE,RICH		
KUOH	177,08	7262	17	40547	3754		LEATHER	9562	
KUOH	177,11	9562	20	47527	3754	2203	LEATHER	7262	
LHA	018,07	0469.0A	09	52900	3757	2941	(ONOMAT.)		
LHA	030,08	0784.0A	11	60018			(ONOMAT.),(PHONETIC)		
LHA	030,09	0812.0B	12	62000	3758	2942	(ONOMAT.)		
LHA	064,05	2139	08	50018	3756	0551	PULL		
LA	018,07	0469	09	52900	3757	2941	TO SLASH		
LA	032,05	0998.0A	08	40118	3755	0545	GARBAGE		
LA	162,15	9380	19	32301	3766	6758	UNTIDY		
LA	195,09	765M	20	52336			PYGOSTEUS SINENSIS		
LAA	030,09	0812	12	62000	3758	2942	(PHONETIC)		
LAH	018,07	0469.0B	09	52900		2941	CRUEL/OBSTINATE		
LAH	030,09	0812.0A	12	62000	3758	2942	RUFFIAN,GANG		
LAH	064,15	237B	18	52016	3762	6837	LEAVE BEHIND	9380.0A	
LAH	104,09	8877	14	00120	3760	2944	SCABIES/SCALD-HEAD		
LAH	130,08	5198	12	74261	3763	1513	PRESERVED(MEAT)	5248	
LAH	130,13	9139	17	74227		4400	CANDLE,WAX	5779	

捆
梱
綑
閫
困
睏
蛞
廓
扩
括
擴
溿
潤
适
闊
鞟
鞹
剌
啦
喇
拉
剌
垃
邋
劗
剌
喇
剌
喇
擸
瘌
腊
臈

ROM	RAD	TEL	TOT	FC	MAT	OSH	TAG	CR	CHAR
LAH	130,15	5248	19	72216	3763	6838	PRESERVED(MEAT),DECEMBER	5198	臘
LAH	140,09	5507.0C	13	44164		1425	LEAVE BEHIND	9380.0A	落
LAH	142,08	5779	14	54161	3764		CANDLE,WAX	5866	蜡
LAH	142,15	5866	21	52116	3764	6840	CANDLE,WAX	5779	蠟
LAH	160,07	6584	14	05496	3761	5524	HOT,PUNGENT		辣
LAH	162,15	9380.0A	19	32301	3766	6758	LEAVE BEHIND	237B	邋
LAH	167,15	4257	23	82116	3767	6835	SOLDER		鑞
LAH	190,09	7590	19	72922			BALD,SCABBY		鬎
.LA	030,08	0784	11	60018		0552	FUSION OF .LE + .A		啦
.LA	140,14	5663.0A	18	44107			KOHLRABI		藍
LHAI	039,14	8312	17	15417	3775	0730	CHILD OF AN OLD MAN		孻
LAI	009,06	0171	08	40908	3768	5429	TO COME		來
LAI	009,08	0206	10	24298	3769		TO COME	1784	俫
LAI	046,08	1503	11	24798		5114	NAME OF A MOUNTAIN IN SZECHWAN		崍
LAI	060,08	1784	11	24298	3769	5432	TO COME	0171	徠
LAI	075,03	0171.1	07	50900	3768		TO COME		来
LAI	085,08	3200	11	34198	3770	5434	BROOK,RIPPLE		淶
LAI	118,08	4610	14	88908			(BAMBOO)		箂
LAI	140,08	5490	12	44908	3772	5435	CHENOPODIUM ALBUM		萊
LAI	167,08	4414	16	84198		5430	RHENIUM		錸
LAI	187,08	7495	18	74398			MARE		騋
LAY	009,08	0206.0A	10	24298	3769		INDUCE/SUMMON	1784.0A	俫
LAY	019,08	8111.0A	10	44927	3769		INDUCE/SUMMON	1784.0A	勑
LAY	060,08	1784.0A	11	24298	3769	5432	INDUCE/SUMMON		徠
LAY	085,16	3471	19	37186	3777	8207	RUSHING OF WATER,NAME OF A RIVER		瀨
LAY	104,16	4088	21	00186	3778	8208	SKIN DISEASE,SCABIES		癩
LAY	109,08	4202	13	64098	3771	5431	GAZE/STARE		睞
LAY	118,16	4704	22	88986	3779	8209	MUSICAL PIPE WITH 3 REEDS,MUSIC		籟
LAY	140,16	5680	20	44986			(FRAGRANT LABIATE PLANT)		蘱
LAY	154,08	6336	15	40806	3773	8219	CONFER,BESTOW		賚
LAY	154,09	6351	16	57986	3776	8203	RELY,TO BLAME,DISCLAIM		賴
LAN	001,04	5695.1	05	80101			ORCHID		兰
LAN	038,08	1245	11	44404	3780	9040	AVARICIOUS		婪

209

ROM	RAD	TEL	TOT	FC	MAT	OSH	TAG	CR	CHAR
LAN	046,09	1526	12	22217	3783	7836	MIST,NAME OF A MOUNTAIN		
LAN	064,05	2374.1	08	58011			HINDER,CUT OFF		
LAN	064,17	2374	20	57020	3790	3509	HINDER,CUT OFF		
LAN	067,17	2433	21	07420	3791	3512	VARIEGATED/PARTI-COLORED		
LAN	075,05	2936.1	09	48911			RAILING		
LAN	075,17	2936	21	47920	3792	3510	RAILING		
LAN	085,17	3482	20	37120	3793	3513	SWELLING WATER		
LAN	118,14	4691	20	88107	3801	0645	BASKET		
LAN	118,17	9025	23	88227			QUIVER,BOW CASE		
LAN	140,14	5663	18	44107	3802	0644	BLUE		
LAN	140,17	5695	21	44227	3795	3514	ORCHID		
LAN	145,14	5996	19	38217	3803	0640	RAGGED GARMENTS		
LAN	145,17	6001	22	37220	3796	3508	GOWN OR ROBE		
LAN	149,17	9301	24	07620	3797	3507	MAKE A FALSE CHARGE		
LAN	167,17	4420	25	87120			LANTHANUM		
LAN	169,09	7061	17	77906	3789	3506	DOOR-SCREEN,LATE,EXHAUSTED		
LAAN	032,13	1087	16	40194	3784	5549	DISAPPOINTED		
LAAN	038,16	1304	19	47486	3786	8206	LAZY	2036	
LAAN	061,16	2036	19	97086	3787	8204	LAZY	1304	
LAAN	064,14	8477	18	78502	3805	3342	SEIZE,MONOPOLIZE	2385	
LAAN	064,21	2385	24	58016	3805	7619	SEIZE,MONOPOLIZE	8477	
LAAN	075,21	2941	25	48916	3806	7620	OLIVE		
LAAN	085,21	3465	24	38116		7622	PICKLE FRUITS		
LAAN	122,09	4493	14	60227			SPRING NET FOR FISHING		
LAAN	147,14	6031	21	78216	3804	7618	LOOK OVER/TO VIEW		
LANN	085,14	3448	17	38117	3800	0643	EXCESSIVE		
LANN	085,17	3482.0A	20	37120	3793	3513	UNINHIBITED		
LANN	086,05	3620.1	09	98811			ROTTEN,OVERCOOKED,SOFT		
LANN	086,17	3620	21	97820	3794	3511	ROTTEN,OVERCOOKED,SOFT		
LANN	120,21	4968	27	28916	3807	7621	HAWSER,TO TIE THE BOAT		
LANN	130,06	9118.0A	10	71227			OVER-COOKED/SOFT	B3620	
LANG	038,10	8288	13	47427	3821	2245	MYTHICAL PLACE NAME		
LANG	053,10	1671	13	00227	3822	2246	PORCH		

嵐
拦
攔
爛
栏
欄
瀾
籃
簡
藍
蘭
禮
襴
讕
钄
闌
壛
嫻
懶
掔
攬
欖
灠
嘼
覽
澹
瀾
烂
爛
纜
胹
嫏
廊

ROM	RAD	TEL	TOT	FC	MAT	OSH	TAG	CR	CHAR
LANG	075,07	2728	11	43932	3809	5920	(PALM)		根
LANG	075,10	2826	14	47927	3823	2243	(TREE)		榔
LANG	085,07	3186.0A	10	33132	3810	5925	FLOWING		浪
LANG	094,07	3708	10	43232	3811	5918	WOLF		狼
LANG	096,07	3809	11	13132	3812	5915	(GEM),TINKLING OF PENDANTS	3858	琅
LANG	096,10	3858	14	17127	3812	2241	(GEM),TINKLING OF PENDANTS	3809	瑯
LANG	115,07	4450	12	23932	3813	5921	GRASS,WEEDS		稂
LANG	118,07	4597	13	88732	3814		YOUNG BAMBOO		筤
LANG	140,07	5456	11	44732	3815	5926	(MARSH GRASS)/BIDENS TRIPARTITA		莨
LANG	140,10	5334	16	44727			WEEDS		蒗
LANG	142,07	5766	13	53132	3816	5923	MANTIS,DRAGONFLY	5788	蜋
LANG	142,10	5788	16	57127	3816	2244	MANTIS,DRAGONFLY	5766	螂
LANG	157,07	6428	14	63132	3942	5917	JUMP		跟
LANG	163,07	6745	10	37727	3820	2240	A YOUTH,(SURNAME)		郎
LANG	167,07	9467	15	83132	3818	5916	ORNAMENT,CHAIN		銀
LAANG	032,11	8243	14	32104			RAISED BANK/MUD WALL		塱
LAANG	074,07	2597	11	37720	3808	3578	CLEAR/BRIGHT		朗
LAANG	086,07	3535	11	93832		5922	BLAZE,LIGHT		烺
LAANG	169,07	7046	15	77732	3819	3516	HIGH DOOR,LOFTY,OUTLYING WASTE		閬
LANQ	032,07	822?	10	43132			WASTELAND/WILD		埌
LANQ	085,07	3186	10	33132	3810	5925	WAVE,DISSIPATED		浪
LANQ	140,07	5456.0A	11	44732	3815	5926	SCOPALIA JAPONICA MAXIN		莨
LANQ	140,10	4538	14	44132			PLACE NAME,(HERB)		蒗
LHAU	064,12	2318	15	59027	3829	4855	FISH UP		撈
LAU	019,10	0525	12	99427	3826	4853	TOIL		勞
LAU	030,12	8167	15	69027	3827	4854	TO CHATTER		嘮
LAU	030,12	088A	15	69027	3827	4854	TALK A LOT,QUARREL,NOISY		嘮
LAU	032,12	8257	15	49127			NAME OF MOUNTAIN IN SHANTUNG	1555	墝
LAU	046,12	1555	15	29727			NAME OF A MOUNTAIN IN SHANTUNG		嶗
LAU	064,12	2318.0A	15	59027	3829	4855	FISH UP		撈
LAU	093,03	3666	07	30502	3824	2521	FIRM/FAST		牢
LAU	104,12	4072	17	00127	3831	4857	TUBERCULOSIS		癆
LAU	164,11	6828	18	17622	3838	4208	WINE OR LIQUOR WITH SEDIMENT		醪

ROM	RAD	TEL	TOT	FC	MAT	OSH	TAG	CR	CHAR
LAO	009,06	0097	08	24211		7170	MALE/MAN(CANTONESE)		佬
LAO	038,06	1209	09	44411	4583	7172	GRANDMA (MATERNAL)		姥
LAO	075,06	2724	10	44911	3835	7171	BASKET		栲
LAO	085,12	3388.0A	15	34196		8424	FLOODED,HEAVY RAIN		潦
LAO	094,06	8800	09	44211			NAME OF A TRIBE		獠
LAO	125,00	5071	06	44711	3833	7168	OLD((IN AGE),TOUGH		老
LAO	159,12	9365	19	54096			SPOKES		轑
LAO	167,06	4553	14	84111	3304	7169	RHODIUM		铑
LAW	019,10	0525.0A	12	99427	3826	4853	TO REWARD/ENCOURAGE		勞
LAW	038,11	1283	14	47422	3837		LUSTFUL,(SURNAME)		嫪
LAW	061,12	2027	15	99027	3828		TO REGRET		憪
LAW	085,12	3388	15	34196	3836	8424	FLOODED	3399	潦
LAW	085,12	3399	15	39127	3830	4856	FLOODED	3388	澇
LAW	086,06	3529	10	97864	4123	1421	BAKE,LARGE CAKE,FLAT IRON		烙
LAW	120,06	4820.0A	12	27964	4125	1423	SMALL NET		絡
LAW	140,09	5507	13	44164	4122	1425	TO FALL/DROP,ALIGHT		落
LAW	164,06	6803	13	17664	4126	1412	CHINESE CREAM/CHEESE		酪
LHE	019,09	0519.0A	11	44527	3841	4806	EXTORT		勒
LHE	145,10	5975.0A	15	31211	4617	7187	UNTIDY(IN DRESS)		褳
LE	019,09	0519.0B	11	44527	3841		COMPEL BY ORDER		勒
LEH	009,02	8021	04	24227	3839	4803	SURPLUS,TITHE		仂
LEH	019,09	0519.0C	11	44527	3841	4806	REIN IN		勒
LEH	032,05	0998	08	40118	3755	0545	GARBAGE		垃
LEH	032,07	1005	10	42142	4133	3287	ENCLOSURE		埒
LEH	064,02	8418	05	54027			DIVINATION BY STRAW		扐
LEH	064,07	2192.0A	10	52049	4134	3288	PULL (WHISKERS)		捋
LEH	075,02	2867.1	06	72904			HAPPY,LAUGH,(SURNAME)		乐
LEH	075,11	2867	15	22904	4129	5411	HAPPY,LAUGH,(SURNAME)		樂
LEH	085,05	3147	08	34127	3843	4805	WRITE		泐
LEH	120,06	4820	12	27964	4125	1423	ESTABLISH CONNECTIONS WITH		絡
LEH	130,02	5132.0A	06	74227	3840	4809	RIB		肋
LEH	140,09	5507.0A	13	44164		1425	TO FALL/DROP,ALIGHT		落
LEH	170,02	7081	05	74227		4804	LAYER,VEIN		阞

ROM	RAD	TEL	TOT	FC	MAT	OSH	TAG	CR	CHAR
LEH	187,06	7482.0A	16	77364	4127	1419	CAMEL		駱
LEH	195,11	5016	22	24327	3842		(SHAD),SPERMARY OF FISH		鰳
.LE	006,01	0055	02	17207	3958	3091	(PART. OF COMPLETION)		了
.LE	030,06	0744.0B	09	62000	3986	2922	(PART. FOR ENUM.)		咧
LHEI	019,09	0519	11	44527	3841	4806	STRANGLE		勒
LEI	030,09	081E	12	66660			PERPHIN		㗊
LEI	038,11	1284	14	46493	4222	8455	(SURNAME)		嫘
LEI	064,13	2341	16	51063	4237	1782	TO GRIND,BEAT		擂
LEI	075,13	8594	17	41963			LOGS ROLLED DOWN IN DEFENSE OF CITY		檑
LEI	120,05	4797.0B	11	60903	4221	8450	CUMBERSOME,ABBR. OF 4959	D4959	累
LEI	120,11	4913	17	26993	4224	8453	BIND,BOND		縲
LEI	120,15	4959	21	60903	4231	8458	BIND,CREEP,DISPIRITED		纍
LEI	121,15	4982	21	60772	4234		JAR,WOODEN DRINKING CUP		罍
LEI	123,13	5035	19	00217	4240	7892	ENTANGLED,LEAN		羸
LEI	140,11	556B	15	44903			RETENE		蔂
LEI	140,21	5703	25	44903	4233		CREEPER/BRAMBLE,DIRT-BASKET		虆
LEI	167,13	7012	21	81163	4239	1781	RADIUM		鐳
LEI	173,05	7191	13	10603	4236	1780	THUNDER,(SURNAME)	A9547	雷
LEI	173,15	9547	23	10666		1746	THUNDER	A7191	靁
LEEI	009,15	8079	17	26260	4227	1744	PUPPET,INJURE		儡
LEEI	032,06	1093.1	09	23104			RAMPART		垒
LEEI	032,15	1093	18	60104	4228	0193	RAMPART		壘
LEEI	075,11	2879	15	46993			MOUNTAIN-CLIMBING SHOES		樏
LEEI	075,21	8605	25	46993			VEHICLE FOR MOUNTAIN TRAVELLING		欙
LEEI	085,11	3374.0A	14	36193		8456	NAME OF A RIVER		漯
LEEI	112,10	4320	15	10661	4225	1103	LUMPY,UNEVEN,ROCK PILE		磊
LEEI	120,05	4797.0A	11	60903	4221	8450	ACCUMULATE		累
LEEI	127,00	5085	06	50900	4241	5489	PLOUGH		耒
LEEI	140,12	3650	16	44666			(PLANT)		蕌
LEEI	140,13	5628	17	44603	4238	1783	BUD	B5670	蕾
LEEI	140,15	5670	19	44666	4235	1745	CREEPER/BRAMBLE,BUD	D5628	藟
LEEI	149,06	6120	13	05690	4242	5490	EULOGY,EULOGIZE THE DEAD		誄
LEEI	196,15	776A	26	67627			FLYING SQUIRREL		鸓

ROM	RAD	TEL	TOT	FC	MAT	OSH	TAG	CR	CHAR
LEY	037,06	7352.1	09	90430			CATEGORY		类
LEY	064,13	2341.0A	16	51063	4237		BEAT(A DRUM)		擂
LEY	085,05	3223.1	08	36100	4243	1703	TEARS		泪
LEY	085,08	3223	11	33134	4243	5091	TEARS		淚
LEY	112,15	4346	20	16660	4230	1743	ROLL STONE DOWN HILL,STONE PILE		礌
LEY	120,05	4797	11	60903	4221	8450	TIRED,IMPLICATE		累
LEY	120,15	4955	21	91986	4245	8316	FLAW,KNOT		纇
LEY	130,02	5132	06	74227	3840	4809	RIB		肋
LEY	164,07	6810	14	12649	4135		POUR OUT LIBATION,SPRINKLE		酹
LEY	181,10	7352	19	91486	4244	8288	CATEGORY		類
LHENG	167,08	9476	16	84147			(METAL)		錂
LENG	032,09	1080	12	46127			ELEVATED BANK DELIMITING A FIELD		塄
LENG	046,08	1515	11	24747	3846	6436	LOFTY (AS OF MOUNTAIN)		崚
LENG	075,08	2789	12	44947	3847	6440	CORNER,SQUARE BEAM	4462	棱
LENG	075,09	2807	13	46927			CORNER,SQUARE BEAMS	2789	楞
LENG	115,08	4462	13	24947	3849	6441	CORNER,SQUARE BEAMS	2789	稜
LENG	140,13	5629	17	44947	3850	6442	OLD NAME FOR SPINACH		蔆
LEENG	015,05	0397	07	38137	3844	2107	COLD		冷
LENQ	061,05	1850	08	91011		0491	BE STARTLED	2807.0A	忙
LENQ	061,09	190C	12	96027		4335	BE STARTLED		愣
LENQ	075,09	2807.0A	13	46927	3845	4336	BE STARTLED	190C	楞
LHI	030,07	0769.0B	10	66014	3859	0431	(ONOMAT.)		哩
LHI	142,07	575F	13	56114			LYGAEUS EQUESTRIS		蝍
LI	001,07	7787.1A	08	11227			KOREA		丽
LI	010,14	0353	16	41211		7557	CENTIGRAM		趨
LI	027,07	0622	09	71214	3883	0443	ONE THOUSANDTH	6853	厘
LI	030,09	5070	12	61014			GRAIN WEIGHT		喱
LI	038,11	1278	14	58244	3880	8986	WIDOW		嫠
LI	075,07	8563	11	46914	3861	0439	BASKET FOR REMOVING EARTH,SPADE		梩
LI	075,08	2746.1	12	22904	3870		PEAR		梨
LI	075,08	2746	12	27904	3870	5367	PEAR		棃
LI	082,11	3036	15	58214	3881	7385	TUFT OF HAIR,TAIL		氂
LI	085,11	3347	14	30127	3897	4073	PATTERING(OF RAIN),SEEP THROUGH	D3287	漓

214

ROM	RAD	TEL	TOT	FC	MAT	OSH	TAG	CR	CHAR
LI	085,11	3372	14	58232	5773		MUCUS/SPITTLE,GO WITH CURRENT		漦
LI	085,19	3287	22	30114			SEEP THROUGH,NAME OF A RIVER	B3347	灕
LI	093,07	3680.1	11	22500	3871	2523	PLOUGH		犁
LI	093,08	3680	12	27502	3871	2531	PLOUGH		犂
LI	093,11	8789	15	58251	3882	2516	BLACK OX,YAK		犛
LI	094,07	3714	10	42200	3872	2947	(MONKEY)		狸
LI	094,07	3706	10	46214	3863	0435	WILD-CAT,(DOG)	A6291	狸
LI	096,11	3863	15	10127	3898	4068	GLASS,COLORED GLAZE	3896	璃
LI	096,15	3896	19	17132		5671	GLASS,COLORED GLAZE	3863	瓈
LI	114,06	4418	11	00227	3896	4067	TO LEAVE,(DISTANT)FROM	7180	离
LI	118,11	4713.1	17	88227	3899	4078	A FENCE		篱
LI	118,19	4713	25	88214	3903	0885	A FENCE		籬
LI	119,09	4760	15	91914		0444	CENTIMETER		粴
LI	120,11	4926	17	20927	3900	4071	BRIDAL VEIL OR KERCHIEF	5976	縭
LI	122,11	5008	16	60914	3892	0877	SORROW,SUFFER FROM,HAPPEN TO		罹
LI	140,12	5602	16	44904			CHENOPODIACEAE		藜
LI	140,15	5668	19	44132	3877	5672	CHENOPODIUM ALBUM		藜
LI	140,19	9201	23	44214	3904		GRACILARIA CONFERVOIDES		蘺
LI	142,07	5774	13	52100	3875	2948	CLAM		蜊
LI	142,15	5867.0A	21	27136	3894	8910	CALABASH		蠡
LI	145,11	5976	16	30227			BRIDE'S VEIL OR KERCHIEF	4926	褵
LI	153,07	6291	14	26214	3863	0436	WILDCAT	A3706	貍
LI	166,11	6853	18	58214	3883	0445	ONE THOUSANDTH	0622	釐
LI	172,11	7180	19	00214	3902	0884	TO LEAVE,(DISTANT)FROM	4418	離
LI	187,19	7537	29	71311	3918	7105	GOOD HORSE,BLACK HORSE		驪
LI	198,08	7787.0A	19	11211		7100	KOREA		麗
LI	202,03	7812	15	27132	3876	5670	BLACK,(SURNAME)		黎
LI	203,08	7824	20	27331	3878	8730	DARK/SALLOW COLOR		黧
LII	009,07	0200	09	26214	3858	0433	RUSTIC		俚
LII	030,07	0769	10	66014	3859	0431	MILE		哩
LII	038,07	1222	10	46414	3860	0441	HUSBAND'S BROTHER'S WIFE		娌
LII	061,07	1887.0A	10	96014		0432	SAD		悝
LII	075,03	2621	07	40407	3852	3145	PLUM,(SURNAME)		李

ROM	RAD	TEL	TOT	FC	MAT	OSH	TAG	CR	CHAR
LII	085,07	3192	10	36114	3862	0442	NAUTICAL MILE		浬
LII	085,13	3430	16	35118	3885	0582	NAME OF A RIVER,(SURNAME)		澧
LII	096,07	3810	11	16114	3864	0429	REASON/PRINCIPLE		理
LII	113,01	4409.1	05	32210	3886	7071	PROPRIETY,RITE,GIFT		礼
LII	113,13	4409	17	35218	3886	0580	PROPRIETY,RITE,GIFT		禮
LII	142,15	5867	21	27136	3894	8910	WOOD-BORING INSECT		蠡
LII	145,07	5937	13	00732	3865	5840	INSIDE	5987	裏
LII	145,07	5987	12	36214	3865	0434	INSIDE	5937	裡
LII	162,19	6710	23	31301	3916	6760	WINDING		邐
LII	164,13	6833	20	15618	3887	0578	SWEET WINE		醴
LII	166,00	6849	07	60104	3857	0427	CHINESE MILE,INSIDE	D5937	里
LII	167,07	9465	15	86114		0430	LITHIUM		鋰
LII	195,07	7642	18	26314	3866	0440	CARP		鯉
LII	195,13	9661	24	25318	3888	0581	SNAKEFISH		鱧
LIH	001,07	7787.1	08	11227			BEAUTIFUL		丽
LIH	009,06	0173	08	22200	3890	2923	EXAMPLE		例
LIH	009,07	0196	09	22200	3868	2946	CLEVER		俐
LIH	009,10	0269	12	21294		5331	LISU(ETHNIC GROUP)		傈
LIH	009,19	0330	21	21211	3915	7104	HUSBAND AND WIFE		儷
LIH	015,10	0411	12	31194	3926		COLD		凓
LIH	018,05	0448	07	22900	3867	2945	PROFIT		利
LIH	019,00	0500	02	40027	3920	4782	STRENGTH		力
LIH	019,05	0536.1	07	74227			EXHORT		励
LIH	019,15	0536	17	74227	3907	4813	EXHORT		勵
LIH	027,02	2479.1	04	71227			CALENDAR		历
LIH	027,03	0632.1	05	71227		4320	SEVERE		厉
LIH	027,10	2479.2	12	71294	3930		CALENDAR		厤
LIH	027,13	0632	15	71227	3906	4096	SEVERE		厲
LIH	030,02	0930	05	64027			(PHONETIC)/SINGAPORE		叻
LIH	030,03	0684	06	50006	3853	6571	MINOR OFFICIAL		吏
LIH	030,07	8140	10	62000	3869		SOUND/NOISE,(FINAL PART.)		唎
LIH	030,08	0789	11	63034	3855	5088	CRY OF A CRANE OR WILD GOOSE		唳

ROM	RAD	TEL	TOT	FC	MAT	OSH	TAG	CR	CHAR
LIH	030,14	8182	17	61011			SOUND OF SPLITTING/CRACKING		噼
LIH	046,02	8321	05	22427			HIGH MOUNTAIN RANGE		屴
LIH	061,10	1961	13	91094	3927	5332	AFRAID/TREMBLING		慄
LIH	063,04	2074	08	30234	3854	5087	DO VIOLENCE,GO AGAINST		戾
LIH	072,12	2479	16	71269	3930	1582	CALENDAR	B2980	曆
LIH	075,06	2698	10	10904	3925	5330	CHESTNUT,(SURNAME)		栗
LIH	075,15	2929	19	42994	3937	5415	OAK/QUERCUS SERRATA		櫟
LIH	075,16	2931	20	41911	3933	0485	STABLE		櫪
LIH	077,12	2980	16	71211	3931	0483	CALENDAR,TO PASS THROUGH	D2479	歷
LIH	085,05	3146	08	38122	6376	4201	MIASMA		沴
LIH	085,07	8674	10	30118	3912	0548	ATTEND(OFFICIAL FUNCTIONS)	5444	涖
LIH	085,10	3303	13	31194	3928	5334	NAME OF A RIVER		溧
LIH	085,16	3468	19	31111	3934	0486	DRIP		瀝
LIH	104,07	4031	12	00120	3873	2949	DYSENTERY		痢
LIH	104,13	4078	18	00127	3908	4100	SORE CAUSED BY VARNISH POISONING		癘
LIH	104,16	4087	21	00111	3935	0487	SCROFULA		癧
LIH	106,15	4119	20	22694			LUSTER(OF PEARLS)		皪
LIH	108,15	4153	20	28107			VIOLENT,UNREASONABLE		盭
LIH	112,04	8930	09	12630			CROSS STREAM BY STEPPING ON STONES		砅
LIH	112,05	4246	10	10618			PLACE NAME		砬
LIH	112,05	4351.1	10	15690			GRAVEL/SMALL STONE		砅
LIH	112,15	4350	20	11627	3909	4097	SANDSTONE,GRIND		礪
LIH	112,15	4351	20	12694	3938	5413	GRAVEL/SMALL STONE		礫
LIH	117,00	4539	05	00108	3921	0544	TO STAND,SET UP		立
LIH	118,05	4567	11	88108	3922	0408	BAMBOO RAIN HAT		笠
LIH	118,10	9018	16	88904	3929		BAMBOOS GOOD FOR POLES,HORN		篥
LIH	119,05	4721	11	90918	3923	0554	A GRAIN/A GRANULE		粒
LIH	119,15	4755	21	91927	3910	4098	COARSE(GRAIN)		糲
LIH	140,05	5380	09	44108	3924	0559	PIG-STY,(HERB)		苙
LIH	140,06	5408	10	44427	3913	4279	LITCHI		荔
LIH	140,07	5444	11	44218	3912	0550	ATTEND(OFFICIAL FUNCTIONS)	5539	莅
LIH	140,07	5461	11	44920	3874	2950	JASMINE		莉
LIH	140,08	547C	12	44234			PERNISECTUM JAPONICUM		蒚

ROM	RAD	TEL	TOT	FC	MAT	OSH	TAG	CR	CHAR
LIH	140,10	5539	14	44118	3912	0549	ATTEND(OFFICIAL FUNCTIONS)	5444	
LIH	140,12	9194	16	44994			SPARSENESS OF VEGETATION		
LIH	140,16	569A	20	44211			DRABANEMEROSA HEBECARPA		
LIH	142,15	5869	21	51127	3911	4099	OYSTER		
LIH	149,05	6091	12	60601	3891	1161	SCOLD,CURSE		
LIH	157,15	6491	22	62194	3939		MOVE/WALK		
LIH	159,15	6577	22	52094	3940	5414	WHEEL-RUT,TO BULLY		
LIH	163,19	6786	22	17227	3917	2251	(SURNAME),ANCIENT PLACE NAME		
LIH	171,00	7152	08	50137	5993	5693	SCRIBE,ATTACHED TO	7153	
LIH	171,09	7153	17	45932	3905	5697	SCRIBE,ATTACHED TO	7152	
LIH	173,16	7225	24	10211	3936		CLAP OF THUNDER		
LIH	190,07	9633	17	72922			BALD/SCABBY		
LIH	195,07	764R	18	22336			CHIMAERA PHANTASMA		
LIH	196,05	770F	16	07127			ALCEDO BENGALENSIS		
LIH	196,19	7765	30	17227	3919	4657	ORIOLE		
LIH	198,08	7787	19	11211	3914	7100	BEAUTIFUL		
.LI	030,07	0769.0A	10	66014	3859	0431	(PART. FOR CONTINUED STATE)		
LEA	009,07	0224.1	09	21227			TWO		
LEA	009,08	0224	10	21227	3954	4022	TWO		
LIAN	022,13	0568	15	71718			DOWERY,DRESSING CASE WITH A MIRROR	D4708	
LIAN	030,11	8163	14	65030	4010		CHATTERING		
LIAN	032,11	1160	14	40716	3997		BRIDAL TROUSSEAU		
LIAN	050,05	1588	08	30227	3998	4001	CURTAIN,WINE SHOP SIGN	A4688	
LIAN	053,10	1670	13	00237	4003	5580	INEXPENSIVE,INCORRUPT		
LIAN	061,05	1995.1	08	98037	3995	2100	TO PITY		
LIAN	061,11	1978	14	95034			FLOW (OF TEARS)		
LIAN	061,12	1995	15	99059	3996	2570	TO PITY		
LIAN	085,11	3353	14	35134	4012	6669	RIPPLE,TEARFUL		
LIAN	085,13	3425	16	30137	4004	5583	NAME OF A RIVER IN HUNAN		
LIAN	086,13	8766	17	90837			UNCEASING(OF FIRE)		
LIAN	096,11	8834	15	15134	4013	6666	SACRIFICIAL VESSEL,CORAL		
LIAN	118,13	4688	19	88237	4005	5585	CURTAIN	A1588	
LIAN	118,17	4708	23	88882		6400	DRESSING CASE WITH A MIRROR	B0568	

蒞蒜蘦蠣罳蹸轢酈隶隸靂影刿燕鳹鸝麗哩俩俩匼嗹盇帘廉怜悡憐連溓爉璉籢廲歛

ROM	RAD	TEL	TOT	FC	MAT	OSH	TAG	CR	CHAR
LIAN	128,06	5114.1	12	18134			UNITE,ALLY		联
LIAN	128,11	5114	17	12172	4008	2792	UNITE,ALLY		聯
LIAN	130,13	5248	17	70237	4006		ECTHYMA		臁
LIAN	140,11	5571	15	44304	4014	6670	LOTUS		蓮
LIAN	142,13	586A	19	50137			COCKROACH		蠊
LIAN	145,11	9260	16	35234	4015		POUCH HUNG FROM BELT		褳
LIAN	162,07	6647	11	35300	4009	6665	JOIN,EVEN/AS,(SURNAME)		連
LIAN	167,10	6962	18	88137	4007	5568	SCYTHE/SICKLE	6991	鎌
LIAN	167,13	6991	21	80137	4007	5581	SCYTHE/SICKLE	6962	鑝
LIAN	190,10	7582	20	72337			HANGING TEMPLE HAIR		鬑
LIAN	195,11	9654	22	25330	4017		HYPOPHTHALMICHTHYS MORITRIX		鰱
LEAN	066,13	2425.0A	17	88840	3999		GATHER,ARRANGE,CONTROL ONESELF		斂
LEAN	076,13	2966.0A	17	87882	2052	4959	GATHER,ARRANGE,CONTROL ONESELF		歛
LEAN	130,13	5245	17	78286	4002	8007	FACE		臉
LEAN	163,15	9414	18	57527			PLACE NAME		鄻
LIANN	061,06	2043.1	10	00333	4299	8693	FEEL ATTACHED TO,LONG FOR		恋
LIANN	061,19	2043	23	22339	4299	8691	FEEL ATTACHED TO,LONG FOR		戀
LIANN	064,19	2381	23	22502	4300	3362	ATTACHED,SPASM		攣
LIANN	066,13	2425	17	88840	3999	6397	GATHER,ARRANGE,CONTROL ONESELF	2966	斂
LIANN	075,09	2808	13	45996	4017A	5532	MELIA JAPONICA		楝
LIANN	076,13	2966	17	87882	2052	4959	GATHER,ARRANGE,CONTROL ONESELF	2425	歛
LIANN	078,13	3003	17	18286	4001	8009	PREPARE BODY FOR COFFIN		殮
LIANN	085,09	3271	12	35196	4018		BOIL RAW SILK		湅
LIANN	085,13	3432	16	38186			FULL OF WATER,TROUGH	3481	渰
LIANN	085,17	3481	20	37182		6398	FULL OF WATER,TROUGE	3432	瀲
LIANN	086,05	3550.1	09	94894			REFINE,SMELT		炼
LIANN	086,09	3550	13	95896	4019	5533	REFINE,SMELT		煉
LIANN	120,05	4886.1	11	24994			TO DRILL/TO TRAIN		练
LIANN	120,09	4886	15	25996	4020	5534	TO DRILL/TO TRAIN		練
LIANN	140,13	563A.0A	17	44886			VITIS SERJAMAEFOLIA	5692	薟
LIANN	140,17	5692	21	44848	4000	6399	VITIS SERJAMAEFOLIA	563A.0A	薟
LIANN	145,13	5990	18	38286		8004	BOW/CURTSY		襝
LIANN	167,09	6937	17	85196	4021	5529	REFINE		鍊

ROM	RAD	TEL	TOT	FC	MAT	OSH	TAG	CR	CHAR
LIANN	167,11	6969	19	85130	4016	6667	CHAIN,LEAD OR TIN ORE		
LIANG	015,08	0404	10	30196	3946	8404	COOL	3213	
LIANG	075,07	2733	11	33904	3951	5364	BRIDGE,(SURNAME),BEAM OF ROOF	G2856	
LIANG	075,11	2856	15	43994	3951	5366	BEAM OF ROOF	C2733	
LIANG	085,08	3213	11	30196	3946	8405	COOL	0404	
LIANG	119,07	4731	13	33904	3952	5448	SORGHUM		
LIANG	119,07	9037	13	93932	3944	5919	PROVISIONS	4752	
LIANG	119,12	4752	18	96914	3944	0447	PROVISIONS	9037	
LIANG	138,01	5328	07	30732	3941	5914	GOOD		
LIANG	157,07	6428.0A	14	63132	3942	5917	JUMP		
LIANG	166,05	6852.0A	12	60104	3943	0446	TO MEASURE		
LEANG	001,05	0357.2	06	10227	3953		TAEL		
LEANG	001,06	0357.1	07	10227	3953	4044	TWO,TAEL		
LEANG	009,07	0224.1A	09	21227			CRAFT/CUNNING		
LEANG	009,08	0224.0A	10	21227	3954	4022	CRAFT/CUNNING		
LEANG	011,06	0357	08	10227	3953	4021	TWO,TAEL		
LEANG	030,08	5084	11	61027			OUNCE		
LEANG	194,08	7619	18	21212	3957		SPRITE/FAIRY		
LIANQ	008,07	0081	09	00217	3949	7878	BRIGHT		
LIANQ	009,08	8054	10	20296			DISTANT,SEARCH		
LIANQ	030,09	8154	12	60017	3950	7879	CLEAR/RESOUNDING		
LIANQ	072,08	8512	12	60096	3945	8400	TO DRY IN THE AIR		
LIANQ	149,08	6156	15	00696	3947	8399	FORGIVE		
LIANQ	157,07	6428.0B	14	63132	3942	5917	STAGGER/SWAY FROM SIDE TO SIDE		
LIANQ	159,07	6538.1	14	51027			AN FOR VEHICLES		
LIANQ	159,08	6538	15	51027	3956	4023	AN. FOR VEHICLES		
LIANQ	166,05	6852	12	60104	3943	0446	QUANTITY,CAPACITY,TO ESTIMATE		
LHIAU	064,12	2316	15	54096		8418	PULL UP(SLEEVE),LIFT UP(SKIRT)		
LHIAU	142,12	584A	18	54196			POMPONIA MACULATIOCOLLIS		
LIAU	009,12	0297	14	24296	3969	8417	BUREAUCRAT		
LIAU	030,12	0882	15	64096	3970	8412	CRY(OF CRANES ETC.),CLEAR SOUND		
LIAU	038,12	8298	15	44496		8423	TO PLAY,SMART,GOOD		
LIAU	040,11	1394	14	30202	3963	4217	EMPTY,LONESOME,VERY FEW		

ROM	RAD	TEL	TOT	FC	MAT	OSH	TAG	CR	CHAR
LIAU	040,12	1402	15	30906	3971	8426	FELLOW-OFFICIAL,HUT,LAOS		寮
LIAU	042,09	1426	12	40906	3968	8410	(SURNAME)		尞
LIAU	044,12	8319	15	77296			PENIS		屌
LIAU	064,12	2316.0A	15	54096	3973	8418	TEASE,STITCH,TAKE		撩
LIAU	066,11	8492	15	28940	3961		SEW,KEEP TIDY AND REPAIRED		敹
LIAU	085,12	3388.0B	15	34196	3836		UNLUCKY IN LIFE,CARELESS		潦
LIAU	086,12	3598.0B	16	94896	3975	8421	SINGE		燎
LIAU	094,12	3750	15	44296	3976	8420	HUNT,FIERCE,NAME OF A TRIBE		獠
LIAU	104,02	4070.1	07	00127			TO CURE/TO TREAT		疗
LIAU	104,12	4070	17	00196	3977	8425	TO CURE/TO TREAT		療
LIAU	116,12	4531	17	30906			DIG,PIERCE		窲
LIAU	120,12	4933	18	24996	3979	8422	WIND ROUND,LINES FOR A SAIL		繚
LIAU	128,05	5108	11	17120	3960	2134	KILL TIME,TO CHAT		聊
LIAU	130,10	5220	14	99227	3980	3624	FAT ON INTESTINES		膋
LIAU	130,12	5220.1	16	74296	3980	8419	FAT ON INTESTINES		膫
LIAU	162,02	6697.1	06	37302			NAME OF A DYNASTY,LIAONING		辽
LIAU	162,12	6697	16	34309	3981	6780	NAME OF A DYNASTY,LIAONING		遼
LIAU	167,12	9507	20	84196	3982	8411	SHACKLES,PURE SILVER,FURNACE		鐐
LIAU	196,11	7740	22	17227			SKYLARK		鷯
LIAU	196,12	7754	23	47927	3983	4663	EASTERN WREN		鷦
LEAU	006,01	0055.0A	02	17207	3958	3091	TO FINISH,CLEAR	D4229	了
LEAU	086,12	3598.0A	16	94896		8421	SINGE		燎
LEAU	109,12	4229	17	64096	3978	8415	CLEAR	B0055.0A	瞭
LEAU	140,11	5578	15	44202	3966	4218	SMARTWEED,POLYGONUM		蓼
LEAU	142,02	573A	08	57127			ORTHETRUM ALBISTYLUM		虰
LEAU	167,02	5100	10	87127		3092	RUTHENIUM		钌
LIAW	053,11	1675	14	00222	3964	4215	(SURNAME)		廖
LIAW	064,11	2297	14	56064		1427	TO LEAVE (IT)		撂
LIAW	068,06	2436	10	94900	3959	2703	MATERIAL,GUESS		料
LIAW	086,12	3598	16	94896	3975	8421	TO BURN		燎
LIAW	109,12	4229.0A	17	64096	3978	8415	LOOK AFAR FROM A HIGH PLACE		瞭
LHIE	030,06	0744.0A	09	62000		2922	CHILD'S CRY		咧

ROM	RAD	TEL	TOT	FC	MAT	OSH	TAG	CR	CHAR
LIE	030,06	0744.0C	09	62000		2922	LIE GLIBLY		唎
LIEE	030,06	0744	09	62000		2922	DRAW BACK CORNERS OF MOUTH		咧
LIEH	015,06	0399	08	32100	3985	2925	COLD AND RAW		冽
LIEH	018,04	0441	06	12200	3984	2921	A ROW/SERIES		列
LIEH	019,04	0503	06	90427	4302	4861	INFERIOR		劣
LIEH	047,12	7588.1	15	22712	3992	6834	MANE,BRISTLES		鼣
LIEH	064,08	2203	11	53034	3856	5090	TWIST,TEAR		捩
LIEH	075,06	8556	10	42900		2924	CASTANEA SATIVA,GROW IN ROWS		栵
LIEH	085,06	3153	09	32100	3987	2926	PURE/CLEANSE		洌
LIEH	086,06	3525	10	12330	3988	8787	ARDENT/INTENSE		烈
LIEH	094,08	3756.1	11	44261		6839	HUNTING		猎
LIEH	094,15	3756	18	42216	3993	6839	HUNTING		獵
LIEH	109,08	8914	13	63034			TO ROLL THE EYEBALLS TO LOOK		睞
LIEH	140,06	5410	10	44220	3989		SEDGES,RUSHES		茢
LIEH	142,06	575B	12	52100			CYRTOXIPHUS RITSEMAE		蛚
LIEH	145,06	5933	12	12732	3990	5821	SPLIT		裂
LIEH	156,06	639B	13	42800	3991	5955	STUMBLE		趔
LIEH	157,15	6489	22	62116	3994	6836	STEP ACROSS		躐
LIEH	190,15	7588	25	72716	3992	6841	MANE,BRISTLES,HYAENA		鬣
LIEH	195,15	767E	26	22316			ZACCO PLATYPUS		鱲
LIEH	196,06	770K	17	12327			WOODPECKER		鴷
LIN	003,08	5259.1	09	38263			JUST BEFORE		临
LIN	030,08	5123	11	64090			(PHONETIC)/LINE IN CHEM. COMPOUNDS		啉
LIN	046,12	1543	15	29759	4029	2568	RANGES OF HILLS		嶙
LIN	075,04	2651	08	44990	4022	5271	WOODS		林
LIN	085,08	3218	11	34190	4023	5274	DRIP,DISEASE OF THE BLADDER		淋
LIN	085,12	3411	15	39159			CLEAR(AS OF WATER)		潾
LIN	086,12	3592	16	99859	4028	2573	PHOSPHOROUS		燐
LIN	096,08	3829	12	14190	4024	5272	GEM		琳
LIN	096,12	3876	16	19159		2567	LUSTER OF GEM		璘
LIN	112,12	4340	17	19659	4074	2569	PHOSPHORUS,WATER IN ROCKS	A3592	磷
LIN	119,06	9036	12	90259	4028	2566	PHOSPHOROUS	3592	粦

ROM	RAD	TEL	TOT	FC	MAT	OSH	TAG	CR	CHAR
LIN	119,08	4736	14	92230		8962	CLEAR(AS OF WATER)		猭
LIN	131,11	5259	17	78766	4027	1081	JUST BEFORE		臨
LIN	159,12	9368	19	59059	4031	2572	RUMBLING OF WHEELS		轔
LIN	162,12	6689	16	39305	4032	6658	SELECT FOR APPOINTMENT,(SURNAME)		遴
LIN	163,05	6775.1	08	87227			NEIGHBOR,NEIGHBORING		邻
LIN	163,12	6775	15	97227	4033	2192	NEIGHBOR,NEIGHBORING	7141	鄰
LIN	170,12	7141	15	79259	4033	2571	NEIGHBOR,NEIGHBORING	6775	隣
LIN	173,08	7207	16	10994	4026	5277	CONTINUED RAIN		霖
LIN	195,05	763A.0A	16	28332			FISH SCALE		鮻
LIN	195,12	7673	23	29359	4034	2575	SCALES(OF FISH)		鱗
LIN	198,07	7782	18	00604	4035		FEMALE UNICORN	7792	麐
LIN	198,12	7792	23	09259		2574	FEMALE UNICORN	7782	麟
LIIN	015,13	0412	15	30191	4036	8352	SHIVER WITH COLD OR FEAR		凜
LIIN	053,13	1686	16	00291	4037	5553	GOVERNMENT GRANARY		廩
LIIN	061,13	2023	16	90091	4038	5550	FEAR		懍
LIIN	075,13	2882	17	40991	4039	5551	RIDGE POLE,CROSS-BEAM		檁
LIIN	085,13	3417	16	30191			CHILLY/COLD		凛
LIIN	140,08	9178	12	44994			ANCIENT NAME FOR EAST ROMAN EMPIRE		菻
LIIN	167,12	9512	20	89159			PHOSPHONIUM(RADICAL)		鏻
LINN	030,04	0690	07	00604	4040	1440	STINGY	B6689.0A	吝
LINN	061,07	0690.1	10	90064	4040	1441	STINGY		悋
LINN	085,08	3218.0A	11	34190	4023	5274	TO DRAIN,DISEASES OF THE BLADDER		淋
LINN	112,12	4340.0A	17	19659	4074	2569	THIN,MICA		磷
LINN	130,12	524A	16	79259			PHOSPHINE		膦
LINN	140,16	5677	20	44227	4041	3446	JUNCUS EFFUSUS		藺
LINN	149,08	6158.0B	15	08627	4253	3794	BY THE/PER		論
LINN	154,06	6324	13	22806	3107	8108	TO RENT		賃
LINN	162,12	6689.0A	16	39305	4032	6658	DIFFICULTY,STINGY	D0690	遴
LING	009,05	0134	07	28237	4044	2101	CLEVER		伶
LING	015,08	0407	10	34147	4062	6445	ENCROACH,SOAR,THICK ICE	K3249	凌
LING	030,05	5129	08	68032			WHISPER,PURINE IN CHEM. COMPOUND		吟
LING	031,05	0941	08	60307	4045	1876	PRISON		囹
LING	032,08	8231	11	47147			MOUND,TOMB	7117	埁

223

ROM	RAD	TEL	TOT	FC	MAT	OSH	TAG	CR	CHAR
LING	075,05	267C	09	48932			EURYA JAPONICA		
LING	075,17	2933	21	41963		1079	LATTICE		
LING	077,09	7881.1	13	28732			AGE		
LING	085,05	3132	08	38137		2108	SOUND OF WATER FLOWING,(SURNAME)		
LING	085,08	3249	11	34147	4063	6446	ENCROACH,SOAR,(SURNAME)	K0407	
LING	086,03	7227.1	07	17809		5611	EFFICACIOUS,ALERT,DEPARTED SOUL		
LING	096,05	3781	09	18132	4047	2096	TINKLING OF GEM-PENDANTS		
LING	098,05	3909	10	81317	4048	7930	CONCAVE CHANNELS OF TILING		
LING	120,08	4866	14	24947	4064	6443	DAMASK,THIN SILK		
LING	123,05	5024	11	88532		2102	ANTELOPE		
LING	124,05	5044	11	87320	4050	3389	TAIL FEATHERS		
LING	128,05	5107	11	18132	4051	2104	HEAR,LISTEN,APPREHEND		
LING	137,05	5309	11	28432	4052		SMALL BOAT WITH WINDOWS		
LING	140,05	5376	09	44302	4053	2109	FUNGUS,TUBER		
LING	140,08	5480	12	44407	4065	6447	WATER CALTROPS,TRAPA NATANS		
LING	140,11	5579	15	44147			WATER-CALTROPS/TRAPA NATANS	5480	
LING	142,05	5749	11	58132	4054	2106	SANDFLY		
LING	159,05	6517	12	58022		2103	WHEEL		
LING	163,17	6784	20	17627	4070		NAME OF A HSIEN IN HUNAN		
LING	164,17	6837	24	11663			NAME OF A WINE		
LING	167,05	6875	13	88132	4056	2097	BELL		
LING	170,08	7117	11	74247	4067	6438	MOUND,TOMB		
LING	173,05	7190	13	10302	4057	2111	ZERO,REMNANT		
LING	173,16	7227	24	10108	4071	0135	EFFICACIOUS,ALERT,DEPARTED SOUL		
LING	195,05	763A	16	28332			LEGLESS WIGGLING ANIMAL		
LING	195,08	765D	19	24347	4068	6444	PANGOLIN/MANIS PENTADACTYLATA		
LING	196,05	7701	16	87327	4060	4622	WAGTAIL/LARK		
LING	196,13	775G	24	17327			BACHSTELZE		
LING	198,17	7793	28	00663			ANTELOPE	5024	
LING	211,05	7881	20	28732	4061	2099	AGE		
LIING	046,05	1545.1	08	28734			MOUNTAIN RANGE		
LIING	046,14	1545	17	22386	4059	8264	MOUNTAIN RANGE		
LIING	181,05	7325	14	81386	4058	8263	TO LEAD,RECEIVE,COLLAR		

ROM	RAD	TEL	TOT	FC	MAT	OSH	TAG	CR	CHAR
LINQ	009,03	0109	05	80307	4043	2095	COMMAND,HONORABLE		令
LINQ	030,02	0659	05	60427	3506	4842	SEPARATELY		另
LINQ	157,20	6497	27	64127	4042	3447	CART-RUT,TRAMPLE DOWN		躏
LHIOU	085,10	3296	13	37162	4085	1792	SLIP AWAY,TO SKATE		溜
LIOU	018,04	0491.1	06	02400		2959	(SURNAME),TO KILL		刘
LIOU	018,13	0491	15	72100	4093	2868	(SURNAME),TO KILL		劉
LIOU	061,15	8406	18	92000	4094		LOVELY/BEAUTIFUL		懰
LIOU	070,09	2471	13	08213	4079	7787	TASSEL		旒
LIOU	075,10	2839	14	47962	4084	1790	POMEGRANATE		榴
LIOU	085,06	3461.1	09	32100			CLEAR/DEEP(OF WATER)		浏
LIOU	085,07	3177	10	30113	4080	7786	FLOW		流
LIOU	085,15	3461	18	32100	4095	2859	CLEAR/DEEP(OF WATER)		瀏
LIOU	096,07	3812	11	10113	4081	7780	PRECIOUS STONE	3845	琉
LIOU	096,10	3845	14	17162	4081	1785	PRECIOUS STONE	3812	瑠
LIOU	096,10	3857	15	30103			JADE ORNAMENT HANGING FROM CAP		瓬
LIOU	102,03	3966.2	08	90600			RETAIN/KEEP,LEAVE(MESSAGE)		甾
LIOU	102,05	3966	10	77602	4083	1784	RETAIN/KEEP,LEAVE(MESSAGE)		留
LIOU	102,07	3966.1	12	10607	4083	1779	RETAIN/KEEP,LEAVE(MESSAGE)		畱
LIOU	104,10	4058	15	00162	4086	1793	TUMOR		瘤
LIOU	104,12	4058.1	17	00167			TUMOR		癅
LIOU	112,07	4288	12	10613	4082	7783	SULFUR		硫
LIOU	162,10	6675.0A	14	37306	4087	6635	TO LINGER		遛
LIOU	167,10	9497	18	30109			BESSEMERIZING OF MATTE		鎏
LIOU	167,10	9490	18	87162		1786	LUTECIUM		鎦
LIOU	167,11	6981	19	87122	4096		PURE GOLD		鏐
LIOU	182,10	7375	19	77216	4089	7841	SOUGHING OF WIND		飀
LIOU	187,07	7483	17	71327			BAY HORSE WITH BLACK MANE	7511	駠
LIOU	187,10	7511	20	77362	4091	1789	BAY HORSE WITH BLACK MANE	7483	騮
LIOU	196,10	7736	21	77627	4092	4619	LARGE HORNED-OWL		鶹
LEOU	075,05	2692	09	47920	4097	2135	WILLOW,(SURNAME)		柳
LEOU	120,08	4859	14	28964	4098	1433	TUFT/LOCK,SKEIN		綹
LEOU	122,10	5005	15	60602		1794	CREEL/FISH BASKET		罶
LEOU	167,07	691A	15	80113			SULFONIUM(RADICAL)		鋶
LIOW	012,02	0362	04	00800	4189	8013	SIX		六

ROM	RAD	TEL	TOT	FC	MAT	OSH	TAG	CR
LIOW	031,04	093C	07	60800			CYCLOHEXANTHRENE	
LIOW	112,04	426A	09	10680			CHALEOGEN	
LIOW	157,10	6448	17	67162			WALK A HORSE,TO STROLL	6675
LIOW	162,10	6675	14	37306	4087	6635	WALK A HORSE,TO STROLL	6448
LIOW	170,05	7120.1A	08	75272			SIX(FRAUDPROOF)	
LIOW	170,08	7120.0A	11	74214	4191	0238	SIX(FRAUDPROOF)	
LIOW	173,10	7211	18	10602	4088	1795	DRIPPING OF RAIN FROM EAVES	
LIOW	184,10	5130	18	87762	4090	1787	REHEAT BY STEAMING	
LIU	075,15	2925	19	47920	4285	3459	PALM TREE	
LIU	104,11	4068.0A	16	00144	4289	9018	HUNCHBACK	
LIU	140,15	9197	19	44236	4294		MADDER	
LIU	169,07	7047	15	77606	4284	3458	GATE OF A VILLAGE,VILLAGE	
LIU	187,04	7533.1	14	73377	4296	4235	DONKEY	
LIU	187,16	7533	26	71317	4296	0662	DONKEY	
LEU	009,07	0188	09	26260	4281	1468	COMPANION	
LEU	030,04	0712	07	60600	4280	1466	(SURNAME)	
LEU	044,09	1459.1	12	77244			TIME AND AGAIN	
LEU	044,11	1459	14	77244	4288	9019	TIME AND AGAIN	
LEU	044,12	1462	15	77247	3893	6415	TO TREAD ON,SHOE	
LEU	064,07	2192.0B	10	52049	4134	3288	STROKE (BEARD)	
LEU	070,06	2464	10	08232	4286	5807	TRAVEL	
LEU	075,07	2632	11	46960	4282	1471	BEAM AT THE EAVES	
LEU	085,11	3377	14	35144			DRIZZLE	
LEU	120,11	4917	17	25944	4290	9016	THREAD,STRAND,STATE IN DETAIL	
LEU	130,10	5219	14	08227	4287	3640	BACKBONE,STRENGTH	
LEU	140,07	5447.0A	11	44606	1569	1475	RUBRENE	
LEU	145,11	5997	16	35244	4291	9010	TATTERED,SOILED	
LEU	167,07	6986	15	86160	4283	1467	ALUMINUM	
LEU	195,07	764Q	18	26360			GARRICK/LICHIA GLANCA	
LIUH	046,09	8345	12	22257		2621	TO TOWER,RISE SHARPLY	
LIUH	060,06	1774	09	25207	4297	2620	LAW	
LIUH	061,06	1982.1	10	21231			ANXIETY	
LIUH	061,11	1982	15	21236	4292	8591	ANXIETY	

CHAR: 囡 砳 蹓 遛 陆 陸 餾 櫊 瘻 藘 閭 駅 驢 侶 呂 屢 屢 履 捋 旅 柩 淒 縷 齊 莒 褸 鋁 鮱 嵂 律 慮 慮

ROM	RAD	TEL	TOT	FC	MAT	OSH	TAG	CR	CHAR
LIUH	084,08	3048	12	80117	4197	7818	CHLORINE	B4845	氣
LIUH	085,10	3459.1	13	31131			TO FILTER		濾
LIUH	085,15	3459	18	31136	4293	8594	TO FILTER		瀘
LIUH	095,06	3764	11	00403	5910	2359	RATE/FREQUENCY		率
LIUH	120,08	4845	14	27932	4197	5666	GREEN,CHLORINE	D3048	綠
LIUH	130,11	9137	15	70243			SACRIFICIAL FLESH		膟
LIUH	140,09	550C	13	44257			HUMULUS JAPONICUS		葎
LIUH	167,15	7008	23	81136	4295	8592	POLISHING TOOL,(SURNAME)		鑢
LIUAN	039,19	1334	22	22407	4213	3149	TWINS		孿
LIUAN	064,19	2381.0A	23	22502	4300	3362[2]	ATTACHED,SPASM		攣
LEUAN	038,19	1309	22	22404	4298	9062	BEAUTIFUL		孌
LIUEH	018,08	0486.0A	10	02900		2976	PLUNDER	2230	剟
LIUEH	064,08	2230	11	50096	4077	8401	PLUNDER	0486.0A	掠
LIUEH	102,06	3970.1	11	60604	4075	1426	SLIGHTLY,STRATEGY,PLUNDER		畧
LIUEH	102,06	3970	11	67064	4075	1411	SLIGHTLY,STRATEGY,PLUNDER	G2230	略
LIUEH	142,08	577D	14	50196			TACHINA LARVARUM		蜋
LIUEH	167,07	9466	15	82142			(ANCIENT UNIT OF WEIGHT)		鋝
LHIUN	064,08	2241.0A	11	58027	4250	3797	WHIRL		掄
LIUN	085,08	3218.0B	11	34190		5274	DRENCH		淋
.LO	030,06	0748	09	67064	4120	1409	PART.INDICATING OBVIOUSNESS		咯
LHONG	170,09	7127.0A	12	77214	4255	0405	SOUND OF DRUMS		隆
LONG	030,16	0918	19	61011	4260	7321	THROAT		嚨
LONG	043,02	7893.1	05	43040			DRAGON		龙
LONG	046,16	8352	19	22211			STEEP/PRECIPITOUS(OF MOUNTAIN)		巄
LONG	072,16	2570	20	61011	4263	7323	BRIGHT		曨
LONG	074,16	2604	20	71211	4264	7327	RISING MOON		朧
LONG	075,16	2934	20	41911	4265	7328	CAGE,GRATINGS,BAR	A4705	櫳
LONG	085,12	8707	15	37114			WATER FROM A HIGH PLACE		瀧
LONG	085,16	3478	19	31111	4266	7330	TORRENTIAL(RAIN)		瀧
LONG	096,16	3891	20	11111	4268	7320	TINKLING OF GEM-PENDANTS		瓏
LONG	104,12	4071	17	00114	4256	0406	INFIRMITY,RETENTION OF URINE		癃
LONG	109,16	4237	21	61011			HAZY/UNCLEAR		矓
LONG	112,16	4352	21	01601	4269	1121	GRIND,MILL		礱

ROM	RAD	TEL	TOT	FC	MAT	OSH	TAG	CR	CHAR
LONG	116,12	9002	17	30214	4257	0407	CAVITY,HOLE		窿
LONG	118,16	4705	22	88211	4271	7336	CAGE,BASKET	A2934	籠
LONG	128,16	5122	22	01401	6402	2740	DEAF		聾
LONG	140,16	5693	20	44211	4273		POLYGONUM POSUMBU		蘢
LONG	142,17	587A	23	53114			TRAPDOOR SPIDER		蠪
LONG	157,16	9352	23	61111	4275		TO WALK		躘
LONG	170,09	7127	12	77214	4255	0405	PROSPEROUS,START(A FIRE)		隆
LONG	212,00	7893	16	01211	4258	7318	DRAGON		龍
LOONG	032,16	1096	19	01104	4261	0236	MONOPOLIZE		壟
LOONG	032,16	8263	19	41111		7319	MOUND		壠
LOONG	064,16	2379	19	51011	4262	7326	COLLECT,DRAW NEAR TO		攏
LOONG	170,16	7150	19	71211	4276	7325	KANSU		隴
LONQ	030,07	8144	10	61041		2796	(PHONETIC),-R + ONE(CHEM.)		哢
LONQ	055,04	1702.0B	07	10441	4278	2795	LANE/ALLEY	5893	弄
LONQ	144,06	5893	12	21221	2554	3032	LANE/ALLEY	1702.0B	衖
LHOU	064,11	2299.0A	14	55044	4142	9011	GRAFT (MONEY),SOLICIT		摟
LHOU	064,09	2299.1A	12	59044	4142	9011	GRAFT(MONEY),SOLICIT		搂
LOU	009,11	0283	13	25244	4137	9008	HUNCHBACK		僂
LOU	030,09	0853.1	12	69044			SUBORDINATES IN GANG OF BANDITS		喽
LOU	030,11	0853	14	65044	4139	9006	SUBORDINATES IN GANG OF BANDITS	C1236.1	嘍
LOU	038,06	1236.1	09	90404	4136		(SURNAME),(STAR),ABBR. OF 0853	G0853	娄
LOU	038,08	1236	11	50404	4136	9002	(SURNAME),(STAR)		婁
LOU	075,09	2869.1	13	49944			HOUSE WITH MORE THAN 1 STORY		楼
LOU	075,11	2869	15	45944	4143	9014	HOUSE WITH MORE THAN 1 STORY		樓
LOU	127,11	5098	17	55944	4145	9015	DRILL FOR SOWING GRAIN		耬
LOU	140,11	5589	15	44404	4146	9021	ARTHEMISIA VULGARIS,PIPER BETLE		蔞
LOU	142,11	5829	17	55144	4147	9017	MOLE-CRICKET/GRYLLOTALPA AFRICONA		螻
LOU	188,11	7551	21	75244	4149	9012	SKULL		髏
LOOU	032,11	1061	14	45144	4140	9003	SMALL MOUND		塿
LOOU	046,11	1530	14	25744	4141	9005	MOUNTAIN PEAK		嶁
LOOU	064,09	2299.1	12	59044			TO EMBRACE		搂
LOOU	064,11	2299	14	55044	4142	9011	TO EMBRACE		摟
LOOU	118,09	4664.1	15	88404			DEEP BASKET		篓

ROM	RAD	TEL	TOI	FC	MAT	OSH	TAG	CR	CHAR
LOOU	118,11	4664	17	88404	4144	9022	DEEP BASKET		篓
LOW	085,11	3345	14	37127	4152	4020	TO LEAK,FUNNEL		漏
LOW	104,11	4076	16	00127	4289		FISTULA,SINUS	4068	瘺
LOW	104,11	4068	16	00144	4289	9018	FISTULA,SINUS	4076	瘻
LOW	167,11	6979	19	85144	4148	9004	ENGRAVE,HARD STEEL		鏤
LOW	170,06	7097	09	71212	4151	0756	LOW/HUMBLE		陋
LOW	173,12	7216.0A	20	10164	4186	1408	TO EXPOSE		露
.LOU	030,09	0853.1A	12	69044			(PART.)		喽
.LOU	030,11	0853.0A	14	65044		9006	(PART.EXPRE. CHAGRIN OR RESENTMENT)		嘍
LHU	030,15	8183	18	67063	4177	1623	GRUMBLE/CHATTER		噜
LU	032,16	1097	19	41117	4157	0654	CLAY,SHOP		墟
LU	053,04	1687.1	07	00277		4240	HUT		庐
LU	053,16	1687	19	00217	4158	0668	HUT		廬
LU	063,01	4151.1	05	21277			(SURNAME)		卢
LU	075,16	5260	20	41917		0663	SMOKE TREE,CAPITAL(OF COLUMN)		櫨
LU	084,11	8646	15	80617		7802	CHLORINE		氯
LU	085,05	3472.1	08	31177			PLACE NAME,NAME OF A RIVER		泸
LU	085,16	3472	19	31117	4159	0667	PLACE NAME,NAME OF A RIVER		瀘
LU	086,04	3619.1	08	93872	4160	4236	STOVE		炉
LU	086,16	3619	20	91817	4160	0664	STOVE		爐
LU	095,06	3766	11	08732		5808	BLACK		玈
LU	108,11	4151	16	21217	4156	0653	(SURNAME)		盧
LU	118,16	4701	22	88217			BASKET MADE OF RUSH,SPEAR-SHAFT		籚
LU	120,16	4963	22	21917	4164	0665	HEMPEN THREAD,TO DRESS HEMP		纑
LU	121,16	4983	22	81717	4165	0656	PILE OF EARTH TO KEEP WINE JARS		罏
LU	130,16	5251	20	71217	4166	0660	SKIN,BELLY,TO STATE		臚
LU	137,16	5325	22	21417	4167	0661	BOW OF SHIP		艫
LU	140,04	5684.1	08	44277		4239	RUSH/REED/PHRAGMITES COMMUNIS		芦
LU	140,16	5684	20	44217	4168	0669	RUSH/REED/PHRAGMITES COMMUNIS		蘆
LU	159,16	6578	23	51017	4169	0658	WINDLASS		轳
LU	167,16	7010	24	81117	4170	0655	STOVE	3619	鑪
LU	181,16	7361	25	21286	4171	8249	SKULL,FOREHEAD		顱
LU	195,16	7678	27	21317	4172	0666	COMMON PERCH		鱸

ROM	RAD	TEL	TOT	FC	MAT	OSH	TAG	CR	CHAR
LU	196,16	7760	27	27227	4173	4603	FISHING CORMORANT		
LUU	025,05	7767.1	07	21600			ABBR. OF 3366 AND 7767	3366	
LUU	032,11	8248	14	41160			SALT/BRINE	B7767	
LUU	064,13	2342	16	51027	4175	4851	TAKE CAPTIVE	5712	
LUU	075,15	2924	19	47963	4178	1625	SCULLING OAR	9161	
LUU	082,15	5272	19	22716	4179	7399	ROUGH SERGE OF YAK'S HAIR		
LUU	085,11	3366	14	31160	4155	1962	GRAVY,BRINE	E7767	
LUU	112,11	4330	16	11660		1951	AMMONIUM		
LUU	115,15	4491	20	27963			WILD RICE		
LUU	137,13	9161	19	21427		4852	SCULLING OAR	2924	
LUU	137,15	2924.1	21	27463	4178	1624	SCULLING OAR		
LUU	141,02	5712.1	08	21227			TAKE CAPTIVE		
LUU	141,07	5712	13	21227	4175	4849	TAKE CAPTIVE	2342	
LUU	167,15	5266	23	87163			LUTECIUM		
LUU	195,04	7627	15	27603	4176	1622	CRASS,PLACE NAME	B7767	
LUU	197,00	7767	11	21600	4153	1950	SALT/BRINE,CRASS,HALOGEN	D7627	
LUH	009,11	0285	13	27222	4208	4209	DESPISE/INSULT		
LUH	012,02	0362.0A	04	00800	4189	8013	SIX		
LUH	019,11	0526	13	14227	4209	4814	UNITE/COMBINE FORCES		
LUH	032,05	8204	08	40104	4190		CLOD OF EARTH,LAND		
LUH	058,05	6922.1	08	17132	4192	5661	TO RECORD/COPY		
LUH	062,11	2068	15	13250	4210	6939	KILL		
LUH	085,08	8692	11	37132	4194		CLEAR(WATER),STRAIN LIQUIDS	D3369	
LUH	085,11	3369	14	30111	4202	7099	STRAIN LIQUIDS	B8692	
LUH	085,13	3406	16	37164	4183	1407	(SURNAME),NAME OF A RIVER		
LUH	096,08	3826	12	17132			(JADE)		
LUH	096,13	3873	17	17164	4184	1405	(JADE)		
LUH	101,01	3939	06	27220			PLACE NAME,(SURNAME)		
LUH	108,08	4143	13	27107			BOX CASE		
LUH	112,08	4294	13	12632	4195	5664	LABORIOUS,SMALL STONE		
LUH	112,11	8961	16	17622		4206	STONE SOIL ROLLER		
LUH	113,08	4389	12	37232	4196	5667	OFFICIAL SALARY,GOOD FORTUNE		
LUH	115,08	8988	13	24914			LATE-PLANTED EARLY-RIPENING GRAIN	4478	

ROM	RAD	TEL	TOT	FC	MAT	OSH	TAG	CR	CHAR
LUH	115,11	4478	16	27922			LATE-PLANTED EARLY-RIPENING GRAIN.	8988	穋
LUH	118,11	4666	17	88211	4205	7113	BOX/BASKET		簏
LUH	118,13	4685	19	88564			(BAMBOO)		簬
LUH	118,16	4700	22	88132	4201	5663	CHART,MEMORANDUM,LIST		籙
LUH	120,08	4845.0A	14	27932	4197	5666	GREEN,CHLORINE		綠
LUH	140,08	5467	12	44132	4198	5669	ARTHRAXON CILIARE,RHODACENE,GREEN		菉
LUH	140,11	5578.0A	15	44202	3966	4218	LUXURIANT GROWTH		蓼
LUH	140,13	564A	17	44164			LEUCACENE		蕗
LUH	148,00	6037.0B	07	27227		3699	(SURNAME)		角
LUH	154,06	6323	13	67864	4180	1422	BRIBE(RY)		賂
LUH	157,06	6424	13	67164	4181	1404	ROAD,(SURNAME)		路
LUH	159,06	6526	13	57064	4188	1414	CHARIOT		輅
LUH	159,11	6564	18	50011	4206	7097	WINDLASS		轆
LUH	162,08	6629	12	37303	4199	6730	GO CAREFULLY,(SURNAME)		逯
LUH	164,08	6838	15	17632			NAME OF A WINE		醁
LUH	167,08	6922	16	87132	4200	5662	TO RECORD/TO COPY		錄
LUH	170,05	7120.1	08	75272			LAND,(SURNAME)		陆
LUH	170,08	7120	11	74214	4191	0238	LAND,(SURNAME)		陸
LUH	173,12	7216	20	10164	4186	1408	DEW		露
LUH	187,08	7498	18	77332			(HORSE)		騄
LUH	195,08	765C	19	24314			BLUEFISH,POMATOMUS SALTATRIX		鯥
LUH	196,12	7752	23	67327		4673	HERON		鷺
LUH	198,00	7773	11	00211	4203	7096	DEER		鹿
LUH	198,08	7785	19	44211	4207	7112	FOOT OF A HILL		麓
.LU	030,15	8183.0A	18	67063		1623	GRUMBLE/CHATTER		嚕
LUAN	031,19	8194.1	22	60993	4212	1931	ROUND		圝
LUAN	031,23	8194	26	60904		1929	ROUND		圞
LUAN	038,19	1309.0A	22	22404	4298	9062	BEAUTIFUL		孌
LUAN	046,19	1551	22	22772	4214	1001	MOUNTAIN RANGES		巒
LUAN	075,19	2940	23	22904	4215	5399	KOELREUTERIA PANICULATA		欒
LUAN	085,23	3497	26	32194	4216	5400	NAME OF A RIVER		灤
LUAN	130,19	5254	23	22227	4301	4064	SLICED MEAT,SKINNY		臠
LUAN	167,19	7019	27	22109	4217	0385	IMPERIAL		鑾

ROM	RAD	TEL	TOT	FC	MAT	OSH	TAG	CR	CHAR
LUAN	196,19	7762	30	22327	4218	4693	(MYTHICAL BIRD)		鸞
LOAN	026,05	0607	07	77720	4219	2150	OVUM		卵
LUANN	005,06	0052.1	07	22610	4220	7059	DISORDERED		乱
LUANN	005,12	0052	13	22210	4220	7068	DISORDERED		亂
LHUEN	064,08	2241	11	58027	4250	3797	WHIRL (ONE'S ARM)		掄
LHUEN	159,08	6544.0A	15	58027	4254	3796	WHIRL(ONE'S ARM)	2241	輪
LUEN	009,06	0178	08	80227	4246	3792	ARRANGE		侖
LUEN	009,08	0243	10	28227	4247	3795	HUMAN RELATIONSHIP		倫
LUEN	031,08	0950	11	60227	4248	1886	COMPLETE		圇
LUEN	046,08	1510	11	22227	4249	3800	KOULKUN MOUNTAINS		崙
LUEN	064,08	2241.0B	11	58027	4250	3797	SELECT		掄
LUEN	085,08	3229	11	38127	4251	3799	PERISH		淪
LUEN	120,08	4858	14	28927	4252	3798	SILK THREAD,TWIST SILK,CLASSIFY		綸
LUEN	149,08	6158.0A	15	08627	4253	3794	(CONFUCIAN)ANALECTS		論
LUEN	159,08	6544	15	58027	4254	3796	WHEEL,ROTATE		輪
LUEN	167,08	9470	16	88127			(METAL)		錀
LUENN	149,08	6158	15	08627	4253	3794	DISCUSS,THEORY,BY THE/PER		論
LHUO	030,19	0925	22	66014	4101	0915	FUSSY,TALKATIVE		囉
LHUO	064,07	2192	10	52049	4134	3288	STRIP (COW/LEAVES/BRANCH)		捋
LUO	009,19	8081	21	26214	4100	0916	SMART/CLEVER		儸
LUO	030,19	0925.0A	22	66014	4101	0915	SUBORDINATE IN A GANG OF BANDITS		囉
LUO	094,19	3762	22	46214			NAME OF A TRIBE		玀
LUO	118,19	4712	25	88914	4104	0918	BASKET		籮
LUO	122,03	5012.1	08	60207		4250	GAUZE,(SURNAME),ABBR. OF 0925.0A		罗
LUO	122,14	5012	19	60914	4099	0913	GAUZE,(SURNAME)		羅
LUO	140,11	5582	15	44903			BASKET FOR CARRYING EARTH		蔂
LUO	140,19	5700	23	44914	4105	0917	RADISH		蘿
LUO	142,11	5828	17	56193	4111	8454	SNAIL,SCREW		螺
LUO	142,13	5856.0A	19	00217	4118	7898	SNAIL	5828	蠃
LUO	147,14	6035	21	16210	4114	7603	EXPLAIN IN DETAIL		覶
LUO	162,19	6709	23	36301	4106	6607	LOGIC,PATROL		邏
LUO	167,19	7017	27	86114	4107	0914	GONG		鑼
LUO	187,11	7512	21	76393	4112	8452	MULE	7529	騾

ROM	RAD	TEL	TOT	FC	MAT	OSH	TAG	CR	CHAR
LUO	187,13	7529	23	00217	4112	7894	MULE	7512	贏
LUOO	009,08	0139	10	26294	4108	5497	NAKED,LOLO	A5953	倮
LUOO	064,13	2342.0A	16	51027	4175	4851	TAKE CAPTIVE	5712.0A	擄
LUOO	104,11	4064	16	00193	4223	8457	SCROFULA,TUBERCULOSIS OF GLANDS		瘰
LUOO	104,21	8888	26	00193			SCROFULA/SWELLING	4064	癭
LUOO	112,05	8931	10	11620	4113	3042	A HEAP/PILE(OF ROCKS)		砢
LUOO	130,17	5252	21	00217	4117	7895	NAKED	5953	臝
LUOO	140,10	5559	14	44232	4119	4991	FRUIT OF PLANTS(NOT OF TREES)		蓏
LUOO	141,02	5712.1A	08	21227			TAKE CAPTIVE		虜
LUOO	141,07	5712.0A	13	21227	4175	4849	TAKE CAPTIVE	2342.0A	虜
LUOO	142,13	5856	19	00217	4118	7898	SOLITARY WASP		蠃
LUOO	145,08	5953	13	36294	4109	5498	NAKED		裸
LUOO	158,08	6505	15	26294	4109	5502	NAKED	5953	躶
LUOH	030,06	0748.0A	09	67064	4120	1409	TO ARGUE/DEBATE,COUGH(BLOOD)		咯
LUOH	064,11	5285	14	56093	4110	8451	PILE UP		摞
LUOH	085,06	3157	09	37164	4121	1424	NAME OF A RIVER,(SURNAME)		洛
LUOH	085,15	3458	18	32194	4130	5417	NAME OF A RIVER		濼
LUOH	093,10	3684	14	99502	4131	2522	EMINENT,CLEAR,BRINDLED OX		犖
LUOH	096,06	3794	10	17164	4124	1402	NECK-ORNAMENT		珞
LUOH	120,19	9077	25	26914			STRING ON WHICH COINS ARE STRUNG		纙
LUOH	140,09	5507.0B	13	44164	4122	1425	TO FALL/DROP,ALIGHT		落
LUOH	164,06	6803.0A	13	17664	4126	1412	MILK		酪
LUOH	172,06	7170	14	23614	4128	0874	BLACK HORSE WITH WHITE MANE,FEARFUL		雒
LUOH	187,06	7482	16	77364	4127	1419	CAMEL		駱
M	030,07	0767	10	61061		1229	NOT(CANTONESE)		唔
MHA	030,11	0860	14	64027			MARK		嘜
MHA	038,10	1265	13	41427	4312	4704	MA/MAMMA	1301	媽
MHA	038,14	1301	17	40432			MA/MAMMA	1265	嬤
MHA	142,10	5818.0A	16	51127	4318	4703	DRAGONFLY		螞
MA	052,00	8010.0A	03	22730		8821	WHAT	7803.0A	么
MA	053,03	7803.1A	06	00232	4540	8823	WHAT		庅
MA	104,08	4034	13	00194	4025	7076	LEPROSY,NUMB	E7802	麻
MA	140,11	5594	15	44294	4307	7075	HEMP	C7802	蔴

ROM	RAD	TEL	TOT	FC	MAT	OSH	TAG	CR	CHAR
MA	142,10	5818.0B	16	51127	4318	4703	LEECH		螞
MA	142,11	5840	17	54134	4309	5017	TOAD		蟆
MA	200,00	7802	11	00294	4303	7073	TO BOTHER,NUMB,HEMP	G5594	麻
MA	200,03	7803.0A	14	00232	4540	8824	WHAT	8010.0A	麼
MAA	030,10	0834.0A	13	61027		4698	MORPHINE		嗎
MAA	085,10	3301	13	31127			NAME OF A RIVER		溤
MAA	096,10	3854	14	11127	4314	4697	AGATE		瑪
MAA	112,10	4316	15	11627	4315	4699	YARD,NUMBER,A WEIGHT		碼
MAA	142,10	5818	16	51127	4318	4703	ANT		螞
MAA	187,00	7456	10	71327	4310	4696	HORSE,21ST OF MONTH(TELE.)		馬
MAH	030,13	5006.1	16	66327		4706	SCOLD/ABUSE		駡
MAH	113,10	4401	14	31227	4316	4702	SACRIFICE TO GOD OF WAR,D(22ND)		禡
MAH	122,10	5006	15	60327	4317	4708	SCOLD/ABUSE		罵
MAH	142,10	5818.0C	16	51127	4318	4703	GRASSHOPPER		螞
.MA	030,10	0834	13	61027	4311	4698	(INTERROG. PART.)	7803.0B	嗎
.MA	030,11	0859	14	60094	4304	7074	(PHONETIC)		嘛
.MA	052,00	8010.0B	03	22730		8821	(INTERROG. PART.)	0834	么
.MA	053,03	7803.1B	06	00232	4540	8823	(INTERROG. PART.)		庅
.MA	142,11	5840.0A	17	54134	4309	5017	TOAD		蟆
.MA	200,03	7803.0B	14	00232	4540	8824	(INTERROG. PART.)	0834	麽
MAI	032,07	1003	10	46114	4319	0428	BURY		埋
MAI	173,14	7223	22	10214	4321	0438	DUST-STORM		霾
MAE	037,03	6314.1	06	17430			BUY		买
MAE	140,12	556F	16	44806			SONCHUS		蕒
MAE	154,05	6314	12	60806	4322	8147	BUY		買
MAY	019,13	0535	15	44227	4324	4812	PUT FORTH EFFORT		勱
MAY	035,04	7796.1	07	50407		6410	WHEAT,(SURNAME)		麦
MAY	037,05	6344.1	08	40430			SELL		卖
MAY	130,05	9115.0A	09	73232	4382	5655	PULSE,MOUNTAIN RANGE	5181.0A	脉
MAY	130,06	5181.0A	10	72232	4382	5805	PULSE,MOUNTAIN RANGE	9115.0A	脈
MAY	143,06	5884.0A	12	22132	4382	5804	PULSE	A5181.0A	蚷
MAY	154,08	6344	15	40806	4323	8148	SELL		賣
MAY	162,03	6701.1	07	31302			TAKE A STEP		迈

ROM	RAD	TEL	TOT	FC	MAT	OSH	TAG	CR	CHAR
MAY	162,13	6701	17	34302	4325	6706	TAKE A STEP		
MAY	196,11	774E	22	47427			ARA MACAW		
MAY	199,00	7796	11	40207	4379	6428	WHEAT,(SURNAME)		
MHAN	181,11	7354	20	41286	4329	8277	DAWDLING		
MAN	032,07	1003.0A	10	46114	4319		TO BLAME		
MAN	075,11	8583	15	44927			(TREE)		
MAN	075,11	2705	15	46947			(TREE)		
MAN	085,11	3355.0A	14	36147	4335	6182	OVERFLOW,FULL		
MAN	109,11	4221	16	64027	4327	4026	CONCEAL FROM		
MAN	140,11	5585.0B	15	44407	4337	6183	BRASSICA CAMPESTRIS		
MAN	142,06	5875.1	12	00136		8950	BARBARIAN,BULLYING		
MAN	142,19	5875	25	22136	4343	8949	BARBARIAN,BULLYING		
MAN	149,11	6211	18	06647	4338	6175	DECEIVE		
MAN	157,11	6466	18	64127	4328	4025	JUMP OVER		
MAN	181,11	7354.0A	20	41286	4329	8277	DAWDLING		
MAN	184,11	7429	19	86747	4340	6177	STEAMED BREAD		
MAN	195,11	7665	22	26347	4341	6180	EEL/ANGUILLA LOSTONIENSIS		
MAAN	085,11	3341	14	34127	4326	4027	FULL,MANCHURIAN		
MAAN	142,11	584E	17	54127			ACARID		
MAAN	145,11	9262	16	34227			PADDED WINTER ROBE		
MAAN	167,12	698A	20	84127			AMERICIUM		
MANN	032,11	1063	14	46147	4331	6173	TO PLASTER		
MANN	038,11	1285	14	46447	4332	6181	INSULT,(SURNAME)		
MANN	050,11	1611	14	46247	4333	6178	CURTAIN		
MANN	061,11	1976	14	96047	4334	6176	SLOW		
MANN	073,07	2581	11	60407	4330	6172	LONG,LARGE,HANDSOME		
MANN	085,11	3355	14	36147	4335	6182	INUNDATE,FREE/UNRESTRAINED		
MANN	086,11	8759	15	96847			TO SPREAD		
MANN	120,11	4915	17	26947	4336	6179	PLAIN THIN SILK,UNADORNED,SLOW		
MANN	140,11	5585	15	44407	4337	6183	CREEPER,TO SPREAD		
MANN	149,11	6211.0A	18	06647	4338	6175	NEGLECT/SLIGHT,DISRESPECT		
MANN	163,11	9411	14	67427			PLACE NAME		
MANN	167,11	6976	19	86147	4339	6174	TROWEL,SIDE OF COIN WITHOUT WORDS		

邁
鷞
麥
顢
埋
橫
槾
漫
瞞
蔓
蠻
繜
謾
跰
滿
顢
饅
鰻
滿
蟎
襔
鏋
墁
嫚
幔
慢
蔓
漫
熳
縵
蔓
謾
鄤
鏝

ROM	RAD	TEL	TOT	FC	MAT	OSH	TAG	CR	CHAR
MANN	190,11	7583	21	72407		6184	PRETTY HAIR,HEAD ORNAMENTS		
MANG	027,07	8118.0A	09	71212		7724	(SURNAME)		
MANG	030,07	8141	10	63012			JARGON		
MANG	043,04	1430.0A	07	42012	4353	7723	STRIPED,SHAGGY DOG		
MANG	061,03	1811	06	90011	4344	0760	BUSY		
MANG	075,03	8531	07	00904	4345		RIDGE-POLE IN ROOF		
MANG	083,04	3047	08	07747	4424	6867	VAGRANT/RUFFIAN	3959	
MANG	093,16	368A	20	21511			GERANACEAE,BLACK AND WHITE COW		
MANG	102,03	3959	08	60010	4424		VAGRANT,RUFFIAN	3047	
MANG	109,03	4159	08	00601	4346	1712	BLIND		
MANG	112,07	8947	12	14610	4349	0764	CRUDE SALTPETER		
MANG	140,03	5345	07	44710	4347	0762	MISCANTHUS SINENSIS		
MANG	140,06	5413	10	44110		0761	VAST,VAGUE		
MANG	163,03	6715	06	07727	4351	2166	NAME OF A HILL		
MANG	167,07	6916	15	84110	4350	0763	SHARP POINT		
MAANG	075,12	289A	16	44943			MANGIFERA INDICA		
MAANG	085,10	3357	13	34143	4355		VAST/EXPANSIVE(OF WATER)		
MAANG	140,08	5462	12	44443	4354	2806	RUDE,ILLICIUM ANISATUM		
MAANG	142,12	5845	18	54143	4356	2807	PYTHON MOLURUS		
MHAU	064,11	2307.0A	14	54034	4560	5013	FEEL WITH THE HAND		
MHAU	094,09	3728	12	44260	4366	1777	CAT	6292	
MHAU	153,09	6292	16	24260	4366	1776	CAT	3728	
MAU	070,06	2463.0A	10	08214	4363	7388	BANNER DECORATED WITH ANIMAL'S TAIL		
MAU	082,00	3029	04	20714	4357	7367	FUR/HAIR		
MAU	082,11	3036.0A	15	58214	3881	7385	TUFT OF HAIR,TAIL		
MAU	110,00	4243	05	17222	4570	3089	LANCE		
MAU	140,05	5403	09	44222	4364	3090	THATCH,(SURNAME)		
MAU	142,09	5801	15	18136	4365	8942	GRAIN-EATING GRUB,SPANISH FLY	5833	
MAU	142,11	5833	17	17136	4365	8909	GRAIN-EATING GRUB,SPANISH FLY	5801	
MAU	167,09	6931	17	84160	4367	1772	ANCHOR		
MAU	190,04	7565	14	72714	4362	7391	FASHIONABLE,BANG(HAIR),MANE	9631	
MAU	190,05	9631	15	72222			FASHIONABLE,BANG(HAIR),MANE	7565	
MAO	026,03	0602	05	77220	4369	2133	4TH EARTH'S BRANCH,5-7 A.M.		

鬘厖嚨尨忙亲氓攏吔盲硭芒莣邙鋩樠漭莽蟒摸猫貓旄毛氂矛茅蝥矛蚰錨髦髳卯

ROM	RAD	TEL	TOT	FC	MAT	OSH	TAG	CR	CHAR
MAO	046,05	1475	08	22727			SINGLE HILL (GEOGRAPHICAL)		屵
MAO	072,05	2510	09	60727	4370	2137	THE PLEIADES		昴
MAO	085,05	3148	08	37120	4371	2136	STILL WATER		泖
MAO	140,05	5374	09	44727	4372	2138	BRASENIA PURPUREA		茆
MAO	167,05	9450	13	87120			RIVETING		鉚
MAW	010,05	6290.2	07	26210	4368		APPEARANCE		皃
MAW	013,07	0379	09	60600	4373	1719	TO COVER,BRAVE DANGER		冒
MAW	038,09	1256	12	46460	4374	1722	ENVIOUS		媢
MAW	050,09	1604	12	46260	4375	1720	CAP/HAT		帽
MAW	061,13	2021	17	44339	4575	8654	EXERT THE MIND,BE GREAT		懋
MAW	070,06	2463	10	08214	4363	7388	AGED	5073	旄
MAW	075,09	8574	13	44990		5270	CYDONIA JAPONICA		楙
MAW	096,09	3847	13	16160	4378		(JADE)		瑁
MAW	109,04	8900	09	62014	4359	7372	HAVING POOR EYESIGHT		眊
MAW	109,09	4214	14	18604	4572	1731	INDISTINCT VISION/DIM		瞀
MAW	125,04	5073	10	44714	4360	7394	AGED	2463	耄
MAW	140,04	5369	08	44714	4361	7390	SELECT,VEGETABLES		芼
MAW	140,05	5399	09	44253	4580	6995	LUXURIANT		茂
MAW	145,05	5924	11	00732	4574	5886	LENGTH/DISTANCE FROM NORTH TO SOUTH		袤
MAW	153,07	6290.1	14	26210	4368	7581	APPEARANCE		貌
MAW	153,08	6290	15	27217	4368	7538	APPEARANCE		貌
MAW	154,05	6319	12	77806	4581	8210	COMMERCE		貿
MAW	163,12	6718	15	77827			ANCIENT PLACE NAME		鄻
.ME	030,15	5886	18	66014		0251	FINAL PART.		嚜
.ME	052,00	8010	03	22730	7282	8821	(INTERROG. SUFF.),ONE ON DICE	7803	么
.ME	053,03	7803.1	06	00232	4540	8823	(INTERROG. SUFF.)		庅
.ME	200,03	7803	14	00232	4540	8824	(INTERROG. SUFF.)	8010	麼
MEI	032,09	8240	12	47167			LOW WALL		堳
MEI	038,09	1252	12	44494	4397	5304	MEDIUM/GO-BETWEEN		媒
MEI	046,08	1520	11	26767	4393	1706	NAME OF A MOUNTAIN IN SZECHWAN		嵋
MEI	075,04	2653	08	48940	4389	6385	AN. FOR SMALL OBJECTS		枚
MEI	075,07	2734	11	48957	4402	4880	PLUM FLOWER		梅
MEI	075,09	2812	13	47967	4394	1707	LINTEL		楣

ROM	RAD	TEL	TOT	FC	MAT	OSH	TAG	CR	CHAR
MEI	085,04	3093	07	37147	4555	6256	HAVE NOT,NOT		沒
MEI	085,04	3093.1	07	37147			HAVE NOT,NOT		没
MEI	085,09	3270	12	37167	4395	1709	BRINK/EDGE		湄
MEI	086,09	3561	13	94894	4398	5303	COAL		煤
MEI	096,04	3780	08	18140	4390	6309	ROSE		玫
MEI	096,09	8831	13	17167			(STONE WHICH RESEMBLES JADE)		瑂
MEI	109,04	4168	09	77267	4391	1705	EYEBROWS		眉
MEI	113,09	4399	13	34294	4399		HEIR-REQUESTING SACRIFICE		禖
MEI	130,06	9119	10	74289			SHOULDER FLESH		胈
MEI	130,07	9123	11	78257			MEAT ON THE BACK OF AN ANIMAL		脢
MEI	140,05	5388	09	44771	4404	4885	(WILD ROSE)		莓
MEI	140,07	5448	11	44507	4404	4883	STRAWBERRY		莓
MEI	163,09	6758	12	77227	4396	2183	ANCIENT PLACE NAME		郿
MEI	164,07	5326	14	18657			ENZYME		酶
MEI	167,07	9469	15	88157			LOCK,METAL DOG COLLAR		鋂
MEI	167,09	5296	17	87167			AMERICIUM		鎇
MEI	173,07	7199	15	10507	4405	4884	MOLDY,FUNGI,BACTERIA	7827	霉
MEI	203,11	7827	23	28240	4415	6405	MOLDY,FUNGI,BACTERIA	7199	黴
MEEI	015,07	8680.1	09	37116	4409	7752	ASK A FAVOR OF		浼
MEEI	038,09	8292	12	48434			BEAUTIFUL	A5019	媄
MEEI	038,10	1275	13	48440	4417	6396	BEAUTIFUL	A5019	嬍
MEEI	080,03	3020	07	80507	4401	4875	EACH/EVERY		每
MEEI	085,07	8680	10	37116	4409	7753	ASK A FAVOR OF		浼
MEEI	085,09	8695	12	38134	4407	5007	RIPPLE PATTERN		渼
MEEI	123,03	5019	09	80430	4406	5005	BEAUTIFUL,AMERICA		美
MEEI	167,09	9485	17	88134		5006	MAGNESIUM		鎂
MEY	038,05	1188	08	45490	4410	5463	YOUNGER SISTER		妹
MEY	038,09	1253	12	47467	4392	1708	FLATTER/CHARM		媚
MEY	040,09	1382	12	30294	4416	5462	SLEEP SOUNDLY		寐
MEY	072,05	2505	09	65090	4411	5460	DARK,CONCEAL		昧
MEY	085,05	3105	08	35190	4412	5464	DAWN,PLACE NAME		沬
MEY	086,09	8752	13	97867			BE RADIANT/FLAMING,DROUGHT		焵
MEY	096,09	3847.0A	13	16160	4378		TORTOISE SHELL		瑁

238

ROM	RAD	TEL	TOT	FC	MAT	OSH	TAG	CR	CHAR
MEY	104,07	8870	12	00157	4403	4882	DISEASE CAUSED BY ANXIETY		
MEY	109,05	4175	10	65090	4413	5461	BLIND/IMPERCEPTIVE		
MEY	113,05	8980	09	35290			GHOST/APPARITION,DEMON		
MEY	145,04	5927	09	35230	4456	5210	SLEEVE OF A ROBE		
MEY	178,05	7283	14	45590			A GRASS THAT GIVES RED DYE		
MEY	194,05	7613	15	25219	4414	7657	TO CHARM,MAGIC,DEMON		
MEY	194,14	7622	24	24215			TO CHARM,MAGIC,DEMON	7613	
MHEN	061,08	1899.0A	12	77337	4420	3535	STUFFY	2030.0A	
MHEN	086,12	3626.0A	16	97820	4421	3536	COOK IN A COVERED VESSEL		
MEN	009,08	0226.0A	10	27220	4419		PERSONAL NOUN PLURALIZER		
MEN	064,08	2204	11	57020	4422	3437	LAY HANDS ON,TO COVER		
MEN	096,11	8838	15	14127			(GEM),ROUGE		
MEN	115,11	8990	16	00904		5560	RICE SPROUTS,PORRIDGE		
MEN	167,08	5330	16	87120			MENDELEVIUM		
MEN	169,00	7024.1	03	27000			DOOR,FIELD OF ENDEAVOR		
MEN	169,00	7024	08	77777	4418	3434	DOOR,FIELD OF ENDEAVOR		
MENN	061,08	1899	12	77337	4420	3535	MELANCHOLY	2030	
MENN	061,14	2030	18	34332	4420	8631	MELANCHOLY	1899	
MENN	086,12	3626	16	97820	4421	3536	COOK IN A COVERED VESSEL		
.MEN	009,08	0226	10	27220	4419	3436	PERSONAL NOUN PLURALIZER		
MHENG	109,14	4235.0A	19	64032	4443	5718	DECEIVE		
MHENG	140,10	5536.0A	14	44232	4437	5716	HOODWINK		
MENG	043,04	1430.0B	07	42012	4353	7723	CONFUSED		
MENG	050,14	1619	17	44232	4438	5722	COVER	5536	
MENG	072,14	2563	18	64032	4439	5717	BEFORE DAY BREAK	5536	
MENG	074,14	2603	18	74232	4440	5720	INDISTINCT,DECEIVE		
MENG	075,14	2916	18	44932	4441	5723	LEMON		
MENG	083,04	3047.0A	08	07747	4424	6867	PEOPLE		
MENG	085,14	3443	17	34132	4442	5725	DRIZZLE/MIST	5536	
MENG	094,14	373D	17	44232			HERPESTES MUNGO		
MENG	098,11	3918	16	44717	4434	7939	RAFTERS SUPPORTING TILES		
MENG	102,03	3959.0A	08	60010	4424		PEOPLE	3047.0A	
MENG	108,08	4145	13	67107	4426	0694	TO ALLY,OATH		

ROM	RAD	TEL	TOT	FC	MAT	OSH	TAG	CR	CHAR
MENG	109,14	4235	19	64032	4443	5718	DIM SIGHTED,IGNORANT		曚
MENG	112,14	8968	19	14632			(MINERAL)		礞
MENG	137,14	5322	20	24432	4444	5721	WAR-BOAT		艨
MENG	140,07	5499	11	44227			FRITILLARIA VERTICILLATA		莔
MENG	140,08	5492	12	44627	4427	3555	SPROUT,PEOPLE		萌
MENG	140,10	5536	14	44232	4437	5716	COVER,MONGOLIA,ABBR. OF 1619/2563		蒙
MENG	142,03	5724	09	50110			TABANUS TRIGONUS/HOUSE FLY		虻
MENG	142,09	5804	15	00136	4425	8904	TABANUS TRIGONUS/HOUSE FLY		蝱
MENG	173,14	7222	22	10232	4442		DRIZZLE/MIST	3443	霥
MENG	196,14	775H	25	37227			TROPIC BIRD		鸏
MEENG	050,14	1619.0A	17	44232		5722	LUXURIANT		幪
MEENG	061,14	2035.1	17	94027	4436	4252	STUPID		懞
MEENG	061,16	2035	19	94062	4436	1713	STUPID		懵
MEENG	094,08	3718	11	47217	4429	0691	FEROCIOUS,SUDDENLY		猛
MEENG	137,08	5313	14	27417	4430	0690	SMALL BOAT		艋
MEENG	142,08	5789	14	57117	4431	0692	GRASSHOPPER	C5817	蜢
MEENG	142,14	5817	20	54132	4445	5724	MIDGE,SANDFLY,GRASSHOPPER	G5789	蠓
MEENG	167,08	7021	16	87117	4432	0689	MANGANESE		錳
MENQ	036,08	1125.1	11	44207		4264	DREAM		梦
MENQ	036,11	1125	14	44207	4433	4251	DREAM		夢
MENQ	039,05	1322	08	17107	4428	0688	FIRST,(SURNAME)		孟
MENQ	109,11	4240	16	44602	4435		BE BLINDED,OBSCURED		薴
MGAN	037,04	1165	07	10430			SKINNY/PUNY (CANTONESE)		奀
MHI	030,06	0743	09	69094		5438	SOUND TO CALL CAT		咪
MHI	109,10	4185	15	69039		6726	TO SQUINT		眯
MI	014,06	0384	08	37904	4447	5445	DEEP		冞
MI	057,05	1736.1	08	17292			TO FILL,FULL,OVERFLOWING	G3483	弥
MI	057,14	1736	17	11227	4459	4031	TO FILL,FULL		彌
MI	085,17	3483	20	31127	4460	4033	OVERFLOWING	C1736.1	瀰
MI	094,17	8813	20	41227	4461	4032	MACAQUE		獼
MI	113,14	4410.0A	18	31227	4651	4035	(SURNAME)		禰
MI	119,11	4745	17	00294	4453	5454	RICE-GRUEL,DISSOLVED,WASTED	G7238.0A	糜
MI	120,11	4919	17	00293	4454	8479	TIE UP		縻

ROM	RAD	TEL	TOT	FC	MAT	OSH	TAG	CR	CHAR
MI	140,10	554C	14	44309			VIBURNUM DELATATUM		蒾
MI	140,19	5701	23	44211		2789	MILLET		蘼
MI	149,10	6193	17	09639	4451	6725	RIDDLE		謎
MI	162,06	6617	10	39309	4450	6724	BEWILDER,CRAZY ABOUT		迷
MI	164,10	5721	17	19639		6727	ETHER		醚
MI	164,17	6843.1	24	10694		5455	UNFILTERED WINE,WINE BREWED TWICE		釀
MI	164,19	6843	26	10611			UNFILTERED WINE,WINE BREWED TWICE		醿
MI	175,11	7238.0A	19	00211	4455	2788	WASTED	C4745	靡
MI	198,06	7780	17	00904	4452	5456	MOOSE,(SURNAME),RIVER BANK		麋
MI	198,09	7789	20	00241	4458		FAWN,YOUNG OF ANIMALS		麛
MII	030,06	0743.0A	09	69094		5438	METER	D4717	咪
MII	057,06	1725	09	11240	4457	2727	TO STOP/REPRESS		弭
MII	066,06	2401	10	98940		6386	PEACEFUL		敉
MII	085,14	8712	17	31127	4650		MANY/NUMEROUS		瀰
MII	109,06	4183	11	69090	4449	5439	BLIND(AS WITH DUST)		眯
MII	119,00	4717	06	90904	4446	5436	UNCOOKED RICE,(SURNAME),METER	G0743.0A	米
MII	119,04	9034	10	97937			METER		釆
MII	130,06	518B	10	79294			AMIDINE		脒
MII	140,03	9090.0A	07	44500			(SURNAME)		芊
MII	140,06	541B	10	44904			MESITYLENE		苿
MII	167,06	690A	14	89194		5437	AMERICIUM		鎂
MII	175,11	7238	19	00211	4455	2788	GO WITH FASHION,EXTRAVAGANT,NOT		靡
MIH	014,00	0382	02	37020	4462	1976	A COVER		冖
MIH	014,14	0389	16	37227	4467	3996	POWER(MATH.TERM)		冪
MIH	030,11	5878	14	63072			(PHONETIC)AS IN PYRIMIDINE		嘧
MIH	032,10	8237	13	47180			TO PLASTER/WHITEWASH(WALL)		墁
MIH	040,05	1348	08	30332	4463	8712	STILL/SILENT,(SURNAME)		宓
MIH	040,08	1378	11	30772	4464	1003	DENSE		密
MIH	050,13	8366	16	70227			CHARIOT CANOPY		幦
MIH	085,04	3075	07	36100	3482	1498	NAME OF A RIVER		汨
MIH	085,05	3125.0A	08	33100	5087		SECRETE		沁
MIH	113,05	4365	09	33200	5088	8709	SECRET	4434	祕
MIH	115,05	4434	10	23900	5088	8708	SECRET	4365	秘

ROM	RAD	TEL	TOT	FC	MAT	OSH	TAG	CR	CHAR
MIH	118,12	4670	18	88253			SCREEN ON CARRIAGE		篾
MIH	120,00	4761.0A	06	20903	5570	8442	FINE SILK		糸
MIH	122,14	5009	19	60227	4467	3995	COVER OF CLOTH FOR FOOD,VEIL	0389	冪
MIH	142,08	5778	14	30136	4465	8951	HONEY		蜜
MIH	147,04	6017.1	11	10216	4469	7628	SEEK		覓
MIH	147,04	6017	11	20216	4469	7626	SEEK		覓
MIH	149,10	6194	17	03617	4468	0727	QUIET		謐
MIH	195,11	766Q	22	23373			HEMIBARBUS BARBUS		鮸
MIH	206,02	7846	15	37221	4466	2855	COVER OF TRIPOD KETTLE		鼏
MIAN	040,00	1336	03	30327	4488	1977	ROOF		宀
MIAN	075,08	2758	12	46927	4505	3968	COTTON		棉
MIAN	109,05	4177	10	67047	4504	6869	SLEEP		眠
MIAN	120,08	4875	14	26927	4506	3969	COTTON,SOFT/DOWNY,INCESSANT	A2758	綿
MIAN	120,09	9066	15	2229	4506	8491	COTTON,SOFT/DOWNY,(SURNAME)	K4875	緜
MIAN	123,08	5022	14	86527			WOOL AS SOFT AS COTTON		羏
MEAN	001,03	0018	04	10207	4489	4531	HIDDEN		丏
MEAN	009,07	0201	09	27216	4493	7747	EXERT,STOOP		倪
MEAN	010,05	0346	07	27416	4492	7745	TO AVOID		免
MEAN	013,09	0380	11	60416	4494	7754	ROYAL CROWN		冕
MEAN	019,07	0517	09	24212	4495	7755	EXHORT		勉
MEAN	019,09	8112	11	14627	4499	4802	EXHORT	0517	勔
MEAN	038,07	1231.0A	10	47416	7012	7751	GIVE BIRTH TO A CHILD		娩
MEAN	061,09	190A	12	91060	4500	1944	SHY		愐
MEAN	085,04	3094	07	31127	4490	4333	INUNDATION,NAME OF A RIVER		沔
MEAN	085,09	3274	12	31160	4501	1948	DRUNK		湎
MEAN	109,04	4165	09	61027	4491	4532	OGLE		眄
MEAN	120,07	9061.0A	13	27916	7144	7750	CAP		絻
MEAN	120,09	4884	15	21960	4502	1947	BURMA,DISTANT		緬
MEAN	130,09	520C	13	71260		1946	BASHFUL	7241	腼
MEAN	176,07	7241	16	16610	6380	7598	BASHFUL		靦
MEAN	195,07	764B	18	27316			SCIAENA ALBIFLORA,OTOLITHOIDESMIIUY		鮸
MIANN	009,08	8058	10	21260	4498		LOOK TOWARDS,OPPOSE		偭
MIANN	109,10	4220.0A	15	67080	4531	8016	DISTURB PHYSICALLY		瞑

242

ROM	RAD	TEL	TOT	FC	MAT	OSH	TAG	CR	CHAR
MIANN	176,00	7240	09	10600	4497	1943	FACE/SURFACE,FLOUR,NOODLES	D9692	面
MIANN	199,04	7797	15	41402	4503	6433	FLOUR,NOODLES	K7240	麪
MIANN	199,09	9692	20	41406	4503	6429	FLOUR/NOODLES	B7240	麵
MHIAU	030,09	081B	12	64060		1773	MEOW(ONOMAT. FOR CAT'S MEWING)		喵
MIAU	064,09	2249	12	54060	4472	1775	DEPICT,TO TRACE (A DRAWING)		描
MIAU	109,09	4178	14	64060	4473A	1774	TO AIM		瞄
MIAU	140,05	5379	09	44600	4470	1771	SPROUT,MIAO TRIBE,(SURNAME)		苗
MEAU	075,04	2641.0A	08	40609	7297	1580	DARK AND QUIET,DISAPPEAR		杳
MEAU	075,04	2634	08	49920	4475	4158	TIP OF BRANCH,THE LIMIT		杪
MEAU	085,08	8693	12	12232		5638	A FLOOD,INFINITY		淼
MEAU	085,09	3267	12	39120	4477	4155	VAGUE/REMOTE		渺
MEAU	109,04	4166	09	69020	4476	4153	SUBTLE,MINUTE(SMALL)		眇
MEAU	115,04	4432	09	29920	4479	4159	A SECOND		秒
MEAU	116,05	4507.0A	10	30727	7274	4840	QUIET AND ELEGANT,DEEP		窈
MEAU	120,09	4893	15	29920	4478	4154	INDISTINCT		緲
MEAU	140,14	5662	18	44216	4480	7582	SMALL,DESPISE		藐
MEAU	162,14	6707	18	36301	4564	6769	REMOTE,PROFOUND		邈
MIAW	038,04	1181	07	49420	4474	4163	CLEVER/WONDERFUL	3765	妙
MIAW	053,05	1680.1	08	00260	4473		TEMPLE/MONASTERY		庙
MIAW	053,12	1680	15	00227	4473	3560	TEMPLE/MONASTERY		廟
MIAW	095,04	3765	09	09720	4474		CLEVER,WONDERFUL	1181	玅
MIAW	120,11	4924.0A	17	27922	4538	4213	(SURNAME)		繆
MHIE	005,01	0045	02	40712	4481	7417	SQUINT		也
MHIE	030,07	077A	10	64050		2410	BLEAT	9090	咩
MHIE	140,03	9090	07	44500			BLEAT	077A	芈
MIEH	050,15	1622	18	44253			CARRIAGE COVER		幭
MIEH	085,10	3319	13	33150	4483	7022	EXTINGUISH	3528	滅
MIEH	086,01	3319.1	05	10809			EXTINGUISH		灭
MIEH	086,06	3528	10	53200	4483	7020	EXTINGUISH	3319	威
MIEH	118,11	4668	17	88253	4484	7036	BAMBOO SPLINTS FOR BASKETS		篾
MIEH	140,11	5583	15	44253	4487	7030	NOTHING,BELITTLE,DEFILED WITH BLOOD	G5885	蔑
MIEH	142,15	5864	21	54153	4486	7035	MINUTE FLIES		蠛
MIEH	143,15	5885	21	24153	4487	7031	DEFILED WITH BLOOD	C5583	衊

ROM	RAD	TEL	TOT	FC	MAT	OSH	TAG	CR	CHAR
MIN	030,05	072C	08	67047			INDAMINE		呡
MIN	046,05	1488	08	27747	4510	6868	NAME OF A RIVER IN SZECHWAN		岷
MIN	083,01	3046	05	77747	4508	6865	PEOPLE,CITIZEN		民
MIN	096,04	3774.0A	08	10140		6547	JADE-LIKE STONE	3787	玟
MIN	096,05	3787	09	17147	4512	6866	JADE-LIKE STONE	8952	珉
MIN	104,08	8874	13	00164			TO BE ILL		瘠
MIN	112,08	8952	13	12664			JADE-LIKE STONE	3787	磻
MIN	120,09	4891	15	27964	4516	1601	FISHING-LINE,CORD,STRING OF COINS		緡
MIN	140,05	9169	09	44747			SKIN OF BAMBOO,MULTITUDE		苠
MIN	169,06	7044	14	77136	4522	3540	FUKIEN		閩
MIIN	061,09	1940	13	78334	4521	8674	SYMPATHIZE,PITY	2006	愍
MIIN	061,11	2046	15	88334			INTELLIGENT		憨
MIIN	061,12	2006	15	97020	4521	3521	SYMPATHIZE/TO PITY	1940	憫
MIIN	064,05	2129	08	57047	4514	6870	TO SMOOTH,PURSE UP (LIPS)		抿
MIIN	066,07	2404	11	88540	4517	6384	KEEN		敏
MIIN	072,09	8513	13	78604	4513		STRONG,VIGOROUS		暋
MIIN	085,05	3139	08	37147	4511	6872	SUBMERGE,OBLITERATE		泯
MIIN	085,13	3427	16	37117	4507	7341	NAME OF A RIVER IN HONAN		澠
MIIN	169,04	7036	12	77400	4520	3520	FEEL COMPASSION FOR,(SURNAME)		閔
MIIN	195,11	7676	22	88336		8783	CODFISH/NIPHON SPINOSUS		鰵
MIIN	205,00	7836	13	77717	4523	7337	TOAD		黽
MING	014,08	0388	10	37800	4528	8014	DARK,DEEP		冥
MING	030,03	0682	06	27600	4524	1358	NAME		名
MING	072,04	2494	08	67020	4534	3554	CLEAR/BRIGHT		明
MING	072,10	2544	14	67080	4529	8015	DARK		暝
MING	075,10	280A	14	47980			CHINESE QUINCE		榠
MING	085,06	3117	09	37160		1424	NAME OF A RIVER		洺
MING	085,10	3298	13	37180	4530	8019	DRIZZLE,SEA		溟
MING	109,10	4220	15	67080	4531	8016	CLOSE THE EYES		瞑
MING	130,06	518E	10	77260	3310		PROTAMINE		眀
MING	140,06	5407.0A	10	44607	4525	1361	THEA SINENSIS/YOUNG LEAVES OF TEA		茗
MING	140,11	5551	15	44800		8020	(MYTHOLOGICAL TREE)		蓂
MING	142,10	5820	16	57180	4533	8018	HELIOTHUS ARMIGERA		螟

ROM	RAD	TEL	TOT	FC	MAT	OSH	TAG	CR	CHAR
MING	163,10	9403	13	37827			PLACE NAME		鄍
MING	164,06	6802	13	17660	4526	1360	DRUNK		酩
MING	167,06	6900	14	87160	4527	1359	INSCRIBED MOTTO		銘
MING	196,03	7686	14	67027	4535	4611	TO CRY(OF BIRDS)		鳴
MIING	108,00	4129	05	77100	4536	0637	VESSEL/UTENSIL		皿
MIING	140,06	5407	10	44607	4525	1361	THEA SINENSIS/YOUNG LEAVES OF TEA		茗
MINQ	030,05	0730	08	80627	4537	2120	LIFE/FATE		命
MINQ	072,10	2544.0A	14	67080	4529	8015	NIGHT,(SURNAME)		暝
MINQ	195,08	765H	19	28327			SEBASTODES MATSUBARAE		鮯
MIOW	149,11	6208	18	07622	4539	4207	ERRONEOUS,ABSURD		謬
MHO	064,11	2307	14	54034	4560	5013	FEEL WITH THE HAND		摸
MO	018,19	0497	21	02200		2890	WHITTLE		劘
MO	038,11	1287	14	44434			UGLY WOMAN		嫫
MO	052,00	8010.0C	03	22730		8821	DIMI.	7803.0C	幺
MO	053,03	7803.1C	06	00232		8823	DIMI.		広
MO	064,11	2302	15	00252	4541	3360	RUB		摩
MO	064,11	2308	15	44502		3351	IMITATE/COPY	2307.0B	摹
MO	064,11	2307.0B	14	54034	4560	5013	IMITATE/COPY	2308	摸
MO	075,11	2875	15	44934	4590	5015	IMITATE,MODEL/NORM	A2308	模
MO	112,11	4333	16	00601	4543	1117	GRIND,RUB		磨
MO	119,11	9044	17	94934	4308	5016	BLURRED		糢
MO	140,15	567C	19	44221	4542		METAPLEXIS STAUNTONI		摩
MO	140,16	5704	20	44261	4542	1119	MUSHROOM		蘑
MO	149,11	6206	18	04634	4591	5010	PLAN,TO PRACTICE		謨
MO	184,11	7418	19	84734		5012	SMALL LOAF OF STEAMED BREAD		饃
MO	194,11	7621	21	00213	4545	7651	DEVIL		魔
MO	200,03	7803.0C	14	00232		8824	DIMI.	8010.0C	麼
MOO	064,05	2130	08	55090	4548	5466	TO SMEAR,PLAY		抹
MOH	032,12	1075	15	60104	4386	0250	INK		墨
MOH	035,04	7796.1A	07	50407		6410	WHEAT,(SURNAME)		麦
MOH	040,11	1389	14	30430	4558	5020	LONESOME		寞
MOH	064,05	2130.0A	08	55090	4548	5466	GIRDLE/BRASSIERE,TO PLASTER	A5920.0A	抹
MOH	075,01	2608	05	50900	4546	5465	END		末

ROM	RAD	TEL	TOT	FC	MAT	OSH	TAG	CR	CHAR
MOH	078,04	8623	08	17220		4483	TO END/TO DIE	A3093	
MOH	078,04	2985	08	17247	4554		TO END/TO DIE	A3093.0A	
MOH	085,04	3093.0A	07	37147	4555	6256	TO END/TO DIE,DROWNED	A2985	
MOH	085,04	3093.1A	07	37147			TO END/TO DIE,DROWNED		
MOH	085,05	3106	08	35190	4412	5464	FOAM,SUDS		
MOH	085,11	3351	14	34134	4561	5018	DESERT,UNCONCERNED		
MOH	104,11	4069	15	00134	4562	5019	SICKNESS,DISTRESS		
MOH	112,05	8934	10	15690			PIECES OF BROKEN ROCK		
MOH	112,11	4333.0A	16	00601	4543	1117	GRINDSTONE		
MOH	115,05	4438	10	25990	4550	5470	FEED A HORSE WITH GRAIN,HORSE FEED		
MOH	120,15	4954	21	26914	4387	0252	CORD,BIND		
MOH	130,05	9115	09	73232	4382	5655	PULSE,MOUNTAIN RANGE	5181	
MOH	130,06	5181	10	72232	4382	5805	PULSE,MOUNTAIN RANGE	9115	
MOH	130,11	5229	15	74234	4563	5014	MEMBRANE		
MOH	140,05	5406	09	44904	4551	5473	JASMINE		
MOH	140,07	5459	11	44430	4557	5009	THERE IS NONE WHO,DO NOT		
MOH	143,06	5884	12	22132	4382	5804	PULSE	A5181	
MOH	145,05	5920.0A	10	35290	4552	5467	GIRDLE/BRASSIERE		
MOH	153,06	6289	13	21260	4380	1690	NAME OF A WILD TRIBE,SILENT		
MOH	153,06	6288.0B	13	27264	2127		NAME OF A WILD TRIBE,SILENT	6289	
MOH	153,11	629A	18	24234	4384		TAPIR		
MOH	163,11	9409	14	47427			(SURNAME)		
MOH	170,06	7099	09	71260	4381	1689	RAISED PATH,STREET		
MOH	173,10	7210	18	10232	4383		DRIZZLING RAIN,SHOWERED WITH FAVORS		
MOH	177,05	9555	14	45590	4553	5468	SOCKS/STOCKINGS,NAME OF A TRIBE		
MOH	187,11	7513	21	44327	4385	4712	LEAP ON OR OVER,SUDDENLY		
MOH	195,05	7628	16	25390			(SALT-WATER FISH)		
MOH	199,00	7796.0A	11	40207	4379	6428	WHEAT,(SURNAME)		
MOH	203,04	7817	16	63334	4388	5086	SILENT,WRITE FROM MEMORY		
MOU	009,06	0177	08	23250	4567	2535	SIMILAR/COMPARABLE/EQUAL		
MOU	093,02	3664	06	23500	4566	2533	TO MOO,USURP,BARLEY	G7799	
MOU	109,06	4188	11	63050	4568	2534	PUPIL OF THE EYE		
MOU	120,11	4924	17	27922	4538	4213	TO WIND ROUND		

勿
歿
没
没
沫
漠
摸
硃
磨
秣
繆
脉
脈
膜
茉
莫
蚥
袜
貊
貉
貘
鄚
陌
霢
靺
鶩
鮇
麥
默
侔
牟
眸
繆

ROM	RAD	TEL	TOT	FC	MAT	OSH	TAG	CR	CHAR
MOU	142,06	5750	12	53150	4569	2537	MARINE CRAB		蛑
MOU	149,09	6180	16	04694	4578	5301	TO PLAN/SEEK		謀
MOU	167,09	9482	17	18109	4573	0381	IRON POT,METAL CAP		鍪
MOU	199,06	7799	17	43405	4566	2536	BARLEY	C3664	麰
MOOU	028,00	0635.0A	02	23700		8816	A CERTAIN	2673	厶
MOOU	075,05	2613	09	44904	4577	5300	A CERTAIN	0635.0A	某
MOOU	075,09	8574.0A	13	44990		5270	CYDONIA JAPONICA		楙
MOOU	093,03	3665.0A	07	24510	4576	0148	MALE		牡
MOOU	102,02	3965.1A	07	00600			(MEASURE-ABOUT1/6 ACRE)		亩
MOOU	102,04	3965.2A	09	02630	4579		(MEASURE-ABOUT1/6 ACRE)		畆
MOOU	102,05	3965.0A	10	07630	4579	4974	(MEASURE-ABOUT1/6 ACRE)		畝
MOW	061,13	2021.0A	17	44339	4575	8654	EXERT THE MIND,BE GREAT		懋
MOW	072,09	8515	13	18604			TO GET GIDDY/DAZZLED		瞀
MU	064,11	2308.0A	15	44502	4588	3351	IMITATE/COPY		摹
MU	075,11	2875.0A	15	44934	4590	5015	MOLD/FORM		模
MUU	038,05	1191	08	47450	4583	4874	GOVERNESS	8281	姆
MUU	038,06	1209.0A	09	44411	4583	7172	GOVERNESS,OLD WOMAN	A1191	姥
MUU	038,07	8281	10	48457			GOVERNESS	1191	娒
MUU	064,05	2136	08	57050	4584	4873	THUMB	9114	拇
MUU	080,01	3018	05	77500	4582	4871	MOTHER,FEMALE		母
MUU	093,03	3665	07	24510	4576	0148	MALE		牡
MUU	093,05	3688	09	27550			(BOVINE)		牳
MUU	102,02	3965.1	07	00600			(MEASURE-ABOUT1/6 ACRE)		亩
MUU	102,04	3965.2	09	02630		8817	(MEASURE-ABOUT1/6 ACRE)		畆
MUU	102,05	3965	10	07630		4974	(MEASURE-ABOUT1/6 ACRE)		畝
MUU	102,07	3977	12	68057			(MEASURE-ABOUT 1/6 ACRE)	3965	晦
MUU	130,05	9114	09	77250			THUMB	2136	胟
MUH	019,11	0527	13	44427	4585	4863	CANVASS FOR CONTRIBUTIONS		募
MUH	032,11	1045	14	44104	4586	0214	TOMB		墓
MUH	050,11	1612	14	44227	4559	3994	STAGE CURTAIN,TENT		幕
MUH	061,11	1970	15	44333	4587	8520	ADMIRE		慕
MUH	072,11	2550	15	44603	4589	1581	SUNSET,EVENING		暮
MUH	075,00	2606	04	40900	4593	5262	WOOD,TREE		木

ROM	RAD	TEL	TOT	FC	MAT	OSH	TAG	CR	CHAR
MUH	075,09	2805	13	18904			ORNAMENTS ON CHARIOT-SHAFT		桼
MUH	085,04	3092	07	34190	4594	5279	BATHE/CLEANSE,RECEIVE FAVORS		沐
MUH	093,04	3668	08	28540	4599	6322	SHEPHERD		牧
MUH	109,00	4158	05	60000	4596	1693	EYE,ITEM		目
MUH	109,08	4207	13	64014	4600	0237	FRIENDLY		睦
MUH	115,11	4476	16	26922	4601	4229	(SURNAME),SOLEMN		穆
MUH	140,05	5382	09	44600	4597	1714	CLOVER		苜
MUH	167,05	9453	13	86100	4598	1694	MOLYBDENUM		鉬
MUH	173,07	7195	15	10194	4595	5280	FINE RAIN,DRIZZLE		霂
MUH	196,09	7726.0A	20	18327	4602	4683	DUCK		鶩
NA	064,05	2144	09	47502	4603	3357	TAKE/APPREHEND	2169	拏
NA	064,06	2150	10	46502	4603	3338	TAKE,APPREHEND	2169	挐
NA	064,06	2169	10	80502	4603	3339	TAKE,APPREHEND	2144	拿
NA	167,10	6014	18	88152			NEPTUNIUM		錼
NAA	030,07	0763	10	67027		2228	WHICH ,HOW	6719.0B	哪
NAA	163,04	6719.0B	07	17527	4604	2227	WHICH/HOW	0763	那
NAH	030,04	0704	07	64027	4609	4047	BATTLE CRY	A6077	吶
NAH	064,08	2205	11	54091	4606	8384	PRESS DOWN FIRMLY		捺
NAH	075,07	273D	11	47927			PODOCARPUS NAGEIA		梛
NAH	120,04	4780	10	24927	4607	4052	TO PAY(TAX ETC.),TO ACCEPT		納
NAH	130,04	514F	08	74227		4050	CASTOR		肭
NAH	140,10	554D	14	44327			IMPATIENS BALSAMINA		蒳
NAH	145,04	5906	09	34227	4608	4049	TO LINE,CASSOCK		衲
NAH	149,04	6077	11	04627	4609	4048	BATTLE CRY,SPEAK CAUTIOUSLY	A0704	訥
NAH	159,04	9360	11	54027	4610		INNER REINS OF A 4-HORSE TEAM		軜
NAH	163,04	6719	07	17527	4604	2227	THAT/THOSE		那
NAH	167,04	6871	12	84127	4611	4046	SODIUM		鈉
.NA	030,07	0763.0E	10	67027	4605	2228	(FINAL PART. PRECEDED BY N)		哪
NAE	004,01	0035	02	17227	4612	4719	THEREUPON		乃
NAE	030,07	0763.0B	10	67027			WHICH(FOLLOWED BY AN. OR NMR.)		哪
NAE	038,02	1168	05	47427	4613	4724	BREAST,MILK,LADY	1248	奶
NAE	038,05	1248	08	47492	4613	8437	MILK,BREAST,LADY	1168	妳
NAE	038,14	1302	17	41427	4613	4034	MILK,BREAST,LADY	1168	嬭

ROM	RAD	TEL	TOT	FC	MAT	OSH	TAG	CR	CHAR
NAE	054,06	1698	09	11400	4612	6811	THEREUPON	0035	迺
NAE	084,02	6036	06	80217		7809	NEON		氖
NAE	162,06	6621	10	31306	4612	6638	THEREUPON	0035	迺
NAY	037,05	1143	08	40901	4615	8383	HOW CAN ONE HELP	B2690	奈
NAY	075,05	2690	09	40901	4615	8385	CRAB-APPLE,HOW CAN ONE HELP	D1143	柰
NAY	126,03	5082	09	14200	4616	3214	ENDURE,PATIENT		耐
NAY	140,08	6055	12	44901			NAPHTHALENE		萘
NAY	142,10	579C	16	21136			ERISTALIS TENAX		蟹
NAY	145,10	5975	15	31211	4617	7187	SUN HAT,IGNORANT		襶
NAY	206,02	7845	15	17221	4614	2856	INCENSE TRIPOD		鼐
NHAN	031,03	8189	06	60404	4618	1932	DAUGHTER(WU DIAL.)		囡
NHAN	031,03	8188.0A	06	60407	0823	1880	CHILD(WU DIAL.)		囝
NAN	024,07	0589	09	40227	4620	3917	SOUTH		南
NAN	030,09	0809	12	63027	4621	3918	MUMBLE IN REPETITION	6177	喃
NAN	072,09	8516	13	64027			NAME OF A COUNTRY		晴
NAN	075,04	8538	08	47950	4622	4108	MACHILUS NANMU	2809	枏
NAN	075,05	2684	09	45947			MACHILUS NANMU	2809	柟
NAN	075,09	2809	13	44927	4622	3922	MACHILUS NANMU	8538	楠
NAN	102,02	3948	07	60427	4619	4845	MALE		男
NAN	142,09	5813.0A	15	54127	4623		IMMATURE LOCUSTS		蝻
NAN	149,09	6177	16	04627	4621	3987	MUMBLE IN REPETITION	0809	諵
NAN	172,02	7181.1	10	70414	4625	0905	DIFFICULT		难
NAN	172,11	7181	19	40514	4625	0897	DIFFICULT,NOT GOOD		難
NAAN	061,19	8408	23	40331	4626	8556	STAND IN AWE		戁
NAAN	142,09	5813	15	54127		3923	IMMATURE LOCUSTS		蝻
NAAN	155,04	6377	11	47347	4624	6101	BLUSH		赧
NANN	172,02	7181.1A	10	70414	4625	0905	DISTRESS,DISASTER		难
NANN	172,11	7181.0A	19	40514	4625	0897	DISTRESS,DISASTER,TO SCOLD		難
NANG	030,19	0926	22	50732	4627	5857	SACK		囊
NAANG	072,17	2571	21	60732	4633	5855	IN FORMER TIMES		曩
NANQ	085,22	3292	25	35132	4631	5860	MUDDY		瀼
NAU	030,05	0726	08	67040	4634	6095	CLAMOR		呶
NAU	046,07	8335	10	47272			NAME OF A MOUNTAIN		猺

ROM	RAD	TEL	TOT	FC	MAT	OSH	TAG	CR	CHAR
NAU	064,12	2321	15	54011	4639	7495	TO SCRATCH		撓
NAU	075,12	2889	16	44911	3087	7497	OAR		橈
NAU	094,09	3733	12	47294	4642	5357	(MONKEY),SCRATCH		猱
NAU	112,06	6257.1	11	16600		1936	SAL-AMMONIAC		硇
NAU	112,07	6257	12	16600			SAL-AMMONIAC		碯
NAU	149,05	9285	12	07640			CLAMOR	0726	詉
NAU	167,12	6984	20	84111	4641	7486	BIG CYMBALS		鐃
NAO	061,06	1925.1	09	90072			GET MAD		恼
NAO	061,09	1925	12	92072	4635	1940	GET MAD		惱
NAO	096,09	3839	13	12162	4637	1938	AGATE	4313	瑙
NAO	112,09	4313	14	12662	4637	1939	AGATE	3839	磠
NAO	130,06	5207.1	10	70272			BRAIN		脑
NAO	130,09	5207	13	72262	4638	1941	BRAIN		腦
NAW	085,08	8681	11	31146	4645	2309	SLUSH/MUD,(SURNAME)		淖
NAW	130,14	9140	18	71227	4647	3771	SHOULDER BLADE,FRONT LEGS OF ANIMAL		臑
NAW	169,05	9527	13	77227	4646	3495	MAKE NOISE OR DISTURBANCE	7593	閙
NAW	191,05	7593	15	77227	4646	3429	MAKE NOISE OR DISTURBANCE	9527	鬧
NEH	149,04	6077.0A	11	04627	4609	4048	LARGE,SPEAK CAUTIOUSLY		訥
NEH	195,04	762D	15	24327			GUITAR-FISH		魶
.NE	030,04	0704.0A	07	64027	4609	4047	(FINAL PART.)	0716	呐
.NE	030,05	0716	08	67011	4656	7160	(FINAL PART.)	0704.0A	呢
.NE	030,07	0763.0D	10	67027			(FINAL PART. FOR CONTINUED STATE)	0716	哪
NEEI	030,07	0763.0A	10	67027			WHICH (FOLLOWED BY AN. OR NMR.)		哪
NEEI	163,04	6719.0C	07	17527	4604	2227	WHICH ONE		那
NEEI	184,07	7407	15	82744	4767	9065	HUNGRY		餒
NEEI	184,08	7407.1	16	82744	4767	9045	HUNGRY		餧
NEY	011,02	0355	04	40227	4766	4045	INTERIOR		內
NEY	084,04	8635	08	80217		7807	NEON		氖
NEY	163,04	6719.0A	07	17527	4604	2227	THAT/THOSE		那
NEE(M)	030,07	0763.0C	10	67027			IN WHAT MANNER		哪
NE(MM)	163,04	6719.0D	07	17527			SO/THUS		那
NENN	038,11	1282.0A	14	4844	4765	6389	TENDER		嫩
NENG	130,06	5174	10	21211	4648	7186	ABLE/CAN,ENERGY		能

ROM	RAD	TEL	TOT	FC	MAT/	OSH	TAG	CR	CHAR
NENG	130,06	5174.1	10	25230			ABLE/CAN,ENERGY		觥
NENG	130,13	5240.0A	17	75232	4773	5787	PUS		膿
NENQ	055,04	1702.0A	07	10441	4278	2795	TOY WITH,FIX		弄
NHI	030,05	0716.0A	08	67011			(FINAL PART.)		呢
NI	009,08	0242	10	27217	4662	7534	(SURNAME)		倪
NI	030,05	0716.0B	08	67011	4656	7160	WOOLEN MATERIAL		呢
NI	032,05	0983	08	47111	4660	7158	MUD	3136	坭
NI	032,08	8228	11	47117			PARAPET/BATTLEMENT		堄
NI	038,05	1200	08	47411	4657	7165	SLAVE GIRL		妮
NI	044,02	1441	05	77211	4654	7157	BUDDHIST NUN		尼
NI	061,05	1842	08	97011	4658	7162	BLUSH		怩
NI	085,05	3136	08	37111	4660	7166	MUD	0983	泥
NI	094,08	3722	11	47217	4663	7536	LION,(MYTHICAL ANIMAL)		猊
NI	140,05	537C	09	44211			ACENAPTHENE		苊
NI	142,08	9224	14	56110		7541	RAINBOW,JAPANESE CICADA	A7206	蜺
NI	159,08	6536	15	57017	4665	7535	CLAMPS FOR CROSSBAR OF CARRIAGE		輗
NI	163,08	9396	11	27227			PLACE NAME		郳
NI	167,05	6281	13	87111		7159	NIOBIUM		鈮
NI	173,08	7206	16	10217	4666	7542	RAINBOW	A9224	霓
NI	195,08	7646	19	27317	4667	7540	CRYPTOBRANCHUS JAPONICUS,SALAMANDER		鯢
NI	198,08	7783	19	00217	4668	7543	FAWN		麑
NII	009,05	0132	07	27292	4649	8435	YOU		你
NII	009,14	0323	16	27281		6034	EMULATE/IMITATE,DOUBTFUL/SUSPICIOUS		儗
NII	064,04	2362.1	07	58000		7986	PLAN TO		拟
NII	064,14	2362	17	57081	4672	6035	PLAN TO		擬
NII	070,07	2459	11	08211	4661	7167	FLUTTERING OF FLAGS		旎
NII	075,05	8544	09	47914	4659		(TREE),TO STOP		柅
NII	113,14	4410	18	31227	4651	4035	TEMPLE OF DECEASED FATHER		禰
NII	140,14	5656	18	44481			LUXURIANT(OF PLANTS)		薿
NIH	023,09	0574	11	71716	4678	0803	TO HIDE		匿
NIH	046,14	1544.0A	17	22481	4671	6038	LOFTY,STEEP		嶷
NIH	061,08	1905	12	27334	4653	8664	FAMISHED,DISTRESSED		惄
NIH	072,05	2511	09	67011	4680	7161	FAMILIAR,TO APPROACH	2551	昵

ROM	RAD	TEL	TOT	FC	MAT	OSH	TAG	CR	CHAR
NIH	072,11	2551	15	61016	4680	0804	FAMILIAR,TO APPROACH	2511	暱
NIH	085,05	3136.0A	08	37111	4660	7166	RESTRAINED		泥
NIH	085,10	3312	13	37127	4652	4750	DROWN		溺
NIH	109,08	4194	13	67017	4664	7533	LOOK ASKANCE		睨
NIH	130,12	5232	16	73240	4673	6886	GREASY,TIRED OF		膩
NIH	142,11	584B	17	10136			TINGIS PYRIOIDES		蟗
NIH	145,04	5909	09	36200	4670	1496	WOMEN'S UNDERGARMENTS		衵
NIH	162,06	6627	10	38304	4677	6708	GO AGAINST/REBEL		逆
NHIAN	140,11	5576	15	44327	7332	4585	FADE/WITHER		蔫
NIAN	051,03	1628	06	80500	4711	2590	YEAR		年
NIAN	064,05	2138	08	51060	4712	1270	PICK UP WITH FINGERS		拈
NIAN	119,05	4724	11	91960	0129	1272	STICKY	7811	粘
NIAN	195,05	7630	16	21360	4713	1276	CATFISH,PARASILURUS ASOTUS		鮎
NIAN	202,05	7811	17	21160	4714	1273	STICKY	4724	黏
NEAN	064,05	2138.0A	08	51060	4712	1270	TWIRL (IN THE FINGERS)	2214	拈
NEAN	064,08	2214	11	58032	4696	8620	TWIRL(IN THE FINGERS)	2138.0A	捻
NEAN	064,12	2324	15	53033	4715	8792	TWIRL(IN THE FINGERS)	2138.0A	撚
NEAN	064,15	2365	18	55056	4721	2668	EXPEL		攆
NEAN	085,07	8679	10	37132			MUDDY WATER		涊
NEAN	085,08	3233	11	38132			CALM WATER		淰
NEAN	112,10	4317	15	17632	4719	5771	STONE ROLLER	B6558.0A	碾
NEAN	120,08	9157.1	14	28932	4717		CAULK		綩
NEAN	137,08	9157	14	28432	4717		CAULK		艌
NEAN	159,08	6542	15	55506	4720	2667	EMPEROR'S CARRIAGE		輦
NEAN	159,10	6558.0A	17	57032	0141	5773	CRUSH BY ROLLING,STONE ROLLER	D4317	輾
NIANN	024,01	0579	03	44000	4710	2793	TWENTY	1700	廿
NIANN	030,08	0911	11	68032		8618	READ ALOUD	A1819	唸
NIANN	032,08	1036	11	48132		8617	DIKE		埝
NIANN	055,00	1700	03	44770	4710	1033	TWENTY	0579	廿
NIANN	061,04	1819	08	80332	4716	8616	READ ALOUD,THINK	A0911	念
NIANN	120,08	9157.1A	14	28932	4717		TOWROPE		綩
NIANN	137,08	9157.0A	14	28432	4717		TOWROPE		艌
NIANN	195,09	7664	20	28332			SHEATFISH/WELS		鯰

ROM	RAD	TEL	TOT	FC	MAT	OSH	TAG	CR	CHAR
NHIANG	038,07	1224.0A	10	43432			AUNT (FATHER'S SISTER OR COUSIN)		娘
NIANG	038,07	1224	10	43432	4683	5924	YOUNG LADY,MOTHER	E8304	娘
NIANG	038,17	8304	20	40432	4684	5853	TROUBLED,MOTHER	E1224	孃
NIANQ	164,07	6840.1	14	13632			FERMENT/BREW		酿
NIANQ	164,17	6840	24	10632	4685	5847	FERMENT/BREW		釀
NEAU	038,10	1272	13	47427	4687	4749	GRACEFUL,DELICATE	5934	娲
NEAU	038,13	8303	16	47432		5824	GRACEFUL,DELICATE	1272	嬝
NEAU	038,14	1303	17	66427	4691	4847	TEASE/DISTURB		嬲
NEAU	140,11	5596	15	44327	4689	4676	GROSSULARIACEAE		蔦
NEAU	145,07	5934	13	27732	4690	5822	GRACEFUL,DELICATE	1272	裊
NEAU	196,00	7680	11	27327	4688	4599	BIRD		鳥
NIAW	044,04	1443	07	77232	4686	5641	URINE	3312.0A	尿
NIAW	085,10	3312.0A	13	37127	4652	4750	URINATE/URINE	1443.0A	溺
NIAW	130,07	6295	11	77232			UREA		脲
NHIE	064,08	2214.0A	11	58032	4696	8620	PINCH		捻
NHIE	064,09	2250	12	57012	4693	0110	PINCH WITH FINGERS		揑
NIE	064,07	8430	10	56014			(SURNAME)		捏
NIEH	030,15	0909	18	61072		0984	GNAW	0929	嚙
NIEH	030,18	0922	21	61041	4706	2724	MOVE THE MOUTH AS IN SPEAKING		囁
NIEH	030,21	0929	24	67072	4704	0986	GNAW	0909	齧
NIEH	039,16	1333	19	20407	4701	3143	CONSEQUENCE OF SIN	5642	孽
NIEH	039,16	5642	20	44407	4701	3142	CONSEQUENCE OF SIN	1333	孼
NIEH	064,10	2378.1A	13	51047			PEACEFUL/PEACE		捻
NIEH	064,18	2378.0A	21	51041	5710	2726	PEACEFUL/PEACE		攝
NIEH	066,08	8489	12	88340			TO FILL UP OR COVER UP A HOLE		敜
NIEH	075,16	2930	20	20904	4702	5345	SHOOTS FROM AN OLD STUMP	5649	櫱
NIEH	085,09	3206	12	37111	4694	0111	BLACKEN		涅
NIEH	119,17	4758	23	44904	4703	5447	FERMENTING GRAIN,SPROUTING GRAIN		糱
NIEH	128,12	5119	18	10141	4705	2721	(SURNAME),WHISPER		聶
NIEH	132,04	5262	10	26904	4697	5328	PROVINCIAL JUDGE		臬
NIEH	132,10	5265	16	27912	4700	7226	TOTTERING/UNSTEADY		臲
NIEH	140,17	5649	21	44904	4702	5344	SHOOTS FROM AN OLD STUMP	2930	蘖
NIEH	157,18	6495	25	61141	4707	2723	TREAD,STEP,CHASE		躡
NIEH	167,10	7015.1	18	81147			FORCEPS,TO NIP		鎳

ROM	RAD	TEL	TOT	FC	MAT	OSH	TAG	CR	CHAR
NIEH	167,10	6996	18	86194	4698	5329	NICKEL		鎳
NIEH	167,18	7015	26	81141	4708	2722	FORCEPS,TO NIP		鑷
NIEH	169,10	9529	18	77904		3505	VERTICAL DIVIDER OF A DOOR WAY		闑
NIEH	170,09	7129	12	77211	4695	0109	DANGEROUS		陧
NIEH	181,18	736B	27	11186	4709	8267	TEMPORAL BONES		顳
NIEH	211,06	7884	21	57772	4704	0985	GNAW,(SURNAME)	A0929	齧
NIN	061,07	1849	11	27339	4722	8689	YOU (HON.)		您
NING	015,14	0413	16	37181	4732	6036	CONGEAL		凝
NING	030,14	0905	17	63021	4727	2998	ENJOIN		嚀
NING	040,02	1337	05	30201			PEACEFUL,RATHER	1380	宁
NING	040,08	1380.3	11	30201	4725		PEACEFUL,RATHER		寧
NING	040,09	1380.2	12	30107	4725	0726	PEACEFUL,RATHER		甯
NING	040,09	3942	12	30447	4724	3713	PEACEFUL,RATHER	1380	寍
NING	040,10	1380.1	13	30201	4725		PEACEFUL,RATHER		寗
NING	040,10	3942.1	13	30447	4724		PEACEFUL,RATHER		寕
NING	040,11	1380	14	30201	4725	2997	PEACEFUL,RATHER	1337	寧
NING	064,14	2349	17	53021	4728	2999	WRING,TO PINCH		擰
NING	075,12	8597	16	43947			LEMON	2899	檸
NING	075,14	2899	18	43921	4729	3001	LEMON	8597	欞
NING	094,14	3761	17	43221	4731	3000	FIERCE-LOOKING		獰
NING	140,12	563B	16	44227			LIMONENE		薴
NIING	064,14	2349.0A	17	53021	4728	2999	TO TWIST,MISTAKE		擰
NINQ	009,05	0156	07	20244	4723	9001	ELOQUENT,TALENT		佞
NINQ	040,02	1337.0A	05	30201			PEACEFUL,RATHER		宁
NINQ	040,08	1380.3A	11	30201			RATHER		寧
NINQ	040,09	1380.2A	12	30107		0726	RATHER		甯
NINQ	040,09	3942.0A	12	30447		3713	PEACEFUL,RATHER		寍
NINQ	040,10	1380.1A	13	30201			RATHER		寗
NINQ	040,10	3942.1A	13	30447		4129	PEACEFUL,RATHER		寕
NINQ	040,11	1380.0A	14	30201		2997	RATHER		寧
NINQ	064,14	2349.0B	17	53021		2999	STUBBORN		擰
NINQ	085,12	3335	15	33147	4730	3002	MUDDY	3438	濘
NINQ	085,14	3438	17	33121	4730	3002	MUDDY	3335	濘

ROM	RAD	TEL	TOT	FC	MAT	OSH	TAG	CR	CHAR
NHIOU	038,04	1310	07	47410	4738	0541	LITTLE GIRL		妞
NIOU	093,00	3662	04	25000	4737	2412	OX/COW		牛
NEOU	061,04	1821	07	97012	4739	0536	BLUSH/BE SHY,ACCUSTOMED TO	D3694	忸
NEOU	064,04	2100	07	57010	4740	0537	WRING		扭
NEOU	075,04	8537	08	47910		0539	RED APRICOT,HANDCUFFS		杻
NEOU	094,04	3694	07	47215	4741	0538	ACCUSTOMED TO	B1821	狃
NEOU	120,04	4781	10	27915	4742	0540	BUTTON		紐
NEOU	167,04	6873	12	87115	4743	0534	BUTTON,(SURNAME)		鈕
NIOW	064,05	2112	08	54027	7272	4838	STUBBORN,CONTRARY	2152	拗
NIOW	064,05	2152	08	54027	7272	4838	STUBBORN/CONTRARY	2112	拗
NIOW	143,03	5882.0A	09	27120	4777	4317	BLEED AT THE NOSE,CHECK IN BATTLE	5880.0A	衄
NIOW	143,04	5880.0A	10	27115	4777	0535	BLEED AT THE NOSE,CHECK IN BATTLE	5882.0A	衂
NIOW	149,11	6208.0A	18	07622	4539	4207	ERRONEOUS,ABSURD		謬
NIUH	061,04	1821.0A	07	97012	4739	0536	BLUSH/BE SHY,ACCUSTOMED TO		忸
NEU	038,00	1166	03	40400	4776	8982	WOMAN,FEMALE		女
NEU	119,03	4719	09	94940	3143		CAKES OF RICE-FLOUR AND HONEY		粔
NEU	167,03	6381	11	84140			NEODYMIUM		釹
NIUH	061,06	1867	10	10332		8630	ASHAMED		恧
NIUH	143,03	5882	09	27120	4777	4317	BLEED AT THE NOSE,CHECK IN BATTLE	5880	衄
NIUH	143,04	5880	10	27115	4777	0535	BLEED AT THE NOSE,CHECK IN BATTLE	5882	衂
NIUEH	104,03	4061.1	08	00114			MALARIA		疟
NIUEH	104,09	4061	14	00114	4735	0858	MALARIA		瘧
NIUEH	141,03	5707	09	21214	4734	0085	OPPRESSIVE/TYRANNICAL		虐
NIUEH	149,09	6195	16	01614	4736	0857	RIDICULE,PLAY TRICKS ON		謔
NONG	009,13	0309	15	25232	4769	5784	YOU(SHANGHAI DIAL.)		儂
NONG	030,13	0901	16	65032	4770	5780	GARRULOUS		噥
NONG	040,04	6593.1	07	30732			AGRICULTURE		农
NONG	085,13	3426	16	35132	4771	5789	CONCENTRATED,DENSE	A6834	濃
NONG	104,13	4077	18	00132			PUS	5240	癑
NONG	115,13	4487	18	25932	4772	5788	THICKLY CLUSTERED(AS BLOSSOMS)		穠
NONG	130,13	5240	17	75232	4773	5787	PUS	4077	膿

ROM	RAD	TEL	TOT	FC	MAT	OSH	TAG	CR	CHAR
NONG	145,13	9264	18	35232		5785	WARM DRESS,BRIGHT LIGHT		襛
NONG	161,06	6593	13	55232	4768	5781	AGRICULTURE		農
NONG	161,08	6593.2	15	44232		5792	AGRICULTURE		辳
NONG	164,13	6834	20	15632	4774	5783	CONCENTRATED,STRONG WINE	A3426	醲
NONQ	055,04	1702	07	10441	4278	2795	TOY WITH,FIX		弄
NONQ	104,13	4077.0A	18	00132			ACHE,ILLNESS		癑
NOW	094,14	3754	17	41227			ANGRY DOG		獳
NOW	127,10	5097	16	51943	4752	3280	HOE		耨
NU	038,02	1167	05	47440	4753	6094	SLAVE		奴
NU	039,05	1325	08	47407	4756	3148	CHILD/OFFSPRING		孥
NU	050,05	1583.0A	08	47227	6123	3998	CHILD/OFFSPRING	1325	帑
NU	130,05	516D	11	47227			GRANULATION,E.G. PTERYGIUM		胬
NU	187,05	7466	15	47327	4762	4714	WORN OUT OLD HORSES		駑
NUU	019,05	0505	07	47427	4755	4865	EXERT		努
NUU	057,05	1722	08	47207	4757	4740	CROSS-BOW		弩
NUU	112,05	4279	10	47601	4760		FLINT		砮
NUH	061,05	1829	09	47334	4758	8665	INDIGNANT		怒
NUAN	200,09	7805	20	00269			FRAGRANT		麝
NOAN	072,09	2541	13	62047	4763	6118	WARM	3557	暖
NOAN	085,09	3557	13	92847	4763	6121	WARM	2541	煖
NOAN	184,09	9598	17	81734	4764	5042	SEND A PRESENT OF A FEAST		餪
NUENN	038,11	1282	14	48440		6389	TENDER		嫩
NUO	038,07	1226	10	47427	4745	2230	ELEGANT/GRACEFUL		娜
NUO	064,07	2186	10	52044	4749	9066	RUB,CRUMPLE		挼
NUO	064,07	2180	10	57027	4748	2229	TO SHIFT,MOVE		挪
NUO	064,08	2186.1	11	52044	4749	9046	RUB,CRUMPLE		捼
NUOO	038,07	1226.0A	10	47427	4745	2230	ELEGANT/GRACEFUL		娜
NUOH	009,19	8080	21	20214	4746	0898	EXORCISE DEMONS		儺
NUOH	030,09	0816.0A	12	64064	3093	1126	TO YES	A6179	喏
NUOH	061,14	2032	17	91027	4750	3766	TIMID,IMBECILE		懦
NUOH	064,10	2286	13	57027	4733	4748	TAKE HOLD		搦
NUOH	119,14	4754	20	91927	4751	3772	GLUTINOUS RICE		糯
NUOH	149,09	6179	16	04664	4747	1127	TO YES,TO PROMISE	A0816.0A	諾

ROM	RAD	TEL	TOT	FC	MAT	OSH	TAG	CR	CHAR
O	030,05	0725.0B	08	61020	2110	3040	(INTERJ.)		呵
O	030,07	0768	10	63050			OH, I SEE	0845.0B	哦
O	030,09	0845.0B	12	67014		0266	OH, I SEE	0768	喔
OR	030,07	0768.0A	10	63050	4780	6926	OH IS THAT SO		哦
OO	030,14	8179.0A	17	64047	2205	6149	(INTERJ. OF SURPRISE)		嘆
OU	023,02	0575.1A	04	71714		0787	(SURNAME),(ANCIENT VOLUME MEASURE)		区
OU	023,09	0575.0A	11	71716		0787	(SURNAME),(ANCIENT VOLUME MEASURE)		區
OU	030,08	086C	11	67082			(EXCLAMATION)		噢
OU	030,11	0868.0B	14	61016		0789	IRRITATE		嘔
OU	076,11	2962	15	77782	4817	4910	EUROPE		歐
OU	079,11	3016	15	77747	4818	6265	BRAWL		毆
OU	085,11	3371.0A	14	31116	4819	0802	BUBBLE,FROTH		漚
OU	098,11	3917	16	71717	4821	7927	BOWL/CUP		甌
OU	149,11	6209	18	01616	4823	0790	SING BALLADS,SONGS		謳
OU	196,11	7743	22	77727	4824	4605	COMMON GULL		鷗
OOU	009,09	0260	11	26227	4801	4089	PAIR/MATE,IMAGE,ACCIDENTAL	A5096	偶
OOU	030,11	0868	14	61016	4815	0789	VOMIT		嘔
OOU	127,09	5096	15	56927	4802	4091	PAIR/MATE/PLOUGHSHARE	A0260	耦
OOU	140,15	5665	19	44927	4803	4092	ROOT OF LOTUS		藕
OW	085,11	3371	14	31116	4819	0802	STEEP		漚
.OU	030,11	0868.0A	14	61016			(FINAL PART.)		嘔
PA	140,09	5518	13	44617	4840	7283	COROLLA OF FLOWER		葩
PA	157,02	640A	09	68100		6510	TO LIE ON ONE'S STOMACH		趴
PAR	064,02	2091.0A	05	58000	4853	6512	CLIMB,CRAWL,SNATCH	A3632	扒
PAR	075,04	2618	08	47917	4830	7291	LOQUAT		杷
PAR	087,04	3632	08	77231	4857	4981	CRAWL/CLIMB	A2091.0A	爬
PAR	096,08	3831	12	11717	4858	7298	(MUS. INSTR.)		琶
PAR	127,04	5090	10	57917	4835	7293	A RAKE		耙
PAR	157,04	9330	11	67117			TO SQUAT/CROUCH		跁
PAH	050,05	1584	08	46200	4855	1659	HANDKERCHIEF		帕
PAH	061,05	1830	08	96000	4856	1656	FEAR/BE AFRAID		怕
PAI	064,05	2143	08	56000	4986	1658	BEAT		拍
PAIR	009,08	0216	10	21211	4868	2776	VARIETY SHOW,NOT SERIOUS,IRRESOLUTE	G1780	俳

ROM	RAD	TEL	TOT	FC	MAT	OSH	TAG	CR	CHAR
PAIR	060,08	1780	11	21211	4869	2777	IRRESOLUTE	C0216	
PAIR	064,08	2226	11	51011	4870	2778	LINE UP,A PLATOON		
PAIR	075,08	8566	12	41911	4870A		RAFT,STERN OF JUNK,SHIELD	A4657	
PAIR	091,08	3654	12	26040	4871	2322	SIGNBOARD,GAME PIECES,CARDS		
PAIR	118,08	9014	14	88406			BAMBOO RAFT	4657	
PAIR	118,11	4657	17	88546		2325	BAMBOO RAFT	9023	
PAIR	118,12	9023	18	88246		2323	BAMBOO RAFT	4657	
PAE	064,08	2226.0A	11	51011		2778	ROW OF LOGS OR BOARDS		
PAY	030,09	081C	12	62032			(PHONETIC)/AS IN PIPERIDINE		
PAY	085,06	3175	09	32132	4873	5806	TO DISPATCH,CLIQUE/SCHOOL		
PAY	085,09	3269	12	31150	4874	2602	SOUND OF WAVES		
PAY	140,09	6397	13	44132			PINANE		
PAN	064,04	2104.0A	07	51047	4899	6109	PULL,CLIMB UP	2372	
PAN	064,15	2372	19	44502	4899	3352	PULL,CLIMB UP	2104.0A	
PAN	085,12	3382	15	32169	4907	1810	(SURNAME)		
PAN	102,07	3972.0A	12	20609	1790	1797	PLACE NAME,(SURNAME)		
PAN	109,04	8903	09	62047			SHOW THE WHITES OF EYES		
PARN	050,10	1609	13	27227			LARGE SCARF		
PARN	075,05	2628	09	49950			PLATE	A4149	
PARN	075,10	2857	14	27904	4902	5381	WOODEN TRAY,BIG		
PARN	108,06	4149.1	11	27107			PLATE,TO COIL		
PARN	108,10	4149	15	27107	4903	0710	PLATE,TO COIL		
PARN	112,10	4323	15	27601	4904	1115	ROCK,FIRM/STABLE		
PARN	112,12	4341	17	12669	4908	1802	NAME OF A RIVER IN SHENSI		
PARN	120,10	9070	16	27903			SMALL BAG/SACK		
PARN	142,12	5847	18	52169	4909	1809	TO COIL,TRICHINA SPIRALIS	B4149	
PARN	145,19	600A	25	34252		3353	LOOP		
PARN	157,11	6466.0A	18	64127	4328	4025	LIMP		
PARN	177,10	7270	19	27506		2630	LARGE BELT		
PANN	015,05	0398	07	39150			TO MELT	3140	
PANN	018,05	0445	07	92500	4893	2884	TO JUDGE		
PANN	029,07	0651	09	92547	4897	6110	REVOLT		
PANN	064,05	2155	08	53040	4898	2814	DISREGARD,REJECT		

徘
排
桖
算
簰
簰
排
咏
派
湃
蒎
扳
攀
潘
番
眅
幋
枰
槃
盘
盘
磐
磻
槃
蟠
襻
蹯
幋
泮
判
叛
拚

ROM	RAD	TEL	TOT	FC	MAT	OSH	TAG	CR	CHAR
PANN	085,05	3140	08	39150	4895	2511	MELT		
PANN	102,05	3961	10	69050	4896	2506	FIELD-PATH,BANK		
PANN	109,04	4162	09	68027	4906	4291	TO HOPE		
PANN	140,07	545A	11	44520			PERYLENE		
PANN	149,05	9286	12	09650			PLEASING/CLEVER TALK		
PANN	181,05	7323	14	91586			DISPERSE		
PANG	003,05	8004	06	72301	4925	7975	BANG(ONOMAT.)		
PANG	085,10	3316	13	30127	4930	4351	RUSHING(WATER)		
PANG	130,10	5218.0C	14	70227		4346	PUFFED(SWOLLEN)		
PARNG	009,10	0266	12	20227	4927	4342	BESIDE	A2460	
PARNG	027,07	8118	09	71212		7724	HUGE	1663	
PARNG	043,04	1430	07	42012		7723	STRIPED,SHAGGY DOG		
PARNG	053,07	1663	10	00212	4352	7725	HUGE	A1690	
PARNG	053,16	1690	19	00211		7332	HUGE,MIXED,(SURNAME)	7894	
PARNG	060,04	1762.0A	07	20227	1805	4326	IRRESOLUTE	1790	
PARNG	060,10	1790	13	20227	4929	4343	IRRESOLUTE	1762.0A	
PARNG	070,06	2460	10	00227	4926	4337	BESIDE,ONE SIDE,OTHER	A0266	
PARNG	130,10	5218.0A	14	70227	4931	4346	BLADDER		
PARNG	142,10	5824	16	50127	4932	4350	CRAB		
PARNG	162,06	6614	10	37305	4934	6660	(SURNAME)		
PARNG	173,04	7188	12	10227		4355	HEAVY FALL OF RAIN OR SNOW	7217	
PARNG	173,13	7217	21	10127		4352	HEAVY FALL OF RAIN OR SNOW	7188	
PARNG	212,02	7894	18	71211		7331	HUGE,MIXED,(SURNAME)	1690	
PAANG	127,10	6590	16	50927		4349	TO WEED		
PANQ	130,05	5160	09	79250	4936	2509	FAT		
PAU	064,04	2141	07	54012	4962	7914	THROW,ABANDON		
PAU	085,05	3133	08	37112		7275	PUFFED/SWOLLEN		
PAU	130,07	5193	11	72247	4961	3154	BLADDER		
PAUR	018,05	0442.0A	07	22700	4942	2964	TO DIG,ELIMINATE,TO QUESTION		
PAUR	020,09	0549	11	47212	4967	7270	BOTTLE-GOURD/LAGENARIA VULGARIS		
PAUR	030,05	0733	08	67012	4963	7262	TO ROAR		
PAUR	053,05	1647	08	00212	4964	7276	KITCHEN		
PAUR	086,05	3519	09	27331	4966	8808	TO ROAST		

ROM	RAD	TEL	TOT	FC	MAT	OSH	TAG	CR	CHAR
PAUR	087,05	3631	09	77231			TO PLANE/WHITTLE		爮
PAUR	094,05	6594	08	47212			(DEER)		狍
PAUR	145,05	5916	10	37212	4970	7266	GOWN(LINED)		袍
PAO	157,05	6410	12	67112	4971	7261	TO RUN		跑
PAW	085,05	3133.0A	08	37112	4965	7275	TO STEEP/SOAK		泡
PAW	086,05	3517	09	97812	4966	7272	FIRECRACKER,CANNON/GUN	D4276	炮
PAW	086,15	3615.0A	19	96832			FIRECRACKER		爆
PAW	104,05	6711	10	00112	4968	7277	PIMPLE		疱
PAW	107,05	6711.1	10	47212	4968	7273	PIMPLE		皰
PAW	112,05	4276	10	17617	4969	7263	GUN/CANNON	B3517	砲
PAW	112,16	4348	21	10648	4969	6535	GUN/CANNON	4276	礮
PEI	030,05	072A	08	61019			TO SPIT(IN CONTEMPT)		呸
PEI	032,05	0999.0A	08	41119		0075	UNBURNT EARTHENWARE		坯
PEI	064,05	2126	08	54047	5145	6240	THROW OVER THE SHOULDERS		披
PEI	075,05	8549	09	41919			TO HATE/BEAR GRUDGE		伾
PEI	130,04	9110	08	71290	5010	7980	FOETUS	5162	胚
PEI	130,05	5162	09	71219	5010	0077	FOETUS	9110	胚
PEI	164,08	6813	15	10661	5013	1241	UNSTRAINED SPIRITS		醅
PEIR	032,08	1014	11	40161	5011	1239	CULTIVATE		培
PEIR	096,08	382A	12	10161			BAKELITE		琣
PEIR	145,08	5952	14	11732	5018	5817	(SURNAME)		裴
PEIR	154,08	6341	15	60861	5012	1249	PAY DAMAGE,LOSE IN TRADE		賠
PEIR	163,05	6729	08	17127	5139	2154	HAPPY,ANCIENT PLACE NAME		邳
PEIR	167,08	6844	16	80161			BERKELIUM		錇
PEIR	170,08	7111	11	70261	5014	1244	KEEP ONE COMPANY		陪
PEY	009,06	0160	08	27210	5015	7826	WEAR(BELT/ETC.),TO RESPECT	B3805	佩
PEY	050,05	1592	08	44247	5144	3983	CAPE		帔
PEY	070,07	2465	11	08227	5022	4016	PENNANT,STREAMER		斾
PEY	085,05	3099	08	30127	5020	4013	COPIOUS/ABUNDANT		沛
PEY	096,06	3805	10	17110	5016	7825	GIRDLE ORNAMENTS,WEAR(BELT/ETC.)	D0160	珮
PEY	159,15	6576	22	22609	5024	1445	REINS,BRIDLE		轡
PEY	164,03	6792	10	17617	5019	7249	TO MATE,FIT TO		配
PEY	173,07	7198	15	10127	5021	4014	TORRENT OF RAIN		霈

ROM	RAD	TEL	TOT	FC	MAT	OSH	TAG	CR	CHAR
PEN	030,05	0899.1	08	64030	5036		TO SPOUT,TO PUFF		味
PEN	030,12	0899	15	64086	5036	8182	TO SPOUT,TO PUFF	2958	噴
PEN	076,12	2958	16	47882	5036	4962	TO SPOUT,TO PUFF	0899	歎
PEN	085,12	3409.0A	15	34186		8185	TO SPOUT,PUFF	0899	濆
PERN	085,09	3288	12	38117	5035	0697	NAME OF A RIVER,FLOWING OF WATER		溢
PERN	108,04	4133	09	80107	5034	0696	BASIN		盆
PENN	030,05	0899.1B	08	64030	5036		SNEEZE,FRAGRANT		味
PENN	030,12	0899.0B	15	64086	5036		FRAGRANT,SNEEZE		噴
PENN	076,12	2958.0A	16	47882	5036	4962	TO SPOUT,TO PUFF	0899.0B	歎
PENG	061,05	1839	08	91049	5049	2421	IMPULSIVE		怦
PENG	064,05	2125	08	51049	5050	2423	IMPEACH,ATTACK		抨
PENG	085,08	8683	11	37120	5308		SOUND OF WATER		湢
PENG	085,11	8704	14	32127	5059		NOISE OF DASHING WAVES		潷
PENG	086,07	3534	11	00332	5052	8788	CUISINE/COOKING		烹
PENG	112,05	4280	10	11649	5051	2419	SOUND OF CRASHING/THUNDER		砰
PERNG	030,12	088F	15	62022			(ONOMAT.)		嘭
PERNG	032,08	8229.0A	11	47120			TARGET IN ARCHERY		堋
PERNG	059,09	1756	12	42122	5060	4171	(SURNAME)		彭
PERNG	074,04	2590	08	77220	5054	3566	FRIEND		朋
PERNG	075,08	2766	12	47920	5055	3568	SHED		棚
PERNG	085,12	3403	15	32122	5061	4174	SOUND OF WAVES		澎
PERNG	112,08	4296	13	17620	5056	3567	BORON		硼
PERNG	118,11	4659	17	88304	5067	6664	SAIL		篷
PERNG	130,12	5191	16	72222	5062	4172	SWOLLEN		膨
PERNG	140,03	5338	07	44217	5065		LUXURIANT GROWTH		芃
PERNG	140,11	5570	15	44304	5068	6663	DISHEVELED,(GRASS)		蓬
PERNG	142,12	5846	18	42136			(LAND-CRAB)/GRAPSUS SP.		蟚
PERNG	142,12	5846.1	18	52122	5063	4173	(LAND-CRAB)/GRAPSUS SP.		蟛
PERNG	187,10	9621	20	70327			VIGOROUS(OF HORSE)		騯
PERNG	190,08	7577	18	72222	5057	3574	DISHEVELLED HAIR	7584	髯
PERNG	190,11	7584	21	72304			DISHEVELLED HAIR	7577	鬔
PERNG	196,08	7720	19	77227	5058	4631	LARGE FABULOUS BIRD		鵬
PEENG	064,08	2201	11	55053	5066	2497	HOLD OR OFFER WITH BOTH HANDS		捧

ROM	RAD	TEL	TOT	FC	MAT	OSH	TAG	CR	CHAR
PENQ	064,08	2267.1	11	58012			TO BUMP,MEET WITH		揌
PENQ	064,09	2267	12	58017	5064	0513	TO BUMP,MEET WITH	4314	搓
PENQ	085,05	3119	08	10232		5664	PUMP		泵
PENQ	112,09	4314	14	18617	5064	0511	TO BUMP,MEET WITH	2267	碰
PF	030,08	0803.0A	11	61011			(INTERJ.)		啡
PI	001,04	0012	05	10109	5137	0074	GRAND		丕
PI	009,05	8030	07	21219			POWERFUL,MULTITUDINOUS		伾
PI.	018,13	0490	15	70227	5174	4286	SPLIT OPEN		劈
PI	023,02	0572	04	71711	5170	0765	AN. FOR HORSES		匹
PI	032,05	0999	08	41119	5008	0075	UNBURNT EARTHENWARE		坯
PI	064,04	2106	07	51010	5151	7085	ACT ON,PASS ON,CRITICIZE		批
PI	064,05	2126.0A	08	54047	5145	6240	SEPARATE,SCATTER		披
PI	094,05	8797	08	41219		0078	PUPPY BADGER		狉
PI	112,04	4268	09	11610	5154	7082	ARSENIC	4321	砒
PI	112,10	4321	15	16611	5154		ARSENIC	4268	磇
PI	115,05	4437	10	21919	5009		(MILLET)		秠
PI	120,04	9055	10	21910	5155	7089	SPOILED SILK,ERROR/CARELESSNESS		紕
PI	167,10	6960	18	86111			KNIFE SHAPED LIKE ARROW-BARB		鈚
PI	173,13	7219	21	10641	5178	2455	CLAP OF THUNDER		霹
PI	187,05	9614	15	71319			(HORSE)		駓
PI	196,04	7688	15	77727	5171		WILD DUCK		鴄
PYI	030,08	0802	11	66040	5161	2316	BEER		啤
PYI	032,08	1020	11	46140	5162	2315	LOW WALL		埤
PYI	075,04	2657	08	41910	5152	7086	LOQUAT		枇
PYI	081,05	3027	09	60711	5158	7126	ADJOIN/BORDER	3026	毗
PYI	081,05	3026	09	61010	5158	7083	ADJOIN/BORDER	3027	毗
PYI	096,08	3832	12	11711	5157	7094	(MUS. INSTR.)		琵
PYI	104,05	4006	10	00147	5146	6251	WEARY		疲
PYI	107,00	4122	05	40247	5142	6226	SKIN,LEATHER		皮
PYI	120,04	9055.0A	10	21910	5155	7089	TASSELS/SILK FRINGES		紕
PYI	122,14	5013	19	60331	5166	8806	(BEAR)		羆
PYI	130,08	5196	12	76240	5164	2326	SPLEEN		脾
PYI	140,04	9167	08	44711			MALVA SYLVESTRIS		芘

ROM	RAD	TEL	TOT	FC	MAT	OSH	TAG	CR	CHAR
PYI	142,08	7023	14	56140			(INSECT),EGG OF MANTIS		蜱
PYI	145,08	5947.0A	13	36240	5072	2320	SMALL,ASSISTANT,(SURNAME)		裨
PYI	153,10	6293	17	26211	5160	7127	(LEOPARD)		貔
PYI	163,08	9395	11	27427		2189	PLACE NAME		郫
PYI	167,05	9448	13	84147		6231	BERYLLIUM		鈹
PYI	170,05	7095	08	74247	5345	6238	RESERVOIR		陂
PYI	170,08	7116	11	76240	5165	2321	PARAPET		陴
PII	009,04	0113	06	21210	5149	7084	TO PART		仳
PII	018,13	0490.0A	15	70227	5174	4286	SPLIT IN TWO/DIVIDE		劈
PII	023,02	0572.0A	04	71711	5170	0765	BOLT(OF FABRIC),ORDINARY PERSON	A3988	匹
PII	030,04	0694.0A	07	10609	1902	1442	EVIL,CLOGGED		否
PII	030,16	8181	19	41669			GREAT,GREAT FORTUNE		噽
PII	032,03	0965	06	47117	5141	7246	DESTROYED,INJURE		圮
PII	053,02	1640	05	00211	5148	7155	PREPARE		庀
PII	103,00	3988	05	17801	5169	6024	A BOLT(OF CLOTH)	A0572.0A	疋
PII	104,07	4028	12	00169	5140	1444	SWELLING OF THE LIVER		痞
PII	104,13	4075	18	00141	5176	2454	HABIT,HOBBY		癖
PII	140,04	535C	08	44711			PICENE		莅
PII	196,13	775A	24	20341			DABCHICK		鸊
PIH	009,13	0306	15	20241	5173	2451	SECLUDED,RUSTIC,LOW		僻
PIH	038,10	1274	13	46411	5159	7128	TO MATCH/TO PAIR		媲
PIH	044,04	1445	07	77211	5150	7093	TO BREAK WIND		屁
PIH	064,13	2352	16	50041	5114	2452	BEAT THE BREAST,SLIT OPEN		擗
PIH	085,08	8685	11	36140			LUXURIANT(OF WATER PLANTS)		淠
PIH	085,13	3437	16	30141	5175	2453	TO CLEAN,BLEACH		澼
PIH	085,14	3456	17	36146			SOUND OF WATER CRASHING		濞
PIH	098,13	3921	18	70717	5116	7940	GLAZED TILE		甓
PIH	149,13	6229	20	70601	5167	1163	GIVE AN EXAMPLE		譬
PIH	160,06	6582.0A	13	70641	5172	2449	OPEN UP,DISPEL	7075	辟
PIH	169,13	7075	21	77641	5177	3479	OPEN UP,DISPEL	6582.0A	闢
PIAN	009,09	0252	11	23227	5246	3781	ONE-SIDED		偏
PIAN	063,05	2078.0A	09	30227	5228	3778	SMALL BOAT,(SURNAME)		扁
PIAN	091,00	3651.0A	04	22021	5256	2853	DISC,SHEET		片

ROM	RAD	TEL	TOT	FC	MAT	OSH	TAG	CR	CHAR
PIAN	118,09	4638	15	88227	5248	3791	CHAPTER/ARTICLE		篇
PIAN	124,09	5055	15	37220	5249	3393	FLY FAST		翩
PIAN	130,09	520E	14	73227			METAPROTEIN		腷
PIAN	140,09	5506	13	44227		3790	POLYGONUM AVICULARE		萹
PYAN	009,07	0189.0A	09	21246	5224	6577	CHEAP,ADVANTAGEOUS		便
PYAN	075,09	2824	13	41946		6579	(TREE)		梗
PYAN	075,09	8577	13	43927			BASKET-COUCH IN COFFIN		楄
PYAN	096,08	3816	12	16140			(PEARL)		玤
PYAN	130,06	5173	10	78241	5254	2439	CALLOUS ON HAND OR FOOT		胼
PYAN	149,09	6163.0A	16	03627	5251	3780	SPECIOUS TALK		諞
PYAN	157,09	6450	16	63127	5252	3779	TO LIMP		蹁
PYAN	187,08	7478	18	78341			LITERARY STYLE		駢
PEAN	149,09	6163	16	03627	5251	3780	BRAG		諞
PIANN	060,09	1786.0A	12	23227	5230	3782	EVERYWHERE	A6664.0A	徧
PIANN	091,00	3651	04	22021	5256	2853	A SLICE/PIECE		片
PIANN	162,09	6664.0A	13	33302	5230	6692	EVERYWHERE,A TIME,TURN		遍
PIANN	187,09	7499	19	73327	5253	3784	DECEIVE/SWINDLE		騙
PIAU	030,11	8166	14	61091			PURINE		嘌
PIAU	085,11	3343	14	31191	5196	8365	DRIFT ABOUT		漂
PIAU	142,11	9237	17	51191	5203	8363	NEST OF EGGS OF MANTIS		螵
PIAU	182,11	7373	20	17910	5205	7835	TO FLOAT		飄
PIAU	182,11	7373.1	20	71219		7848	TO FLOAT		飍
PYAU	038,11	1276	14	41491	5195	8364	VISIT A PROSTITUTE		嫖
PYAU	097,11	3903	16	12930	5198	4994	DIPPER/LADLE		瓢
PYAU	140,14	9195	18	44191			(FLOATING WATER-PLANT)		藻
PEAU	064,11	2315.0A	14	51091	5179	8357	TO FALL		摽
PEAU	078,07	2993	11	12247	5191		DIE OF STARVATION	5457.0A	殍
PEAU	085,11	3343.0A	14	31191	5196	8365	TO BLEACH		漂
PEAU	106,11	4120	16	20631			WHITE		皫
PEAU	109,11	8918	16	61091	5200	8355	CAST A GLANCE		瞟
PEAU	120,11	4918.0A	17	21391	5201	8361	MISTY/INDISTINCT		縹
PEAU	140,07	5457.0A	11	44407	1940	3159	DIE OF STARVATION	2993	莩
PIAW	018,11	0484	13	12900	5194	2977	ROB		剽

ROM	RAD	TEL	TOT	FC	MAT	OSH	TAG	CR	CHAR
PIAW	019,11	8114	13	14927			SEIZE BY FORCE/TO PLUNDER		勡
PIAW	061,11	1969	14	91091			AGILE-BODIED		憳
PIAW	085,11	3343.0B	14	31191	5196	8365	ELEGANT,POLISHED		漂
PIAW	113,06	4384	11	10901	5192	8353	TICKET,BANK NOTE		票
PIAW	120,11	4918	17	21391	5201	8361	CLEAR BRIGHT COLOR		縹
PIAW	187,11	7516	21	71391	5206	8359	WHITE HORSE		驃
PIE	038,12	8297	15	98404			IRRITABLE,HASTY		嫳
PIE	064,12	2317	15	58040	5216	6358	CAST AWAY		撇
PIE	064,12	2317.1	16	98502	5216		CAST AWAY		撆
PIE	084,01	305A	05	80217			PROTIUM		氕
PIE	109,12	4224	17	98604	5218	1732	BLINK,GLANCE		瞥
PIEE	004,00	0033	01	20000	5215		DOWNSTROKE TO THE LEFT		丿
PIEE	064,12	2317.0A	15	58040	5216	6358	THROW		撇
PIEE	064,12	2317.1A	16	98502	5216		THROW		撆
PIEE	140,05	7154	09	44109		0080	BRASSICA CAMPESTRIS SUBSP. RAPA		苤
PIN	038,06	8280	09	48441	5297	2443	BE A MISTRESS OR LOVER		姘
PIN	038,08	8280.1	11	48441	5297	2443	BE A MISTRESS OR LOVER		姘
PIN	064,05	2155.0A	08	52043	4898	2814	STAKE ALL	D2210	拼
PIN	064,08	2178	11	58041	5294	2438	STAKE (ALL),PIECE TOGETHER	2210	拼
PIN	064,08	2210	11	58041	5294	2438	PIECE TOGETHER,STAKE ALL	2178	拼
PYN	030,16	0914	19	61086	5276	8280	KNIT THE BROWS	7360	嚬
PYN	038,14	1300	17	43486	5261	8198	VIRTUOUS WOMAN		嬪
PYN	140,16	5689.0A	20	44286	5278	8282	MARSILIACEAE		蘋
PYN	154,04	6302	11	80806	5274	8211	POOR		貧
PYN	181,07	7340	16	21286	5275	8279	FREQUENTLY/REPETITIOUS		頻
PYN	181,15	7360	24	21406	5276	2335	KNIT THE BROWS	0914	顰
PYN	186,14	9611	23	23686			DENSE FRAGRANT VAPOR		馪
PIIN	030,06	0756	09	60660	5281	1080	GRADE,CONDUCT,THING		品
PINN	093,02	3663	06	22510		7148	FEMALE		牝
PINN	128,07	5111	13	15127	5313	4542	ENGAGE(TEACHER),BETROTHED		聘
PING	004,05	8003	06	72201	5302	4169	BING(ONOMAT.)		乒
PING	009,07	8048	09	27227			FORLORN		俜
PING	038,07	1219	10	45427	5312	4544	GRACEFUL		娉

ROM	RAD	TEL	TOT	FC	MAT	OSH	TAG	CR	CHAR
PYNG	016,06	0417	08	22217	5309	7871	PROOF,LEAN AGAINST	1996	凭
PYNG	016,12	1996.1	14	31217	5310	7884	PROOF,LEAN AGAINST		憑
PYNG	032,05	0988	08	41149	5304	2418	A PLAIN		坪
PYNG	044,08	1456	11	77241	5298	2445	STANDING SCREEN		屏
PYNG	050,08	1594	11	48241		2440	SHELTER		帡
PYNG	050,09	8362	12	47241			STANDING SCREEN	1456	幈
PYNG	051,02	1627	05	10409	5303	2417	LEVEL		平
PYNG	061,12	1996	16	31332	5310	8644	PROOF,LEAN AGAINST	0417	憑
PYNG	075,05	2695	09	41949		2424	CHESS-LIKE GAME		枰
PYNG	085,05	3130	08	31149	4895	2511	SOUND OF WATER SPLASHING		泙
PYNG	085,06	8671	09	38141			WASH/BLEACH(FABRIC)		洴
PYNG	085,08	8671.1	11	38141	5300	2444	WASH/BLEACH(FABRIC)		淜
PYNG	096,05	8820	09	11149			(JADE)		玶
PYNG	098,08	3910	13	81417	5301	7931	VASE,BOTTLE,PITCHER	4973	瓶
PYNG	115,05	4439.0A	10	21949	0382	2425	BALANCE		秤
PYNG	121,06	4973	12	88741	5301	2435	VASE/BOTTLE/PITCHER	3910	缾
PYNG	140,05	5393	09	44409	5305	2426	(ARTEMISIA),DUCK WEED,APPLE	G5689	苹
PYNG	140,08	5493	12	44149		2427	DUCKWEED		萍
PYNG	140,08	548D	12	44441			IRIS ENSATA		荓
PYNG	140,16	5689	20	44286	5278	8282	APPLE	C5393	蘋
PYNG	142,05	574C	11	51149			LEPTUS/CHIGGER		蚲
PYNG	149,05	6097	12	01649	5306	2420	COMMENT ON,TO JUDGE		評
PYNG	159,08	6548	15	58041			CARRIAGE WITH SCREEN(FOR WOMEN)		軿
PYNG	195,05	763B	16	21349			PSEUDOPLEURONECLES OLIVACEUS		鮃
PYNG	208,05	785B	18	71712			ARVICOLA HATANEZUMI/VOLES		鼫
PINQ	128,07	5111.0A	13	15127	5313	4542	BETROTH		聘
PO	030,02	066A	05	63600			POR (AS IN PORPHIN)		卟
PO	032,05	0980	08	44147	5343	6229	SLOPE		坡
PO	085,12	3380	15	32147	5358	6291	TO SPILL,SPLASH		潑
PO	167,02	9437	10	83100			POLONIUM		釙
PO	167,05	7182	13	81116			PROMETHIUM		鉅
PO	170,05	7095.0A	08	74247	5345	6238	UNEVEN,RUGGED		陂
PO	181,05	7324	14	41286	5346	8297	UNEVEN/SLOPING,QUITE/RATHER		頗

ROM	RAD	TEL	TOT	FC	MAT	OSH	TAG	CR	CHAR
POR	038,08	1237	11	34404	5347	9052	MATRON,MOTHER-IN-LAW,GRANDMOTHER		婆
POR	106,12	4115	17	22669	5351	1803	WHITE		皤
POR	112,08	8949	13	34601			STONES FOR ARROWHEADS		碆
POR	163,12	6776	15	27627	5352	2184	NAME OF A LAKE		鄱
POO	030,02	0672	05	71716	5349	0786	NOT,THEREUPON	8315	叵
POO	041,05	8315	08	74700	5349		NOT,THEREUPON	0672	叵
POO	118,05	457A	11	88716	5350		FLAT BASKET-TRAY		筐
POO	181,05	7324.0A	14	41286	5346	8297	QUITE/RATHER		頗
POH	054,05	1695	08	16400	4982		COMPEL	6612	迫
POH	075,02	2613.0A	06	43900		1996	CELTIS SINENSIS VAR. JAPONICA		朴
POH	096,05	3789	09	16100	5348	1654	AMBER		珀
POH	112,05	4275	10	14647	5344	6234	BREAK/BROKEN		破
POH	119,05	4722	11	96900	5353	1662	GRAINS IN DISTILLED LIQUOR		粕
POH	162,05	6612	09	36300	4982	6630	COMPEL	1695	迫
POH	194,05	7611	15	26613	4988	7637	SOUL		魄
POU	018,08	0472	10	02600	5358		TO CUT		剖
POUR	064,04	2120	07	51090	5357	7979	TAKE UP IN BOTH HANDS	2221	杯
POUR	064,08	2221	11	50061	5359	1245	TAKE UP IN BOTH HANDS	2120	掊
POUR	145,07	5938	13	00732		5866	COLLECT		裒
POOU	018,08	0472.0A	10	02600	5358		BREAK UP	A2221.0A	剖
POOU	064,08	2221.0A	11	50061	5359	1245	BREAK UP,HIT	A0472.0A	掊
POOU	098,08	3916	13	01617	5361	7928	JAR/POT		瓿
PU	009,02	0091.0A	04	23200	1953	1993	FALL PROSTRATE		什
PU	030,12	086E	15	62034		5247	SOUND OF ESCAPING LAUGHTER/WATER		噗
PU	064,02	2090	05	53000	5402	1994	TO RUSH ON	2333	扑
PU	064,12	2333	15	52034	5402	5254	RUSH ON	2090	撲
PU	066,00	2391	04	21407	5399	6197	TO RAP/TO TAP		攴
PU	066,00	2391.1	04	80400	5399	6305	TO RAP/TO TAP		攵
PU	104,07	4030	12	00127		3743	SICK/DISABLED		痡
PU	167,07	6917.0A	15	83127	5396	3727	TO SPREAD		鋪
PWU	009,02	0091	04	23200			SERVANT	0295	什
PWU	009,12	0295	14	22234	5401	5249	SERVANT	0091.0A	僕
PWU	020,07	0548	09	27220	5388	4449	CRAWL/LIE PROSTRATE		匍

ROM	RAD	TEL	TOT	FC	MAT	OSH	TAG	CR	CHAR
PWU	050,12	8363	15	43234		5255	HOOD/TURBAN		幞
PWU	075,02	2613	06	43900	5354	1996	SIMPLE AND UNADORNED	2883	朴
PWU	075,12	2883	16	42934	5354	5256	SIMPLE AND UNADORNED	2613	樸
PWU	085,14	3450	17	32134	5383	5252	NAME OF A RIVER		濮
PWU	096,12	3877	16	12134	5355	5244	UNPOLISHED GEM		璞
PWU	130,07	5194.0A	11	73227	1944	3737	CHEST(THORAX)		脯
PWU	140,07	5455	11	44227	5393	3744	PLACE NAME		莆
PWU	140,08	5476	12	44601	5387	1251	BODHISATTVA		菩
PWU	140,09	5515	13	44227	5389	4450	GRAPES		葡
PWU	140,10	5543	14	44127	5392	3741	CALAMUS		蒲
PWU	140,10	5567	14	44527	5398	3736	SEDGES,GAMBLING-GAME		莆
PWU	142,12	584F	18	52134			PROMACHUS YESONICUS		蟆
PWU	145,12	9272.1	17	32234	5380	5253	HOOD/TURBAN,HEMLESS SKIRT		襆
PWU	145,14	9272	19	32234		5251	HOOD/TURBAN,HEMLESS SKIRT	A8363	襥
PWU	157,12	9349	19	62134	5381	5246	WEBBED FEET		蹼
PWU	164,07	6811	14	13627	5395	3731	DRINK HEAVILY,DRINK IN COMPANY		酺
PWU	167,12	7235	20	82134		5245	PROTOACTINIUM		鏷
PWU	195,07	764C	18	23327	5397		SKATE/RAY/BATOIDEI		鯆
PUU	031,07	0944	10	60227	5368	1885	GARDEN/ORCHARD		圃
PUU	032,07	1033	10	43127	5369	3726	PORT		埔
PUU	072,08	2528	12	80601	5384	1504	UNIVERSAL		普
PUU	082,12	7239	16	28716	5385	7398	THICK ROUGH SERGE FROM TIBET		氆
PUU	085,07	3184	10	33127	5390	3740	BEACH		浦
PUU	085,10	3302	13	33142	5391	3268	EXTENSIVE/PERVADING		溥
PUU	086,07	8739	11	93827			TO TRAVEL BY THE LIGHT OF TORCH		炻
PUU	149,13	6225	20	08661	5386	1505	LIST,CHART,SCORE(MUSIC)		譜
PUU	167,12	9506	20	88161			PRASEODYMIUM		錯
PUH	032,09	1027.0A	12	26104	4947	0219	STRONGHOLD		堡
PUH	072,15	2566	19	66032	5403	5679	TO SUN,TO AIR		曝
PUH	085,15	3462	18	36132	4959	5683	WATERFALL		瀑
PUH	135,09	5291	15	83627	5394	3729	A STORE	A6917	舖
PUH	167,07	6917	15	83127	5396	3727	STORE,AN FOR BED	A5291	鋪
PUH	208,12	785H	25	72713			RAT KANGAROO		鼺

ROM	RAD	TEL	TOT	FC	MAT	OSH	TAG	CR	CHAR
RAN	086,08	3544	12	23333	3072	8791	SO/THUS,-LY		然
RAN	086,12	3595	16	93833	3073	8793	BURN,COMBUSTION		燃
RAN	142,04	5744	10	57140	3069	4132	(SURNAME),BOA CONSTRICTOR		蚺
RAN	142,05	5744.1	11	55147	3069	4115	(SURNAME),BOA CONSTRICTOR		蚺
RAN	142,05	574A	11	55147	3069	4115	BOA CONSTRICTOR,PYTHON MOLURUS		蚺
RAN	190,05	7570	15	72447	3075	4127	WHISKERS,BEARD		髥
RAAN	013,03	0373	05	50447	3067	4114	(SURNAME),PASSING(OF TIME)	E5375	冉
RAAN	075,05	2676	09	34904	3071	5394	TO DYE		染
RAAN	124,05	504A	11	57020			DOWNY		翆
RAAN	140,05	5375	09	44447	3068	4126	LUXURIANT GROWTH,PASSING(OF TIME)	E0373	苒
RHANG	030,17	0924.0A	20	60032			TO SHOUT,BLURT OUT		嚷
RANG	019,17	0537	19	04727	3076	4824	HASTE		勷
RANG	064,17	2376	20	50032	3079	5849	TAKE BY FORCE,REJECT		攘
RANG	085,17	3475	20	30132	3080	5854	DEWY		瀼
RANG	097,17	3905	22	02730	3081	4993	PULP OF FRUIT		瓤
RANG	113,16	4412	20	30232	3082	3185	SACRIFICE FOR AVOIDING CALAMITY		禳
RANG	115,17	4492	22	20932	3083	5851	STALK OF GRAIN,ABUNDANT,(SURNAME)		穰
RAANG	030,17	0924	20	60032	3077	5845	TO SHOUT		嚷
RAANG	032,17	1099	20	40132	3078	5842	SOIL/EARTH		壤
RAANG	064,17	2376.0A	20	50032	3079	5849	THROW INTO CONFUSION		攘
RAANG	140,17	569B	21	44732	3084		GINGER		蘘
RANQ	149,03	6245.1	10	01610			YIELD		訕
RANQ	149,17	6245	24	00632	3085	5846	YIELD		讓
RAU	038,12	1290	15	44411	3086	7500	GRACEFUL		嬈
RAU	140,12	5609	16	44211	3089	7502	GRASS,FUEL		蕘
RAU	142,12	7455	18	54111	3090	7500	OXYURIS VERMICULARIS		蟯
RAU	184,12	7437	20	84711	3091	7494	TO SPARE,(SURNAME)		饒
RAO	038,12	1290.0A	15	44411	3086		DISTURBANCE		嬈
RAO	064,04	2371.1	07	53014			DISTURB		扰
RAO	064,15	2371	18	51047	3092	6480	DISTURB		擾
RAW	120,12	4935	18	24911	3088	7499	TO WIND(AROUND),GO AROUND	6691	繞
RAW	162,12	6691	16	34301	3088	6768	TO WIND(AROUND),GO AROUND	4935	遶
REE	030,09	0816	12	64064	3093	1126	TO SALUTE/MAKE ONE'S CURTSY		喏

ROM	RAD	TEL	TOT	FC	MAT	OSH	TAG	CR	CHAR
REE	061,09	1931	13	44336	3094	8561	ANNOY		惹
REH	086,06	3583.1	10	54331		8812	HOT(OF WEATHER),WARM UP		热
REH	086,08	8742	12	94827			TO BURN,HEAT	3616.0A	焫
REH	086,11	3583	15	44331	3095	8809	HOT(OF WEATHER),WARM UP		熱
REH	086,11	3583.2	15	44331	3095	8810	HOT(OF WEATHER),WARM UP		熱
REH	086,15	3616.0A	19	44331	3096		TO BURN,HEAT	8742	爇
REN	009,00	0086	02	80000	3097	4891	MAN/PERSON/PEOPLE		人
REN	009,02	0088	04	21210	3099	0003	HUMANE		仁
REN	010,00	0334.0B	02	22010	3098	7455	MAN		儿
REN	033,01	1103	04	20104	3100	0291	9TH HEAVEN'S STEM		壬
REEN	061,03	1804	07	17332	3112	8636	ENDURE		忍
REEN	115,08	4457	13	28932	3120	8622	RIPE GRAIN		稔
REEN	130,08	9129	12	78232			GOOD-TASTING,COOKED,BE SATIATED		腍
REEN	140,06	5432	10	44214	3105	0296	PERILLA OCIMOIDES,SOFT		荏
REEN	140,07	545B	11	44337			POLEMONIUM		葱
REEN	184,04	7387	12	82714	3108	0298	COOK THOROUGHLY		飪
RENN	009,03	0105	05	27220	3111	4306	(MEASURE)		仞
RENN	009,04	0117	06	22214	3101	0292	RESPONSIBILITY		任
RENN	018,01	0432	03	17320	3110	4304	EDGE OF BLADE		刃
RENN	018,01	0432.1	03	17440	3110	4316	EDGE OF BLADE		刄
RENN	038,04	1175	07	42414	3102	0300	BE PREGNANT	1206	妊
RENN	038,06	1206	09	42414	3102	0295	PREGNANT	1175	姙
RENN	061,06	1851	10	22331	3103	8540	IN THIS WAY		恁
RENN	075,09	2795.0A	13	44911			FRUIT OF MULBERRY	5513.0A	椹
RENN	093,03	3667	07	27520	3114	4307	TO STUFF,FILL UP		牣
RENN	120,03	4771	09	27940		4312	TO THREAD(NEEDLE),TO STRING		紉
RENN	120,04	4777	10	22914		0299	THREAD USED FOR WEAVING		紝
RENN	140,09	5513.0A	13	44711		0773	FRUIT OF MULBERRY	2795.0A	葚
RENN	145,04	5910	09	32214	3106	6561	OVERLAPPING PART OF CHINESE GOWN	5929	衽
RENN	145,06	5929	11	32214	3106	0293	OVERLAPPING PART OF CHINESE GOWN	5910	袵
RENN	149,02	6126.1	09	08600			RECOGNIZE,ADMIT		訒
RENN	149,03	6072	10	07620	3117	4305	SLOW IN SPEECH		訒
RENN	149,07	6126	14	07632	3113	8637	RECOGNIZE,ADMIT		認

ROM	RAD	TEL	TOT	FC	MAT	OSH	TAG	CR	CHAR
RENN	154,06	6324.0A	13	22806	3107	8108	TO VENT		賃
RENN	159,03	6514	10	57020	3118	4310	BRAKE		靭
RENN	177,03	7282.1	12	47520	3119	4309	PLIABLE BUT STRONG,ANNEALED		靭
RENN	178,03	7282	12	47520	3119	4308	PLIABLE BUT STRONG,ANNEALED		靭
RENN	196,06	7706	17	21327	3109	4669	HOOPOE		鵀
RHENG	064,02	2093	05	57027	3122	4722	THROW		扔
RENG	009,02	0095	04	27227	3121	4721	STILL		仍
RENG	113,02	4356	06	37227	3123	4723	BLESSINGS		祊
RENG	170,09	9534	12	71234		5043	SOUND OF STONEMASON'S SHOVEL		陾
REENG	064,02	2093.0A	05	57027	3122	4722	THROW		扔
RONG	040,07	1369	10	30608	7560	1389	COUNTENANCE,CONTAIN		容
RONG	046,14	1539	17	29794	7583	5336	LOFTY		嶸
RONG	062,02	2051	06	53400	3181	6968	WEAPON,(SURNAME)		戎
RONG	075,10	2827	14	45968	7561	1391	BANYON TREE/FICUS WIGHTIANA		榕
RONG	075,10	2837	14	99904	7582	5335	GLORY,HONORED		榮
RONG	082,07	3031	11	23715	3182	7404	DOWN,FELT		毧
RONG	085,10	3310	13	33168	7562	1393	DISSOLVE		溶
RONG	085,14	3484	17	39194	7584		EDDY		瀜
RONG	086,10	3579	14	93868	7564	1392	TO SMELT,FUSE	6954	熔
RONG	094,06	8799	09	43250			HAPALE JACCHUS		狨
RONG	096,10	8833	14	13168			GEM ORNAMENTS FOR BELTS		瑢
RONG	120,06	4823	12	23950	3183	6970	VELVET,WOOLEN		絨
RONG	123,06	5027	12	83550	3184		WOOL OF SHEEP		羢
RONG	130,03	9109	07	72222	7549		(SURNAME)		肜
RONG	140,06	5422	10	44401	3185	2735	LUXURIANT GROWTH,FLUFFY,CONFUSED		茸
RONG	140,10	5554	14	44608	7563	1394	LOTUS		蓉
RONG	142,10	5816	16	15236	7566	8901	MELT,MILD,HARMONIOUS		融
RONG	142,14	5828	20	54194			SALAMANDER		蠑
RONG	167,10	6954	18	83168	7564	1390	TO SMELT/FUSE	3579	鎔
ROONG	014,02	0383	04	37217	3180	7875	EXTRANEOUS	1340	冗
ROONG	040,02	1340	05	30217	3180	7880	EXTRANEOUS	0383	宂
ROONG	082,12	3040	16	12214	3186	7375	DOWN OR FINE HAIR	A5422.0A	氄
ROONG	140,06	5422.0A	10	44401	3185	2735	DOWN OR FINE HAIR,DENSE GROWTH	A3040	茸

271

ROM	RAD	TEL	TOT	FC	MAT	OSH	TAG	CR	CHAR
ROU	028,02	0636.0A	04	40731			TO TRAMPLE	6451	
ROU	064,09	2?48	12	57094	3134	5356	KNEAD,MASSAGE		
ROU	075,05	2677	09	17904	3133	5352	SOFT		
ROU	114,00	4415	05	40227	3132	4066	TRAMPLE	6451	
ROU	140,09	550A	13	44904			ELSHOLTRIA PALTRINI		
ROU	157,09	6451	16	67194	3135	5353	TRAMPLE	0636.0A	
ROU	159,09	6555	16	57094	3136	5355	WHEEL BAND		
ROU	177,09	7558	18	47594		5354	SUEDE/CHAMOIS,TO TAN,TANNIN		
ROOU	119,09	9041	15	97994	4744	5358	MIXED,ASSORTED		
ROW	130,00	5131	06	40227	3153	4057	FLESH/MEAT		
RU	009,14	0320	16	21227	3145	3767	SCHOLAR/CONFUCIAN		
RU	030,14	0906	17	61027	3146	3765	CHATTERING		
RU	038,03	1172	06	46400	3137	1096	AS,IF		
RU	039,14	1332	17	11427	3147	3769	CHILD,(SURNAME)		
RU	085,06	3168	09	36100	3138	1099	MARSHY		
RU	085,14	3446	17	31127	3149	3775	TO MOISTEN,DILATORY		
RU	118,06	4588	12	88463			THIN OUTSIDE SKIN OF BAMBOO		
RU	120,14	4948.0A	20	21927	2845	3773	FINE SILK		
RU	140,06	5423	10	44460	3139	1100	EAT,RUBICENE(CHEM.)		
RU	140,14	565A	18	44227			ELSHOTRIA PALTRINI		
RU	142,09	9229.0A	15	51134			WRIGGLE	5862.0A	
RU	142,14	5862.0A	20	51127	3164	3774	WRIGGLE	9229.0A	
RU	145,06	9256	11	36200	3140	1098	OLD RAGS		
RU	145,14	5993	19	31227	3150	3768	SHORT COAT,JACKET		
RU	164,14	9430	21	11627			STRONG(OF WINE)		
RU	167,06	7560	14	86100		1097	RUBIDIUM		
RU	181,14	736A	23	11286	3151	8275	TEMPLES(ANATOMY)		
RU	196,06	7705	17	46327	3141	4672	QUAIL-LIKE BIRD		
RUU	005,07	0050	08	22410	3144	7065	MILK		
RUU	011,00	0354.0A	02	80000	3152	6517	TO MISPLACE,HAND OVER IN DARKNESS		
RUU	085,03	3067	06	34140	3142	8985	THOU		
RUU	161,03	6592	10	71403	3154	3277	INSULT,DISGRACE		
RUH	011,00	0354	02	80000	3152	6517	ENTER		

ROM	RAD	TEL	TOT	FC	MAT	OSH	TAG	CR	CHAR
RUH	085,10	3314	13	31143	3155	3283	DAMP/MUGGY		
RUH	120,10	4904	16	21943	3156	3281	ADORNED,BEAUTIFUL		
RUH	140,10	5562	14	44343	3157	3284	RUSHES,MAT		
RUH	145,10	5970	15	31243	3158	3279	MATTRESS		
RUH	161,03	6592.0A	10	71403	3154	3277	INSULT,DISGRACE		
RUH	163,10	9405	13	77327		2207	PLACE NAME		
RUAN	032,14	1092	17	41127		3763	LAND ON WATER EDGE OR UNDER WALL		
ROAN	032,09	8236	12	41134	3160	5038	SPACES ENCLOSED BY CITY WALL		
ROAN	096,14	3897	18	11127		3764	OPAQUE/WHITE QUARTZ		
ROAN	126,03	5081	09	10430	3159	5037	PLIABLE		
ROAN	130,04	5140	08	71211			PROTEIN		
ROAN	142,09	9229	15	51134			WRIGGLE	5862	
ROAN	142,14	5862	20	51127	3164	3774	WRIGGLE	9229	
ROAN	159,04	6516	11	57082	3165	4925	SOFT	6554	
ROAN	159,09	6554	16	51034	3165	5044	SOFT	6516	
ROAN	170,04	7086	07	71211	7710	7467	(SURNAME)		
RUEI	100,07	8856	12	14231	3175		OVERLADEN WITH FRUIT		
RUEI	120,08	4864	14	22944	3171	9048	STRINGS OF CAP		
RUEI	140,12	5624	16	45231	3175	5747	OVERLADEN WITH FLOWERS,FRINGE		
ROEI	075,12	8588	16	33904			DANGLE,HANG LOOSELY	9075	
ROEI	120,12	9075	18	33903		8482	DANGLE,HANG LOOSELY	8588	
ROEI	140,12	5605	16	44333	3172	8529	STAMEN OR PISTIL OF A FLOWER	5687	
ROEI	140,16	5687	20	44904	3173		STAMEN OR PISTIL OF A FLOWER	5605	
RUEY	029,14	0653	16	27640	3176	6060	ASTUTE/PERSPICACIOUS	4213	
RUEY	075,04	2660	08	44927	3167	4051	TOOL HANDLE		
RUEY	085,04	3103	07	34127	3168	4054	RIVER-BEND		
RUEY	096,09	3843	13	12127	5924	3755	PROPITIOUS,RAYL(ACOUSTICAL UNIT)		
RUEY	109,09	4213	14	21608	3176	1724	ASTUTE,PERSPICACIOUS	0653	
RUEY	140,04	5360	08	44227	3170	4055	SMALL,(SURNAME)		
RUEY	142,04	5731	10	54127	3169	4053	(MOSQUITO)/SIMULIA LUGUBRIS		
RUEY	142,08	5761	14	54127	3169	4056	(MOSQUITO)/SIMULIA LUGUBRIS	5731	
RUEY	167,07	6904	15	88116	3174	7566	ACUTE		
RUEN	093,08	3681	12	20547			OX		

溽
縟
蓐
褥
鄏
壖
堧
礝
耎
朊
蝡
蠕
軟
輭
阮
豲
綾
蕤
橤
蕊
蕊
蘂
叡
柄
汭
瑞
睿
芮
蚋
蜹
銳
犉

273

ROM	RAD	TEL	TOT	FC	MAT	OSH	TAG	CR	CHAR
RUENN	085,12	3387	15	37120	3178	3443	MOIST		潤
RUENN	169,04	7032	12	77104	3177	3442	INTERCALARY		閏
RUO	064,07	2186.0A	10	52044		9066	RUB,CRUMPLE		接
RUO	064,08	2186.1A	11	52044		9046	RUB,CRUMPLE		捼
RUOH	009,09	8067	11	24264		1128	TO SUCH A DEGREE/SUCH		偌
RUOH	057,07	1726	10	17127	3128	4747	WEAK		弱
RUOH	086,15	3616	19	44331	3096		BURN,HEAT		爇
RUOH	118,09	4627	15	88604	3127	1129	(BAMBOO),SKIN OF BAMBOO		箬
RUOH	140,05	5387	09	44604	3126	1125	AS,IF		若
RUOH	140,10	554A	14	44127	3130	4751	KONYAKU		蒻
RUOH	163,09	9397	12	47627		2169	PLACE NAME		鄀
RUOH	195,10	765T	21	27327			SARDINE		鰙
RUOH	196,10	774B	21	17127			SISKIN		鶸
RYH	072,00	2480	04	60000	3124	1492	SUN,DAY,JAPAN		日
RYH	187,04	7462	14	76300	3125	1497	HORSE FOR RELAYING DISPATCHES		馹
SA	064,12	2320	15	58040	5406	6345	LET GO		撒
SA	130,06	518D	10	74294			OSAZONE		脎
SAA	064,12	2320.0A	15	58040		6345	TO SCATTER		撒
SAA	085,06	3155	09	31460	5624	1961	SPRINKLE,SPILL	3491	洒
SAA	085,19	3491	22	31111	5624	7109	SPRINKLE,SPILL	3155	灑
SAA	177,04	7251.0A	13	47547	5409	6502	SLIPPERS,LABORERS, SHOES		鞡
SAH	024,02	0580	04	44000	5404	2841	THIRTY		卅
SAH	140,14	5646	18	44214	5410	0398	BODHISATTVA,(SURNAME)		薩
SAH	182,05	7366	14	07110	5405	7830	SOUND OF WIND,DECLINING		颯
SAI	032,10	1049	13	30104	5446	0212	STOP UP		塞
SAI	082,09	3038	13	26713			FLUSTERED,UNKEMPT		毸
SAI	130,09	5210	13	76230	5412	8583	LOWER PART OF CHEEKS,GILLS	7343	腮
SAI	181,09	7343	18	61386	5412	8318	LOWER PART OF CHEEKS,GILLS	5210	顋
SAI	195,09	7658	20	26330	5413	8586	GILLS OF FISH		鰓
SAI	196,09	772F	20	67327			SYNTHLIBORHAMPHUS ANTIQUUS		鶍
SAY	030,13	0865	16	63014			(PHONETIC)		嗄
SAY	032,10	1049.0B	13	30104	5446	0212	STRATEGIC PASS		塞
SAY	096,17	8845	21	13186			(PHONETIC)USED IN CELLOPHANE		璹

ROM	RAD	TEL	TOT	FC	MAT	OSH	TAG	CR	CHAR
SAY	154,10	6357	17	30806	5414	8214	COMPETE		賽
SAN	001,02	0005	03	10101	5415	0008	THREE		三
SAN	028,06	0638	08	23101	5415	0010	THREE(FRAUD PROOF)		叁
SAN	056,03	8383	06	43100		6879	THREE	0005	弎
SAN	082,11	8633	15	22214		7376	LONG-HAIRED/SHAGGY		髟
SAAN	009,04	0270.1	06	80409			UMBRELLA/PARASOL		伞
SAAN	009,10	0270	12	80408	5420	2368	UMBRELLA/PARASOL		傘
SAAN	066,08	2414.0A	12	48240	5421	6343	POWDERED MEDICINE,LIESURELY,LOOSEN		散
SAAN	119,11	4746	17	93922	5419	4224	TO MIX (OF POWDERS)		糁
SAAN	120,12	4894	18	28940	5420	6346	UMBRELLA/PARASOL	0270	繖
SANN	066,08	2414	12	48240	5421	6343	SCATTER,ADJOURN		散
SANG	024,04	0828.1	08	40732			MOURNING/FUNERAL		丧
SANG	030,09	0828	12	40732	5429	5769	MOURNING/FUNERAL		喪
SANG	075,06	2718	10	77904	5424	5378	MULBERRY TREE		桑
SAANG	030,10	0837	13	67094	5425	5379	THROAT,VOICE		嗓
SAANG	064,10	8459	13	57094	5426	5380	PUSH OVER,PUSH BACK		搡
SAANG	112,10	4327	15	17694	5427		STONE PLINTH		磉
SAANG	181,10	7350	19	71986	5428	8290	FOREHEAD,KOWTOW		顙
SANQ	024,04	0828.1A	08	40732			LOSE(BY DEATH)		丧
SANQ	030,09	0828.0A	12	40732	5429	5769	LOSE(BY DEATH)		喪
SAU	064,10	2279	13	57036	5431	8939	TO SCRATCH,DISTURB		搔
SAU	120,11	4923	17	22994	5441	5514	REEL SILK FROM COCOONS		繰
SAU	130,10	5246.1	14	77236	5442	8940	SMELL OF URINE		臊
SAU	130,13	5246	17	76294	5442	5315	SMELL OF URINE		臊
SAU	137,10	5318	16	27447	5435	6163	AN. FOR WARSHIPS		艘
SAU	187,10	7510	20	77336	5433	8941	HAVE SEX APPEAL		騷
SAO	038,10	1269	13	47447	5434	6164	ELDER BROTHER'S WIFE		嫂
SAO	064,03	2217.1	06	57070			SWEEP		扫
SAO	064,08	2217	11	57027	5437	3976	SWEEP		掃
SAW	032,08	8227	11	47127	5436	3973	BROOM,DIKE	A2217.0A	埽
SAW	064,03	2217.1A	06	57070			BROOM		扫
SAW	064,08	2217.0A	11	57027	5437	3976	BROOM	A8227	掃
SAW	130,10	5246.1A	14	77236	5442	8940	BASHFULNESS		臊

275

ROM	RAD	TEL	TOT	FC	MAT	OSH	TAG	CR	CHAR
SAW	130,13	5246.0A	17	76294	5442	5315	BASHFULNESS		臊
SEH	030,08	0835.1	11	40601			STINGY		嗇
SEH	030,10	0835	13	40601	5447	1855	STINGY		嗇
SEH	032,04	0969.0A	07	47147		6497	GARBAGE		圾
SEH	032,10	1049.0C	13	30104	5446	0212	UNENLIGHTENED,PISTON		塞
SEH	085,07	3396.1	10	37111			TART/ACERB,GRATING(OF SURFACES)		涩
SEH	085,12	8721	15	31111		0474	TART/ACERB,GRATING(OF SURFACES)	3396	澁
SEH	085,13	3435	16	34161	5448	1863	GRATING(OF SURFACES)	B3396	濇
SEH	085,14	3396	17	37111	5448	0475	TART/ACERB,GRATING(OF SURFACES)	D3435	澀
SEH	096,09	3844	13	11331	5451	8711	(MUS. INSTR.)		瑟
SEH	115,13	4484	18	24961	5449	1861	GATHER IN HARVEST		穡
SEH	139,00	5331	06	27717	5445	7310	COLOR		色
SEH	142,13	586E	19	54161			PACHYTYLUS MIGRATATORIUS		蟖
SEH	149,14	9299	21	07611			TALKATIVE/LOQUACIOUS		譅
SEH	159,13	6572	20	54061	5450	1858	LEATHER TOP OF A CART		轖
SEH	167,06	7597	14	87117			CESIUM		鉋
SEI	032,10	1049.0A	13	30104		0212	TO STOP UP		塞
SEN	075,08	2773	12	40994	5722	5278	FOREST		森
SENG	009,12	0300	14	28266	5453	1555	MONK		僧
SENG	190,12	7585	22	72606	5454		SHORT HAIR/UNKEMPT		鬙
SHA	018,06	0458.0A	08	42900		0110	TO BRAKE(CAR)		刹
SHA	075,02	3010.1	06	40904			KILL		杀
SHA	075,03	2619.0A	07	42922	5626		(PINE)		杉
SHA	075,07	8560	11	39904	5607		(TREE)		梁
SHA	075,11	281A	15	47947			ZANTHOXYLUM AILANTHOIDES		樧
SHA	079,06	3010	10	47947	5615	6295	KILL		殺
SHA	085,04	3097	07	39120	5606	4164	SAND,GRANULE,HOARSE/RASPY	A4263	沙
SHA	086,09	3559.0A	13	28334		8796	TIGHTEN,DECREASE		煞
SHA	104,07	4025	12	00129	5608	4167	CHOLERA		痧
SHA	112,04	4263	09	19620	5610	4152	SAND/GRAVEL/GRANULE	A3097	砂
SHA	120,04	4784	10	29920	5611	4161	COTTON YARN,MUSLIN		紗
SHA	140,07	5446.0A	11	44129	5458	4168	(INSECT),(PHONETIC)		莎
SHA	145,07	5945	13	39732	5612		BUDDHIST MONK'S ROBE		裟

ROM	RAD	TEL	TOT	FC	MAT	OSH	TAG	CR	CHAR
SHA	167,11	9494	19	87147			SPEAR		鎩
SHA	195,07	7644	18	39336	5613	8777	SHARK		鯊
SHAR	030,08	0798	11	68064		1326	WHAT (DIAL.)		啥
SHAA	009,11	0247.1	13	26247	5614	6457	FOOLISH		傻
SHAA	009,13	0247	15	22247		6453	FOOLISH		儍
SHAH	027,10	0633.0A	12	71247		6426	TALL BUILDING	1669.0A	廈
SHAH	030,10	084A.0A	13	61047		6424	HOARSE		嗄
SHAH	053,10	1669.0A	13	00247		6427	TALL BUILDING	0633.0A	廋
SHAH	076,09	2955	13	27782	5618	4914	DRINK		歃
SHAH	086,09	3559	13	28334	5617	8796	BALEFUL,BRING TO A STOP,VERY		煞
SHAH	118,08	4623	14	88801	0791	6048	FAN		箑
SHAH	124,08	5052	14	17404	5619	8992	WOODEN FAN CARRIED IN PROCESSION		翣
SHAH	140,08	9176	12	44801			(AUSPICIOUS HERB)		萐
SHAH	173,08	7203	16	10404	5620	8993	ALL OF A SUDDEN,DRIZZLE		霎
.SHA	086,09	3559.0B	13	28334		8796	PART. OF INSISTENCE OR IMPATIENCE		煞
SHAI	118,10	4652	16	88727	5621	4006	SIEVE	9026	筛
SHAI	118,19	9026	25	88211			SIEVE	4652	籭
SHAE	139,00	5331.0A	06	27717	5445	7310	COLOR,DICE	D7544.0A	色
SHAE	188,04	7544.0A	14	77247	6491	6280	DICE,CUBOID BONE	B5331.0A	骰
SHAY	072,06	2488	10	61060	5623	1957	TO SUN	2572	晒
SHAY	072,19	2572	23	61011	5623	7102	TO SUN	2488	曬
SHAN	018,04	5348.1	06	72400	5635		SCYTHE,MOW,CUT DOWN		刐
SHAN	018,05	0444.1	07	72200		2907	DELETE		刪
SHAN	018,05	0444	07	72400	5628	2916	DELETE		删
SHAN	032,07	1007.0A	10	42141	7343	6802	TO MIX WATER WITH CLAY		埏
SHAN	038,05	1194	08	47440	5416	4105	DEPRECATE,LITHE (OF WOMAN'S WALK)		姍
SHAN	046,00	1472	03	22770	5630	0987	MOUNTAIN/HILL		山
SHAN	059,00	1747	03	20202	5625	4170	FEATHERS		彡
SHAN	063,06	2082.0A	10	30227	5642	3398	TO FAN	2271	扇
SHAN	064,10	2271	13	53027	5643	3400	TO FAN		搧
SHAN	064,11	2296.0A	14	53022	5636	4222	DELICATE HAND		掺
SHAN	075,03	2619	07	42922	5626	4181	(PINE)		杉
SHAN	085,12	3394.1	15	34127	5629	3637	TEARFULLY		潸

ROM	RAD	TEL	TOT	FC	MAT	OSH	TAG	CR	CHAR
SHAN	085,12	3394	15	34169		1603	TEARFULLY		
SHAN	086,10	3569	14	93827	5644	3402	INCITE,FAN INTO A FLAME		
SHAN	096,05	3790	09	17140	5417	4102	CORAL		
SHAN	115,11	448A	16	23922			PANICUM FRUMENTACEUM		
SHAN	120,11	9073	17	2392			FRINGE/ORNAMENT OF BANNER		
SHAN	123,12	5034.1	18	80551	5656	2348	RANK ODOR(OF SHEEP OR GOATS)		
SHAN	123,13	5034	19	80416	5656	0044	RANK ODOR(OF SHEEP OR GOATS)	5238	
SHAN	130,13	5238	17	70216			RANK ODOR (OF SHEEP OR GOATS)	5034	
SHAN	137,03	9152	09	22470	5633	0990	SAMPAN		
SHAN	140,04	5348	08	44407	5635	6304	SCYTHE,MOW,CUT DOWN		
SHAN	140,05	5390	09	44601	5641	1284	THATCH,STRAW MAT		
SHAN	145,03	5904	08	32222	5627	4175	CHINESE GOWN(UNLINED)		
SHAN	157,05	6413	12	67140	5418	4103	LIMP		
SHAN	167,03	9438	11	82122			SAMARIUM		
SHAAN	064,11	2296.0B	14	53022	5636		TO GRASP		
SHAAN	109,08	8913	13	69089	5640	5628	FURTIVELY GLANCE,GLITTERING		
SHAAN	169,02	7026	10	77807	5638	3497	FLASH,LIGHTNING		
SHAAN	170,07	7104	10	74238	5637	5117	SHENSI		
SHANN	009,12	8074.0A	14	26250			SHAN NATIONALITY		
SHANN	018,08	0470.0A	10	92800			RIVER IN CHEKIANG		
SHANN	024,06	0830.1A	08	80506	6030		(SURNAME)		
SHANN	030,09	0830.0A	12	66506	6030		(SURNAME)		
SHANN	030,09	0810	12	80605	5657	1219	GOOD		
SHANN	032,12	8253	15	46156	5647	2633	LEVEL SPOT FOR SACRIFICES		
SHANN	038,13	1296	16	40416	5652	0048	CHANGES AND SUCCESSION		
SHANN	063,06	2082	10	30227	5642	3398	FAN		
SHANN	064,08	2242	11	59089	5639	5629	EASY,QUIET		
SHANN	064,11	8463	14	52021			TO CUT DOWN/MOW		
SHANN	064,12	8472	15	58065			TO EXTEND/STRETCH TO THE LIMIT		
SHANN	064,13	2343	16	50016	5653	0045	USURP,WITHOUT AUTHORITY		
SHANN	075,05	2694.0A	09	47940	0093	4104	FENCE		
SHANN	085,03	3073	06	32170	5631	0992	SWATOW		
SHANN	104,03	3999	08	00172	5632	0993	HERNIA		

潜 煽 珊 穆 繆 羴 羶 膻 舢 荍 苫 衫 跚 釤 掺 睒 閃 陝 僤 剡 單 單 善 墠 嬗 扇 掞 撣 搀 擅 柵 汕 疝

ROM	RAD	TEL	TOT	FC	MAT	OSH	TAG	CR	CHAR
SHANN	113,12	4407.0A	16	36256	5650	2640	ABDICATE	8473.0A	禪
SHANN	120,12	4931	18	28965	5658	1223	MAKE A FAIR COPY OF		繕
SHANN	130,12	5234	16	78265	5659	1222	MEALS	9603	膳
SHANN	142,12	5807	18	58165	5660	1225	EARTHWORM		蟮
SHANN	149,03	6065	10	02670	5634	0988	ABUSE,SLANDER		訕
SHANN	149,10	6189	17	03627	5645	3399	BEGUILE,CAJOLE		謆
SHANN	154,13	6365	20	67861	5664	1184	TO SUPPORT/PROVIDE FOR		贍
SHANN	163,12	6781	15	87627	5661	2173	NAME OF A HSIEN IN SINKIANG		鄯
SHANN	184,12	9603	20	88765	5659	1221	MEALS	5234	饍
SHANN	187,10	7509	20	73327	5646	3401	TO GELD		騸
SHANN	195,12	9659	23	26356	5662	2641	CHINESE YELLOW EEL	1668	鱓
SHANN	195,12	7668	23	28365	5662	1224	CHINESE YELLOW EEL	9659	鱔
SHANG	009,04	0281.1	06	28227			INJURE/INJURY		伤
SHANG	009,11	0281	13	28227	5666	4501	INJURE/INJURY		傷
SHANG	030,08	0794	11	00227	5673	3875	COMMERCE,CONSULT		商
SHANG	061,09	8400.0A	12	96027			BE RESOLUTE/DEDICATED		慯
SHANG	078,11	2999	15	18227	5667	4504	DIE PREMATURELY		殤
SHANG	086,11	7772	15	90828			ENTROPY		熵
SHANG	145,08	5951	14	90732	5671	5814	CLOTHES		裳
SHANG	148,11	6050	18	28227	5668	4503	GOBLET,FEAST		觴
SHAANG	032,06	1010	09	47120		3927	UNIT OF AREA		垧
SHAANG	072,06	2517	10	67020	2550	3929	AROUND NOON		晌
SHAANG	154,08	6339	15	90806	5672	8143	GIVE,ENJOY THE BEAUTY OF		賞
SHANQ	001,02	0006	03	21100	5669	0081	UP,ABOVE,GO TO		上
SHANQ	042,05	1424	08	90227	5670	3855	STILL		尚
SHANQ	142,17	588C	23	50141			CERAMBYX RUGICOLLIS		蠰
SHAU	057,07	1727	10	19227	5677	3668	ENDS OF A BOW		弰
SHAU	064,07	2200	10	59027	5678	3666	BRING OR TAKE (ALONG)		捎
SHAU	075,07	2744	11	49927	5679	3669	TIP OF BRANCH		梢
SHAU	086,12	3599	16	94811	5692	7498	TO BURN/ROAST,FEVER		燒
SHAU	115,07	4455	12	29927	5680	3670	SOMEWHAT/A LITTLE		稍
SHAU	118,07	4603	13	88227	5682	3678	BASKET,BUCKET		筲
SHAU	137,07	5314	13	29427	5683	3667	STERN OF BOAT		艄

ROM	RAD	TEL	TOT	FC	MAT	OSH	TAG	CR	CHAR
SHAU	140,07	9174	11	44227			JUNGLE GRASS,LAIR		荀
SHAU	142,07	5768.0A	13	58127	5684	3672	LONG-LEGGED SPIDER		蛸
SHAUR	020,01	0541	03	27320	5829	4358	SPOON		勺
SHAUR	075,03	2626	07	47920	5831	4364	LADLE		杓
SHAUR	117,03	4548	08	07120			CENTILITER		竕
SHAUR	140,03	5342	07	44327	5833	4370	PAEONIA ALBIFLORA		芍
SHAUR	180,05	7300	14	07662	5691	1366	HARMONIOUS,EXCELLENT,(MUSIC)		韶
SHAO	042,01	1421	04	90200	5675	4148	FEW,LACK		少
SHAW	009,05	4801.1	07	27262	5689	1367	CONNECT,TO INTRODUCE		佋
SHAW	019,05	0508	07	14627	5687	4800	STIMULATE TO EFFORT,(SURNAME)		劭
SHAW	026,05	0605	07	17620	5688	2121	(SURNAME)		邵
SHAW	030,02	0664.0A	05	17602	0234	1362	(SURNAME),NAME OF AN ANCIENT STATE		召
SHAW	030,07	0783	10	69027	5676	3660	SENTRY,A WHISTLE		哨
SHAW	042,01	1421.0A	04	90200	5675	4148	YOUNG		少
SHAW	120,05	4801	11	27962	5689	1372	CONNECT,TO INTRODUCE		紹
SHAW	163,05	6730	08	17627	5690	2178	PLACE NAME,(SURNAME)		邵
SHE	037,06	1151.0A	09	40207	0074		EXTRAVAGANT	1158	奢
SHE	037,09	1158	12	40604	5696	1650	EXTRAVAGANT	1151.0A	奢
SHE	154,07	6332	14	68891	5695	8382	BUY ON CREDIT		賒
SHER	009,05	0152	07	80901	5694	8380	(SURNAME)		佘
SHER	064,04	2124.0A	07	52021	0267	2029	BROKEN (AS OF ROPE/STICK)		折
SHER	064,08	8440	11	54094	5708		SORT OUT DIVINING STALKS		揲
SHER	135,00	5286	06	20604	5705	1314	TONGUE		舌
SHER	142,05	5748	11	53111	5698	7184	SNAKE		蛇
SHER	169,09	7062.0A	17	77604	6502	3475	USED IN BUDDHIST TRANSLITERATION		闍
SHER(M)	009,02	0087.0A	04	24200	5808		WHAT	3928.0A	什
SHER(M)	099,04	3928.0A	09	44718		0766	WHAT	0087.0A	甚
SHEE	064,08	2202	11	58064	5700	1328	GIVE UP	5287.0A	捨
SHEE	135,02	5287.0A	08	80604	5699	1325	GIVE UP	2202	舍
SHEH	027,07	0623	09	71256	5697		(SURNAME)		厙
SHEH	030,02	0673.0A	05	64000			NAME OF A HSIEN IN HONAN	5509.0A	叶
SHEH	041,07	1410	10	24200	5703	3215	SHOOT,RADIO-(CHEM.)		射
SHEH	053,07	1655.0A	10	00256	3496	2650	(SURNAME)		庫

ROM	RAD	TEL	TOI	FC	MAT	OSH	TAG	CR	CHAR
SHEH	061,18	2042.0A	21	91041	0272	2725	AFRAID,BE FEARED		懾
SHEH	064,10	2378.1	13	51047			COLLECT,ASSIST		摄
SHEH	064,18	2378	21	51041	5710	2726	COLLECT,ASSIST		攝
SHEH	076,12	2965.0A	16	87182	2476	4932	NAME OF A HSIEN IN ANHWEI		歙
SHEH	085,07	3195	10	31121	5707	4147	WADE,INVOLVE/CONCERN		涉
SHEH	085,18	3490	21	31141			NAME OF A RIVER		灄
SHEH	094,08	3721	11	48264		1329	(WILD-CAT)		猞
SHEH	113,03	4357	07	34210	5701	0152	SOCIETY		社
SHEH	135,02	5287	08	80604	5699	1325	RESIDENCE		舍
SHEH	140,08	549A	12	44604			XYLENE		荅
SHEH	140,09	5509.0A	13	44904	7319	5297	NAME OF A HSIEN IN HONAN	0673.0A	葉
SHEH	140,11	556C	15	44647			THEA SINENSIS		蔎
SHEH	142,13	586F	19	54194			PODISMA MIKADO		蝶
SHEH	149,04	6080	11	07647	5711	6267	ESTABLISH,DISPLAY		設
SHEH	155,04	6376	11	48340	5702	6101	TO PARDON(A CONVICT)		赦
SHEH	178,09	7288	18	44594	5709		ARCHER'S THUMB RING		韘
SHEH	198,10	7790	21	00241	5704	3218	MUSK DEER		麝
SHEIR	149,08	6142.0A	15	00614	5923	0872	WHO		誰
SHEN	009,05	0135	07	25206	5713	2689	STRETCH OUT		伸
SHEN	009,06	8042	08	24211	5721		LARGE CROWD	7476	侁
SHEN	028,06	0639.1B	08	23202			GINSENG		参
SHEN	028,09	0639.0B	11	23202	6685	4219	GINSENG		参
SHEN	028,10	0640.0B	12	23338	6685		GINSENG		蔘
SHEN	030,05	0728	08	65006	5714	2687	GROAN		呻
SHEN	038,07	1228	10	41432	0312	5779	PREGNANT		娠
SHEN	038,07	1228.1	10	47440	0312	4135	PREGNANT		媷
SHEN	085,08	3234	11	37194	5719	5393	DEEP		深
SHEN	086,12	8590	16	90904			BRISK/VIGOROUS(OF FIRE)		燊
SHEN	100,05	3933	10	25114	5740	0390	MULTITUDE/CROWD		甡
SHEN	102,00	3947	05	50006	5712	2685	EXTEND,(SURNAME),3-5 P.M.		申
SHEN	112,05	8938	10	15605	5715	2688	ARSENIC		砷
SHEN	119,03	4753	09	97910			RESIDUE FROM OIL MAKING		籸
SHEN	120,05	4800	11	25906	5717	2690	MEMBER OF GENTRY		紳

ROM	RAD	TEL	TOT	FC	MAT	OSH	TAG	CR	CHAR
SHEN	140,07	5450.0A	11	44401	2740	2475	LONG,NUMEROUS		莘
SHEN	140,09	9185	13	44247		6188	GINSENG	0639.0B	葠
SHEN	149,06	6123	13	04611		7520	INQUIRE,INFORM		詵
SHEN	158,00	6500	07	27220	5718	4134	BODY		身
SHEN	187,06	7476	16	74311	5721	7521	LARGE CROWD	8042	駪
SHERN	113,05	4377	09	35206	5716	2691	SPIRITUAL BEING,GOD,LIVELY		神
SHERN	167,05	688A	13	85106			ARSONIUM(RADICAL)		鉮
SHEEN	030,06	0757	09	61060	5728	1955	SMILE		哂
SHEEN	038,15	1306	18	43469	5730	1815	WIFE OF FATHER'S YOUNGER BROTHER		嬸
SHEEN	040,05	1399.1	08	30506			TRY (IN COURT),INVESTIGATE		审
SHEEN	040,12	1399	15	30609	5729	1813	TRY (IN COURT),INVESTIGATE	9300	審
SHEEN	085,04	3088.0A	07	34112	0332	7743	(SURNAME),PLACE NAME	E3476	沈
SHEEN	085,15	3476	18	33169	5731	1816	POUR,PLACE NAME	E3088.0A	瀋
SHEEN	109,12	8919	17	61046			(SURNAME)		瞫
SHEEN	111,04	4250	09	82400	5732	1981	(INTERROG.)		矧
SHEEN	149,08	6159	15	08632	5733	8619	CONSULT		諗
SHEEN	149,15	9300	22	03669		1814	TRY(IN COURT),INVESTIGATE	1399	讅
SHENN	061,10	1957	13	94034	5734	8085	CAUTIOUS		慎
SHENN	075,09	2795	13	44911	0320	0771	FRUIT OF MULBERRY	5513	椹
SHENN	085,08	3334.1	11	33122			SEEP THROUGH		渗
SHENN	085,11	3334	14	33122	5735	4226	SEEP THROUGH		滲
SHENN	099,04	3928	09	44718	5724	0766	VERY		甚
SHENN	130,05	516A	09	75206			ARSINE		胂
SHENN	130,07	5187	11	71232		5777	SACRIFICIAL MEAT(RAW)		脤
SHENN	130,08	5200	12	77227	5736	3647	KIDNEYS		腎
SHENN	140,09	5513	13	44711	5725	0773	FRUIT OF MULBERRY	2795	葚
SHENN	142,07	5763	13	71136	5737	8937	(MYTHICAL ANIMAL),CLAM,SEA-SERPENT		蜃
SHENN	203,09	7828	21	64318			DARK AND HEAVY(AS RAIN CLOUDS)		黮
SHENG	019,10	0524.0A	12	79227	5754	4864	ABLE TO BEAR	B516B	勝
SHENG	024,02	0581	04	24400	5745	2822	RISE,PINT		升
SHENG	033,04	5116.1	07	40277	5748	4241	SOUND/VOICE,NOISE,TONE		声
SHENG	072,04	2573	08	60440	5746	2823	ASCEND,PEACEFUL		昇
SHENG	085,05	3327	08	35114			RISING OF WATER		泩

ROM	RAD	TEL	TOT	FC	MAT	OSH	TAG	CR	CHAR
SHENG	093,05	3673	09	25510	5739	0393	DOMESTIC ANIMAL		牲
SHENG	100,00	3932	05	25104	5738	0389	LIFE,GIVE BIRTH		生
SHENG	100,07	3935	12	26127	5743	4846	NEPHEW		甥
SHENG	117,04	454E	09	04100			LITER		竔
SHENG	118,05	4563	11	88104	5742	0408	(MUS. INSTR.)		笙
SHENG	128,11	5116	17	47401	5748	2738	SOUND/VOICE,NOISE,TONE		聲
SHENG	130,05	516B	09	75210			PEPTIDE,BE ABLE TO BEAR	D0524.0A	胜
SHENG	170,07	7105	10	74214	5747	0203	PROMOTED		陞
SHENG	208,05	9696	18	75711			STOAT,WEASEL		鼪
SHERNG	085,13	3427.0A	16	37117	4507	7341	NAME OF A RIVER IN SHANTUNG		澠
SHERNG	120,08	4939.1	14	26916			ROPE		繩
SHERNG	120,13	4939	19	27917	5749	7339	ROPE		繩
SHEENG	109,04	4164	09	90602	5744	1723	FRUGAL,SAVE,PROVINCE		省
SHEENG	109,05	8904	10	25601	5741	1711	CATARACT OF THE EYE,ERROR		眚
SHENQ	018,10	0476	12	22900	5750	2951	HAVE AS REMAINDER	6359	剩
SHENQ	019,10	0524	12	79227	5754	4864	VICTORIOUS	516B.0A	勝
SHENQ	032,02	5110.1	05	77104	5753	0222	SAGE,HOLY		圣
SHENQ	046,10	1522	13	22791	0364	5565	NAME OF A HSIEN IN CHEKIANG		嵊
SHENQ	072,06	8508	10	60253	5751	7019	BRIGHTNESS OF SUN,SPLENDOR		晟
SHENQ	108,06	4141.0A	11	53107	5752	0721	FLOURISHING,(SURNAME)		盛
SHENQ	128,07	5110	13	16104	5753	0306	SAGE,HOLY		聖
SHENQ	130,05	516B.0A	09	75210			VICTORIOUS	0524	胜
SHENQ	154,10	6359	17	79286	5750	8217	HAVE AS REMAINDER	0476	賸
SHI	009,10	0268	12	22134	2426	5057	SERVANT,OF KIANGSI PROVINCE		傒
SHI	009,12	0296	14	24265	2435	1255	CAUTIOUS,MERRY/JOYFUL,(SURNAME)		僖
SHI	012,02	0363	04	80207	2414	4546	(PART.)		兮
SHI	030,04	0705	07	67047	2471	6500	INHALE,ABSORB		吸
SHI	030,07	0785	10	64027	2417	3951	SOUND OF SOBBING		唏
SHI	030,12	0883	15	64065	2436	1253	LAUGH/GIGGLE		嘻
SHI	030,12	0890	15	68027	2471	3404	INHALE,ABSORB	0705	噏
SHI	036,00	1119	03	27200	2485	4247	EVENING		夕
SHI	037,07	1153	10	20430	2425	5054	WHAT WHY		奚
SHI	038,12	1291	15	44465	2437	1258	AMUSEMENT		嬉

ROM	RAD	TEL	TOT	FC	MAT	OSH	TAG	CR	CHAR
SHI	046,17	8353	20	23750	2453		MOUNTAIN-GORGE,RAVINE		
SHI	050,04	1585	07	40227	2416	3950	RARE/INFREQUENT		
SHI	060,10	1793	13	22234	2427	5058	FOOTPATH,WAIT FOR	A6459	
SHI	061,06	8394	09	91060	2461	1958	TROUBLED/VEXED		
SHI	061,07	1885	11	20339	2506	8656	KNOW,IN ALL CASES		
SHI	064,04	2103	07	57047	2472	6503	COLLECT/RECEIVE		
SHI	064,10	2377.1	13	50027	2443	4725	BRING,HOLD		
SHI	064,12	2322.0A	15	52021	5577	2041	TO SUPPORT,AROUSE		
SHI	064,18	2377	21	52027	2443	3899	BRING,HOLD		
SHI	072,07	2522	11	64027	2418	3952	DRY IN THE SUN,DAWN		
SHI	072,08	2531	12	42602	2490	1570	BRIGHT,DISCRIMINATE		
SHI	072,08	2530	12	62021	2490	2034	UNDERSTANDING		
SHI	072,16	2569	20	68053	2432	6941	LIGHT OF DAY		
SHI	075,04	2649	08	42921	2488	2033	ANALYZE/ANALYSIS		
SHI	075,06	2722.0A	10	41960	2462	1959	TO ROOST	2776.0A	
SHI	075,08	2776.0A	12	45944	2462	8997	TO ROOST	2722.0A	
SHI	075,12	2898	16	47953		2519	OSMANTHUS FRAGRANS		
SHI	076,07	2950	11	47282	2419	4933	TO SOB		
SHI	084,06	8639	10	80617			XENON		
SHI	085,07	3054	10	34127			NAME OF A RIVER IN HUPEI		
SHI	085,08	3215	11	32121	2491	2036	SOUND OF RAIN/SLEET ETC.		
SHI	085,10	3305	13	32134		5060	CREEK	6254	
SHI	086,07	7910	11	94827			ALKENE		
SHI	086,09	3556	13	77331	2451	8807	SPLENDID,PROSPEROUS		
SHI	086,12	3588	16	40336	2439	8769	WARM,BRIGHT	3587	
SHI	086,12	3587	16	94865			WARM,BRIGHT	3588	
SHI	086,13	8764	17	98853			FIRE		
SHI	093,06	3686.1	10	21560			SACRIFICE		
SHI	093,08	3679	12	77253	2463	2517	RHINOCEROS		
SHI	093,16	3686	20	28553	2433	6942	SACRIFICE		
SHI	102,06	3971	11	64014	2442	0165	50 MUU,SMALL PLOT OF FARM LAND		
SHI	106,08	4112	13	42602	2490	1665	WHITE		
SHI	112,06	8970	11	11660		1956	SELENIUM		

ROM	RAD	TEL	TOT	FC	MAT	OSH	TAG	CR	CHAR
SHI	113,12	4406	16	34265	2440	1256	JOY		禧
SHI	115,07	4449	12	24927	2421	3955	SPARSE,DILUTED		稀
SHI	116,11	4527	16	30339		8658	DISTURBING NOISES		窸
SHI	119,06	9035	12	91960		1960	THRESH RICE,GROUND RICE		粞
SHI	123,10	5032	16	80253	2431		NAME OF AN EMPEROR,(SURNAME)		羲
SHI	130'11	5230	15	74232	2508	5674	KNEE		膝
SHI	142,08	5782	14	52121	0270	2035	CHAMELEON/EUMECES LATISCUTATUS		蜥
SHI	142,10	7911	16	56130			(INTESTINAL WORM)		螅
SHI	142,11	5842	17	52139	2507	8657	CRICKET		蟋
SHI	142,17	587E	23	58112			AENARIA LEWISI		蟻
SHI	146,00	6007	06	10600	2460	1953	WEST		西
SHI	148,18	6054	25	22227	2445	3900	IVORY BODKIN FOR UNDOING KNOTS		觿
SHI	149,04	6082.0A	11	02621	2728	2018	VAPOR RISING FROM EARTH		訴
SHI	149,12	9298	19	04665		1254	OH (DENOTING FRIGHT)		譆
SHI	150,10	6254	17	28468	0511	1386	CREEK	3305	谿
SHI	150,10	9314	17	82634			CREEK	6254	谷
SHI	152,07	6274	14	14227	2422	3956	SWINE		豨
SHI	157,10	6459	17	62134	2429	5055	FOOTPATH	A1793	蹊
SHI	163,18	9417	21	27227	2446		PLACE NAME		酅
SHI	164,12	6832	19	10617	2448	0724	ACYL		醯
SHI	170,17	9537	20	73250			PRECIPITOUS,PERILOUS,TO DAMAGE		隵
SHI	184,06	7400	14	80732			UNIT OF GOODS IN BARTER		飻
SHI	191,08	7594	18	77217	2482	3432	QUARREL		鬩
SHI	196,13	9682	24	37127			BIRD-LIKE MANDARIN DUCK		鸂
SHI	208,10	7863	23	72713	2430		MOUSE		鼷
SHYI	018,01	5045.1	03	17120			TO PRACTICE		习
SHYI	038,10	1261	13	46430	2496	8577	DAUGHTER-IN-LAW		媳
SHYI	050,07	1598	10	00227	2502	3959	WOVEN MAT,BANQUET	A5553	席
SHYI	061,06	1873	10	26330	2495	8574	TO REST		息
SHYI	061,08	1917	11	94061	2494	1510	TO PITY,TO BE SPARING OF		惜
SHYI	072,04	2497	08	44601	2493	1506	FORMERLY		昔
SHYI	075,13	2907	17	48940	2484	6374	ORDER,DISPATCH		檄
SHYI	085,12	3384	15	37127	2510	4518	SALT-LAND LEFT BY TIDE		潟

ROM	RAD	TEL	TOT	FC	MAT	OSH	TAG	CR	CHAR
SHYI	086,10	3571	14	96830	2497	8576	EXTINGUISH(FIRE)		
SHYI	104,08	8875	13	00161			DISEASE		
SHYI	124,05	5045	11	17602	2499	1666	TO PRACTICE		
SHYI	140,10	5553	14	44227	2503	3961	WOVEN MAT	A1598	
SHYI	145,08	5954	13	36227	2504	4511	TAKE OFF UPPER GARMENT		
SHYI	145,11	5977.0A	16	37262	6324	1669	BREECHES		
SHYI	145,16	6002	22	01732	2512	5829	RAID,INHERIT,SUIT OF CLOTHES		
SHYI	147,07	6021	14	16110	2483	7585	WIZARD		
SHYI	167,08	6932	16	86127	2505	4507	TIN,GIVE,(SURNAME)		
SHYI	170,14	7147	17	76233	2511	8814	LOW/MARSHY LAND,(SURNAME)		
SHYI	195,11	9667	22	27362			LOACH,MUDFISH		
SHII	030,09	0823	12	40605	2434	1252	GLAD,LIKE		
SHII	044,11	1460	14	77281	2449	5975	SLIPPERS	9344	
SHII	060,08	1781	11	21281	2468	5972	CHANGE ONE'S RESIDENCE		
SHII	061,12	8404	16	40336	2438	8563	BE DELIGHTED WITH		
SHII	075,05	2662	09	23904	2464	5323	MALE NETTLE-HEMP		
SHII	085,06	3156	09	34111	2465	7522	WASH		
SHII	096,14	3886	19	10103	2469	0353	RULER'S SEAL		
SHII	113,12	4406.0A	16	34265	2440	1256	JOY		
SHII	140,09	5527	13	44336	2466	8590	FEEL INSECURE,UNHAPPY		
SHII	140,09	551F	13	44902			XANTHIUM STRUMARIUM		
SHII	140,11	5572	15	44281	2450	5976	INCREASE FIVE FOLD,(GRASS)		
SHII	142,12	9240	18	54165	2441	1257	(SPIDER)		
SHII	157,11	9344	18	61181	2449	5973	SLIPPERS	1460	
SHII	157,19	9353	26	61111	2449	7101	SLIPPERS	1460	
SHII	167,06	690C	14	80100			SELENIUM (RADICAL)		
SHII	195,12	766U	23	24365			WHITING/SILLAGO SP.		
SHIH	009,07	0190	09	22293	2424	8486	BE,TIE UP/BIND,CONNECTION/RELATION	B4762	
SHIH	009,12	8073	14	28227			UNITE,ALL,IN HARMONY	5047	
SHIH	023,00	0571	02	71710	2413	0774	A BOX		
SHIH	030,06	8134	09	61014	2456	0257	LOUD LAUGH		
SHIH	042,07	7138.1	10	90906	2481		CRACK,OCCASION FOR DISLIKE		
SHIH	044,21	1467	24	77286	2459	8102	GIGANTIC STRENGTH		

ROM	RAD	TEL	TOT	FC	MAT	OSH	TAG	CR	CHAR
SHIH	061,10	1958.0A	13	98017	2454	7813	TO SIGH		愾
SHIH	062,02	2070.1	06	73450			A PLAY,TRICK		戏
SHIH	062,11	2070.2	15	23250	2452	6897	A PLAY,TRICK		戲
SHIH	062,13	2070	17	23250	2452	6898	A PLAY,TRICK		戯
SHIH	064,03	8419.0A	06	5801			SPRIGHTFUL		抴
SHIH	076,12	2965	16	87182	2476	4932	TO SHUT,CONTRACT,BREATH		歙
SHIH	085,03	3071	06	37120	2486	4249	EVENING TIDE		汐
SHIH	085,12	3405	15	38127	2477		FLOWING WATER		潝
SHIH	093,10	8788	14	28517			STARVED(OF CATTLE)		犤
SHIH	109,04	4171	09	68027	2415	4547	GLARE AT		盻
SHIH	112,03	8928	08	17620		4248	SILICON	9441	矽
SHIH	113,09	4397	13	37234	2457		PURIFICATION CEREMONY		禊
SHIH	116,03	4497	08	30207	2487	4265	GLOOM OF THE GRAVE,TOMB,DEATH		穸
SHIH	120,01	4762	07	20903	2423	8484	SYSTEM,BE,TO TIE	D0190	系
SHIH	120,05	4798	11	26300	2467	1749	FINE,MINUTELY		細
SHIH	120,07	4838	13	28968	2473	1387	COARSE HEMPEN FABRIC		綌
SHIH	120,13	4941	19	57903	2458	8470	TO TIE/CONNECT	C4762	繫
SHIH	124,06	5047	12	80127	2475	3403	UNITE,ALL,IN HARMONY		翕
SHIH	130,04	5222	08	77282			BEEF		欯
SHIH	130,04	5150	08	78240	2470	2337	SCATTER,GIGGLE		肸
SHIH	134,06	5278	12	77327	2509	4589	SHOE/SLIPPER		舄
SHIH	141,12	5720	18	91917	2480	7672	TERRIFIED		虩
SHIH	163,06	6742	09	47727	2474	2263	CRACK,OCCASION FOR DISLIKE,(SURNAME)	6748	郄
SHIH	163,07	6748	10	87627	2474	2179	CRACK,OCCASION FOR DISLIKE,(SURNAME)	K7138	郤
SHIH	163,10	9404	13	27327			PLACE NAME		鄎
SHIH	167,03	9441	11	87120			SILICON	8928	鉽
SHIH	170,10	7138	13	79296	2481	8427	CRACK,OCCASION FOR DISLIKE	K6748	隙
SHIH	184,10	7426	18	88717	2455	7814	SACRIFICIAL VICTIM,GRAIN RATION		饎
SHIA	109,10	4219	15	63061	2535	1344	BLIND		瞎
SHIA	142,03	5802.1	09	51130			SHRIMP/PRAWN		虾
SHIA	142,09	5802	15	57147	2516	6134	SHRIMP/PRAWN		蝦
SHIA	195,09	7657	20	27347	2519	6133	GOBY		鰕
SHYA	009,07	0204	09	24238	2631	5115	HEROIC		侠

ROM	RAD	TEL	TOT	FC	MAT	OSH	TAG	CR	CHAR
SHYA	022,05	0563	07	71715	2525	0806	BOX		匣
SHYA	030,05	0727	08	66050	2526	2680	SIP A DRINK		呷
SHYA	046,07	1499	10	24738	2531	5114	GORGE		峽
SHYA	064,07	2188.0A	10	54038	2632	5118	COERCE,CLASP UNDER THE ARM		挾
SHYA	072,09	2538	13	67047			LEISURE		暇
SHYA	075,05	2679	09	46950	2527	2684	PEN,CAGE,SCABBARD		柙
SHYA	085,06	3174.0A	09	38161	2529	1197	ACCORD,MAKE CONTACT		洽
SHYA	093,10	5295.0A	14	40503			GIB/CHOCK		牽
SHYA	094,05	3697	08	46250	2528	2683	BE INTIMATE WITH		狎
SHYA	094,07	3707	10	44238	2532	5119	NARROW-MINDED,NARROW		狹
SHYA	096,09	3838	13	17147	2515	6127	FLAW IN JADE,BLEMISH		瑕
SHYA	112,07	4286	12	14638	2533		PLACE NAME		硤
SHYA	113,06	4380	10	38261	2530		TRIENNIAL SACRIFICE TO ANCESTORS		祫
SHYA	124,05	504B	11	67220			DIGITAL WEBS		翈
SHYA	137,05	9154	11	26450			(BOAT)		舺
SHYA	140,13	5627	17	44304			WATER-LILY LEAVES		蕸
SHYA	159,10	6561	17	53061	2536	1345	HAVE JURISDICTION OVER		轄
SHYA	162,09	6667	13	37304	2517	6753	DISTANT,ABANDON		遐
SHYA	173,09	7209	17	10247	2518	6137	RED CLOUDS		霞
SHYA	1⁸⁷,0⁹	9620	19	77347			(HORSE)		騢
SHYA	203,06	7822	18	64361	2537	1215	CRAFTY,(PHONETIC)		點
SHIAH	001,02	0007	03	10230	2520	2005	DOWN,BELOW,GO DOWN		下
SHIAH	027,10	0633	12	71247	2522	6426	TALL BUILDING	1669	廈
SHIAH	030,02	0687	05	61030		2006	FRIGHTEN	0907	吓
SHIAH	030,14	0907	17	64031	2092	8515	FRIGHTEN	0687	嚇
SHIAH	035,07	1115	10	10247	2521	6423	SUMMER		夏
SHIAH	053,10	1669	13	00247	2522	6427	TALL BUILDING	0633	廎
SHIAH	072,09	2538.0A	13	67047	2514	6129	LEISURE		暇
SHIAH	086,06	8738	10	98861			FIERY,TO BOIL		焰
SHIAH	112,11	8963	16	11649			CLEFT IN ROCK		磇
SHIAH	121,11	4978	17	81749	2523	3319	CRACK,GRUDGE		罅
SHIAH	146,00	6006	06	10227	2524	2858	COVER		西
SHIAH	149,08	0907.1	15	01617		7667	FRIGHTEN		諕

ROM	RAD	TEL	TOT	FC	MAT	OSH	TAG	CR	CHAR
SHIAN	009,03	0103	05	22270	2707	0989	IMMORTAL	8070	
SHIAN	009,11	8070	13	21212	2707	7233	IMMORTAL	0103	
SHIAN	010,04	0341	06	24211	2702	7517	BE FIRST		
SHIAN	038,05	1194.0A	08	47440	5416		DEPRECATE,LITHE (OF WOMAN'S WALK)		
SHIAN	038,17	1308	20	43450	2720		SLENDER,CUNNING		
SHIAN	061,13	2012	16	98086	2688		ARTFUL,FLATTERING		
SHIAN	064,08	2216	11	57082	2659	4922	LIFT (COVER)		
SHIAN	072,12	2554	16	36301	2712	6606	SIAM		
SHIAN	084,03	7912	07	80717		7799	XENON		
SHIAN	094,12	8810	15	42227			DOG WITH SHORT SNOUT		
SHIAN	115,03	4425	08	22970	2708	0991	COMMON RICE	4729	
SHIAN	119,03	4729	09	92907	2708		COMMON RICE	4425	
SHIAN	120,03	4928.1A	09	2294			FINE/DELICATE(ABBR. OF 4960)	4960	
SHIAN	120,17	4960	22	23950	2721	6991	FINE/DELICATE	4928.1A	
SHIAN	157,16	6494	23	61131	2710	6762	WALK AROUND,MANNER OF DANCING		
SHIAN	164,06	7913	13	14611			ACYL		
SHIAN	167,06	6901	14	82164	2711	1315	SHARP,FISH-SPEAR		
SHIAN	167,08	9475	16	87182			(IRON) SHOVEL		
SHIAN	195,06	7639	17	28351	2716	2553	FRESH	9666	
SHIAN	195,22	9666	33	27336	2716	8774	FRESH	7639	
SHIAN	196,10	7728	21	30327	2701	4677	SOAR		
SHYAN	030,06	0752	09	53200	2666	6999	ALL,IN ALL CASES,SALTY	G7768	
SHYAN	030,09	0792	12	67020	2682	2116	HOLD IN MOUTH	A6902	
SHYAN	030,10	0840.0A	13	68037	0883	5570	TO HOLD IN MOUTH,TO HATE		
SHYAN	038,10	1273	13	48437	2669	5579	DISLIKE		
SHYAN	038,12	1288	15	47420	2674	3492	ELEGANT/REFINED	8300	
SHYAN	038,12	8300	15	47420	2674	3504	ELEGANT/REFINED	1288	
SHYAN	057,05	1720	08	10232	2661	8884	BOW STRING,STRING OF MUS. INSTR.	D4808	
SHYAN	064,12	8469	15	57046	2713	3243	TAKE,PULL OUT HAIR,SELECT		
SHYAN	085,07	3241	10	32141	2714	6807	SALIVA,SHAMELESSLY		
SHYAN	104,05	3996	10	00132	2662	8891	INDIGESTION/DYSPEPSIA		
SHYAN	104,12	4073	17	00127	2677	3493	EPILEPSY,INSANITY		
SHYAN	109,12	4228.0A	17	67020	2678	3490	(SURNAME)		

仙 僊 先 姍 孅 憸 掀 暹 氙 獮 秈 籼 纖 躚 酰 鈷 鈂 鮮 鱻 騫 咸 唅 嗛 嫌 嫻 嫻 弦 撏 涎 痃 癇 睍

ROM	RAD	TEL	TOT	FC	MAT	OSH	TAG	CR	CHAR
SHYAN	120,05	4808	11	20932	2663	8886	STRING OF MUS. INSTR.	B1720	絃
SHYAN	137,05	5304	11	20432	2664	8883	SIDES OF BOAT		舷
SHYAN	149,09	6185	16	03650	2667	7003	SINCERITY,BRING INTO ACCORD		誠
SHYAN	154,08	6343	15	77806	2671	8220	WORTHY(PERSON)		賢
SHYAN	154,14	6343.1	21	75806	2671	8239	WORTHY(PERSON)		贒
SHYAN	164,09	9427	16	13650		7005	SALTY	7768	醎
SHYAN	167,06	6902	14	21221	2681	3016	HOLD IN MOUTH,NOMINAL OFFICE	A0792	銜
SHYAN	169,04	7034	12	77227	2672	3489	IDLE	A7033	閒
SHYAN	169,04	7033	12	77904	2679	3503	IDLE,ENCLOSURE	A7034	閑
SHYAN	195,09	765G	20	23350			UGUI MINNOW/TRIBOLODON HAKIENSIS		鹹
SHYAN	196,12	7755	23	77227		4628	PHASIANUS NYCTHEMERUS		鷴
SHYAN	197,09	7768	20	23650	2668	7004	SALTY	C0752	鹹
SHEAN	009,07	8044	09	26210			WEATHER-COCK		倪
SHEAN	015,06	0405	08	34111			(SURNAME)		冼
SHEAN	038,06	8277	09	44411	5720		NAME OF AN ANCIENT STATE		姺
SHEAN	042,10	1425	13	49720		4150	RARE,FEW	7639.0A	尟
SHEAN	042,10	8316	13	69802			RARE,FEW	7639.0A	尠
SHEAN	046,13	8349	16	28786			RUGGED,PRECIPITOUS	B7145	嶮
SHEAN	050,16	1624	19	43236	2698		CURTAIN AT FRONT OF CARRIAGE		幰
SHEAN	072,05	7359.1	09	60102			PROMINENT/CONSPICUOUS		显
SHEAN	085,17	3286	20	38151			NAME OF A RIVER		瀗
SHEAN	086,14	3611	18	11_{809}	2719	5634	CONFLAGRATION		燹
SHEAN	094,13	8811	16	48286		8008	LONG-SNOUT DOG	3760	獫
SHEAN	094,14	3751	17	41227	2722	4030	TO HUNT/KILL		獮
SHEAN	094,20	3760	23	46_{248}		6333	LONG-SNOUT DOG	8811	玁
SHEAN	112,13	8969	18	18686			RUGGED	B7145	礥
SHEAN	118,06	4580	12	88211	2704	7524	BAMBOO BRUSH FOR UTENSILS		筅
SHEAN	140,17	5691	21	44351	2718	2555	MOSSES ON DAMP WALLS		蘚
SHEAN	142,07	9223	13	56110	2687	7615	CYCLINA ORIENTALIS		蜆
SHEAN	157,06	6420	13	64111	2705	7519	BAREFOOTED		跣
SHEAN	167,06	6897	14	84111	2706	7518	SHINING METAL		銑
SHEAN	170,13	7145	16	78286	2689	8005	DANGER(OUS),RUGGED	D8969	險
SHEAN	177,14	9563	23	46533			LEATHER GIRTH ON HORSE		韅

ROM	RAD	TEL	TOT	FC	MAT	OSH	TAG	CR	CHAR
SHEAN	181,14	7359	23	61386	2692	8321	PROMINENT/CONSPICUOUS		顯
SHEAN	195,06	7639.0A	17	28351	2716	2553	RARE/FEW		鮮
SHIANN	009,12	0293	14	27220	2673	3491	COURAGEOUS/VALIANT		倜
SHIANN	040,06	2009.1	09	30211			CONSTITUTION		宪
SHIANN	046,07	1501	10	26710	2683	7593	STEEP HILL		峴
SHIANN	061,12	2009	16	30336	2697	8595	CONSTITUTION		憲
SHIANN	064,12	8468	15	57020	2676		WRATHFUL,VALIANT		撊
SHIANN	072,07	8509	11	66010			TO APPEAR(OF SUN)		睍
SHIANN	075,11	2860	15	47920			BIG TREE		櫚
SHIANN	094,09	3759.1	13	43234	2699	5084	TO OFFER		献
SHIANN	094,16	3759	20	23234	2699	5081	TO OFFER		獻
SHIANN	096,07	3807	11	16110	2684	7586	APPEAR,PRESENT/NOW	A6015.0A	現
SHIANN	109,03	4905.1	08	77731			A DISTRICT/HSIEN		县
SHIANN	109,07	4198	12	66010	2685	7597	GOGGLE-EYED		睍
SHIANN	120,08	4848	14	23953	2723	6958	THREAD,LINE,WIRE	4775	線
SHIANN	120,09	4775	15	26932	2723	5647	THREAD,LINE,WIRE	4848	綫
SHIANN	120,10	4905	16	62993	2700	8492	A DISTRICT/HSIEN		縣
SHIANN	123,07	5029	13	80182	2715	4966	TO ENVY		羡
SHIANN	130,09	5177	13	76232	2724	5646	GLAND		腺
SHIANN	140,07	5454	11	44216	2686	7625	AMARANTUS MANGOSTANUS		莧
SHIANN	147,00	6015.0A	07	60210	0860	7583	APPEAR	A3807	見
SHIANN	151,10	6268	17	18137	2670	5569	HALF-GROWN BEANS,D(29TH)		豏
SHIANN	167,09	696A	17	86132			WIRE	C4848	鏉
SHIANN	170,06	7098	09	77232	2696	5908	LIMIT		限
SHIANN	170,08	7119	11	77277	2694	1054	TO FALL,TRAP		陷
SHIANN	173,12	7213	20	10248	2725	6347	SLEET		霰
SHIANN	184,08	7414	16	87777	2695	1053	STUFFING/FORCEMEAT		餡
SHIANG	019,17	0537.0A	19	04727	3076		ASSIST	5980	勷
SHIANG	052,00	6763.1	03	22720			COUNTRY/VILLAGE		乡
SHIANG	053,09	1666	12	00260	2563	1698	SIDE ROOM,BOX (IN THEATER)		廂
SHIANG	085,09	3276	12	36100	2565	1697	NAME OF A RIVER		湘
SHIANG	096,17	8844	21	10132	2573	5843	ORNAMENTS,TO INLAY	D7013	瓖
SHIANG	109,04	4161	09	46900	2562	1695	MUTUALLY		相

ROM	RAD	TEL	TOT	FC	MAT	OSH	TAG	CR	CHAR
SHIANG	118,09	4630	15	88963	2566	1702	BOX/TRUNK/CHEST		箱
SHIANG	120,09	4889	15	26900	2567	1696	LIGHT YELLOW COLOR		緗
SHIANG	120,17	9076	23	20932			CORD TO HOLD UP SLEEVES		纕
SHIANG	130,12	9138	16	77227			SOUP,HASHED BEEF		膷
SHIANG	137,03	5299	09	21410	2548	0091	BOAT		舡
SHIANG	140,09	551E	13	44960			CELOSIA ARGENTEA		葙
SHIANG	140,13	5577	17	44727			(FUKIEN DRAMA)		薌
SHIANG	145,11	5980	17	00732	2571	5841	ASSIST		襄
SHIANG	163,10	6763	13	27727	2556	2187	COUNTRY/VILLAGE		鄉
SHIANG	167,17	7013	25	80132	2574	5844	INLAY	88844	鑲
SHIANG	186,00	7449	09	20609	2547	1581	FRAGRANT,INCENSE		香
SHIANG	187,17	7534	27	70332	2575	5850	PRANCE(AS A HORSE)		驤
SHYANG	034,03	7100.1A	06	27504	0654		SURRENDER		牟
SHYANG	053,06	1651	09	00251	2576	2557	ASYLUM FOR THE AGED,SCHOOL		庠
SHYANG	113,06	4382	10	38251	2577	2522	AUSPICIOUS/PROPITIOUS		祥
SHYANG	124,06	5046	12	87520	2578	3392	SOAR		翔
SHYANG	149,06	6116	13	08651	2579	2544	DETAILED		詳
SHYANG	170,06	7100.0A	09	77254	0654	2587	SURRENDER		降
SHEANG	008,06	0078	08	00407	2552	3116	ENJOY		享
SHEANG	030,06	0742	09	67020	2559	3928	SOUND	7302	响
SHEANG	061,09	1927	13	46330	2564	8573	THINK		想
SHEANG	180,13	7302	22	27601	2559	1526	SOUND	0742	響
SHEANG	184,06	7401	14	87720	2551	3930	SOLDIER'S PAY	7442	飨
SHEANG	184,13	7440	22	27732	2560	5936	OFFER OR ENJOY SACRIFICE		饗
SHEANG	184,17	7442	25	80732		5848	SOLDIER'S PAY	7401	饟
SHEANG	195,08	7638	19	80336		8779	WINE-PRESERVED POMFRET		鯗
SHIANQ	009,12	0288	14	27232	2569	5758	RESEMBLE,SEEM,IMAGE/PORTRAIT		像
SHIANQ	030,03	0686	06	27220	2549	3926	GUIDE,OPPOSITE TOWARDS	K0915	向
SHIANQ	030,16	0915	19	27227	2561	3931	GUIDE,OPPOSITE	K0686	嚮
SHIANQ	049,06	1574	09	44717	2553	7257	LANE/ALLEY		巷
SHIANQ	072,13	2561	17	60727	2557	2254	FORMERLY		曏
SHIANQ	075,12	2895	16	47932	2570	5760	OAK/QUERCUS SERRATA		橡
SHIANQ	109,04	4161.0A	09	46900	2562	1695	APPEARANCE,PORTRAIT	F0288	相

ROM	RAD	TEL	TOT	FC	MAT	OSH	TAG	CR	CHAR
SHIANQ	142,13	5858	19	27136	2558	8929	LARVAE		蠁
SHIANQ	144,06	5893.0A	12	21221	2554	3032	LANE/ALLEY	1574	衖
SHIANQ	152,05	6272	12	27232	2568	5757	ELEPHANT,ABBR. OF 0288	D0288	象
SHIANQ	181,03	7309	12	11186	2555	8244	ITEM,(SURNAME),BACK OF NECK		項
SHIAU	018,07	0465	09	92200	2785	2906	TO SCRAPE		削
SHIAU	030,07	0771	10	64047	2602	3108	PANT/ROAR/BARK(OF ANIMALS)		哮
SHIAU	030,11	8161	14	67022	2592	4205	BOASTFUL/BOMBASTIC		嘐
SHIAU	030,12	0879	15	64011	2593	7489	QUERULOUS,A CRY OF ALARM		嘵
SHIAU	030,18	0923	21	66668	2596	1078	CLAMOR		囂
SHIAU	040,07	1366	10	30227	2607	3675	NIGHT		宵
SHIAU	075,05	2664	09	46927	2590	4539	HOLLOW OF A TREE,EMPTY		枵
SHIAU	075,07	2743	11	27904	2589	5368	OWL/STRIX URALENSIS,BRAVE		梟
SHIAU	076,10	8619	14	07282			VAPOR/STEAM		歊
SHIAU	085,07	3194	10	39127	2607	3673	SUBSIDE,CONSUME,NEWS		消
SHIAU	085,12	8711	15	35127			SOUND OF RAIN AND WIND	3469	潇
SHIAU	085,16	3469	19	34127	2622	2093	RIVER NAME,SOUND OF RAIN AND WIND	8711	瀟
SHIAU	086,06	3526	10	24339	2581	8795	TO BOIL OR FUMIGATE		烋
SHIAU	104,07	4005	12	00147	2603		ASTHMA,DIFFICULTY IN BREATHING		痟
SHIAU	112,07	4285	12	19627	2608	3661	SALTPETER,TO TAN(LEATHER)		硝
SHIAU	118,11	4682.1	17	88227			PAN PIPES,(FLUTE)		箫
SHIAU	118,12	4682	18	88227	2619	2094	PAN PIPES,(FLUTE)		簫
SHIAU	120,07	4843	13	29927	2609	3671	RAW SILK		綃
SHIAU	124,07	5048	13	17227	2617		RUFFLED FEATHERS,LONELY		翛
SHIAU	140,11	5618.1	15	44227			MOURNFUL		萧
SHIAU	140,12	5618	16	44227	2620	2091	MOURNFUL		蕭
SHIAU	141,04	5708	10	41017	2582	7671	ROAR OF A TIGER		虓
SHIAU	142,07	5768	13	58127	5684	3672	MANTIS EGG NEST,OCTOPUS OCTOPODIA		蛸
SHIAU	142,16	5870	22	54127		2092	LONG-LEGGED SPIDER		蟏
SHIAU	162,07	6630	11	39302	2610	6688	LEISURELY/EASY-GOING		逍
SHIAU	164,07	6806.0A	14	14647	0720	3109	YEAST		酵
SHIAU	167,07	6906	15	89127	2611	3658	SELL,MELT METAL		銷
SHIAU	173,07	7197	15	10227	2612	3676	FIRMAMENT/HEAVEN		霄
SHIAU	187,12	7522	22	74311	2595	7496	GOOD HORSE,STRONG,BRAVE		驍

ROM	RAD	TEL	TOT	FC	MAT	OSH	TAG	CR	CHAR
SHIAU	194,07	7617	17	29212	2614	7654	ELF		魈
SHIAU	196,05	7697	16	67227	2591	4642	URAL OWL		鴞
SHYAU	039,05	1331.2A	08	90407			LEARN/STUDY,IMITATE		学
SHYAU	039,11	1331.1A	14	27407			LEARN/STUDY,IMITATE		學
SHYAU	039,13	1331.0A	16	77407			LEARN/STUDY,IMITATE		學
SHYAU	130,04	5149.0A	08	40227	2584	3592	JELLIED PORK	7413.0A	肴
SHYAU	184,08	7413.0A	16	84727	2588	3594	JELLIED PORK	5149.0A	餚
SHEAU	042,00	1420	03	90000	2605	8346	SMALL,YOUNG		小
SHEAU	072,12	2556	16	64011	2594	7492	DAWN,KNOW		曉
SHEAU	118,07	4607	13	88248	2616	6320	DWARF BAMBOO	4646	筱
SHEAU	118,10	4646	16	88294	2616	5386	DWARF BAMBOO	4607	篠
SHEAU	149,10	6203	17	07647	5476	6159	SMALL		謏
SHIAW	009,10	0272	12	28240	2600	6392	IMITATE		傚
SHIAW	019,06	0509	08	04427	2597	4826	EXERT		効
SHIAW	030,06	4562.1	09	68034	2615	5148	LAUGH/SMILE		咲
SHIAW	030,07	0771.0A	10	64047	2602	3108	TO SHOUT		哮
SHIAW	030,12	0876	15	65027	2618	2087	TO WHISTLE,TO HISS	8620	嘯
SHIAW	039,04	1321	07	44407	2601	3107	FILIAL		孝
SHIAW	061,06	8395	09	90048	2598	6528	CHEERFUL		恔
SHIAW	066,06	2400	10	08440	2599	6391	EFFICACY,EFFECT,IMITATE		效
SHIAW	066,16	2427	20	78440	2604	6336	TEACH,PERCEIVE		斅
SHIAW	075,06	2699	10	40948	0706	6536	SCHOOL		校
SHIAW	076,12	8620	16	57282	2618	4926	TO WHISTLE,TO HISS	0876	歗
SHIAW	118,04	4562	10	88430	2615	5140	LAUGH/SMILE		笑
SHIAW	130,03	5135	07	90227	2606	3657	SIMILAR/RESEMBLING		肖
SHIAW	149,06	9292	13	00648			TO SHOUT/TO HAIL		詨
SHIE	007,05	0067	07	21101	2623	0005	SOME		些
SHIE	075,09	2801	13	47934	2651	5049	TO WEDGE,WEDGE		楔
SHIE	075,10	2838	14	47927			SPHENE		楯
SHIE	076,09	2957	13	67782	2642	4943	TO REST		歇
SHIE	094,09	8806	12	46227	2643		SHORT-SNOUT DOG		猲
SHIE	142,09	5791	15	56127	2124	4395	SCORPION	5861	蝎
SHIE	142,13	5861	19	57182	2644	4944	SCORPION	5791	蠍

ROM	RAD	TEL	TOT	FC	MAT	OSH	TAG	CR	CHAR
SHYE	009,09	0253.0A	11	21262	0621	1676	IN COMPANY WITH		偕
SHYE	019,13	0533	15	46430			HARMONIOUS	6168	龤
SHYE	024,04	0588.1	06	44037			COOPERATE,HARMONIZE		协
SHYE	024,06	0588	08	44027	2639	4817	COOPERATE,HARMONIZE	D0673.0B	協
SHYE	030,02	0673.0B	05	64000	2633	2267	HARMONIZE	B0588	叶
SHYE	064,07	2188	10	54038	2632	5118	COERCE,CLASP UNDER THE ARM		挾
SHYE	064,10	2377.1A	13	50027	2443	4725	BRING,HOLD(HANDS)		擷
SHYE	064,15	2355	18	51086	2636	8258	COLLECT		攜
SHYE	064,18	2377.0A	21	52027	2443	3899	BRING,HOLD(HANDS)		攜
SHYE	068,06	2438	10	84900	2624	2706	SLANTING		斜
SHYE	120,06	4817	12	57903	2634	8462	MARKING LINE,REGULATE,PURE		絜
SHYE	120,15	4956	21	21986	2637	8259	TIE A KNOT,KNOT		纈
SHYE	130,04	5178.1	08	40000			SIDE OF BODY,THREATEN		胁
SHYE	130,06	5178	10	40227	2641	3633	SIDE OF BODY,THREATEN	5179	脅
SHYE	130,06	5179	10	74227	2641	4818	SIDE OF BODY,THREATEN	5178	脇
SHYE	145,04	9253	10	00732			BUSKIN,INIQUITOUS/NEFARIOUS	D6723	袤
SHYE	145,15	5999	20	31286	2638	8257	CARRY WITH THE FRONT OF A ROBE		襭
SHYE	149,09	6168	16	01662	2546	1675	HARMONIOUS		諧
SHYE	163,04	6723	07	77227	2625	2209	INIQUITOUS/NEFARIOUS,DEMONICAL	B9253	邪
SHYE	177,06	7256	15	44514	2545	0168	SHOES		鞋
SHYE	177,10	7256.1	19	42534	2545	5059	SHOES		鞵
SHYE	181,06	7327	15	41686	2635	8256	FLY UPWARDS,NECK,(SURNAME)		頡
SHYE	214,09	6168.1	26	81262	2546	1679	HARMONIOUS		龤
SHIEE	014,04	1400.1	06	37127			WRITE		写
SHIEE	014,12	1400.2	14	37327	2627	4519	WRITE		寫
SHIEE	040,12	1400	15	30327	2627	4520	WRITE		寫
SHIEE	143,00	5877	06	27100	2901	0745	BLOOD		血
SHIEH	026,07	0609	09	87120	2626	2115	UNLOAD/TAKE OFF		卸
SHIEH	038,09	1255	12	44494	2648	5295	TO LUST FOR		媟
SHIEH	044,07	1454	10	77227	2652	3674	CRUMBS,FILINGS,WORTH WHILE		屑
SHIEH	044,12	1463	15	77294		5291	WOODEN SHOES		屧
SHIEH	046,13	8350	16	27752		2526	MOUNTAIN VALLEY		嶰
SHIEH	053,13	1685	16	00241			OFFICE		廨

ROM	RAD	TEL	TOT	FC	MAT	OSH	TAG	CR	CHAR
SHIEH	061,13	2018	16	97041	2539	2527	LAX/NEGLIGENT		懈
SHIEH	072,11	2549	15	44601			LICENTIOUS	5978	勢
SHIEH	075,07	2750	11	43950	2538	6974	TOOLS		械
SHIEH	075,09	2801.0A	13	47934	2651	5049	WEDGE		楔
SHIEH	075,10	2836	14	44900	2629	3217	PAVILLION		榭
SHIEH	085,05	3118	08	34117	2950	0853	LEAK OUT,DIVULGE	3129	泄
SHIEH	085,05	3454.1	08	37127			TO FLOW,HAVE DIARRHEA		瀉
SHIEH	085,06	3129	09	35106	2649	7055	LEAKOUT,DIVULGE	3118	洩
SHIEH	085,09	8699	12	34194	6318	5296	GET RID OF,SCATTER,(SURNAME)		渫
SHIEH	085,10	3365.0A	13	38117			SALT POOL		澙
SHIEH	085,12	3428	15	37141	2540		CREEK,BECOME WATERY		澥
SHIEH	085,15	3454	18	33127	2628	4521	FLOW,HAVE DIARRHEA		瀉
SHIEH	085,16	3474	19	37111	2544	0506	MIST/VAPOR		灺
SHIEH	086,03	8731	07	94812	2646		CANDLE STUB	3523	炧
SHIEH	086,05	3523	09	98812		7435	CANDLE STUB	8731	爕
SHIEH	086,13	3610	17	99407	2655	6257	HARMONY/HARMONIZE,(SURNAME)		獬
SHIEH	094,13	3749	16	47241	2541	2528	(MYTHICAL ANIMAL)		疷
SHIEH	104,05	8868	10	00117			DYSENTERY		紲
SHIEH	120,05	9057	11	24917	2647		REIN,LEASH	4879	綫
SHIEH	120,06	4813	12	25906	2650		REIN,LEASH	9057	緤
SHIEH	120,09	4879	15	24994			REIN,LEASH	9057	薢
SHIEH	140,12	5630	16	44252			(GRASS)		薤
SHIEH	140,13	5648	17	44211	2645	0504	SHALLOT/SCALLION,ALLIUM BAKERI		蟹
SHIEH	142,13	5851	19	27136	2542	8930	CRAB		蠏
SHIEH	142,13	5851.1	19	57152		2529	CRAB		褻
SHIEH	145,06	5978.1	12	00732			LICENTIOUS		褻
SHIEH	145,11	5978	17	00732	2654	5895	LICENTIOUS		解
SHIEH	148,06	6043.0B	13	27252	0626	2525	(SURNAME)		觧
SHIEH	148,06	6043.1B	13	28251	0626	2550	(SURNAME)		謝
SHIEH	149,10	6200	17	04600	2630	3216	TO THANK,(SURNAME)		躠
SHIEH	157,17	9351	24	69147	2656	6258	TO WALK		邂
SHIEH	162,13	6702	17	37305	2543	6650	MEET UNEXPECTEDLY		駴
SHIEH	187,07	9616	17	73350			THUNDEROUS BEATING OF DRUMS		

ROM	RAD	TEL	TOT	FC	MAT	OSH	TAG	CR	CHAR
SHIEH	188,04	7543	14	78220			JOINT OF BONES		骱
SHIN	030,07	0778	10	60041			XANTHENE		哞
SHIN	061,00	1800	04	33000	2735	8526	HEART,MIND		忻
SHIN	061,04	1823	07	92021	2727	2021	HAPPY	2946	新
SHIN	069,09	2450	13	02921	2737	2037	NEW,NEWLY,MESO-(CHEM.)		昕
SHIN	072,04	2500	08	62021	2726		DAWN		欣
SHIN	076,04	2946	08	77282	2727	4921	HAPPY	6082	歆
SHIN	076,09	2956	13	07682	2729	4918	PLEASED/MOVED		炘
SHIN	086,04	3512	08	92821			MID-DAY GLARE/HEAT		芯
SHIN	140,04	5361	08	44330	2736	8614	LAMP PITH		莘
SHIN	140,07	5450	11	44401	2740	2475	ASARUM SIEBOLDI		薪
SHIN	140,13	5647	17	44921	2738	2038	FUEL,SALARY		訢
SHIN	149,04	6082	11	02621	2728	2018	HAPPY	1823	辛
SHIN	160,00	6580	07	00401	2739	2447	TIRED,8TH HEAVEN'S STEM		鈊
SHIN	167,04	9444	12	83100			CADOLINIUM		鋅
SHIN	167,07	6854	15	80141	2741	2448	ZINC		鑫
SHIN	167,16	9515	24	80119	2732	0370	(USED IN NAMES)		馨
SHIN	186,11	7451	20	47609	2769	1585	FRAGRANT		鄩
SHYN	163,12	9412	15	17327	2928		PLACE NAME,(SURNAME)		鬵
SHYN	193,08	7603	18	71227	2743	3916	CALDRON OR BOILER		伈
SHIIN	009,04	8023	06	23200	5727	8527	NERVOUS/FEARFUL		信
SHINN	009,07	0207	09	20261	2748	1156	BELIEVE,A LETTER		囟
SHINN	031,03	093A	06	26000	2752		TOP OF HEAD,SKULL	735A	焮
SHINN	086,08	3624	12	97882	2730	4923	HEAT/FLAME,INFLAMMATION		釁
SHINN	134,13	5284	20	77106			OFFER BLOOD IN SACRIFICE	6841	葷
SHINN	140,12	5622.0A	16	44406	1720	2298	MUSHROOM,MOLD		蕈
SHINN	143,05	5881	11	29150	2734	2505	OFFER BLOOD IN SACRIFICE	6841	衅
SHINN	164,07	681C	14	12627			LACTIM		酳
SHINN	164,18	6841	25	77227	2734	4299	OFFER BLOOD IN SACRIFICE	5881	釁
SHINN	181,10	735A	19	21386	2752	8319	TOP OF HEAD,SKULL	093A	顖
SHING	012,04	5281.1	06	90801			FLOURISH,IT IS THE FASHION TO		兴
SHING	061,09	1932	12	96014	2773	0402	TRANQUIL,UNDERSTAND		惺
SHING	072,05	2502	09	60104	2772	0400	A STAR		星

ROM	RAD	TEL	TOT	FC	MAT	OSH	TAG	CR	CHAR
SHING	094,09	3726	12	46214	2774	0404	APE		猩
SHING	130,09	5206	13	76214	2775	0403	FISHY(SMELL)		腥
SHING	134,09	5281	16	77801	2753	8064	FLOURISH,IT IS THE FASHION TO		興
SHING	142,07	576A	13	51111			DRAGONFLY		蜓
SHING	167,05	9451	13	85110			RUST ON IRON		銈
SHING	187,07	7490	17	70341	2777	2463	BAY HORSE		騂
SHYNG	009,06	8043	08	22200			STATUTE,SHAPE	D1748	俐
SHYNG	018,04	0438	06	12400	2755	2891	CORPOREAL PUNISHMENT		刑
SHYNG	032,06	0992	09	12104	2756	0204	MODEL		型
SHYNG	059,04	1748	07	12422	2759	4178	SHAPE		形
SHYNG	059,06	1748.1	09	12422	2759	4177	SHAPE		形
SHYNG	085,10	3322	14	99232	7586	5648	PLACE NAME		滎
SHYNG	112,06	4283	11	12600	2757	2893	WHETSTONE		研
SHYNG	144,00	5887	06	21221	2754	3020	WALK/GO,WILL DO		行
SHYNG	163,04	6717	07	17427	2760	2200	PLACE NAME,(SURNAME)	9388	邢
SHYNG	163,06	9388	09	17427		2191	PLACE NAME,(SURNAME)	6717	郉
SHYNG	167,04	9446	12	81140			LONG-NECKED WINE FLASK		鉶
SHYNG	167,06	9446.1	14	81140		2388	LONG-NECKED WINE FLASK		鋞
SHYNG	167,06	6889	14	82100	2758	2892	CALDRON FOR SOUP		鉶
SHYNG	170,07	7102	10	71211	2762	0125	DEFILE/PASS,BORDER THE STOVE		陘
SHYNG	184,09	7424	17	86727	2778	4489	MALT-SUGAR		餳
SHIING	061,09	1932.0A	12	96014	2773	0402	TRANQUIL,UNDERSTAND		惺
SHIING	064,14	237A	17	56046	2768	2756	BLOW NOSE		擤
SHIING	109,04	4164.0A	09	90602	5744	1723	INTROSPECT,VISIT,COMPREHEND		省
SHIING	164,09	6821	16	16614	2776	0401	AWAKE		醒
SHINQ	009,08	0228	10	24241	2765	2478	LUCKY		倖
SHINQ	012,04	5281.1A	06	90801			INTEREST		兴
SHINQ	038,05	1198	08	45410	2770	0395	SURNAME/FAMILY NAME		姓
SHINQ	038,08	8284	11	44441			UPRIGHT		婞
SHINQ	051,05	1630	08	40401	2764	2476	FORTUNATE		幸
SHINQ	061,05	1840	08	95010	2771	0391	NATURE,SEX		性
SHINQ	061,08	1901	11	94041	2766	2477	ANGRY		悻
SHINQ	075,03	2622	07	40609	2763	1398	APRICOT		杏

ROM	RAD	TEL	TOT	FC	MAT	OSH	TAG	CR	CHAR
SHINQ	134,09	5281.0A	16	77801	2753	8064	INTEREST		興
SHINQ	140,06	5429	10	44221		3023	LIMNANTHEMUI NYMPHOIDES		荇
SHINQ	140,07	544A	11	44609			NYMPHOIDES PELTATUM		荇
SHINQ	144,00	5887.0A	06	21221	2754	3020	CONDUCT,BEHAVIOR		行
SHIONG	010,03	0338	05	60210	2807	7544	ELDER BROTHER		兄
SHIONG	010,04	0343	06	22217	2809	7531	FIERCE		兇
SHIONG	017,02	0423	04	22770	2808	0979	OMINOUS		凶
SHIONG	020,04	0546	06	27720	2812	4401	HUNGARY,THORAX/CHEST	D5172	匈
SHIONG	085,04	3081	07	32170		0982	TORRENTIAL RUSH,TUMULTUOUS	3170	汹
SHIONG	085,06	3170	09	37120	2811	4405	TORRENTIAL RUSH,TUMULTUOUS	3081	洶
SHIONG	130,06	5172	10	77220	2812	4404	THORAX/CHEST		胸
SHIONG	149,04	6081	11	02670	2813	0980	BRAWL,UPROAR	9290	訩
SHIONG	149,06	9290	13	07620	2813	4402	BRAWL,UPROAR	6081	詾
SHYONG	086,10	3574	14	21331	2815	8805	A BEAR		熊
SHYONG	172,04	7160	12	40014	2814	0919	MALE,HEROIC		雄
SHIONQ	066,11	2416	15	27407		6421	(SURNAME)		夐
SHIONQ	149,05	9287	12	07620	2817	3821	TO SPY,TO GOSSIP,CLEVER		詗
SHIOU	009,04	0128	06	24290	2786	5263	TO REST		休
SHIOU	009,08	0208	10	28222	2794	4228	REPAIR,CULTIVATE		修
SHIOU	030,06	8136	09	64090	2787	5264	CALL OUT,JEER		咻
SHIOU	053,06	1652	09	00294	2788	5267	SHADE,PROTECTION		庥
SHIOU	085,10	3331	13	37127	2796	3650	WATER IN WHICH RICE WAS BOILED		滫
SHIOU	123,05	5026	11	80215	27970	542	BASHFUL,TO SHAME		羞
SHIOU	130,07	5190	11	28227	2795	3649	REPAIR,CULTIVATE,TEACHER'S PAY	K0208	脩
SHIOU	140,10	554G	14	44222			RUMEX ACETOSA		蓨
SHIOU	142,11	584C	17	58127			LONCHODES NIPONENSIS		蟏
SHIOU	153,06	6287	13	24290	2789	5266	(LEOPARD)		貅
SHIOU	184,11	7430	19	88715	2798	0543	DELICACIES		饈
SHIOU	190,06	7574	16	72294		5268	RED LACQUER,TO LACQUER		髹
SHIOU	196,06	7707	17	27227	2790	4649	OWL		鵂
SHEOU	040,08	1372.0B	11	30261	5498	1685	(A) NIGHT		宿
SHEOU	075,02	2615	06	41927	2791	4536	ROTTEN		朽
SHEOU	075,10	8580	14	46934			CLERODENDRON TRICOTOMUM		模

ROM	RAD	TEL	TOT	FC	MAT	OSH	TAG	CR	CHAR
SHEOU	119,10	9043	16	93936			TO WASH(RICE/ETC.)		糔
SHIOW	030,10	0833	13	66034	2792	5094	SENSE OF SMELL	B5263.0A	嗅
SHIOW	040,08	1372.0A	11	30261	5498	1685	CONSTELLATION		宿
SHIOW	046,05	1485	08	25760	2800	1832	MOUNTAIN PEAK,CAVE		岫
SHIOW	085,10	8700	13	36134		5096	BROMINE		溴
SHIOW	096,06	8821	10	14127			QUICKLY-DETERIORATING JADE		琇
SHIOW	096,07	3811	11	12127	2804	4727	(JADE)		琇
SHIOW	115,02	4423	07	20227	2803	4726	HANDSOME/ELEGANT		秀
SHIOW	120,07	4836	13	22927	2805	4730	EMBROIDER(Y)	4937	綉
SHIOW	120,11	4937.1	17	25927			EMBROIDER(Y)		繡
SHIOW	120,12	4937	18	25927	2805	2090	EMBROIDER(Y)	4836	繍
SHIOW	132,04	5263.0A	10	26430	1331	5093	SMELL BAD,SENSE OF SMELL	D0833	臭
SHIOW	145,05	5918	10	35260	2801	1833	SLEEVE		袖
SHIOW	167,07	6907	15	82127	2806	4728	RUST		銹
SHIOW	167,12	6907.1	20	85127	2806	2086	RUST		鏽
SHIOW	209,10	7869	24	26434	2793		SENSE OF SMELL	0833	齅
SHIU	030,03	0675.0A	06	61040	2818	3308	SH/HUSH		吁
SHIU	030,12	0864	15	61017	2822	0509	HISS,EXHALE		噓
SHIU	032,12	1074	15	41117	2823	0508	OLD BURIAL GROUNDS		墟
SHIU	038,12	1294	15	21404		9061	ELDER SISTER		嬃
SHIU	062,02	2049	06	53200	2861	6996	11TH EARTH'S BRANCH,7-9 P.M.		戌
SHIU	072,03	8501	07	61040			DAWN		旴
SHIU	075,12	2898.0A	16	47953		2519	OSMANTHUS FRAGRANS		樨
SHIU	076,12	2963	16	27282	2824	4908	TO SNORT		歔
SHIU	085,06	3164	09	37110	2856	0748	DITCH,GUTTER		洫
SHIU	085,09	3291	12	31186	2847	8324	NECESSARY/MUST	A7312	湏
SHIU	104,03	8863	08	00127			TO BE SICK,DISEASE/AFFLICTION		疔
SHIU	109,03	4173	08	61040	2819	3310	STARE,ANXIOUS,(SURNAME)		盱
SHIU	120,09	9067	15	28921			FINE SILK	4948	繪
SHIU	120,14	4948	20	21927	2845	3773	FINE SILK	9067	繻
SHIU	130,05	5171	09	17227	2835	3641	ALL,TO STORE,ASSIST		胥
SHIU	141,06	5711	12	21217	2821	0507	VOID,DEVOID OF CONTENT		虛
SHIU	149,03	6070	10	01640	2820	3309	TO BOAST/GREAT/LARGE		訏

ROM	RAD	TEL	TOI	FC	MAT	OSH	TAG	CR	CHAR
SHIU	173,06	7194	14	10227	2844	3762	TO NEED		需
SHIU	181,03	7312	12	21286	2847	8283	NECESSARY/MUST,BEARD	D7586	須
SHIU	190,12	7586	22	72286	2848	8284	BEARD	B7312	鬚
SHYU	060,07	1776	10	28294	2841	8501	SLOW,(SURNAME)		徐
SHEU	013,08	8098	10	60641			CAP OF YIN DYNASTY		冔
SHEU	030,06	8136.0A	09	64090	2787	5264	TO GROAN/SHRIEK		咻
SHEU	038,05	8274	08	47420	2829		CHEERFUL,CHATTER LIKE OLD WOMAN		姁
SHEU	075,06	2700	10	47920	2826	3395	QUERCUS SERRATA		栩
SHEU	085,09	8689	12	37127	2837	3646	STRAIN SPIRITS,ABUNDANT,BRIGHT		湑
SHEU	086,09	3563	13	67332	2831	8790	GENIAL/WARM		煦
SHEU	119,09	4738	15	97927	2838	3644	SACRIFICIAL RICE,OFFICIAL PAY		糈
SHEU	149,04	6079	11	08640	2825	2429	TO PERMIT,(SURNAME)		許
SHEU	149,06	6103	13	07620	2827	3387	BRAG,MAKE KNOWN,HARMONY		詡
SHEU	149,09	6162	16	07627	2839		KNOWLEDGE,DECEIT		諝
SHEU	164,09	9428	16	17627	2840	3643	STRAIN SPIRITS,SPIRITUS		醑
SHIUH	009,06	8041	08	27210			STILL/SILENT		侐
SHIUH	019,09	0521.1	11	60127	2858	4793	EXHORT,STIMULATE		勖
SHIUH	019,09	0521	11	64627	2858	4801	EXHORT,STIMULATE	2587	勗
SHIUH	026,06	0614	08	27120	2862	2118	GIVE RELIEF,SYMPATHY	1865	卹
SHIUH	029,07	0650	09	87940	2842	6093	NARRATE,ARRANGE	2402	叙
SHIUH	033,09	1107	12	47127	2836	3642	SON-IN-LAW	8296	壻
SHIUH	038,09	8296	12	47427	2836	3645	SON-IN-LAW		婿
SHIUH	053,04	1645	07	00222	2851	3087	ORDER,PREFACE		序
SHIUH	061,06	1865	09	97010	2862	0746	SYMPATHY,GIVE RELIEF	0614	恤
SHIUH	061,10	8402	13	90063			TO FOSTER/TO BEAR		慉
SHIUH	066,07	2402	11	81947	2842	6203	NARRATE	0650	敍
SHIUH	072,02	2485	06	46010	2855	7912	DAWN/RISING SUN		旭
SHIUH	073,08	2587	12	60127			EXHORT,STIMULATE	0521	朂
SHIUH	078,06	8624	10	17210			DAMAGE EGG SO IT DOES NOT HATCH		殈
SHIUH	085,11	3375	14	38140			NAME OF A RIVER		漵
SHIUH	094,09	372A	12	47227			MIDAS		猇
SHIUH	094,12	8809	15	47227			FLUTTER WITH FEAR(AS BIRDS)		獝
SHIUH	102,05	3964.0A	10	00603	1412	1820	TO RAISE(ANIMALS)		畜

ROM	RAD	TEL	TOT	FC	MAT	OSH	TAG	CR	CHAR
SHIUH	120,06	4825	12	46903	2849	8449	LINE WITH COTTON WADDING		
SHIUH	120,09	4872	15	24960	2850	1639	CLUES,BEGINNINGS		
SHIUH	120,15	4958	21	24986	2865	8156	CONTINUE,REPLENISH		
SHIUH	128,06	9105	12	17401		2741	SON-IN-LAW	1107	
SHIUH	140,04	5352	08	44202		3088	SCIRPIS MARITIMUS/SMALL CHESTNUT		
SHIUH	140,10	5552	14	44603	2860	1822	TO STORE		
SHIUH	140,14	5658	18	44801			(SURNAME),BEAUTIFUL		
SHIUH	140,15	5667	19	44806		8160	ALISMA PLANTAGO		
SHIUH	154,06	6330	13	67810	2863	0747	GIVE ALMS		
SHIUH	164,04	6796	11	12670	2834	0981	DRUNK		
SHIUH	181,04	7320	13	11186	2859	8246	ANXIOUS,WORRIED		
SHIUH	194,05	9635	15	23215			BEGUILE,SUDDENLY		
SHIUH	195,09	765N	20	27327			UPENEUS CHRYSOPHEURON		
SHIUH	195,14	9663	25	27381	2854	8062	HYPOPHTHALMICHTHYS MORITRIX		
SHIUAN	007,04	8017	06	10106	2889	0021	REVOLVE		
SHIUAN	009,13	0318	15	26232	2876	5871	INGENIOUS/FRIVOLOUS		
SHIUAN	030,09	0826	12	63016	2869	0031	CLAMOR/NOISE	A6165	
SHIUAN	038,13	1298	16	46432	2877	5876	CLEVER/PRETTY		
SHIUAN	040,06	1357	09	30106	2890	0030	DECLARE PUBLICLY		
SHIUAN	061,09	8399	12	93016			WELL-BEING		
SHIUAN	064,09	8445	12	53016	2891	0034	PULL UP SLEEVES,STRIKE WITH FISTS		
SHIUAN	072,06	8507	10	61016	2867		TO DRY/PARCH		
SHIUAN	072,09	2537	13	63016	2870	0033	GENIAL AND WARM		
SHIUAN	086,09	3551	13	93816		0036	RADIANCE,WARM		
SHIUAN	096,09	8830	13	13116	2893		ORNAMENTAL PIECE OF JADE		
SHIUAN	109,09	8916	14	63016			LARGE EYES		
SHIUAN	113,11	8983	15	36227			(SURNAME)		
SHIUAN	120,09	9068	15	23916	2872		BRIGHT COLOR		
SHIUAN	124,13	5067	19	67720		3396	SHORT FLIGHT,FLIRTATIOUS		
SHIUAN	140,09	5503	13	44106	2873	0038	HEMEROCALLIS FLAVA	A6178	
SHIUAN	140,16	9199	20	44647		6117	HEMEROCALLIS FLAVA,MOTHER	A5503	
SHIUAN	149,09	6178	16	02647	2875	6116	HEMEROCALLIS FLAVA,FALSE,FORGET	A9199	
SHIUAN	149,09	6165	16	03616	2874	0032	CLAMOR,NOISE,DECEITFUL	A0826	

絮緒續耵芧蕦薲賉酗頊魊鰰亘儇喧嬛宣愃擅昍暄煊瑄瞘褑縜翾萱護諼

ROM	RAD	TEL	TOT	FC	MAT	OSH	TAG	CR	CHAR
SHIUAN	159,03	6513	10	51040	2660	2380	PAVILION,COVERED CARRIAGE		軒
SHIUAN	167,09	9488	17	83116			SPADE/HOE		鍠
SHIUAN	187,07	9617.0A	17	76327			GREY HORSE		駽
SHIUAN	195,11	766R	22	28381			SEBASTODES MATSUBARAE		鰁
SHYUAN	061,08	2038.1	12	77333			SUSPEND,HANG		悬
SHYUAN	061,16	2038	20	62339	2887	8692	SUSPEND,HANG		懸
SHYUAN	070,07	2467	11	08281	2894	6025	REVOLVE		旋
SHYUAN	085,11	3373	14	38181	2895	6028	EDDY		漩
SHYUAN	095,00	3763.1	04	00712	2881	0602	BLACK,MYSTERIOUS		亥
SHYUAN	095,00	3763	05	00732	2881	8880	BLACK,MYSTERIOUS		玄
SHYUAN	096,11	3872	15	18181	2896	6026	(JADE)	3894	琁
SHYUAN	096,14	3894	18	11168	2896	1725	(JADE)	3872	璿
SHYUAN	140,12	7915	16	44346	6070	3247	NETTLE,URTICA		蕁
SHEUAN	030,06	0753	08	61016	2866	0023	GLORIOUS,SOB/WEEP		咺
SHEUAN	086,06	3531	10	91816	2867		BRILLIANT		烜
SHEUAN	104,17	4089	22	00151	2717	2554	RINGWORM		癬
SHEUAN	162,06	6693.1	10	34301			SELECT,ELECT		选
SHEUAN	162,12	6693	16	37308	2898	6775	SELECT,ELECT		選
SHEUAN	167,05	6881	13	80132	2886	8881	WIRE,RINGS ON A TRIPOD		鉉
SHIUANN	070,07	2467.0A	11	08281	2894	6025	SPECIALLY FOR AN OCCASION,LATHE	D9500	旋
SHIUANN	075,09	2775	13	43916	2871	0035	STRETCH(SHOE),BLOCK(HAT)		楦
SHIUANN	085,05	3138	08	30132	2882	8890	WEEP		泫
SHIUANN	085,09	8694	12	33116	2892	0037	WASH(COLOR)		渲
SHIUANN	086,05	3514	09	90832	2883	8885	DAZZLE,TO SHOW OFF		炫
SHIUANN	109,05	4181	10	60032	2884	8882	DIZZY/DAZZLED	8909	眩
SHIUANN	109,06	8909	11	67020			DAZZLED/DIZZY	4181	眴
SHIUANN	120,06	4821	12	27920	2888	4442	ADORNED,SWIFT		絢
SHIUANN	140,11	9193	15	44281			(HERB)		蔙
SHIUANN	144,05	5891	11	21221	2885	3034	TO BOAST/TO SHOW OFF		衒
SHIUANN	167,11	9500	19	88181	2897	6027	LATHE,THREAD IN SCREW	B2467.0A	鏇
SHIUANN	170,08	7119.0A	11	77277	2694	1054	SINK IN		陷
SHIUE	140,13	5641	17	44741	2653	2460	WORMWOOD,(SURNAME)		薛
SHIUE	160,09	6585	16	20741		2459	WORMWOOD,(SURNAME)	5641	辪

ROM	RAD	TEL	TOT	FC	MAT	OSH	TAG	CR	CHAR
SHIUE	177,04	7247	13	44510	2902	7145	BOOTS	7273	
SHIUE	177,12	7273	21	44554	2902	2609	BOOTS	7247	
SHIUE	178,12	9570	21	44554	2902	2609	BOOTS	7247	
SHYUE	039,05	1331.2	08	90407	2780	3141	LEARN/STUDY,SCIENCE		
SHYUE	039,11	1331.1	14	27407	2780		LEARN/STUDY,SCIENCE		
SHYUE	039,13	1331	16	77407	2780	3140	LEARN/STUDY,SCIENCE		
SHYUE	140,05	9166	09	44802			CONTAINER FOR STORING PROVISIONS		
SHYUE	148,13	9280	20	77227			TO POLISH HORN		
SHYUE	157,07	643A.0A	14	52801		5983	TO WALK AROUND/TURN BACK MIDWAY		
SHYUE	196,13	7759	24	77327	2781	4675	ORIENTAL BULLFINCH		
SHEUE	173,03	7185	11	10177	2903	0864	SNOW		
SHEUE	195,11	7914	22	21377		0865	CODFISH/GADUS MACROCEPHALUS		
SHIUEH	018,07	0465.0A	09	92200	2785	2906	TO SCRAPE		
SHIUEH	094,05	8798	08	43250			TO SCAMPER(AS A TERRIFIED ANIMAL)		
SHIUEH	116,00	4494	05	30802	2899	6513	HOLE/CAVE/DEN		
SHIUEH	142,05	574E	11	53187			NECROPHORUS JAPONICUS		
SHIUEH	143,00	5877.0A	06	27100	2901	0745	BLOOD		
SHIUEH	173,03	7185.0A	11	10177	2903	0864	WASH AWAY(SHAME),WHITE		
SHIUN	019,10	8113	12	64827	2907	4833	MERIT,MEDAL	0534	
SHIUN	019,14	0534	16	24327	2907	4833	MERIT,MEDAL	8113	
SHIUN	032,10	1053	13	46186	2908	8136	ANCIENT PORCELAIN WIND-INSTRUMENT	1088	
SHIUN	032,14	1088	17	42131	2908	8734	ANCIENT PORCELAIN WIND-INSTRUMENT	1053	
SHIUN	072,14	2564	18	62031	2909	8735	TWILIGHT/SUNSET		
SHIUN	086,07	8740·	11	17336	2905	8768	FUMES FROM SACRIFICE		
SHIUN	086,10	3575	14	20331	2906	8733	TO SMOKE,SCENT,FUMIGATE	3609	
SHIUN	086,14	3609	18	92831	2906	8738	TO SMOKE/SCENT/FUMIGATE	3575	
SHIUN	094,14	3753	17	42231	2910	8737	NAME OF A TRIBE		
SHIUN	116,09	4518.0A	14	30601	7422	1527	TO SCENT TEA WITH FLOWERS		
SHIUN	120,14	4950	20	22931	2911	8739	CRIMSON		
SHIUN	130,14	9142	18	72231			LAMB SOUP		
SHIUN	140,14	5651	18	44331	2912	8740	COUMAROUNA ODORATA		
SHIUN	164,14	6836	21	12631	2913	8736	HELPLESSLY INTOXICATED		
SHYUN	030,12	088D	15	67041			A FATHOM		

ROM	RAD	TEL	TOT	FC	MAT	OSH	TAG	CR	CHAR
SHYUN	041,03	1416.2	06	17347			SEEK		
SHYUN	041,09	1416.1	12	17341			SEEK		
SHYUN	041,09	1416	12	17346	2744	3242	SEEK		
SHYUN	046,06	1493	09	27720	2916	4435	RANGES OF HILLS		
SHYUN	047,03	1559.1	06	12403	2927		TO PATROL		
SHYUN	047,04	1559	07	32303	2927	6786	TO PATROL		
SHYUN	060,06	1770.0A	09	27220	2917		COMPREHENSIVE		
SHYUN	060,09	1789	12	22264	2926	1716	FOLLOW (A RULE)		
SHYUN	061,06	1852	09	97020	2918	4437	SINCERE		
SHYUN	064,09	8442	12	52064			TO STROKE,ENCOURAGE		
SHYUN	072,02	2484	06	27620	2915	4433	TEN DAYS		
SHYUN	075,12	8591	16	47941			FRAXINUS BUNGEANA		
SHYUN	085,06	3169	09	37120	2921	4443	TRULY,WHIRLPOOL		
SHYUN	085,12	3410	15	37141	2745	3246	STEEP BANK,NAME OF A RIVER		
SHYUN	085,23	8720	27	26232			A GROUP OF SPRINGS		
SHYUN	086,12	3593	16	97841	2746	3244	WARM UP(FOOD)		
SHYUN	094,06	3702.0A	09	47220	2920	4440	COMPREHENSIVE/COMPLY WITH		
SHYUN	096,06	3800	10	17120		4434	(GEM)		
SHYUN	120,03	9052	09	22900			SILKCORDS,BIND		
SHYUN	140,06	5424	10	44627	2922	4444	(SURNAME)		
SHYUN	142,12	5854	18	57141			(HAIRY SEA-CRAB)		
SHYUN	149,06	6104	13	07620	2923	4436	INQUIRE		
SHYUN	163,06	6737	09	27627	2925	2221	NAME OF A FEUDAL STATE		
SHYUN	187,03	7460	13	72300	2929	2836	TAME,ATTAIN GRADUALLY		
SHYUN	195,12	9658	23	21346			PSEPHURUS SP.		
SHYUN	195,12	7669	23	27341	2747	3245	STURGEON,ACIPENSER SP.		
SHEUN	075,06	8558	10	47920	2919		FRAME FOR HANGING BELLS		
SHIUNN	009,06	8039	08	27220	2920		DIE FOR A CAUSE,BURIED WITH DEAD	2991	
SHIUNN	030,12	8170	15	67081	5551	8040	SPURT OUT OF THE MOUTH	3407	
SHIUNN	049,09	1575	12	77801		8039	A SIGN IN THE TRIGRAM,OBEY		
SHIUNN	060,06	1770	09	27220	2917	4438	FOLLOW,QUICK		
SHIUNN	078,06	2991	10	17220	2920	4441	DIE FOR A CAUSE,BURIED WITH DEAD	3702	
SHIUNN	085,03	3065	06	37110	2749	7791	HIGH WATER,SPRINKLE WATER		

寻尋尋岣巡巡徇循恂揗旬橁洵潯矗燿狥珣紃荀蟳詢郇馴鱏鱒枸侚噀巽徇殉汛

ROM	RAD	TEL	TOT	FC	MAT	OSH	TAG	CR	CHAR
SHIUNN	085,12	3407	15	37181			SPURT OUT OF THE MOUTH	8170	
SHIUNN	094,06	3702	09	47220	2920	4440	DIE FOR A CAUSE,BURIED WITH DEAD	2991	
SHIUNN	140,12	5622	16	44406	1720	2298	MUSHROOM,MOLD		
SHIUNN	149,03	6064	10	02600	2914	2835	INSTRUCTION		
SHIUNN	149,03	6061	10	07610	2750	7790	NEWS/INFORMATION		
SHIUNN	162,03	6598	07	37301	2751	6773	RAPID		
SHIUNN	162,06	6676.1	10	39300			TO YIELD		
SHIUNN	162,10	6676	14	32309	5545	6779	TO YIELD		
SHOU	029,02	2392.1	04	27740	5837		RECEIVE,COLLECT		
SHOU	066,02	2392	06	28740	5837	6324	RECEIVE,COLLECT		
SHOUR	086,11	3578.0A	15	04331	5895	8811	RIPE,COOKED		
SHOOU	040,03	1343	06	30342	5844	3255	TO GUARD		
SHOOU	064,00	2087	04	20500	5838	3335	HAND		
SHOOU	064,08	8479	12	20552			PICKPOCKET		
SHOOU	185,00	7445	09	80601	5839	1739	HEAD,AN. FOR POEMS		
SHOW	029,06	0649	08	20407	5840	6194	RECEIVE		
SHOW	030,08	0786	11	20601	5843	1259	SELL		
SHOW	030,08	3757.1	11	80601			BEAST,QUADRUPED		
SHOW	033,11	1108	14	40641	5846	3174	LONG LIFE		
SHOW	041,04	1108.1	07	50404			LONG LIFE		
SHOW	064,08	2219	11	52047	5841	6195	GIVE		
SHOW	094,06	3704	09	43242	5845	3257	HUNTING-DOG,IMPERIAL TOUR		
SHOW	094,15	3757	18	63634	5847	5071	BEAST,QUADRUPED		
SHOW	104,09	4060	14	00147	5848	6167	THIN/LEAN		
SHOW	120,08	4849	14	22947	5842	6196	CORD ON A SEAL		
SHU	002,03	2579.1	04	53027			BOOK/LETTER		
SHU	029,06	0647.0A	08	27940	5881		UNCLE(AS IN 0647) IN DIRECT ADDRESS		
SHU	038,06	1204	09	45490	5850	5485	PRETTY WOMAN		
SHU	064,04	2118	07	57022	5854	3084	TO STRAIN/POUR OUT		
SHU	064,11	2314	14	51027	5899	4557	DICE/GAMBLING,TO RELEASE		
SHU	064,15	2373	18	51036	5858	8593	TO SPREAD,SET FORTH		
SHU	073,06	2579	10	50601	5857	1502	BOOK/LETTER		
SHU	075,07	2752	11	40913	5860	7785	COMB		

渫狗葷訓 訊迅遜遜收收熟守手扌首受售獸壽寿授狩獸瘦綬书叔姝抒摴攄書梳

ROM	RAD	TEL	TOT	FC	MAT	OSH	TAG	CR	CHAR
SHU	075,11	2873	15	41916	5859	0800	HINGE		樞
SHU	075,11	2880	15	41927	5863	4558	AILANTHUS GLANDULOSA		樗
SHU	078,06	2992	10	15290	5851	5482	UNIQUE		殊
SHU	079,00	3007	04	77407	5849	6259	SPEAR,(SURNAME)		殳
SHU	082,09	3039	13	82214		7384	RUG		毹
SHU	085,06	3178	09	35190			NAME OF A RIVER,(SURNAME)		洙
SHU	103,06	3989	11	15192	5861	5520	SPARSE,NEGLIGENT,(SURNAME)	K3990	疎
SHU	103,07	3990	13	10113	5861	7781	SPARSE,NEGLIGENT	K3989	疏
SHU	120,04	4782	10	27922	5855	3086	SLOW,TO FREE FROM		紓
SHU	135,06	5289	12	87622	5856	3083	RELAX(SURNAME)		舒
SHU	140,11	5600.0A	15	44113	5862	7782	VEGETABLES		蔬
SHU	159,09	6551	16	58021	5864	8972	LOSE,TRANSPORT		輸
SHU	159,09	6551.1	16	58032	5864	8972	LOSE,TRANSPORT		輸
SHWU	029,06	0647	08	27940	5881	6086	UNCLE(FATHER'S YOUNGER BROTHER)		叔
SHWU	032,11	1060	14	04104	5894	0230	PRIVATE TUTORAGE		塾
SHWU	039,08	1328	11	04417	5893	7919	WHO/WHICH/WHAT		孰
SHWU	085,05	3145	08	33194	5887		NAME OF A RIVER		沐
SHWU	085,08	3219	11	37140	5883	6090	PURE/VIRTUOUS,SKILLFUL		淑
SHWU	086,11	3578	15	04331	5895	8811	RIPE,COOKED		熟
SHWU	115,05	4443	10	23994	5888	7079	PANICUM ITALICUM		秫
SHWU	140,08	5486	12	44947	5884	6092	LEGUMINOUS PLANTS		菽
SHWU	145,13	9269	18	36227			SHORT SKIRT OR TUNIC		襡
SHWU	154,15	6370	22	64886	5903		REDEEM/TO RANSOM		贖
SHUU	044,05	1466.2	08	77227	5896		BELONG,CLASS		属
SHUU	044,09	1466.1	12	77227	5896		BELONG,CLASS		属
SHUU	044,18	1466	21	77227	5896	4476	BELONG,CLASS		屬
SHUU	066,09	2422.1A	13	98440	5865		TO COUNT		数
SHUU	066,11	2422.0A	15	58440	5865	6406	TO COUNT		數
SHUU	072,09	2540	13	60604	5866	1644	SUMMER HEAT		暑
SHUU	104,13	8885	18	00116			HIDDEN/SECRET,SCROFULA		癙
SHUU	122,09	5002	14	60604	5867	1645	OFFICE/BUREAU		署
SHUU	140,14	5620	18	44604	5869	1647	POTATO,YAM	5675.0A	薯
SHUU	140,16	5675.0A	20	44664	5869	1631	POTATO,YAM	5620	藷

ROM	RAD	TEL	TOT	FC	MAT	OSH	TAG	CR	CHAR
SHUU	142,07	5771	13	60127	5901	4465	SZECHWAN		
SHUU	142,13	9241	19	56127	5902	4474	MAGGOT,LARVA		
SHUU	167,21	701A	29	87127			METAL		
SHUU	195,14	767B	25	26364			DOLPHIN/CORPHAENA		
SHUU	202,00	7810	12	20132	5870	5676	GLUTINOUS MILLET		
SHUU	208,00	7857	13	77717	5871	6820	RAT/MOUSE		
SHUH	009,08	0225	10	27234	5885	5098	SUDDENLY		
SHUH	009,08	0225.1	10	27289	5885	5635	SUDDENLY		
SHUH	032,11	1065	14	67104	5876	0205	VILLA		
SHUH	053,08	1659	11	00237	5874	8763	ORDINARY		
SHUH	061,06	1859	10	46330	5875	8560	FORGIVE		
SHUH	062,02	2050	06	53200	5873	7029	GARRISON		
SHUH	066,09	2422.1	13	98440	5865		NUMBER,SEVERAL		
SHUH	066,11	2422	15	58440	5865	6406	NUMBER,SEVERAL		
SHUH	072,14	2562	18	66064	5868	1646	DAWN		
SHUH	075,01	2611	05	43900			METHOD/TECHNIQUE	5890	
SHUH	075,03	2631	07	50906	5891	5519	BIND,TO CONTROL		
SHUH	075,05	2885.1	09	44900			TREE		
SHUH	075,12	2885	16	44900	5879	3168	TREE		
SHUH	085,11	3359	14	37182	5483	4950	TO RINSE(MOUTH)		
SHUH	085,12	3412	15	34100	5880	3169	MOISTURE,TIMELY RAIN		
SHUH	103,07	3990.0B	13	10113	5861	7781	STATEMENT,RUNNING COMMENTARY		
SHUH	117,08	4549	13	77108	5877	0561	VERTICAL,TO ERECT	6264	
SHUH	118,15	4697	21	88448			16 PECKS		
SHUH	122,09	5002.0A	14	60604	5867	1645	TO SIGN(ONE'S NAME),TO MANAGE		
SHUH	124,07	5048.0A	13	17227	2617		HASTINESS		
SHUH	140,09	551G	13	44309			CURCUMA LONGA		
SHUH	144,05	5890	11	21221	5889	3031	METHOD/TECHNIQUE	2611.0A	
SHUH	145,07	9258	12	31218	5878		COARSE CLOTHING OF CAMEL'S HAIR		
SHUH	151,08	6264	15	77108	5877	0601	VERTICAL,TO ERECT	4549	
SHUH	157,11	6468	18	63161	5898	1686	WALK CAREFULLY		
SHUH	162,05	6615	09	33309	5890	6759	NARRATE/RELATE		
SHUH	167,05	9452	13	83194			ACMITE		

蜀蠋钃鱪泰鼠倏儵墅庶恕戍数數曙术束树樹漱澍疏豎籔署僗透術襡豎躅述鉥

ROM	RAD	TEL	TOT	FC	MAT	OSH	TAG	CR	CHAR
.SHU	050,05	1590.0C	08	17227			BROOM		帚
SHUA	018,06	0456	08	72200	5905	2911	BRUSH		刷
SHOA	126,03	5080	09	10404	5904	9036	PLAY WITH,TO JUGGLE		耍
SHUAH	018,06	0456.0A	08	72200	5905	2911	TO SELECT		刷
SHUAI	064,11	2292	14	50043	5911	2371	TO FALL,THROW ON GROUND	A6469	摔
SHUAI	094,10	373A	13	40240			HYAENA STRIATA		猭
SHUAI	145,04	5905	10	00732	5908	5861	DECAY,DECLINE		衰
SHUAI	157,11	6469	18	60143		2360	TO FALL	A2292	蹂
SHOAI	101,00	3943	05	77212	5907	7454	FLING		甩
SHUAY	050,02	1596.1	05	34027			TO COMMAND,COMMANDER-IN-CHIEF		帅
SHUAY	050,06	1596	09	24727	5909	3945	TO COMMAND,COMMANDER-IN-CHIEF	A3764.0A	帥
SHUAY	095,06	3764.0A	11	00403	5910	2359	TO LEAD/COMMAND	A1596	率
SHUAY	142,11	5839	17	50143	5836		CRICKET		蟀
SHUAN	064,06	2165	09	58014	5912	0342	TIE UP		拴
SHUAN	075,06	2633	10	48914	5913	0343	WOODEN PIN,BOTTLE STOPPER		栓
SHUAN	169,01	7025	09	77107	5914	3438	TO BOLT		閂
SHUANN	085,08	7795	11	32100	5906	2912	RINSE		涮
SHUANN	149,09	6178.0A	16	02647	2875	6116	TO FOOL		譔
SHUANG	029,02	7175.1	04	77440	5915		PAIR		双
SHUANG	038,17	1307	20	41463	5920	1701	WIDOW		孀
SHUANG	085,16	3478.0A	19	31111		7330	NAME OF A RIVER IN KWANTUNG		瀧
SHUANG	137,18	5323	24	20447	5916	6141	BOAT		艭
SHUANG	172,10	7175	18	20407	5915	6139	PAIR		雙
SHUANG	173,09	7208	17	10963	5919	1699	FROST		霜
SHUANG	187,17	9622	27	71363		1700	GOOD HORSE		驦
SHUANG	196,17	9684	28	17927			TURQUOISE KINGFISHER		鸘
SHOANG	032,11	8249	14	44134			ELEVATED PROMINENT GROUND		塽
SHOANG	089,07	3642	11	40034	5917	5125	INVIGORATING,STRAIGHTFORWARD		爽
SHOANG	187,11	7519	21	54334			(HORSE)		驦
SHUANQ	029,02	7175.1A	04	77440	5915		(SURNAME)		双
SHUANQ	172,10	7175.0A	18	20407	5915	6139	(SURNAME)		雙
SHWEI	149,08	6142	15	00614	5923	0872	WHO		誰
SHOEI	085,00	3055	04	12230	5922	5637	WATER		水

ROM	RAD	TEL	TOT	FC	MAT	OSH	TAG	CR	CHAR
SHUEY	050,07	1599	10	48216	5926	7570	HANDKERCHIEF		帨
SHUEY	109,08	4204	13	62014	5925	0413	TO SLEEP		睡
SHUEY	115,07	4451	12	28916	5927	7572	TAXES/DUTIES		稅
SHUEY	142,07	5770	13	58116	5928	7573	EXUVIAE OF INSECTS OR REPTILES		蛻
SHUEY	149,07	6141.0A	14	08616	5939	7567	PERSUADE(POLITICALLY)		說
SHWEN	086,08	3545	12	90847			BLAZING/BRIGHT		焞
SHOEN	030,04	0700	07	63010	5929	7682	SUCK		吮
SHOEN	075,09	2815	13	42964	5934	1718	HORIZONTAL RAILING,DRAW FORTH		楯
SHOEN	109,04	4163.0A	09	72264	6578		A SHIELD		盾
SHUENN	109,12	4226	17	62052	5937	2564	TO WINK		瞬
SHUENN	136,06	5293	12	20252	5936	2563	NAME OF AN EMPEROR		舜
SHUENN	140,12	556G	16	44252	5938		HIBISCUS SYRIACUS		蕣
SHUENN	181,03	7311	12	21086	5935	8270	FAVORABLE,ALONG		順
SHUO	149,07	6141	14	08616	5939	7567	SAY		說
SHWO	085,03	3248	06	37120	5832		TO BUBBLE(OF WATER)		沟
SHUOH	038,03	1171	06	47420			MATCHMAKER,(SURNAME)		妁
SHUOH	060,03	8385	06	27220			PLANK FOR CROSSING STREAM		彴
SHUOH	064,10	2283	13	57020	5941	3576	DAUB/THRUST		搠
SHUOH	066,09	2422.1B	13	98440	5865		FREQUENTLY/REPEATEDLY		數
SHUOH	066,11	2422.0B	15	58440	5865	6406	FREQUENTLY/REPEATEDLY		數
SHUOH	074,05	2592	09	87420	5940	3575	BEGINNING;FIRST DAY OF LUNAR MONTH		朔
SHUOH	075,10	2844	14	87904	5942	5360	LONG LANCE	8925	槊
SHUOH	086,15	3617	19	92894	5834	5416	BRIGHT/LUMINOUS	B7007	爍
SHUOH	095,06	3764.0B	11	00403	5910		TO LEAD/COMMAND		率
SHUOH	110,07	8925	12	19227			LONG LANCE	2844	矟
SHUOH	112,09	4311.0A	14	11686	5815	8255	LARGE/BIG		碩
SHUOH	118,09	4633	15	88223	2619		HIT WITH A POLE/POLE DANCE		箾
SHUOH	140,10	7801	14	44427			POD/CAPSULE		蒴
SHUOH	142,11	5839.0A	17	50143	5836		CRICKET		蟀
SHUOH	167,05	7007.1	13	82194			MELT/FUSE(METAL),BRIGHT		鑠
SHUOH	167,15	7007	23	82194	5835	5412	MELT/FUSE(METAL),BRIGHT	D3617	鑠
SHY	037,02	1136	05	25030	5806	5193	LOSE		失
SHY	044,00	1437	03	77270	1045	4233	CORPSE	1451	尸

ROM	RAD	TEL	TOT	FC	MAT	OSH	TAG	CR	CHAR
SHY	044,06	1451	09	77212	5759	7150	CORPSE	1437	屍
SHY	050,03	1597.1	06	31027			TEACHER,A DIVISION (MILIT.)		师
SHY	050,07	1597	10	21727	5760	4003	TEACHER,A DIVISION (MILIT.)		師
SHY	070,05	2457	09	08212	5768	7430	DISTRIBUTE(ALMS),(SURNAME)		施
SHY	085,09	3440.1	12	36112			WET		湿
SHY	085,10	3313	13	31114	5823	0254	WET	3440	溼
SHY	085,14	3440	17	36133	5823	8815	WET	3313	濕
SHY	094,10	3740	13	41227	5761	4004	LION		獅
SHY	140,09	5532	13	44212		7433	XANTHIUM STRUMARIUM		蒒
SHY	140,10	5558	14	44601	5801	1615	ACHILLEA SIBIRICA		蓍
SHY	140,10	5548	14	44727			CAREX MACRECEPHALA		蒒
SHY	142,02	5723	08	17110	5452	7793	LOUSE	5810	虱
SHY	142,09	5810	15	17136	5452	8915	LOUSE	5723	蝨
SHY	149,06	6108	13	04641	5783	3228	POEM		詩
SHY	163,06	9389	09	47427			PLACE NAME		邿
SHY	195,10	766A	21	21327			SERIOLA QINQUERADIATA,YELLOW TAIL		鰤
SHY	196,03	7684	14	77227	5758	4639	TURTLE DOVE		鳲
SHYR	009,02	0087	04	24200	5808	2269	TENTH		什
SHYR	010,07	8088	09	44210		7559	DECAGRAM		尅
SHYR	024,00	0577	02	40000	5807	2264	TEN		十
SHYR	032,10	1054	13	44141		3230	HEN ROOST		埘
SHYR	040,05	1395.1	08	30430	5821		REALLY,SOLID		实
SHYR	040,09	1385	12	30801	5821	6012	REALLY,SOLID	1395	寔
SHYR	040,11	1395	14	30806	5821	8168	REALLY,SOLID	1385	實
SHYR	064,06	2168	09	58061	5809	1193	PICK UP,TEN(FRAUDPROOF)		拾
SHYR	072,03	2514.1	07	64000			TIME,O,CLOCK,WHEN		时
SHYR	072,06	2514	10	64041	5780	3229	TIME,O,CLOCK,WHEN		時
SHYR	085,09	3290	12	36181		6011	CLEAR WATER,PURE		湜
SHYR	112,00	4258	05	10600	5813	1101	STONE/ROCK		石
SHYR	112,09	4311	14	11686	5815	8255	LARGE/BIG		碩
SHYR	113,05	4367	09	31260	5814		STONE SHRINE		祏
SHYR	117,02	454A	07	04100		2266	DECALITER		竍
SHYR	119,02	472A	08	94900			DECAMETER		籿

ROM	RAD	TEL	TOT	FC	MAT	OSH	TAG	CR	CHAR
SHYR	140,10	5535	14	44641	5781	3232	TO PLANT,PEUCECLANUM GRAVELENS		
SHYR	142,08	5793	16	85736	5811	8900	EAT UP SLOWLY,ECLIPSE		
SHYR	149,12	6221.0A	19	03650	5825	6907	LEARN CHARACTERS		
SHYR	184,00	7380	09	80732	5810	5927	EAT,ANIMAL FEED		
SHYR	195,10	7661	21	24341	5782	3231	SHAD/ILISHA ELONGATA		
SHYR	208,05	7859	18	71716	5816	1106	LONG-TAILED MARMOT		
SHYY	009,06	0169	08	25206	5770	6572	CAUSE,EMPLOY,MESSENGER		
SHYY	030,02	0670	05	50006	5769	6569	HISTORY		
SHYY	038,05	1193	08	43460	5772	1461	BEGIN		
SHYY	040,06	1358.0A	09	30104			ROOM		
SHYY	044,06	1452	09	77294	5757	5441	STOOL/FECES		
SHYY	057,03	1716	06	14212	5767	7424	RELAX		
SHYY	111,00	4247	05	80430	5784	5154	DART,ARROW		
SHYY	120,11	4927	17	21381	5774	5974	BAND FOR THE HAIR	4967	
SHYY	120,19	4967	25	21911	5775	7106	BAND FOR THE HAIR	4927	
SHYY	152,00	6269	07	10232	5766	5708	HOG/SWINE		
SHYY	187,05	7471	15	75346	5771	6570	SAIL A VESSEL,HASTEN,PROCEED TO		
SHYH	001,04	0013	05	44717	5790	0850	WORLD,A LIFETIME		
SHYH	006,07	0057	08	50007	5787	3377	WORK/AFFAIR		
SHYH	009,03	0099	05	24210	5777	0141	AN OFFICIAL		
SHYH	009,06	0174	08	24241	5778	3235	ATTEND ON		
SHYH	019,06	0528.1	08	54427		4870	TENDENCY,INFLUENCE,CONDITIONS		
SHYH	019,11	0528	13	44427	5799	4869	TENDENCY,INFLUENCE,CONDITIONS		
SHYH	030,10	0841	13	64061	5800	1612	FOND OF,ADDICTED TO		
SHYH	030,13	0896	16	68018	5764	0138	TO BITE,DEVOUR		
SHYH	033,00	1102	03	40100	5776	0140	SCHOLAR,WARRIOR		
SHYH	037,12	1163	15	40036	5827	5111	ANGRY,(SURNAME)		
SHYH	040,06	1358	09	30104	5820	0278	ROOM		
SHYH	050,02	1579	05	00227	5792	4011	MARKET		
SHYH	056,03	1709	06	43100	5817	6880	FORM/STYLE		
SHYH	056,09	1710	12	43940	5797	6884	MURDER A SUPERIOR		
SHYH	061,06	1853	09	94041	5779	3234	RELY UPON		
SHYH	063,03	8416.1	07	30217			DOOR PIVOT		

蒔蝕識食鱒鼫使史始室屎弛矢縰纚豕駛世事仕侍势勢嗜噬士螫室市式弒恃扅

ROM	RAD	TEL	TOT	FC	MAT	OSH	TAG	CR	CHAR
SHYH	063,03	8416	07	37217			DOOR PIVOT		戹
SHYH	064,05	2160	08	53040	5815		WIPE		拭
SHYH	072,04	2508.1	08	60308	5794		TO BE,THIS		昰
SHYH	072,05	8505	09	60101			TO BE,THIS	2508	昰
SHYH	072,05	2508	09	60801	5794	6002	TO BE,THIS		是
SHYH	075,05	2636	09	40927	1842	4009	PERSIMMON		柹
SHYH	075,05	267B	09	47927			PERSIMMON	2636	柿
SHYH	075,06	8550	10	43940			(TREE)		柿
SHYH	083,00	3044	04	72740	5785	6842	CLAN NAME,MAIDEN NAME		氏
SHYH	085,13	3431	16	38118	5765	0139	NAME OF A RIVER,BANK/SHORE		澨
SHYH	109,04	8902	09	62040			LOOK AT	6018	眡
SHYH	109,05	8906	10	61091	5789		LOOK AT	6018	眎
SHYH	113,00	4355	05	10901	5788	8347	TO SHOW/REVEAL		示
SHYH	118,07	4602	13	88108	5763	0137	DIVINE BY STALK		筮
SHYH	130,05	516C	09	70201			PROTEOSE		胨
SHYH	135,04	5288	10	22640	5786	6843	TO LICK/LAP		舐
SHYH	135,08	5288.1	14	26627	5786	4509	TO LICK/LAP		舓
SHYH	142,11	5826.0A	17	48136	5826	8944	TO STING		螫
SHYH	142,12	585A	16	53150			MACROCHEIRA KAMPFERI		蟤
SHYH	145,15	5998	20	34236	5828		RAINCOAT		襫
SHYH	147,04	6018	11	36210	5789	7614	LOOK AT		視
SHYH	149,06	6107	13	03640	5798	6881	TRY/TO TEST		試
SHYH	149,07	6129	14	52601	5803	1162	OATH/VOW		誓
SHYH	149,09	6164	16	06681	5795	6005	EXAMINE,JUDGE		諟
SHYH	149,09	6184	16	08617	5802	0699	POSTHUMOUS TITLE,CONFER SUCH TITLE	6198	諡
SHYH	149,10	6198	17	08617	5802	0715	POSTHUMOUS TITLE,CONFER SUCH TITLE	6184	謚
SHYH	149,12	6221	19	03650	5825	6907	KNOW/RECOGNIZE		識
SHYH	151,04	6262.0A	11	14147	5805	6209	SALTED FERMENTED BEANS		豉
SHYH	153,05	628A	12	26240			PERODICTICUS POTTO		貃
SHYH	154,05	6322	12	44806	5791	8132	BUY ON CREDIT,BORROW,RENT OUT		貰
SHYH	159,06	6524	13	53040	5819	6882	CROSSBAR IN CARRIAGE FRONT		軾
SHYH	162,06	6624	10	32306			FIT/SUITABLE	6684	适
SHYH	162,07	6641	11	32302	5804	6641	DEPART,DIE		逝

ROM	RAD	TEL	TOT	FC	MAT	OSH	TAG	CR	CHAR
SHYH	162,11	6684	15	30302	5822	6694	FIT/SUITABLE	6624	
SHYH	165,13	6847	20	26941	5824	2488	TO RELEASE,EXPLAIN		
SHYH	167,05	7775	13	80127		4008	CERIUM		
SHYH	184,05	7395	13	88727	5812	3958	ADORN,ORNAMENTS		
SHYH	195,05	763D	16	20322			OSTRACION IMMACULATUM		
.SHY	021,09	0555.0A	11	61801	5796	6014	KEY		
SH	030,12	0864.0A	15	61017	2822	0509	TO HISS/BOO		
SONG	038,06	8279	09	43450	5560	6971	NAME OF AN ANCIENT STATE		
SONG	046,08	1516	11	22932	5554	8851	NAME OF A MOUNTAIN IN HONAN, LOFTY	1529	
SONG	046,10	1529	13	22227	5554	3837	NAME OF A MOUNTAIN IN HONAN,LOFTY	1516	
SONG	075,04	2646	08	48932	5552	8849	PINE,LOOSE	D7575	
SONG	075,07	1370	11	30904			PINE		
SONG	085,08	3247	11	38132	5555	8850	NAME OF A RIVER		
SONG	130,04	514E	08	78232			OSONE		
SONG	140,08	5473	12	44932	5556	8852	(CABBAGE)/BRASSICA CHINENSIS		
SONG	190,08	7575	18	72932	5557	8853	LOOSE	B2646	
SORNG	061,07	1884.0A	10	95096	5561	5523	COWARD		
SOONG	061,07	1884	10	95096	5561	5523	FRIGHTENED		
SOONG	061,11	1981	15	28338	5563	8663	AROUSE		
SOONG	117,07	4548	12	05196	5562	5521	HORRIFIED,RAISE,INCITE		
SOONG	128,11	5117	17	22401	5564	2737	TO SHRUG,EXCITE,RAISE UP		
SONQ	040,04	1345	07	30904	5565	5338	SUNG DYNASTY,(SURNAME)		
SONQ	149,04	6075	11	08632	5558	8847	LITIGATION		
SONQ	149,07	6139	14	07627	5567	3717	READ ALOUD		
SONQ	162,06	6623	10	38303	5566	6722	SEND,SEE OFF,PRESENT WITH		
SONQ	181,04	7313	13	81786	5559	8322	TO PRAISE		
SOU	053,09	8372	12	00227			TO SEARCH,BE CONCEALED	1672	
SOU	053,10	1672	13	00247	5471	6166	TO SEARCH/BE CONCEALED	8372	
SOU	064,09	8456	12	53027			TO SEARCH	2282	
SOU	064,10	2282	13	57047	5472	6162	TO SEARCH		
SOU	085,10	3309	13	37147	5473	6165	URINATE		
SOU	094,10	8807	13	47247			DOG(DIAL.),TO HUNT		
SOU	137,10	5318.0A	16	27447	5435	6163	AN. FOR WARSHIPS		

適釋鉓鰤匙噓娀崟嵩松窰淞胗菘鬆悚悚愯竦聳宋訟誦送頌慶廋摠搜溲獀艘

ROM	RAD	TEL	TOT	FC	MAT	OSH	TAG	CR	CHAR
SOU	140,10	5533	14	44213	5469	7649	SEARCH OUT(AS DATA)		蒐
SOU	163,09	9400	12	77427			NAME OF A TRIBE		鄋
SOU	182,10	7372	19	77214	5478	7846	SOUND OF WIND,BLOW(AS OF WIND)		颼
SOU	184,10	9600	18	87747	5479	6161	RANCID/SOURED(AS FOOD)		餿
SOOU	009,09	8062	11	27247			OLD GENTLEMAN	0652	傁
SOOU	029,08	0652	10	77407	5470	6157	OLD GENTLEMAN		叟
SOOU	030,11	0871	14	68034		5161	TO URGE ON/INCITE		嗾
SOOU	064,15	2370	18	58040	5480	6407	SHAKE/TREMBLING		擻
SOOU	109,10	4218	15	67047	5474	6160	BLIND		瞍
SOOU	118,15	4697.0A	21	88448			BASKET FOR DRAINING RICE		籔
SOOU	140,15	5674	19	44448	5481	6408	PLACE OF CONCOURSE,MARSH		藪
SOOU	140,15	567D	19	44731			LIRIOPE SPICATA		蓃
SOOU	149,10	6203.0A	17	07647	5476	6159	INDUCE		謏
SOW	030,11	0870	14	67082	5482	4949	COUGH	8882	嗽
SOW	030,11	0870.1	14	68040	5482	6388	COUGH		嗽
SOW	085,11	3359.0A	14	37182	5483	4950	TO RINSE(MOUTH)		漱
SOW	104,11	8882	16	00182	5482		COUGH	0870	瘷
SU	100,07	3936	12	15401	5487	6588	REVIVE	C5685	甦
SU	103,06	3989.0A	11	15192	5861		SPARSE,NEGLIGENT,(SURNAME)	K3990.0A	疎
SU	103,07	3990.0A	13	10113	5861	7781	SPARSE,NEGLIGENT	K3989.0A	疏
SU	115,11	4479	16	22394	5487	5543	REVIVE	3936	穌
SU	140,04	5685.1	08	44337			PLACE NAME,(PLANT),REVIVE		苏
SU	140,11	5600	15	44113	5862	7782	VEGETABLES		蔬
SU	140,16	5685	20	44394	5488	5544	PLACE NAME,(PLANT),REVIVE	G3936	蘇
SU	164,05	6798	12	12694	5486	5541	FLAKY		酥
SWU	009,07	0198	09	28268	5497	1384	VULGAR		俗
SUH	009,12	0287	14	21294		5444	LISU(ETHNIC GROUP)		傈
SUH	024,06	5126.1	08	50227			RESPECTFUL,KANSU		肃
SUH	030,10	0851	13	65093	5491	8446	CROP(OF BIRD)	A9135	嗉
SUH	032,10	1043	13	87104	5492	0206	TO MODEL(A FIGURE) IN CLAY		塑
SUH	036,03	1121	06	77210	5502	7827	MORNING		夙
SUH	040,08	1372	11	30261	5498	1685	LODGE FOR THE NIGHT,OLD/FORMER		宿
SUH	061,10	1954	14	87332	5494		TELL,COMPLAIN,SUE	K6083	愬

ROM	RAD	TEL	TOT	FC	MAT	OSH	TAG	CR	CHAR
SUH	061,10	1953	13	95093	5493	8447	GUILELESS/SINCERE		愫
SUH	075,10	2870	14	47982			QUERCUS DENTATA		橭
SUH	075,12	8595	16	45927			TALL AND STRAIGHT(OF TREES)		橚
SUH	085,05	3149	08	32131	5496	2057	GO UP STREAM,TRACE THE SOURCE	3307	沂
SUH	085,07	3208	10	35196	5503	5527	NAME OF A RIVER		涑
SUH	085,10	3307	13	37120	5495	3577	GO UP STREAM,TRACE THE SOURCE	3149	溯
SUH	116,08	4528	13	30408	5501	2358	RUSH OUT OF A DEN,RUSTLING		窣
SUH	118,11	4665	17	88982			SIEVE,DENSE VEGETATION		簌
SUH	119,06	4725	12	10904	5500	5443	GRAIN,MILLET		粟
SUH	120,04	4790	10	50903	5490	8445	PLAIN		素
SUH	129,08	5126	13	50227	5509	2085	RESPECTFUL,KANSU		肅
SUH	130,10	9135	14	75293	5491	8448	CROP OF A BIRD,FAT	A0851	膆
SUH	140,11	5581	15	44261	5499	1688	CLOVER,MEDICAGO		蓿
SUH	140,11	5565	15	44982	5508	4951	VEGETABLES,(SURNAME)		蔌
SUH	142,08	577E	14	50148			SYROMASTES		蜉
SUH	148,07	6046	14	25296	5504	5525	TREMBLE WITH FEAR		觫
SUH	149,05	6083	12	02631	5494	2054	TELL,COMPLAIN,SUE		訴
SUH	149,10	6204	17	06647	5900	6455	RISE,TO BEGIN,COMPOSED		謖
SUH	162,07	6643	11	35309	5505	6728	RAPID		速
SUH	162,10	6679	14	37302	5496	6684	GO UPSTREAM,TRACE THE SOURCE	3307	遡
SUH	162,11	9377	15	37308			NIMBLE,QUICK,ALERT		遬
SUH	184,07	7406	15	85796	5506		POT OF COOKED RICE		餗
SUH	187,12	7525	22	75327	5510	2088	(HORSE)		驌
SUH	195,12	9660	23	25327			DRIED FISH		鱐
SUH	196,12	9681	23	57227		4621	(OMINOUS MYTHICAL BIRD),TEAL		鷫
SUAN	094,07	3710	10	43247	5512	6469	(MYTHICAL ANIMAL)		狻
SUAN	104,07	4000	12	00147	5513	6473	ACHING OF LIMBS		痠
SUAN	164,07	6808	14	13647	5514	6464	SOUR,ACID,SORE		酸
SUANN	118,07	9013	13	88441	5516	2797	TO FIGURE,REGARD AS	4615	筭
SUANN	118,08	4615	14	88446	5516	2804	TO FIGURE,REGARD AS	9013	算
SUANN	140,10	5537	14	44991	5515	8349	GARLIC		蒜
SUEI	035,00	1114	03	40407	5517	6565	MOVING SLOWLY		夊
SUEI	044,04	1443.0A	07	77232	4686	5641	URINATE/URINE		尿

ROM	RAD	TEL	TOT	FC	MAT	OSH	TAG	CR	CHAR
SUEI	085,13	3285	16	30114			NAME OF A RIVER		濰
SUEI	109,06	4242	11	64014			EVIL LOOK OF DEEP-SET EYES		眭
SUEI	109,08	4205	13	60014	5518	0875	STARE,(SURNAME)		睢
SUEI	120,07	4840	13	22944	5520	9068	PACIFY		綏
SUEI	140,07	5443	11	44404	5521		CORIANDER		荽
SUEI	142,03	7173.1A	09	60136			ALTHOUGH		虽
SUEI	172,09	7173.0A	17	60114	5519	0921	ALTHOUGH		雖
SWEI	120,07	4840.0A	13	22944	5520	9068	PACIFY		綏
SWEI	142,03	7173.1	09	60136			ALTHOUGH		虽
SWEI	170,09	7131	12	74227	5522	3597	SUI DYNASTY		隋
SWEI	170,10	9536	13	74232		6685	FOLLOW,(SURNAME)	7151	随
SWEI	170,13	7151	16	74232	5523	6686	FOLLOW,(SURNAME)	9536	隨
SWEI	172,09	7173	17	60114	5519	0921	ALTHOUGH		雖
SOEI	085,16	3473	19	34132	5524		SLIPPERY		濰
SOEI	172,10	7172	18	22227	2447	3897	PLACE NAME IN SZECHWAN		巂
SOEI	188,13	7557	23	74232	5525	6687	MARROW		髓
SUEY	046,02	2979.4	05	22101	5538	0004	YEAR/YEARS OLD		岁
SUEY	046,03	2979.1	06	22207			YEAR/YEARS OLD		歳
SUEY	046,04	2979.2	07	22207	5538		YEAR/YEARS OLD		岁
SUEY	046,09	2979.3	12	22253	5538	7015	YEAR/YEARS OLD		歲
SUEY	075,13	2903	17	48933			(TREE)		檖
SUEY	077,09	2979	13	21253	5538	7011	YEAR/YEARS OLD		歲
SUEY	086,13	3606	17	98833	5531	6740	SPECULUM,FIRE	A9511	燧
SUEY	096,13	3887	17	18133	5532		PENDANT GIRDLE-ORNAMENTS		璲
SUEY	109,08	4210	13	60048	6877	2344	CLEAR,BRIGHT EYE		睟
SUEY	112,08	4295	13	10648	5528	2341	BREAK/BROKEN/FRAGMENTARY		碎
SUEY	113,05	4378	10	22901	5539	8350	EVIL SPIRIT		祟
SUEY	115,12	4482	17	25933	5526	8699	EAR OF GRAIN		穗
SUEY	115,13	4485	18	28933	5533	6741	EAR OF GRAIN	4482	檖
SUEY	120,12	4934	18	25933	5527	8700	TASSEL,FINE AND LOOSE CLOTH	A494A	繐
SUEY	120,13	494A	19	28933	5535	6742	TASSEL	A4934	繸
SUEY	145,13	5985	18	38233	5536	6738	GRAVE-CLOTHES		襚
SUEY	149,08	6144	15	00648	5529	2342	ABUSE		誶

ROM	RAD	TEL	TOT	FC	MAT	OSH	TAG	CR	CHAR
SUEY	162,09	6659	13	38303	5530	6736	FORTHWITH		遂
SUEY	162,14	6706	18	33303		6743	DEEP,DISTANT,MYSTERIOUS		邃
SUEY	167,13	9511	21	88133			SPECULUM	A3606	鐩
SUEY	170,13	7143	16	78233	5537	6739	SUBTERRANEAN,UNDERGROUND PASSAGE		隧
SUEN	039,03	1327.1	06	19400			GRANDSON		孙
SUEN	039,07	1327	10	12493	5541	8487	GRANDSON		孫
SUEN	094,10	3735	13	42293	5543	8489	(MONKEY)		猻
SUEN	140,10	5549	14	44493	5544	8490	FRAGRANT GRASS		蓀
SUEN	184,03	7385	12	28232	5546	5928	SUPPER		飧
SOEN	064,10	2275	13	56086	5548	8140	TO DAMAGE/INJURE		損
SOEN	075,10	2835	14	40941	5549	2272	TENON AND MORTISE		榫
SOEN	118,04	4571	10	88507	5547	4246	BAMBOO SHOOT	4587	笋
SOEN	118,06	4587	12	88627	5547	4445	BAMBOO SHOOT	4571	筍
SOEN	118,12	4680	18	88801	2919		CROSS-BEAM FOR HANGING BELLS		簨
SUENN	030,12	8170.0A	15	67081	5551	8040	SPURT OUT OF THE MOUTH	3407.0A	喸
SUENN	049,09	1575.0A	12	77801	5550	8039	A SIGN IN THE TRIGRAM,OBEY		巽
SUENN	085,12	3407.0A	15	37181			SPURT OUT OF THE MOUTH	8170.0A	潠
SUENN	162,06	6676.1A	10	39300			TO YIELD		逊
SUENN	162,10	6676.0A	14	32309	5545	6779	TO YIELD		遜
SUO	009,10	0273	12	28211		0102	UNEVEN/UNSTEADY(IN DANCING)		傞
SUO	030,07	0778	10	63047	5462	6461	SUCK,INCITE		唆
SUO	038,07	1223	10	39404	5455	9037	(PHONETIC),LOOSE		娑
SUO	064,07	2199	11	39502	5456	3346	FEEL,TO FONDLE	8431	挲
SUO	064,07	8431	10	59020	5456	4166	TO FEEL,TO FONDLE	2199	挱
SUO	075,07	2747	11	43947	5463	6471	SHUTTLE		梭
SUO	075,07	2726	11	49920	5457		STEWARTIA PSEUDOCAMELLIA		桫
SUO	118,10	4649	16	88732		5865	RAINCAPE MADE OF GRASS	5560	簑
SUO	120,11	4799	17	23961	5897	1687	SHRINK/REDUCE		縮
SUO	123,07	502A	13	83547			CARBOXYL(RADICAL)		羧
SUO	140,07	5446	11	44129	5458	4168	(GRASS)/CYPERUS ROTUNDUS		莎
SUO	140,10	5560	14	44732	5464	5864	RAINCAPE MADE OF GRASS	4649	蓑
SWO	120,04	4792.0A	10	40903	5459	8459	MIGHT AS WELL		索
SUOO	027,05	2076.1	07	71228			PLACE,ACTUALLY		所

ROM	RAD	TEL	TOT	FC	MAT	OSH	TAG	CR	CHAR
SUOO	063,04	2076	08	72221	5465	2032	PLACE,ACTUALLY		所
SUOO	096,10	3851	14	19186	5466	8235	FRAGMENTARY,TRIFLING	8837	瑣
SUOO	096,11	8837	15	12194	5467	5512	FRAGMENTARY/TRIFLING	3851	璅
SUOO	120,04	4792	10	40903	5459	8459	TO EXACT,SEARCH INTO,ISOLATED		索
SUOO	142,10	582F	16	54193			ANISODACTYLUS SIGNATUS		蟆
SUOO	167,10	6956.1	18	82186	5468		LOCK		鎖
SUOO	167,10	6956	18	89186	5468	8236	LOCK		鎖
SUOH	030,10	7624	13	69086			SMALL TRUMPET		唢
SY	009,09	8059	11	26230	5581	8582	TALENTED,URGENT		偲
SY	027,12	0631	14	71221	5575	2044	SERVANT	1678	廝
SY	028,00	0635	02	23700	5568	8816	SELFISH,PRIVATE	4424	ム
SY	030,02	0674	05	17620	5585	3378	CONTROL,COMPANY		司
SY	030,12	0880	15	62021	5576	2040	NEIGH,HISS		嘶
SY	030,12	0888	15	62093	5572		(PHONETIC)		嗦
SY	032,05	098A	08	47120			SLERE		坷
SY	053,12	1678	15	00221	5575	2045	SERVANT	0631	廝
SY	061,05	1835	09	60330	5580	8579	THINK		思
SY	064,12	2322	15	52021	5577	2041	TO TEAR		撕
SY	069,08	2448	12	42821	5574	2039	THIS,(PHONETIC)		斯
SY	085,12	3402	15	32121	5578	2043	TO EXHAUST,DRAIN DRY		澌
SY	113,10	4404	14	32217			FELICITY/BLESSING		禠
SY	115,02	4424	07	22930	5569	8820	PRIVATE,SELFISH		私
SY	120,00	4761	06	20903	5570	8442	SILK	4828	糸
SY	120,06	4828	12	22993	5571	8444	SILK		絲
SY	120,07	4828.1	13	22993		8494	SILK		絲
SY	120,09	4880	15	26930	5582	8585	FINE LINEN		總
SY	122,09	5003	14	60336	5583	8589	SCREEN		罳
SY	141,04	9213	10	72217	5579	7673	AMPHIBIOUS ANIMAL WITH ONE HORN		虒
SY	142,10	5825	16	51127	5762	4005	SNAIL		螄
SY	164,19	9432	26	11611		7103	TO FILTER(WINE)		釃
SY	167,09	7600	17	86130		8580	STRONTIUM		鍶
SY	182,09	7368	18	76213	5584	7849	COOL BREEZE OF AUTUMN		颸
SY	195,10	766H	21	22317			DRACISCUS SACHI		鰤

319

ROM	RAD	TEL	TOT	FC	MAT	OSH	TAG	CR	CHAR
SY	196,12	7748	23	22327	5573	4692	HERON		鷥
SYY	078,02	2984	06	10212	5589	7149	DIE		死
SYH	009,05	0136.0A	07	27220	6969	3380	TO EXAMINE/SPY		伺
SYH	009,05	0138	07	28200	5593	7985	RESEMBLE		似
SYH	009,07	0203	09	23234	5595	5178	WAIT FOR/UNTIL		俟
SYH	009,15	8077	17	26227		4513	TO FINISH,THE END		儩
SYH	010,06	0349	08	77217	5603	7659	RHINOCEROS INDICUS		兕
SYH	010,06	8087	08	77217	5603	7659	BOVINE ANIMAL WITH ONE HORN		兕
SYH	027,09	0627.0B	11	71220	6987	2974	LATRINE	1665.0B	厠
SYH	030,10	0843	13	67220	5588	3382	SUCCESSION,OFFSPRING		嗣
SYH	031,02	0934	05	60210	5598	1925	FOUR		四
SYH	038,04	1197	07	48400	5594	7987	WIFE OF OLDER BROTHER,(SURNAME)		姒
SYH	041,03	1408	06	40341	5597	3226	BUDDHIST TEMPLE		寺
SYH	049,00	1570	03	77717	5590	7252	9-11 A.M., 6TH EARTH'S BRANCH		巳
SYH	053,09	1665.0B	12	00220	6987	2975	LATRINE	0627.0B	廁
SYH	075,05	8548	09	46900			SPOON/LADLE		柶
SYH	085,03	3066	06	37117	5591	7255	STREAM WHICH RETURNS AFTER BRANCHING		汜
SYH	085,05	3128	08	36100	5600	1927	SNIVEL,PLACE NAME		泗
SYH	085,07	3201	10	33134	5596	5181	RIVER-BANK		涘
SYH	113,03	4358	07	37217	5592	7254	OFFER SACRIFICE TO		祀
SYH	117,07	9004	12	03134	5595	5175	WAIT FOR/UNTIL	0203	竢
SYH	118,05	4568	11	88627	5586	3384	HAMPER,TRUNK		笥
SYH	127,05	5091	11	57977	5604	1478	PLOUGH,PLOUGHSHARE		耜
SYH	129,07	5127	13	75707	5598	2623	FOUR(FRAUDPROOF),MARKET		肆
SYH	154,08	6337.0A	15	66827	6988	4512	GIVE/BESTOW		賜
SYH	184,00	7380.0A	09	80732	5810	5927	TO FEED	7393	食
SYH	184,05	7393	13	87720	5587	3381	TO FEED	7380.0A	飼
SYH	187,05	7475	10	76300		1926	TEAM OF 4 HORSES		駟
SYH	195,03	762B	14	27311			GIRELLA PUNCTATA		鮖
TA	009,03	0100	05	24212	5961	7421	HE/SHE		他
TA	032,10	1042	13	46127	5967	3406	COLLAPSE		塌
TA	038,03	1247	06	44412	5961	7426	SHE		她
TA	040,02	1338	05	30711	6439	7174	IT		它

ROM	RAD	TEL	TOT	FC	MAT	OSH	TAG	CR	CHAR
TA	093,03	3671	07	24512	5961	7422	IT		坔
TA	157,10	6488	17	66127	5973	3408	SHUFFLE ALONG(IN SLIPPERS)	7251	蹋
TA	167,05	7809	13	83111			THALLIUM		鉈
TA	177,04	7251	13	47547	5409	6502	SHUFFLE ALONG IN(SLIPPERS)	6488	鞳
TAA	032,10	1044	13	44161	5978	1199	PAGODA		塔
TAA	085,10	7814	13	34161			TAR		溚
TAA	094,16	3758.0A	19	47286	5985	8205	OTTER		獺
TAH	030,10	0852	13	64061	5977	1200	TO DESPAIR		嗒
TAH	030,14	8180	17	66033		6721	TO DRINK/TO SWALLOW		嚃
TAH	064,05	2148.0A	08	51060	6460	1104	MAKE RUBBING	2287	拓
TAH	064,10	2287	13	56027	5968	3410	MAKE RUBBING	2148.0A	搨
TAH	064,13	2337	16	54034	5979	6656	FLOG,RAPID		撻
TAH	075,10	2840	14	46927	5969	3411	COUCH		榻
TAH	085,04	3101	07	12603	5962	1586	AGAIN AND AGAIN,MANY,(SURNAME)		沓
TAH	085,11	3374	14	36193	5984	8456	NAME OF A RIVER		漯
TAH	094,06	8801	09	42264			TO EAT(OF DOGS),DOG-FOOD		猲
TAH	094,16	3758	19	47286	5985	8205	OTTER		獺
TAH	157,08	6431	15	62163	5964	1588	STEP ON		踏
TAH	157,10	6488.0A	17	66127	5973	3408	STEP ON	6431	蹋
TAH	162,10	6681	14	36302	5974	6683	CARELESS,UNTIDY		邋
TAH	162,10	6682	14	36303	5983	6720	MIXED,ABUNDANT		遝
TAH	167,08	9474	16	82163	5965	1587	ENCASE THE END WITH METAL		錔
TAH	167,10	9489	18	86127		3407	THALLIUM		鐋
TAH	169,10	7069	18	77127	5975	3488	DOOR OR WINDOW IN AN UPPER STORY		闒
TAH	169,13	7077	21	77304	5982	3524	DOOR OF AN INNER ROOM		闥
TAH	195,10	766W	21	26327	5976		COMMON SOLE/SOLEA SOLEA		鰨
TAI	030,05	8130.0A	08	63060			(SURNAME)		咍
TAI	130,05	5158	09	73260	6010	1454	FOETUS,LITTER		胎
TAI	140,05	5377.0A	09	44603	6011	1464	COATING(OF TONGUE)		苔
TAIR	030,02	0669	05	23600	6008	1447	ABBR. OF 2918/5270/7376,YOUR		台
TAIR	064,05	2127	08	53060	6018	1453	LIFT OR CARRY (SOMETHING HEAVY)	2358	抬
TAIR	064,14	2358	17	54014	6018	0275	LIFT OR CARRY(SOMETHING HEAVY)	2127	擡
TAIR	075,05	2918.1	09	43960		1457	DESK,PLATFORM		枱

ROM	RAD	TEL	TOT	FC	MAT	OSH	TAG	CR	CHAR
TAIR	075,14	2918	18	44914		0276	DESK,PLATFORM	A0669	檯
TAIR	086,05	3520	09	23809	6009	5612	SOOT		炱
TAIR	133,08	5270	14	40104	6016	0273	PLATFORM,STATION	A0669	臺
TAIR	140,05	5377	09	44603	6011	1464	MOSS		苔
TAIR	140,14	5653	18	44104	6019	0277	CAREX DISPALATHA		薹
TAIR	163,05	6733	08	27627	6013	2180	NAME OF A FEUDAL STATE,(SURNAME)		邰
TAIR	182,05	7376	14	73216		7840	TYPHOON	A0669	颱
TAIR	187,05	7469	15	73360	6014	1456	WORN OUT HORSE,TIRED		駘
TAIR	195,05	7632	16	23360	6015	1460	GLOBEFISH		鮐
TAY	009,10	7831	12	25232			THAI		傣
TAY	037,01	1132	04	40030	6020	5061	TOO/EXCESSIVELY		太
TAY	061,04	1966.1	08	40333			ATTITUDE		态
TAY	061,10	1966	14	21331	6024	8682	ATTITUDE		態
TAY	085,04	3077	07	34130	6022	5065	TOO,ELIMINATE		汰
TAY	085,05	3141	10	50132	6023	5687	GRAND		泰
TAY	130,04	514B	08	74230			PEPTIDE		肽
TAY	164,04	679B	11	14630			PHTHALEIN		酞
TAY	167,04	7835	12	84130		5062	TITANIUM		鈦
TAN	030,12	8171	15	66056	6071		TO SNORT/PANT		嘽
TAN	032,04	0973	07	47140	6056	4107	COLLAPSE		坍
TAN	061,06	1848	10	44331		8686	HE/SHE (HON.)		她
TAN	064,10	2382.1	13	50014			SPREAD OUT,VENDOR'S STAND		摊
TAN	064,19	2382	22	50014	6082	0899	SPREAD OUT,VENDOR'S STAND		攤
TAN	085,10	3492.1	13	30114			BEACH		滩
TAN	085,19	3492	22	30114	6083	0900	BEACH		灘
TAN	104,10	4093.1	15	00114			PARALYZED		瘫
TAN	104,19	4093	24	00114	6084	0901	PARALYZED		癱
TAN	154,04	6304	11	80806	6055	8187	GREEDY		貪
TARN	032,04	1086.1	07	41131	6059	8857	ALTAR,EARTHEN JAR	D1098	坛
TARN	032,12	8258	15	41146	6069	2290	EARTHEN JAR	1098	壇
TARN	032,13	1086	16	40116	6059	0041	ALTAR		墰
TARN	032,16	1098	19	46131	6069	8871	EARTHEN JAR	B1086.1	壜
TARN	059,12	1734.0A	15	16256	6072	2639	PLUCK A STRING,IMPEACH		彈

ROM	RAD	TEL	TOT	FC	MAT	OSH	TAG	CR	CHAR
TARN	072,12	2560	16	60731	6068	8879	DARK CLOUDS		
TARN	075,13	2905	17	40916	6060	0046	SANDAL WOOD		
TARN	085,12	3389	15	31146	6063	2297	DEEP,(SURNAME)		
TARN	085,13	3422.0A	16	37161	6045	1186	(SURNAME)		
TARN	104,08	4033	13	00189	6076	5632	PHLEGM,SPITTLE		
TARN	121,12	9084.1	18	81746	6069	2291	EARTHEN JAR		
TARN	121,16	9084	22	86732		8872	EARTHEN JAR	1098	
TARN	146,06	6009	12	10406	6061	2289	(SURNAME),DEEP		
TARN	149,08	6151	15	09689	6078	5627	TO CHAT/DISCUSS,(SURNAME)		
TARN	149,12	6223	19	01646	6066	2292	(SURNAME)		
TARN	163,08	6756	11	97827	6079	2239	NAME OF AN ANCIENT CITY,(SURNAME)		
TARN	167,08	9477	16	89189			LONG SPEAR		
TARN	167,12	9509	20	81146	2742		KNOB ON A SWORD-HANDLE,(SURNAME)		
TARN	184,08	9596.0A	16	89789	6080		TO ADVANCE		
TAAN	030,11	8160	14	68086			SOUND OF MANY PEOPLE EATING		
TAAN	032,05	0982	08	46110	6057	0022	FLAT,OPEN-HEARTED		
TAAN	061,03	1809	07	21331	6074	8535	NERVOUS		
TAAN	061,08	8397	11	99089			TO BURN,BE AFFLICTED		
TAAN	082,08	3034	12	29718	6075	7401	BLANKET,RUG		
TAAN	113,12	4405	16	31246	6065	2296	SACRIFICE AT THE END OF MOURNING		
TAAN	140,08	5485	12	44809	6077	5633	MISCANTHUS SACCHARIFLORUS		
TAAN	145,05	5917	10	36210	6058	0016	TO BARE	9270	
TAAN	145,13	9270	18	30216	6058	0042	TO BARE	5917	
TAAN	154,12	6374	19	61846		2295	PAY AN ADVANCE,SILK BOOK COVER		
TAAN	164,09	6822	16	14617	6086	0723	BRINE OF PICKLED MEAT		
TAAN	190,04	7566	14	72412	6086A	7744	HAIR HANGING DOWN OVER THE FOREHEAD		
TANN	030,02	0855.1	05	67040			TO SIGH		
TANN	030,11	0855	14	64034	6081	5258	TO SIGH	2961	
TANN	064,08	2232	11	57094	6054	5392	SEARCH		
TANN	076,11	2961	15	47582	6081	4947	TO SIGH	0855	
TANN	086,05	3516	09	22289	6085	5609	CHARCOAL,CARBON	D8955	
TANN	112,09	8955	14	12689		5610	CARBON	B3516	
TANG	085,09	3282	12	36127	6101	4496	SOUP,(SURNAME)		

ROM	RAD	TEL	TOT	FC	MAT	OSH	TAG	CR	CHAR
TANG	123,09	7856	15	82589			CARBONYL(RADICAL)		
TANG	156,09	639C	16	46802	6104	5961	WADE/GET FEET WET	A6499	
TANG	157,11	6499	18	69114			WADE		
TANG	167,11	6974	19	89114	6110	0188	NOISE OF DRUMS		
TARNG	030,07	0781	10	00267	6116	1346	T'ANG DYNASTY,(SURNAME)		
TARNG	032,08	1016	11	90104	6107	0187	HALL		
TARNG	032,10	1048	13	40167	6117	1347	POND		
TARNG	064,10	2288	13	50067	6118	1349	KEEP OUT		
TARNG	075,08	2768	12	90904	6111	5321	CHERRY-APPLE		
TARNG	085,10	8697	13	30167		1354	POND,NONCOAGULATIVE		
TARNG	096,10	8835	14	10167			(JADE)		
TARNG	119,10	4743	16	90967	6121	1350	SUGAR/CANDY		
TARNG	130,11	5228	15	79214	6108	0190	CHEST(OF BODY),HOLLOW SPACE		
TARNG	142,10	9236	16	50167	6122	1353	(CICADA)		
TARNG	142,11	5838	17	59114	6109	0191	PRAYING MANTIS		
TARNG	164,10	7864	17	10667			CARBOHYDRATE		
TARNG	184,09	7424.0A	17	86727	2778	4489	MALT-SUGAR		
TARNG	184,10	7425	18	80767	6121	1348	SUGAR/CANDY	4743	
TAANG	009,08	0229	10	29227	6106	3858	IF	A0331	
TAANG	009,20	0331	22	29231	6106	8728	IF,UNEXPECTEDLY	A0229	
TAANG	050,05	1583	08	47227	6123	3998	TREASURY		
TAANG	061,08	1918.0A	11	99027	0227	3857	DISAPPOINTED		
TAANG	061,09	8400	12	96027			DISSOLUTE,EXTRAVAGANT		
TAANG	085,08	3358	11	39127	6112	3861	DRIP,TO SHED(TEARS)		
TAANG	158,08	6507	15	29227	6114	3860	LIE DOWN		
TANQ	086,12	3594	16	36809	6102	5617	HOT,SCALD,TO IRON		
TANQ	108,12	4155	17	36107	6097	0698	A TIME,A TRIP	6396	
TANQ	156,08	6396	15	49802	6113	5958	A TIME,A TRIP	4155	
TAU	030,02	0660.0A	05	67020	6141	4275	BE IN RECEIPT OF		
TAU	057,05	1718	08	12247	6145	6252	TO COVER,BOW CASE	7290	
TAU	061,10	1962	13	92077	7285A	1064	REJOICE		
TAU	064,08	2223	11	57020	6143	4409	FISH OUT (FROM POCKET)	2272	
TAU	064,10	2272	13	52077	6143	1066	FISH OUT (FROM POCKET)		

ROM	RAD	TEL	TOT	FC	MAT	OSH	TAG	CR	CHAR
TAU	085,10	3325	13	32177	6144	1068	OVERFLOW,TORRENT-DASH		
TAU	085,14	3447.0A	17	34141	6159	3186	BIG WAVE		
TAU	120,07	4816	13	27293	6146	8471	SASH,BRAID,CORD	9072	
TAU	120,10	9072	16	22977	6146		SASH,BAND,CORD	4816	
TAU	120,11	4969	17	27994			SASH,BRAID,CORD	4816	
TAU	140,05	538C	09	44627			TOLUENE		
TAU	149,10	6201	17	02677		1063	DOUBT		
TAU	177,10	7269	19	42577			TO COVER,BOW-CASE	7290	
TAU	178,10	7290	19	42577	6145	1065	TO COVER,BOW-CASE	1718	
TAU	184,13	7439	22	61732	6147	5941	GLUTTONOUS		
TAUR	020,06	7118.1	08	27720	6156	4406	POTTERY,PLEASED,(SURNAME)		
TAUR	030,06	0751	09	62013	6152	7693	WAIL		
TAUR	030,08	0751.1	11	67020	6152	4407	WAIL		
TAUR	075,06	2711	10	42913	6148	7700	PEACH		
TAUR	075,14	2917	18	44941	6158	3184	WOOD-BLOCK,BLOCKHEAD		
TAUR	085,06	3165	09	32113	6149	7703	CLEANSE,NAME OF A RIVER	A3221	
TAUR	085,08	3221	11	37120	6153	4411	CLEANSE,ELIMINATE		
TAUR	085,14	3447	17	34141	6159	3186	BIG WAVES		
TAUR	086,14	3614	18	40334		8789	COVER OVER,TO ENVELOPE		
TAUR	120,08	4871	14	27920	6154	4410	BIND,TWIST,CORD		
TAUR	140,08	5426	12	44727	6155	4412	GRAPES		
TAUR	162,06	6625	10	32301	6150	6771	TO ESCAPE		
TAUR	170,08	7118	11	77220	6156	4408	POTTERY,PLEASED,(SURNAME)		
TAUR	177,05	7252	14	47562	6151		HAND DRUM USED BY PEDDLERS	7253	
TAUR	177,06	7253	15	42513	6151	7696	HAND DRUM USED BY PEDDLERS	7851	
TAUR	207,06	7851	19	32147	6151	6212	HAND DRUM USED BY PEDDLERS	7252	
TAO	149,03	6062	10	04600	6157	3188	ASK FOR,SEND PUNITIVE EXPEDITION		
TAW	037,07	1152	10	40731	6160	8831	COVERING/SHEATH		
.TAU	140,08	5426.0A	12	44727	6155	4412	GRAPES		
TEH	061,03	1810	07	10333	6164	8607	NERVOUS		
TEH	061,03	1805	07	43300	6163	6888	EXCESSIVE,TO CHANGE		
TEH	061,11	1973	15	71331	6166	8547	EVIL THOUGHT		
TEH	093,06	3676	10	24541	6165	3237	SPECIAL(-LY),MALE ANIMAL	D8785	
TEH	093,08	8785	12	24517			MALE ANIMAL	B3676	

ROM	RAD	TEL	TOT	FC	MAT	OSH	TAG	CR	CHAR
TEH	142,10	5822.0A	16	79236	6184	8935	RICE PLANT EATING INSECT		螣
TEH	167,07	7870	15	83140		6889	TERBIUM		鋱
TERNG	085,11	3326	15	79232	6181	5684	(SURNAME),PLACE NAME		滕
TERNG	104,05	4012	10	00133	6180	9074	(IT)HURTS,LOVE FONDLY		疼
TERNG	118,15	4696	21	88232	6182	5686	RATTAN/CANE	5671	籐
TERNG	120,10	4910	16	79293	6183	8467	BIND,TIE UP,CORD		縢
TERNG	140,15	5671	19	44232	6182	5685	RATTAN/CANE	4696	藤
TERNG	142,10	5822	16	79236	6184	8935	FLYING DRAGON		螣
TERNG	149,06	6187.1	13	90601			MAKE A(CLEAN)COPY		誊
TERNG	149,10	6187	17	79261	6185	1168	MAKE A (CLEAN)COPY		謄
TERNG	187,10	7506	20	79227	6186	4713	SOAR/HOVER,MOVE OUT		騰
TERNG	195,10	766J	21	73236			PELOR		䲢
TI	018,08	0471	10	62200	6262	2931	PICK(AS TEETH)		剔
TI	075,07	2748	11	48927	6249	4762	LADDER		梯
TI	157,08	6437	15	66127	6264	4508	TO KICK		踢
TI	167,07	6982	15	88127	6254	4759	ANTIMONY		銻
TYI	030,09	0805	12	60027	6242	3985	TO CRY,MOURN		啼
TYI	030,10	8158	13	62017	6242	7675	TO CRY,MOURN	0805	嗁
TYI	032,09	1029	12	46181	6231	6003	DIKE	7125	堤
TYI	038,09	8293	12	46481	6232		AT EASE,FASCINATINGLY BEAUTIFUL		媞
TYI	064,09	2251	12	56081	6233	6008	LIFT (FROM ABOVE),MENTION		提
TYI	094,09	372B	12	46281			HOUND		猻
TYI	113,09	4398	13	36481	6234	6009	WELL-BEING		禔
TYI	115,07	4456	12	28927	6252	4763	TARES,GRASS		稊
TYI	120,07	4835	13	28927	6253	4764	COARSE GREENISH BLACK PONGEE		綈
TYI	120,09	4895	15	26981	6235	6010	ORANGE RED SILK		緹
TYI	140,06	5434	10	44532	6245	5242	(GRASS)		荑
TYI	157,09	6452	16	60127	6244	3984	HOOF,PORK SHOULDER	9343	蹄
TYI	157,10	9343	17	62117	6244		HOOF,PORK SHOULDER	6452	蹏
TYI	162,09	6696	13	30302			(SURNAME)		逓
TYI	164,09	6819	16	16681	6237	6006	ESSENTIAL OIL OF BUTTER		醍
TYI	170,09	7125	12	76281	6210	6007	DIKE	1029	隄
TYI	181,09	7344	18	61808	6238	6015	SUBJECT,SUPERSCRIBE		題

ROM	RAD	TEL	TOT	FC	MAT	OSH	TAG	CR	CHAR
TYI	187,09	7501	19	76381	6239		SPIRITED HORSE		騠
TYI	195,09	7666	20	26381	6240		SHEATFISH,ANCHOVY		鯷
TYI	196,07	7708	18	87227	6255	4644	PELICAN		鵜
TYI	196,10	774A	21	77227			PODICEPS RUFICOLUS		鷈
TII	009,05	7555.1	07	25230	6246	5424	BODY		体
TII	188,13	7555	23	75218	6246	0579	BODY		體
TIH	009,08	0232	10	27220	6266	3887	ENERGETIC/EXALTED/MAGNANIMOUS	0209.0A	倜
TIH	009,08	0209.0A	10	27240	5882	6088	ENERGETIC,EXALTED,MAGNANIMOUS	0232	傲
TIH	018,07	0461	09	82200	6247	2933	SHAVE		剃
TIH	030,09	0804.0A	12	00602			(NOT)JUST/(NOT)ONLY		啻
TIH	030,14	0908	17	64081	6258	5999	SNEEZE		嚏
TIH	044,05	1449	08	77217	6259	0854	TIER,TRAY,DRAWER	8318	屉
TIH	044,08	8318	11	77217		0851	TIER,TRAY,DRAWER	1449	屜
TIH	061,07	1879	10	98027	6248	4761	DO ONE'S DUTY AS A YOUNGER BROTHER		悌
TIH	061,08	1912	11	96027	6263	4510	RESPECTFUL,FEARFUL		惕
TIH	064,09	8447	12	50027			IVORY HAIRPIN,GET RID OF		掃
TIH	073,08	2583	12	55603	6257	1572	TO SUBSTITUTE FOR		替
TIH	078,11	3001	15	14227			FATIGUE		殢
TIH	085,07	3199	10	38127	6250	4766	TEARS,NASAL MUCUS		涕
TIH	118,14	4692	20	88214	6226		LONG BAMBOO(FOR FISHING ROD)		籊
TIH	130,07	519A	11	78227			STIBINE		睇
TIH	140,13	5640	17	44414	6256	0896	SHAVE,TO WEED		薙
TIH	156,14	9327	21	47801	7504	5945	TO JUMP,WAY OF STROKE IN CALLIGRAPH		趯
TIH	162,07	6636	11	39308	6265	6729	FAR	6655	逖
TIH	162,08	6655	12	36302	6265	6715	FAR	6636	邊
TIH	190,03	7563	13	72712	6260	7436	FALSE HAIR		髢
TIAN	037,01	1131	04	10430	6361	5151	SKY,HEAVEN,DAY		天
TIAN	085,04	3096	09	10132			ADD,REPLENISH	3240	汆
TIAN	085,08	3240	11	32133	6370	8524	ADD,REPLENISH	3096	添
TIAN	174,10	9552	18	58217	6361		SKY/HEAVEN,DAY	1131	靝
TYAN	032,10	1050	13	44181	6373	8080	FILL IN		填
TYAN	061,06	1815	09	92064	6365	1317	QUIET		恬
TYAN	085,10	3329.0A	13	34181	6334	8090	YUNNAN		滇

ROM	RAD	TEL	TOT	FC	MAT	OSH	TAG	CR	CHAR
TYAN	099,06	3929	11	24670	6366	1037	SWEET		甜
TYAN	102,00	3944	05	60000	6362	1740	FIELD/FARM,(SURNAME)		田
TYAN	102,04	3953	09	68040	6363	6318	TO HUNT,CULTIVATE(LAND)		畋
TYAN	102,05	3524	09	96802		1748	DRY FIELD		畑
TYAN	116,10	9001	15	30801			FILL IN	1050	寶
TYAN	130,05	518F	09	76200			PROTEAN		胂
TYAN	140,08	7875	12	44333			SUGAR BEET		菾
TYAN	167,05	6879.0A	13	86100	6364	1741	GOLD INLAID WORK		鈿
TYAN	169,10	7063	18	77801	6374	3533	FILL UP,RUMBLING SOUND		闐
TEAN	061,04	1812	08	20333	6368	8521	TO SHAME		忝
TEAN	078,05	2989	09	18222	6375	4199	EXTERMINATE		殄
TEAN	085,08	8682	11	35181	6378	8076	TURBID/MUDDY		澱
TEAN	130,08	5197	12	75281	6379	8075	MAKE STRONG(AS LIQUORS),VIRTUOUS		腆
TEAN	130,09	520C.0A	13	71260			ASHAMED	7241.0A	腼
TEAN	135,08	7897	14	22633	6371	8522	LICK/LAP	7397	舔
TEAN	147,08	6033	15	56810			ASHAMED/BASHFUL	A7241.0A	蜆
TEAN	176,07	7241.0A	16	16610	6380	7598	ASHAMED,SHAMELESS(COLL.)	A6033	靦
TEAN	184,06	7397	14	82764	6371	1319	LICK/LAP	7897	餂
TIANN	096,10	3859	14	14134		8081	JADE EAR-PLUG		瑱
TIAU	061,06	1856	09	92013			FRIVOLOUS		佻
TIAU	064,06	2176	09	52013	6282	7697	CHOOSE,CARRY ON A POLE		挑
TIAU	113,06	4383	10	32213	6285	7771	ANCESTRAL HALL		祧
TYAU	009,06	0167	08	22213	6281	7695	FRIVOLOUS,ACT FURTIVELY		佻
TYAU	046,05	8330	08	22602	6291	1374	LOFTY PEAK		岧
TYAU	075,03	2742.1	07	27904		5382	AN. FOR RIBBON/RIVER/ETC,A STRIP		条
TYAU	075,07	2742	11	27294	6300	5383	AN. FOR RIBBON/RIVER/ETC.,A STRIP		條
TYAU	118,05	4566	11	88602	6292	1377	BROOM		笤
TYAU	140,05	5378	09	44602	6293	1375	TEOCOMA GRANDIFLORA		苕
TYAU	142,08	5781	14	57120	6297	3892	CICADA		蜩
TYAU	149,08	6148.0A	15	07620	6298	3885	HARMONIZE,RECONCILE		調
TYAU	162,05	6606	09	37306	6294	6617	REMOTE		迢
TYAU	177,07	7257	16	27256			REINS OF LEATHER		鞗
TYAU	190,05	7567	15	72602	6295	1376	TUFTS OF HAIR ON CHILDREN		髫

ROM	RAD	TEL	TOT	FC	MAT	OSH	TAG	CR	CHAR
TYAU	195,11	9655	22	27394			CHUB LEUCIEHTHYS		鰷
TYAU	211,05	7882	20	27762	6296	1363	SHED THE MILK TEETH,YOUNG		齠
TEAU	064,06	2176.0A	09	52013	6282	7697	INCITE		挑
TEAU	116,06	4511	11	30113	6286	7706	QUIET AND ELEGANT		窕
TIAW	074,06	2594	10	72213	6283	7698	WESTERN MOON BEFORE SUNRISE,SCORCH		朓
TIAW	109,06	4189	11	62013	6284	7694	GAZE AFAR		眺
TIAW	119,05	4759.1	11	22904		5442	SELL(GRAIN FROM GRANARY)		粜
TIAW	119,19	4759	25	27914	6303	0952	SELL(GRAIN FROM GRANARY)		糶
TIAW	121,06	4974	12	82713			EARTHEN JAR		瓹
TIAW	147,06	6020	13	36110	6290	7612	HAVE AN AUDIENCE		覜
TIAW	157,06	6426	13	62113	6287	7692	JUMP/HOP,SKIP(A GRADE)		跳
TIE	050,05	1586.0A	08	41260	6328	1271	FIT SNUGLY	B6317	帖
TIE	061,05	1832	08	91060	6329	1267	PEACEFUL/QUIET		怗
TIE	154,05	6317	12	61860	6330	1274	TO PASTE/STICK,FIT SNUGLY	D1586.0A	貼
TIEE	050,05	1586	08	41260	6328	1271	NOTICE,INVITATION CARD		帖
TIEE	142,08	9226.0A	14	55181		6045	BUTTERFLY	5805.0A	蜨
TIEE	142,09	5805.0A	15	54194		5294	BUTTERFLY	9226.0A	蝶
TIEE	167,05	6993.1	13	85130	6332	5194	IRON		鉄
TIEE	167,06	6993.2	14	85132	6332	5236	IRON		銕
TIEE	167,13	6993	21	83150	6332	6976	IRON		鐵
TIEE	187,13	7523	23	73350			DARK BROWN HORSE		驖
TIEH	050,05	1586.0B	08	41260	6328	1271	RUBBING FROM INCISED INSCRIPTION		帖
TIEH	140,08	547D	12	44261			TERPANE		萜
TIEH	184,09	7421	18	18732	6331	5937	GLUTTONOUS		餮
TING	027,02	1689.1	04	71221			RECEPTION HALL		厅
TING	030,04	8126	07	62021	6402	2016	LISTEN/HEAR,OBEY	5121	听
TING	053,22	1689	25	00231	6403	8534	RECEPTION HALL		廳
TING	075,02	8527	06	41920	6396		POST/STAKE,NAME OF AN ANCIENT STATE		杍
TING	075,07	2756	11	46914			BED SIDE STAND		程
TING	085,02	3060	05	31120	6397	2995	SAND-BANK		汀
TING	086,07	7899	11	91811			HYDROCARBON		烴
TING	120,07	9059	13	22941			SILK BRAIDED CORD		綎
TING	128,14	5121.1	20	14131			LISTEN/HEAR,OBEY		聽

ROM	RAD	TEL	TOT	FC	MAT	OSH	TAG	CR	CHAR
TING	128,16	5121	22	14131	6402	8532	LISTEN/HEAR,OBEY	8126	聽
TYNG	008,07	0080	09	00201	6399	3003	PAVILION		亭
TYNG	009,09	0255	11	20221	6400	3004	TO STOP		停
TYNG	038,09	1250	12	40421	6401	3005	GRACEFUL		婷
TYNG	053,07	1656	10	00241	6405	6797	COURTYARD		庭
TYNG	054,04	1694	07	12401	6404	6789	PALACE COURTYARD		廷
TYNG	085,09	8687	12	30121		3006	STAGNANT WATER		渟
TYNG	118,07	9011	13	88401		6799	SPINDLE,BAMBOO POLE		筳
TYNG	140,07	5438	11	44401	6411	6798	STALK OF GRASS		莛
TYNG	140,09	550E	13	44201		3007	DRABA NEMEROSA BEBE CARPA		葶
TYNG	142,07	5767	13	52141	6412	6796	DRAGONFLY		蜓
TYNG	142,09	9228	15	50121			(INSECT)/LEPTOGASTER BASIRALIS		蟶
TYNG	173,07	7200	15	10401	6414	6800	CLAP OF THUNDER		霆
TIING	064,07	2185	10	52041	6406	6791	BE STRAIGHT AND STIFF,RATHER (GOOD)		挺
TIING	075,07	2732	11	42941	6407	6795	A CLUB(WEAPON)		梃
TIING	075,09	7903	13	40921			(TREE)		楟
TIING	096,07	3806	11	12141	6408		SCEPTER		珽
TIING	102,02	3957	07	61020	6398	2988	RAISED PATH BETWEEN FIELDS		町
TIING	130,07	9121	11	72241	6409	6792	BRISKET MEAT,STRAIGHT		脡
TIING	137,07	5312	13	22441	6410	6793	SMALL BOAT		艇
TIING	167,07	6910	15	82141	6413	6790	BIG ARROW,WALK FAST		鋌
TIING	181,07	9576	16	11486			NARROW FOREHEAD		頲
TINQ	030,04	8126.0A	07	62021	6402	2016	LET/ALLOW	5121.0A	听
TINQ	128,14	5121.1A	20	14131			LET/ALLOW		聴
TINQ	128,16	5121.0A	22	14131	6402	8532	LET/ALLOW	8126.0A	聽
TONG	061,06	1871	09	97020	6618	3866	MOANING IN PAIN	4020	恫
TONG	075,11	2697	15	47932			(TREE)		樋
TONG	104,06	4020	11	00127	6620	3872	MOANING IN PAIN	1871	痌
TONG	140,11	9186	15	44302	6639		ARALIA PAPYRIFERA		蓪
TONG	162,07	6639	11	37302	6638	6689	GO THROUGH,KNOW WELL		通
TORNG	009,03	0104	05	80101	6615	0112	TOGETHER/SAME	0681	仝
TORNG	009,05	0157	07	27233	6624	9072	(SURNAME)		佟
TORNG	009,06	0179	08	27220	6616	3867	IGNORANT		侗

ROM	RAD	TEL	TOT	FC	MAT	OSH	TAG	CR	CHAR
TORNG	009,12	0302	14	20214	6627	0453	BOY		僮
TORNG	030,03	0681	06	77220	6615	3862	TOGETHER/SAME	0104	同
TORNG	046,06	1491	09	27720	6617	3864	NAME OF A MOUNTAIN		峒
TORNG	059,04	1749	07	72422	6625	4180	RED,(SURNAME)		彤
TORNG	072,12	2559	16	60014	6628	0450	SUN ABOUT TO RISE		曈
TORNG	074,12	8525	16	70214	6629	0455	LIGHT FROM THE RISING MOON		朣
TORNG	075,06	2717	10	47920	6619	3869	ALEURITES CORDATA		桐
TORNG	085,12	3392	15	30114	6631	0460	HIGH,NAME OF A PASS		潼
TORNG	086,06	7906	10	97820			HOT/HEATED		烔
TORNG	109,12	4227	17	60014	6633	0451	PUPIL OF THE EYE		瞳
TORNG	112,06	8943	11	17620			TO PLANE,TO SMOOTH		硐
TORNG	115,12	4483	17	20914			EARLY-PLANTED LATE-RIPENING GRAIN		穜
TORNG	117,07	4547	12	00104	6626	0448	BOY,CHILD,(SURNAME)		童
TORNG	118,07	4601	13	88227	6637	3724	BAMBOO PIPE		筒
TORNG	122,12	5011	17	60104		0461	BIRD NET		罿
TORNG	137,12	5321	18	20414	1530	0457	LONG/SWIFT BOAT		艟
TORNG	140,06	7905	10	44227		3873	CHRYSANTHEMUM CORONARIUM		茼
TORNG	142,06	5750	12	57120			XANTHOCHROA LUPEIPENNIS		蛧
TORNG	164,06	7904	13	17620		3865	KETONE		酮
TORNG	167,06	6894	14	87120	6623	3863	COPPER		銅
TOONG	032,06	8211	09	47120			(SURNAME)		垌
TOONG	064,07	218A	10	57027	6634	3719	POKE THROUGH		捅
TOONG	075,07	2729	11	47927	6635	3720	PAIL		桶
TOONG	118,06	4592	12	88227	6621	3874	TUBE/CYLINDER		筒
TOONG	118,07	4601.0A	13	88227	6637	3724	TUBE/CYLINDER	4592	筒
TOONG	120,06	4827	12	20913	6641	7687	WHOLE,TO UNIFY		統
TONQ	061,11	1975	14	94027	6640	4788	GRIEF		慟
TONQ	104,07	4027	12	00127	6636	3723	PAIN,THOROUGHLY		痛
TONQ	130,08	0616	12	75296			PEPTONE		腖
TONQ	144,06	5892	12	21221	6622	3027	LANE		衕
TOU	009,09	0262	11	28221	6488	8970	TO STEAL		偷
TOU	038,09	8295.0A	12	48421	7630	8977	IMPROPER,IRREGULAR		媮
TOUR	008,00	0071	02	00000	6486		ABOVE		亠

ROM	RAD	TEL	TOT	FC	MAT	OSH	TAG	CR	CHAR
TOUR	037,02	7333.1	05	34030			HEAD		
TOUR	064,04	2121	07	57047	6490	6277	THROW		
TOUR	091,09	8778	13	28021		8973	SHORT BOARD/PLANK		
TOUR	181,07	7333	16	11186	6489	8247	HEAD		
TOUR	188,04	7544	14	77247	6491	6280	DICE,CUBOID BONE		
TOOU	038,05	8273	08	40414			BEAUTIFUL/FAIR,(FEMININE NAME)		
TOOU	068,12	2442	16	44800			TO PLUNDER		
TOOU	201,05	7807	17	40814			A YELLOW COLOR		
TOW	140,12	556H	16	44302			TERPENES		
TOW	162,07	6631	11	32302	6493	6717	THOROUGH,THROUGH,PIERCE		
.TOU	037,02	7333.1A	05	34030			SUFF. FOR NOUNS		
.TOU	181,07	7333.0A	16	11186	6489	8247	SUFF. FOR NOUNS		
TSA	064,10	2258.0A	13	54094	0102	8494	APPLY (OINTMENT/POWDER)		
TSA	064,14	2361	17	53091	6648	8396	WIPE,TO POLISH		
TSAI	094,08	3719	11	45227	6659	3691	TO GUESS		
TSAIR	064,00	2088	03	40200	6660	3301	JUST,NOT UNTIL,TALENT	K4965	
TSAIR	075,03	2624	07	44900	6661	3304	MATERIAL		
TSAIR	120,17	4965	23	27913	6672	7769	JUST,NOT UNTIL	K2088	
TSAIR	145,06	5932	12	43750	6664	6984	CUT OUT(AS A DRESS)		
TSAIR	154,03	6299	10	64800	6662	3305	WEALTH		
TSAE	040,08	1371	11	30904	6666	5408	GOVERNMENT HAND,OFFICIALS		
TSAE	059,07	1752	10	22922	6667	4183	BRIGHT COLORS,PRIZE	B6846	
TSAE	064,08	2231	11	52094	6668	5406	GATHER	A6846	
TSAE	109,07	4174	12	62094	6669	5405	PAY ATTENTION/TAKE NOTICE OF		
TSAE	120,08	4857	14	22994	6670	5407	COLORED,VARIEGATED		
TSAE	157,05	6425.1	12	61110			STEP ON		
TSAE	157,06	6401	13	61160		1954	CAPTURE,STEP ON	D6425	
TSAE	157,08	6425	15	62194		5404	STEP ON	B6401	
TSAE	165,01	6846	08	20904	6665	5403	GATHER,BRIGHT COLORS,AFFAIRS	A2231	
TSAY	032,08	8234	11	42194			ALLOTMENTS TO FEUDAL NOBLES	6846.0A	
TSAY	140,08	5475	12	44904	6671	5409	VEGETABLE		
TSAY	140,11	5591	15	44901	6673	8397	(SURNAME)		
TSAY	165,01	6846.0A	08	20904	6665	5403	ALLOTMENT TO A FEUDAL NOBLE	8234	

ROM	RAD	TEL	TOT	FC	MAT	OSH	TAG	CR	CHAR
TSAN	028,06	0639.1	08	23202		4227	PARTICIPATE,TO COUNSEL		參
TSAN	028,09	0639	11	23202	6685	4219	PARTICIPATE,TO COUNSEL	0640	參
TSAN	028,10	0640	12	23338	6685		PARTICIPATE,TO COUNSEL	0639	叄
TSAN	184,02	7381	11	38132	6694	5930	MEAL	7404	飡
TSAN	184,07	7404	16	27732	6694	5940	MEAL	7381	餐
TSAN	187,11	7515	21	73322	6687	4223	OUTSIDE HORSES OF A TEAM OF 4		驂
TSAN	195,11	766F	22	23322			HORSE MACKEREL		鯵
TSARN	061,11	1972	15	52332	6690	8608	ASHAMED	1974	慙
TSARN	061,11	1974	14	92021	6690	2026	ASHAMED	1972	慚
TSARN	078,08	2995	12	13253	6689	6954	REMNANT,CRIPPLED		殘
TSARN	119,07	4732	13	27904	6691	5450	BRIGHT,LAUGHING		粲
TSARN	142,04	5729	10	20136	6698	8934	SILKWORM	5874	蚕
TSARN	142,18	5874	24	11136	6698	8908	SILKWORM	5729	蠶
TSAAN	061,08	1971.1	11	93022			TRAGIC		惨
TSAAN	061,11	1971	14	93022	6686	4221	TRAGIC		慘
TSAAN	061,12	2008	15	91061	6697	1618	SORROWFUL,ALREADY		憯
TSANN	039,09	1329.0A	12	77247	0169	3100	DODGER		孱
TSANN	086,03	3503	07	92870			RESPLENDENT/BRILLIANT	3605	灿
TSANN	086,13	3605	17	97894	6692	5452	RESPLENDENT/BRILLIANT	3503	燦
TSANN	096,13	3881	17	17194	6693	5451	LUSTER OF GEM,GEM		璨
TSANG	009,02	0221.1	04	80712			GRANARY,CABIN/HOLD(IN SHIP)		仓
TSANG	009,08	0221	10	80607	6707	1130	GRANARY,CABIN/HOLD(IN SHIP)	D5319	倉
TSANG	009,10	0263	12	28267	6708	1135	LOW FELLOW/RUSTIC		傖
TSANG	015,10	3318.1	12	38167	6709	1141	COLD		滄
TSANG	085,10	3318	13	38167	6711	1142	VAST(OF WATER),COLD		滄
TSANG	137,10	5319	16	28467	6713	1137	CABIN,HOLD(IN SHIP)	B0221	艙
TSANG	140,10	5547	14	44607	6714	1144	DARK BLUE,FLY/MUSCA	D9234	蒼
TSANG	142,10	9234	16	58167		1140	FLY/MUSCA	B5547	蠅
TSANG	195,08	7647	19	26360	6716		POMFRET/STROMATEOIDES ARGENTEUS		鯧
TSANG	196,10	7735	21	87627	6717	4612	ORIOLE		鶬
TSARNG	140,14	5661	18	44253	6718	7048	TO HIDE		藏
TSAANG	187,05	9615.0A	15	77310	6701	0612	RASCAL,INFERIOR		馬
TSANQ	140,14	5661.0A	18	44253	6718	7048	STOVE,TREASURE,TIBET		藏

ROM	RAD	TEL	TOT	FC	MAT	OSH	TAG	CR	CHAR
TSAU	064,13	2347	16	56094	6732	5314	TO DRILL,INTEGRITY		
TSAU	119,11	4751	17	94936	6742	6614	ROUGH/COARSE(IN TEXTURE)		
TSAUR	030,11	0856	14	65066	6734	1563	NOISY/BUSTLING		
TSAUR	073,07	2580	11	55606	6733	1561	(SURNAME)		
TSAUR	075,11	2864	15	45966	6736	1564	TROUGH		
TSAUR	085,11	3378	14	35166	6737	1567	TRANSPORT BY WATER,WATERCOURSE		
TSAUR	137,11	9159	17	25466			SEA-GOING JUNK		
TSAUR	142,11	5834	17	55166	6738	1566	LARVA OF MIMELA LUCIDULA		
TSAO	061,13	2015.0A	16	96094	6725		SAD,ANXIOUS		
TSAO	140,00	5335	06	22447	6739	2692	GRASS	A5430	
TSAO	140,06	5430	10	44406	6739	2312	GRASS,HASTY		
TSAW	061,11	1993.0A	14	94036	6741	6613	SINCERE		
TSAW	064,13	2347.0A	16	56094	6732	5314	INTEGRITY		
TSAW	119,11	4751.0A	17	94936	6742	6614	ROUGH/COARSE(IN TEXTURE)		
TSEH	009,09	0258	11	22200	6757	2971	LATERAL,SIDE,INCLINED		
TSEH	013,03	0374	05	77440	6756	4101	BOOKLET,AN. FOR VOLUME		
TSEH	013,03	0374.1	05	77440	6756	3777	BOOKLET,AN. FOR VOLUME		
TSEH	027,09	0627	11	71220	6987	2974	REST ROOM	1665	
TSEH	053,09	1665	12	00220	6987	2975	REST ROOM	0627	
TSEH	061,09	1933	12	92020	6758	2970	SORROWFUL		
TSEH	085,09	3261	12	32100	6759	2973	TO MEASURE		
TSEH	102,05	3967	10	60407		6454	SHARP		
TSEH	118,06	4595	12	88902	6760	5518	POLICY,SCHEME	4604	
TSEH	118,07	4604	13	88438	6761	5124	POLICY,SCHEME	4595	
TSEH	140,06	5411	10	44902			TO PRICK,POINTED GRASSBLADE		
TSEN	028,06	0639.1A	08	23202			UNEVEN/NOT UNIFORM		
TSEN	028,09	0639.0A	11	23202	6685	4219	UNEVEN/NOT UNIFORM		
TSEN	028,10	0640.0A	12	23338	6685		UNEVEN/NOT UNIFORM		
TSEN	046,11	1533	14	22202			UNEVEN/NOT UNIFORM	0639.0A	
TSERN	046,04	1478	07	22207	0329	2850	(SURNAME),SMALL HIGH HILL		
TSERN	085,07	3198	10	32127	0330	2851	TEARFUL		
TSENG	030,12	0886	15	68066		1553	SCOLD		
TSERNG	044,04	1461.1	07	77231			LAYER,STORY		

操 糙 嘈 曹 槽 漕 艚 螬 懆 艸 草 慥 操 糙 側 冊 册 厠 厠 惻 測 戻 策 筴 萗 参 参 糁 嵾 岑 涔 渗 嘈 層

ROM	RAD	TEL	TOT	FC	MAT	OSH	TAG	CR	CHAR
TSERNG	044,12	1461	15	77266	6772	1559	LAYER,STORY		層
TSERNG	046,12	1537	15	28766		1552	LOFTY,PRECIPITOUS		嶒
TSERNG	073,08	2582	12	80606	6771	1549	ONCE,BEFORE		曾
TSERNG	163,12	6773	15	87627	6770		NAME OF A FEUDAL STATE		鄫
TSEENG	030,12	0886.0B	15	68066		1553	TO SEVER/BREAK UP(FRIENDSHIP)		噌
TSENQ	157,12	6479	19	68166	6773	1551	RUB AGAINST,WALK SLOWLY		蹭
TSONG	009,02	1783.1A	04	88000	6919	4893	UNHURRIED		从
TSONG	020,03	8116	05	27420	6915	4515	HURRIED	1846	匆
TSONG	031,04	0935	07	26000	6914	1933	CHIMNEY		囱
TSONG	060,08	1783.0A	11	28281	6919	5992	UNHURRIED		從
TSONG	061,05	1846	09	27332	6915	8641	HURRIED		忽
TSONG	061,07	1892	11	26330	6915	8600	HURRIED	1846	悤
TSONG	075,09	276A	13	47932			ARALIA SPINOSA		楤
TSONG	075,11	2878	15	48981		5994	ABIES FIRMA		樅
TSONG	095,11	3865	15	18181	6920		TINKLING OF JADE PENDANTS		琮
TSONG	096,11	3867	15	16130			(GEM)		璁
TSONG	128,09	5115.1	15	18436			ACUTE/INTELLIGENT		聡
TSONG	128,11	5115	17	16130	6916	8601	ACUTE/INTELLIGENT		聰
TSONG	140,09	5523	13	44332	6917	8643	SCALLION	5595	葱
TSONG	140,11	9190	15	44281			BOSCHNIAKIA GLABRA		蓯
TSONG	140,11	5595	15	44336		8605	SCALLION	5523	蔥
TSONG	142,09	579B	15	57132			CALOPTERYX ATRATA		蠟
TSONG	167,11	9498	19	88181			SPEAR,TO PLUNGE(WITH SPEAR)		鏦
TSONG	187,11	7500	21	76330	6918	8603	BUCKSKIN HORSE		驄
TSORNG	001,04	0654.1	05	88100			THICKET,COLLECTION OF BOOKS		丛
TSORNG	009,02	1783.1	04	88000	6919	4893	FROM,FOLLOW		从
TSORNG	029,16	0654	18	32147	6921	6069	THICKET,COLLECTION OF BOOKS		叢
TSORNG	060,08	1783	11	28281	6919	5992	FROM,FOLLOW		從
TSORNG	061,08	1922	11	93091		8370	JOY		悰
TSORNG	085,08	3222	11	33191	1460	8375	NOISE OF WATER		淙
TSORNG	096,08	3827	12	13191	6899	8368	OCTAGONAL JADE BADGE,(SURNAME)		琮
TSORNG	154,08	9323.1	15	30801	6903	8237	TRIBUTE PAID BY HAN DYNASTY TRIBES		賨
TSORNG	154,08	9323	15	63891	6903	8237	TRIBUTE PAID BY HAN DYNASTY TRIBES		賨

ROM	RAD	TEL	TOT	FC	MAT	OSH	TAG	CR	CHAR
TSOW	015,09	0410	11	35134	6809	5138	COME TOGETHER	3272	湊
TSOW	085,09	3272	12	35134	6809	5139	COME TOGETHER	0410	湊
TSOW	130,09	5216	13	75234	6810	5137	BETWEEN SKIN AND FLESH		腠
TSOW	159,09	6550	16	55034	6811	5135	HUB OF WHEEL,CONVERGE		輳
TSU	093,07	6042	11	57027	6833	3702	COARSE,ROUGH,RUDE	4723	牾
TSU	119,05	4723	11	97910	6833	0613	COARSE,ROUGH,RUDE		粗
TSU	198,04	4723.1	15	80211	6833	7111	COARSE		麁
TSU	198,22	7794	33	00211	6833	7098	COARSE,ROUGH,RUDE	4723	麤
TSWU	060,05	1768	08	27210	6813	0608	TO GO,TO REACH		徂
TSWU	078,05	2987	09	17210	6814	0611	DIE		殂
TSUH	009,07	0191	09	26281	6838	5979	HURRY		促
TSUH	024,02	0586.1A	04	40401			ABRUPTLY/HURRIEDLY	3720	卆
TSUH	024,06	0586.0A	08	00408	6827	2339	ABRUPTLY/HURRIEDLY	3720	卒
TSUH	094,08	3720	11	40248	6837	2349	ABRUPTLY/HURRIEDLY	0586.0A	猝
TSUH	104,11	8881	16	00134			(SKIN DISEASE)		瘯
TSUH	118,11	4662	17	88234	6841	5163	FRAME WORK FOR SILKWORMS,CROWDED	A5590	簇
TSUH	140,11	5590	15	44234	6841	5162	FRAME FOR SILK WORM,NEST,COLLECT	A4662	蔟
TSUH	157,08	9340	15	60148			BUTT AGAINST		踤
TSUH	157,08	6439	15	67140	6228	6087	LEVEL/SMOOTH,CAREFULLY		踧
TSUH	157,11	6464	18	53801	6843	5988	WRINKLED,URGENT,KICK		蹙
TSUH	157,12	6473	19	63114	6842	7719	TREAD ON,KICK,CAREFULLY		蹴
TSUH	164,08	6818	15	14661	6835	1509	VINEGAR		醋
TSUH	167,08	6934.0A	16	84161	6793	1507	ARRANGE		錯
TSUAN	064,18	238A	21	53017	6853	6824	STIR UP,RUSH,THROW		攛
TSUAN	085,02	8660	05	80232		5651	BOIL FOR A SHORT TIME		氽
TSUAN	167,17	0381	25	83117			(DRILLING TOOL)		鑹
TSWAN	064,19	2380.0A	22	54086	6845	8230	BRING TOGETHER		攢
TSWAN	075,19	8604	23	44986			SHED TO COVER A COFFIN		欑
TSUANN	086,25	3627	29	77809	6855	5620	COOKING-STOVE,TO COOK,(SURNAME)		爨
TSUANN	116,07	4533.1	12	30506			TO ESCAPE,TO LEAP		窜
TSUANN	116,13	4533	18	30717	6852	6821	TO ESCAPE,TO LEAP		竄
TSUANN	118,10	4647	16	88733	1449	8845	USURP(THE THRONE)		篡
TSUEI	009,11	0275	13	22214	6865	0928	URGE/PROMPT/HURRY(V.T.)		催

ROM	RAD	TEL	TOT	FC	MAT	OSH	TAG	CR	CHAR
TSUEI	046,08	1508	11	22214	6864	0926	HIGH MOUNTAIN,PRECIPITOUS,(SURNAME)		崔
TSUEI	064,11	2301	14	52014	6866	0929	DESTROY,REPRESS		摧
TSUEI	075,10	2838	14	40932	6869	5862	SMALL RAFTER		榱
TSUEI	120,10	4901	16	20932	6870	5863	MOURNING GARMENTS	5905.0A	縗
TSUEI	145,04	5905.0A	10	00732	5908	5861	MOURNING GARMENTS	4901	衰
TSOEI	096,11	3862	15	12114	6868	0927	LUSTER OF GEMS		璀
TSOEI	156,08	9325	15	40801			PLACE NAME		趡
TSUEY	009,08	8052	10	20248	6871	2347	DEPUTY,SUB-,SECOND		倅
TSUEY	030,08	8148	11	60048	6872	2340	SPIT,SIP		啐
TSUEY	061,08	1897	11	90048	6873	2346	HAGGARD		忰
TSUEY	082,08	3035	12	20714	6883	7381	FINE ANIMAL HAIR,CRISP/BRITTLE	D5186	毳
TSUEY	085,08	3231	11	30148	6874	2353	DIP(IN WATER),TO TEMPER		淬
TSUEY	086,08	3546	12	90848	6875	2352	TO TEMPER(AS STEEL)		焠
TSUEY	104,08	4041	13	00148	6876	2354	SICK,WEARY		瘁
TSUEY	116,12	4532	17	30714			DIG A HOLE		竁
TSUEY	119,08	4733	14	90948	6878	2351	ESSENCE,PURE		粹
TSUEY	124,08	5050	14	17408	6879	2357	GREEN JADE		翠
TSUEY	130,06	5186	10	27212	6882	7224	CRISP/BRITTLE		脆
TSUEY	130,06	9117	10	77217	6882	7313	CRISP/BRITTLE	5186	脃
TSUEY	130,12	5211	16	74248	6881	2356	PANCREAS		膵
TSUEY	140,08	5488	12	44408	6880	2355	DENSE,COLLECTION,COLLECT		萃
TSUEY	140,12	5611.0A	16	44917			COARSE GRASS USED TO SHOW RANK		蕝
TSUEY	181,08	7342	17	01486		8266	HAGGARD	1897	頖
TSUEN	075,03	2625	07	44900	6895	3219	VILLAGE	6722	村
TSUEN	107,09	4123	12	24447	6890	6245	CHAPPED		皴
TSUEN	163,04	6722	07	57727	6895	2255	VILLAGE	2625	邨
TSWEN	039,03	1317	06	40247	6891	3110	EXIST,TO STORE		存
TSWEN	157,12	6472.0A	19	68146	6576	3250	CROUCH/SQUAT		蹲
TSOEN	061,03	1806	06	94000	6894	3191	PONDER		忖
TSUENN	030,03	8120	06	64000	6893	3173	INCH(ENGLISH)		吋
TSUENN	032,07	099A	10	32104			DREGS,SEDIMENT		坋
TSUENN	041,00	1407	03	40300	6892	3162	CHINESE INCH		寸

ROM	RAD	TEL	TOT	FC	MAT	OSH	TAG	CR	CHAR
TSUO	064,09	2278	12	58011	6788		RUB,TWIST		搓
TSUO	064,12	2331	15	56047	6800	6072	BRING TOGETHER,SHOVEL LITTLE BIT		撮
TSUO	112,10	4322	15	18211	6790	0100	TO POLISH,DELIBERATE		磋
TSUO	157,10	6458	17	68111	6791	0097	SLIP,ERROR		蹉
TSUO	164,10	9429	17	68611			WHITE WINE		醝
TSWO	046,05	8329.1A	08	22211			LOFTY/HIGH(OF MOUNTAINS)		岝
TSWO	046,05	8329.0A	08	28711			LOFTY/HIGH(OF MOUNTAINS)		岠
TSWO	046,10	1532	13	28711	6787	0098	LOFTY (AS OF MOUNTAIN)		嵯
TSWO	104,10	4059.0A	15	00111	0123	0105	DISEASE		瘥
TSWO	111,07	8926	12	88414	6796	0285	SHORT/DWARFISH		矬
TSWO	197,10	7771	21	28611	6792	0101	BRINE,SALT		鹾
TSUOO	096,10	3860	14	18111	6789		LUSTER OF GEMS		瑳
TSUOO	130,07	9120	11	78214	6796	0284	CHOPPED MEAT,TRIFLES		脞
TSUOH	018,07	0464	09	82100	6794	2866	TO FILE		剉
TSUOH	027,08	0625	10	71261	6799	1⁵17	TO PLACE/DISPOSE		厝
TSUOH	064,07	2181	10	58014	6795	0283	BEND BACK,DAMPEN		挫
TSUOH	064,08	2238	11	54061	6834	1512	TAKE ACTION ON		措
TSUOH	140,10	9180	14	44407			TO SQUAT(IN SALUTATION)		蓌
TSUOH	167,07	6908	15	88114	6798	0282	FILE		銼
TSUOH	167,08	6934	16	84161	6793	1507	WRONG,MISTAKE,UNEVEN		錯
TSY	048,07	1567.0B	10	80211	0105	0096	UNEVEN		差
TSY	061,06	1864.0A	10	37338	6925	8647	THROW OFF RESTRAINT,CONCEITED		恣
TSY	104,05	4009	10	00111	6976	7139	BLEMISH/FLAW		疵
TSY	172,05	7166.0A	13	20114	6979	0906	FEMALE		雌
TSYR	061,10	1964	14	44333	6965	8696	COMPASSIONATE/GENTLE		慈
TSYR	098,06	3911	11	37717	6966	7942	CHINAWARE	8851	瓷
TSYR	098,10	8851	15	80717		7947	CHINAWARE	3911	甆
TSYR	104,05	4009.0A	10	00111	6976		BLEMISH/FLAW		疵
TSYR	112,10	4318	15	18632	6966	8896	MAGNETISM,PORCELAIN	D3911	磁
TSYR	113,05	4379	09	37220	6970	3383	ANCESTRAL HALL		祠
TSYR	119,09	0371	15	98932			FRIED RICE CAKE	9595	糍
TSYR	140,05	5402.0B	09	44111	6978		WATER CHESTNUT		茈
TSYR	140,06	5412	10	44182	6982	4903	THATCHED HUT,TRIBULUS TERRESTRIS		茨

ROM	RAD	TEL	TOT	FC	MAT	OSH	TAG	CR	CHAR
TSYR	149,05	6101	12	07620	6971	3379	DICTION,PHRASE,WORD	C6588	詞
TSYR	160,06	6588.1	13	23641	6984	2458	RESIGN,BID FAREWELL,DICTION		辝
TSYR	160,08	6588.2	15	20441	6984	2468	RESIGN,BID FAREWELL,DICTION		辞
TSYR	160,12	6588	19	20241	6984	2461	RESIGN,BID FAREWELL,DICTION	G6101	辭
TSYR	172,05	7166	13	20114	6979	0906	FEMALE		雌
TSYR	184,06	9595	15	37732	6983	5939	FRIED RICE CAKE	0371	餈
TSYR	196,09	7732	20	80327			PHALACROCORAX CAPILLATUS		鶿
TSYR	196,09	7732.1	20	87727	6968	4666	PHALACROCORAX CAPILLATUS		鷀
TSYY	009,05	8036	07	21210			PETTY/WRETCHED		佌
TSYY	077,02	2974	06	21110	6972	7131	THIS		此
TSYY	096,05	3793	09	11110	6975	7132	CLEAR(AS IN A GEM)		玼
TSYH	009,05	0136	07	27220	6969	3380	WAIT ON		伺
TSYH	009,06	8031	08	27282	6981	4900	TO HELP,NIMBLE,(SURNAME)		佽
TSYH	018,06	0459	08	52900	6985	2940	THORN		刺
TSYH	027,09	0627.0A	11	71220	6987	2974	RESTROOM	1665.0A	厠
TSYH	053,09	1665.0A	12	00220	6987	2975	RESTROOM	0627.0A	廁
TSYH	076,02	2945	06	37182	6980	4899	INFERIOR,SECOND		次
TSYH	140,08	549B	12	44920			URTICA THUNBERGIANA		莿
TSYH	142,06	9221	12	43150			(LARVA)		蚝
TSYH	154,08	6337	15	66827	6988	4512	GIVE/BESTOW		賜
TU	115,02	4422	07	20217	6537	7661	BALD,BLUNT		秃
TWU	015,07	8094	09	38194			SMEAR/DAUB	A3205	涂
TWU	017,03	0424	05	77777	6305	1975	CONVEX		凸
TWU	030,08	0956.2	11	60604			DIAGRAM,TO PLAN		昌
TWU	031,05	0956.1	08	60303			DIAGRAM,TO PLAN		图
TWU	031,11	0956	14	60604	6531	1874	DIAGRAM,TO PLAN		圖
TWU	032,10	1047	13	38104	6525	0249	TO SMEAR/DAUB	A3205	塗
TWU	044,09	1458	12	77264	6529	1643	SLAUGHTER,SLAUGHTER MAN		屠
TWU	046,07	8334	10	80772			NAME OF A MOUNTAIN		嵞
TWU	060,07	1778	10	24281	6536	5943	DISCIPLE,APPRENTICE		徒
TWU	085,07	3205	10	38194	6524	8508	SMEAR/DAUB,(SURNAME)	A1047	涂
TWU	104,09	4047	14	00164	6530	1642	BE INJURED/ILL(OF ANIMALS)		瘏
TWU	115,07	4454	12	28994	6494	8506	GLUTINOUS RICE		稌

ROM	RAD	TEL	TOT	FC	MAT	OSH	TAG	CR	CHAR
TWU	116,04	4499	09	30430	6540	5101	SUDDENLY		
TWU	130,09	9132	13	72264			FAT(OF PIGS)		
TWU	140,07	5442	11	44904	6526	8509	SONCHUS OLERACEUS		
TWU	162,07	6634	11	38309	6527	6782	ROAD		
TWU	164,07	6809	14	18694	6528	8500	YEAST		
TUU	030,03	0685.0A	06	64010	6533	0147	SPIT		
TUU	032,00	0960	03	40100	6532	0144	EARTH/DUST		
TUU	120,04	4776	10	24900			YELLOW COLOR(OF SILK)		
TUU	167,03	7907	11	84110		0146	THORIUM		
TUH	010,06	0347	08	17413	6534	7756	RABBIT		
TUH	010,06	0347.1	08	20413	6534	7771	RABBIT		
TUH	030,03	0685	06	64010	6533	0147	VOMIT		
TUH	030,08	0790.0A	11	62014	6458	0411	SALIVA,SPIT AT		
TUH	032,08	8239	11	47113		7757	SIDE OF BRIDGE		
TUH	140,08	551H	12	44213	6535		DODDER/CUSCUTA		
TUH	140,08	5460	12	44413	6535	7760	DODDER/CUSCUTA		
TUH	196,08	772D	19	27127			SCOPS SEMITORQUES		
TUAN	085,09	3273	12	32127	6554	3761	TO RUSH(OF WATER)		
TWAN	018,11	0483	13	52300			SLASH		
TWAN	031,03	0957.1	06	60240			ROUND,REGIMENT,DUMPLING	C 9046	
TWAN	031,11	0957	14	60343	6549	1881	ROUND,REGIMENT		
TWAN	064,11	2306	14	55043	6551	3295	ROLL ROUND WITH HAND		
TWAN	085,11	3350	14	35143	6552	3299	HEAVY DEW		
TWAN	119,11	9046.1	17	95943	6553	3297	DUMPLING		
TWAN	119,14	9046	20	96900	6553	1882	DUMPLING	C0957.1	
TOAN	102,09	3980	14	62014	6555	0465	PLACE TRODDEN BY ANIMALS	8859	
TOAN	102,12	8859	17	60014	6555		PLACE TRODDEN BY ANIMALS	3980	
TUANN	058,06	1740	09	27232	6556	5735	RUNNING HOG		
TUEI	064,08	2236	11	53014	6564	0880	PUSH,REFUSE (RESPONSIBILITY)		
TUEI	140,11	9191	15	44514		0881	LEONURUS MACRANTHUS		
TWEI	115,14	4488	19	25286			DECADENT,BECOME BALD	7339	
TWEI	140,16	5678	20	44286			(PLANT)		

ROM	RAD	TEL	TOT	FC	MAT	OSH	TAG	CR	CHAR
TWEI	170,12	7142	15	75286	6566	8124	FALL IN RUINS,SOFT		隤
TWEI	181,07	7339	16	21286	6567	8304	DECADENT,BECOME BALD	4488	頹
TWEI	194,08	9636	18	20211	6565	7652	JAPANESE BROWN BEAR		魋
TOEI	130,10	5217	14	77233	6569	6751	LEG	7548	腿
TOEI	157,10	9342	16	67133			LEG	5217	跟
TOEI	188,07	7548	17	72244	6569	9067	LEG	5217	骽
TUEY	142,07	5770.0A	13	58116	5928	7573	EXUVIAE OF INSECTS OR REPTILES		蛻
TUEY	162,06	6622	10	37303	6568	6749	RETREAT/WITHDRAW		退
TUEY	187,07	9618	17	78316			APPROACH AT SWIFT GALLOP(ON HORSES)		駾
TUEN	030,04	0691	07	20603	6587	1397	TO SWALLOW		吞
TUEN	030,08	8149	11	60047	6588		MOVE SLOWLY		哼
TUEN	072,12	2557	16	68040	6590	6341	SUN ABOVE THE HORIZON		暾
TUEN	085,07	8675	10	37167	6591		VOMIT,PLANET JUPITER		涒
TWEN	031,04	0937.0A	07	60717	6593	1924	TO STORE/HOARD		囤
TWEN	045,01	1470	04	50717	6592	7405	TO STATION (SOLDIERS),TO STORE UP		屯
TWEN	130,13	5241	17	77227	6602	3648	BUTTOCKS		臀
TWEN	152,04	6270	11	71232	6600	5709	SUCKLING PIG		豚
TWEN	159,04	9359	11	55017			WAR-CHARIOT		軘
TWEN	162,04	6600	08	35301	6597	6764	WALK WITH DIFFICULTY/LITTLE PROGRES		迍
TWEN	184,04	7386	12	85717	6598	7408	CHINESE RAVIOLI		飩
TWEN	195,04	9639	15	25317	6599	7414	LEATHERFISH		魨
TUENN	022,04	056A	06	71711			TANK		匰
TUENN	145,10	5963	15	37233	6601	6750	TAKE OFF(CLOTHES),FADE		褪
TUO	009,05	0150	07	23211	6439	7177	THAT,HE		佗
TUO	064,03	2094	06	52014	6460	7359	SUPPORT ON PALM		托
TUO	064,03	8421	06	54012			DRAG ALONG	2151	扡
TUO	064,05	8427	08	53012	6440		DRAG ALONG	2151	挖
TUO	064,05	2151	08	58012	6440	7429	DRAG ALONG		拖
TUO	130,07	5192	11	78216	6468	7569	TAKE OFF,GET AWAY FROM		脫
TUO	149,03	6067	10	02614	6461	7358	ENTRUST		託
TUO	184,03	9594	11	82714			(CAKE)		飥
TWO	009,05	0150.0A	07	23211	6439	7177	CARRY ON THE BACK		佗
TWO	032,05	1001	08	43111		7158	LUMP,SPHERIC SUBSTANCE		坨

ROM	RAD	TEL	TOT	FC	MAT	OSH	TAG	CR	CHAR
TWO	075,05	2670	09	43911	6441	7182	MAIN BEAM OF ROOF		椯
TWO	075,12	2891	16	50904	6465	5320	SACK,TUBE FOR BLOWING FIRE		橐
TWO	085,05	3108	08	33111	6442	7185	TO BRANCH(OF RIVER),TEARFUL		沱
TWO	112,05	8932	10	13614	6444		STEELYARD WEIGHT		砣
TWO	112,09	8932.1	14	14627	6444		STEELYARD WEIGHT		磋
TWO	120,05	4779	11	23911			BRAID ON A ROBE		綐
TWO	157,05	6408	12	63111	6445	7175	STUMBLE		跎
TWO	164,05	6801	12	13611	6446	7176	FLUSHED(FROM DRINKING)		酡
TWO	170,03	7083	06	74212	1033		HILLSIDE,BANK		阤
TWO	170,05	7094	08	73211	6447	7178	(PHONETIC),STEEP BANK,DECLIVITY		陀
TWO	187,03	7461	13	74330	6452	5002	CARRY ON BACK		馱
TWO	187,05	7474	15	73311	6448	7181	HUMPBACK		駝
TWO	187,12	7527	22	76356			(HORSE)		驒
TWO	195,05	9640	16	23311	6449	7183	(FISH)		鮀
TWO	196,05	9676	16	23311	6450	7180	OSTRICH		鴕
TWO	205,12	7842	25	66717	6453	7342	LARGE WATER LIZARD		鼉
TUO	038,04	1185	07	20404	6454	9064	SECURE/SOUND		妥
TUO	053,08	1641	11	00287	6464	4970	LENGTH OF 2 OUTSTRETCHED ARMS		庹
TUO	064,12	8461	15	54027	6456		SHORTEN,CLIP,THROW AWAY		撱
TUO	075,09	2900.1	13	44927			ELLIPSE		橢
TUO	075,12	2900	16	44927	6457	3598	ELLIPSE		橢
TUO	130,07	5192.0A	11	78216	6468	7569	GET AWAY FROM		脫
TUO	158,12	6506	19	26256			HANG/SLOPE(SHOULDERS/SLEEVES)		軃
TUO	196,07	771E	18	27727			TOCO TOUCAN		鵎
TUOH	030,08	0790	11	62014	6458	0411	SALIVA,SPIT AT		唾
TUOH	064,05	2148	08	51060	6460	1104	EXPAND,SUPPORT ON PALM		沰
TUOH	075,05	2682	09	42931	6462	2056	WATCHMAN'S RATTLE		柝
TUOH	118,16	4703	22	88541	6466	2486	SHEATH AROUND JOINTS OF BAMBOO		籜
TUOH	140,16	5690	20	44541	6467	2485	FALLEN LEAVES AND BARK		蘀
TUOH	157,05	6406	12	62131	6463	2053	CARELESS		跅
TZ	030,11	0862	14	65086	6749	8112	(INTERJ. OF ADMIRATION,OF DISGUST)		嗻
TZA	022,03	0559	05	71712	6642	0811	GO ROUND	1578	匝
TZA	030,05	0715	08	61012	6643	0812	SMACK ONE'S LIPS		咂

ROM	RAD	TEL	TOT	FC	MAT	OSH	TAG	CR	CHAR
TZA	050,01	1578	04	10227	6642	4002	GO ROUND	0559	
TZA	120,04	4796.1B	10	52903		8477	TIE WITH STRING OR RIBBON		
TZA	120,05	4796.0B	11	42903	6647	8478	TIE WITH STRING OR RIBBON		
TZA	196,04	769B	15	17227			NUTHATCH/SITTA CAESIS AMURENSIS		
TZAR	030,06	0749	09	66000	6645	1737	WE(INCL.)		
TZAR	030,11	086A.0A	14	63050			SHY		
TZAR	064,06	8429	09	52027		4254	TO FORCE OUT,OPPRESS		
TZAR	075,02	7177.1	06	40904	6419		MIXED/MISCELLANEOUS		
TZAR	075,06	2740	10	42927			FORCE (ONE'S WAY)		
TZAR	112,05	4271	10	11612	6644	0813	SMASH/SMASHED		
TZAR	140,18	569E	22	44914			MYRIOPHYLLUM		
TZAR	145,12	9265	17	30294	6646	5299	MIXED/MISCELLANEOUS	7177	
TZAR	172,10	7177	18	00914	6646	0903	MIXED/MISCELLANEOUS	9265	
TZAI	030,06	0762	09	43650	6650	6978	(EXCLAMATORY OR INTERROG. PART.)		
TZAI	075,06	2707	10	43950	6651	6982	TO PLANT		
TZAI	086,03	3505	07	22809	6652	5636	DISASTER/CALAMITY	3506	
TZAI	086,03	3506	07	30809	6652		DISASTER/CALAMITY	3505	
TZAI	086,06	8736	10	43850	6652	7020	DISASTER/CALAMITY	3505	
TZAI	102,03	3951	08	22603	6932	1823	STEROID NUCLEUS		
TZAI	140,08	5469.0A	12	44603	6932	1828	DISASTER/CALAMITY	3505	
TZAI	140,09	5512.0A	13	44603			DISASTER/CALAMITY	3505	
TZAE	009,03	0098.0B	05	27247	6940	3099	DIMI.(CANTONESE)		
TZAE	031,03	8188.0B	06	60407	0823	1880	CHILD		
TZAE	040,07	1363	10	30401	6655	2473	SLAUGHTER,OFFICIAL		
TZAE	046,09	8342	12	22336	6656	8587	YOUNG OF ANIMALS		
TZAE	159,06	6528.0A	13	43550	6653	6979	YEAR		
TZAY	009,13	0314	15	23250	6654	6980	CONVEY/LOAD WITH	A6528	
TZAY	013,04	0375	06	10447	6658	4116	AGAIN		
TZAY	032,03	0961	06	40214	6657	0156	EXIST,BE AT		
TZAY	159,06	6528	13	43550	6653	6979	CONVEY/LOADED WITH,CARRY		
TZAN	118,12	4681	18	88601	6679	1621	HAIRPIN		
TZARN	009,09	2501.2	11	28264	6674	1592	WE(INCL.)		
TZARN	030,06	0749.0A	09	66000	6645	1737	WE(INCL.)	2501	

币紮綵鵏咱喊撥架楼砸蘸襍雜哉栽災突救甾蒅薔仔囝宰嵗載儀再在載簪偺咱

ROM	RAD	TEL	TOT	FC	MAT	OSH	TAG	CR	CHAR
TZARN	030,09	2501.1	12	68064	6674	1591	WE(INCL.)		
TZARN	072,05	2501	09	28604	6674	1590	WE(INCL.)	0749.0A	
TZARN	119,08	9048	14	93964			TIBETAN CEREAL DISH		
TZARN	119,09	9048.1	15	93964		1594	TIBETAN CEREAL DISH		
TZAAN	040,08	1373	11	30801		6047	SWIFT		
TZAAN	064,06	8429.0A	09	52027		4254	PUNISH BY SQUEEZING FINGERS		
TZAAN	064,19	2380	22	54086	6845	8230	COLLECT,HOARD		
TZAAN	075,06	2740.0A	10	42927			FINGER-SQUEEZING PUNISHMENT		
TZAAN	156,19	9328	26	44808	6682	5970	HASTEN,URGE		
TZANN	072,09	2548.0A	13	52602	6683	1568	TEMPORARILY		
TZANN	096,19	3895	23	14186		8226	LIBATION CUP		
TZANN	149,19	6247	26	04686	6681	8229	TO PRAISE	6363	
TZANN	154,08	6363.1	15	55806	6676	8216	TO PRAISE		
TZANN	154,12	6363	19	24806	6676	8225	TO PRAISE	6247	
TZANN	163,19	6783	22	27827		2258	PLACE NAME,GROUP OF 100 FAMILIES		
TZANN	167,11	6983	19	52109	6684	0376	ENGRAVE		
TZANG	090,06	3647	10	28251	6699	2547	FEMALE SHEEP,PLACE NAME		
TZANG	130,06	5253.1A	10	70214			DIRTY	7554	
TZANG	131,08	5258	14	23250	6704	7046	GOOD/LUCKY,(SURNAME)		
TZANG	154,06	6368.1	13	60814	6705	0155	BOOTY/SPOILS		
TZANG	154,14	6368	21	63850	6705	7047	BOOTY/SPOILS		
TZANG	188,13	7554	23	74241	6703	2810	DIRTY	5253.1A	
TZAANG	187,05	9615	15	77310	6701	0612	POWERFUL HORSE		
TZANQ	032,10	5520.1	13	44104	6702	0235	BURY(THE DEAD)		
TZANQ	037,07	1155.0A	10	24430		5004	GREAT		
TZANQ	130,06	5253.1	10	70214			VISCERA		
TZANQ	130,18	5253	22	74253	6706	7049	VISCERA		
TZANQ	140,09	5520	13	44441	6702	2809	BURY(THE DEAD)		
TZAU	119,11	4748	17	95966	6719	1565	DREGS,TO WASTE/SPOIL		
TZAU	157,11	9346	18	65166	6720	1562	TO WASTE/SPOIL	B4748	
TZAU	162,11	6685	15	35306	6720	6629	MEET BY CHANCE,INCIDENT,A TIME		
TZAU	164,11	6827	18	15666	6719		DREGS	A4748	
TZAUR	017,10	7020.1	12	32772			CHISEL		

ROM	RAD	TEL	TOT	FC	MAT	OSH	TAG	CR	CHAR
TZAUR	167,20	7020	28	37109	6786	0380	CHISEL		鑿
TZAO	072,02	2483	06	60400	6721	2277	EARLY,MORNING		早
TZAO	075,04	2764.1	08	50303			JUJUBE		枣
TZAO	075,08	2764	12	50902	6723	5517	JUJUBE		棗
TZAO	085,13	3416	16	36194	6726	5317	BATH		澡
TZAO	096,13	3884	17	16194	6728		PENDANT OF PEARLS ON CORONET		璪
TZAO	140,16	5679	20	44194	6727	5318	(AQUATIC GRASSES),ELEGANT		藻
TZAO	142,04	5734	10	77136	6724	8938	FLEA		蚤
TZAO	142,10	5734.1	16	77136	6724	8911	FLEA		蝨
TZAW	030,13	0894	16	66094	5438	5312	CHIRPING/BUZZING,CLAMOR		噪
TZAW	061,11	1993	14	94036	6741	6613	SINCERE		慥
TZAW	061,13	2015	16	96094	6725		SAD,ANXIOUS		懆
TZAW	085,11	3378.0A	14	35166	6737	1567	TRANSPORT BY WATER,(SURNAME)		漕
TZAW	086,03	3501	07	94810	6731	0151	KITCHEN STOVE	4536	灶
TZAW	086,13	3604	17	96894	5440	5316	DRY/PARCHED,IMPATIENT		燥
TZAW	106,02	4103.1	07	26400	6722	2313	BLACK		皁
TZAW	106,02	4103	07	26714	6722	7354	BLACK		皂
TZAW	116,16	4536	21	30717	6731	7343	KITCHEN STOVE	3501	竈
TZAW	118,11	9020	17	88306		6615	SECOND DEGREE,COLLATERAL		簉
TZAW	149,13	6227	20	06694	5443	5313	NOISE OF CROWD,DISTURBANCE		譟
TZAW	157,13	6481	20	66194	6729	5311	IMPATIENT,HOT-TEMPERED		躁
TZAW	162,07	6644	11	34306	6730	6612	BUILD/MANUFACTURE		造
TZER	018,07	0463	09	62800	6746	2968	PRINCIPLE,THEN		則
TZER	030,05	0738	08	68011	6743	2059	GNAW		咋
TZER	030,11	0862.0A	14	65086	6749	8111	(INTERJ. OF ADMIRATION,OF DISGUST)		嘖
TZER	046,05	8329.1	08	22211			NAME OF A MOUNTAIN		岞
TZER	046,05	8329	08	28711			NAME OF A MOUNTAIN		岝
TZER	050,11	1614	14	45286	6750	8115	CONICAL CAP		幘
TZER	064,13	2344	16	56041	0276	2484	SELECT		擇
TZER	085,13	3419	16	36141	0277	2491	MARSH,BENEFICENCE		澤
TZER	116,05	4504.0A	10	30211	6744	2076	NARROW		窄
TZER	118,05	4575	11	88211		2080	NARROW,BOARD UNDER TILES ON ROOF	A4504.0A	笮
TZER	118,11	4660	17	88806	6751	8119	MAT,BED MAT		簀

ROM	RAD	TEL	TOT	FC	MAT	OSH	TAG	CR	CHAR
TZER	137,05	5311	11	28411		2069	SMALL BOAT		舴
TZER	140,09	9181	13	44820			(MEDICINAL HERB)		荝
TZER	154,04	6307	11	50806	6748	8109	DUTY/RESPONSIBILITY		責
TZER	154,06	6329.0A	13	63850	6752	6969	THIEF		賾
TZER	154,10	6358	17	75786	0274	8111	MYSTERIOUS		賾
TZER	162,05	9374	09	38301		6642	TO PRESS,HASTE		迮
TZER	195,09	9649	20	22300	6747	2972	CUTTLEFISH		鰂
TZEH	009,02	0090	04	71280	6754		OBLIQUE TONE		仄
TZEH	046,09	1528	12	22827			LOFTY (AS OF MOUNTAIN)		崱
TZEH	072,04	2493	08	60281	6755	4895	AFTERNOON,DECLINE		昃
TZEIR	154,06	6329	13	63850	6752	6969	THIEF		賊
TZE(MM)	162,03	6638.2B	07	34300	0265	6678	SO/THUS/(IN)THIS WAY		迠
TZE(MM)	162,04	6638.1B	08	30304	0265	6757	SO/THUS/(IN)THIS WAY		这
TZE(MM)	162,07	6638.0B	11	30306	0265	6611	SO/THUS/(IN)THIS WAY		這
TZEEN	061,05	1827	09	80331	6762	8609	HOW		怎
TZENN	149,12	6220	19	01661	0323	1617	SLANDER		譖
TZENG	032,12	1073	15	48166	6763	1550	ADD/INCREASE		增
TZENG	061,12	1999	15	98066	6764	1554	DETEST		憎
TZENG	073,08	2582.0A	12	80606	6771	1549	GREAT-GRAND(FATHER),(SURNAME)		曾
TZENG	075,12	2896	16	48966			DWELLING ON TOP OF WOODEN STAKES		橧
TZENG	111,12	4254	17	88466	6766	1556	ARROW WITH A STREAMER		矰
TZENG	120,12	4938	18	28966	6767	1558	SILK FABRICS,(SURNAME)		繒
TZENG	122,12	9088	17	60606	6768	1560	LARGE SQUARE NET		罾
TZENQ	098,12	3920	17	81617	6765	7929	CALDRON/RICE POT		甑
TZENQ	120,12	4938.0A	18	28966	6767	1558	TO TIE/TO BIND		繒
TZENQ	154,12	6362	19	68866	6769	1557	GIVE PRESENT		贈
TZONG	040,05	1350	08	30901	6896	8367	ANCESTOR,FAMILY		宗
TZONG	075,08	2762	12	43991	6897	8372	PALM	2820	棕
TZONG	075,09	2820	13	42947	6897	6451	(PALM)	2762	椶
TZONG	075,13	2820.1	17	42947			(PALM)		樬
TZONG	120,04	4912.1A	10	28900			VERTICAL		纵
TZONG	120,09	4881	15	22947			FISH-NET		緵
TZONG	120,11	4912.0A	17	28981	6910	5995	VERTICAL		縱

ROM	RAD	TEL	TOT	FC	MAT	OSH	TAG	CR	CHAR
TZONG	124,09	9098	15	12147			UNEVEN FLIGHT OF A BIRD		翪
TZONG	130,08	5208	12	73291			HYDRAZONE		腙
TZONG	152,11	6280	18	18281	6902		LITTER OF PIGS,LITTLE PIG		豵
TZONG	157,08	9338	15	63191	6904	8369	FOOTPRINT/TRACE	6467	踪
TZONG	157,11	6467	18	68181	6904	5993	FOOTPRINT,TRACE	9338	蹤
TZONG	187,08	7487	18	73391	6905	8371	HORSE'S MANE,BRISTLES	7502	騌
TZONG	187,09	7502	19	72347	6905	6450	HORSE'S MANE,BRISTLES	7487	騣
TZONG	190,08	7571	18	72901	6906	8377	MANE,BRISTLE	K3732	鬃
TZONG	193,09	7604	19	12247		6449	KETTLE ON LEGS		鬷
TZOONG	009,09	8064	11	27232	6911		BUSY/HURRIED,DESPONDENT	1991.1	偬
TZOONG	009,11	8064.1	13	26230	6911		BUSY/HURRIED,DESPONDENT	1991	傯
TZOONG	061,05	4920.1	09	80336			GENERAL/IN EVERY CASE		总
TZOONG	061,09	1991.1	12	97032			BUSY/HURRIED,DESPONDENT	8064	惚
TZOONG	061,11	1991	14	96030			BUSY/HURRIED,DESPONDENT	8064.1	憁
TZOONG	064,09	8460.1	12	56036			GENERAL/IN EVERY CASE,TO HOLD		捴
TZOONG	064,11	8460	14	56030	6912		GENERAL/IN EVERY CASE,TO HOLD	A4920	摠
TZOONG	120,11	4920	17	26930	6912	8604	GENERAL/IN EVERY CASE		總
TZONQ	009,02	1783.1B	04	88000	6919	4893	SECOND COUSIN		从
TZONQ	060,08	1783.0B	11	28281	6919	5992	SECOND COUSIN		從
TZONQ	094,08	3732	11	43291	6898		MANE,BRISTLE,NAME OF A TRIBE	K7571	猔
TZONQ	119,08	9040	14	93991	6900	8373	RICE DUMPLINGS WRAPPED IN LEAVES	4740	粽
TZONQ	119,09	4740	15	92947	6900	6452	RICE DUMPLINGS WRAPPED IN LEAVES	9040	糉
TZONQ	119,13	4740.1	19	92947			RICE DUMPLINGS WRAPPED IN LEAVES		糉
TZONQ	120,04	4912.1	10	28900			RELEASE,EVEN IF		纵
TZONQ	120,08	4844	14	23991	6901	8374	SYNTHESIZE,SYNTHESIS		综
TZONQ	120,11	4912	17	28981	6910	5995	RELEASE,EVEN IF		縱
TZOU	064,08	2244	11	57040	6802	6066	BEAT THE NIGHT WATCHES,GRASP		掫
TZOU	075,08	8569	12	17904			(SURNAME)		棸
TZOU	120,08	4863	14	27940	6803	6067	PURPLE SILK		緅
TZOU	140,08	9177	12	44147			WEEDS,ARROW		菆
TZOU	149,08	6155	15	07640	6804	6063	CONSULT,CHOOSE		諏
TZOU	149,10	6188	17	07627	1308	4452	MAKE UP(A STORY)		謅
TZOU	163,10	6760	13	27427	1309	2222	(SURNAME),NAME OF HSIEN IN SHANTUNG		鄒

ROM	RAD	TEL	TOT	FC	MAT	OSH	TAG	CR	CHAR
TZOU	170,08	7112	11	77240	6805	6064	CORNER,FOOT OF MOUNTAIN		
TZOU	187,10	7507	20	77327	1310	4454	GO,MYTHICAL ANIMAL		
TZOU	195,08	9646	19	27340	6806	6068	SMALL FISH,MINNOWS,(SURNAME)		
TZOOU	156,00	6382	07	40801	6807	5942	WALK,GO		
TZOW	037,06	1146	09	50430	6808	5134	PRESENT A MEMORIAL		
TZOW	064,09	2213	12	55034		5136	BEAT UP,BREAK TO PIECES		
TZOW	163,08	6780.1	11	17127	1311	2247	HOME TOWN OF CONFUCIUS		
TZOW	163,14	6780	17	17227	1311	2231	HOME TOWN OF CONFUCIUS,(SURNAME)		
TZOW	187,14	7532	24	77332	1312	5706	SUDDEN(LY)		
TZU	115,05	4436	10	27910	6816	0614	RENT,TAXES		
TZWU	024,02	0586.1	04	40401			DIE,SOLDIER		
TZWU	024,06	0586	08	00408	6827	2339	DIE,A SOLDIER		
TZWU	030,11	0871.0A	14	68034		5161	TO URGE ON/INCITE		
TZWU	064,08	2215	11	50048	6828	2348	SEIZE		
TZWU	070,07	2469	11	08234	6830	5159	CLAN/RACE		
TZWU	157,00	6398.1	06	60308			FOOT,SUFFICIENT		
TZWU	157,00	6398	07	60801	6824	5977	FOOT,SUFFICIENT		
TZWU	167,11	6968	19	88134	6831	5160	ARROWHEAD,SHARP		
TZUU	009,07	0194	09	87810	6812	0615	A STAND FOR FOOD AT SACRIFICE		
TZUU	096,05	3785	09	17110			CARVING ON JADE		
TZUU	113,05	4371	09	37210	6815	0618	ANCESTOR,GRAND-(AS IN GRANDFATHER)		
TZUU	120,05	4809	11	27910	6817	0617	CORD,ORGANIZE		
TZUU	140,10	554F	14	44917			STACHY ASPERS		
TZUU	149,05	6100	12	07610	6818	0607	CURSE,SWEAR(OATH)		
TZUU	170,05	7091	08	77210	6819	0609	OBSTRUCT(ION)		
TZUH	096,05	3785.0A	09	17110			CARVING ON JADE		
TZUAN	167,05	9449.0A	13	81160			ENTER(A HOLE),PROBE	7018.0A	
TZUAN	167,19	7018.0A	27	84186	6848	8227	ENTER(A HOLE),PROBE	9449.0A	
TZOAN	118,19	4711	25	88806			BAMBOO UTENSIL		
TZOAN	120,14	4951	20	88903	6850	8465	COMPILE		
TZOAN	120,19	4957	25	24986	6846	8232	CARRY ON		

陬
騶
鯫
走
奏
揍
郰
郰
驟
租
九
卒
嗾
捽
族
足
鏃
俎
珇
祖
組
葅
詛
阻
珇
鑽
鑽
簒
纘

ROM	RAD	TEL	TOT	FC	MAT	OSH	TAG	CR	CHAR
TZOAN	167,05	9449	13	81160			TO BORE(WITH AN AUGER)	7018	鉆
TZOAN	167,19	7018	27	84186	6848	8227	TO BORE(WITH AN AUGER)	9449	鑽
TZUANN	154,10	6354.0A	17	68837	1437	5576	CHEAT/SWINDLE		賺
TZUANN	167,05	9449.0B	13	81160			AN AUGER,DIAMOND	7018.0B	鉆
TZUANN	167,19	7018.0B	27	8418	6848	8227	AN AUGER,DIAMOND	9449.0B	鑽
TZUEI	032,08	1018.0A	11	40114		0867	A PILE(SMALL)		堆
TZOEI	030,12	0878	15	61027	6857	3705	MOUTH	9278.0A	嘴
TZOEI	148,05	9278.0A	12	21227	6856	3704	MOUTH	0878	觜
TZUEY	072,08	2536	12	60048	6861	2343	1ST BIRTHDAY OF A CHILD		晬
TZUEY	073,08	2584	12	60147	6858	6070	MOST		最
TZUEY	075,13	8593	17	40927	6863	4140	WOODEN PESTLE OR RAMMER		橇
TZUEY	122,08	4997	13	60111	6860	2785	CRIME,SIN		罪
TZUEY	140,12	5612	16	44147	6859	6073	ASSEMBLE,SMALL		叢
TZUEY	157,08	9340.0A	15	60148			ROOST TOGETHER(OF FOWLS)		踤
TZUEY	160,06	6583	13	26401	6860		CRIME,SIN	4997	辠
TZUEY	164,08	6816	15	10648	6862	2345	INTOXICATED		醉
TZUEN	032,12	8254	15	48146	6886		GOBLET/BOTTLE/WINE-JAR	4979	墫
TZUEN	041,09	1415	12	80346	6884	3248	TO HONOR		尊
TZUEN	075,12	2886	16	48946	6886	3254	GOBLET/BOTTLE/WINE-JAR	4979	樽
TZUEN	121,12	4979	18	88746	6886	3251	GOBLET/BOTTLE/WINE-JAR	8254	罇
TZUEN	162,12	6690	16	38304	6887	6680	OBEY		遵
TZUEN	167,12	9508	20	88146	6888	3249	BUTT END OF SPEAR		鐏
TZOEN	030,12	8169	15	68046	6884A	3252	TALK TOGETHER		噂
TZOEN	064,12	2323	15	58046	6885	3253	REGULATE,RESTRAIN		撙
TZUENN	009,12	8071	14	27281	6889	8042	MASTER AT A VILLAGE FEAST		僎
TZUENN	195,12	7923	23	28346			SEA TROUT		鱒
TZUO	009,05	0155.0A	07	28211	6780	2065	TO DO,MAKE		作
TZUO	030,12	0872	15	66047	1427	6071	SUCK		嗺
TZWO	009,05	0155.0B	07	28211	6780		TO DO,MAKE		作
TZWO	064,08	2215.0A	11	50048	6828	2348	SEIZE		捽
TZWO	072,05	2506	09	68011	6782	2062	YESTERDAY		昨
TZUOO	009,05	0146	07	24211	6775	0107	ASSIST		佐
TZUOO	048,02	1563	05	40011	6774	0106	LEFT		左

ROM	RAD	TEL	TOT	FC	MAT	OSH	TAG	CR	CHAR
TZUOH	009,05	0155	07	28211	6780	2065	DO,MAKE	0254	作
TZUOH	009,09	0254	11	28240	6776	6316	DO,MAKE	0155	做
TZUOH	017,10	7020.1A	12	32772			CHISEL		凿
TZUOH	030,07	8143	10	68014			(PHONETIC)/-Z + OLE(CHEM.)		唑
TZUOH	032,04	0976	07	88104	6778	0281	SIT		坐
TZUOH	053,07	1654	10	00214	6779	0286	SEAT		座
TZUOH	061,05	1826	08	98011	6781	2064	ASHAMED		怍
TZUOH	075,05	2683	09	48911	6783	2070	OAK/QUERCUS SERRATA		柞
TZUOH	104,07	8871	12	00114		0287	ACNE VALGARIS		痤
TZUOH	113,05	4373	09	38211	6822	2072	BLESSING,THE THRONE		祚
TZUOH	119,16	9047	22	37904			POUNDED/WHITENED RICE		鑿
TZUOH	130,05	5161	09	78211	6823	2068	SACRIFICIAL FLESH,CONFER UPON		胙
TZUOH	140,09	9182	13	44211			STRAW CUSHION/PILLOW		莋
TZUOH	162,05	9374.0A	09	38301		6642	TO PRESS,HASTE		迮
TZUOH	164,05	6797	12	18611	6785	2063	TOAST TO HOST BY GUEST		酢
TZUOH	167,20	7020.0A	28	37109	6786	0380	CHISEL		鑿
TZUOH	170,05	7092	08	78211	6777	2067	STEPS LEADING TO THE EASTERN DOOR		阼
TZY	009,03	0098.0A	05	27247	6940	3099	DUTY/RESPONSIBILITY		仔
TZY	030,04	8123	07	64047	6922	6214	(PHONETIC)		吱
TZY	030,06	0745	09	37608	6923	1395	CONSULT	6171	咨
TZY	038,07	1217	10	37404	6924	9038	BEAUTY,DISPOSITION		姿
TZY	039,04	1320	07	48440	6943	6335	UNWEARIED EFFORT		孜
TZY	039,09	1330	12	80407	6936	3160	INDUSTRIOUS,PRODUCE/BEAR		孳
TZY	046,09	1521	12	28732	6936A	8894	NAME OF A MOUNTAIN IN KANSU		嵫
TZY	085,08	3245	11	32163	6930	1827	BLACK,NAME OF A RIVER		淄
TZY	085,09	3320	12	38132	6937	8897	NOURISH,EXCITE		滋
TZY	085,13	3439	16	37186			TO RAIN CONTINUOUSLY		濨
TZY	095,06	5417.1	09	80732	6935		HEREWITH		兹
TZY	119,06	4726	12	37904	6926	5449	COMMON MILLET		粢
TZY	120,08	4867	14	22963	6931	1826	BLACK SILK,DARK,BUDDHISTS		緇
TZY	140,06	5417	10	44732	6935	8898	HEREWITH		兹
TZY	140,08	5469	12	44603	6932	1828	ONE-YEAR-OLD FIELD,(SURNAME)		菑
TZY	140,09	5512	13	44603			ONE-YEAR-OLD FIELD	5469	蓄

ROM	RAD	TEL	TOT	FC	MAT	OSH	TAG	CR	CHAR
TZY	148,05	9278	12	21227	6856	3704	(ZODIACAL SIGN)		
TZY	149,05	6088.0A	12	21601	6956	1172	BACKBITE,WEALTH,(SURNAME)		
TZY	149,09	6171	16	07668	6923	1396	CONSULT	0745	
TZY	154,05	6309	12	21806	6957	8223	PROPERTY,FINE INSTEAD OF PUNISHMENT		
TZY	154,06	6327	13	37806	6927	8215	RESOURCES/CAPITAL		
TZY	156,09	6394	16	47806		5950	MARK TIME,HESITATE		
TZY	159,08	6539	15	52063	6933	1825	MILIT. SUPPLY		
TZY	163,10	9407	13	17627			PLACE NAME		
TZY	167,08	6926	16	82163	6934	1824	ANCIENT WEIGHT,ONE-EIGHTH OF A TAEL		
TZY	167,10	6961	18	88132	6938	8893	HOE		
TZY	181,08	7347	17	21186			MUSTACHE	7568	
TZY	190,05	7568	15	72111	6958	7140	MUSTACHE		
TZY	195,08	9647	19	22363			MUGIL CEPHALUS/GREY MULLET		
TZY	206,03	7847	16	40221	6964	2857	TRIPOD WITH A SMALL OPENING ON TOP		
TZY	211,05	788A	20	21710		7134	PROJECTING TEETH		
TZYY	009,03	0098	05	27247	6940	3099	MINUTELY		
TZYY	038,05	1192	08	45427	6948	4755	OLDER SISTER		
TZYY	039,00	1311	03	17407	6939	3098	CHILD,SON		
TZYY	039,03	8311	06	17447	6941		TWINS,A PAIR		
TZYY	075,07	2737	11	40941	6951	2466	CATALPA KAEMPFERI		
TZYY	085,05	8669	08	31110		7138	CLEAN,FRESH,TO MOISTEN		
TZYY	085,10	3324	13	33141	6952	2474	SEDIMENT,DREGS		
TZYY	115,05	4444	10	25927	6949	4754	BILLION		
TZYY	118,05	4573	11	88227		4756	PLANKS OF BED,SLEEPING-MAT		
TZYY	119,03	4750	09	97947	6945	3103	SEEDS		
TZYY	120,05	4793	11	21903	6954	8480	PURPLE		
TZYY	127,03	5086	09	57947	6946	3104	HOE UP SOIL AROUND PLANTS		
TZYY	130,05	5159	09	75227	6950	4753	DRIED MEAT WITH BONE		
TZYY	140,05	5402	09	44111	6978		LITHOSPERMUM OFFICINALE		
TZYY	142,03	573B	09	57147			NARAGA DIFFUSA		
TZYY	149,05	6088	12	21601	6956	1172	BACKBITE,DISLIKE		
TZYH	018,08	0493	10	52000	6961	2897	STAB,ERECT		
TZYH	039,03	1316	06	30407	6942	3127	WORD		

ROM	RAD	TEL	TOT	FC	MAT	OSH	TAG	CR	CHAR
TZYH	061,06	1864	10	37338	6925	8647	THROW OFF RESTRAINT		恣
TZYH	085,11	3356	14	35186	6962	8118	SOAK,SATURATE		潰
TZYH	093,06	8784.1	10	23547	6944	3128	FEMALE OF DOMESTIC ANIMALS		牸
TZYH	093,07	8784	11	24547			FEMALE OF DOMESTIC ANIMALS		特
TZYH	109,05	4179	10	21601	6953	1733	CANTHUS	4180	眥
TZYH	109,05	4180	10	61010	6953	7137	CANTHUS	4179	眦
TZYH	130,05	5156	09	21227	6955	4063	PUTRID CARCASS		胔
TZYH	130,06	5175	12	43250	6963	6981	DICED MEAT,CUT MEAT INTO PIECES		胾
TZYH	132,00	5261	06	26000	6960	1736	SELF/ONESELF,FROM,SINCE		自
.TZ	039,00	1311.0A	03	17407	6939	3098	(NOUN SUFF.)		子
U	030,10	0839	13	67027	7167	4593	(ONOMAT. FOR HUMMING)		嗚
U	032,03	0963	06	41127	7174	4572	TO PLASTER,WHITE-WASH	8528	圬
U	044,06	1450	09	77214	7212	0264	ROOM,HOUSE		屋
U	048,04	1566	07	10108	7164	0133	WITCH		巫
U	075,03	8528	07	41927	7174	4574	TO PLASTER,WHITEWASH	0963	杇
U	085,03	3064	06	31127	7175	4575	DIRT/FILTH		污
U	085,03	3064.1	06	31140	7175	3312	DIRT/FILTH		汙
U	085,06	3176	09	34127	7175	4570	STAGNANT WATER,DIG(A POND)		洿
U	086,06	3527	10	27327	7166	4590	A CROW,BLACK		烏
U	149,07	6136.0A	14	01618	7165	0134	ACCUSE FALSELY		誣
U	163,10	6762	13	27327	7171	2226	ANCIENT PLACE NAME,(SURNAME)		鄔
U	167,10	7005	18	87127	7172	4592	TUNGSTEN		鎢
U	196,07	771B	18	17127			SPARROW/EMBERIZA CIOPSIS		鵐
WU	030,04	0710	07	10601	7188	1226	I/MY		吾
WU	030,04	0702	07	26430	7201	5102	(SURNAME),PROVINCE OF KIANGSU		吳
WU	030,07	0767.0A	10	61061		1229	SOUND OF A TUNE,I(DIAL.)		唔
WU	030,09	0845.0A	12	67014		0266	CACKLING OF FOWLS		喔
WU	046,07	1480	10	21761			NAME OF A MOUNTAIN		峿
WU	071,00	2477	04	10410			NOT TO HAVE,-LESS	3541	无
WU	075,07	2745	11	41961	7191	1237	STERCULIA PLATANIFOLIA		梧
WU	080,00	3019	04	77550	7193	4890	DO NOT ...		毋
WU	086,08	3541	12	80331	7180	8742	NOT TO HAVE,-LESS	2477	無
WU	140,12	5617	16	44331	7184	8749	OVERGROWN WITH WEEDS		蕪

ROM	RAD	TEL	TOT	FC	MAT	OSH	TAG	CR	CHAR
WU	142,07	5765	13	56134	7203	5106	CENTIPEDE		蜈
WU	149,07	6136	14	01618	7165	0134	ACCUSE FALSELY		誣
WU	163,07	9392	10	17627			PLACE NAME		鄅
WU	167,04	687A	12	81117			NEBULIUM		鈺
WU	167,07	6918.0A	15	81161	7652		HOE		鋘
WU	167,07	9461	15	86134			TROWEL,TO PLASTER		鏝
WU	208,07	7861	20	71716		6827	PETAURISTA LEUCOGENYS		鼯
WUU	007,02	0063	04	10107	7187	0531	FIVE		五
WUU	009,04	0124	06	21217	7187A	0532	FIVE,COMPANY,ASSOCIATE WITH		伍
WUU	009,04	0114	06	28240	7176	2432	OPPONENT		仵
WUU	009,07	0185	09	28257	7194	4879	INSULT		侮
WUU	024,02	0582	04	80400	7177	2428	NOON/11 A.M.-1 P.M.		午
WUU	030,08	1822.1	11	81461	7178	1234	DISOBEDIENT/UNFILIAL		啎
WUU	030,12	8172	15	68031			UNCLEAR/UNINTELLIGENT		嘸
WUU	031,04	093B	07	60107			5-MEMBER RING		囮
WUU	032,10	1051.0A	13	47127			DOCK		塢
WUU	038,08	8286	11	43440	7181	6894	TO PLEASE,FLATTER	8301	娬
WUU	038,12	8301	15	48431	7181	8747	TO PLEASE,FLATTER	8286	嫵
WUU	053,12	1682	15	00231	7182	8748	VERANDA		廡
WUU	061,04	1822	07	98040	7178	2431	DISOBEDIENT/UNFILIAL		忤
WUU	061,12	2007	15	98031	7183	8743	STARTLED,DISAPPOINTED		憮
WUU	077,04	2976	08	13140	7195	6890	MARTIAL/MILITARY		武
WUU	096,08	3814	12	13140			INFERIOR GEM	4300	珷
WUU	098,12	8852	17	81317		7937	(VASE/JAR)		甒
WUU	112,08	4300	13	13640		6891	INFERIOR GEM	3814	砆
WUU	130,12	5236.0A	16	78231		8745	THICK		膴
WUU	136,08	5294	14	80251	7185	2561	DANCE		舞
WUU	196,07	7713	18	17127		4654	PARROT		鵡
WUH	010,01	0335	03	10210	7205	7456	CUT OFF THE FEET,(SURNAME)		兀
WUH	019,03	0523-1	05	27427			BUSINESS/AFFAIR		务
WUH	019,09	0523	11	17227	7198	4866	BUSINESS/AFFAIR		務
WUH	020,02	0543	04	27220	7208	4480	DO NOT		勿
WUH	026,07	8117	09	17212	7211	7227	UNCOMFORTABLE,UNSTEADY		阢

ROM	RAD	TEL	TOT	FC	MAT	OSH	TAG	CR	CHAR
WUH	032,08	7916	11	41117		0517	DOCK,LOW WALL	1051	堨
WUH	032,10	1051	13	47127	7168	4591	DOCK,LOW WALL	7135	塢
WUH	038,09	1251	12	18404	7200	9053	BEAUTIFUL		嫵
WUH	040,11	1393	14	30261	7192	1233	AWAKE FROM SLEEP		寤
WUH	046,03	8322	06	21710	7206		BARE HILL		屼
WUH	061,06	1921.1B	10	10331			LOATHE		惡
WUH	061,07	1889	10	91061	7189	1232	COMPREHEND		悟
WUH	061,07	1888	10	96034	7202	5104	TO DELAY,NEGLECT	6137	悞
WUH	061,08	1921.0B	12	10331	4809	8544	LOATHE		惡
WUH	062,01	2048	05	53200	7197	6994	5TH HEAVEN'S STEM		戊
WUH	064,03	8420	06	51010			TO MOVE/SWAY		扤
WUH	072,07	2524	11	61061	7190	1231	MEET(SOCIALLY)		晤
WUH	075,03	2620	07	41910	7207	7458	LOW STOOL		杌
WUH	085,04	8663	07	37120			PROFOUND,ABSTRUSE		沕
WUH	093,04	3670	08	27520	7209	4482	THING/OBJECT/MATTER		物
WUH	104,07	403A	12	00161			(FLAT) MOLE		痦
WUH	140,04	537A	08	44227			FLUORENE		芴
WUH	149,07	6137	14	06634	7204	5103	TO DELAY,TO NEGLECT	1888	誤
WUH	162,04	6605	08	38304	7179	6645	TO ENCOUNTER,RECALCITRANT	9379	迕
WUH	162,12	9379	16	36307			TO ENCOUNTER,RECALCITRANT	6605	遻
WUH	167,07	6909	15	32109		0378	PLATED,TO PLATE		鋈
WUH	170,10	7135	13	77227	7168	4594	DOCK,LOW WALL	1051	隖
WUH	173,05	7212.1	13	10427			FOG/MIST		雺
WUH	173,11	7212	19	10227	7199	4867	FOG/MIST		霧
WUH	187,09	7497	19	18327		4715	FAST,RUN RAPIDLY,GREEDY		騖
WUH	196,09	7726	20	18327	4602	4683	TAME DUCK		鶩
UA	017,03	0425.0A	05	77770	7268	1974	CONCAVE		凹
UA	030,05	0722	08	62030	5995	4984	CRYING SOUND OF CHILD	0760	呱
UA	030,06	0760	09	64014	6989	0162	SOUND OF CHILD'S CRYING	0722	哇
UA	038,09	1257	12	47427	6997	3940	SISTER OF FWU SHI,(SURNAME)		媧
UA	064,06	2177	09	53017	6999	7973	DIG,SCOOP OUT		挖
UA	085,06	3173	09	34114	6991	0174	WINDING DITCH,ABBR. OF 4520		洼
UA	085,10	3295	13	33132			TO FORM HOLLOW/PIT		滧

ROM	RAD	TEL	TOT	FC	MAT	OSH	TAG	CR	CHAR
UA	116,01	4495	06	30717		7972	DIG,SCOOP OUT	2177	窀
UA	116,05	8999	10	30232	6994	4995	LOWLAND SWAMP	D4520	窊
UA	116,09	4520	14	30114	6992	0175	SWAMP,SUNKEN,DEPRESSION	3173	窪
UA	142,06	5752	12	54114	6993	0172	FROG	7838	蛙
UA	205,06	7838	19	40717	6993	7344	FROG	5752	鼃
WA	038,06	1216	09	44414	6990	0173	BABY,DOLL		娃
WA	064,06	2177.0A	09	53017			EAR PICK		挖
WA	116,01	4495.0A	06	30717		7972	EAR PICK	2177.0A	窫
WAA	009,04	7908	06	21217			KAWA		低
WAA	030,05	072B	08	61017			(PHONETIC)		呱
WAA	098,00	3907	05	10717	6998	7925	TILE		瓦
WAH	130,03	514C	07	71227			OXIME		肟
WAH	130,10	522A	14	76217		0677	CASTOR		膃
WAH	145,05	5920	10	35290	4552	5467	SOCKS/STOCKINGS	5994	袜
WAH	145,15	5994	20	34253	7000	7032	SOCKS/STOCKINGS	5920	襪
WAH	177,15	7292.1	24	44553	7000	7034	SOCKS/STOCKINGS		韈
WAH	178,15	7292	24	44553	7000	7033	SOCKS/STOCKINGS	5994	韤
UAI	030,09	0808.0A	12	66032		5762	HELLO		喂
UAI	046,09	8343	12	22253	7003	7027	MOUNTAINOUS		崴
UAI	077,05	2977	09	10101	7002	0497	ASKEW		歪
WOAI	077,05	2977.0A	09	10101	7002	0497	SPRAIN(ANKLE)		歪
WOAI	134,04	5276.0A	10	20777	7299	1061	TO SCOOP		舀
WAY	036,02	1120	05	23200	7001	1995	OUTSIDE		外
UAN	018,08	0468	10	32200	7017	2963	SCOOP OUT		剜
UAN	032,22	1081	25	40127			BAY	3494	壪
UAN	057,06	1737.1	09	00207	7028	4745	BEND/BENT		弯
UAN	057,19	1737	22	22207	7028	4743	BEND/BENT		彎
UAN	085,09	3494.1	12	30127		4746	BAY		湾
UAN	085,22	3494	25	32127	7029	4744	BAY		灣
UAN	142,08	5800	14	53112	7025	7207	TO MOVE(AS SNAKE)		蜿
UAN	151,08	6261	15	13112	7026	7198	PEAS		豌
WAN	003,02	0029	03	40017	7004	7915	PILL		丸
WAN	018,04	8101	06	12200			ROUND OFF CORNERS,TO TRIM		刓

ROM	RAD	TEL	TOT	FC	MAT	OSH	TAG	CR	CHAR
WAN	032,07	8219	10	43111			BANK/DIKE		垸
WAN	040,04	1346	07	30211	7008	7470	FINISHED		完
WAN	085,03	3304	06	34117	7005	7923	SHED TEARS		汍
WAN	086,07	7909	11	93811		7476	ALKANE		烷
WAN	096,04	3779	08	11111	7009	7464	TO PLAY,CURIOS/ANTIQUES	C7316	玩
WAN	096,20	3893	24	13134			JADE TABLET INDICATING RANK		瓛
WAN	120,03	4770	09	24917	7006	7922	WHITE SILK,WHITE		紈
WAN	140,03	5339	07	44417		7924	METAPLEXIS STAUNTONI		芄
WAN	181,04	7316	13	11286	7010	8303	OBSTINATE,MISCHIEVOUS,TO PLAY	G3779	頑
WAN	195,07	764S	18	23311			CTENOPHARYNGODON IDELLUS		鯇
WOAN	032,08	8225	11	43112			BOWL/CUP	4297	埦
WOAN	038,07	1231	10	47416	7012	7751	COMPLAISANT/AGREEABLE		婉
WOAN	038,08	1238	11	43412	7018	7208	GRACEFUL,TACTFUL		婉
WOAN	040,05	1354	08	30212	7016	7196	SIMILAR,WINDING (SURNAME)		宛
WOAN	064,07	2187	10	57016	7013	7749	PULL,DRAW,SEND FUNERAL ODE	6533	挽
WOAN	072,07	2519	11	67016	7014	7746	LATE,EVENING		晚
WOAN	075,08	2782	12	43912	7022	7205	BOWL/CUP	4297	椀
WOAN	085,07	3183.0A	10	33111	2244		CLEANSE/BATHE	3418.0A	浣
WOAN	085,13	3418.0A	16	38141	2244	2413	CLEANSE,BATHE	3183.0A	澣
WOAN	096,08	3834	12	13112		7197	ENSIGN OF ROYALTY		琬
WOAN	102,08	3979	13	63012		7200	A FIELD OF 20 OR 30 MOU		畹
WOAN	106,07	4111	12	23611	2245	7472	ANHWEI		皖
WOAN	108,05	4136	10	27107	7022	0722	BOWL/CUP	4297	盌
WOAN	112,08	4297	13	13612	7022	7199	BOWL/CUP	4136	碗
WOAN	120,08	4852	14	23977	7027	1486	STRING TOGETHER,BIND UP		綰
WOAN	140,07	5451	11	44211	2247	7478	SMILE		莞
WOAN	140,08	5463	12	44212	7024	7209	LUXURIANCE OF GROWTH		菀
WOAN	142,08	5800.0A	14	53112	7025	7207	TO MOVE(AS SNAKE)		蜿
WOAN	159,07	6533	14	57016	7015	7748	PULL A CART,SEND FUNERAL ODE	2187	輓
WANN	001,02	8001	03	10227	7030	4319	10,000,(SURNAME)	5502	万
WANN	024,04	0591	06	12217	7032	0855	SWASTIKA		卍
WANN	061,08	1923	11	93012	7020	7201	ALARMED		惋
WANN	073,07	2581.0A	11	60407	4330	6172	LONG,LARGE,HANDSOME		曼

ROM	RAD	TEL	TOT	FC	MAT	OSH	TAG	CR	CHAR
WANN	096,04	3779.0A	08	11111		7464	CURIOS/ANTIQUES		玩
WANN	124,09	9097	15	11611	7011	7466	PLAY WITH		翫
WANN	130,08	5205	12	73212	7023	7203	WRIST		腕
WANN	140,09	5502	13	44227	7030	4095	10,000,(SURNAME)	8001	萬
WANN	140,11	5585.0A	15	44407	4337	6183	CREEPER,TO SPREAD		蔓
UANG	043,00	1428	03	40010	7033	7707	LAME,FEEBLE	1431	尢
UANG	043,04	1431.1	08	81211	7038	7680	FEEBLE,LAME		尫
UANG	043,05	1431	08	41011		7708	FEEBLE,LAME	1428	尪
UANG	085,04	3076	07	31114	7041	0322	EXPANSE OF WATER,(SURNAME),OOZE		汪
WANG	008,01	0072	03	00710	7034	0759	PERISH		亡
WANG	096,00	3769	04	10104	7037	0314	KING,(SURNAME)		王
WANG	180,09	9573.0A	18	06614			SOUND OF BRONZE PERCUSSION		韹
WOANG	060,05	1766	08	20214	7050	0360	GO TO/TOWARDS		往
WOANG	061,08	1913	11	97020	7046	3810	DESOLATE		惘
WOANG	075,04	2648	08	41914	7040	0320	IN THE WRONG,IN VAIN		枉
WOANG	120,08	4853	14	27920	7047	3812	A NET	4986	網
WOANG	122,00	4986	06	77220	7044	3924	A NET	4853	网
WOANG	122,03	4987	08	77220	7045	3809	DECEIVE,THERE IS NONE		罔
WOANG	140,06	541C	10	44227			ILLICIUM ANISATUM		莽
WOANG	140,08	549C	12	44220			BECKMANNIA		菵
WOANG	159,08	6545	15	57020	7048	3811	WHEEL BAND,TIRE		輞
WOANG	194,08	7618	18	27212	7049	7655	ELF,SPRITE		魍
WANQ	038,03	1174	06	00404	7035	8994	ABSURD/FANTASTIC		妄
WANQ	061,03	1808	07	00331	7036	8546	FORGET		忘
WANQ	072,04	2489	08	61014	7039	0316	PROSPEROUS		旺
WANQ	074,07	2598	11	07104	7043	0309	LOOK TOWARDS,HOPE,TOWARDS		望
WANQ	074,10	2602	14	77104	7043	0310	15TH DAY OF MONTH(LUNAR CALENDAR)		朢
WANQ	162,04	6599	08	31301	7042		TO TRAVEL,SCARE,DECEIVE		迋
UEI	009,08	0244.0A	10	22244	7153		WINDING AND DISTANT(OF ROAD)		倭
UEI	009,09	0246	11	26232	7070	5763	TO CUDDLE		偎
UEI	030,09	8153	12	63050			(PHONETIC)		喴
UEI	038,05	1201.0A	08	20404	7098	9041	CROOKED		委
UEI	038,06	1218	09	53200	7051	7026	PRESTIGE		威

ROM	RAD	TEL	TOT	FC	MAT	OSH	TAG	CR	CHAR
UEI	060,10	1792.0A	13	28240	7061		TINY		
UEI	085,10	8691	13	38140			LIGHT RAIN		
UEI	086,06	8737	10	94814			THREE-CORNERED STOVE		
UEI	086,09	3566	13	96832	7072	5767	TO ROAST IN ASHES,SIMMER		
UEI	140,08	5494.0A	12	44404	7100	9050	WITHERED,SPIRITLESS		
UEI	140,09	5524	13	44253	7052	7028	LUXURIANT		
UEI	140,09	552A	13	44741			CUDRANIA		
UEI	170,09	7128	12	76232	7074	5764	COVE,BAY		
UEI	195,09	765P	20	23312			PODOTHECUS TOKUBIRE		
WEI	002,03	7279.1	04	50002			(SURNAME),SOFT LEATHER		
WEI	019,02	3634.2	04	34027			ACT AS,TO BE,TAKE...TO BE		
WEI	026,04	0604	06	27212	7056	7219	PERILOUS		
WEI	030,08	0787	11	60014	7064	0870	ONLY,-ISM	1919	
WEI	031,00	0931	03	60000	7054	1889	ENCLOSURE		
WEI	031,09	0953	12	60506	7082	1878	SURROUND		
WEI	032,03	0962.0A	06	41140	7593	3307	DIKE		
WEI	046,10	1531	13	22213	7096	7648	ROCKY		
WEI	046,18	1550	21	22413	7105	7647	LOFTY/EMINENT		
WEI	050,08	1602	11	40214	7065	0883	CURTAIN/SCREEN		
WEI	050,09	1605	12	44256	7083	2581	CURTAIN,WOMEN'S APARTMENT		
WEI	060,10	1792	13	28240	7061	6394	TINY		
WEI	061,08	1919	11	90014	7066	0876	ONLY,-ISM	0787	
WEI	075,06	2712	10	47912	7057	7225	MAST		
WEI	085,09	8698	12	34156			TO FLOW BACK(OF WATER)		
WEI	085,14	3452	17	30114	7068	0912	NAME OF A RIVER		
WEI	086,05	3634.1	09	34027			ACT AS,TO BE,TAKE...TO BE		
WEI	087,08	3634	12	20227	7059	4523	ACT AS,TO BE,TAKE... TO BE		
WEI	120,08	4850	14	20914	7067	0911	MAINTAIN		
WEI	140,13	5633	17	44248	7062	6395	WILD ROSE,OSMUNDA REGALIS		
WEI	162,09	6672	13	34305	7093	6659	GO AGAINST,DISOBEY		
WEI	163,12	9413	15	27227			PLACE NAME		
WEI	167,09	9492	17	84156			SPADE		
WEI	169,09	7057	17	77506	7094	3480	DOOR TO WOMEN'S ROOM,GATE TO PALACE		

微 溦 娃 煨 葳 薆 隈 鰄 韦 为 危 唯 囗 圍 圩 嵬 巍 帷 幃 微 帷 桅 潍 潍 為 爲 維 薇 違 鄃 鍏 闈

358

ROM	RAD	TEL	TOT	FC	MAT	OSH	TAG	CR	CHAR
WEI	178,00	7279	09	40506	7080	2576	(SURNAME),SOFT LEATHER		韋
WEI	195,09	765Q	20	26341			HOLOCENTRUS SPINOSISSIMUS		鰃
WOEI	008,19	0084	21	00107	7118	0631	RESOLUTE		亹
WOEI	009,09	0251	11	24256	7081	2579	GREAT		偉
WOEI	030,08	0787.0A	11	60014	7064	0870	YES		唯
WOEI	038,05	1201	08	20404	7098	9041	TO COMMISSION,GIVE UP,INDEED		委
WOEI	038,07	1232	10	47414	7110	7387	COMPLY WITH,ACTIVE		娓
WOEI	040,12	8314	15	30227			(SURNAME)		寪
WOEI	044,04	1442	07	77214	7109	7386	TAIL		尾
WOEI	085,06	3161	09	34127	7106	3589	NAME OF A RIVER		洧
WOEI	086,09	3555	13	94856	7085	2582	RAGING FIRE,GLOW		煒
WOEI	094,09	3725	12	46232	7073		PLENTIFUL,HUMBLE/RUSTIC		猥
WOEI	096,09	3837	13	14156	7086	2577	(REDDISH JADE),RARE,PRECIOUS		瑋
WOEI	104,08	4039	13	00144	7099	9049	ATROPHY		痿
WOEI	106,16	9200.1	21	24627			FLOWER/BLOSSOM		曠
WOEI	112,10	4343	15	16613			ROCKY/STONY		磈
WOEI	120,09	4885	15	24956	7087	2583	LATITUDE		緯
WOEI	140,08	5494	12	44404	7100	9050	WITHER		萎
WOEI	140,09	5517	13	44506	7088	2585	REED/RUSH/PHRAGMITES COMMUNIS		葦
WOEI	140,12	5666	16	44227			(SURNAME),EURYALE FEROX		蔿
WOEI	140,14	5652	18	44303			(SURNAME),(GRASS)		薳
WOEI	140,17	9200	21	44627			FLOWER/BLOSSOM		蘤
WOEI	149,08	6152	15	02644	7101	9043	SHIRK/GIVE EXCUSES		諉
WOEI	170,10	7136	13	76213	7097	7642	(SURNAME),LOFTY,EMINENT		隗
WOEI	178,09	7289	18	65805	7095	6013	RIGHT,CORRECT		韙
WOEI	181,06	9579	15	21286			EASEFUL CARRIAGE OF ONE'S HEAD		頠
WOEI	188,02	7540	12	74217			BE BENT/CROOKED(OF BONES)		骫
WOEI	188,03	7540.1	13	77210	7119	7921	BE BENT/CROOKED(OF BONES)		骪
WOEI	195,06	7635	17	24327	7108	3587	LITTLE TUNA/EUTHNNUS ALLECTERATUS		鮪
WEY	001,02	5898.2	03	17102			PROTECT,(SURNAME)		卫
WEY	009,04	0298.1	06	24227			FALSE,ARTIFICIAL		伪
WEY	009,05	0143	07	20218	7116	0547	AN. FOR PERSON,SEAT,POSITION		位
WEY	009,12	0298	14	22227	7060	4525	FALSE,ARTIFICIAL		偽

ROM	RAD	TEL	TOT	FC	MAT	OSH	TAG	CR	CHAR
WEY	019,02	3634.2A	04	34027			FOR,BECAUSE OF		为
WEY	030,05	0724	08	65090	7115	5459	TASTE		味
WEY	030,09	0808	12	66032	7103	5762	TO FEED	9597	喂
WEY	041,08	1414	11	74200	7111	3222	TO QUIET,MILIT. OFFICIAL,(SURNAME)		尉
WEY	061,11	1983	15	74330	7112	8625	REASSURE		慰
WEY	075,01	2607	05	50900	7114	5458	NOT YET,1-3 P.M.		未
WEY	085,09	3262	12	36127	7077	3620	NAME OF A RIVER		渭
WEY	086,05	3634.1A	09	34027			FOR,BECAUSE OF		為
WEY	086,09	8754	13	96827			RADIANCE OF FIRE		煟
WEY	087,08	3634.0A	12	20227	7059	4523	FOR,BECAUSE OF		爲
WEY	102,04	3956	09	60732	7069	5761	TO FEAR		畏
WEY	112,10	4328	15	12618	7122	0572	MILL		磑
WEY	122,11	9087	16	60240			BIRD-NET		罻
WEY	130,05	5152	09	60227	7075	3615	STOMACH		胃
WEY	140,11	5588	15	44240	7113	3223	ARTEMISIA JAPONICA,LUXURIANT		蔚
WEY	140,13	5635	17	44253			WEEDY		葳
WEY	142,09	5798	15	56127	7078	3619	HEDGEHOG		蝟
WEY	142,11	5827	17	74136			WHITE ANT/LEUCOTERMES SPERATUS		蟨
WEY	144,09	5898.1	15	25221	7089.	3025	PROTECT,(SURNAME)		衛
WEY	144,10	5898	16	21221	7089	3028	PROTECT,(SURNAME)		衞
WEY	145,11	9261	17	74732			COLLAR		尉
WEY	149,09	6182	16	06627	7079	3617	SPEAK OF		謂
WEY	157,15	9350	22	21801	2358		EXAGGERATE		躗
WEY	159,11	9364	18	55077	7120	0862	END OF AXLETREE		轊
WEY	162,08	6653	12	32304	7102	6787	WINDING		透
WEY	173,11	7229	19	10243			RISING OF CLOUDS		靅
WEY	184,08	9597.1	16	82744	7103	9045	TO FEED		餧
WEY	184,09	9597	17	86732		5765	TO FEED	0808	餵
WEY	194,08	7614	18	26413	7104	7646	NAME OF A DYNASTY,(SURNAME)		魏
WEY	195,11	766S	22	24300			BLENNIES/BLENNIIDAE		鰃
UEN	075,10	283A	14	46917		0678	QUINCE		榲
UEN	085,09	3306	12	36112	7125	0684	LUKEWARM,TO REVIEW		温
UEN	104,09	4054	14	00117	7127	0685	EPIDEMIC/PESTILENCE		瘟

ROM	RAD	TEL	TOT	FC	MAT	OSH	TAG	CR	CHAR
UEN	140,10	552B	14	44107			RHODEA JAPONICA		蒕
UEN	159,10	6563	17	56017	7128	0675	HEARSE		轀
UEN	195,10	766C	21	26317			(SARDINE)		鰮
WEN	067,00	2429	04	00400	7129	6545	WRITING,LITERARY		文
WEN	096,04	3774	08	10140		6547	VEINS IN JADE		玟
WEN	120,04	4773	10	20940	7132	6550	LINE/TRACE/MARK		紋
WEN	128,08	5113	14	77401	7142	3483	HEAR,SNIFF AT,(SURNAME)		聞
WEN	142,04	5730	10	50140	7134	6551	MOSQUITO	9238	蚊
WEN	142,05	9238.1	11	57147	7134		MOSQUITO		[illegible]
WEN	142,11	9238	17	77136	7134	8914	MOSQUITO	5730	蟁
WEN	169,08	7064	16	77407	7143	3522	LOOK DOWN		闅
WEN	173,04	7186	12	10400	7135	6556	MULTICOLORED CLOUDS		雯
WOEN	018,04	0437	06	22200	7137	2930	CUT ACROSS(THROAT)		刎
WOEN	030,04	0708	07	67020	7138	4481	MOUTH,KISS		吻
WOEN	115,09	4489.1	14	27937			STEADY,SETTLED		稳
WOEN	115,14	4489	19	22937	7140	8551	STEADY,SETTLED		穩
WOEN	130,07	9127	11	77262	7139	1378	JOIN,FIT TOGETHER		脗
WENN	030,08	0795	11	77607	7141	3450	ASK		問
WENN	064,04	2114	07	50040	7130	6549	WIPE		抆
WENN	064,10	8453	13	56017	7124	0676	WIPE,PRESS WITH FINGER	A2114	搵
WENN	085,04	3080	07	30140	7131	6552	NAME OF A RIVER		汶
WENN	120,04	4772	10	00903	7133	8476	TANGLED,INVOLVED		紊
WENN	120,07	9061	13	27916	7144	7750	MOURNING,ROPE TO THE BIER		絻
UENG	030,10	084D	13	68027		3421	-OIN(CHEM.)AS IN ANISOIN		嗡
UENG	124,04	5040	10	80127	7146	3420	ELDERLY PERSON,(SURNAME)		翁
UENG	142,10	9235	16	58127	7150		AMMOPHILA INFESTA		螉
UENG	195,10	766K	21	28327			CIRRHITICHTHYS AUREUS		[illegible]
UENG	196,10	773A	21	87127			SIBERIAN FLYCATCHER		鶲
WENQ	098,04	3908	09	80717	7151	7946	EARTHEN JAR,URN	3922	瓮
WENQ	098,13	3922	18	00717	7151	7938	EARTHEN JAR,URN	4980	甕
WENQ	121,13	4980	19	00772	7151	1007	EARTHEN JAR,URN	3922	罋
WOENG	085,10	3317	13	38127	7149	3422	FLOAT(OF CLOUDS)		滃
WOENG	140,10	5555	14	44127		3423	THICK,A PLANT IN BLOOM		蓊

ROM	RAD	TEL	TOT	FC	MAT	OSH	TAG	CR	CHAR
UO	009,08	0244	10	22244	7153	9044	DWARF,JAPANESE		
UO	085,09	3260	12	37127	7154	3941	EDDY/WHIRLPOOL		
UO	116,09	4519	14	30227	7155	3943	NEST		
UO	140,09	5504	13	44227	7156	3942	(LETTUCE)/LACTUCA SATIVA		
WOO	062,03	2053	07	23550	4778	6924	I/ME		
WOH	030,09	0845	12	67014	7159	0266	CACKLING OF FOWLS		
WOH	050,09	1606	12	47214	7160	0269	TENT		
WOH	064,09	2259	12	57014	7161	0268	SHAKE HANDS		
WOH	068,10	2441	14	48440	3570	2710	TO TURN		
WOH	085,04	3087	07	32134	7210	5133	FERTILE,RICH		
WOH	085,08	3243	11	33112			TO SOIL		
WOH	085,09	3259	12	37114	7162	0270	MOISTEN,ENRICH		
WOH	130,02	5257	08	78700	7158	1991	LYING DOWN		
WOH	142,14	5863.0A	20	54147		6156	LOOPER CATERPILLAR		
WOH	172,10	7174.0A	18	74447	2210	6152	RED EARTH USED FOR PAINTS		
WOH	211,09	7891	24	27714	7163	0265	SMALL-MINDED,DIRTY		
	009,12	0290	14	26231					
	015,07	0409	09	31146					
TWUSHUGOAN	031,10	0959	13	60601	6531		LIBRARY		
	032,04	8200	07	47120					
	032,05	8207	08	47147					
	032,05	8206	08	47170					
	032,06	8215	09	40148					
	032,07	8220	10	41121					
	046,04	8324	07	20772					
	046,05	8336	08	20780					
	046,06	8332	09	22700					
	061,13	2024	16	92047					
	064,04	8428	08	80502					
	064,07	2146	10	57094					
	069,12	2449	16	62521					
	075,04	8536	08	43934					
	075,05	267A	09	47950			TSUGA SIEBELDII		

倭渦窩蒿我喔幄握幹沃涴渥臥蠖朧蠡偓涹圖圯垠坳坺岙岆岄岞慢挐捼斳枖栦

ROM	RAD	TEL	TOT	FC	MAT	OSH	TAG	CR	CHAR
	075,11	8585	15	43917					槭
	075,11	286A	15	47914			OAK/QUERCUS GLAUCA(JAPAN.)		樫
	082,03	3043	07	29710					[illegible]
	085,10	3250	13	38140					滧
	086,04	3513	08	90830					炞
	086,08	8745	12	94827					焴
	086,10	8755	14	94860					[illegible]
	094,13	8812	16	40236					[illegible]
	096,11	3869	15	14134					[illegible]
	100,10	3937	15	25114					[illegible]
	104,04	8866	09	00147					[illegible]
	112,05	8940	10	17620					硧
	112,06	8945	11	14681					硔
	112,07	8971	12	11660					[illegible]
	112,08	8953	13	10661					[illegible]
	112,08	8957	13	78601					硻
	112,12	8964	17	18646					[illegible]
	113,09	4413	13	37247					[illegible]
	130,10	522B	14	75294					膝
	137,06	9155	12	24427					舿
	137,07	9156	13	24438					[illegible]
	140,04	535B	08	44107					[illegible]
	140,12	557C	16	44840					[illegible]
	142,08	585B	14	52133					[illegible]
	145,04	9252	09	37240					[illegible]
	145,12	9263	17	32253					[illegible]
	145,13	9266	18	34234					[illegible]
	154,07	9324	14	66814					[illegible]
	159,03	6579	10	52070					軕
	170,10	9538	13	77262					[illegible]
	173,06	9544	14	10294					霖
	184,14	9605	22	85717					[illegible]

ROM	RAD	TEL	TOT	FC	MAT	OSH	TAG	CR	CHAR
	195,06	7648	17	24321			GREY MULLET(JAPAN.)		鯐

EXPERIENCE CANADA

A GEOGRAPHY

EXPERIENCE CANADA
A GEOGRAPHY

Dennis DesRivieres
Lead Author

Colin M. Bain

Robert Harshman

OXFORD
UNIVERSITY PRESS

OXFORD
UNIVERSITY PRESS

70 Wynford Drive, Don Mills, Ontario M3C 1J9
www.oup.com/ca

Oxford University Press is a department of the University of Oxford.

It furthers the University's objective of excellence in research,
scholarship, and education by publishing worldwide in

Oxford New York

*Auckland Bangkok Buenos Aires Cape Town
Chennai Dar es Salaam Delhi Hong Kong Istanbul
Karachi Kolkata Kuala Lumpur Madrid Melbourne Mexico City
Mumbai Nairobi São Paulo Shanghai Taipei Tokyo Toronto*

Oxford is a registered trademark of Oxford University Press in the UK
and in certain other countries

Published in Canada
by Oxford University Press

Copyright © Oxford University Press Canada 2003

The moral rights of the author have been asserted

Database right Oxford University Press (maker)

First published 2003

National Library of Canada Cataloguing in Publication Data

DesRivieres, Dennis, 1947-
Experience Canada: a geography / Dennis DesRivieres,
Colin Bain, Robert Harshman.

Includes index.
ISBN 0-19-541846-8

1. Canada—Geography—Textbooks. I. Bain, Colin M.
II. Harshman, Robert III. Title.

FC75.D474 2003   917.1   C2003-900739-1
F1017.D474 2003

Printed in Canada
1 2 3 4 – 06 05 04 03

Acquisitions editor: Patti Henderson
Managing editor: Monica Schwalbe
Lead developmental editor: Margaret Hoogeveen
Developmental editors: Chelsea Donaldson, Evelyn Maksimovich
Copy editor: Francine Geraci
Photo and permissions researcher: Maria DeCambra
Production editor: Heather Kidd
Text design: Brett Miller
Cover design: Joan Dempsey
Formatting and art: VISU*TronX*

Acknowledgements

We have benefited a great deal from the combined
experience of the excellent administrative and editorial team
at Oxford University Press. We appreciate the initiative of
MaryLynne Meschino and Patti Henderson, who launched
the book. We are indebted to lead editor Margaret
Hoogeveen and editors Chelsea Donaldson and Evelyn
Maksimovich, who skillfully shaped what we wrote. As
well, our thanks to Monica Schwalbe, Heather Kidd,
Francine Geraci, and Maria DeCambra, who steered
Experience Canada through production.

Thank you to our GIS consultant, Archie Robinson
(Geography Department Head, Thames Valley District
School Board), for his contribution and to the ten young
people featured in our GeoSkills career features for giving us
a personal look into their lives and career choices. We also
appreciate the many helpful suggestions offered by our
perceptive reviewers and the assistance of the following
companies (which provided technical assistance and
photographs for this book): High Liner Foods Inc., UBE
Automotive North America Sarnia Plant Inc., Pilkington
North America Inc., Toyota Motor Manufacturing Canada
Inc., EBTech, Dofasco Inc., and G.A.P Adventures.

Finally, we are particularly thankful for the assistance and
patience of our families in this endeavour: Vi Bain, for her
research assistance; Shirley, Robert, and Debbie DesRivieres,
for feature materials provided; and Susan, Michelle, and
Kristen Harshman for their encouragement and support.

Experience is the best teacher.

We hope that students will actively participate in learning
with *Experience Canada*. As authors, we have applied many
years of classroom experience to help them meet provincial
curriculum standards. In this, we take full responsibility for
the content and activities of the textbook.

Colin Bain
Dennis DesRivieres
Robert Harshman

Cover images: Chinatown, night: Angelo Cavalli/Getty
Images; Woman on mountain bike: VCL/Getty Images.

CONTENTS

FEATURES

Performance Tasks

INTRODUCTION

Wouldn't it be great to visit one of Canada's sandy beaches? or the Rocky Mountains? or some other part of this huge country? Well, this textbook can take you there. It will let you experience the variety and excitement of our land. That's why we called this book *Experience Canada: A Geography*.

◀ Where the natural world and the human world meet

The Main Ideas

Our Earth is made up of two worlds: the natural world and the human world. The photograph shown above—of footprints in the sand—illustrates the main idea behind this book by reminding us that these two worlds continually come into contact, interacting with and affecting one another.

Sometimes the effects of humans on the Earth are minimal, no more than footprints that are washed away with the next wave. But imagine the damage caused to the shore shown above if an oil tanker were to crash on the rocks. Of course, the interaction can go the other way too. For example, severe storm waves have been known to tear apart homes built too close to the shoreline.

Interaction between the natural and human worlds is an important concept throughout *Experience Canada*. For example, you'll see how Canadians have been able to build a number of major industries by taking advantage of some of the natural resources our land has to offer. In turn, you'll see how Canada's economic growth has affected the environment. You'll also learn how we are linked to the rest of the world—through our cultural, historical, political, and economic ties as well as through our need to solve international environmental problems by working together. This is called *interdependence*.

Experience Canada is divided into five units of study, all of which show the interactions between natural and human worlds:

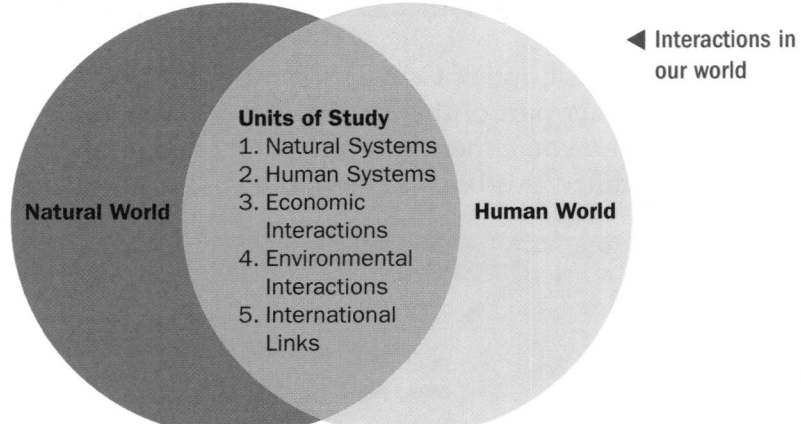

◀ Interactions in our world

Units of Study
1. Natural Systems
2. Human Systems
3. Economic Interactions
4. Environmental Interactions
5. International Links

Natural World   **Human World**

Here's another important concept you'll learn about in *Experience Canada*: The natural and human worlds come together to form unique areas called *regions*. You will examine different types of regions, including your neighbourhood, local bioregions, and larger areas called *ecozones*. In each of these regions, both natural systems and human systems are at work.

Using this Book

This textbook has been designed with you in mind. It includes many special features:

- Do you like to use clues to make an educated guess? Each of the five units starts with a *Somewhere in Canada Contest*, in which you guess where the featured photograph was taken.

- Are you attracted by the strange little details of life? If so, the *GeoTrivia* facts in every chapter are made for you.

- Do you like games of chance with easy rules to follow? Play the *GeoGames* that appear throughout the book; you'll learn something important about our world in every one.

- Ever wondered about life after high school? Meet the ten young adults profiled in the *GeoCareers* features, and find out why they like their geography-related jobs.

- Do you enjoy finding out about interesting places or topics? Read about some unusual Canadian locations (like the Great Lakes Alvar "moonscapes") in the *Case Studies* features.

- Do you enjoy learning by doing? You can learn "hands-on" skills when you actually need them in the *GeoSkills* features. These features help you master a geography skill step-by-step and then give you the opportunity to practise each skill right on the spot.

This textbook also has a few useful tools at the back: an *index* to help you find information quickly and a *glossary* for definitions and examples of important geography words. (These words are highlighted in **bold** and defined within the chapters.)

Your Geographic Toolbox

Skilled professionals use the tools of their trade to do their jobs well. For example, dentists have precise drills and auto mechanics have big rolling tool chests. Professionals also have skills they have learned at school or on the job; in a sense, these skills are also tools. Dentists have a skill for drilling teeth and auto mechanics have a skill for replacing brake pads.

In the field of geography, skills are important too. You can make sure you have the necessary geography "tools" by working through the opening chapter, called "Your Geographic Toolbox". It's packed with five important *GeoSkills* that you'll use over and over in this course. For example, many assignments in this book depend on skilled map construction and use, so four of the *GeoSkills* features in the chapter review the skills you'll need to draw and interpret various kinds of maps at different scales.

Perhaps the most important tool in the geographer's toolbox, though, is the skill of problem solving. Two of the *GeoSkills* in this text help you learn this skill. The first, called "Using Geographic Inquiry," helps you review and practise a five-step method for doing research and answering questions. Later in the book, you'll encounter another *GeoSkill* called "Using Geographic Inquiry to Solve a Problem," which expands your problem-solving skills.

In this course, geographic inquiry will help you do research, prepare projects, and solve problems. Yet, it will also prove useful to you generally, not only throughout your time as a student but also in your future career.

Show Your Learning

If you play sports, you know that practices lead up to "game day". *Experience Canada* is designed this way too: you work through the chapter material, skills, and ideas, and then, at the end of each unit, you show off what you've learned by doing a performance task.

What is a performance task? It's a realistic, hands-on activity, such as planning a snowmobile trail, setting up your own business, or designing an environment-friendly home. Each performance task is broken down into four smaller steps (called assignments) that lead you through the job. You will file these with your teacher in order to build up a collection of work. This portfolio will be like a book of artist sketches—an authentic way to judge how well you can apply what you've learned.

*   *   *

Look back at the picture of the footprints in the sand. Think about the many ways that you interact with the Earth every day. Do you understand *why* we all must be more careful about how we affect Earth's natural systems? Do you know *how* we can use the Earth wisely and still enjoy what it offers to us? *Experience Canada* will lead you farther in these directions.

YOUR GEOGRAPHIC TOOLBOX

The Play

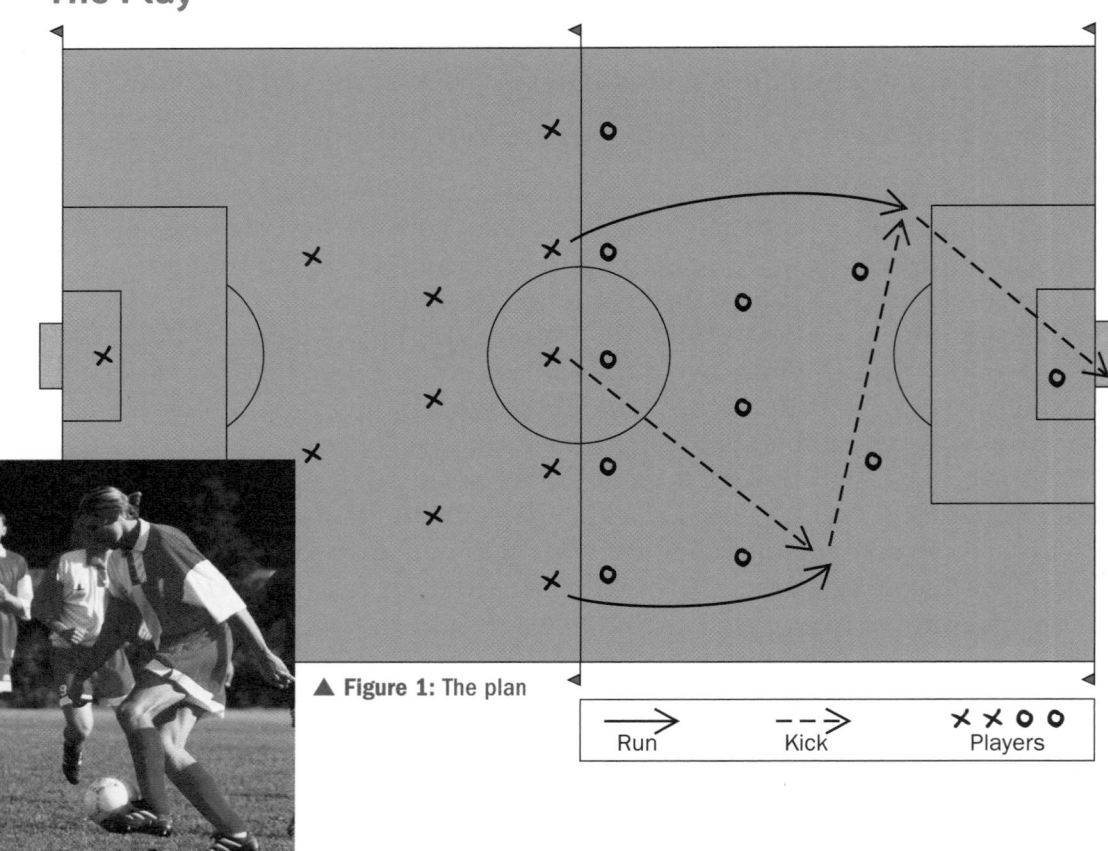

▲ Figure 1: The plan

→ Run	- - → Kick	✗ ✗ ○ ○ Players

◀ Figure 2: Executing the play

1. Look at the plan in Figure 1 and then describe the play that the coach wants the team to execute.

2. How should the opposing team defend against this play?

3. If you were a coach for the opposing team, what plan would you make for getting a goal?

4. Would you call the plan, above, a map? Why or why not?

5. In your notebook, make a labelled plan to show a play in the sport that interests you most.

In this chapter, you will

- learn what geography is about
- use map grids, compass direction, and latitude and longitude
- draw a small-area map
- use a street map, road map, and atlas map

What Is Geography?

Geography is the study of the Earth. Chances are good that some of your favourite activities involve geography. This statement may seem strange. You may think that geography is about the whole world, or about important environmental issues like endangered species and global warming. That's true—geography does involve these. But it works on a small scale, too. The sports fields, parks, and shopping malls you visit are all parts of the Earth, so they're included in geography as well. Your daily life and some of your interests are connected to the Earth.

You might also think that geography doesn't have very much to do with you because geography is about the Earth, not people. In fact, geography involves two aspects of Earth: its **physical geography** (natural things) and its **human geography** (people, and things related to people, such as cities).

> **GeoTrivia #1**
> The word *geography* comes from the ancient Greek words *geo*, meaning "Earth," and *grapho*, which means "I write."

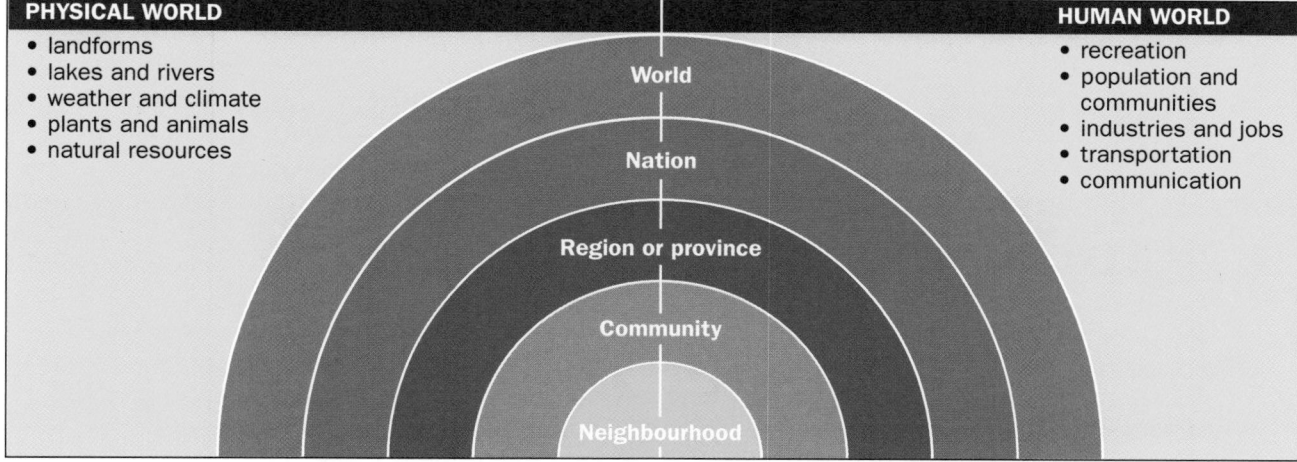

PHYSICAL WORLD	HUMAN WORLD
• landforms	• recreation
• lakes and rivers	• population and communities
• weather and climate	• industries and jobs
• plants and animals	• transportation
• natural resources	• communication

World
Nation
Region or province
Community
Neighbourhood

▲ **Figure 3:** In geography, we study the physical world and the human world on many different levels.

6. Make a drawing like Figure 3 in your notebook, leaving space to fill in examples.
   a) Put these examples in the best place on the drawing.
      • the river or lake closest to your home
      • salmon from the Pacific Ocean, eaten in Prince George, BC
      • a car made in Korea, driven in the USA
      • a TV hockey game played in Edmonton, watched in Ontario
   b) Fill in your own examples in the remaining spaces on your diagram.

Geographers try to answer three questions:
   • Where are things located on Earth?
   • What are the connections between people and the Earth?
   • How can we illustrate this information to understand it better?

"Where?" is the question asked most frequently in geography. The answer usually describes the location and distribution of things on the surface of the Earth. For example, geographers know where Canada's population is growing fastest—in the large cities.

In answering the second geographical question, we try to link physical and human geography. For example, geographers know that rapid population growth in our cities is taking excellent farmland out of production.

To answer the third question, we try to show locations, distributions, and connections using visual aids such as maps and photographs. For example, geographers compare satellite images from space to see the rates of city expansion. Geography is a very visual subject. If something can be mapped, it's probably about geography.

7. a) Use an atlas or a wall map to describe the location of Canada's biggest cities.
   b) Suggest reasons why population growth and loss of farmland are connected.

This chapter will show you how physical geography and human geography relate to you. You'll do this by looking at neighbourhood geography, regional geography, and world geography. You'll also build up a toolbox full of skills to help you succeed in this course. To get started, try drawing a small-area map—the kind of map you probably use every time you go to the local mall.

GeoSkills

DRAWING A SMALL-AREA MAP AND ROUTE

Purpose

Small-area maps show a specific area in great detail. Businesses often create these maps to help us find our way around theme parks, museums, and shopping malls, like the Bigenough Shopping Mall, mapped on the opposite page.

A good map is attractive and easy to read. When you draw a small-area map, take the following steps so you can be sure that others will understand it.

Step 1

Using a ruler, put a frame around your map. This sets it off, like a frame around a picture.

Step 2

Put a title at the top of your map to tell the map's subject and location.

Step 3

Make an organized legend to show the meaning of the colours and symbols you will use. Avoid crowding by boxing off a space labelled "Legend" before you draw your map.

Step 4

Show the compass direction "north." North is usually at the top of the page. Draw a letter *N* with an arrow pointing in the right direction.

Step 5

Show a map scale in one of the lower corners of the map. The **scale** compares measurements on the map to actual distances on the Earth's surface, for example, 2 cm : 1 km. To make a linear scale (sometimes called a bar scale), draw a line and label it like this:

1 kilometre

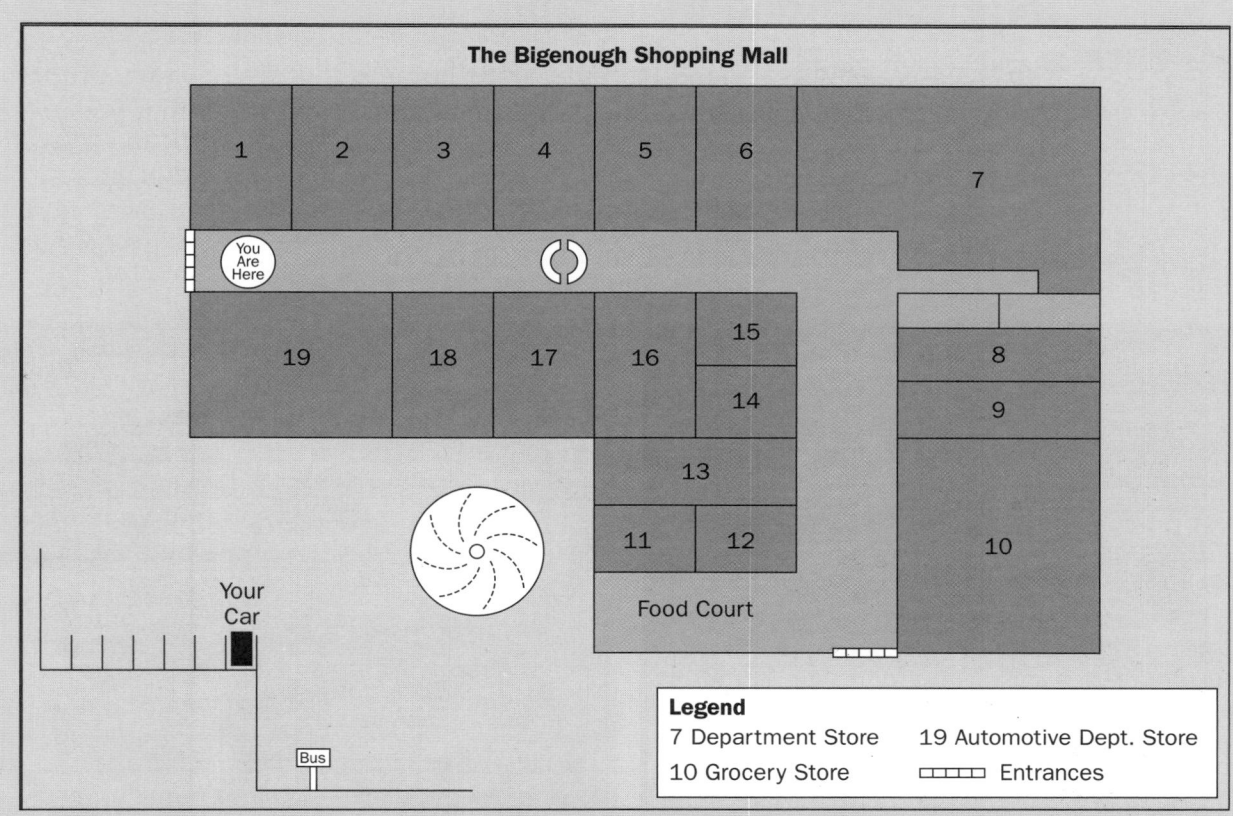

▲ **Figure 4:** An incomplete map of the Bigenough Shopping Mall. What is missing?

Step 6
Draw and label features on the map. Always print labels, using the same size and style of lettering for most items. Print across the map (not up and down), except for features such as rivers, mountain chains, and streets.

Step 7
Plot a route from one place to another by drawing a neat line with arrows to show the direction of movement.

Practise It!
1. a) In your notebook, follow Steps 1–7 to make a complete map of the Bigenough Shopping Mall. Add everything that is missing. Complete the legend by naming the unnamed stores (or types of stores) in this mall. Label the information booth, washrooms, and an outdoor fountain.
   b) Plan a shopping trip to visit at least five stores and the food court. Starting from the bus stop or the car in the parking lot, draw a line with arrows to show

To make a small-area map...
✔ use a ruler to make a frame
✔ add a title and a legend
✔ indicate north
✔ include a map scale
✔ draw the features
✔ print the labels
✔ draw a route with a neat line and some arrows

your route. Use the outside mall entrances shown on the map.

Neighbourhood Geography

You live in a neighbourhood, whether your home is in a city, a town, or the countryside. Your neighbourhood is the small area of the Earth that you connect with every day. It may be only a few blocks, or it could cover a few square kilometres, depending on the population and how far apart people live. Your neighbourhood probably has services that you use regularly, such as a park, variety store, school, and bus service.

▲ **Figure 5:** Two types of neighbourhoods. What is your neighbourhood like?

Geographers are interested in neighbourhood studies to help them solve bigger problems. For example, they might ask the following questions:

- Where do people live, work, or go to school in this neighbourhood?

- Do routes in the neighbourhood encourage people to use cars (which pollute the air) or bicycles (which do not)?

- How can we map the neighbourhood to understand the situation and make some changes?

The answers to these questions could result in planning bicycle routes to reduce pollution in the neighbourhood. Street maps would be very useful to the geographers designing these routes. They are called **large-scale maps** because they show a small part of the Earth in great detail.

GeoTrivia #2
The oldest existing map is a 4500-year-old clay slab from Babylonia, part of present-day Iraq.

8. Make up a set of three questions a geographer might ask about crosswalks in your neighbourhood. Make sure your questions ask "Where?," "What are the connections?," and "How can we illustrate this information to understand it better?"

Compass Direction

A compass is a useful tool to find your way in unfamiliar areas. Here's how it works. The Earth has magnetic poles, and the compass's magnetized metal needle points to the nearest one. The Magnetic North Pole is located in the Canadian Arctic; therefore, compass direction is based on north. North is always at the top, or 12 o'clock position, on a compass. Like a circle, the face of a compass has 360 divisions measured in degrees. Each division is called a **compass bearing**, a number that increases clockwise through the circle. (See Figure 6.) The four cardinal directions, travelling clockwise around the circle, are north, east, south, and west. Ordinal directions, such as northeast or north-northeast, are found between these basic four, as you can see on the compass face below.

9. Look at the compass face in Figure 6. Give the direction that is the same as the following compass bearings.
   a) 360 degrees   b) 225 degrees   c) 45 degrees   d) 22.5 degrees

10. Give the compass bearing that is the same as the following directions.
    a) South   b) NW   c) SE   d) SSE

11. Draw a compass to show where the directions NNE and ENE would be.

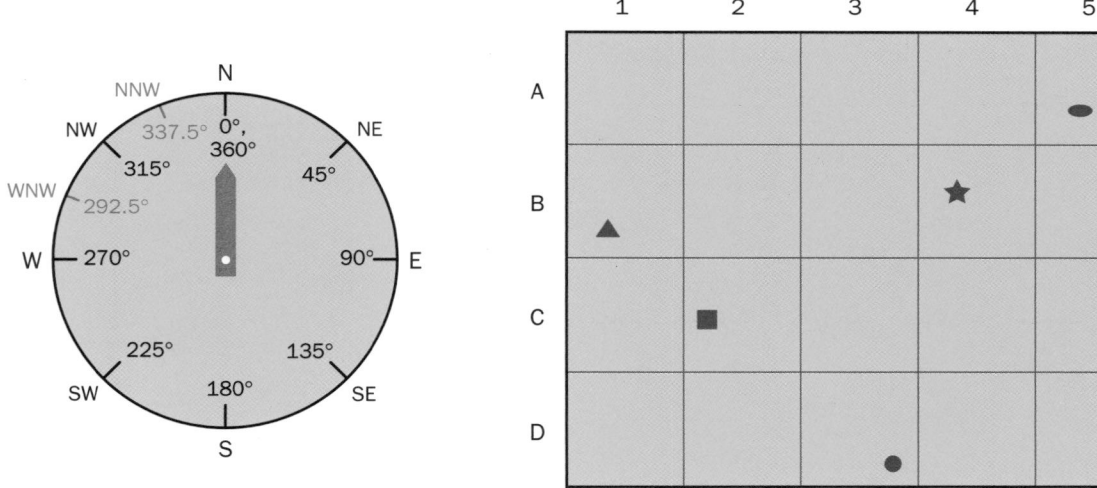

▲ **Figure 6:** A compass face, showing the major directions   ▲ **Figure 7:** An alpha-numeric grid

Grid Location

Street maps often use a simple method to help you locate places. Thin lines called grid lines run up and down and from side to side, dividing the map into even-sized squares or rectangles. Letters and numbers identify the spaces between the lines. Therefore, any place or feature can be identified by a letter–number combination, such as C3. This method of location is called an **alpha-numeric grid**. Usually, a map index will give the grid location of the street you want to find. You can see a grid in Figure 7.

12. Identify the grid locations of the five shapes in Figure 7.

GeoSkills

Using a Street Map

Purpose

Using a street map, you can find your way around virtually any community. All of us—whether we're geographers researching an area, or teenagers looking for a sub shop—use street maps. Follow these steps to make street maps work for you.

Step 1

Check for the north arrow or compass rose (a stylized compass face) to find direction. If neither is shown, assume that north is at the top of the page.

Step 2

If you're travelling, turn the map so that it points the way you're moving.

Step 3

Check for a distance scale. This can help you know if you've already passed your destination.

Step 4

Check the legend to see the meaning of symbols used on the map. For example, hospitals are often marked by a capital letter *H*.

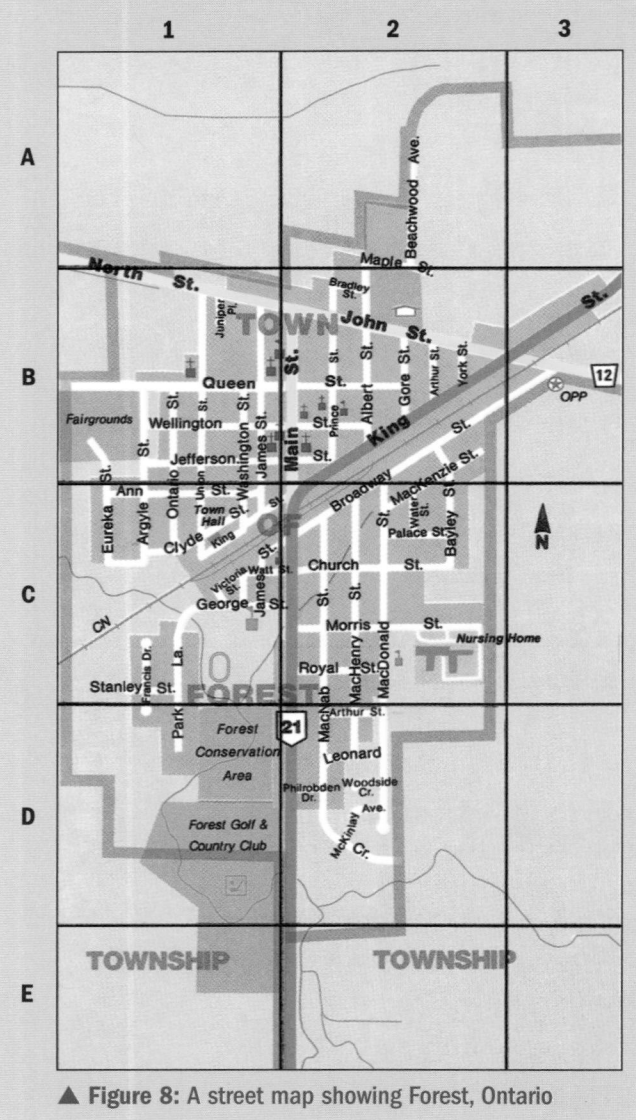

Partial Index

Albert St	B2
Ann St	C1
Argyle St	C1
Arthur St	B2, D2
Bayley St	C2
Beachwood Ave	A2
Bradley St	B2
Broadway St	B2, C2

Legend

- Major building
- School
- Place of worship
- Arena
- Police station
- Railroad
- 21 Highway
- Major street
- Built-up area
- Parkland
- Open space
- Government institution

▲ **Figure 8:** A street map showing Forest, Ontario

Step 5
To tell where you are, check the map to find the physical or human landmarks that you pass. Many street maps show lakes, parkland, schools, and other roadside features.

Step 6
If you want to find a particular street, check to see if there is an alphabetical list of streets. Then use the alpha-numeric grid to find the general location of the street.

Practise It!
1. Identify three types of landmarks you would pass if you were bicycling north on Highway 21 and Main Street from Philrobden Drive to North Street.

2. Find the grid location of these places.
   a) Victoria Street   c) fairgrounds
   b) OPP station   d) the arena

3. a) What municipal building is in C1?
   b) How many places of worship are in B1 and B2?

To make use of a street map...
- ✔ check for north
- ✔ point the map the way you're moving
- ✔ check for a distance scale
- ✔ check the legend
- ✔ check for landmarks
- ✔ use the alpha-numeric grid

4. Use a street map of your own community to find the location of your home. Describe its location using your full address, the alpha-numeric grid on the map, and the compass direction from two landmarks.

Regional Geography

Street maps help us get around communities. But, if you're taking a road trip, you may need a road map to get there. Road maps cover much bigger areas than street maps do. Road maps usually cover regions, such as a province or group of smaller provinces. They are designed to help us understand the region we're travelling through, and to help us choose the best travel route.

Using Map Symbols

Any type of map uses three main types of symbols: area, line, and point.

- *Area symbols* use colours to represent large features, such as green for parks or forests, and blue for a lake.

- *Line symbols* either connect places to one another (as a road does), or divide up areas (as boundaries do).

- *Point symbols* are simple pictures or icons that show the location of places or services, including hospitals, airports, houses, and schools.

▲ **Figure 9:** Typical map symbols

13. a) Sort the symbols in Figure 9, on the previous page, into the three categories: area, line, and point.
    b) Guess what each symbol means. Use the road map legend on page 11 to check your answers.

14. Find ten symbols on a map of your community. What do the symbols you found represent?

Finding Road Distance

How far is your community from other nearby places? Road maps tell you in several ways. If the map has a linear scale, you can use a ruler to measure the distance between two places. For example, on the map below, 1 cm on the map represents 7 km on the Earth's surface. Two places 2 cm apart on the map are really 14 km apart. Road maps also use small stars and numbers to show the actual travel distance between two places. This **road distance** is usually longer than scale measurement because roads curve around obstacles and climb up hills. On the map below, the small red number on Highway 540 is the kilometric distance between the two red stars on that highway.

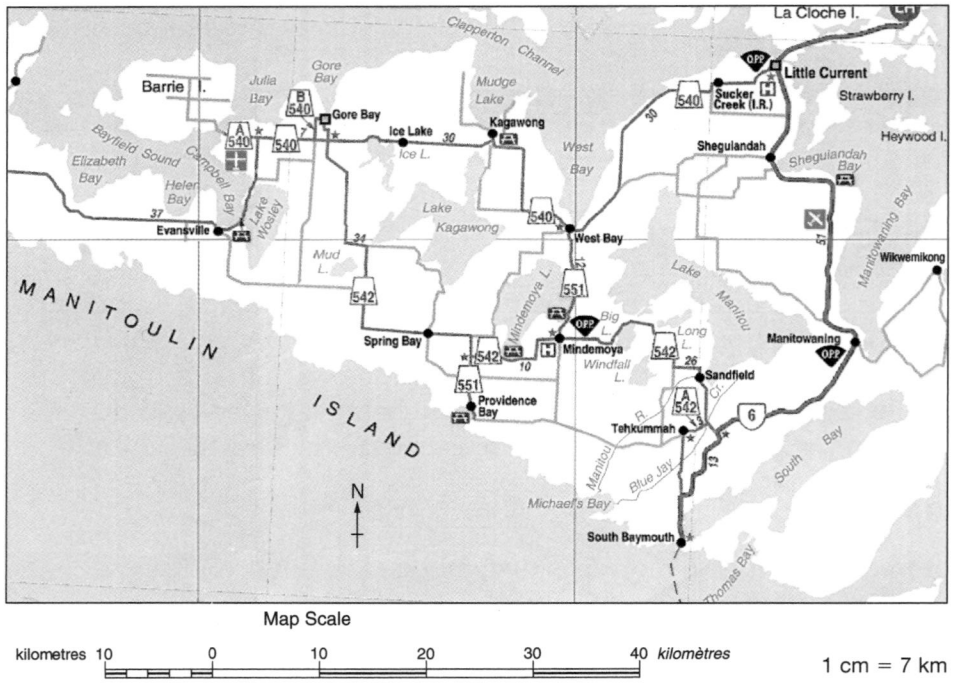

▲ **Figure 10:** A small section of an Ontario road map

15. Use Figure 10 to find the following road distances.
    a) from South Baymouth to Little Current
    b) from Little Current to Mindemoya OPP

16. Use the line scale and a ruler to find the following straight-line distances.
    a) from South Baymouth to Little Current
    b) from Little Current to Mindemoya OPP

17. Why are scale distance and actual road distance not always the same?

GeoSkills

Using a Road Map

Purpose

The skill of reading a road map can help you get around whenever you travel beyond your own community. The steps on the next page should help you use a road map efficiently.

- Express Toll Route *407 ETR*
- Multi-lane divided
- Multi-lane undivided
- Under construction
- Major Roads – Two-lane, hard surface
- Minor Roads – Two-lane, loose surface
- Regional Municipality/District/County/City/Town/Village boundary
- International boundary
- Province or state boundary
- Built-up area
- Railway, passenger service
- GO Train Station
- Ferry Route
- Major Airport
- Secondary Airport
- Local Airport
- Kilometric Distance
- Trans-Canada Highway
- Carpool Parking
- Ontario Provincial Police Detachment
- First Nations Police
- Border Crossing
- Travel Information Centre
- Major Tourist Attraction
- National Park with camping facilities
- National Park without camping facilities
- Provincial Park with camping facilities
- Provincial Park without camping facilities
- Park Commission with camping facilities
- Conservation Area with camping facilities
- Picnic Park
- Service Centre
- Hospital
- First aid/Nursing station

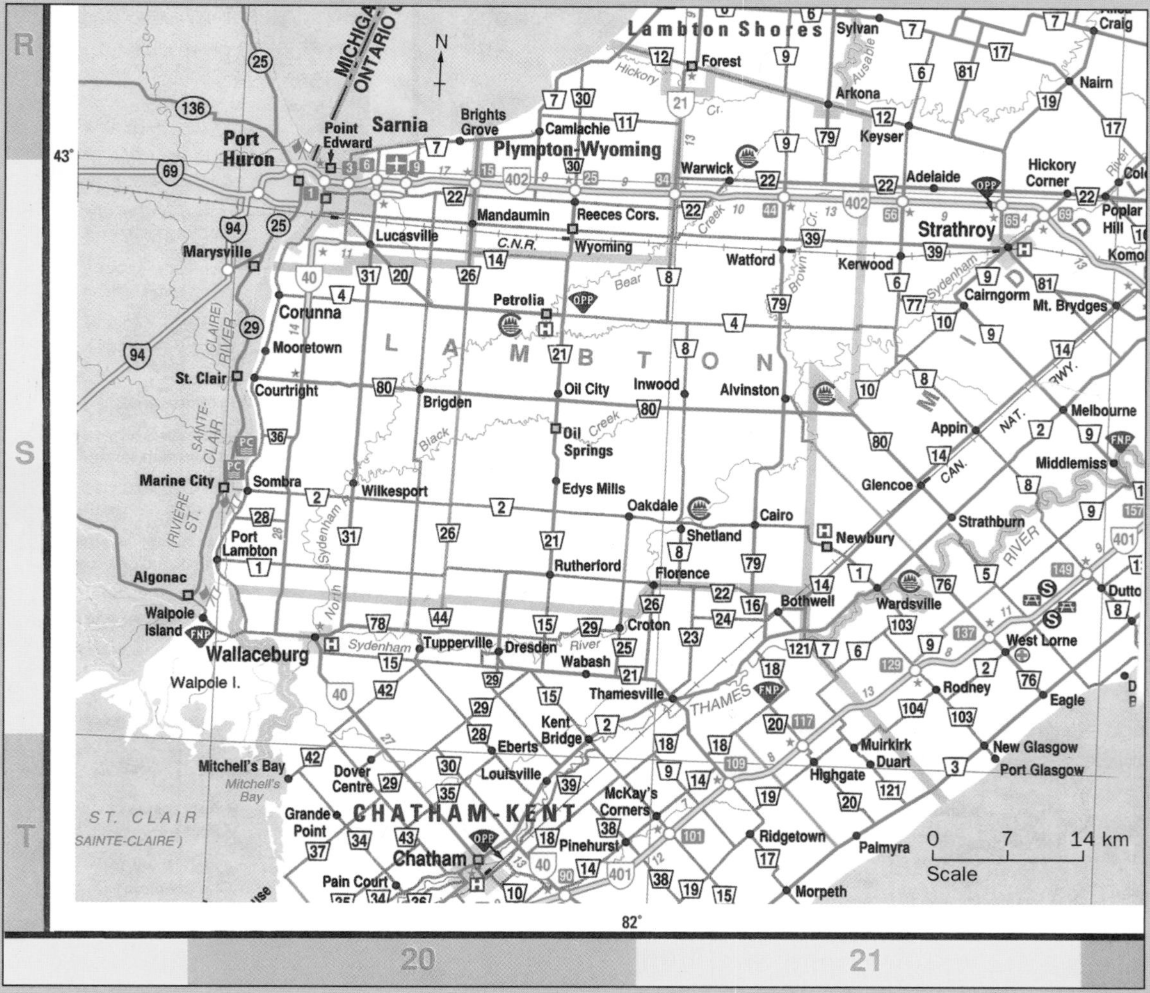

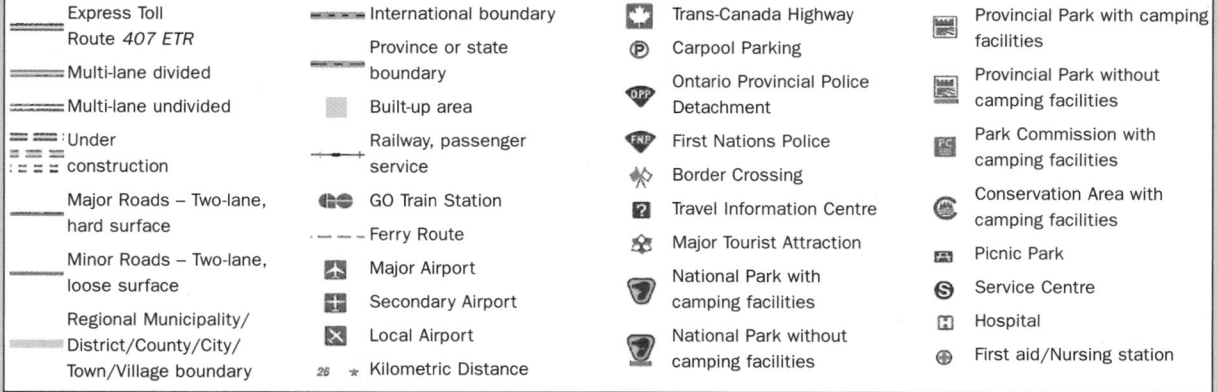

▲ **Figure 11:** A portion of the official Ontario road map, showing the southwest section of the province

Step 1
Examine the road map legend to review the area, line, and point symbols on the map.

Step 2
Look for the compass direction and map scale in the corners of the map or in the legend.

Step 3
To find road distance between communities, use the small red stars and numbers.

Step 4
To find a particular place, use the alpha-numeric grid and the alphabetical listing of places.

Step 5
Make a simple sketch map to plan the best route. The fastest route will follow major highways, while scenic routes may follow smaller, curving roads near lakes and rivers.

Practise It!

1. a) While visiting the area shown in the map, where would you go for help from the Ontario Provincial Police?
   b) Draw and identify eight different symbols in grid square S20.

To make use of a road map...
✔ examine the legend
✔ look for compass direction and map scale
✔ use the small stars and numbers to find road distance
✔ use the alpha-numeric grid to find places
✔ make a sketch map to plan the best route

2. a) Locate the town of Forest in grid R21. Which major highways (by number) lead to Sarnia?
   b) Identify the road distance from Forest to the multi-lane divided highway.
   c) Calculate the total road distance from Forest to the Canada–US border.

3. You're heading from Wallaceburg north to Lucasville.
   a) Plan the fastest route.
   b) Plan the most scenic route.

4. Give the grid location for each of these cities and large towns.
   a) Sarnia   c) Wallaceburg
   b) Chatham   d) Strathroy

5. Make a map to plan a trip by plane.
   a) In your notebook, draw a map to show a simple flight plan of a trip from Sarnia to Wallaceburg to Chatham to Strathroy, and then back to Sarnia.
   b) On your map, record the compass direction you would be travelling between each place.
   c) Use the map scale to calculate the straight-line distance in kilometres between the centres of each place. (For Sarnia, use the airport symbol as the centre.) Record the answers on your map.
   d) Finish your map by adding a frame, a title, and a compass rose.

Solving Neighbourhood and Regional Issues

Knowing how to interpret different types of maps may help you find your way on a road trip to a friend's cottage. But maps play a role in serious research, too. They can be key in solving neighbourhood and regional problems. Another important tool of the geographer is **geographic inquiry**, a five-step process for solving problems. Using these two tools, geographers can investigate many different types of issues and questions. In this section, we will look at one community's transportation problem, and use maps and geographic inquiry to try solving it.

Byron, Ontario, was once a small town located a few kilometres southwest of the city of London, Ontario. Today, London is Canada's tenth-largest city, with a population of 426 300 in 2001. Housing subdivisions multiplied between Byron and London, eventually filling in all the rural spaces between the two communities. Now London includes Byron within its boundaries. Two serious transportation problems have developed.

A natural feature of the landscape, the River Thames, divides London. One narrow bridge, crossing the wide Thames River valley, connects Byron to the city. A great deal of traffic uses this bridge, resulting in long backups and delays for commuters and other drivers heading west toward Highway 401. Secondly, a great deal of traffic clogs Commissioners Road, right through Byron's otherwise pleasant business district. Geographers could use maps and the inquiry method to try to solve these problems.

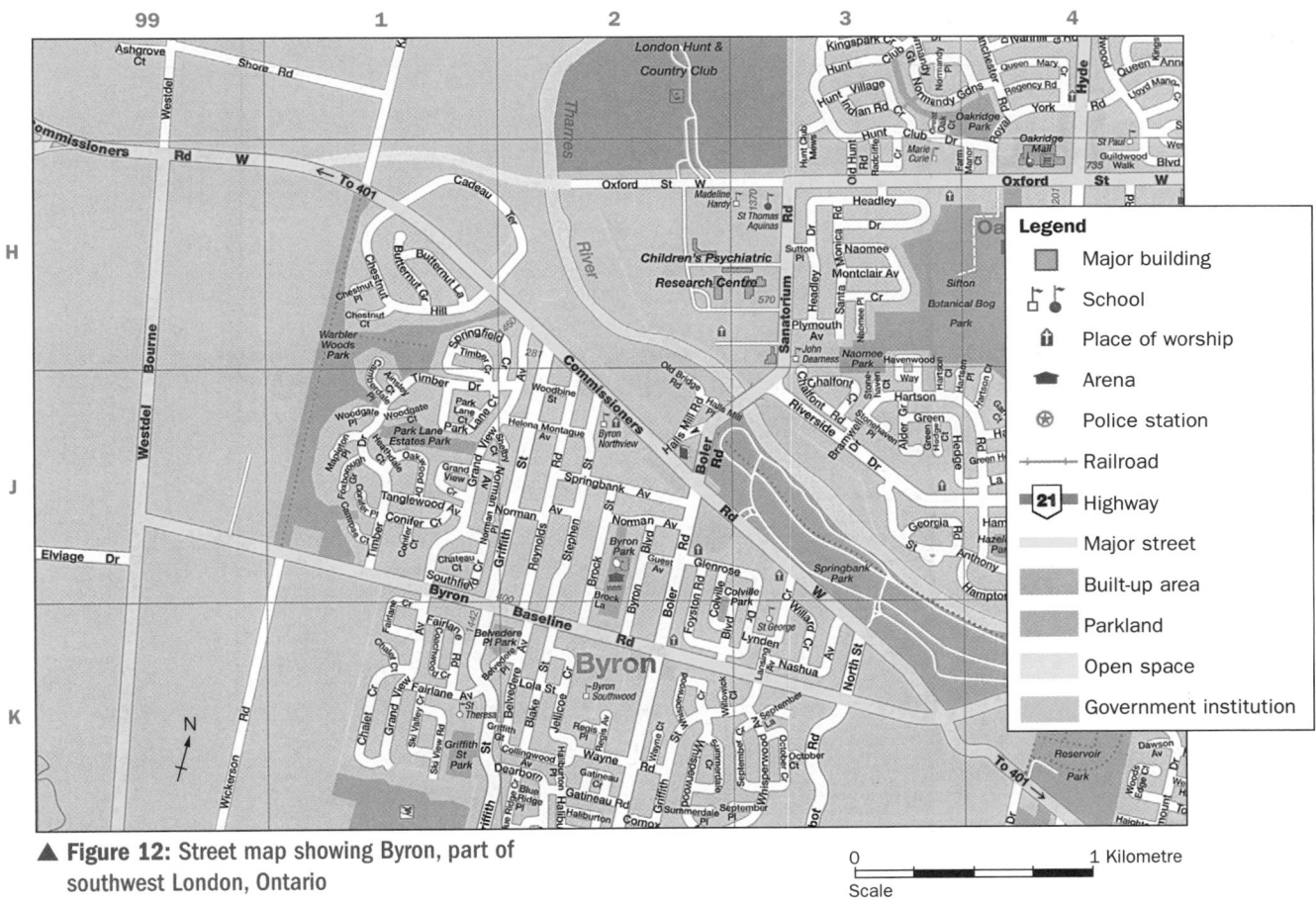

▲ **Figure 12:** Street map showing Byron, part of southwest London, Ontario

18. a) Use the street map to locate Byron, the bridge, and Commissioners Road.
    b) Suggest three problems that heavy traffic volume causes in Byron.

19. a) Find Oxford Street, a major London artery, on the map.
    b) Oxford Street stops at the river. Describe how extending Oxford Street might solve the traffic problems.

GeoSkills

Using Geographic Inquiry

Purpose

When you have a question to answer or a problem to solve, it is useful to follow logical steps to find your answer. Geographers use geographic inquiry to reach sound decisions.

This problem-solving model could help us decide what to do about Byron's transportation problems.

Step 1

Focus on the issue. Start your investigation by asking two types of focus questions:

- Speculative questions, that is, questions that aim for possible answers. For example, "How could adding a bypass route solve the traffic problems?"
- Comparative questions, that is, focus questions that compare different parts of the problem. For example, "What are the benefits and problems of directing traffic away from Byron?"

Step 2

Locate information. You can find information from two main types of sources:

- A **primary source** is information from a person who originates the information. This includes geographic material from field research, surveys, interviews, and photographs.
- A **secondary source** is a summary of primary information. This includes articles, encyclopedias, and a variety of maps.

Step 3

Record information. Choose appropriate methods for displaying the geographic data that you find most useful.

Step 4

Reach conclusions. Describe the best way to solve the problem or answer the inquiry question. Be sure that your evidence supports your conclusion.

Step 5

Communicate findings. Present the results of your investigation to an audience, or to people who can use your results.

Practise It!

1. Use a copy of the map in Figure 12 to sketch two traffic routes:
   a) south across the old bridge and through Byron
   b) west along Oxford Street, bypassing Byron

2. a) Discuss some ways you could get some primary information to help you answer the comparative question, "What are the benefits and problems of directing traffic away from Byron?" (Step 2).
   b) Make an organizing chart to compare the possible benefits and problems of redirecting traffic (Step 3). Be sure to consider the effects of the extension of

To use geographic inquiry...
- ✔ ask different types of focus questions
- ✔ locate information from a range of sources
- ✔ record information in an organized way
- ✔ reach conclusions supported by evidence
- ✔ communicate your findings

Oxford Street on the environment, residents, and businesspeople in the area.
   c) Why is it important for transportation planners to find out what people want?

3. Use the five steps of geographic inquiry to solve a pedestrian "traffic" problem related to your school. For example, students might be cutting through people's backyards to avoid a long walk out of a subdivision.

World Geography

There probably are times when you use maps of malls, streets, and roads to find your way. We use world maps for other reasons. You'll find many world maps in an atlas, in the form of either a book or a CD-ROM. Atlases contain **small-scale maps**, which show large areas in broad detail.

Flip through an atlas, and you'll see that world maps follow certain themes, such as population, pollution, and climate. A geographer might begin studying a world problem with thematic maps like these. Sometimes geographers discover important connections by comparing two or more thematic maps of the same area.

20. Locate thematic maps of two topics, such as landforms and population, in an atlas. What conclusions can you draw when you compare the maps?

> **GeoTrivia #3**
> Atlases are named after the Greek god Atlas, who was forced to hold the sky on his shoulders as punishment for rebelling against other gods.

Latitude and Longitude

You know that street maps and road maps use an alpha-numeric grid to give location. World maps are criss-crossed by a different system of imaginary lines called latitude and longitude. These lines give physical and human locations on the surface of the Earth. Unlike an alpha-numeric grid, every place has a specific latitude and longitude that does not change from map to map.

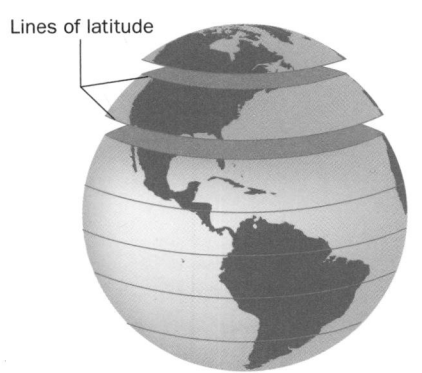
Lines of latitude

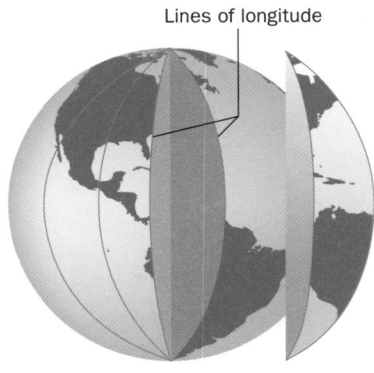
Lines of longitude

▲ **Figure 13:** Latitude divides the world into flat slices, while longitude divides it into orange sections.

21. How might you remember which way latitude and longitude lines run? (*Hint:* Look at the letters "a" and "o" in the caption for Figure 13.)

Lines of **latitude** run in the same direction as the Equator. This imaginary line splits the Earth into two halves, the Northern Hemisphere and the Southern Hemisphere. Latitude lines are numbered in each direction away from the Equator, from 0° at the Equator to 90°N at the North Pole and 90°S at the South Pole.

Longitude lines run from pole to pole. The most important one is the Prime Meridian, passing through historic Greenwich Observatory in London, England. The Prime Meridian, along with the International Date Line at the other side of the world, splits the world into two halves: the Eastern Hemisphere and the Western Hemisphere. Longitude lines are numbered in each direction away from the Prime Meridian, from 0° at Greenwich to 180° in the Pacific Ocean.

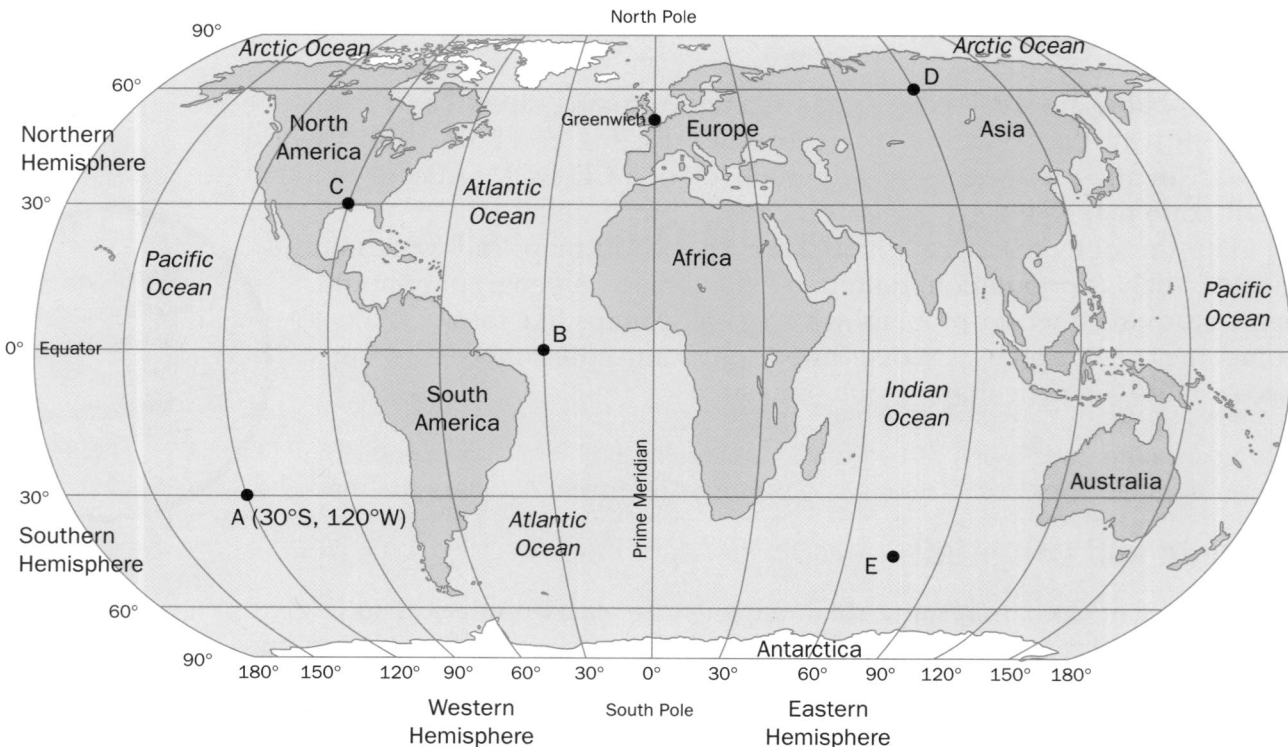

▲ **Figure 14:** Latitude and longitude around the world

22. Use Figure 14 to give the latitude and longitude locations of points B, C, D, and E. Use point A as a guide to help you.

23. In which hemispheres are each of these places located?
    a) Canada   b) Australia   c) Europe

The Gazetteer

Most atlases contain alphabetical listings of streets and communities. These organized lists of locations are called **gazetteers**. Some atlases may have two gazetteers at the back, one for Canadian places and another for places in the rest of the world.

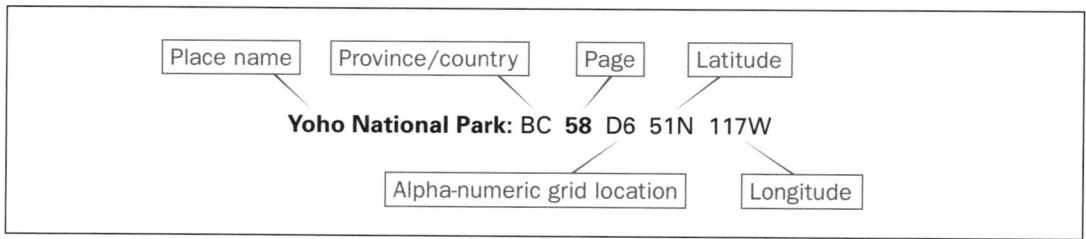

▲ **Figure 15:** A sample gazetteer entry

24. a) Use an atlas gazetteer to find the first and last entries in the Canada gazetteer and the world gazetteer. Use the information to find these places on a map. Describe their locations.
    b) Find your own community (or a larger one near you) in a gazetteer, then locate it on a map. Describe its location.

GeoSkills

Using Thematic Maps

Purpose

Knowing how to use thematic maps gives us access to a huge amount of information useful to the subject of geography.

Use these steps to locate and interpret thematic maps. Let's suppose that you want to find out how deep the water is in Labrador Basin, where a submarine sank recently.

Step 1

To find the region and topics you are seeking, check the table of contents at the front of the atlas. In this case, you can refer to the physical relief map of North America in Figure 16 on the next page. Relief maps give ocean depths as well as land elevations (heights).

Step 2

If you can't find the specific place you're looking for, check the gazetteer. You'll find that Labrador Basin is located at 55°N latitude and 50°W longitude.

Step 3

Examine the map legend. Atlas maps show the height of land by using many different colours. Usually the lowest areas are green, while high mountains are purple and white. In the oceans, darker blues show deeper water.

Step 4

Find the specific information you need. In this case, match the colour at Labrador Basin with the colours in the legend. The depth of Labrador Basin is between 3000 m and 4000 m.

Step 5

Examine the map to identify general patterns. For example, the Atlantic Ocean becomes even deeper south of the Labrador Basin.

Practise It!

Use the map of North America in Figure 16, on the next page, to answer the following questions.

1. Which water bodies are found at the following locations?
   a) 25°N, 90°W   c) 60°N, 90°W
   b) 75°N, 135°W

2. Give the latitude and longitude of the following Canadian locations.
   a) the north end of Vancouver Island, British Columbia
   b) the east end of Newfoundland
   c) the south part of Baffin Island

3. a) How deep is the Atlantic Ocean at 27°N, 60°W?
   b) How high is the Smallwood Reservoir at 53°N, 65°W?

To use an atlas map...
- ✔ check the table of contents to find the map you need
- ✔ check the gazetteer to find a specific location
- ✔ use the legend to help you understand the map
- ✔ find the specific information you need
- ✔ look for patterns within the map

   c) How high are the highest peaks in the Appalachian Mountains in the eastern United States?

4. a) How does the depth in the ocean compare with the distance from land?
   b) Compare the height of the eastern and western sides of North America.
   c) Compare the shape and characteristics of Canada's three ocean coastlines.

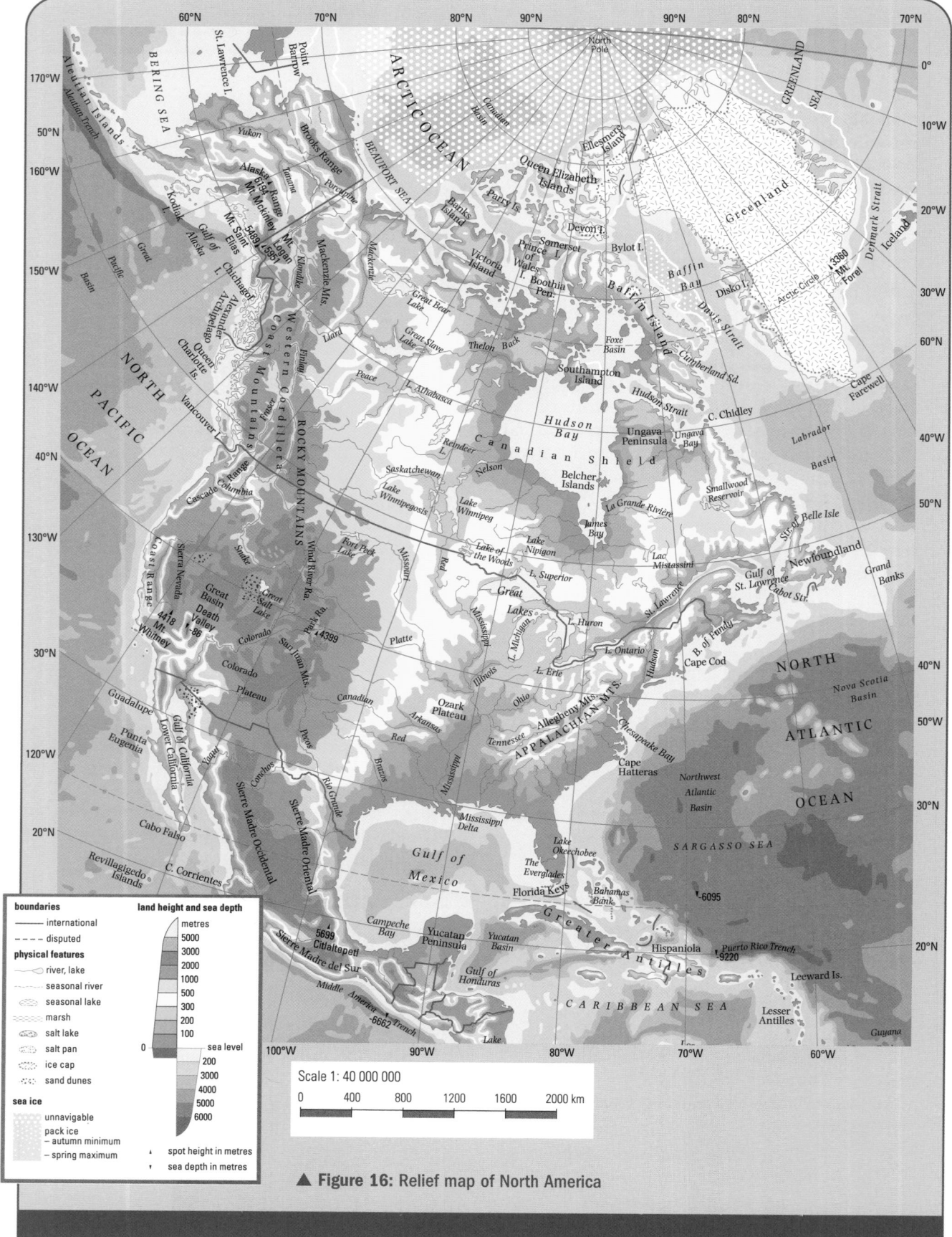

boundaries
—— international
– – – disputed

physical features
river, lake
seasonal river
seasonal lake
marsh
salt lake
salt pan
ice cap
sand dunes

sea ice
unnavigable
pack ice
– autumn minimum
– spring maximum

land height and sea depth
metres
5000
3000
2000
1000
500
300
200
100
0 — sea level
200
3000
4000
5000
6000

spot height in metres
sea depth in metres

Scale 1: 40 000 000

0   400   800   1200   1600   2000 km

▲ **Figure 16**: Relief map of North America

Conclusion

This chapter started with a soccer field and ended with a continent. Both of these are part of geography and the world you live in. Everyone lives in many different "worlds" at the same time. Although you are most familiar with your own community, your world is really much larger. You have connections of many kinds to the neighbourhood, the region, and the rest of the globe.

This chapter has focused on physical and human geography, the topics of the first two units of this book. Physical and human geography are both central to the three final units, too. These sections examine Canada's economy, environment, and global connections.

By the time you complete all five units of study, you will recognize many different ways in which physical and human geography are both central to the Canadian experience.

Wrap It Up

1. a) What are the two main topics of interest in geography? Describe four examples of each topic.
   b) What three questions are most commonly asked in the study of geography? Give an example of each one for your neighbourhood.

2. Four of the GeoSkills features in this chapter practise map-reading at different scales. Name the four kinds of maps used in them, and describe three different purposes for each kind.

3. Refer to Figure 14 on page 16. Then try these riddles.
   a) This continent is located in every hemisphere.
   b) This continent passes through every degree of longitude.
   c) This ocean covers part of every hemisphere.

4. Look at a series of thematic maps of North America in an atlas. Compare the maps to make a list of "connections" between one map and another. For example, at what elevation are most large cities found? Make a list of five different "connections" you found, giving a good example for each one.

5. Use a street map of your neighbourhood or community to plan a bike route. The route should take cyclists through interesting areas where they can see local landmarks and enjoy wooded parkland. Include places to rest. Use a frame, title, legend, and north arrow.

6. Use the official Ontario road map to plan a two-day road trip that starts and ends in your community. Make a neat map to show your route. Include places where you will stop for activities and where you will stay overnight. Explain your trip to a partner, using your map.

CANADA'S NATURAL SYSTEMS

The Somewhere in Canada Contest #1

Where in Canada do you think this photograph might have been taken? Win the Somewhere in Canada Contest #1 by guessing the correct answer before anyone else in your class. If you're not sure, look at the clues below.

CLUE 1 ▶ The photograph shows a large city beside an ocean.

CLUE 2 ▶ What do you see in the background? In the winter months, city residents and tourists flock to the local ski runs.

CLUE 3 ▶ Almost two million people live here, in the third-largest city in the nation.

CLUE 4 ▶ Do you see many boats? A large commercial fishing industry operates out of the city's harbour.

CLUE 5 ▶ This city bid to host the 2010 Winter Olympic Games.

What Will You Study in This Unit?

What clue best helped you identify the city pictured in the photograph? Perhaps it was the presence of mountains. Mountains don't occur everywhere in Canada. They are one of the identifying features that geographers use to decide how to define regions: does the region feature mountains or not? In this unit, you will see that every region has particular characteristics of landforms, climate, soil, and natural vegetation. These are all part of Canada's physical systems, sometimes called natural systems.

In this unit, you will learn about the great variety of landform regions, bioregions, and ecozones in Canada, and the forces that shaped these differences. For example, why is Ontario relatively low-lying, while massive mountains dominate in British Columbia and Yukon? Why is Winnipeg hotter than Halifax in summer but colder in winter? You will learn how climate and landforms combine to affect what natural vegetation and wildlife are found in various parts of the country.

To sum up, this unit is about the foundations of Canadian geography: the physical systems. However, as you progress through upcoming units, you will also learn how people interact with the environment. You will see how Canada's physical geography is linked to our cultural and economic systems.

How does all this affect you? The characteristics of regions influence the ways that Canadians live their lives. To show this, you will develop a snowmobile or canoe route through the North Bay–Sudbury area of Ontario at the end of this unit.

In this unit, you will

- show that you know some of Canada's important geographic patterns
- understand that Canada is divided into different types of regions, including bioregions and ecozones
- recognize that Canada's regions have very different characteristics
- understand how people and environment are linked together in Canada's regions

For a challenge, try the Unit 1 GIS activity, "Volcano Investigator," on page 338.

Chapter 1

CANADIAN LANDFORMS AND CLIMATE

◀ **Figure 1.1:** True or false: After flying in a tornado, this Canadian bull landed safely.

Can You Believe It? Canadian Fact and Fancy

Ready for a challenge? Canada is home to some pretty strange landforms and weather, but don't bet that all of the following statements are true. Which ones are true? Which are false? Time to take your best guess.

1. A tornado in Canada picked up a bull in a stable, and dropped it 20 metres away. The bull lived.
2. Canada has volcanoes that could erupt one day.
3. Because of its ocean location, Halifax, Nova Scotia, has the mildest climate of any large city in Canada.
4. A good place to find fossils of ancient sea life is high in the Rocky Mountains.
5. In Calgary, Alberta, a "snow-eater" causes snow to disappear without leaving meltwater behind.
6. We like it cold. That's why very few of Canada's cities are located close to the US border.
7. Canadian scientist J.T. Wilson thought up the theory that continents drift across the Earth's surface.
8. A Saskatchewan snowstorm was so heavy that it buried an entire train for almost a week.
9. A shelf of shallow ocean floor connects the Atlantic region of Canada with South America.
10. Another Canadian tornado ripped off a man's pants.

Words to Know
continental drift
lithosphere
mantle
core
plate tectonics
Pacific Ring of Fire
relief profile
erosion
continental shelf
chinook
weather
precipitation
climate
climate graph
mean
growing season

In this chapter, you will
- **discover what forces build up the Earth and wear it down**
- **tell the difference between weather and climate**
- **see how weather and climate influence all our lives, including yours**
- **draw a relief profile and a climate graph**

Building Mountains

A geologic tug-of-war has been going on for the past four billion years or so. Stresses and strains inside the Earth have been heaving up mountains. Meanwhile, the forces of erosion keep wearing them down. The first half of this chapter will examine these two opposing forces shaping the Earth's surface.

The Earth in Motion

If you cut out the continents on a world map, you'd be surprised at how well some of them fit together. Almost a century ago, German geographer Alfred Wegener noticed this pattern. Wegener believed that the continents had once been joined in one land mass that he called Pangaea, meaning "all lands." He proposed the theory of **continental drift**, which suggests that the continents gradually moved away from one another over time.

> Wegener was like a crime detective with a suspect but no weapon. He could not explain how massive continents could move across the face of the Earth. Most scientists rejected continental drift theory. Years later, it turned out that Wegener was right—and it was a Canadian who helped discover the reason why.

GeoTrivia #1
Alfred Wegener died on a blizzard-swept expedition to Greenland in 1930, while searching for new evidence to support his theory.

1. Why did scientists reject the theory of continental drift when it was first put forward?

Plate Tectonics

Think of the Earth as a round egg. Canada sits on the thin, brittle outer shell, called the **lithosphere**, or crust. Beneath the lithosphere is the **mantle**, a zone of molten magma where you'd find the egg white. At the centre, the Earth's **core** is like the yolk. It is the nuclear furnace that melts the rocks of the mantle above it.

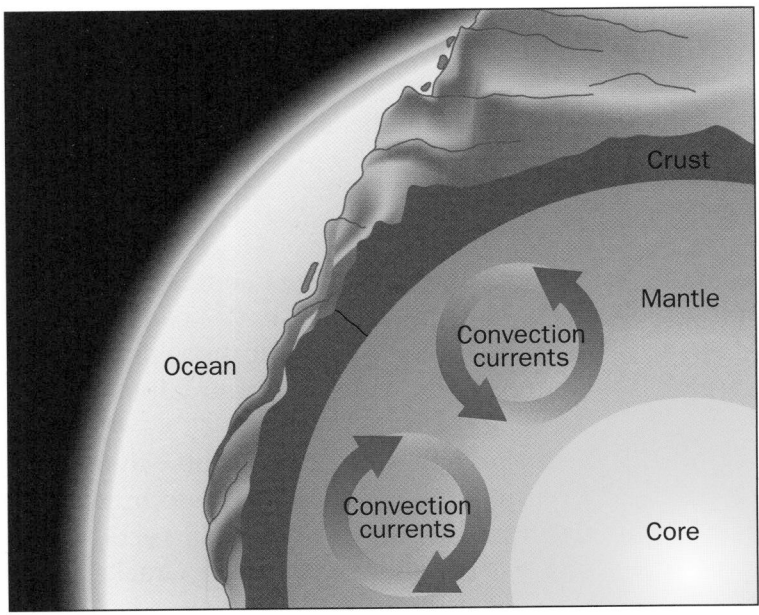

Crust

Mantle

Ocean

Convection currents

Convection currents

Core

◀ **Figure 1.2:** Earth's layers

2. a) Make a chart to compare the Earth with an egg.
   b) What is the purpose of using this image? Think of another comparison that could be used.

In the 1960s, Canadian J. Tuzo Wilson got people interested in continental drift again. He recognized that "hot spots" could form deep in the mantle, and that currents could circulate above these hot spots, just as boiling water swirls in a heated pot on a stove. These *convection currents* might provide enough force to push the crust apart, as Wegener suggested.

Since then, geologists have confirmed that the lithosphere has many pieces, called plates. These plates are still moving. The field of **plate tectonics** investigates how moving plates can create volcanoes, build mountains, and trigger earthquakes. Let's look at how each of these processes occurs.

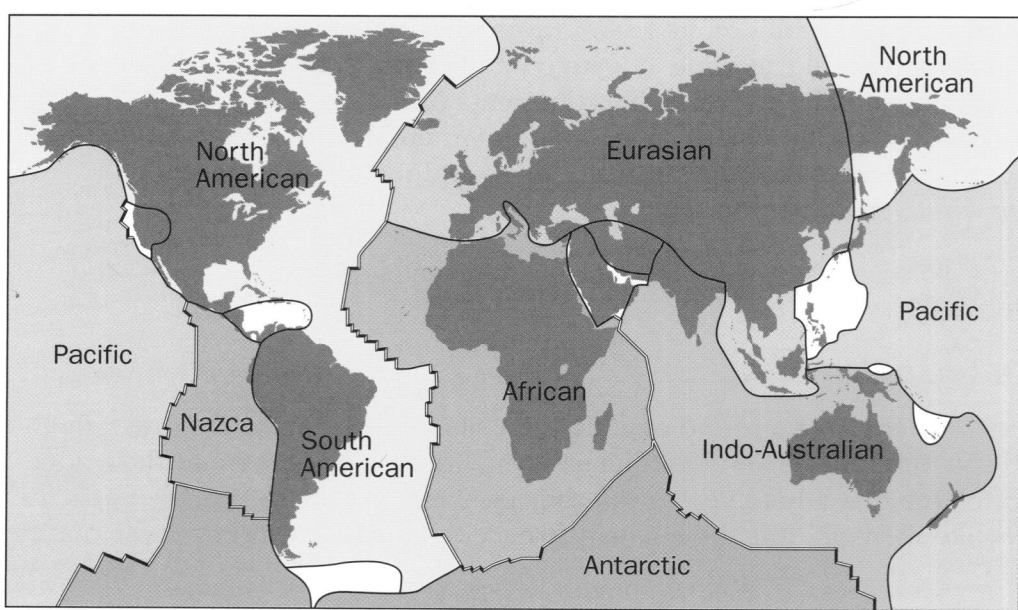

Figure 1.3: Major tectonic plates ▶

3. Look at the map in Figure 1.3. Compare the plate pattern of the Pacific Ocean with that of the Atlantic and Indian Oceans.

4. Use the map to suggest where molten rock from beneath the Earth could reach the surface.

Volcanoes

Canada has no active volcanoes today, but some along the Pacific Coast are classed as dormant (sleeping) volcanoes. This means they have been active in the recent past and could erupt again. These West Coast volcanoes are part of the **Pacific Ring of Fire**, a global system of active volcanic mountains that circle the Pacific Ocean.

What causes volcanoes? Scientists believe there are "hot spots" in the Earth's core. Rising heat sets the molten material of the mantle into huge circular motions, like warm air circulating in a room. As these convection currents swirl, they drag the plates of the lithosphere with them. Cracks open along the plate edges, and magma forces its way through.

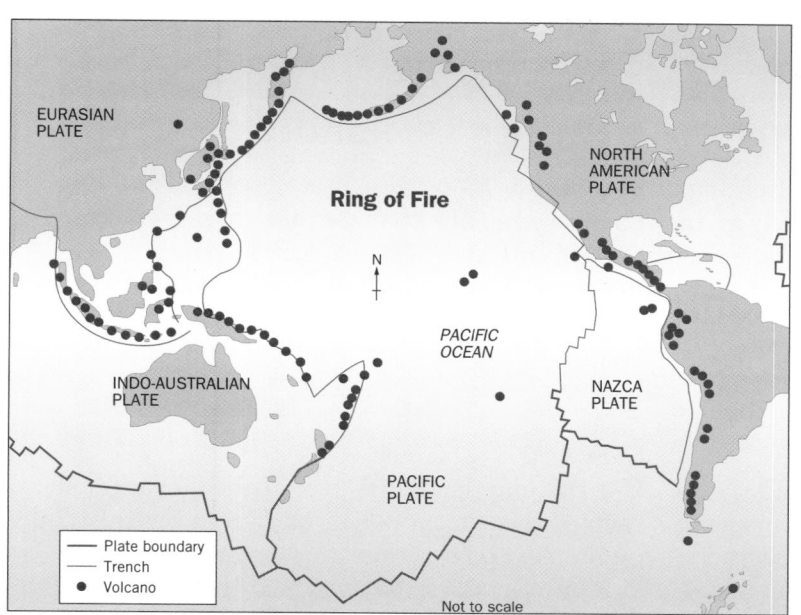

◀ **Figure 1.4:** The Pacific Ring of Fire

GeoTrivia #2
According to an Aboriginal legend, lava flows occurred near Terrace, BC about 200 years ago. Scientific evidence supports this claim.

5. Look at the map in Figure 1.4. Follow the location of the Pacific Ring of Fire. Which parts of Canada does it pass through?

6. Compare the location of volcanoes in the Ring of Fire with plate boundaries. What pattern do you notice? What might explain this pattern?

Fold Mountains

Try this. Put a thin pile of binder paper between two textbooks on your desk. Slowly push the two books together, and you will make a fold mountain. The textbooks are like thick plates, carrying continents, while the paper represents soft sedimentary rock layers on an ocean plate. Your arms are like convection currents dragging the plates together to build mountains. This is how most of Canada's mountain ranges were formed. For example, the Rocky Mountains were folded by the collision of the Pacific and North American Plates.

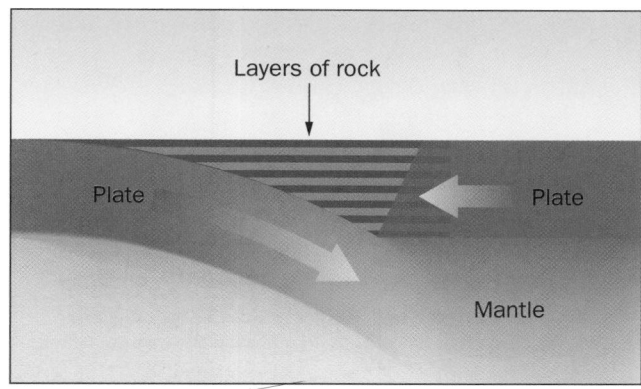
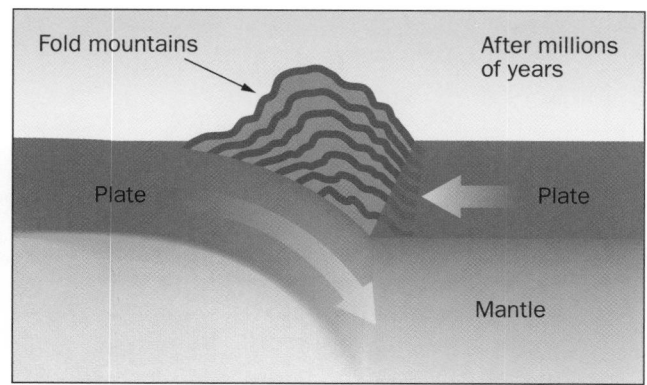

▲ **Figure 1.5:** How fold mountains are formed

7. a) How does folding change the length of the Earth's crust?
   b) In what direction do convection currents move to cause folding?

8. a) Why is there sedimentary rock in the ocean basins of the world?
   b) Why are fold mountains like the Rockies usually found in long chains?

GeoSkills

Constructing a Relief Profile

When you look at mountains on a relief map like the one in Figure 1.6, the changes in height, or elevation, are marked by changes in colour. But it is not always easy to imagine how the land looks. A **relief profile** is a side view of the land that shows its height.

Purpose

By drawing a relief profile, we can easily see the variations in the height of the land. Here you will learn, step by step, how to construct a profile using the relief colours on a thematic map.

Step 1

Start with a straight line labelled XY, marked across the area on the map you wish to profile (see Figure 1.6). A useful map profile usually slices across a valley, hill, or mountain.

Step 2

Lay the edge of a straight piece of paper along the XY line on the map. Mark X and Y onto the paper. Next, carefully make a mark on the paper strip at each place where the relief colour on the map changes. Mark large bodies of water as well.

Step 3

Use the map legend to record the elevation at each of these locations as shown in Figure 1.7 on the next page. For example, the map legend in Figure 1.6 uses 100 m of height to divide the dark green zone from the mid-green zone.

Step 4

On a piece of graph paper, draw a base for your profile graph like the one in Figure 1.8. The line along the bottom should be the same length as the XY line. Use your paper strip to measure it. The vertical line shows the

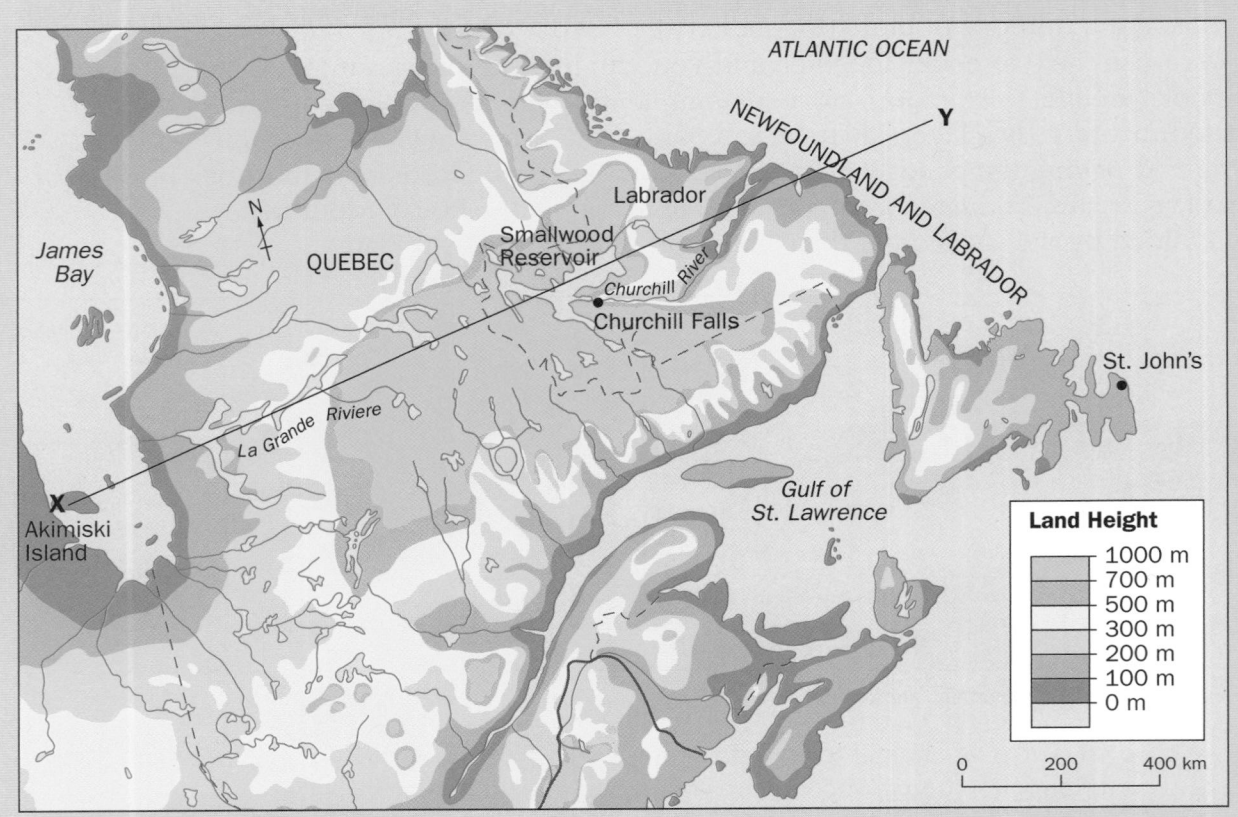

▲ **Figure 1.6:** Relief map of Northern Quebec

height. Write a number scale in metres along this line.

Step 5

Put the strip of paper along the base of the graph you prepared in Step 4. Transfer the relief points from the paper onto the base of the graph (see Figure 1.9). Use the graph scale

to put a dot above each point at the correct height on the graph itself.

Step 6

Finish the profile by connecting the points with a smooth line. Add a title, and label important features such as towns or rivers along the profile line.

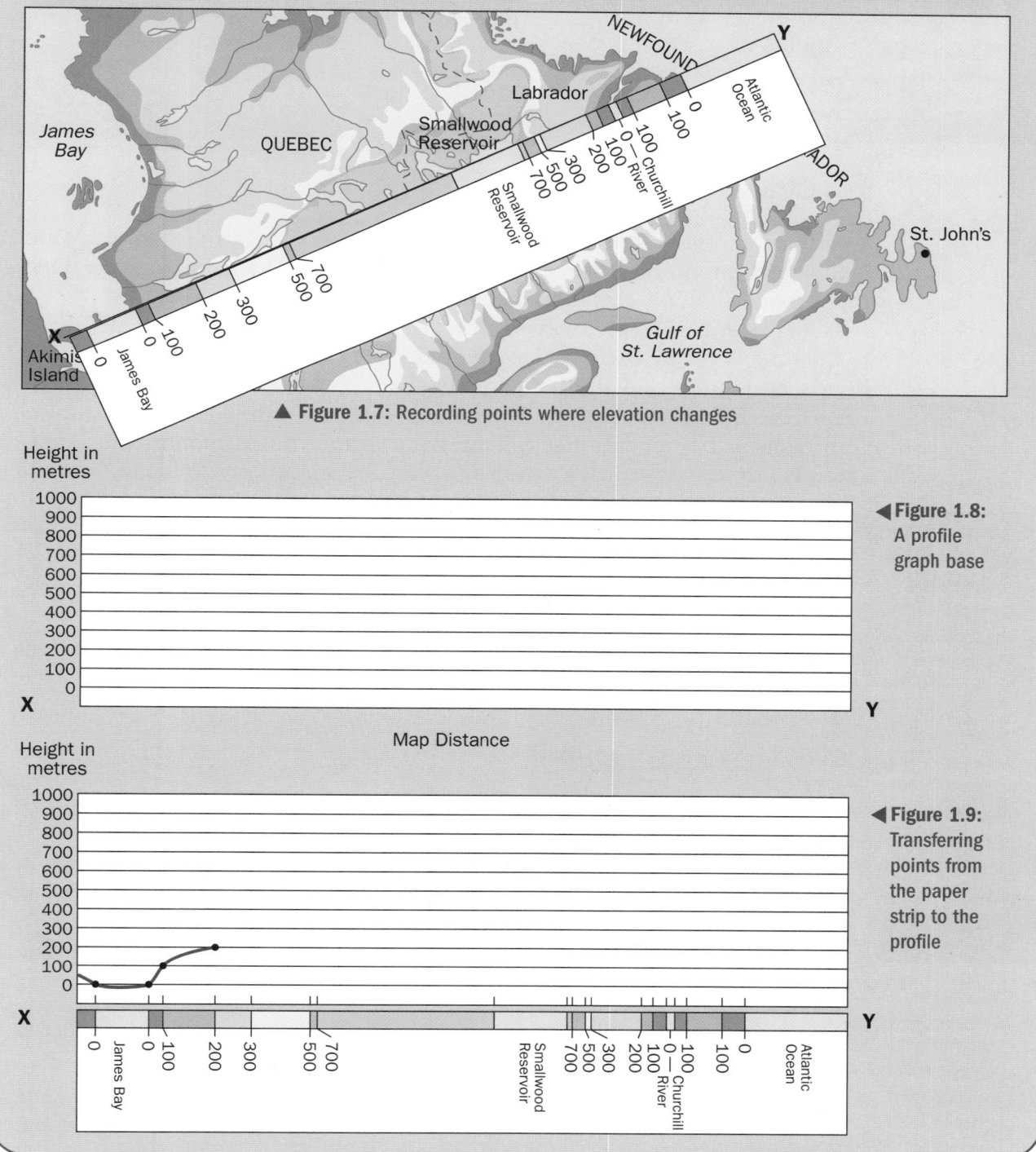

▲ **Figure 1.7:** Recording points where elevation changes

◄ **Figure 1.8:** A profile graph base

◄ **Figure 1.9:** Transferring points from the paper strip to the profile

Practise It!

1. Follow the instructions in Steps 1–6 to make a profile across Quebec and Labrador along line XY.

2. Label the following on your profile: James Bay, La Grande Riviere, Smallwood Reservoir, Churchill Falls, Atlantic Ocean.

3. Describe the land between James Bay and the Atlantic Ocean.

To construct a relief profile...
- ✔ mark each change in elevation on a paper strip
- ✔ make a profile graph base
- ✔ write a number scale in metres on the right
- ✔ transfer the elevation points to the graph
- ✔ join the dots to form a profile
- ✔ add labels and a title

Forces of Erosion

Weathering, or **erosion**, continually works to level the Earth's surface. Water is the most important force of erosion. Other agents of erosion include wind, plant roots, animals, and humans.

As material is worn away from high places, river systems carry it down to the oceans where ocean waves and currents move it along the coast. This builds the **continental shelf**, an area of shallow water reaching many kilometres offshore before the ocean deeps begin. Continental shelves link continents as part of a global system. For example, a wide continental shelf extends into the Atlantic Ocean from Labrador all the way to South America.

▲ **Figure 1.10:** Water, the most important agent of erosion

9. Look at the photographs in Figure 1.10. In what other ways can water act as a force of erosion?

10. Look at a world map showing ocean depths (for example, Figure 16 on page 18). Compare the zones of shallow water along Canada's three ocean coasts. What do you observe about our continental shelf?

Glaciers and the Ice Ages

Have you ever made pancakes? When you pour the batter onto the hot pan, it flows outward in all directions from the thick centre. This is how thick sheets of ice slowly moved across the continents during the ice ages. Ice ages are periods when the Earth's climate cools enough to allow large continental glaciers to flow from the polar regions to regions farther south. There have been at least four ice ages during the past million years. The last ice age ended about 10 000 years ago.

As huge ice sheets advanced over Canada, they changed the land. The bottom of the ice picked up large rocks, which acted like gritty sandpaper to grind and polish solid rock across northern Canada. Soil and other material was bulldozed at the front of the glacier, or pinched up in a ridge between two meeting glaciers. This jumbled material is called a moraine. The Oak Ridges Moraine north of Toronto is a good example of a moraine pushed between meeting ice sheets.

When the ice ages ended, large areas of southern Canada were flooded. Today, the flat bottoms of these former glacial lakes surround the Great Lakes and extend across much of southern Manitoba and Saskatchewan. Rich soil makes these regions some of the most important agricultural land in Canada.

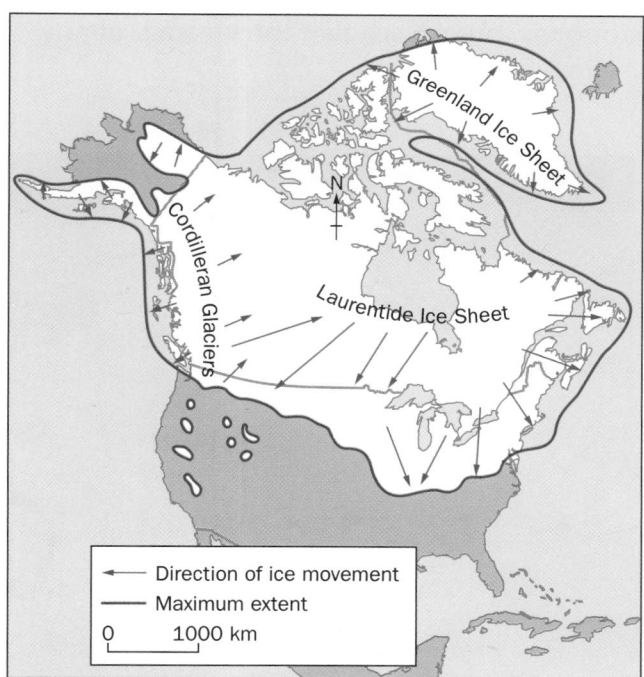

▲ **Figure 1.11:** Extent of glaciation in North America

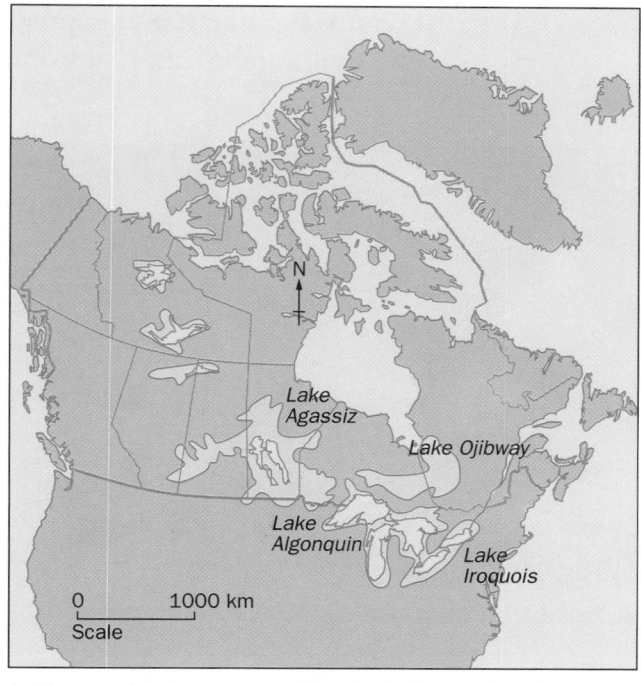

▲ **Figure 1.12:** Areas covered by glacial lakes after the last ice age

11. Use Figure 1.11 to estimate how much of the following areas were covered during the ice ages:
    a) Canada   b) North America   c) United States

12. Compare the map of glacial lakes in Figure 1.12 to a map showing Canada's lakes today. Name lakes that remain where the glaciers melted.

13. Make a chart to show how the glaciers affected
    a) northern Canada   c) southern Ontario
    b) southern Manitoba and Saskatchewan

Weather and Climate: What's the Difference?

Remember the "Can You Believe It?" challenge at the beginning of this chapter? Tornadoes have carried away bulls and ripped off a man's pants, while snowstorms have buried whole trains. And, believe it or not, the mystery "snow-eater" is the **chinook**, a warm wind that blows East from the Rockies to evaporate Calgary's snow with little or no trace.

Weather conditions in Canada can vary greatly from season to season and from place to place. **Weather** refers to the day-to-day conditions in the Earth's atmosphere. To find out about the weather we check measurements of its characteristics: temperature, precipitation, cloud cover, wind speed and direction, and relative humidity. **Precipitation** includes rain, snow, hail, and sleet. Relative humidity tells us how much moisture is in the air compared with how much the air could possibly hold at that temperature. It helps us predict rain.

Climate tells us the average weather conditions of a certain place over a long period of time. For example, Halifax, Nova Scotia, typically has fairly mild, short winters. One year, however, Halifax's weather reports might warn about very cold, harsh winter conditions. You can see that the weather at any one time can be different from the climate of a place.

▲ **Figure 1.13:** Weather versus climate

14. Which of these photographs shows weather? Which shows climate? Explain.

15. If you were deciding where to move in Canada, would you try to find out about climate or weather? Give reasons for your answer.

16. Which two weather characteristics are most important to you? Explain.

17. What has the weather been like in your area during the past few weeks? Are these conditions normal for your area at this time of year?

How Weather Affects You

Weather and its everyday changes affect most Canadians. You probably check out the weather report to help you choose what to wear to school, figure out if the baseball game is still on, or decide where to go skiing.

Canada's tourism industry, as well as its agriculture, depends on weather conditions. Even slight variations from average weather conditions can hurt these industries. For example, cool and rainy weather in the spring can delay the planting of crops, and possibly cost farmers millions of dollars.

Weather affects certain groups of Canadians more than others. Seniors who have difficulty walking may be confined to their homes by heavy snowfalls. People who suffer from asthma may have trouble breathing on hot days when pollution is trapped close to the ground.

GeoTrivia #3
Every year, approximately 80 tornadoes rip through parts of Canada, in total killing two people and seriously injuring about 20 others.

▲ **Figure 1.14:** An Ottawa cyclist braves the elements in a blizzard.

18. Imagine that the severe blizzard shown in this photograph left 1 m of snow on the ground in your community. Suggest three ways the snow would affect each of the following.
    a) stores
    b) schools
    c) road-maintenance crews
    d) homeowners

19. a) Give six examples of ways that very hot summer weather would affect your activities and choice of clothing.
    b) List six summer jobs you might take that would be particularly affected by weather conditions.
    c) For each job you listed, briefly explain the influence of the weather.

20. What modern technologies have been developed to help us cope with each of
    a) snowfalls, b) hail, c) tornadoes, and d) heat waves?

GeoGames

The Playoffs: Sports versus Weather

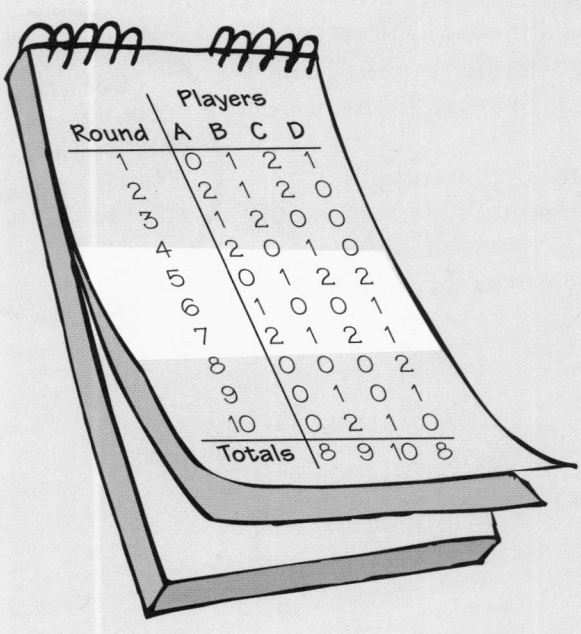

Round	A	B	C	D
1	0	1	2	1
2	2	1	2	0
3	1	2	0	0
4	2	0	1	0
5	0	1	2	2
6	1	0	0	1
7	2	1	2	1
8	0	0	0	2
9	0	1	0	1
10	0	2	1	0
Totals	8	9	10	8

▲ **Figure 1.15:** Score sheet for the Weather Game

Purpose:

To realize how much weather affects what we do; to become more familiar with temperature measurements.

Supplies:

One die, score sheet, pencil

Method:

A. Form groups of two to four players.

B. Set up a score sheet with the players' names listed in order of date of birth, starting with January 1.

C. Seat yourselves clockwise around a table, in the order on your score sheet.

D. The first player (the youngest) rolls the die to identify an outdoor recreational activity, as follows:
   1. downhill skiing
   2. boat or canoe trip
   3. beach volleyball
   4. hockey or skating
   5. walking or cycling to the park
   6. watching a soccer match

E. The same player then rolls the die to determine the sky conditions as follows:
   1. bright sunshine 4. a few clouds
   2. high humidity   5. light precipitation
   3. very windy   6. heavy precipitation

F. Finally, the same player rolls the die a third time, to determine the temperature, as follows:
   1. 30°C   3. 10°C   5. −10°C
   2. 20°C   4. 0°C   6. −20°C

G. To what degree are the weather conditions suitable for the outdoor recreational activity identified on the first roll? Enter points on the score sheet as follows:
   • great conditions: 2 points
   • okay conditions: 1 point
   • save-it-for-another-day conditions: 0 points

H. Play moves clockwise, each player rolling three times at each turn. After ten rounds, add up the total points to declare a table winner.

Wrap-Up:

How important is the weather in our recreational activities? Use an example from your favourite sport to support your conclusion.

Understanding Climate Patterns

Climates are different across Canada, but the overall pattern does make sense. First, temperatures tend to become colder as you travel north, so places in southern Canada are warmer than communities in the Arctic. Most people like to live where it's warm. Businesses tend to set up shop in the same areas, partly because they need access to people to work for them. Farmers, of course, are seriously affected by Canada's temperature pattern. Not many people farm north of the Arctic Circle!

According to the second part of the Canadian major climate pattern, places near the coast are usually wetter than places in the interior. This pattern demonstrates the strong impact that the oceans have on precipitation. Large water bodies also affect the temperatures of regions near the coast. For example, the Pacific, Lower Lakes, and Atlantic climate regions are milder in winter, when stored heat is released from the water around them.

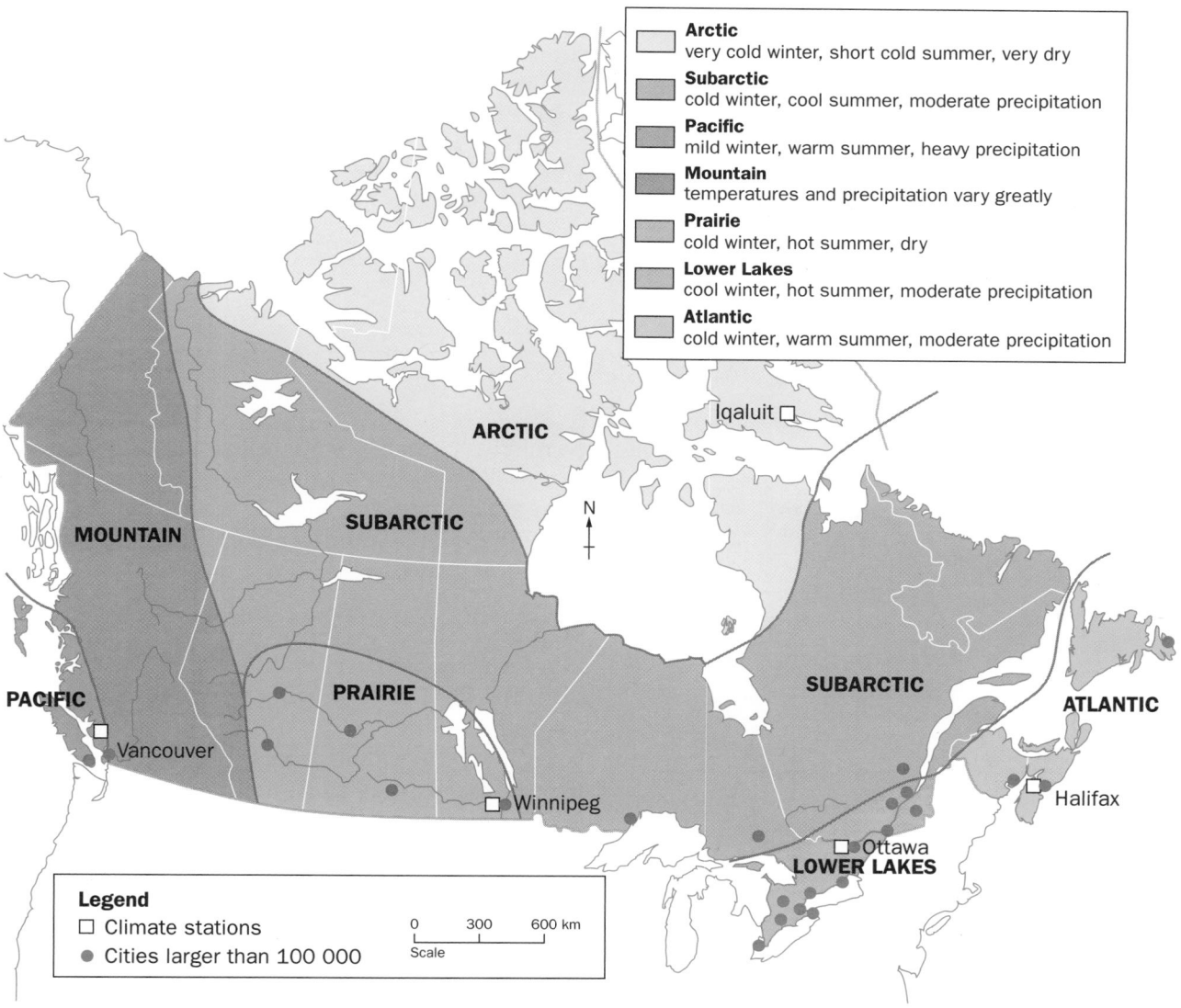

▲ **Figure 1.16:** Climate regions of Canada

21. Using the map on page 33, name the Canadian climate region where you live. What are its characteristics?

22. Which climate region of Canada has conditions that you would most like to live in? Explain why.

23. How close do you live to the US border? Look at the map. How many of Canada's major cities lie within 300 km of our southern neighbour? How can climate help explain this pattern?

GeoSkills

Drawing Climate Graphs with Growing Season

One method of showing the climate of a city or other climate station is to draw a **climate graph**.

Purpose
Climate graphs give scientists researching the climate an easy way to analyze long-term conditions and to compare climate stations. A climate graph is both a bar graph and a line graph. The blue bars show the **mean**, or average, precipitation per month, while the red line shows the mean daily temperature for each month. The graph in Figure 1.18 is a climate graph for Ottawa based on the climate statistics given in Figure 1.17.

Months	J	F	M	A	M	J	J	A	S	O	N	D	Year
Daily mean temperature (°C)	−11	−9	−3	6	13	18	21	19	14	8	1	−8	5.8
Monthly mean precipitation (mm)	58	59	65	69	76	77	88	92	83	75	86	83	911

Source: Environment Canada Web, <http://www.msc-smc.ec.gc.ca/climate>, May 2002.

▲ **Figure 1.17:** Climate statistics for Ottawa, Ontario

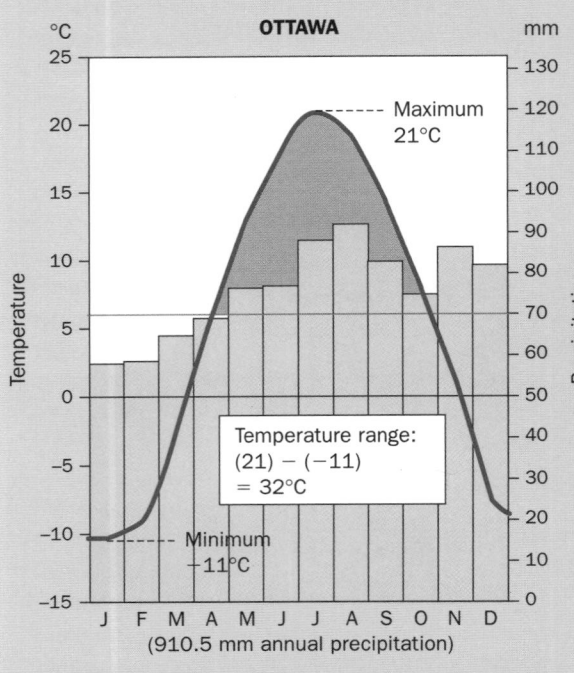

▲ **Figure 1.18:** Climate graph for Ottawa, Ontario

To make a climate graph, follow these steps.

Step 1
Mark the twelve months across the bottom of a sheet of grid paper.

Step 2
Mark a scale for precipitation along the right side. Try for a scale starting with 0 mm at the base and going up by 10-mm steps. Mark "mm" at the top of your scale. Then, for every month, mark a line to show the precipitation for that month. Shade the bars blue.

Step 3
Mark a scale for temperature along the left side. Try for a scale starting at –30°C and going up by five-degree steps to 30°C. Mark "°C" at the top of your scale. Then, for every

City	T/P	J	F	M	A	M	J	J	A	S	O	N	D	Year
Vancouver, BC (3 m)	°C	3	5	6	9	12	15	17	17	14	10	6	4	9.8
	mm	150	124	109	75	62	46	36	38	64	115	170	179	1168
Winnipeg, Man. (239 m)	°C	−18	−15	−7	4	12	17	20	18	12	6	−5	−15	2.4
	mm	19	15	23	36	60	84	72	75	51	30	21	19	505
Iqaluit, Nunavut (34 m)	°C	−26	−27	−24	−15	−4	3	8	7	2	−5	−13	−22	−9.7
	mm	22	19	22	28	30	37	58	64	52	42	31	20	425
Halifax, NS (126 m)	°C	−6	−6	−2	4	9	15	18	18	14	9	3	−3	6.1
	mm	147	119	123	124	111	98	97	110	95	129	154	167	1474

Source: Environment Canada Web, <http://www.msc-smc.ec.gc.ca/climate>, May 2002.

▲ **Figure 1.19:** Daily mean temperature and monthly mean precipitation for four selected stations across Canada. (You can see these stations on the climate region map in Figure 1.16, page 33.)

month, mark a dot in the middle of the month to show the average daily temperature for that month. Connect the dots with a smooth red line that goes right to the edge of the graph.

Step 4

Draw a green line across the graph at 6°C. This is the average temperature at which many plants can begin to grow.

Step 5

Then shade in green the zone that is under the temperature curve and above the 6°C line. (Don't colour over the precipitation bars.) This zone is called the **growing season**, the average period of time during which plants can grow.

Step 6

Write the station name at the top or bottom, along with the annual precipitation.

Practise It!

1. Divide the climate stations in Figure 1.19 among four students. Follow Steps 1 to 6 to construct the four climate graphs at the same scale.

2. As a group, compare the four climate graphs. Be sure to consider summer and winter temperatures, precipitation, and the length of the growing season in each place.

3. Which of these climates would you prefer to live in? Explain your choice.

4. On the climate graph you made in Question 1, mark the maximum and minimum temperatures. Then, calculate the temperature range by subtracting the minimum temperature from the maximum temperature.

To make a climate graph...
- ✔ mark the month of the year
- ✔ put a temperature scale on the left
- ✔ put a precipitation scale on the right
- ✔ label the units of measure
- ✔ add blue bars showing precipitation
- ✔ connect temperatures with a red line
- ✔ add a green line at 6°C
- ✔ shade the growing season green
- ✔ add a title indicating location

Conclusion

Landforms and climate are both very important parts of the Earth's natural system. Mountain-building and erosion are locked in a tug-of-war as they continually reshape the face of the Earth. Some of Canada's landforms are parts of larger global systems, such as the Pacific Ring of Fire and the continental shelf. We use relief maps and relief profiles to show the characteristic patterns of landforms.

Weather and climate have great effects upon the land and all living things. The variable weather shapes our daily activities, while weather extremes can shake up our lives. Canada has a great size, so temperature and precipitation varies a great deal across the country's seven climate regions. Within each region, the length of the growing season directs the seasonal cycle of plants and wildlife.

Wrap It Up

1. Use labelled diagrams to show how Earth's plates and convection currents can explain a) fold mountains, and b) volcanic eruptions.

2. On the Internet, find monthly temperature and precipitation data for your community or one close by. Use this information to draw a climate graph. Compare your completed graph with the climate graph you already drew for this chapter.

3. Explore continental drift yourself.
   a) Cut the continents from an outline map of the world.
   b) Glue Africa onto the centre of a blank page.
   c) Next, glue South America beside Africa, and Eurasia above it.
   d) Then, position North America and Australia where they seem to fit best.
   e) Finally, cut out a circle about the size of Australia to represent Antarctica, and decide where to put it.

4. How has your local region or community been affected by the forces described in this chapter? Look for information about a) evidence of mountain-building, b) evidence of the ice ages, c) sources of present-day water erosion.

5. Review weather reports on two different television stations. Which television station and forecaster do you think is better? Explain reasons for your choice, including such factors as personality, weather technology used, media presentation, and accuracy of report.

6. Examine the two sets of world climate statistics given in Figure 1.20. Which is in the Northern Hemisphere, and which is in the Southern Hemisphere? (*Hint:* Look carefully at temperature and precipitation patterns.) Explain your reasoning for your answer.

7. For a challenge, try the Unit 1 GIS activity, "Volcano Investigator," on page 338.

City	T/P	J	F	M	A	M	J	J	A	S	O	N	D	Year
Station A	°C	1	3	4	6	8	11	13	13	11	8	4	2	7.0
	mm	251	217	188	181	142	120	113	163	245	379	284	270	2553
Station B	°C	15	13	9	5	2	−1	−3	1	5	8	12	14	6.7
	mm	8	5	7	9	10	13	25	24	24	13	9	7	154

Source: Environment Canada Web, <http://www.msc-smc.ec.gc.ca/climate>, May 2002.

▲ **Figure 1.20:** Climate data, two unnamed stations

Chapter 2

OUR DIVERSE REGIONS

Cross-Canada Slogan Match

You have been put in charge of promoting Canada's seven landform regions. A promotions firm has come up with a list of catchy slogans, but they haven't told you what regions they apply to. See if you can match each of the following slogans to one of the regions shown on the map in Figure 2.1. (Some regions have more than one slogan.) Write your answers in your notebook. If you don't get them all the first time, don't worry; all the answers are in this chapter.

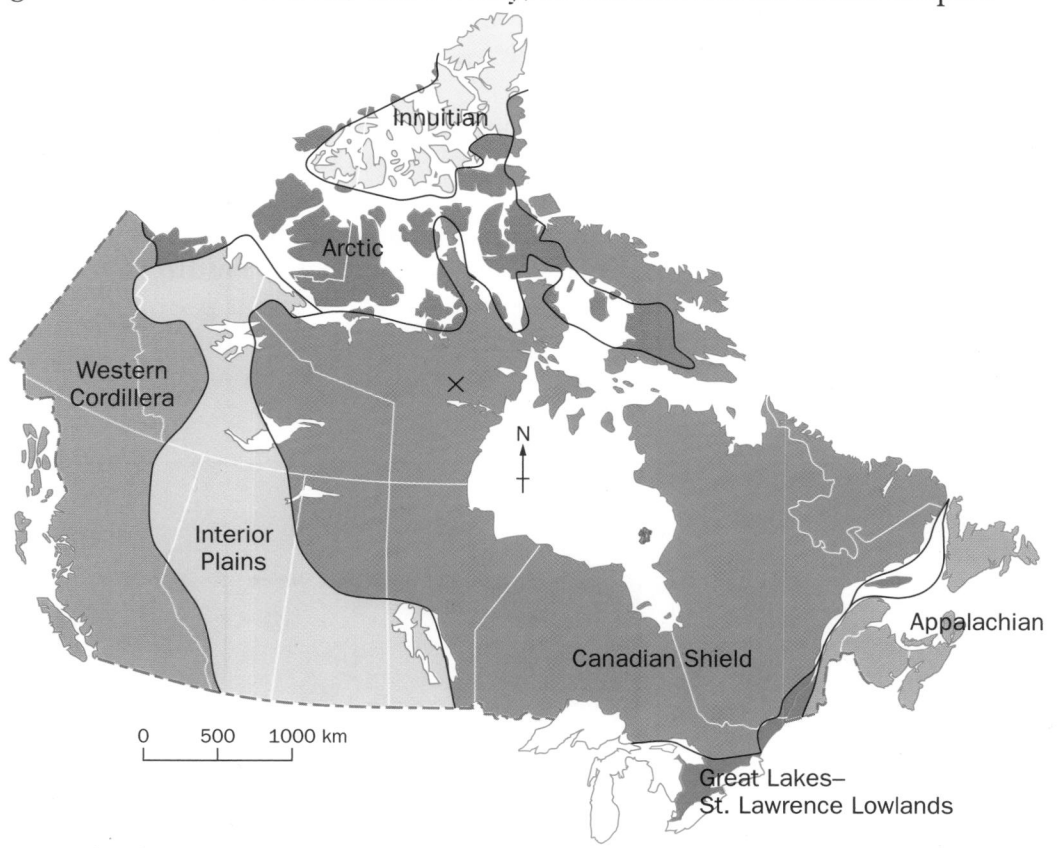

◀ **Figure 2.1:**
The seven landform regions of Canada

1. Reach new heights in Canada's highest mountains

2. Find peace in our many natural harbours

3. Everything is in "plain" view out here

4. You'll love our lakes!

5. Mountains, islands, and ice

6. We've got the brightest lights and the biggest cities!

7. Discover the Northwest Passage

8. Come watch the wheat grow

9. Stand tall among the towering coastal trees

10. Our mines are yours to discover!

GeoTrivia #1
In Figure 2.1, the small "X" near Baker Lake marks the geographical centre of the country. It's surprisingly far north!

In this chapter, you will

- find out what a region is
- see how Canada's seven landform regions were formed
- examine how people live in these regions and use regional resources
- learn about the landforms and people of Nunavut
- read a topographic map

What Is a Landform Region?

If you have a lot to learn, dividing it up into smaller parts makes the job easier. When geographers divide the Earth into regions, they can understand it better. A **region** is an area with certain characteristics that set it apart from other areas.

The two regions shown in Figure 2.2 have completely different landforms and natural vegetation. The mountain region seems to offer more possibilities for human activity, with forests and rivers for industry and recreation. The desert seems to be a harsh and barren region, but don't count it out. There could be oil under the surface, just like in the Middle East. A **landform region** is a part of the Earth with a unique set of physical features that people often use to meet their needs. In this chapter, you will look at seven different landform regions, each with a different set of natural and human characteristics.

▲ **Figure 2.2:** Two very different landform regions

Canada's Landform Regions

Look at a tree stump and you'll see how the tree grew outward from the centre. Canada grew the same way. The oldest part of the country, the Canadian Shield, is in the centre, surrounded by younger landform regions. As the ancient rocks of the Shield eroded, they were deposited in the surrounding oceans as sediment. Later, the ocean floors folded up into great mountain ranges, forming new regions. We'll look at Canada's landform regions from the centre outward, starting with the Canadian Shield.

1. Explain how Canada's basic structure can be compared to a tree. How is it different?

2. Describe the features of the Earth's surface in your area. How have people made use of them?

3. Make a map to name the seven major landform regions of Canada. Locate and name your community on the map.

The Canadian Shield

This region covers almost half of Canada. Figure 2.1 on page 37 shows that it is shaped like a doughnut, with Hudson Bay as the hole. The Canadian Shield formed in stages starting about three billion years ago. Massive volcanic eruptions raised mountains from the sea to form the core of a new continent. Rich veins of metallic minerals, such as gold, silver, and nickel, squeezed into these igneous rocks (rocks created from molten magma). Then, billions of years of erosion levelled the mountains, putting the minerals within reach of miners. During the ice ages, moving glaciers scraped much of the soil from the Shield. As they moved, the glaciers marked the land with hollows and depressions. Today, this region is covered by thousands of lakes and swamps left in these hollows.

GeoTrivia #2
The Canadian Shield is 100 to 200 million times older than you are.

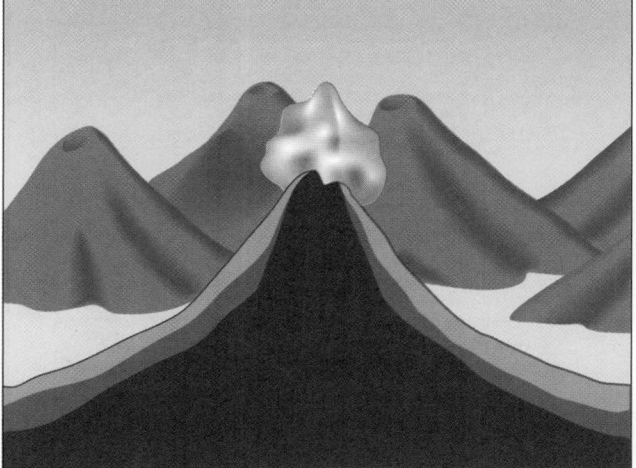

▲ **Figure 2.3:** Formation of the Canadian Shield

▲ **Figure 2.4:** The Canadian Shield

4. Why does the Shield have igneous rock? Why does the region have rich deposits of metallic minerals?

5. Look at the photograph in Figure 2.4. List three different Shield characteristics shown in the picture. Suggest recreational uses for the area.

The Human Geography of the Shield

Mining, hydroelectric power, and forestry are all important resources in this landform region. The southern Canadian Shield has pockets of farmland, called **clay belts**. These areas were once the bottoms of glacial lakes.

    The population of the Canadian Shield is widely scattered, but most people live in the southern parts. Only a few cities have 100 000 people—Sudbury and Thunder Bay in Ontario, and Chicoutimi–Jonquiere (now called Saguenay) in Quebec. In the summertime, lakes, forests, and parkland attract boaters, cottagers, and campers. But for most of the year, the Canadian Shield is a region with many natural resources and few people.

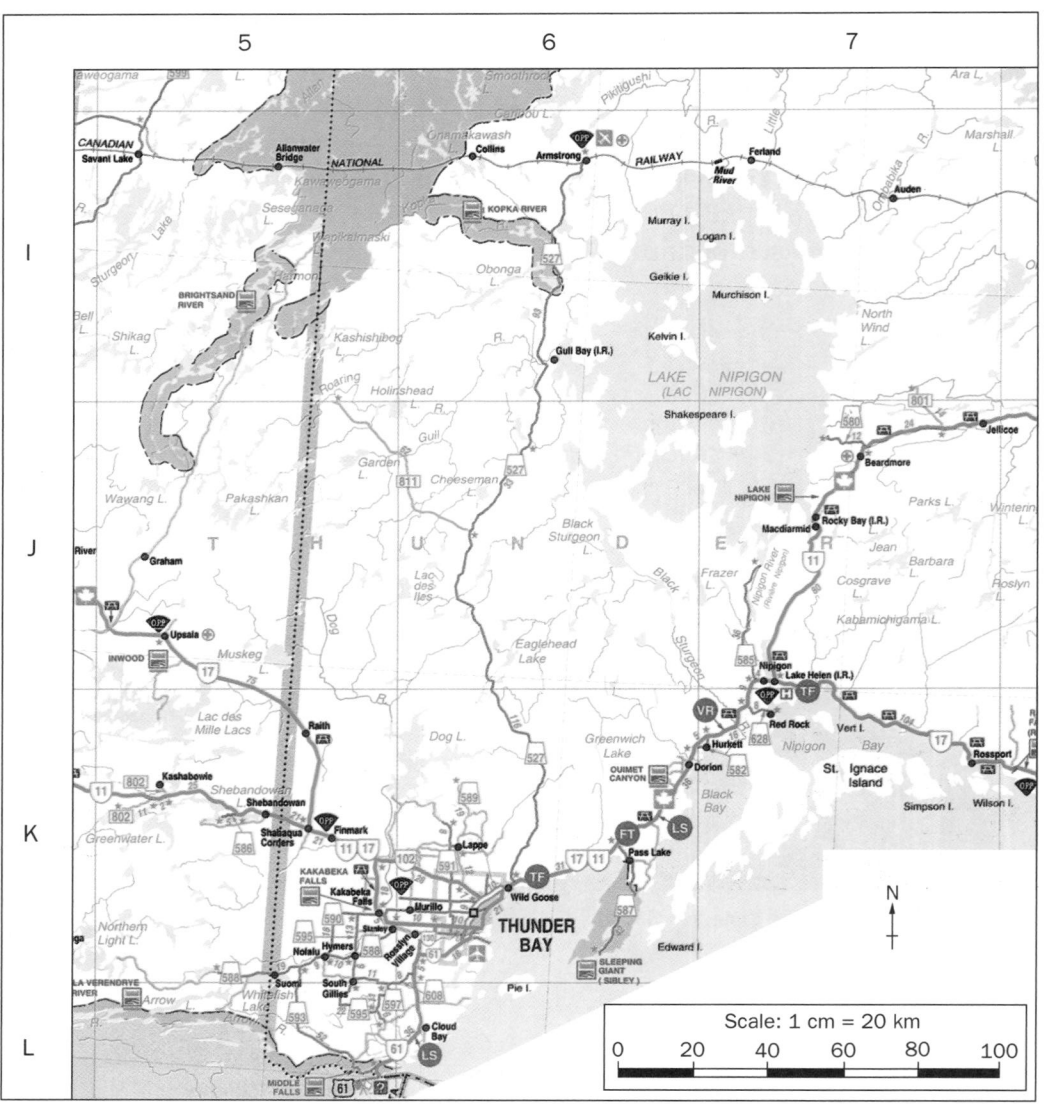

▲ **Figure 2.5:** Northern Ontario: the Canadian Shield

6. Use the map in Figure 2.5 to describe the following Shield characteristics. Give specific examples.

    a) amount of lakes and rivers   c) important provincial parks

    b) amount and pattern of roads   d) amount and pattern of population

The Great Lakes–St. Lawrence Lowlands

This is a low-lying area located (as you probably guessed) around the Great Lakes and along the St. Lawrence River. Half of this small landform region is in Ontario, and the other half is in Quebec. It is a region of sedimentary rock—material deposited in ancient seas as the Canadian Shield eroded. Eventually, parts of the seas filled up with sedimentary rock, creating new land areas. Much of this rock is about half a billion years old. It comes from a time when living things had not yet emerged on land.

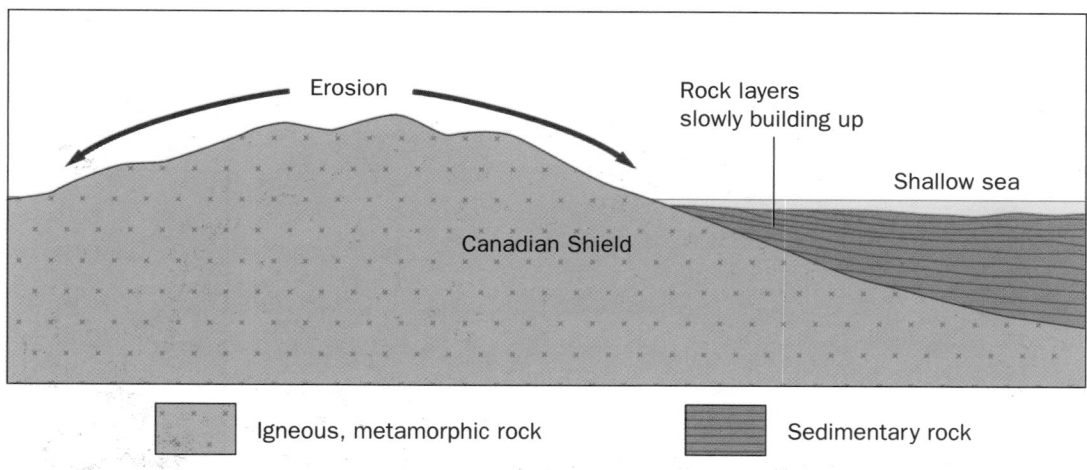

▲ **Figure 2.6:** The formation of the Great Lakes–St. Lawrence Lowlands

7. Where did the material come from to form the Lowlands? Why are the Lowlands made up of sedimentary rock rather than igneous rock?

During the ice ages, ice sheets moved south into the region, pushing earth and rock along with them. For this reason, much of the region is covered with deep layers of soil. Huge glaciers scraped out basins, which filled with water as the glaciers melted. These basins became the Great Lakes.

8. Give two different ways in which ice affected this region.

The Niagara Escarpment

You've probably seen pictures of Niagara Falls. Perhaps you've even visited it. What you may not have realized is that all that water is falling down a ridge that runs right across Southern Ontario—all the way from Niagara Falls to Manitoulin Island. It is called the Niagara Escarpment. An **escarpment** is a sharp change in height caused by the rapid erosion of soft sedimentary rock. The Niagara Escarpment has a hard layer of limestone rock formed from the remains of coral reef and other ancient fossils. Softer shales and sandstones above this layer have worn away and left the cliff that Niagara Falls drops over.

The Escarpment provides stone and cement for the building industry, and recreation for people in the region. Many popular ski resorts use the Escarpment, and the Bruce Trail takes hikers along its crest.

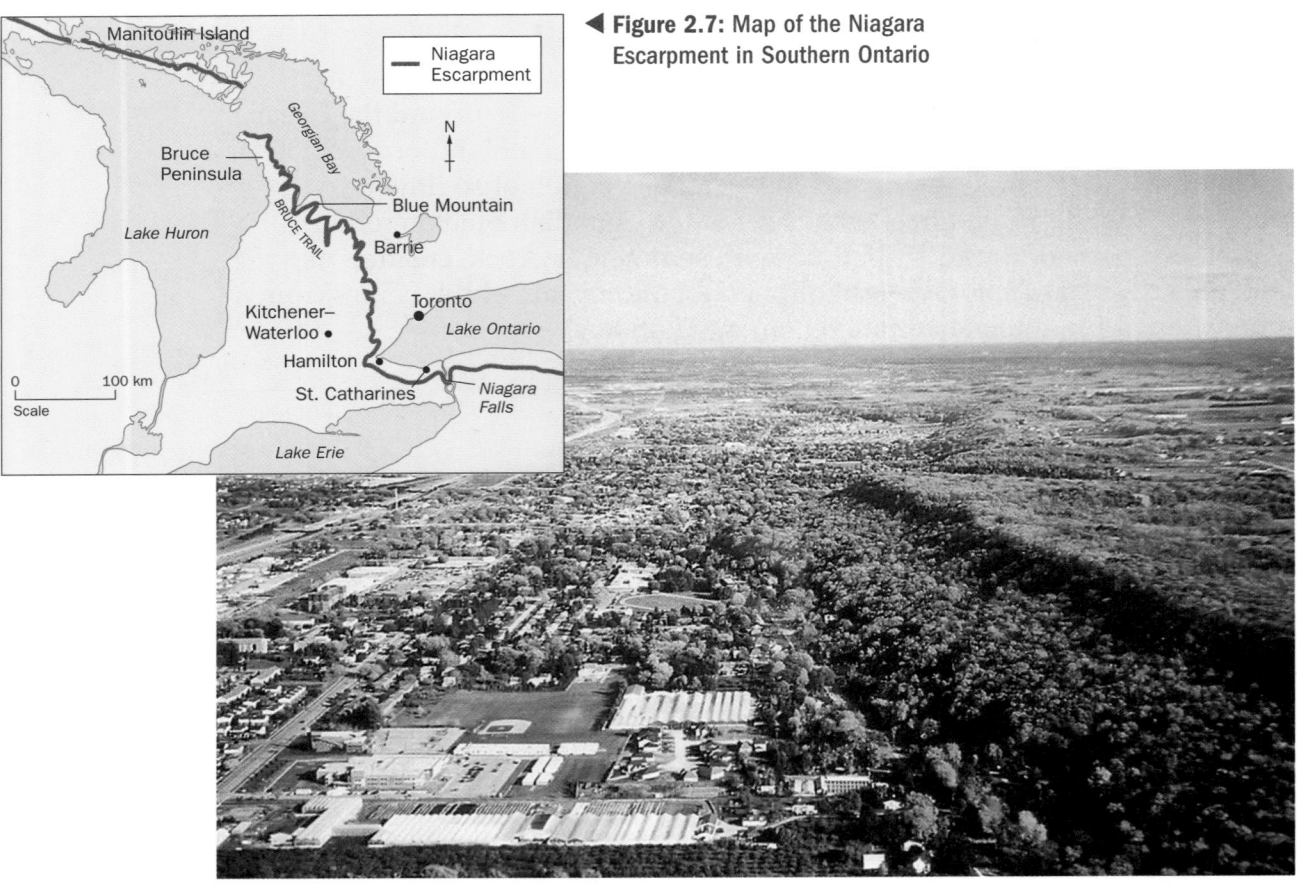

▶ **Figure 2.7:** Map of the Niagara Escarpment in Southern Ontario

▲ **Figure 2.8:** A view of the Escarpment

9. Explain how the Niagara Escarpment was formed.

10. Use a road map or an atlas map to locate your own community in relation to the Niagara Escarpment. How close to this feature do you live?

The Human Geography of the Lowlands

The Great Lakes–St. Lawrence Lowlands region is very heavily populated, especially along the major waterways. Two-thirds of Canada's people live here, particularly clustered in the Greater Toronto Area and Metropolitan Montreal. The region is the manufacturing heart of Canada, particularly for the automobile industry. Prosperous farms are located between the cities, but this fertile farmland is threatened by urban sprawl. Farmers raise livestock and produce a wide range of fruits, vegetables, and grains. This small region faces the pressures of a large and growing population.

11. Brainstorm a list of five reasons why the Great Lakes–St. Lawrence Lowlands is so heavily populated.

12. Make a simple sketch to show the highway, the plain, and the Niagara Escarpment in Figure 2.8. Suggest why the Escarpment is heavily forested.

13. Make a list of five ways people use the land below the Escarpment in Figure 2.8. Which uses might threaten fruit orchards in the area?

The Appalachians

The Appalachian region in eastern Canada is a very popular summer tourist destination, with a unique mix of landforms and people. The rugged old mountains found in the region began to form about 250 million years ago. Plate movements forced the sedimentary rock on the ocean floor to fold upwards, and in some places metallic minerals squeezed into cracks in the rock.

Then, erosion forces ground these mountain ranges down to a fraction of their original height, and formed flatter plains areas between them. Rising oceans drowned some lowland areas, creating a jagged coastline with many excellent natural harbours. Part of the Appalachian region extends far inland, forming the southern edge of Quebec.

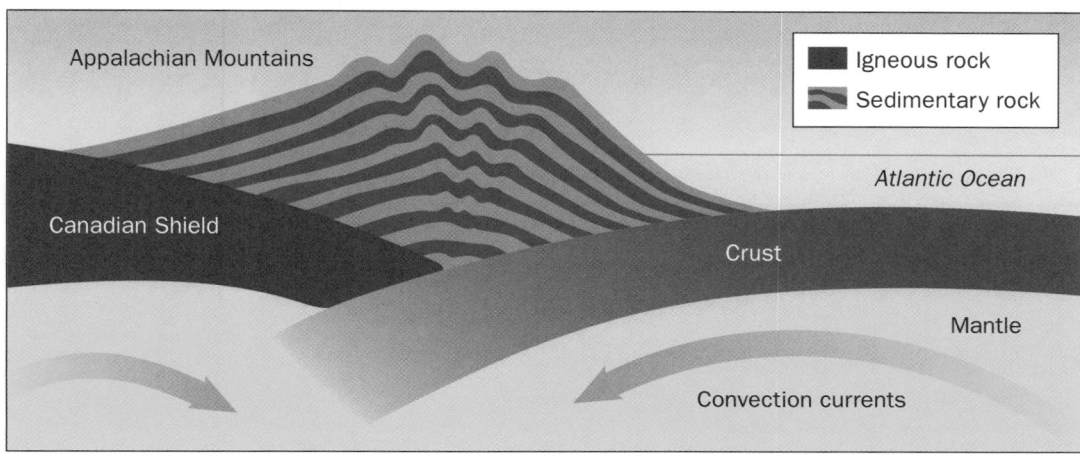

▲ **Figure 2.9:** The formation of the Appalachian Mountains

14. Make a list of steps to detail how the Appalachians developed.

15. If you were an early explorer, what geographical characteristics would you look for when choosing a place to land? Why are natural harbours common along the Atlantic coast?

The Human Geography of the Appalachians

Aboriginal hunters and fishers were the first residents of this region. The Mi'kmaq lived on the mainland, while the Beothuk inhabited Newfoundland. Later, European explorers set up colonies along the region's coastline.

Today, the Appalachian region has about one-tenth of Canada's total population. There are only four cities of 100 000 people: Sherbrooke (Quebec), Halifax (Nova Scotia), Saint John (New Brunswick), and St. John's (Newfoundland and Labrador). Lately, problems in the fishing industry have forced many people in small coastal fishing communities to look for work in the cities.

Next time you grab a bag of potato chips or wolf down some french fries, thank the farmers of the Appalachian region! The fertile soils of Prince Edward Island and New Brunswick are perfect for growing potatoes, which are sold in Canadian and world markets. This is a landform region with many unique characteristics.

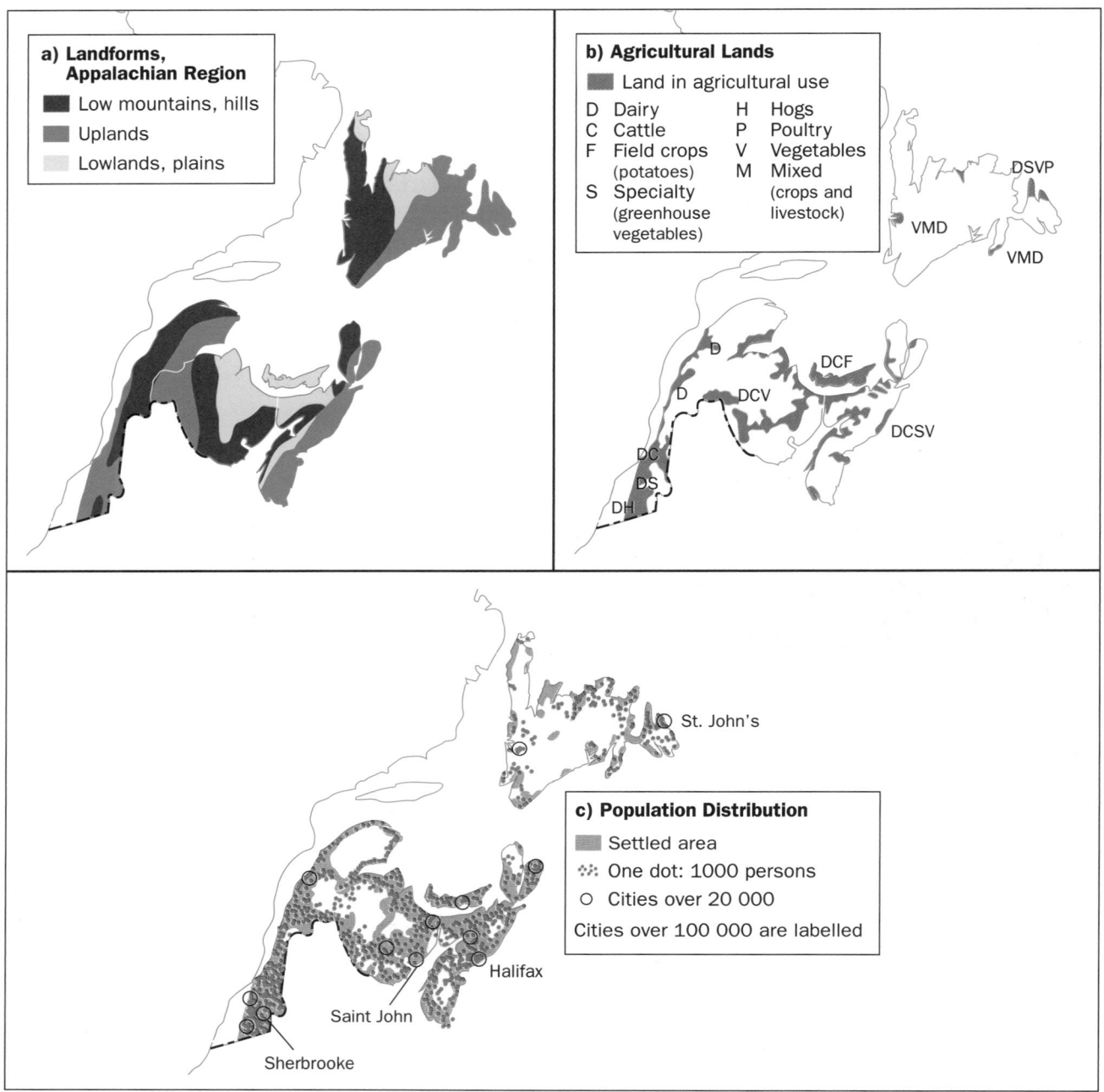

▲ **Figure 2.10:** The Appalachian region, showing a) physical features, b) agricultural land, and c) population distribution

16. Examine the maps in Figures 2.10a and 2.10b. Which types of landform have most of the Appalachian region's farmland? Which type of agriculture is most common in the region?

17. Examine the maps in Figures 2.10a and 2.10c. Is the Appalachian region's population pattern caused by landforms or by the sea? Explain your answer with map evidence.

18. Compare the maps in Figures 2.10b and 2.10c. Where do you find populated areas without agriculture in the region? What other jobs would support communities in these areas?

The Interior Plains

In the nineteenth century, an explorer named William Francis Butler called this western region "The Great Lone Land." This is the Interior Plains region—a large, wide-open area, without mountains or trees to limit the horizon.

Much of the Interior Plains is 200-million-year-old sedimentary rock. As inland seas filled with sediment, fossilized sea life was chemically changed into oil and natural gas. Gradually, erosion carved the region into the three levels shown in Figure 2.11, divided by escarpments in Manitoba and Saskatchewan. The ice ages came and went, leaving the Interior Plains region covered by thick soil layers suited for agriculture.

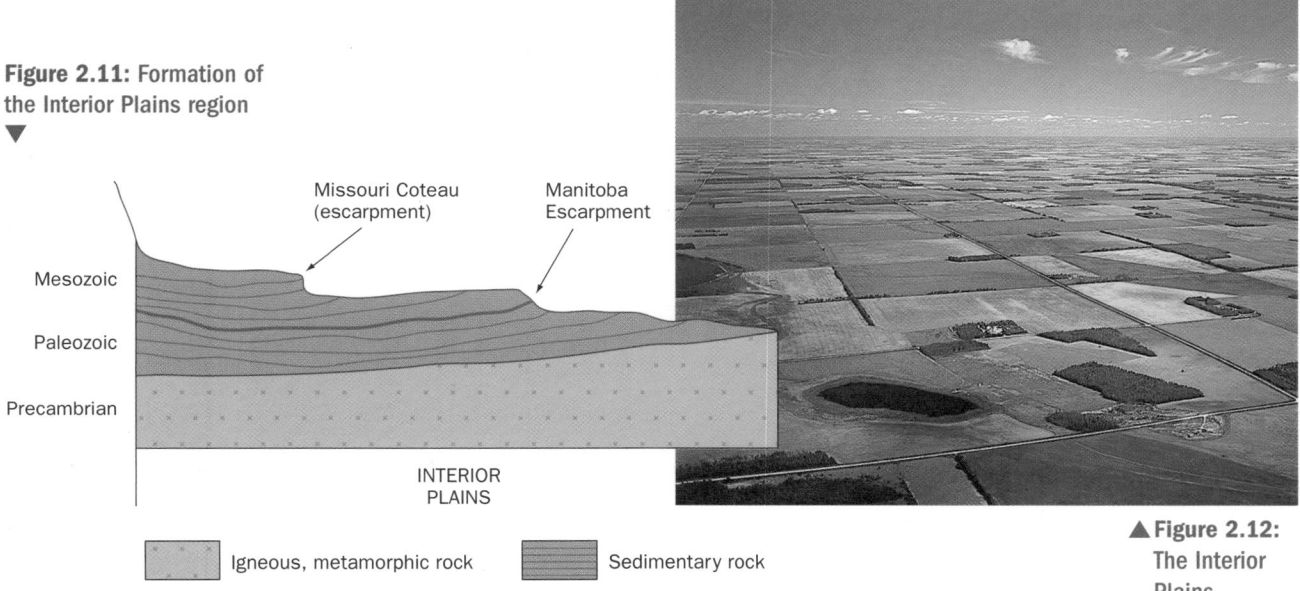

Figure 2.11: Formation of the Interior Plains region ▼

Missouri Coteau (escarpment)

Manitoba Escarpment

Mesozoic

Paleozoic

Precambrian

INTERIOR PLAINS

Igneous, metamorphic rock   Sedimentary rock

▲ **Figure 2.12:** The Interior Plains

19. Look at the photograph of the Interior Plains in Figure 2.12. Use it to list five different characteristics of the region.

20. Brainstorm a chart of benefits and problems of this region, from the point of view of the pioneers who settled it.

The Human Geography of the Plains

Seen from an airplane, the Interior Plains look like a patchwork quilt of squares. That's because the flat-to-rolling land was easily measured into square parcels by government surveyors. Wheat and other field crops are grown on large farms, while even larger beef cattle ranches are found in dry areas of southern Alberta. Two cities in the region have populations approaching one million. Edmonton is the centre of Canada's oil industry, and Calgary is the hub of our natural gas development.

21. Use the topographic map in Figure 2.13 on page 46 to record evidence of a) the way surveyors divided up the land in the region, and b) three regional resources.

GEOSKILLS

READING TOPOGRAPHIC MAPS

A **topographic map** is a detailed map that shows both physical and human features. This type of map includes map symbols to show human features such as buildings and bridges. **Contour lines**, thin brown lines that trace the surface elevation, show how high the land is above sea level. Topographic maps also use a special distance scale and a grid system for finding exact locations.

Purpose

These large-scale maps are used for hiking and other outdoor recreation, for military planning, and for geographic studies.

Here are some steps to follow to help you read a topographic map.

Step 1

Get to know the symbols used in the map legend. Topographic maps use many area, line, and point symbols. The map legend in Figure 2.13 shows some of these.

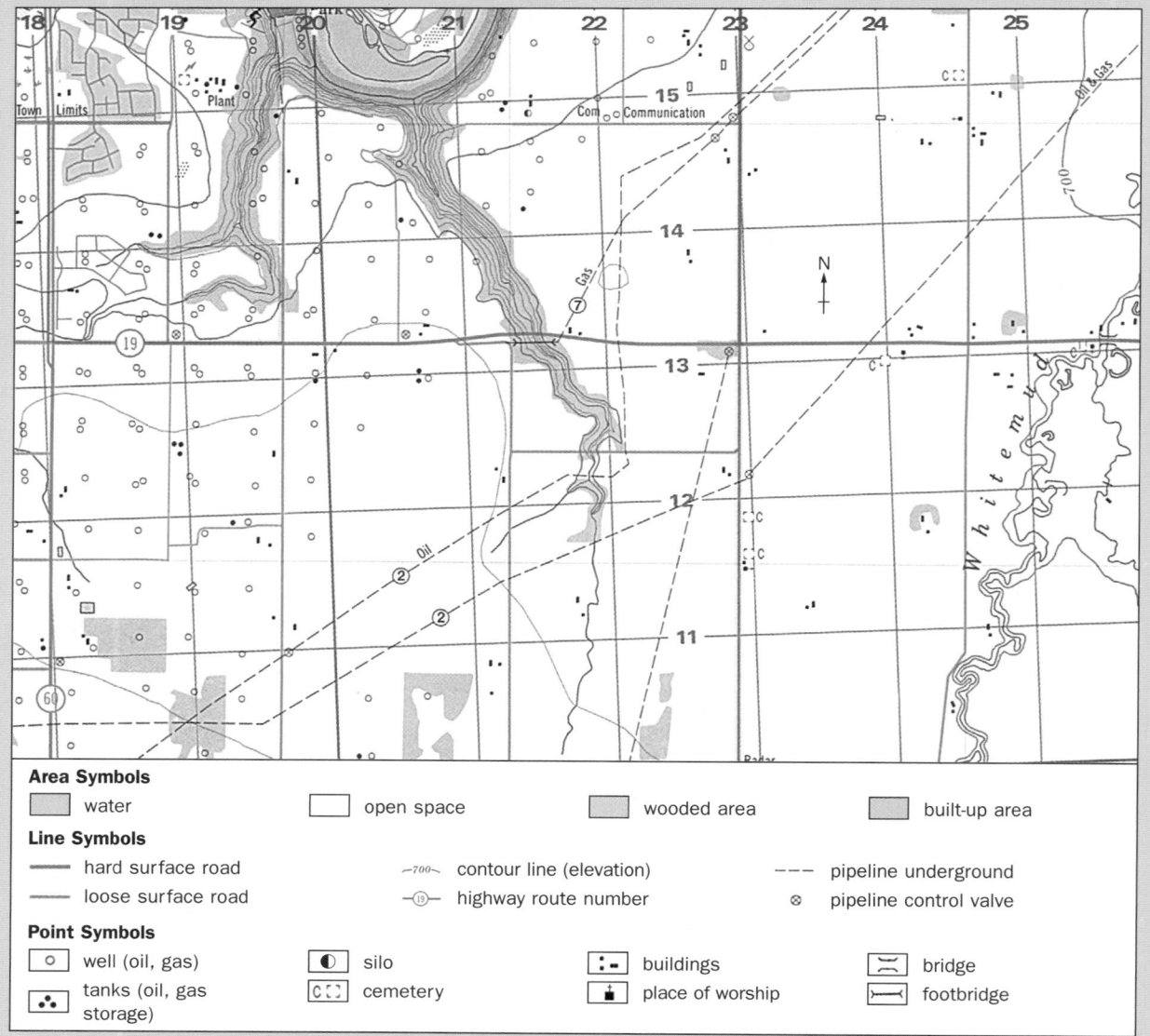

Area Symbols

▮ water   ▯ open space   ▤ wooded area   ▨ built-up area

Line Symbols

── hard surface road   ～700～ contour line (elevation)   --- pipeline underground

── loose surface road   ─⑲─ highway route number   ⊗ pipeline control valve

Point Symbols

⊙ well (oil, gas)   ◑ silo   :– buildings   ⊠ bridge

∴ tanks (oil, gas storage)   [C∷] cemetery   ▪ place of worship   ⊢⊣ footbridge

▲ **Figure 2.13:** Topographic map of the interior plains of Alberta, 1:50 000 scale

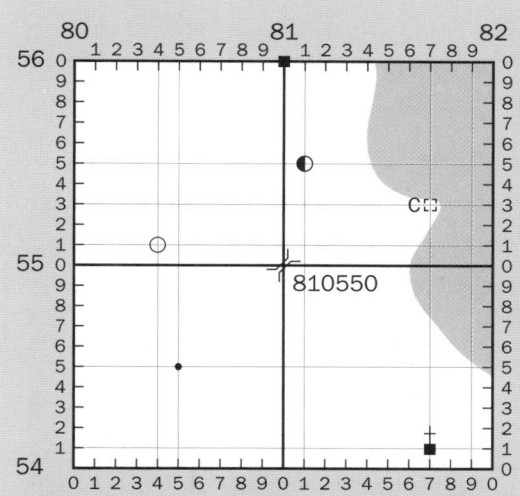

▲ **Figure 2.14:** Military grid

Step 2

Use the **military grid** to describe exact locations. Armies use these maps to locate enemy positions, so they need to be accurate! Lines numbered from 00 to 99 cross the map in both directions. Read the north–south lines first. For example, the bridge in Figure 2.14 is on the 81 north–south and 55 east–west lines.

This position can be written 81.0 by 55.0, or 810550.

Step 3

Read the map scale to find distances. Topographic maps use a ratio scale instead of the line scale on road maps. A **ratio scale** compares map distance to actual distance with a ratio number. If a map has a ratio scale of 1:100 000, then 1 cm on the map represents 100 000 cm (or 1 km) on the Earth. The most commonly used topographic scale is 1:50 000. It means 1 cm = 0.5 km.

Step 4

Identify physical characteristics of the land by looking at the contour lines. Hills are closed circles, while river valleys have a V-shape pointing upstream to the source of the river. The examples in Figure 2.15 show a hill and a river valley drawn normally and topographically. Can you locate points A, B, C, and D on the topographic diagrams?

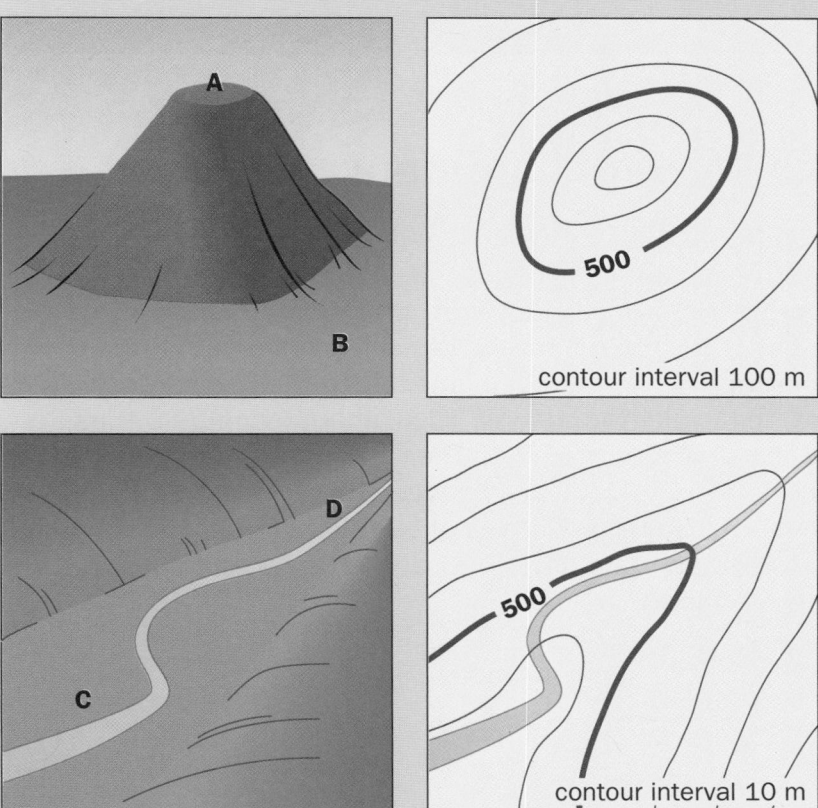

▲ **Figure 2.15:** How hills and river valleys appear on topographic maps

Contour lines close together mean the land is steep, while land with few contours is flat. The height between the lines is the **contour interval**. Find the contour interval by comparing the numbers on neighbouring contour lines. For example, if you see contours marked 90 and 95, the contour interval is five metres.

Practise It!

Use the topographic map of the interior plains of Alberta, and its legend, in Figure 2.13 on page 46 to answer these questions.

1. Draw three symbols that prove this is an important oil-producing region.

2. What is found at each of these locations?
   i) 210140   ii) 229115   iii) 186123

3. a) Find the map ratio scale. How much actual distance does one centimetre represent?
   b) How far is it from the plant building at 193153 to the cemetery to the east-southeast (at 240130)?

To read a topographic map...
- ✔ look at the legend to understand the symbols
- ✔ use the military grid to pinpoint specific locations
- ✔ check the ratio scale to calculate distances
- ✔ analyze contour lines to identify physical features

c) Which side of the map relies most on the oil industry?
d) How can you tell that farming occurs across this whole map?

4. Is the area flat or rugged? Explain.

The Western Cordillera

British Columbia, the Yukon, and small parts of Alberta and the Northwest Territories make up a complicated landform region. The Western Cordillera ("cordillera" is a Spanish word for mountains) is a fairly young geologic region. It has three main parts, each formed in a different way. During the dinosaur age, plate movements folded the Earth's crust up to form the oldest part, the Rocky Mountains. Then, about 65 million years ago, volcanic eruptions farther west built the Coast Range along the Pacific Ocean. The lava flowed over the area between the Rockies and the Coast Range to form the interior **plateau**, an area of elevated land. Finally, alpine glaciers sharpened mountaintops into jagged peaks and cut wide, U-shaped valleys between them.

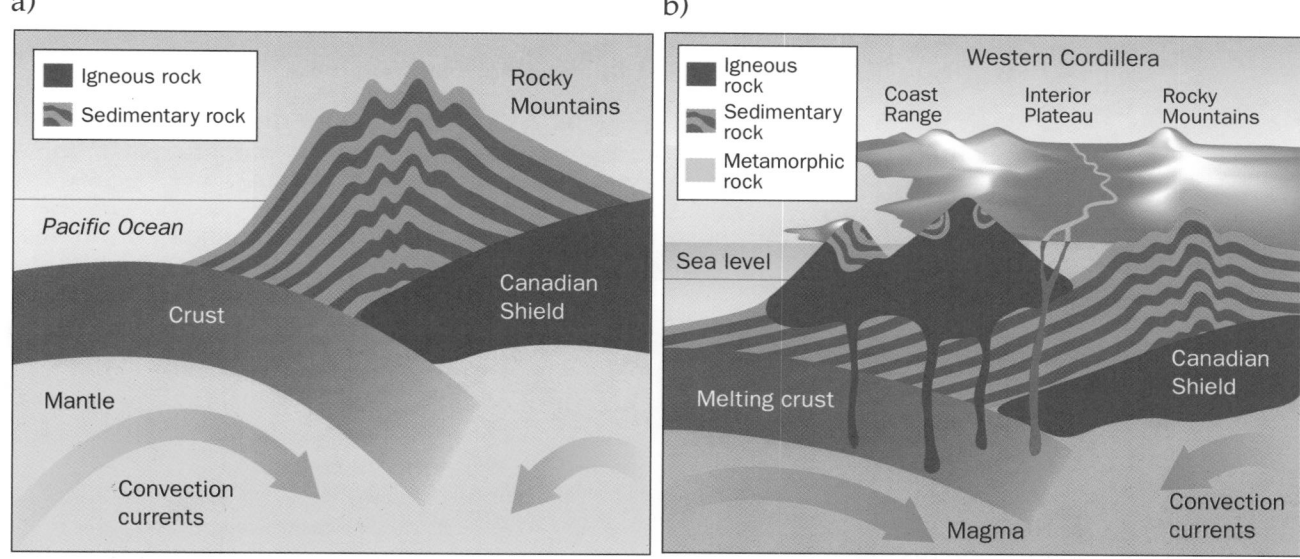

▲ **Figure 2.16:** Geologic formation of the Western Cordillera: a) folding of the Rocky Mountains; b) volcanism in the interior and coastal regions

22. Record one sentence in the text that describes what is happening in Figure 2.16a.

23. Record the sentence that describes the process shown in Figure 2.16b.

The Human Geography of the Cordillera

The Western Cordillera is rich in resources. Coal deposits are found in the Rocky Mountains, while metallic minerals are mined in the Coast Range and on the interior plateau. Forests cover all three areas, while orchards in sheltered interior valleys yield grapes, cherries, and peaches. Mountain slopes and wilderness scenery attract tourists year round.

About one-eighth of Canada's people live in the region, with most concentrated in Greater Vancouver and Victoria. Smaller resource- and tourist-based communities are scattered along the coast and interior valleys. The Western Cordillera is a complex region with a growing population.

24. What natural resources help explain why so many people live in the Cordillera region?

Figure 2.18 on the next page is a satellite image of part of the Western Cordillera region. A **satellite image** is a picture taken from space. Sensors detect light reflected from objects on Earth. A computer adds colour cues. Canada is a world leader in developing and using satellite information. Geographers use satellite images like this one to study physical features and natural resources.

25. Look at the photo of Jasper in Figure 2.17 below.
    a) List the natural resources that you see.
    b) Why is this a good location for a tourist community?

26. Look at the satellite image in Figure 2.18. What colours represent valleys and mountains in the image? Describe the appearance of the mountains. Do they appear as separate peaks or as chains?

27. How can you tell that these are folded mountains? What evidence do you see that alpine glaciers have shaped this area?

▲ **Figure 2.17:** Jasper, Alberta, in the Rocky Mountains

▲ **Figure 2.18:** Satellite image of the Rocky Mountains in Jasper National Park, Alberta

The Innuitians

Canada is a bit like a car that has been in a lot of accidents. The surface has been crumpled up on almost every side by collisions. The Appalachians, the Rockies, and the Innuitian Mountains are all folded sedimentary rock pushed up from the ocean floor by plate movements.

The Innuitians, in Canada's far North, are younger than the Appalachians and older than the Rockies. They are mostly located on Ellesmere Island, with some low-lying parts on the Parry Islands and Queen Elizabeth Islands. Oil and gas deposits have been discovered here, good evidence that the Innuitian region was once covered by warm tropical seas. But it's not like that anymore; now these mountains are covered by large glaciers.

28. Explain in your own words how the Innuitian region was formed.

The Arctic

It would be very easy to get lost in a blizzard in the Arctic region. In fact, many Arctic explorers died this way while searching for the Northwest Passage to the Pacific Ocean. The Inuit, who have lived here for thousands of years, have a deep respect for the power of nature.

The Arctic region is largely made up of islands formed from sedimentary rock. Most of the region was first scraped bare by moving ice, then drowned by rising sea levels as the ice melted. The surface is very stony, with **outcrops** of bare rock and very little vegetation. Oil and natural-gas deposits have been found near Inuvik. Both the Innuitian and Arctic regions are part of the new territory of Nunavut.

GeoTrivia #3
The coldest day ever recorded in Canada was a "wind chill" reading of -91 °C, at the community of Pelly Bay, Nunavut, on 13 January 1975. Now, that's cold!

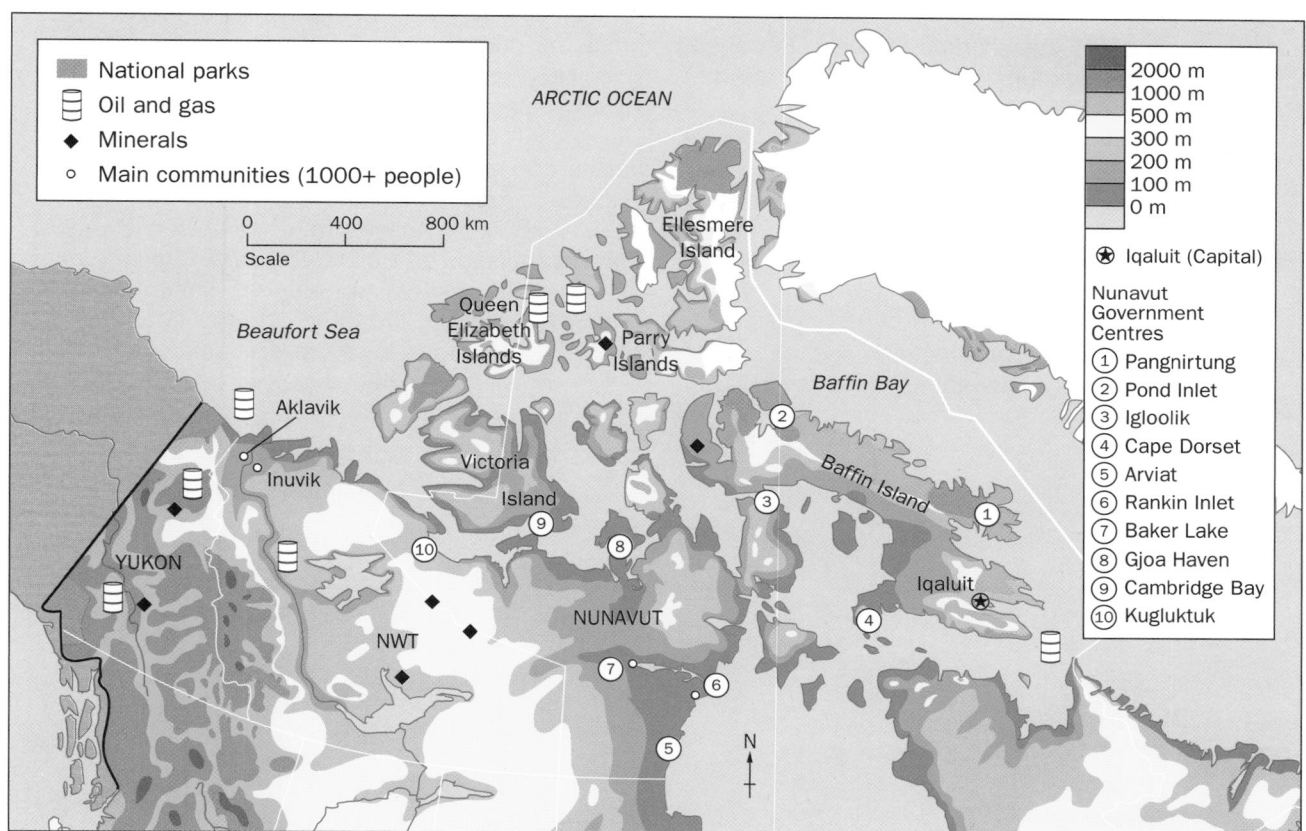

▲ **Figure 2.19:** The Arctic region

29. Look at Figure 2.19. Compare the elevations of the eastern and western Arctic. What challenges to survival do each of these regions present?

30. Why do both the Innuitian and Arctic regions have small populations?

31. Describe the map distribution of each of the following.
    a) Arctic communities   b) oil and gas deposits   c) national parks

CASE STUDY

NUNAVUT:
MEETING REGIONAL NEEDS

Nunavut became Canada's third territory on 1 April 1999. The name means "our land" in Inuktitut, the language of the Inuit. The Inuit have always seen this northeastern Arctic region as a part of themselves, even after European traders of the Hudson Bay Company claimed it. After almost 15 years of negotiations with Canada, Inuit negotiators succeeded in getting direct ownership of about 350 000 km² (or 18 per cent) of the territory in 1993. They agreed to work with Canada to manage the resources in the rest of Nunavut.

The territorial government is faced with some unique challenges. Although Nunavut covers around 1 600 000 km², it contains only about 27 000 people (about the same as the number of people living in Stratford, Ontario). As a result, government officials have had to find ways to serve small, isolated communities that are far from Iqaluit, the capital city.

Delivering government services, such as health care and education, is difficult. Even delivering the mail can be a challenge! Winter temperatures of –50°C and frequent blizzards mean there are few roads to connect communities. In fact, Nunavut has a total of only 21 kilometres of highway! What's more, many settlements in the region are on large islands, cut off from the mainland. Any bridges would be torn apart by the annual movement of ice in the sea.

Air service is the best way to solve the problems of landforms, distance, and climate in Nunavut. *First Air*, the regional airline, connects sixteen communities to one another, to the capital city Iqaluit, and to the rest of Canada. This northern airline is owned by the Inuit of northern Quebec. A regular schedule is followed during the peak Arctic flying season from March to October. Doctors, nurses, and midwives, for example, can make regular visits to isolated communities. During the rest of the year, though, bitter cold, blizzards, and long periods of darkness make flights more hazardous and less frequent.

▲ **Figure 2.20:** Iqaluit, Canada's newest capital

These transportation problems led Nunavut officials to use a very decentralized form of government. This means that local government departments and agencies are being set up in ten communities besides Iqaluit. You can see these on the map in Figure 2.19 on page 51. This decentralization will help create jobs in all areas of the territory. It also makes sense because smaller, isolated communities know best how to meet their own needs.

Local government makes sense in another way. The Inuit have always had a very strong sense of responsibility to the community. For example, according to the Inuit concept of *Innuqatigiinniq* (community ties), the raising and education of children is everyone's responsibility. Therefore, local control over services such as education make perfect sense both because of the land's daunting features and because of Inuit culture.

1. Summarize the reasons why transportation is difficult in Nunavut.
2. Brainstorm lists of advantages and disadvantages for Nunavut's type of government.
3. Suppose you lead the territorial government of Nunavut. Use the map in Figure 2.19 on page 51 to plan the following.
   a) locations for airports to distribute supplies from Iqaluit
   b) places that tourists might like to visit, and ways to get them there
   c) ways to get the territory's oil, natural gas, and minerals to the rest of Canada

Conclusion

In this chapter, you learned that many different landform processes have shaped our country during its long history. Searing volcanoes and slow, grinding plates built mountains. Water, ice, and wind continually wore down the surface and carried it to the sea. Four factors—size, time, mountain-building, and erosion—have created a country with seven different landform regions. People have populated each of these regions and used the resources to develop unique communities.

Wrap It Up

1. Make a chart with the headings shown below. Fill it in with brief point-form notes about each of the seven landform regions you have studied in this chapter.

2. Explain the meaning of each of the following ideas used in the chapter.
   a) Canada's land surface grew like a tree.
   b) Canada is like a car that has been in a lot of accidents.
   c) Nunavut is a new kind of territory.

3. Find out what types of landforms are located in your community and area. How have they affected the economy and population of your area? Prepare a short report, illustrated with a map, pictures, or both.

4. Look at the map of Canada's climate regions on page 33. Compare it to the map of Canada's landform regions in Figure 2.1 on page 37. Describe the climate patterns in each of the seven landform regions.

5. Look at an atlas map of Canada's population. Compare it to the map of Canada's landform regions. Record how population is distributed in each landform region.

Landform Region	Formation	Resources	Population

Chapter 3

BIOREGIONS: BALANCED COMMUNITIES

What Do These Animals Have in Common?

Each of these animals lives in a different bioregion of Canada. See if you can figure out what they all have in common. You will find the answer later in the chapter. (*Hint:* It has something to do with where they live!)

Banff Springs Snail

The Banff Springs snail lives exclusively in a very specific location: the hot springs in Banff National Park. It has adapted to conditions in which temperatures are high and there is very little oxygen.

◄ **Figure 3.1:** A snail that loves hot water!

Burrowing Owl

Yes, an owl that lives underground! These small, brown birds take over burrows made by badgers, gophers, or prairie dogs. They redecorate by making the burrow bigger and adding leaves and grasses before laying their eggs. The burrowing owl can be found in Alberta, Saskatchewan, and British Columbia.

◄ **Figure 3.2:** An owl that digs!

Leatherback Turtle

These are the largest reptiles in the world; they can grow as long as two metres and weigh up to 636 kg. They are found in the Atlantic, Pacific, and Indian Oceans. In Canada, leatherbacks appear on the east and west coasts in the summer, where they feed on jellyfish. Leatherbacks are the only turtles in the world with a soft shell.

◄ **Figure 3.3:** A turtle with a soft shell!

In this chapter, you will
- **find out what a bioregion is and what some particular bioregions are like**
- **look closely at some characteristics of bioregions**
- **examine how human activity affects living things in sensitive areas**
- **look at what you can do locally to help restore the ecological balance**

Words to Know

bioregion
wetland
biodiversity
habitat
soil profile
humus
chernozem
podzol
producer
consumer
alvar
fragmentation
natural corridor

What Is a Bioregion?

Remember your first day in high school? You probably felt like a fish out of water. It took a while to figure out where your classrooms were, good places to go during lunch, what group you wanted to be around, and which ones you wanted to avoid. After a few weeks in your new environment, though, you had probably adapted pretty well.

A bioregion is like that. The living and non-living inhabitants of a bioregion have learned to adapt to that particular place and to one another. Landform regions, which you learned about in Chapter 2: Our Diverse Regions, are large areas of the Earth defined by the type of landform found there. A **bioregion**, on the other hand, is a part of the Earth's surface identified by its combination of natural and human characteristics. Some bioregions are large and some are small. Regardless of its size, every bioregion combines living species (including humans) and the non-living factors that support them. The result is a part of the Earth's surface with distinct characteristics—an ecological community.

To get a better sense of how these communities work, let's look at three bioregions found in different parts of Canada: tundra, swamp, and woodlot.

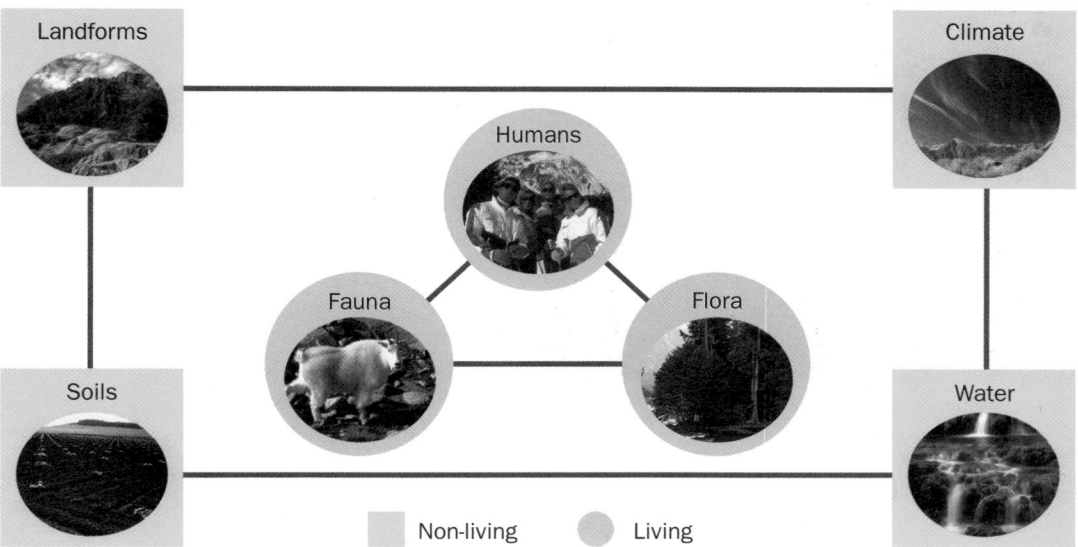

Landforms   Climate

Humans

Fauna   Flora

Soils   Water

◻ Non-living   ● Living

▲ **Figure 3.4:** The parts of a bioregion

1. Examine the flow chart in Figure 3.4. Which region of Canada does it show? How can you tell?

2. What is a bioregion? How can each of the living parts of the bioregion affect the non-living parts? Give examples.

Tundra

In the Arctic, living things must adapt to a harsh climate. Arctic Canada has long, cold winters, resulting in a very short growing season. This is the time when temperatures are warm enough for plants to grow. Most plants don't come up as soon as the snow melts, because they require temperatures of about 6°C. The tundra vegetation you see in the picture in Figure 3.5 is small: shrubs, wildflowers, moss, and lichen—the colourful plant growth found on rocks. These plants can complete their annual growth cycle in a very short time, so they are well suited to the Arctic environment. Caribou herds graze on the sparse vegetation, and then, like the birds, migrate south to forested regions at the end of summer. Human habitation is sparse. Inuit who hunt take advantage of the seasonal changes, hunting caribou in summer and seal in winter.

GeoTrivia #1
During the summer day, the Arctic poppy actually turns its head to follow the sun. The extra heat ripens the seeds more rapidly.

▲ **Figure 3.5:** Arctic tundra in summertime

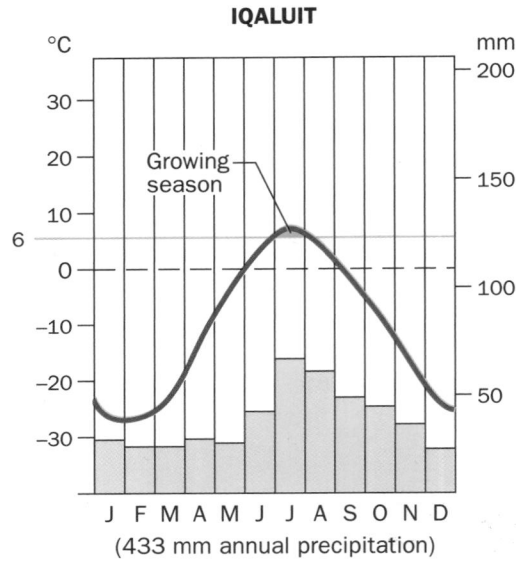

▲ **Figure 3.6:** Climate graph for Iqaluit, Nunavut, showing the growing season

3. Give two examples of how animals might adapt to the long, cold winter of the Arctic tundra.

4. Give two examples of how plants adapt to the short growing season in the Arctic.

5. Look at the climate graph for Iqaluit in Figure 3.6. Identify the maximum and minimum temperatures. Which months are above freezing? Which months are counted as part of the growing season?

Wetlands

In the Canadian Shield region, the rock is usually not very far beneath the surface. Water will not soak through the rock, and is often trapped in low-lying areas. **Wetlands** are areas of swamp and marsh, home to plants that thrive with wet roots. You may think of these areas as useless land, but from an ecological point of view, wetlands are very important. That's because they have **biodiversity**—a great variety of plants and animals. Although few people live in wetlands, many visit to see the wildlife or to hunt or fish.

For example, have you ever seen lily pads floating on water, each with one large white or yellow flower? They actually have a long stem, rooted in the soil at the bottom. Nutrients from the soil travel up the stem to feed the plant. Water plants like these thrive in wetland areas. They also attract moose, another wetland inhabitant, whose long legs and big hooves are well suited to wading into northern swamps to feed on a buffet of water plants.

◀ **Figure 3.7:** A northern wetland

6. Compare the photograph of the tundra (Figure 3.5 on page 56) and that of the wetland (Figure 3.7). Make a list of differences you can see between these two bioregions.

7. What is biodiversity? Suggest reasons why a wetland has more biodiversity than tundra.

Woodlot

European settlers in the Great Lakes–St. Lawrence region cleared the forests to establish farms. But they often left a block of forest at the back of the farm for firewood and maple sugar bush. These woodlots are cool and damp. They are good places to find Ontario's provincial flower, the trillium. They also provide **habitat**, or homes, for deer and raccoon, two species that help themselves to farmers' crops in neighbouring fields by night. Both species are often victims of speeding traffic when their habitat is near roads and highways. Living things in these bioregions must adapt to large human populations.

▲ **Figure 3.8:** A woodlot

8. Look at the picture of a woodlot in Figure 3.8. What are the advantages and the dangers for animals of living at the forest edge?

9. Tundra, wetland, and woodlot are three bioregions. Name another one. See how many living and non-living parts of this bioregion you can describe.

Characteristics of a Bioregion

Bioregions are defined by many characteristics, including their soil type, flora (plants), and fauna (animals).

Soils

Soil is formed from the combination of the landforms, climate, flora, and fauna in a bioregion. First, the forces of erosion (especially water) slowly break up the bedrock into smaller pieces. Then, plant roots begin wedging cracks in the broken rock. Worms and burrowing animals such as chipmunks help by loosening the soil layers and allowing air and water underground.

A side view of soil layers like the one in Figure 3.9 is called a **soil profile**. The upper layer of the soil is usually richer and darker than lower layers. This colour comes from **humus**, the decayed leaves, needles, or grasses that pile up on the surface. Humus is very rich in nutrients, such as nitrogen, that

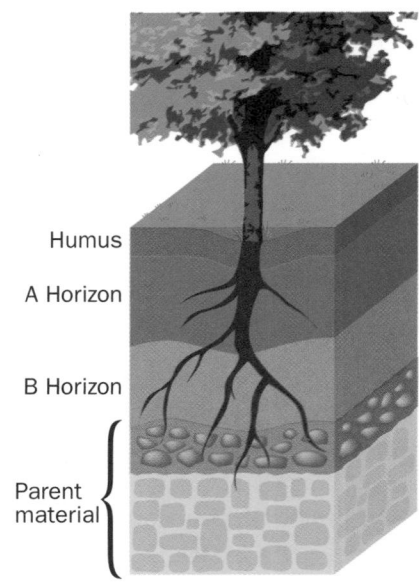

Humus

A Horizon

B Horizon

Parent material

▲ **Figure 3.9:** A soil profile

help plant growth. As water filters downward, some of these nutrients are carried to the lower horizons (layers) to feed deep roots.

Canada's bioregions have different soil profiles because they are formed from different combinations of factors. Thick grassland soils called **chernozems** cover large areas of the Prairie provinces and part of the Northwest Territories. Chernozems range from brown to black in colour, depending on their humus content. Black chernozems are very fertile soils. Forest soils are called **podzols**. They develop in areas that are covered by trees (or once were). The podzolic soils that form under leafy trees, cone-bearing trees, and in mountainous regions all have different profiles. Bog soils are very wet or waterlogged because water doesn't drain well in flat areas.

GeoTrivia #2
Canada's bioregions are similar to those of Russia. That's why we use Russian words like podzol and chernozem to describe our soils.

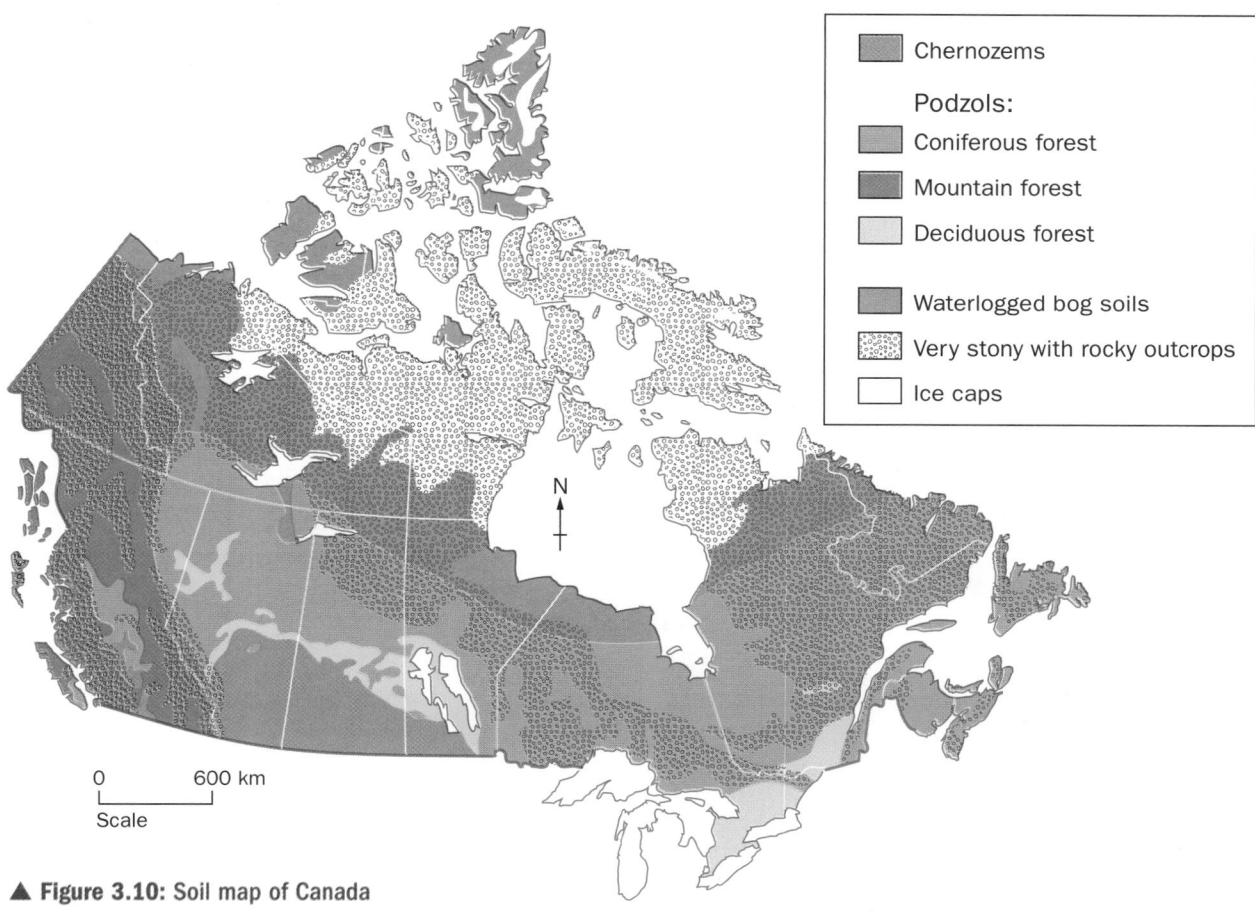

▲ **Figure 3.10:** Soil map of Canada

10. Explain how both the living and non-living parts of the bioregion create its soil layers. Use examples.

11. Describe the characteristics of podzol and chernozem soils. Why are black chernozem soils very fertile?

12. Locate your community on the soil map of Canada. Which type of soil is found in your area? Are there farms in your area? If so, what crops are grown there? If not, what crops are grown in nearby areas with the same type of soil?

Flora

Why won't the inner parts of trees and shrubs grow any leaves or needles? This part of the tree doesn't get enough sunlight. Plant leaves need sunlight to make their own food in a process called photosynthesis. Because they make plant sugar, flora (plants) are called **producers**. Producers are the most important food source for the animals in any bioregion.

Deciduous and Coniferous Trees

There are two basic types of trees. Deciduous trees, such as maple, birch, and ash, lose their leaves in the fall, and have deep root systems to store plant food for winter. For this reason, deciduous trees are found only in warm regions of southern Canada. In the early spring, sap from the roots provides energy until the new buds open. Then, during the summer, the tree stores extra plant sugar in its roots for the following year. The brilliant colours of autumn are caused by chemical changes in the leaves.

Coniferous trees, such as pine and spruce, reproduce by dropping seeds clustered in cones. They can tolerate much colder winters than deciduous trees, and are located farther north. Most conifers have needles, an excellent adaptation to cold. Needles have a small surface area and a tough, waxy coating to help the tree retain heat and moisture. The needles stay on the tree year-round, and begin producing food right away in spring. Since they do not need a deep root system to store food, conifers can grow where soils are thin and rocky. The large conifers that grow in these conditions in British Columbia create mountain forests.

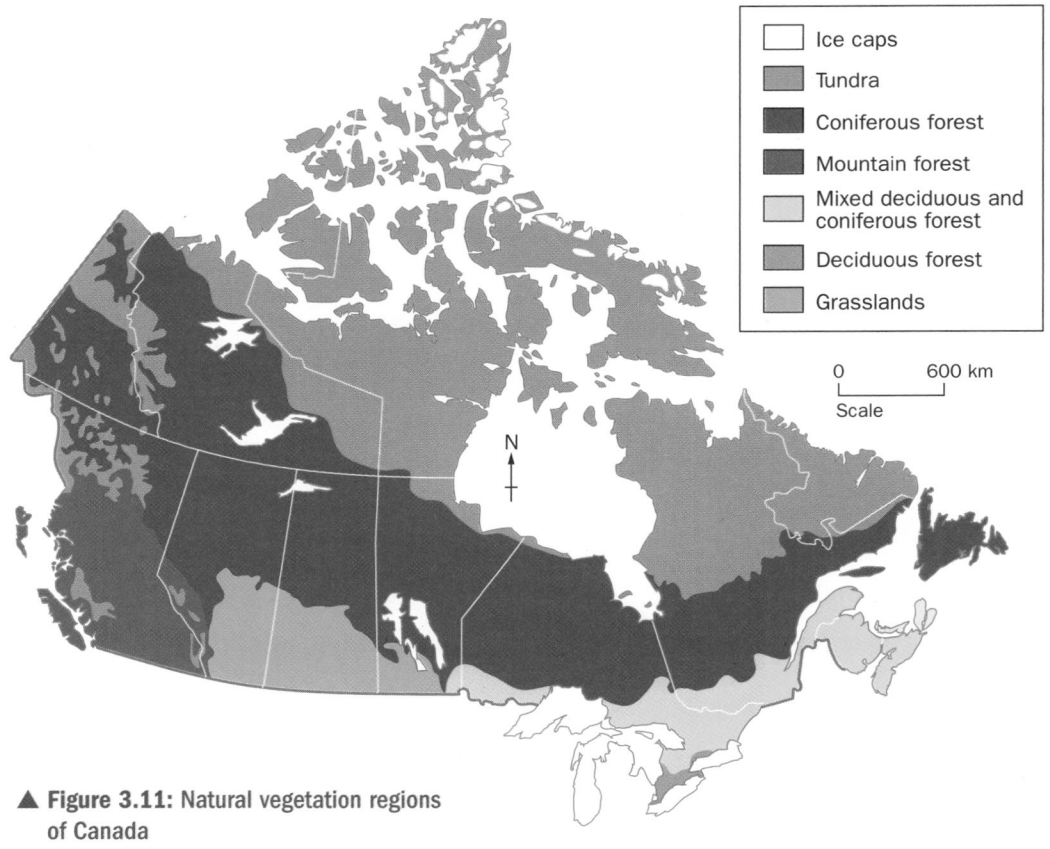

	Ice caps
	Tundra
	Coniferous forest
	Mountain forest
	Mixed deciduous and coniferous forest
	Deciduous forest
	Grasslands

0   600 km
Scale

N

▲ **Figure 3.11:** Natural vegetation regions of Canada

13. Make a chart to compare coniferous and deciduous trees, using these headings.
    a) Type of Foliage
    b) Root System
    c) Adaptation to Cold
    d) Locations in Canada

14. Locate your community on the natural vegetation map of Canada. What type of vegetation is found in your area?

15. Compare the maps of Canadian soil (Figure 3.10, page 59) and natural vegetation (Figure 3.11, page 60). List three similarities between the two maps.

Fauna

All fauna (animals) are called **consumers**, because they can't make their own food and must consume plants or one another to survive. Consumers that rely on plant fibres and seeds are herbivores. Flesh-eating carnivores must hunt prey to survive. Flora and fauna together form a balanced ecological community. This food chain creates an upward flow of energy, from producers to herbivores to carnivores.

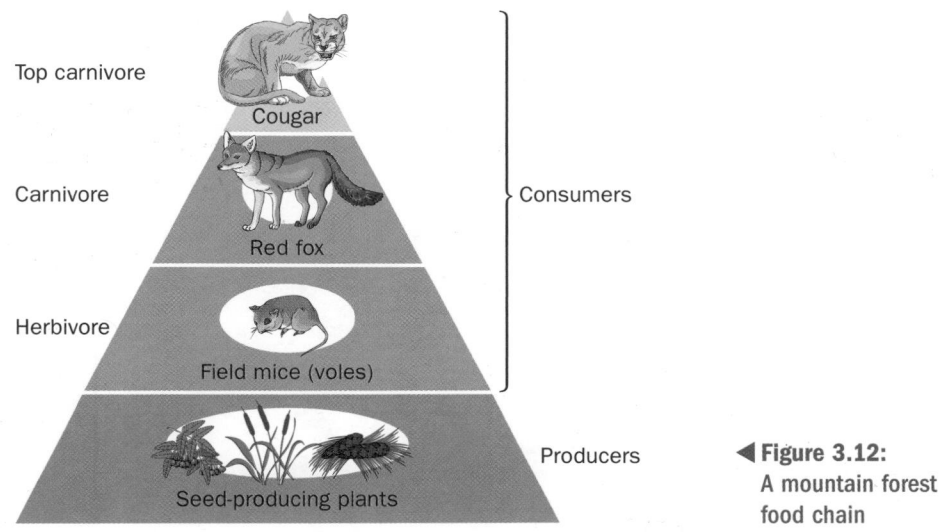

Top carnivore — Cougar

Carnivore — Red fox

Herbivore — Field mice (voles)

Producers — Seed-producing plants

Consumers

◀ **Figure 3.12:** A mountain forest food chain

16. Make a list of eight herbivores living in Canada. Then, try to identify a carnivore (other than humans) that preys on each animal.

17. Look at the food chain diagram in Figure 3.12. Why are there more species lower in the food chain than higher up?

18. Create a food chain diagram like the one in Figure 3.12 for a local bioregion. Include both plants and animals, and use arrows to show the movement of energy from producers to consumers.

Did you ever figure out what those creatures at the beginning of the chapter had in common? They are all endangered because their habitat is being threatened by humans. The Banff Springs snail gets crunched by hikers, and its habitat gets destroyed when people bathe in the hot springs. The burrowing owl is losing its habitat to development. And leatherback turtles are scared away from their nests by sunbathers and other curious humans. When humans disturb one of the inhabitants of a bioregion, they disturb the balance in the whole ecological community.

CASE STUDY

GREAT LAKES ALVARS: LAND OF EXTREMES

There are bioregions called alvars in the Great Lakes region that are found nowhere else except a small part of northern Europe. Physically, an **alvar** is an area of flat limestone bedrock with the soil removed by forces of erosion. These areas are most common in the Bruce Peninsula and on Manitoulin Island, both in Ontario. They are difficult environments for living things, so they have few trees or large animals. But these regions also hold surprises; for example, some of the small, twisted trees clinging to bare rock are up to 500 years old!

Together, the living and non-living parts of an alvar create a balanced ecological community. Plants and animals in alvars are specially adapted to survive the harsh conditions in these bioregions. In fact, "Only the strong survive" would be an appropriate alvar motto.

Non-living Characteristics

Limestone is a sedimentary rock that was once under water, so alvars are good places to find ancient sea fossils. All the softer materials have worn away, leaving the hard limestone exposed, usually with little or no soil cover. Because limestone slowly dissolves in water, alvar surfaces often have little hollows that look like Swiss cheese along with loose pieces of worn or broken rock.

▲ **Figure 3.13:** Wide view of an alvar surface

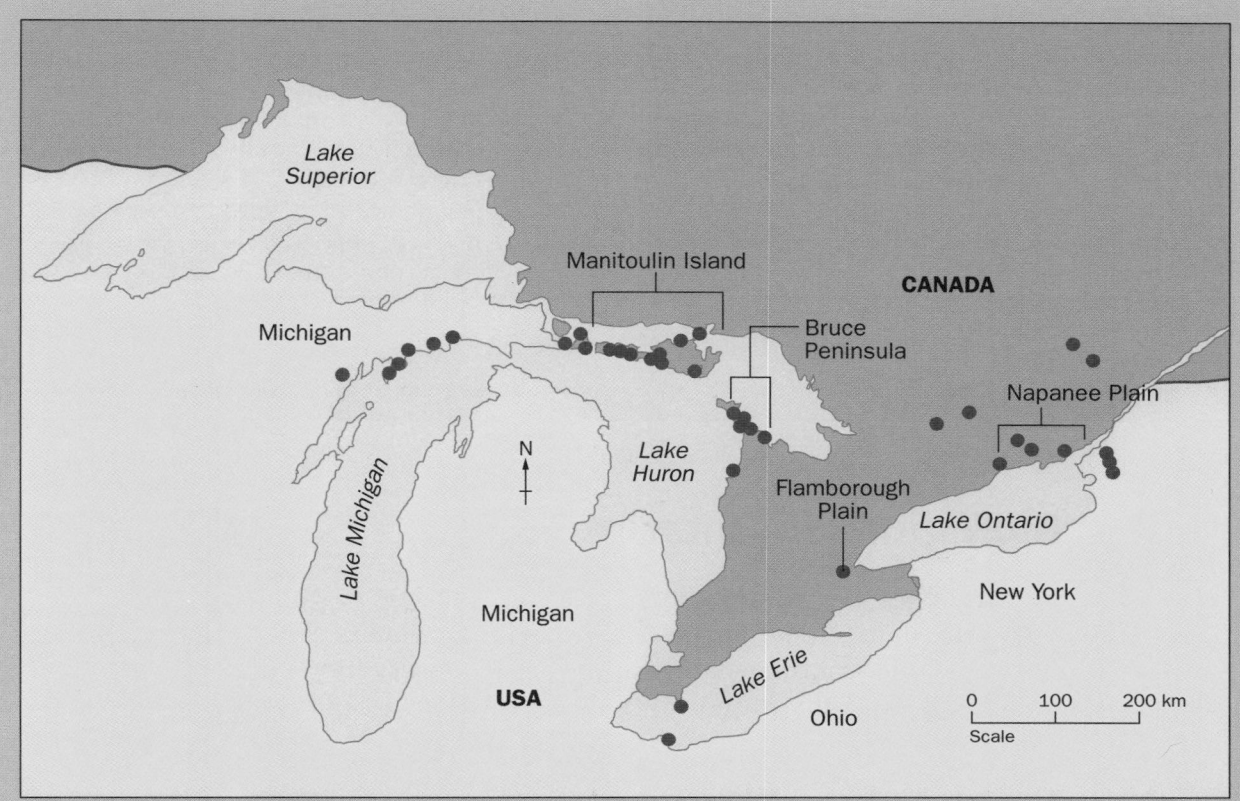

▲ **Figure 3.14:** Distribution of alvars in North America

Alvars are either really wet or really dry. In the spring when the snow melts, a lot of water collects in the rock hollows—too much for most plants. But when these little pools evaporate in hot weather, the alvar is parched. The bare rock causes extremes in temperature as well. Summer temperatures on the rock surface can be as high as 43°C, while in winter, winds blowing across the unprotected surface make it feel much colder than more protected areas.

Living Characteristics

The vegetation of bare-rock alvars is like that of the Arctic tundra. Moss, lichen, and wildflowers grow in the tiny pockets of soil left in hollows or cracks. In some cases, dwarf shrubs and slow-growing old cedar trees can survive. Alvars with a thin soil layer can support natural grasslands.

Insect- and seed-eaters, such as frogs, birds, and field mice, are near the bottom of the food chain, while big reptiles, such as the Massassauga rattler, are at the top. These snakes adapt to extreme temperatures by taking shelter under rocks in summer and hibernating in winter.

▲ **Figure 3.15:** Plants growing on an alvar surface

Humans threaten fragile alvar environments in several ways. Limestone quarries, forest clearing, and cattle grazing are all economic threats. Shoreline cottages and off-road vehicles also pose problems for alvars. The alvar is a harsh but rare environment that must be protected.

1. Use the photographs in Figure 3.13 on page 62 and Figure 3.15 on page 63 to list five characteristics of an alvar bioregion.

2. Use Figure 3.4 on page 55 to make an alvar bioregion chart showing how non-living and living parts of the region affect one another.
3. Do you think an alvar would be a good place for recreational activities? What types of visitors might an alvar attract?
4. Use a road map or an atlas to find out how far you live from the nearest alvar bioregion. Have you ever seen one of these areas?

Bioregions in Ontario

In many parts of Ontario, bioregions are suffering. Population growth, especially in the Great Lakes–St. Lawrence Lowlands region, has put many pressures on local plants and animals. But conservation efforts are also underway. As you will see, all of us can play a part in preserving our bioregions.

Threats to Local Bioregions

Ontario has changed a great deal over the course of the twentieth century. Population pressures, industry, and development now threaten many local bioregions. For example, less than 30 per cent of Ontario's original wetland areas still exist. More than 200 species living in the province are endangered, and some animals are already extinct. The eastern cougar shown in Figure 3.16 is considered extremely endangered and possibly extinct.

GeoTrivia #3
The Eastern Massassauga Rattlesnake is on the Canadian List of Endangered Species, protected by law even outside of provincial and national park areas.

▲ **Figure 3.16:** The eastern cougar

19. Brainstorm a list of three different reasons that could account for the possible extinction of the eastern cougar. Which of your reasons are natural, and which are caused by humans?

20. List three positive steps you can take to help preserve endangered species.

Much of the Ontario countryside has been carved into farm-sized pieces, and many of these are being divided into smaller lots for homes. This situation is called **fragmentation**. When patches of forest, wetland, and other natural environments become too small, they can't support a healthy variety of flora or fauna. This is because competition for territory becomes too intense. For example, a woodlot smaller than 300 metres square won't have many songbirds because it does not offer enough protection. Larger, more aggressive birds can penetrate a small forest, steal songbirds' eggs, and occupy their nests.

Small wooded areas in towns and cities are great places to hike and walk dogs, or for kids to play. But this human intrusion can also fragment the forest and even destroy it. Visitors enjoying the woods may unknowingly trample small trees, and their footsteps may compact the soil so that less water reaches tree roots. Gradually, the forest is divided into shrinking patches of mature trees, with few young replacement trees. Forest animals are also affected. Their habitat, territory, and food supply are lost, and many species will not survive or reproduce. Unless people stay on a few clearly marked paths, these small forest bioregions are threatened systems.

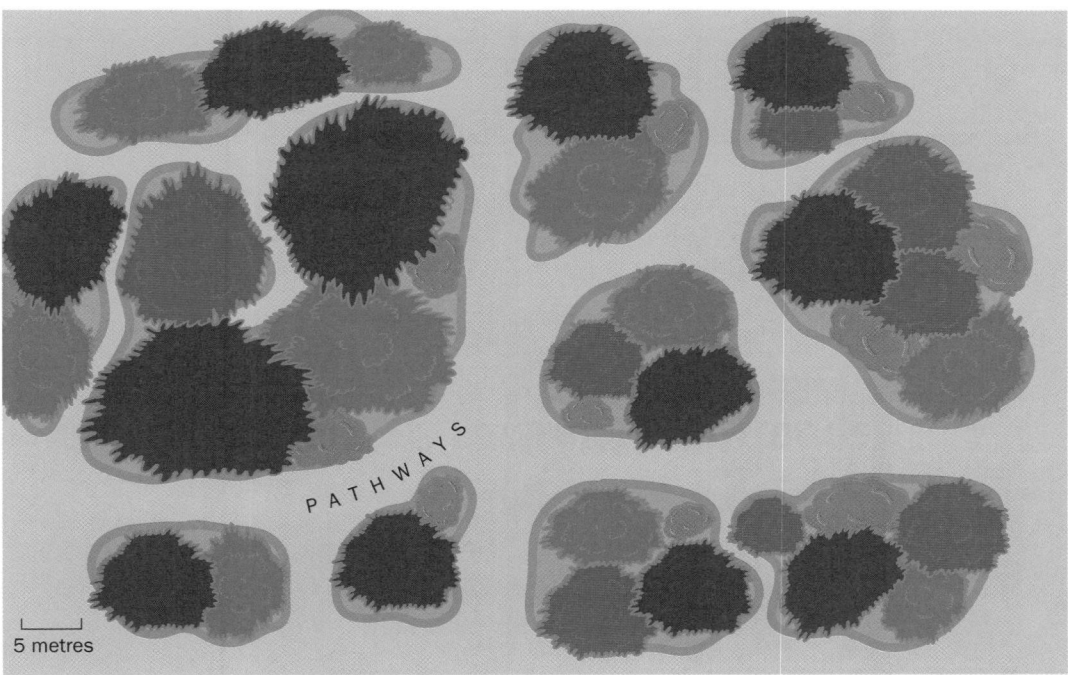

PATHWAYS

5 metres

▲ **Figure 3.17:** A fragmented small forest

21. Make a list of bioregion problems caused by people intruding on a small forest. Are any forests or wooded parks in your area facing such problems? Explain.

22. What do you think should be done to stop fragmentation of bioregions?

GeoGames

Motocross Challenge!

Wetland and woodlot areas near a city have been bought up by a big corporation. The company wants to use the land to build a large motocross course, with spectator areas. Unhappy local citizens try to block the plan. Can the bioregion be saved? Play this board game to find out.

Purpose:

To become familiar with issues regarding human use of bioregions

Supplies:

One die; a marker for each player (2–4 players can play)

Method:

A. Roll to decide the order of play.

B. On your turn, roll the die once and move your marker the number of spaces shown.

C. When you land on a square with a vine, move up. If you get tire tracks, move down. You need the exact number to land on the final square to win the game.

Wrap-Up:

Could the motocross go ahead without destroying the natural balance of the bioregion? Explain your position.

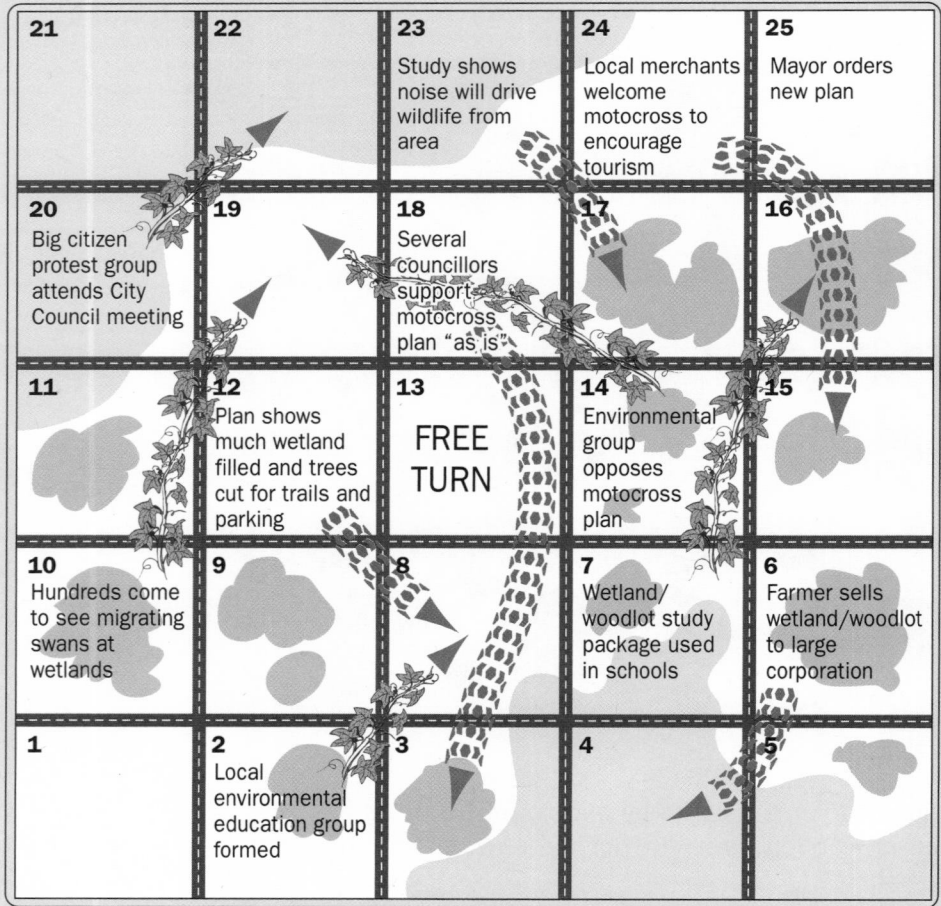

◄ **Figure 3.18:**
Motocross Challenge

Natural Corridors

One way to protect local bioregions is by creating **natural corridors**—wide passageways of trees, grassland, or water. These interconnected areas allow animals to avoid roads and open spaces. Natural corridors are like school hallways. They let you move from room to room without the risks of climbing through the windows!

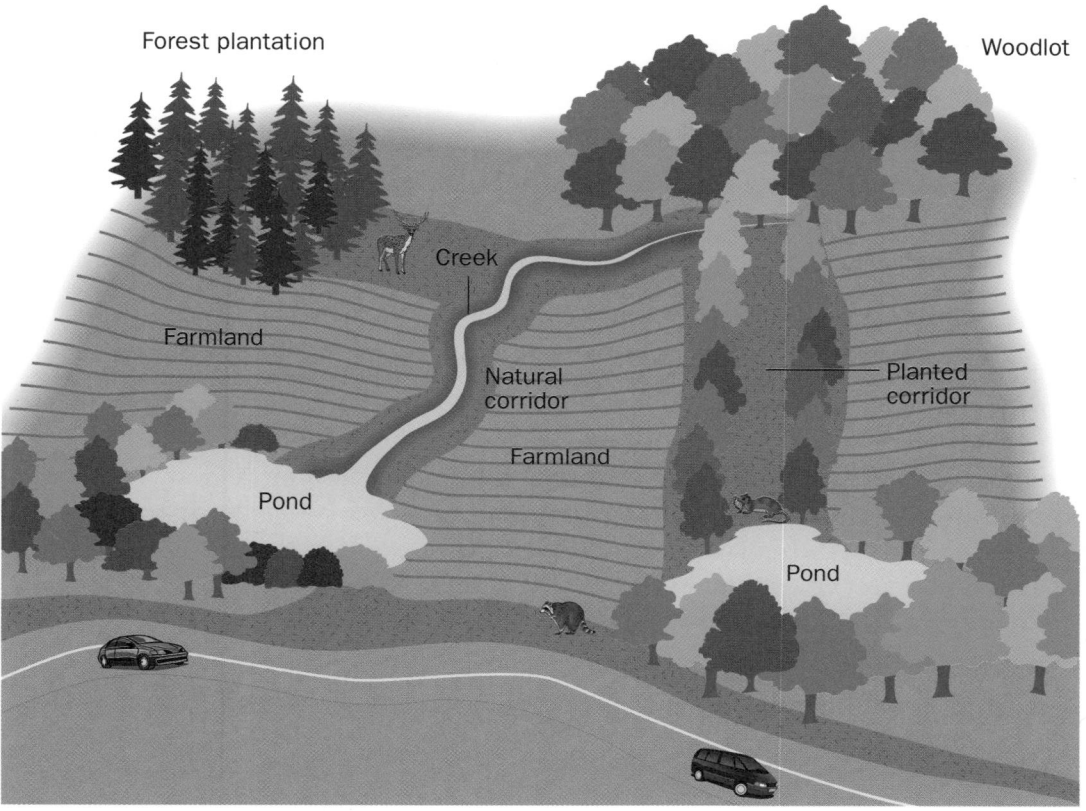

▲ **Figure 3.19:** A natural corridor

23. In your own words, explain "natural corridors." Suggest three to five specific advantages of natural corridors for animals. Why do river valleys make good natural corridors?

24. Look at a road map of Northern Ontario. Name examples of provincial parks that provide natural corridors along rivers. Should motorboats be allowed in these parks? Explain your opinion.

Investigating and Restoring Local Bioregions

We have already seen how people can disturb the natural systems found in a bioregion. But we can also improve local bioregions, if we decide they are important enough. Most places already have environmental groups eager for volunteers to help them with projects. Here are some ways of improving your local bioregion.

- **Pick up garbage.** Garbage ruins the quality of a bioregion. For example, animals become entangled in six-pack plastic packaging, and fish cannot spawn (lay eggs) in littered streams. Good cleanup projects include shallow creeks, roadside ditches, and popular walking routes.
- **Make and mark trails.** People will usually stay on a good trail covered with woodchips that keep it dry in wet weather. Use old logs to block off pathways that are carving up the forest.
- **Plant trees and bushes.** Encourage birds by planting bushes with plenty of berries and seeds. Give small animals hiding places in a small, open forest by planting conifers along the outer edges.

25. Make a list of bioregions found in your neighbourhood or community. Are they fragmented from one another, or linked by natural corridors? Give examples.

26. If you were preparing a media campaign to convince people your age to respect the local environment, what slogan would you use? What arguments would convince your peers to help restore their local bioregion?

Conclusion

Wetlands, forests, tundra, alvars, woodlots—Canada has a stunning variety of bioregions, each of which is home to living things that have adapted to the particular environmental conditions found there. In this chapter, you read about the living and non-living elements that make up a bioregion. You also found out how the delicate balance of a bioregion can be easily disturbed by human activities. Industry, housing development, and even recreational activities can all pose threats to habitat. We need to be sensitive to the way natural systems work when we interact with these areas.

Wrap It Up

1. List the four non-living and the three living parts of a bioregion. Explain how they are connected, using examples from the text or your own experience.

2. Detail four different types of changes that are threatening bioregions in Ontario.

3. Provincial parks must try to protect their bioregion from the many visitors who come to enjoy it. Create a poster promoting bioregion protection in provincial parks. Include a catchy slogan, as well as suggestions for visitors to help prevent destruction of natural areas in the park.

4. Visit a local bioregion and take notes on the flora and fauna in the area. Also look for evidence of how humans interact with the natural systems (garbage, pathways, etc.). Make a drawing or other graphic representation of the area. Label your work to show each of the seven living and non-living elements listed in Figure 3.4 on page 55.

5. Research ways to improve the balance between people and nature in a local bioregion. Would any of the projects suggested in this chapter restore the area? What other types of projects are being undertaken by local environmental groups?

Chapter 4

INTERACTIONS IN CANADA'S ECOZONES

Going to Extremes

Extreme sports are very popular. You may even have tried some yourself—and lived to tell about it! Extreme sports are dangerous, but that is part of the adrenaline rush that players are after. For example, in helicopter skiing you're whisked to the top of a mountain and dropped in full skiing gear onto the peak. Only a helicopter can get skiers to the unmarked runs high above the limit of the ski lifts. In this sport, you have to cope with both steep slopes and deep snow. In whitewater rafting, another extreme sport, you hurtle down steep river slopes and get tumbled about in fast-flowing, rough water.

▲ **Figure 4.1:** Many extreme sports rely on natural systems.

1. What is meant by "extreme sports"? List three extreme sports that take place in natural environments.

2. How are landforms, climate, or river systems important to these activities?

3. Where in Canada would the environmental conditions be best for each of the activities that you named? Give your reasons.

4. How might extreme sports be important to nearby communities? Give examples.

Words to Know
ecozone
biome
boundary
transition zone
permafrost
smog
old-growth forest
drainage basin

In this chapter, you will
- **identify how and why Canada has been divided into ecozones**
- **understand the issues and problems of selected Canadian ecozones**
- **recognize that many Canadian artists paint landscapes typical of these ecozones**
- **evaluate the possibility of a career as a landscape designer**

What Is an Ecozone?

Extreme sports like helicopter skiing and whitewater rafting require certain environmental conditions. These are found only in particular kinds of ecozones.

An **ecozone** is a large geographical area in which human activities interact with the natural world. In that sense, an ecozone is just like a bioregion but much larger. A bioregion might be a five-hectare swamp, whereas an ecozone can include all the swamps, bog, forests, and meadows of a mixed forest.

The ecozone approach was developed by Canadian geographers to help them identify environmental issues and find solutions. Canada is currently divided into fifteen terrestrial ecozones and five marine ecozones, each having an area of at least 200 000 square kilometres (see pages 74–75). By studying ecozones, geographers are able to find out what effect people are having on landforms, climate, soil, river systems, natural vegetation, and wildlife. In short, ecozones are used to measure the ecological health of a region.

5. Explain "ecozone" in your own words. Why did geographers create the idea?

6. Use the map in Figure 4.7 on pages 74–75 to find the ecozone you live in.

An Ecozone Is Not a Biome

As large as ecozones are in scale, they are smaller than biomes. A **biome** is a scientific term used to describe a very large area with a typical community of plants and animals. Biomes are organized into zones based on plants that provide food and habitat for certain animal species. Unlike ecozones, biomes do not consider the impact of human population and activities on Nature. Canada's biomes are much like those of Europe and Asia at similar latitudes north of the Equator. These biomes are part of a global system. They are shaped by factors such as temperature, precipitation, and landforms.

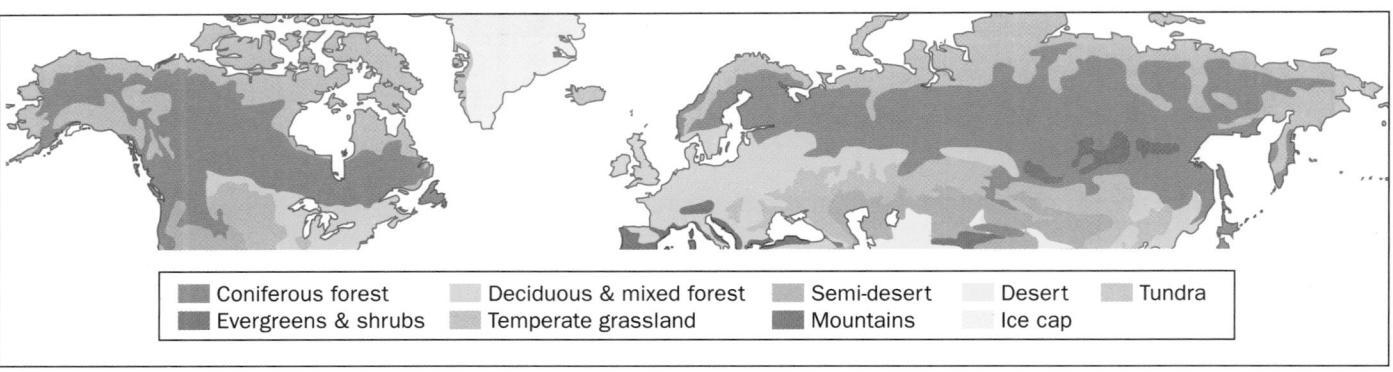

Coniferous forest   Deciduous & mixed forest   Semi-desert   Desert   Tundra
Evergreens & shrubs   Temperate grassland   Mountains   Ice cap

▲ **Figure 4.2:** Natural vegetation biomes in the Northern Hemisphere, from 40°N to 75°N

7. What is a biome? List two differences between a biome and an ecozone.

8. a) Which Canadian biomes are also found in Europe and Asia?
   b) Which biomes of Europe and Asia are *not* found in Canada?

9. Identify two reasons why biomes change as you go north.

Ecozone Boundaries

A **boundary** is a line that divides one area from another. A good example is a line on a map that shows the political division between countries. But the boundaries between ecozones are not exact because physical and human characteristics can be shared by neighbouring ecozones.

Ecozones combine many different physical and human characteristics at once: landforms, climate, soils, flora, fauna, and human activities. The distribution of each characteristic on the Earth's surface is not identical. This is why a huge area like the Canadian Shield is actually shared by four ecozones. It is important to remember, therefore, that ecozone boundary lines on a map are not as exact as they look.

GeoTrivia #1
With global warming, plant and animal species will be able to survive farther north. Geographers will need to draw new boundaries for Canada's ecozones.

▲ **Figure 4.3a:** Is nature like this?

▲ **Figure 4.3b:** Or is nature like this?

10. Look at the diagrams above. Does nature change like Figure 4.3a or like Figure 4.3b? Explain, giving reasons for your choice.

11. Why is it more difficult to draw ecozone boundaries than it is to draw national boundaries?

Transition Zones

It is easy to identify a blue hat from a purple hat. Or is it? There are so many shades in between! Ecozones are like this too. It is easier to see the typical characteristics of an ecozone in the centre of the region. But out along the edges, it is a lot more difficult. For example, in Figure 4.3a, locations A and C are in completely different ecozones. Location B, however, has similarities to both A and C. This is called a **transition zone**, an area in which the characteristics of one region gradually blend into the next. Location B contains a mixture of natural vegetation, soils, and wildlife found in the two neighbouring regions. Although maps show sharp lines between ecozones, there are actually transition zones of shared characteristics between ecozones.

12. Try dividing students in your class into groups based on postal code or hair colour. What difficulties, if any, did you experience? What was different about making these two groupings?

13. Define "transition zone" in your own words. Use another example, such as a city, to explain the idea.

CASE STUDY

THE HUDSON PLAIN ECOZONE

A profile across Canada resembles a giant lopsided saucer. The raised outer rim represents folded mountains, while the centre hollow, where a cup would sit, is flooded by Hudson Bay. South and west of Hudson Bay is a flat, featureless ecozone called the Hudson Plain. During the ice ages, a larger and deeper Hudson Bay covered this ecozone. It remains soggy today, partly because the ground below the northern Hudson Plain is permanently frozen. This **permafrost** prevents water from filtering through the soil, causing it to pool in swamps at the surface.

1. Locate the Hudson Plain ecozone using the map in Figure 4.7 on pages 74–75. Which provinces or territories are within its boundaries?

2. Draw a side-view diagram of a saucer, assuming a cup would sit in the centre. Label these features: Hudson Bay, Appalachian Mountains, and Western Cordillera. Title the diagram.

3. Why is the Hudson Plain a "soggy" region?

4. Suggest three reasons why this ecozone has a low population.

Many large rivers cross the Hudson Plain on their path down into Hudson Bay. Two centuries ago, during the fur trade, the Hudson's Bay Company built forts and trading posts at the mouths of these rivers to collect furs from Aboriginal hunters for shipment to Britain. Today, the Cree, who live in permanent settlements at these same locations, make up much of the ecozone's population.

Physical Characteristics		Human Characteristics	
Landforms	plains	Population	10 000
Climate	cold winters, mild summers dry all year	Population density	0.03 per km²
Soils	bog sand and gravel	Portion of Canada's population	less than 1%
Natural vegetation	wetlands tundra	Major communities	Manitoba: Churchill Ontario: Moosonee
Wildlife	polar bear black bear moose Arctic fox	Economic activities	hunting trapping recreation/tourism cargo handling
Waters	Bays: Hudson, James Rivers: Nelson, Albany, Severn	Major parks	Wapusk National Park Polar Bear Provincial Park

Source: Environment Canada, Canadian Council on Ecological Areas.

▲ **Figure 4.4:** Hudson Plain characteristics

Churchill, Manitoba, is the largest community in the Hudson Plain ecozone. It has an ocean port that is connected to Prairie wheat farms by railroad. In recent years, national and provincial parks have been created to protect the Hudson Plain polar bears. "Tundra buggy" tours out of Churchill bring tourists into close but safe contact with these dangerous carnivores.

Figure 4.5: Tundra buggy tour ▶

▼ **Figure 4.6:** Churchill, Manitoba, 1:250 000 scale

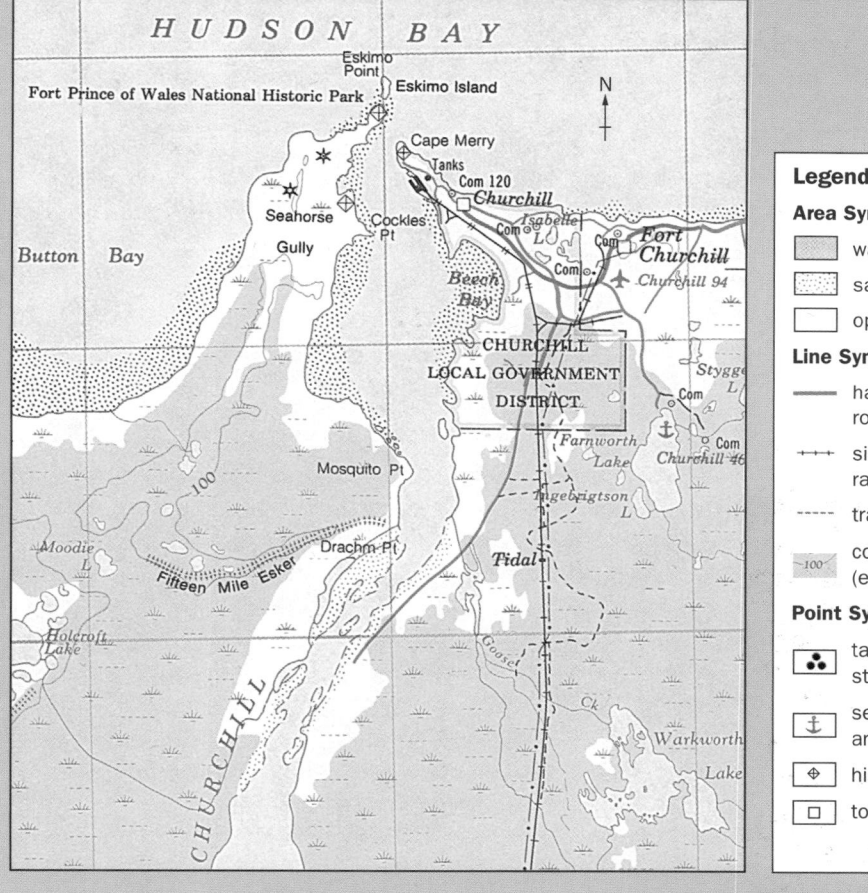

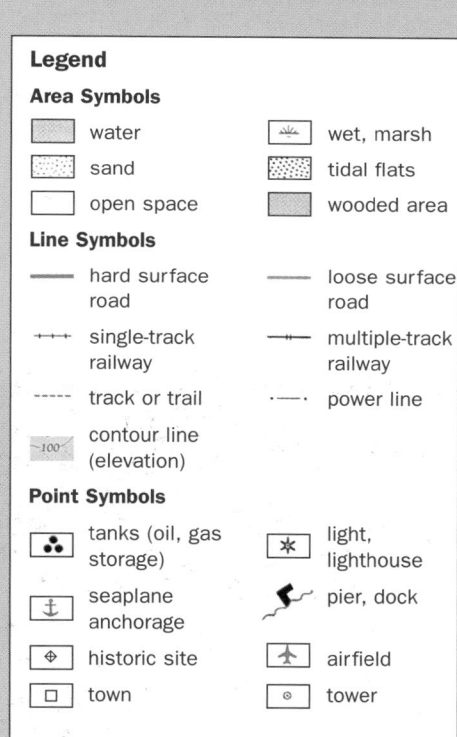

Legend

Area Symbols

▨	water	⩊	wet, marsh
▦	sand	▩	tidal flats
☐	open space	▨	wooded area

Line Symbols

——	hard surface road	——	loose surface road
+—+—+	single-track railway	++—++	multiple-track railway
-----	track or trail	·—·—·	power line
~100~	contour line (elevation)		

Point Symbols

⁘	tanks (oil, gas storage)	✳	light, lighthouse
⚓	seaplane anchorage	↰	pier, dock
⊕	historic site	✈	airfield
☐	town	⊙	tower

5. Find map evidence for the following statements.
   a) The Hudson Plain is flat and wet.
   b) The Hudson Plain has a small population.
6. Find map evidence to prove the following statements.
   a) Churchill has an ocean harbour.
   b) Churchill is connected to Prairie wheat farms.

7. Sketch a neat, labelled map of the area around Hudson Bay that shows the following.
   • Waters: Hudson Bay, Churchill River
   • Places: Churchill, Fort Churchill, Fort Prince of Wales
   • Communications: railroad, airport, seaplane base (anchor symbol), navigation lights
   • Bioregion: swampy woods

Ecozones of Canada

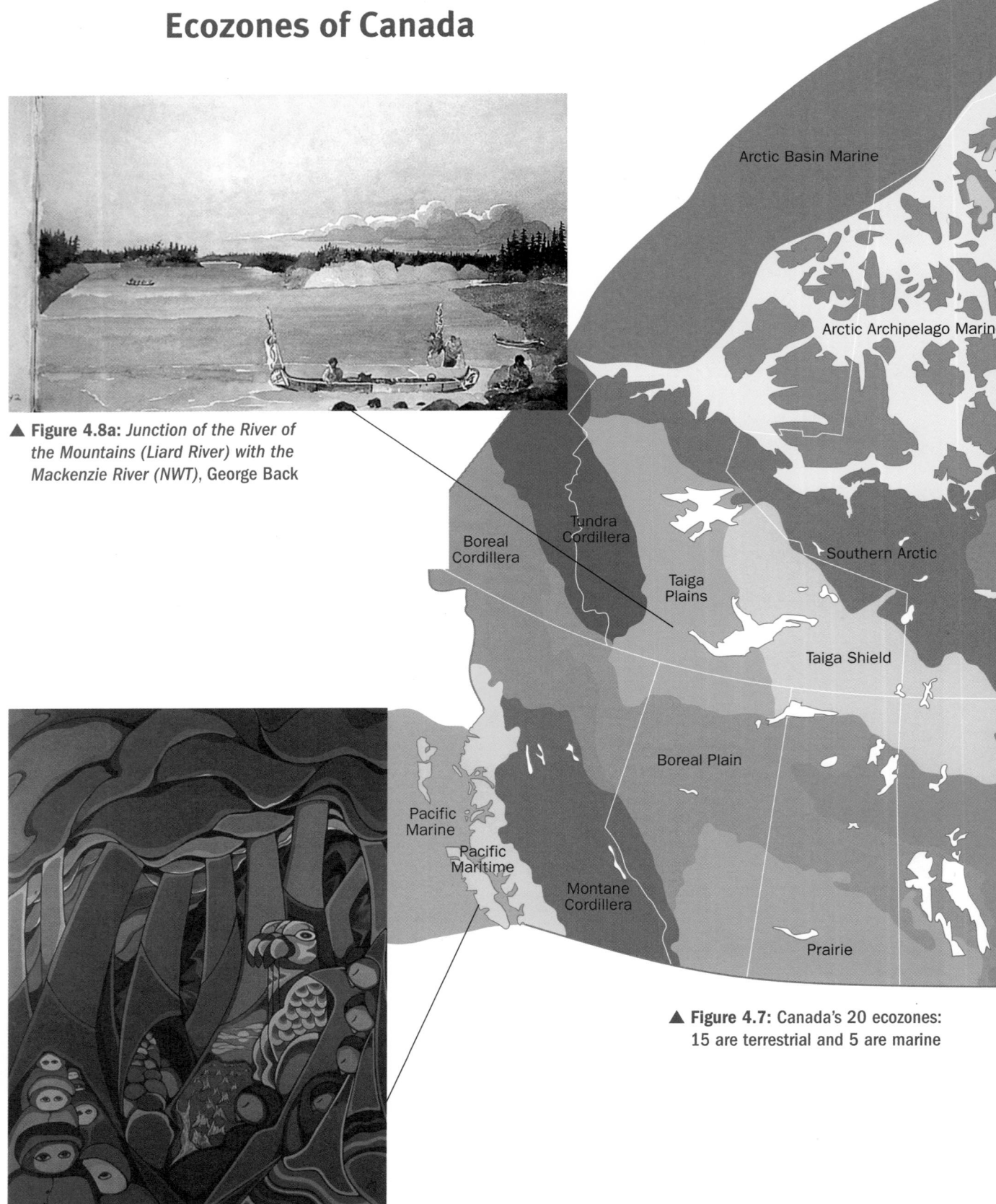

▲ **Figure 4.8a:** *Junction of the River of the Mountains (Liard River) with the Mackenzie River (NWT)*, George Back

▲ **Figure 4.8b:** *Meares Island*, Daphne Odjig

Arctic Basin Marine

Arctic Archipelago Marine

Tundra Cordillera

Boreal Cordillera

Taiga Plains

Southern Arctic

Taiga Shield

Pacific Marine

Pacific Maritime

Boreal Plain

Montane Cordillera

Prairie

▲ **Figure 4.7:** Canada's 20 ecozones: 15 are terrestrial and 5 are marine

14. Which of the landscape paintings do you like most? Why? What ecozone does it show?

15. Which ecozone does *Laurentian Hills* (Figure 4.8c) show? Use it to record the landforms and vegetation of this ecozone.

16. Which ecozone does Figure 4.8d, *Spring, Lower Canada (Maples, Early Spring)* show? Use it to record the landforms and vegetation of this ecozone.

17. Discuss with a classmate why you think landscape painting has been popular with Canadian artists and the public alike.

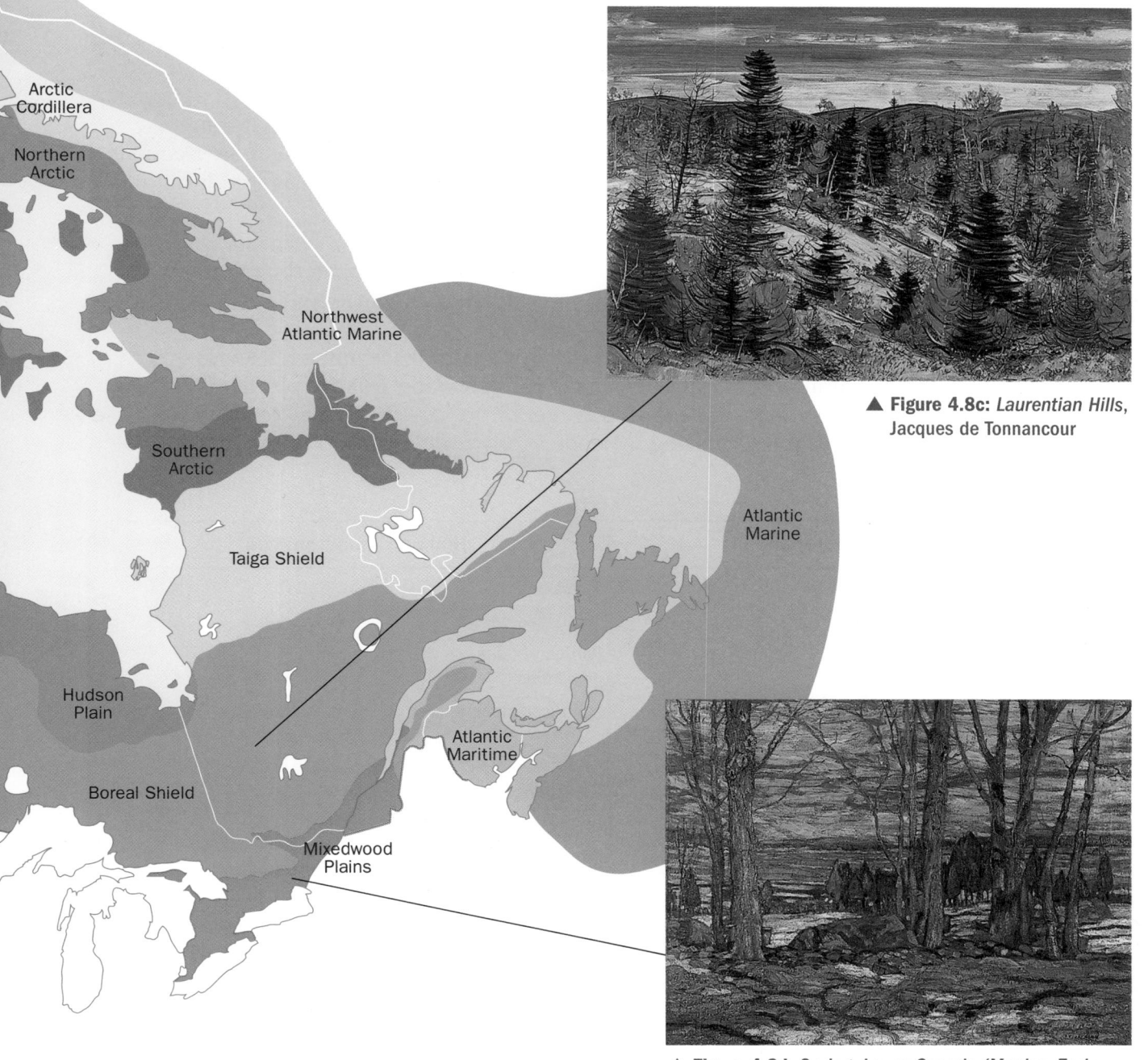

▲ **Figure 4.8c:** *Laurentian Hills,* Jacques de Tonnancour

▲ **Figure 4.8d:** *Spring, Lower Canada (Maples, Early Spring),* A.Y. Jackson

Issues in Selected Ecozones

As we have seen, Canada is made up of twenty ecozones. In this section of the chapter, we'll focus on issues affecting four of them: Mixedwood Plains, Boreal Shield, Pacific Maritime, and Taiga Plains. The people and activities in these four regions have had a strong and often negative impact on the natural environment.

Mixedwood Plains Ecozone

GeoTrivia #2
In 2000, Toronto began exporting waste to landfill sites in Michigan. Even garbage is covered by the North American Free Trade Agreement (NAFTA)!

The Mixedwood Plains ecozone, a narrow band that stretches across southern central Canada, is densely populated and heavily industrialized. This makes pollution a pressing issue. Air pollution caused by **smog** (industrial and automotive *smoke* mixed with *fog* or humidity) is dangerous for people, especially those with breathing problems. This is why Environment Canada issues smog advisories. These advisories become more frequent during the summer months, when intense sunshine, increased humidity, and limited rainfall make the problem worse.

Land pollution is another issue affecting this ecozone, especially as major cities find it harder and harder to dispose of their garbage safely. Toronto, for example, presently trucks much of its waste to landfill sites in other parts of the ecozone and beyond.

Water pollution is also a hazard. For example, seventeen Canadian locations along the Great Lakes have serious water-quality problems caused by industrial waste and urban sewage. Efforts are underway to clean up these locations, but more funding is needed for the measures to be successful.

Physical Characteristics		**Human Characteristics**	
Landforms	plains hills	Population	14 630 000
		Population density	96.4 per km²
Climate	cool to cold winters, mild to hot summers moderate precipitation	Portion of Canada's population	52%
Soils	podzols clay soils glacial moraine	Major communities	Ontario: Ottawa, Toronto, Mississauga, Hamilton Quebec: Montreal, Quebec City
Natural vegetation	deciduous forest mixed forest	Economic activities	agriculture manufacturing business and finance tourism/recreation
Wildlife	white-tailed deer red fox raccoon		
		Major parks	Point Pelee National Park Bruce Peninsula National Park Sandbanks Provincial Park
Waters	Lakes: Huron, Erie, Ontario Rivers: St. Lawrence, Grand		

Source: Environment Canada, Canadian Council on Ecological Areas.

▲ **Figure 4.9:** Mixedwood Plains characteristics

18. Locate the Mixedwood Plains ecozone using the map in Figure 4.7 on pages 74–75. Describe its general size and location in Canada.

19. Explain the three major issues affecting the Mixedwood Plains ecozone.

Boreal Shield Ecozone

A number of important environmental issues are affecting the Boreal Shield ecozone as well. This huge area stretches from Saskatchewan all the way to Newfoundland. It is fragile, with thin soil cover in most areas, and is changing rapidly because of human activities.

Physical Characteristics		Human Characteristics	
Landforms	plains uplands	Population	2 711 000
		Population density	1.6 per km²
Climate	cold winters warm to hot summers moderate precipitation	Portion of Canada's population	10%
Soils	podzols clay belts some rock outcrops	Major communities	Ontario: Sudbury, Thunder Bay Quebec: Chicoutimi-Jonquiere Newfoundland: St. John's
Natural vegetation	coniferous forest mixed forest	Economic activities	forestry mining tourism agriculture hunting/trapping
Wildlife	moose black bear		
Waters	Lakes: Superior, Georgian Bay Rivers: Nelson, Ottawa, Saguenay	Major parks	Gros Morne National Park Algonquin Provincial Park

Source: Environment Canada, Canadian Council on Ecological Areas.

▲ **Figure 4.10:** Boreal Shield characteristics

Several problems affecting this ecozone are getting worse, especially in the more developed eastern half of the Boreal Shield.

- Acid rain from industries and power plants in the United States and Canada is affecting lakes, soil, and forests.

- Toxic chemicals are building in river systems that are used for electric power dams, pulp and paper mills, and metal refining.

- Forests are changing, not only because of clear-cutting, but also because a limited number of tree species are being replanted.

These problems are causing the ecozone's biodiversity—the variety of plant and animal species in the region—to decline.

20. The Boreal Shield stretches across five provinces. Use the map in Figure 4.7 on pages 74–75 to name them.

21. What is biodiversity? Choose two issues affecting the Boreal Shield ecozone. Explain how each one reduces biodiversity.

22. How does the Boreal Shield's location north of the Mixedwood Plains cause more pressure on the Shield environment?

Pacific Maritime Ecozone

The Pacific Maritime ecozone is rich in natural resources. The use (and misuse) of these resources is a very important issue in this region. For example, overfishing by Canadian and American boats has hurt commercial salmon fishing. Pollution in the rivers has also reduced salmon populations because it has affected the spawning beds, where the fish lay their eggs.

The forest industry is the most important economic activity in this ecozone, but there is bitter disagreement about some logging practices used by big international companies. Clear-cutting, as shown in Figure 4.11, is a cheap way to cut timber, but it has destroyed whole ecological communities. Environmentalists regularly protest this practice, particularly when it involves **old-growth forest**—the original trees in an ecozone.

◀ **Figure 4.11:** A clear-cut mountainside in British Columbia

23. Give examples to show that this ecozone is "rich in natural resources."

24. Sketch and then label a diagram of Figure 4.11 to show the following.
    a) uncut forests   c) logging roads
    b) clear-cut area   d) small mountain-stream valleys

25. Why should there be national and provincial/territorial parks in each ecozone? Use information about the Pacific Maritime ecozone in your answer.

Taiga Plains Ecozone

The Taiga Plains, an ecozone in northwest Canada, has harsh conditions. It contained only 22 000 people at the time of the 1996 Census, which was less than 1 per cent of Canada's population. The ecozone's large Dene Nation population relies on tourism, and traditional hunting and fishing. Most live in small communities along the Mackenzie River. This river system is one of the longest in the world, providing a natural corridor and transportation route.

In Chapter 2: Our Diverse Regions, you learned that there are oil and natural gas deposits in the Arctic. During the late 1970s, the Dene people rejected a plan to build a pipeline along the Mackenzie River to carry Arctic natural gas south. Since then, the Canadian government has signed Aboriginal land treaties in the ecozone. This action has led to divided opinions about a pipeline. Some Aboriginal leaders worry about potential environmental and cultural problems, while others welcome the jobs that a natural gas pipeline would bring to the region.

GeoTrivia #3
Taiga means "land of little sticks" in Russian. The word refers to the open stands of small coniferous trees that grow in this cold ecozone.

26. Locate the Taiga Plains ecozone using the map in Figure 4.7 on pages 74–75. Describe its location in Canada. Which provinces and territories are part of this ecozone?

27. Summarize the two opinions on the pipeline issue presented in the paragraph on the previous page. Explain what you think should be done to make sure a fair decision is reached.

Rivers and other bodies of water are an important natural system in Canada's ecozones, and the Taiga Plains ecozone contains some of the largest. A **drainage basin** is the area of land that is drained by river systems. Canada has five drainage basins, each named for the body of water that receives the run-off: Arctic, Pacific, Hudson Bay, Atlantic, and Gulf of Mexico.

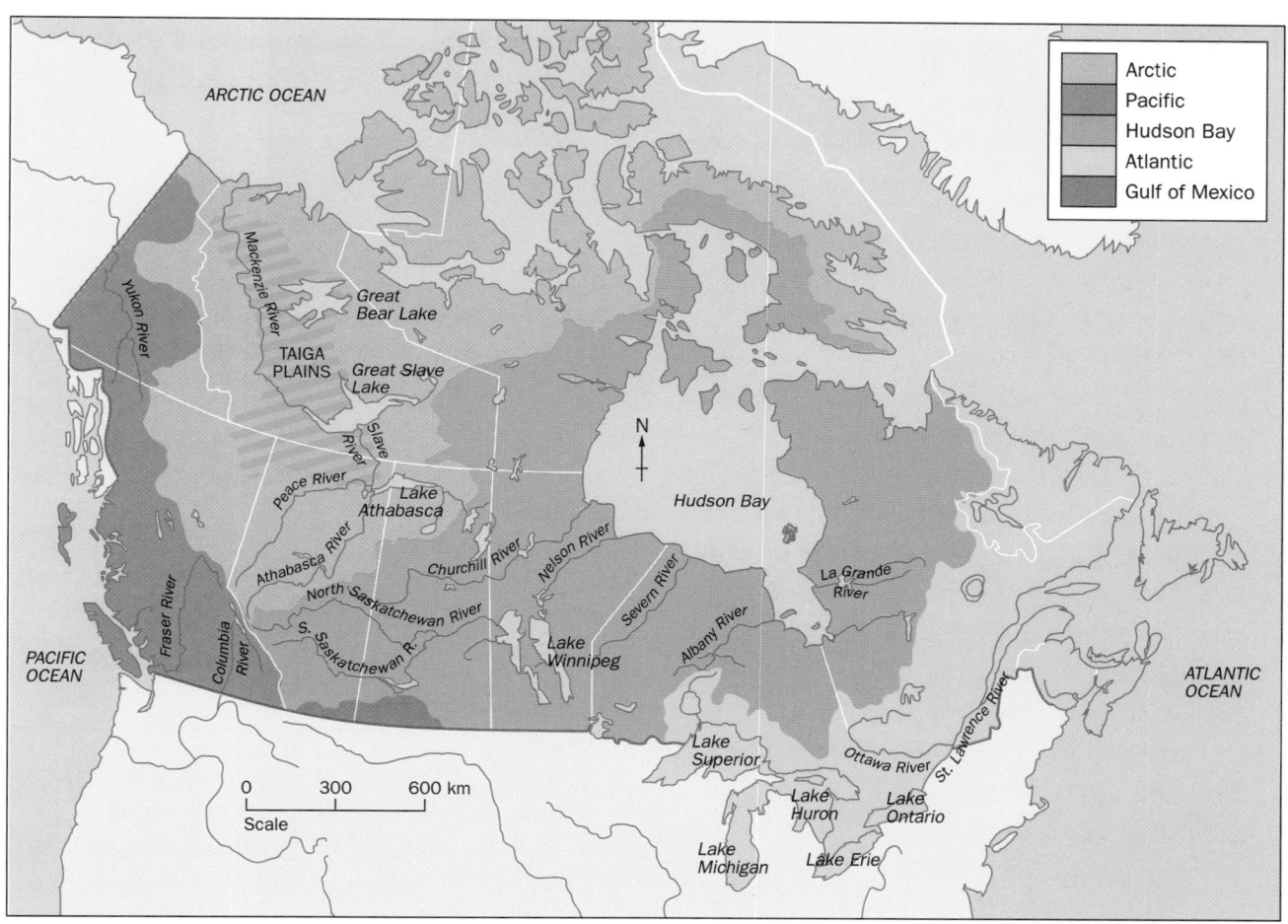

▲ **Figure 4.12:** Canada's five drainage basins, with major lakes and rivers

28. Use Figure 4.12 to list the large rivers and lakes of the Taiga Plains ecozone. Why are they so important to the region?

29. What is a drainage basin? Use the map to rank the Canadian basins from largest to smallest.

30. Look at Figure 4.12. Which major river and lake is nearest to your community? Name the drainage basin in which you live.

GEO CAREERS   LANDSCAPE DESIGNER

Name: Ida Karelsen
High School: Lambton Christian High School, Sarnia, Ontario
Job Title: Landscape Designer

Ecozones and landscape designers have something in common. They both combine physical and human characteristics to make an area unique. Although ecozone landscapes are not always very scenic, the mini-ecozones created by landscape designers must always be attractive. By combining soil, plants, walkways, ponds, and even fish, landscape designers create beautiful outdoor spaces. Just ask Ida Karelsen, landscape designer for DeGroot's Nurseries in Sarnia, Ontario.

"I always loved to draw. In fact, my three favourite subjects in high school were art, geography, and biology—all part of landscape design. My parents operated a commercial bedding plant greenhouse, where I used to help out. So, I was always around plants. I took the three-year Landscape Design diploma course at Fanshawe College in London, Ontario. The best part of the program was the weekly studio classes, where I worked on different types of design projects. It was so practical for the work that I do now."

Ida's landscape designs start with a visit to the customer's home or business. There, she discusses the client's request and carefully checks the sun, wind, and soil characteristics at the location. Before leaving, she takes measurements of the area to use on the design. A landscape plan is developed back at the office, using her rough sketches and a computer design program called LANDCADD. Then, the plan is run through an estimating program to calculate the costs of all materials and labour. Finally, the customer either accepts the plan or requests changes.

What I like about my work: *"The landscapers carry out the actual construction job, and I really enjoy seeing the results. Of course, it is especially nice when customers are very happy with what I've designed for them."*

1. What reasons did Ida give for her career choice?
2. List the technical and personal skills she needs to do this job well.
3. Do you find her career interesting? Give your reasons.

Conclusion

Ecozones are unique regions that combine physical and human characteristics. By studying these large-scale areas, geographers can find out what impact human activities have on plant and animal populations. Serious issues threaten the balance between natural and human systems in every Canadian ecozone. But by treating both terrestrial and marine ecosystems wisely and with respect, Canadians can make sure our ecozones have a future.

Wrap It Up

1. What is an ecozone? What specific characteristics does it include? Use an atlas or the Internet to make a chart for the Taiga Plains or Pacific Maritime ecozone, just like those used for the other ecozones examined in this chapter. (See pages 76 and 77.)

2. a) All of Ontario's ecozones are examined in this chapter. Identify them using the map in Figure 4.7 on pages 74–75. Then, compare the landforms, climate, natural vegetation, wildlife, population densities, and economic activities of two of them. Use a chart like the one at the bottom of the page.

   b) Work with the class to create one master chart on the board, comparing all three Ontario ecozones.

   c) What major changes would you notice if you travelled from southern Ontario to Hudson Bay?

3. Use the Parks Canada Web site to plan a visit to one of the national parks in one of the five ecozones featured in this chapter. Prepare a map of the park, and describe some outdoor activities that you would participate in during your visit.

4. The work of Aboriginal artists often reflects close ties to the land, as Daphne Odjig's *Meares Island* shows (see Figure 4.8b, page 74). Research the work of another Aboriginal artist, such as Bill Reid, Norval Morrisseau, or Allen Sapp. How does the artist express the link between the land and its people?

5. Make a poster, bulletin-board display, or computerized presentation program based on a tourism theme, such as "See Canada's Great Outdoors." Use pictures of Canadian landscapes taken from old magazines, calendars, CD-ROMs, or the Internet. Organize your display based on different regions of Canada.

Characteristics	Ecozone:	Ecozone:
Landforms		
Climate		
Natural vegetation		
Wildlife		
Population densities		
Economic activities		

Unit 1 Performance Task

NORTHERN ONTARIO RECREATION

The area north of Lake Huron is one of the most popular recreational regions in Canada. Some people, including several First Nations,

▲ **Figure 1:** Summer or winter, people enjoy outdoor recreation.

make this region their home. Others boost the population when they visit.

Let's assume that the superintendent of Marten River Provincial Park, near North Bay, has hired you as a tourism consultant. He wants you to decide what to develop in the area: either a canoe route or a snowmobile route. Your task will be to investigate the climate and characteristics of the region by interpreting photographs, maps, and climate information. Then, you will plan a canoe or snowmobile route through the region using a topographic map. You will submit your findings in a report to the Park Superintendent.

There are three parts to this assignment. Your teacher will collect each one as you complete it. Good luck.

Assignment **1**: Interpreting the Road Map

Start your trip to the North Bay–Sudbury area by completing these questions using the road map in Figure 2 on the facing page. See Figure 11 on page 11 if you need to refer to a road map legend.

1. Name four large provincial parks in this area.

2. Use place names to identify two metallic minerals found in the Sudbury area.

3. Give the alpha-numeric grid locations for the following places.
   a) North Bay
   b) South River Airfield
   c) Lady Evelyn–Smoothwater Provincial Park
   d) Marten River Provincial Park

4. What are the following compass directions?
   a) from Lady Evelyn–Smoothwater Provincial Park to North Bay
   b) from South River to Cobalt

5. Find the following road distances in kilometres.
   a) from North Bay northeast to Temiscaming
   b) from North Bay north on Highways 11 and 11B to the Cobalt OPP station

6. a) Which landform region of Canada is shown on this map? List three different pieces of evidence from the map to support your choice.
   b) Record two important differences between the northern and southern halves of the map.

7. From map evidence, explain reasons why this area is so popular with tourists.

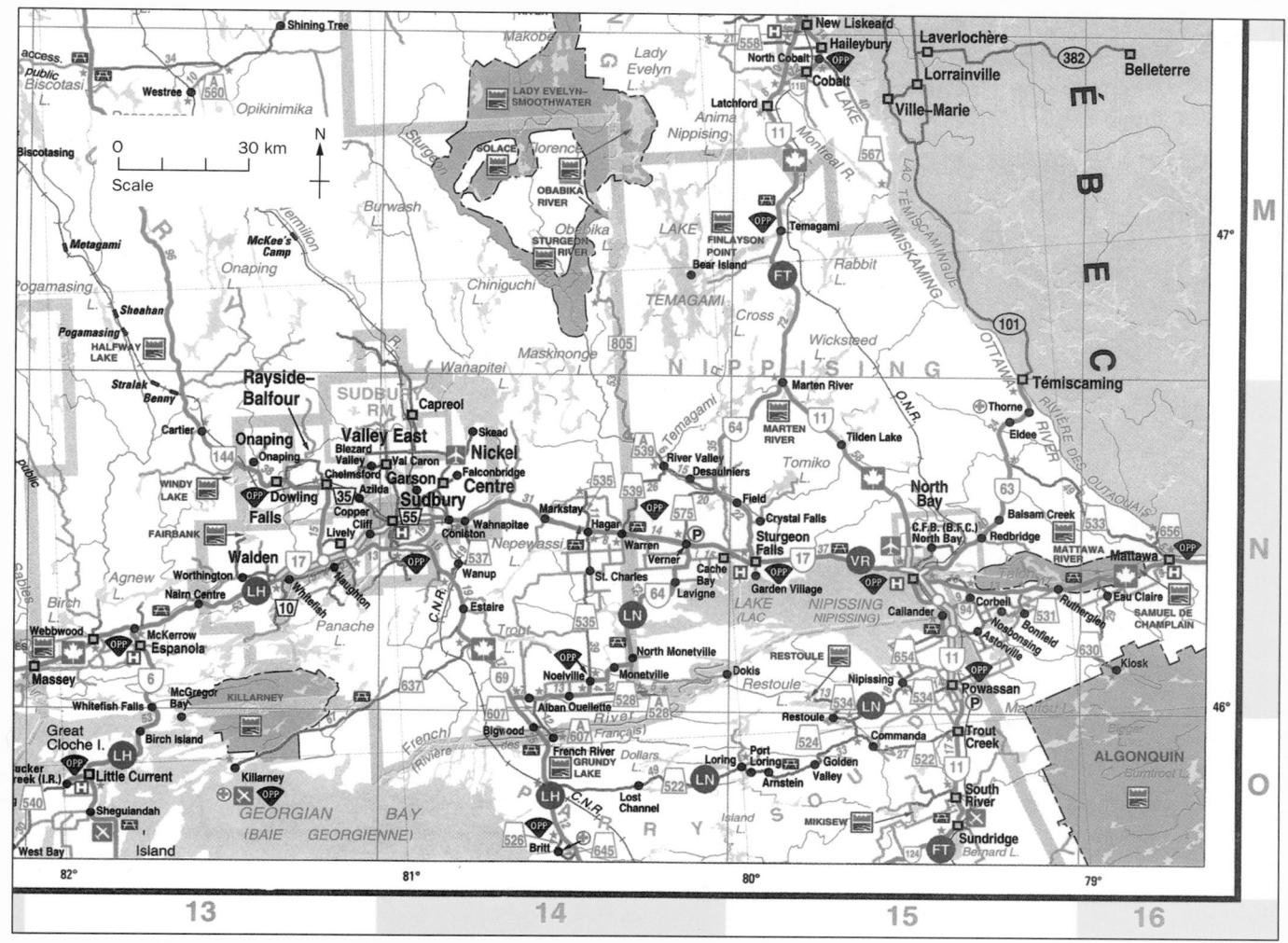

▲ **Figure 2:** An important tourist region in Northern Ontario

Assignment **2**: Assessing the Characteristics of the Region

Interpret the following information about climate and natural vegetation in the North Bay–Sudbury area. This activity will help you understand factors that affect summer and winter recreation in the region.

Month	J	F	M	A	M	J	J	A	S	O	N	D
Temp. (°C)	-12	-10	-4	4	11	17	20	18	14	8	1	-9
Precip. (mm)	60	51	56	64	66	85	98	81	105	82	80	71

Source: Environment Canada Web, <http://www.msc-smc.ec.gc.ca/climate>, May 2002.

▲ **Figure 3:** Climatic statistics for North Bay, Ontario, elevation 369 m

1. Neatly draw and label a standard climate graph for North Bay. Shade the precipitation bars blue and the temperature line red. (If you wish, refer to the climate graph GeoSkills feature on pages 34–35.)

▲ **Figure 4:** A photograph from the area shown on the map

2. a) Draw and label the growing season on your graph.
   b) How long is North Bay's growing season?

3. Use Figure 3 to identify North Bay's maximum and minimum average monthly temperatures.

4. Use your graph to describe North Bay's temperature and precipitation characteristics in one paragraph.

5. What type of trees do you see in the photograph in Figure 4? Use the correct name.

6. What is the name of this natural vegetation region?

7. Identify the large animal and the type of bioregion in which it is shown.

8. What name is given to the ecozone shown in this photograph?

9. Are the climate and other characteristics of the North Bay–Sudbury region suitable for canoeing and snowmobiling? Explain your reasoning.

Assignment 3: Planning a Canoe or Snowmobile Route

Use the topographic map in Figure 5 on the facing page to demonstrate your map-reading skills. Then, follow the instructions to plan your recreational route through the beautiful game preserve in the Marten Lake–Wicksteed Lake area. (If you wish, refer to the topographic map in the GeoSkills feature on pages 46–48.)

A. Demonstrating Your Map-Reading Skills
1. What human or natural features are found at these locations?
   a) 942722
   b) 965737
   c) 915760
   d) 965726
   e) 916717

2. What are the compass directions for the following?
   a) from Wicksteed Lake Dam to the motel
   b) from the motel to Marten River Provincial Park
   c) from Beach Lake to Finlayson Lake

3. a) What is the straight-line distance in kilometres from Wicksteed Lake Dam to the motel by Frenchman's Bay?
   b) What is the road distance in kilometres along Highway 11, from the motel by Frenchman's Bay to the Marten River Provincial Park entrance?

B. Creating Your Own Map
4. Decide whether you would like to recommend a snowmobile route or a canoe route. Then, use an outline map of the area shown on the topographical map to complete *one* of the following options.

Option One: Canoe Route. Starting from Marten River Provincial Park, draw a summer canoe loop route through the map area. (A loop route ends where it begins.) Show the direction of travel, and mark any places where you make a short portage (carry the canoes) from one body of water to another. Recommend three or four good locations along the route where parks officials should locate campsites near the water for canoeists. Complete your map with the appropriate colours, legend, title, and frame.

Option Two: Snowmobile Route. Starting from Marten River Provincial Park, draw a winter snowmobile loop route through the map area. Recommend three or four good locations along the route where parks officials should locate storm shelters with firewood.

5. Prepare a report to the Marten River Provincial Park Superintendent. In it, summarize the plans you have made. Why would canoeists or snowmobilers enjoy the route you chose? Explain the advantages for each of the spots you picked for campsites or winter shelters.

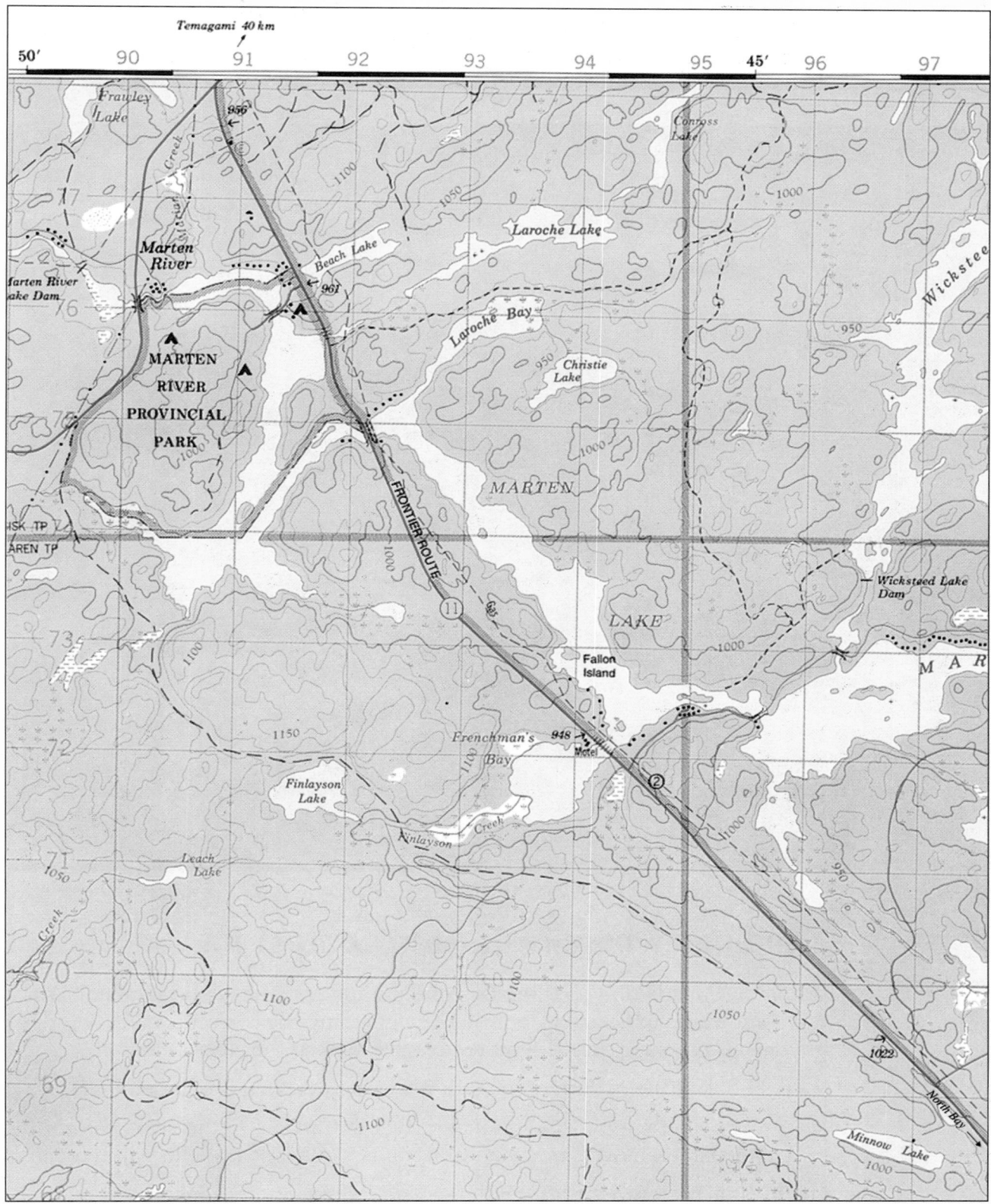

▲ **Figure 5:** The Marten River–Wicksteed Lake area in Northern Ontario (scale 1:50 000)

CANADA'S HUMAN SYSTEMS

The Somewhere in Canada Contest #2

Where in Canada do you think this photograph might have been taken? Win the Somewhere in Canada Contest #2 by guessing the correct answer before anyone else in your class. If you're not sure, look at the clues below.

CLUE 1 Look at the pattern of long, thin rectangles. What are these?

CLUE 2 The photograph shows a major river in Canada. In the years before airplanes, most European immigrants to Canada travelled up this river.

CLUE 3 This river flows through the second largest city in Canada.

CLUE 4 This river flows into the Atlantic Ocean.

CLUE 5 This river flows mostly through one province, and passes that province's capital city.

What Will You Study in This Unit?

As you looked at the photograph on the previous page, you probably noticed that long, narrow farms run back from the river. This land has been farmed continuously for the past four centuries. The outline of these farm fields has changed little, from the time when the first plough dug into the soil, all the way to the present. You can see that the mark we leave on the land can last a very long time.

The impact of people on the land area of Canada has been and is very important. So is the influence of the land on the Canadian people: the main reason people settled on those farms by the river was to take advantage of fertile land. To understand Canada more fully, we need to find out more about who lives in this country. Who are Canadians? What are our origins and our cultures? What patterns have we left on the land? How have Aboriginal peoples adapted to the arrival of others in their traditional territories? How do they maintain their culture today? By learning more about the human systems in Canada, we can better understand Canadian geography as a whole.

In this unit, you will explore the settled areas of Canada including its farmland, villages, and cities. Although Canada began as a rural nation, most Canadians now live in cities. You will learn about our relationships with the natural environment, the rural environment, and the urban environment. Then you will wrap up the unit by making a scrapbook about Canadian urban places and their problems.

In this unit, you will

- recognize the cultural diversity of the people who live in Canada and the ways that people preserve their cultures

- show that you understand important characteristics of our population

- compare rural and urban patterns in different regions of Canada

- understand how people and the environment are linked in rural and urban areas of Canada

For a challenge, try the Unit 2 GIS activity, "Settlement Sleuth," on pages 338–339.

Chapter 5

ANALYZING POPULATION PATTERNS

Take a Mini-Census!

▲ **Figure 5.1:** Sorting returns from the 2001 Census

Every five years, the Canadian government conducts a **census**, or survey of the population. The Census gives a picture of many aspects of Canada's population. Many of the statistics in this chapter come from the Census. To conduct a mini-census of your class, answer the following questions on a sheet of paper. Do not put your name on the sheet. Afterwards, collect all the answers and follow the instructions below.

1. How many people live in your household?

2. What is the age of each person?

3. How many people in your household were born outside Canada?

-   To calculate the size of the average household in your class, add up all the answers to Question 1, and divide this number by the number of people surveyed. For example, if 25 people in your class answered the census questions, and the total for Question 1 was 75, then on average there are three people per household (75 ÷ 25 = 3). The average household in Canada has 2.6 people.

-   The **median** age of a population is the age at which half the people are younger and half are older. To find the median age for your mini-census, write down all the ages recorded in Question 2 from highest to lowest. Count along the ages until you are half-way along the sequence. This is the median age. The median age of Canadians is 37.6.

-   Finally, add up all the answers to Question 3 to find out how many people were born outside Canada. Then, divide this number by the total number of people in all households (from Question 1). Multiply this number by 100 to find out what percentage of people were born outside Canada. For example, if your total for Question 3 was 25, and the total for Question 1 was 75, your answer would be one-third (25 ÷ 75 = 1/3 or 0.3), or 30% (0.3 × 100 = 30%). The percentage of Canadians who were born outside Canada is 37%.

Write down your general conclusions. In what ways is your class typically Canadian? In what ways is it not? Congratulations! You are on your way to being a census taker.

In this chapter, you will

- find out about population density and population growth
- look at the age distribution of the Canadian population now and in the future
- compare Aboriginal population trends with those for the whole country
- learn how to draw a population pyramid
- examine the impact of migration on population

Words to Know

census
median
population density
reserve
age distribution
population pyramid
dependency load
migration
migrant
immigrant
emigrant
internal migrant

▲ **Figure 5.2:** Two regions of Canada with very different population densities

Population Density

How many people would you say live in a downtown area of a major city that is about six blocks long by six blocks wide? What about in the same-sized area in the countryside? or near the Arctic Circle?

Geographers refer to the number of people per square kilometre as the **population density** of an area. Although Canada is the second-largest country in the world, it has a relatively small population. That means its population density is low compared with that of many other countries. In fact, even if the entire population lived in the province of Ontario, our population density would be about the same as that of the United States. If we all decided to move to Newfoundland and Labrador, we'd be about as crowded as Greece or Spain!

To understand the information in Figure 5.3 on the next page, first read the headings on each of the four columns. Read *down* the columns to compare the total population, area, or population density of different countries. Read *across* the rows to find all the data for a particular country.

Country	Area (km²)	Population	Density (people/km²)
Australia	7 686 900	19 358 000	2.5
Canada	9 976 100	31 082 000*	3.1
China	9 597 000	1 273 111 000	132.6
Greece	131 900	10 624 000	80.5
Iceland	103 000	278 000	2.7
Japan	377 800	126 772 000	335.5
Netherlands	41 500	15 981 000	385.0
Russia	17 075 200	145 470 000	8.5
Saudi Arabia	1 960 600	22 757 000	11.6
Spain	504 800	40 038 000	79.3
Sri Lanka	65 600	19 409 000	295.9
Sweden	449 900	8 875 000	19.7
United Kingdom	244 800	59 648 000	243.6
United States	9 629 100	278 059 000	28.9
Zimbabwe	390 600	11 365 000	29.0

* Canadian population statistics based on Statistics Canada, 2001 Census figures.
Sources: US Census Bureau, International Database and *The World Factbook, 2000.*

▲ **Figure 5.3:** Population density for Canada and selected countries, 2001 estimates

GeoTrivia #1
Canada has the second-lowest population density (after Australia) of any industrialized nation in the world.

1. Look down the fourth column on the table. Which country has the highest population density? Which has the lowest? Where does Canada rank in terms of population density compared with other countries on the table?

2. Look across the rows. How many countries have a lower population than Canada but a higher population density? What might account for this difference?

3. Do you think the population density in your area is more or less than three people per square kilometre? What might account for Canada's low overall population density?

Calculating Population Density

To find the population density of an area, divide the number of people by the area (in square kilometres). Canada's total area is close to 10 million km², and its total population in 2001 was about 31 million.

$$\frac{31\ 000\ 000\ \text{people}}{10\ 000\ 000\ \text{km}^2} = 3.1 \text{ people per square kilometre}$$

4. a) The population of India is 1 000 000 000 (1 billion), and its total area is 3 287 590 km². Use the formula above to calculate India's population density.
   b) What problems might a high population density like India's cause?
   c) What problems might a low population density like Canada's create?

Canadian Population Patterns

Canada's overall population density may be low, but some parts of the country are much more crowded than others. If you've ever been in downtown Montreal at rush hour, that's easy to believe! In fact, more than half of us live in large cities with dense populations. The area in and around Toronto alone has a population of almost five million people.

You may be surprised to know that this pattern has been around for only about eighty years. In the 1920s, many farm workers moved to cities to find work in the factories. As well, a huge wave of immigrants entered Canada at this time. Most settled in the cities, where work was easier to find. That's when Canada became an urban nation.

Another interesting population pattern in Canada is the split between north and south. By far, the majority of Canadians live in southern Canada. The strip from Windsor, Ontario, to Quebec City, Quebec, is known as the Windsor–Quebec corridor. This area is only about 1100 km long, but it contains nearly half the total population of the country! By contrast, Yukon, Northwest Territories, and Nunavut have about 39 per cent of Canada's total land. But they contain only about 0.3 per cent of the total population.

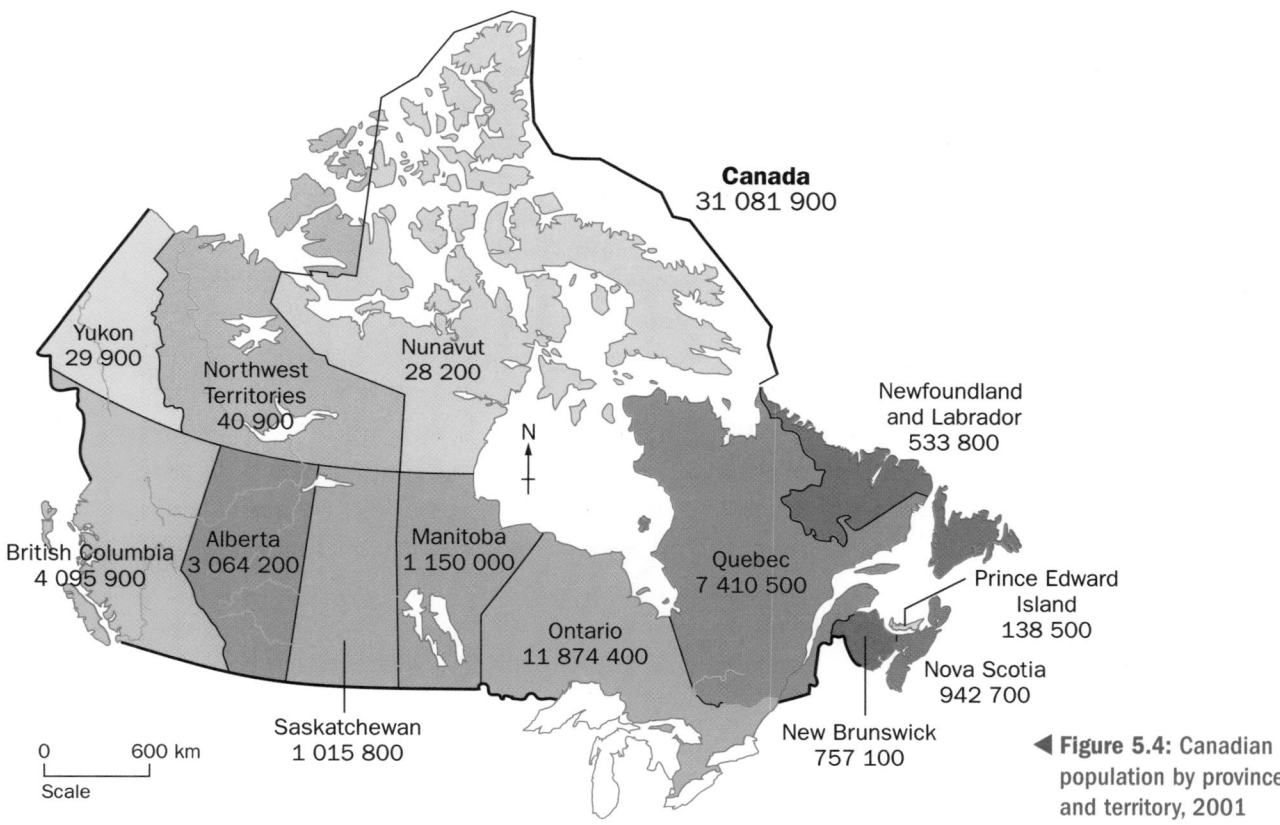

◀ **Figure 5.4:** Canadian population by province and territory, 2001

5. Describe two population patterns in Canada. Give a reason for each.

6. Look at the map in Figure 5.4. Which provinces or territories have populations under one million? Where are these areas of low population located? What reasons might explain the low population figures in these areas?

7. Make a chart to list the benefits and drawbacks of living in a densely populated area or a sparsely populated area. Write a short response explaining which type of area you would rather live in, and why.

Using Circle Graphs to Show Population Patterns

The circle graph in Figure 5.5 shows the population of each province and territory as a slice of a pie. The whole pie represents the total population of Canada. By looking at how big a slice is allotted to each area, you can tell at a glance what portion of the total population lives there.

To read a circle graph, it helps to remember that the whole circle represents 100 per cent. Half the circle equals 50 per cent, and one-quarter of the circle represents 25 per cent. Read the graph starting at the top and working clockwise. Notice how Ontario takes up the largest part of the circle, and Nunavut the smallest. The circle graph quickly illustrates the differences in percentages.

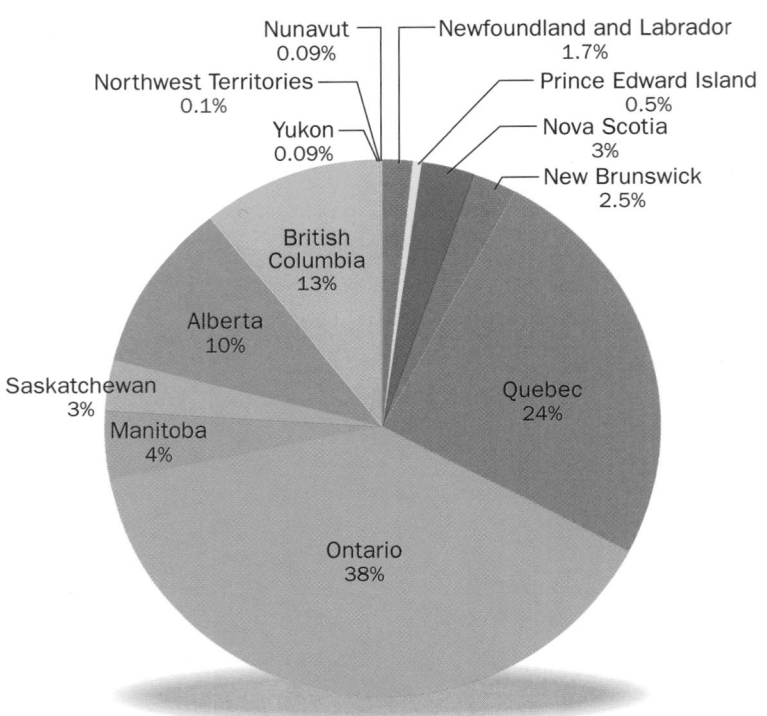

▲ **Figure 5.5:** Population of provinces and territories as per cent of total population, 2001

8. Look at the circle graph in Figure 5.5.
   a) Which two provinces account for more than half of Canada's total population?
   b) What reasons can you think of to explain the large populations of these provinces?

9. In the federal government, Ontario is represented by 103 elected members of Parliament. Alberta has 26 MPs, and Prince Edward Island has only four. What geographical factor do you think lies behind these numbers?

Aboriginal Population Patterns

Aboriginal populations vary in size from region to region. Some areas in southern Ontario and British Columbia were once densely populated by First Nations. They settled there mainly because of the abundant resources and fertile soil. In the 1600s, European settlers brought new wars and diseases. Some Aboriginal populations, especially in the east, were greatly reduced or even wiped out.

Still later, many Aboriginal peoples signed treaties with the government. They gave up large areas of their traditional lands in exchange for various rights and protections. The government granted them control over parcels of land, called **reserves**. Today, Canada has more than 2000 reserves. They are home to slightly less than half of the Aboriginal population. Many other Aboriginal people live off-reserve, often in urban centres such as Winnipeg or Vancouver.

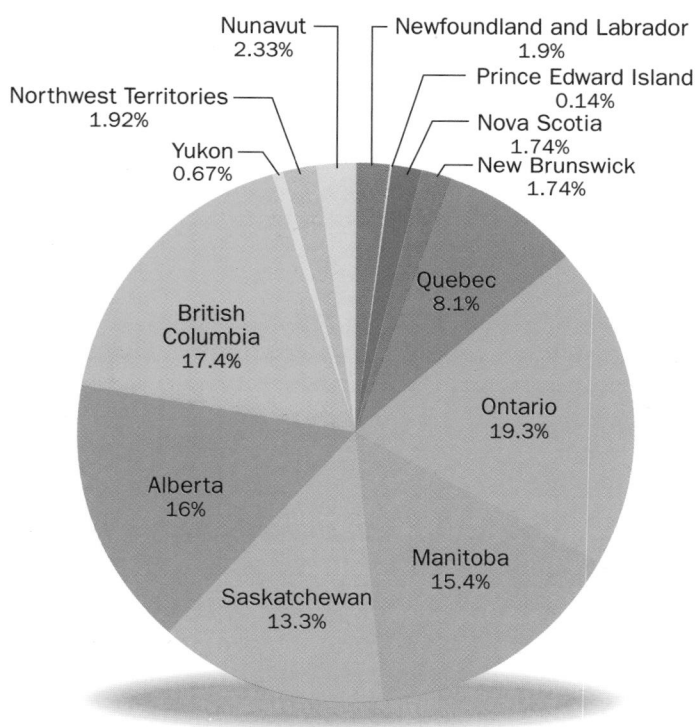

▲ **Figure 5.6:** Aboriginal population distribution by province and territory, 2001

10. Compare the circle graph in Figure 5.6 with the one for the total Canadian population (Figure 5.5, on the previous page). What conclusions can you draw from this comparison?

11. a) In your own words, explain why circle graphs are useful visual tools for geographers.

    b) What other things can you think of that could be effectively shown in a circle graph?

Population Growth

Are there areas near your home where new housing developments are being built? Is your community planning to build new schools or hospitals? Are roads being widened? If you live in a city or suburb, chances are you've observed at least some of these signs of growth. And you are likely to keep observing them for most of your lifetime.

Actually, such growth is nothing new. Ever since Canada became an independent nation in 1867, its population has been rising. In 1867, Canada's population was 3 230 000 people. By 2001, this figure had grown to over 31 million people. And this trend is expected to continue, according to Statistics Canada, the federal government agency in charge of collecting statistics about all aspects of Canada.

The bar graph in Figure 5.7 shows how the population has grown since 1861, and how it is expected to grow to the year 2021. Each bar represents the population of Canada in a given year. The year is shown at the bottom of each bar. To find the total population for that year, look along the vertical line at the left. For example, in 1901 the population was about 5.4 million. In 1921, it had risen to about 8.8 million. The number at the top of the bar shows that this represented a 63.6 per cent increase in the total population over the previous decade.

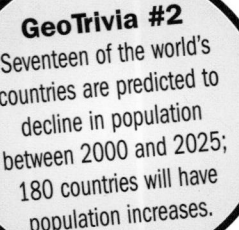

GeoTrivia #2
Seventeen of the world's countries are predicted to decline in population between 2000 and 2025; 180 countries will have population increases.

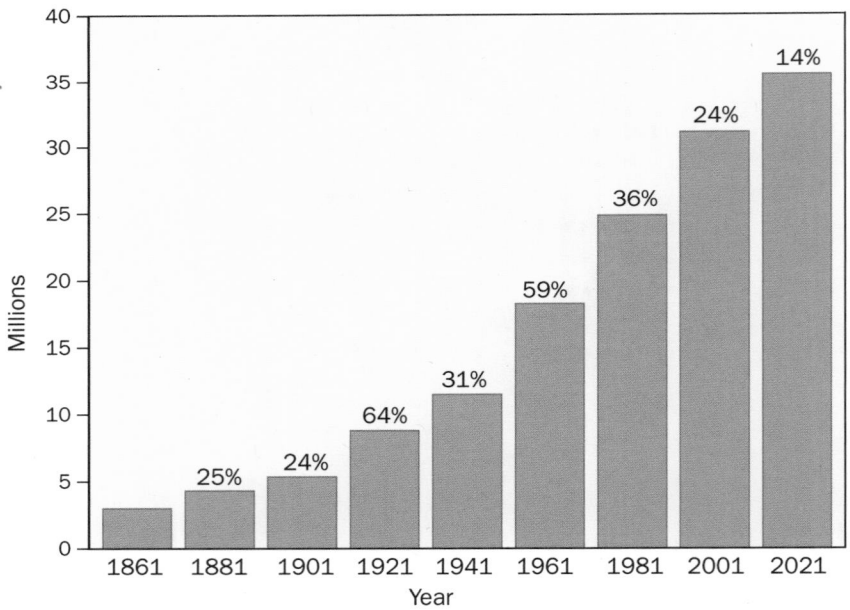

▲ **Figure 5.7:** Canada's population by decades, 1861–2001, plus 2021 (projected)

12. What other signs of population growth have you observed or can you think of?

13. a) Why do you think population growth is good for Canada?
    b) What problems can you think of that might be caused by an expanding population?

Age Distribution

One of the many aspects of population that geographers study is its **age distribution**—how many people fall into different age groups. They often show this information on **population pyramids** like the one in Figure 5.8. A country that has more young people is likely to experience higher population growth. A nation with more people in older age groups is likely to have a slower population growth.

Canada's population pyramid has a bulge in the middle. Its shape is like that of many industrialized countries. From 1946 to the mid-1960s, the number of births in these countries exploded. The Second World War had ended, and people were settling down to have large families. Many of these "baby boom" children are now in their fifties and sixties. Since most of them did not have big families, the generation coming after them is much smaller. In many non-industrialized countries, the situation is quite different. Many of these countries have a large number of young people and fewer elderly people.

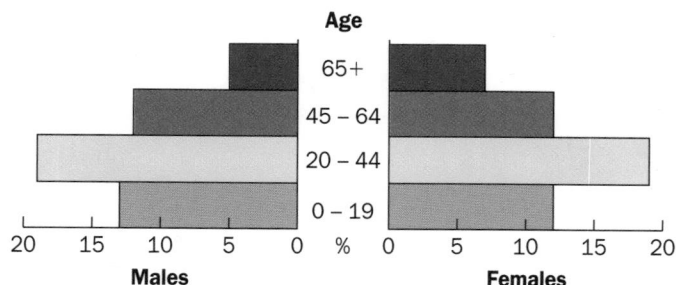

▲ **Figure 5.8:** Canada's population by age groups, 2001

14. Why does the population pyramid for Canada in Figure 5.8 look different from a typical pyramid shape?

15. Look at the population pyramid for Canada.
    a) In which age groups do males outnumber females? In which groups do females outnumber males?
    b) What conclusions can you draw from this about life expectancy for males and females?

16. Look at the data for Question 2 of the census you conducted at the beginning of this chapter.
    a) How many people would fall in each of the four categories on the population pyramid in Figure 5.8?
    b) What do you think a population pyramid would look like for this group?

Dependency Load

People under age 15 and over age 65 usually do not form part of the labour force. Geographers use the term **dependency load** to describe this segment of the population because these people depend on others for support. If a country's dependency load is high, it places more of a burden on the working population. For example, working people may have to pay more taxes to meet the health care needs of the elderly and the schooling needs of the young. (As you will read in the next section, immigration and emigration rates can change this pattern.)

Future Trends

What will Canada's population look like when you are an adult? The population pyramid in Figure 5.10 shows what our age distribution will look like in the future. When you compare it with the population pyramid for 2001 in Figure 5.8 on page 95, you will notice some significant differences. Most important, the over-65 age group will be the fastest-growing population group in Canada in the next twenty years!

▲ **Figure 5.9:** Three generations in one family

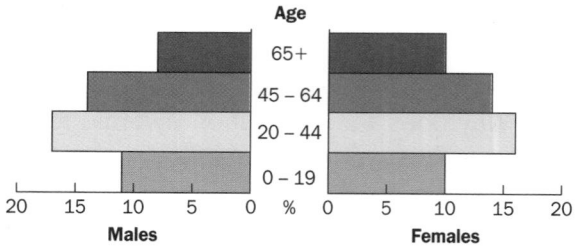

▲ **Figure 5.10:** Population by age group, Canada, 2021 (estimated)

17. Which age groups are projected to grow as a percentage of the total by 2021? Which are projected to get smaller? Use figures to support your conclusion.

18. If these projections are accurate, what sorts of products and services are likely to be in greater demand in 2021? Which are likely to be less in demand? Consider hip replacement surgery, dance clubs, and day care. Explain your reasoning.

19. Look at the photograph in Figure 5.9. Which of the people pictured here would be counted as part of the dependency load? What kind of strain might a high dependency load place on people who are in the workforce?

GeoSkills

Making Population Pyramids

You already know that population pyramids are a useful way of showing the age distribution of a population. They can also show the number of males and females in each age group. In this GeoSkills feature, you will learn how to create a population pyramid of your own. The population pyramid in Figure 5.12 was constructed using the information from the table in Figure 5.11.

Purpose

Geographers use population pyramids to learn more about a population and what services that group may need in the future. They also use population pyramids to help compare the populations of different countries.

Here are the steps to follow when you create a population pyramid.

Step 1

Draw two lines in the middle of a sheet of graph paper to make an upside-down letter "T."

Step 2

Starting from the bottom, label the age groups from the chart on the vertical line, an equal distance apart. For the population pyramid shown here, the age groups are 0–19, 20–44, 45–64, and 65+.

Step 3

Number each square on the horizontal line by fives, starting from 0 in the middle, to 20 at both the left and right edges. Label the left side "Males (%)" and the right side "Females (%)."

Step 4

Using the data from the chart in Figure 5.11, draw a bar to the left of the centre line to show male percentages in the 0–19 age group, and to the right of the centre line to show female percentages in the same group. Draw bars for the other age groups in a similar manner.

Step 5

Colour the male and female bars. Use a different colour for each age group.

Step 6

Title your population pyramid "Population of Ontario by Age and Sex, 2001."

Age Group	Males (%)	Females (%)
0–19	14	13
20–44	18	19
45–64	12	12
65+	5	7

Source: Statistics Canada, CANSIM II, table 051-0001.

▲ **Figure 5.11:** Age distribution by sex, Ontario, 2001

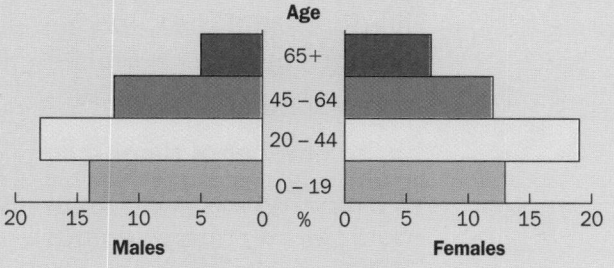

▲ **Figure 5.12:** Population pyramid for Ontario, 2001

Practise It!

1. Use the figures from the table in Figure 5.13 to make a population pyramid for the Aboriginal population of Canada. Follow Steps 1–6 as outlined on the previous page. Use the age groupings shown in the table.

Age Group	Males (%)	Females (%)
0–19	21.2	20.5
20–44	18.4	20.9
45–64	7.3	8.0
65+	1.7	2.0

Source: Statistics Canada, Census of Canada, 2001, Catalogue no. 97F0011XCB01003.

▲ **Figure 5.13:** Aboriginal population by age group, Canada, 2001

To make a population pyramid...
- ✔ mark the age groups along the vertical bar
- ✔ mark percentages along the horizontal bar, starting from 0 in the middle
- ✔ draw bars for males to the left of the centre line
- ✔ draw bars for females to the right of the centre line
- ✔ colour the bars for each age group
- ✔ add a title and year

2. Compare your population pyramid with that for Canada (Figure 5.8 on page 95).
   a) How do the two pyramids differ in shape?
   b) What is the greatest difference between the two populations?

3. Why do you think the age groupings for the Aboriginal population pyramid are different from those for Canada?

4. What conclusion can you draw from this population pyramid about the future growth of the Canadian Aboriginal population?

Factors in Population Change

So far in this chapter, you have been reading about the growth and distribution of the Canadian population. Now we need to identify the factors that can cause the population to change in size. These factors are as follows:

a) the number of births

b) the number of deaths

c) **migration**, or movement into and out of an area (migration into an area is immigration; migration out of an area is emigration)

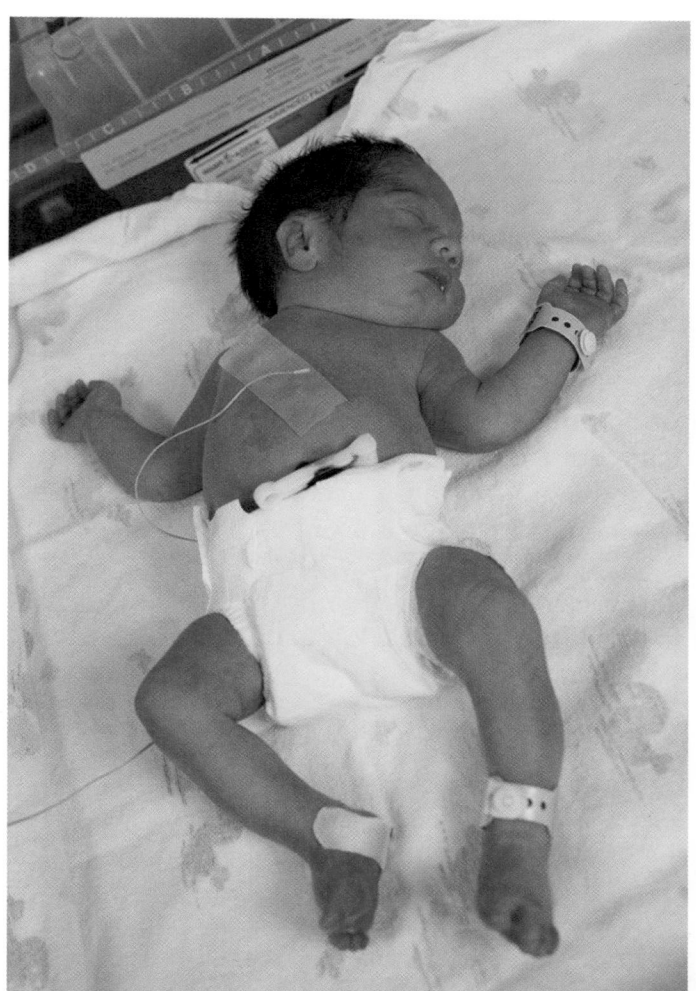

▲ **Figure 5.14:** Three important factors in population change: births, deaths, and migration

2000 Population	Births (+)	Immigrants (+)	Deaths (−)	Emigrants (−)
30 792 567	329 791	252 088	227 076	65 483

Source: Statistics Canada, CANSIM II, table 051-0004.

▲ **Figure 5.15:** Population growth factors, Canada, 2000–2001

20. a) What are the factors in population change?
    b) Which ones would cause the Canadian population to rise? Which ones would cause it to fall?

21. Calculate Canada's population for 2001 by taking the 2000 population figure, adding the births and immigration figures, and then subtracting the deaths and emigration figures.

The Impact of Migration

Take an informal poll in your class. Find out how many students have moved at least once in the last five years. Did anyone move from another country? another province? another city within your province?

Migrants are people who move their home from one place to another. The term includes **immigrants** (people who come from another country), **emigrants** (people who leave for another country), and **internal migrants** (people who move from one part of the country to another).

The graph in Figure 5.16 examines Canadians' migration patterns over a five-year period, from July 1996 to July 2001. Compared with people in other countries, Canadians move around quite a lot. Most provinces have grown through migration in recent years. But Saskatchewan and Newfoundland and Labrador had more out-migration than in-migration. The economies in these provinces have been suffering, as family farms go out of business and the fishery shrinks.

Immigration from other countries has played an important role in Canada's population growth for hundreds of years. We'll look more closely at this aspect of migration in the next chapter.

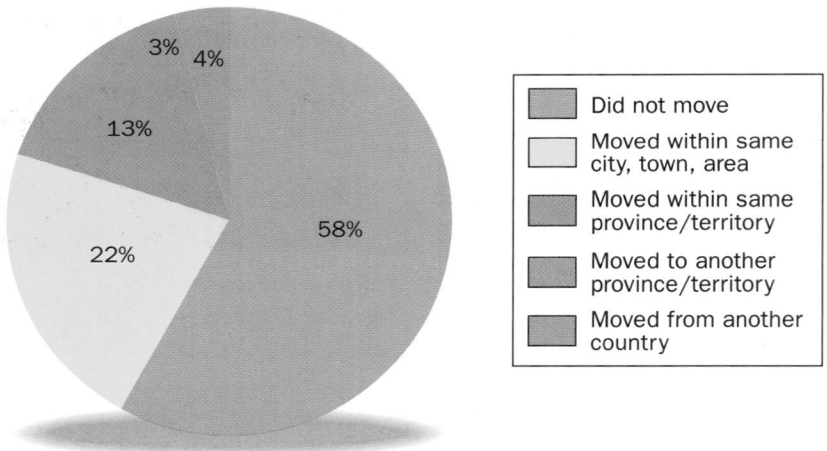

▲ **Figure 5.16:** Population and migration status over 5 years, Canada, 1996–2001

22. In your own words, explain the term "migrant."

23. a) Draw an organizer or other diagram to illustrate the results of the informal migration poll you took among people in your class.
    b) How does your chart compare with the statistics on Canadian migration in the circle graph in Figure 5.16?

24. What problems might a city or region experience if it lost population through migration for an extended period of time?

25. a) Does your region or municipality attract a significant number of migrants? What makes you think so?
    b) What reasons can you think of to explain this pattern?

GeoGames
The Population Growth Game

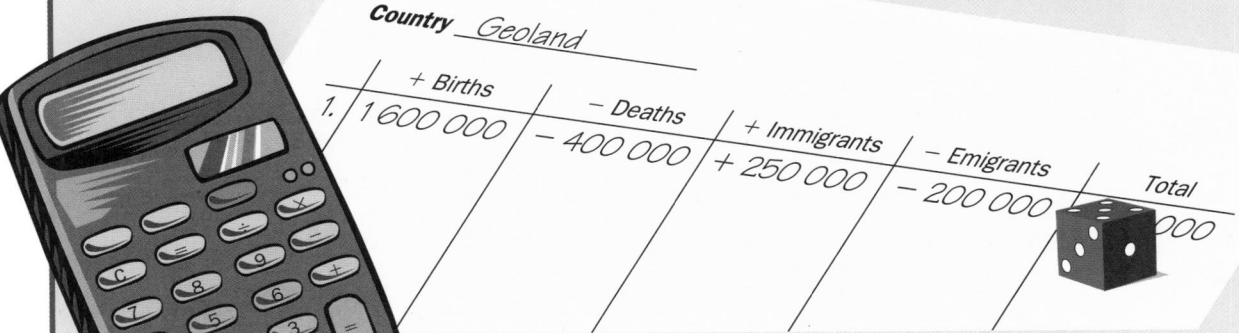

▲ **Figure 5.17:** Equipment needed for the Population Growth Game

Purpose:

To become familiar with the four factors that affect population

Supplies:

All you will need is one die, a calculator, and a scoresheet.

Method:

A. Form two teams of two players each. Each team represents a country with a population of 30 million people. Decide on a name for your country and write it at the top of the score sheet provided by your teacher.

B. Seat yourself at a table in the order of play: the youngest player goes first, followed by his or her teammate. The youngest player on the other team goes next, followed by his or her teammate.

C. Each team will roll four times to determine their country's population growth for a two-year period. The first player (the youngest) rolls twice to determine the number of births and deaths. The second player rolls twice to determine the number of immigrants and emigrants. Play then moves to the other team.

D. Calculate your total population using the scoring chart in Figure 5.18 and record the numbers on your score sheet. For example, if your team rolled 5, 3, 2, and 6, you would score as follows:

1 600 000 − 400 000 + 250 000 − 200 000
= 1 250 000

E. After ten rounds (twenty years), add your total population growth to the 30 million you started with. The winner is the country with the largest population.

If You Roll...	Births (Roll 1)	Deaths (Roll 2)	Immigrants (Roll 3)	Emigrants (Roll 4)
1 or 2	+400 000	−200 000	+250 000	−50 000
3 or 4	+800 000	−400 000	+500 000	−100 000
5 or 6	+1 600 000	−800 000	+1 000 000	−200 000

▲ **Figure 5.18:** Scoring chart

Wrap-Up:
From 2001 to 2021, it is estimated that Canada's population will grow by about four million people. Was your total growth higher or lower than this? Do you think the game presents a realistic model of population growth? Why or why not?

Conclusion

In this chapter, you have seen that Canada's population varies over time and in different parts of the country. You also learned that Canada's population is getting older. This aging population is likely to mean a lower birth rate over the next twenty years. However, other factors, such as migration, can also affect the population growth rate of the country. As we will see in Chapter 6: Reflecting Our Diverse Cultures, immigration has always had a particularly strong impact on Canada's population patterns. No wonder Canadians are so varied!

Wrap It Up

1. Explain why each of the following aspects of population is important to geographers.
   a) population density
   b) population growth
   c) population distribution

2. What are the factors that affect population growth? Explain whether each has a negative or positive effect.

3. Imagine that you are a member of the federal government in Ottawa, and your job is to prepare Canada for the increased number of persons over 65 in 2021. Identify three things that you think the government should do to prepare. Compare your answers with those of a classmate. What have you learned from this experience?

4. Look at Figure 5.3 on page 90. Pick one high population density country, and one low population density country other than Canada. Do some research about the two countries to find out whether their populations have been rising, falling, or stable in recent years. What similarities and differences do you observe between the two countries?

5. Use the data in Figure 5.19 to draw a population pyramid for South Africa. How does this pyramid differ from Canada's population pyramid (Figure 5.8 on page 95)? Setting aside migration as a factor, what prediction can you make about population trends over the next twenty years in South Africa?

Age Group	Males (%)	Females (%)
0–19	21	21
20–44	18	20
45–64	7	7
65+	2	3

Source: US Census Bureau.

▲ **Figure 5.19:** Population by age and sex for South Africa

Chapter 6

REFLECTING OUR DIVERSE CULTURES

Cultural Bingo

You're probably familiar with most of the words in the squares below. But can you identify in what culture they originated? Cut a piece of paper into nine small squares. Write the culture of origin of each item on a separate piece of paper, and place each on the correct square on the board. As soon as you get three in a row going across, down, or diagonally, call out BINGO! Leave the answers in place until your teacher has checked them.

◄ **Figure 6.1:** Cultural Bingo game board

tae kwon do	souvlaki	pizza
fireworks	karaoke	reggae
tortilla	toboggan	sari

Canada's unique mix of cultures is an important part of who we are as a nation. In this chapter, we'll look at our cultural origins from a geographical point of view. This means we will look at patterns of immigration from other nations into Canada, what cultures make up the population, how they are distributed across the country, and what languages are spoken here. We will also look at some of the original inhabitants of Canada, who have maintained strong independent cultures in the midst of huge changes.

Words to Know

cultural diversity
multiculturalism
ethnic origin
visible minority
mother tongue
pull factor
chain migration
cultural imprint
ethnically diverse
nomadic

In this chapter, you will

- investigate Canada's cultural diversity
- learn why new immigrants usually choose to live in large cities
- look closely at a neighbourhood with a strong cultural imprint
- find out about some Aboriginal groups that are working to preserve their traditional cultures

The Cultural Diversity of Canadians

What are your cultural roots? Where did your parents grow up? your grandparents? your great-grandparents? For most Canadians, the answer to at least one of these questions is likely to be "somewhere else." That's because, apart from Aboriginal peoples, who are the original occupants of the land, we are all either immigrants, or descended from immigrants.

Canada is a nation that prides itself on its **cultural diversity**. This term means that the population is drawn from many cultural backgrounds, illustrating a wide range of practices and beliefs. What's more, Canada has an official policy of **multiculturalism**, which means people are encouraged to retain their cultural heritage while also being committed Canadians. So it is quite normal for many of us to say that we are, for example, "Italian," "Korean," or "Nigerian," even after several generations in this country. As you will see, there are many ways of measuring the cultural diversity of the Canadian people.

▲ **Figure 6.2:** Students at Hugh Boyd Secondary School, a culturally diverse Canadian high school in Richmond, BC

1. What is meant by a) cultural diversity? b) multiculturalism? How are they related?

2. Did your family or ancestors immigrate to Canada? If so, where did they come from and how long ago did they come? (If you aren't sure, interview a parent or older relative to find out.) If not, have you or your older relatives noticed any changes over the years in the cultural diversity of the area where you live? Explain.

3. Do many people in your area share the same cultural background as you? How do you know?

Ethnic Origins

Canadians frequently think of themselves in terms of their **ethnic origins**, or cultural background. Ethnic origins are not always the same as nationality, especially in Canada. Canadian citizens—both those who were born here and those who came as immigrants and took out Canadian citizenship—have the same nationality, but a wide array of ethnic origins.

Canada was once a colony of France. Later, it became a British colony. So it is understandable that many Canadians have European origins. In fact, until the 1970s, most immigrants to Canada came from Europe. Beginning in the 1980s, however, immigrants began to come from many other places. The table in Figure 6.3 shows the ethnic origins of Canadians who were already living here in 2001. The map shows where immigrants who came to Canada in 2000–2001 arrived from. See the difference.

GeoTrivia #1
In 2000-2001, 6030 immigrants came to Canada from the USA; 29 139 immigrants came from India.

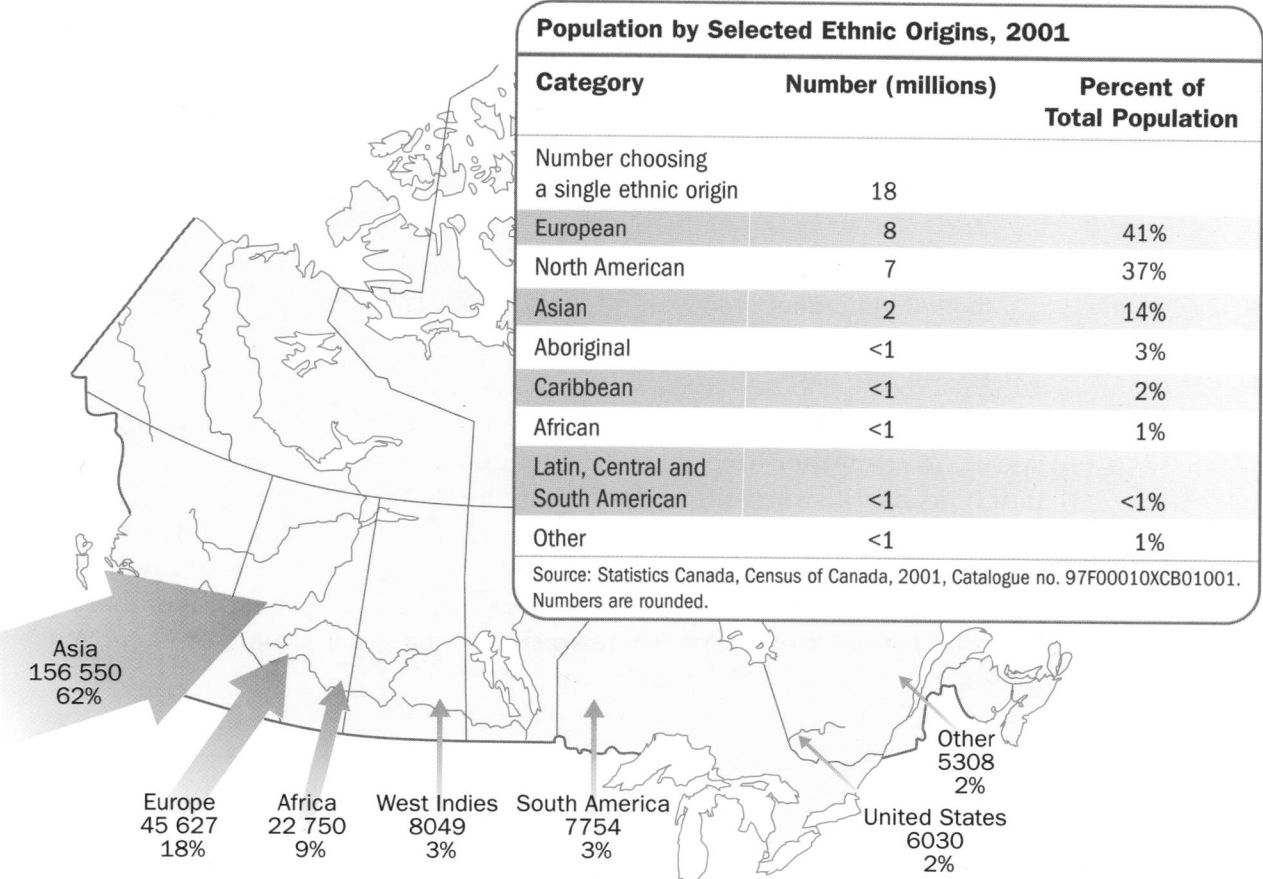

Population by Selected Ethnic Origins, 2001

Category	Number (millions)	Percent of Total Population
Number choosing a single ethnic origin	18	
European	8	41%
North American	7	37%
Asian	2	14%
Aboriginal	<1	3%
Caribbean	<1	2%
African	<1	1%
Latin, Central and South American	<1	<1%
Other	<1	1%

Source: Statistics Canada, Census of Canada, 2001, Catalogue no. 97F00010XCB01001. Numbers are rounded.

Asia
156 550
62%

Europe
45 627
18%

Africa
22 750
9%

West Indies
8049
3%

South America
7754
3%

Other
5308
2%

United States
6030
2%

▲ **Figure 6.3:** Ethnic origins of Canadians in 2001 and immigrants to Canada by region of last residence, 2000–2001

4. Look at the table in Figure 6.3. What is the largest ethnic origin listed? Why do so many Canadians claim this ethnic origin?

5. Look at the table in Figure 6.3 and the bar graph in Figure 6.4 on the next page. Write three sentences comparing Canada's immigration patterns in the early twenty-first century with the pattern in previous years as described in the text above.

Visible Minorities

When you walk down the street in your community, do you feel you stand out because of your ethnic origin? Many people within Canada think of themselves as belonging to a visible minority. **Visible minorities** are ethnic groups within society who look different from the majority. In 2001, 31.6 per cent of Toronto's population were part of a visible minority (see Figure 6.4). Visible minorities are less common in other Ontario cities, but still form a significant part of the population.

Figure 6.4: Visible ▶ minorities in Toronto, 2001

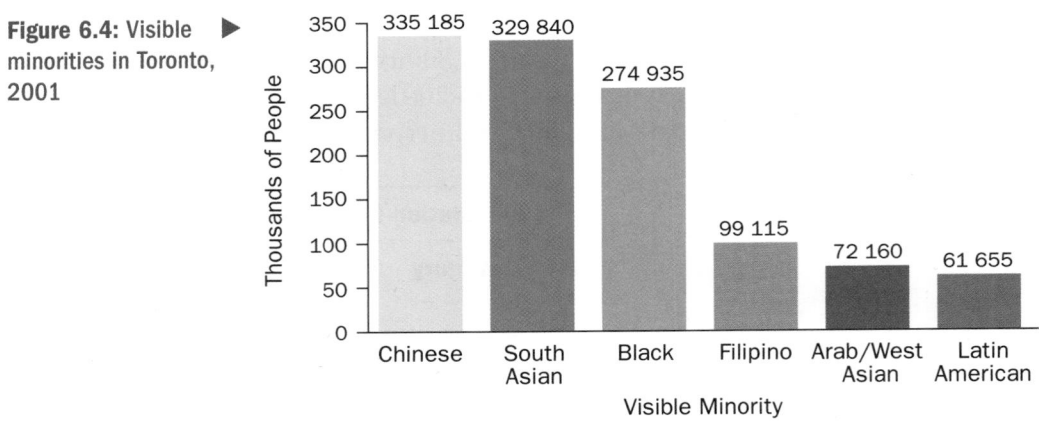

6. Are all immigrants members of visible minorities? Are all members of visible minorities recent immigrants? Explain your answers.

Mother Tongue

Another way of looking at our cultural diversity is by what languages we speak. Your **mother tongue**, or first language, is the language you were first taught as a child and still understand. The table in Figure 6.5 shows the most common mother tongues in two provinces: Ontario and Saskatchewan. In Ontario, Chinese is the most commonly spoken language after English and French. Saskatchewan has a higher percentage of English speakers than Ontario. But a lot of people there speak German, Ukrainian, or Cree. What languages are spoken in your community?

Language	Canada (%)	Ontario (%)	Saskatchewan (%)
English	59	72	86
French	23	4	2
Chinese	3	4	<1
Italian	2	3	<1
German	1	1	3
Ukrainian	<1	<1	2
Cree	<1	<0.1	2

Source: Statistics Canada, Population by mother tongue, 2001 Census, Catalogue no. 97F0007XCB1001.

▲ **Figure 6.5:** Most widely spoken mother tongues, Canada, Ontario, and Saskatchewan, 2001

7. Look at Figure 6.5. Write down two ways the Ontario and Saskatchewan first-language statistics are similar and two ways they are different.

8. a) If your mother tongue is shown in the table, find out what percentage of the population of Ontario and of Canada speak it. Otherwise, find out from relatives what part of Canada has a community of people who speak this language.

    b) Were you surprised by what you found out about your mother tongue? Why or why not?

◀ **Figure 6.6:** Two Canadian cultural events that have been imported and adapted: Chinese New Year (Vancouver, top) and Carnival (Toronto, bottom)

9. Look at the photographs in Figure 6.6. Name some local cultural events (for example, festivals, fairs, or parades) and explain how they reflect the cultural origins of your community or region.

Big City Bound

Canada's big cities have large immigrant populations. The 2001 Census showed that almost 42 per cent of Toronto's population was not born in Canada. The figure for Vancouver was almost 35 per cent, and Montreal's was just under 18 per cent. The number of immigrants living in big cities is much higher than in smaller towns and rural areas. Why is this?

Cities have what geographers call **pull factors**. This term refers to the qualities of big cities that attract, or pull, immigrants to live there. Let's consider some of them.

- Many immigrants are sponsored by family members already living in cities. The new immigrants naturally want to be near their relatives.

- Immigrants who speak neither English nor French are attracted to communities in cities where their language is spoken.

- Big cities often have more jobs available.

- Cities are already culturally diverse. New immigrants find them welcoming.

These factors combine to create **chain migration**. One wave of immigrants settles in a Canadian city. The first wave encourages a second wave to come, and so on. Individual ethnic neighbourhoods are gradually formed as particular ethnic groups settle in one area of the city.

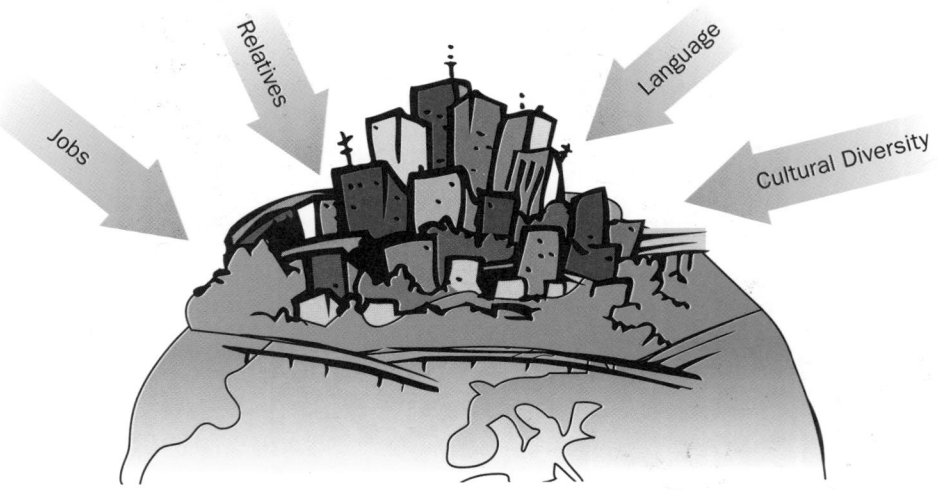

▲ **Figure 6.7:** Pull factors that draw new immigrants to cities

10. What are the four main pull factors that make cities attractive to new immigrants?

11. What other attractions do cities offer to migrants?

Leaving a Cultural Imprint

When you put your hand on a soft surface, your fingers often leave a mark. This mark, or imprint, is distinctly yours. Ethnic groups often give neighbourhoods where they settle a **cultural imprint**. That is, they make their neighbourhood distinctive by bringing some of their own culture to the area. Have you ever lived in, or visited, a city or town that had an area known as "Chinatown"? If so, then you have seen this process at work. Businesses place foreign-language signs on the streetfront. Stores sell goods imported from the home country. Restaurants provide culturally familiar foods. These changes are all part of the process of cultural imprinting.

12. Does your community have any areas that have a particular cultural imprint? If so, describe the area and the impact the particular ethnic group has had on it. If your region has no such communities, why do you think this is?

CASE STUDY

KENSINGTON MARKET, TORONTO

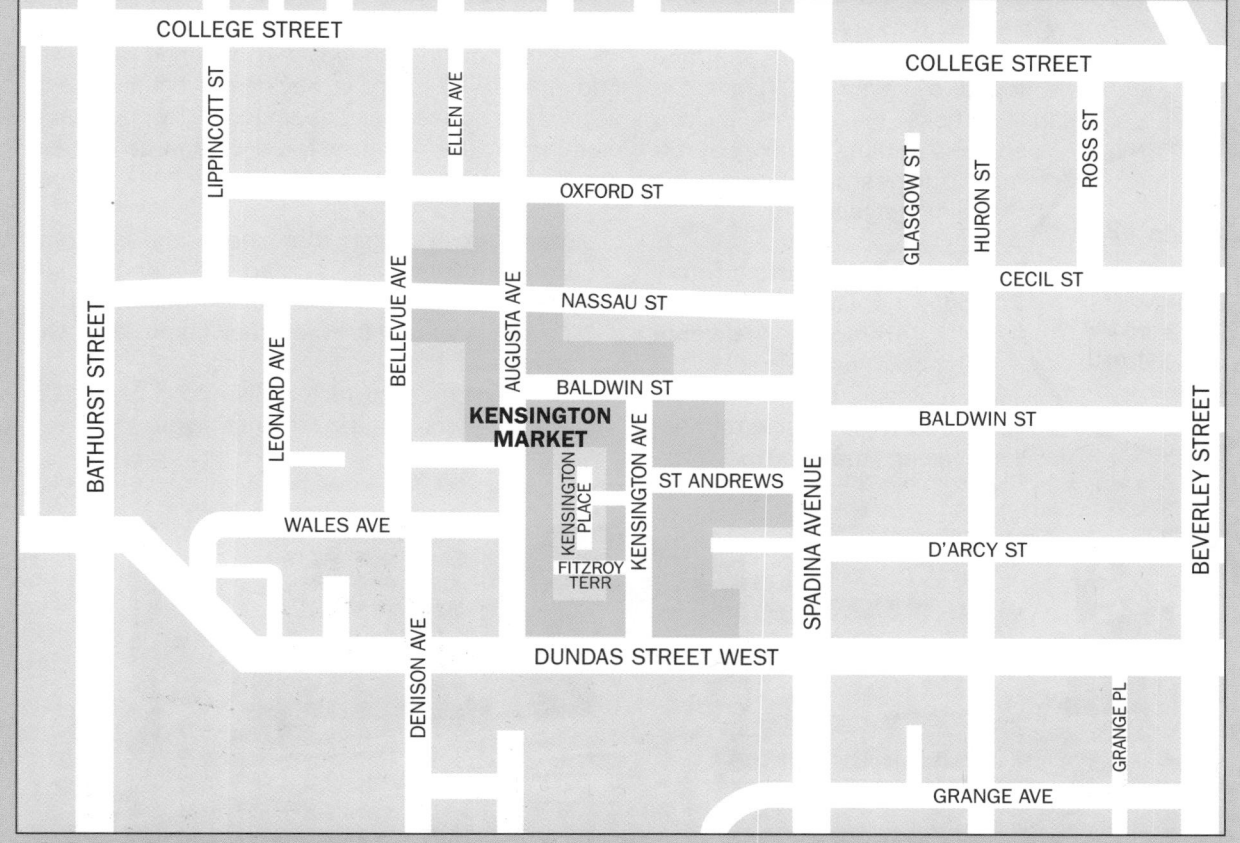

▲ **Figure 6.8:** Kensington Market

One of the most famous culturally diverse areas in Canada is Toronto's Kensington Market. It takes up about five square city blocks in an area just west of the downtown, and right on the border of Chinatown. The streets of Kensington are narrow and lined with old red-brick houses. The many small shops along the streets display their wares on the sidewalks, enticing shoppers to enter. A variety of delicious smells fill the air—everything from salted fish to fresh baked bread to exotic spices.

History

The land that would later become known as Kensington Market was originally the home of the Ojibwa. They fished and traded beside the lakes and rivers of the region. Europeans began to arrive in the 1790s. Wealthy aristocrats were offered parcels of land to encourage them to build large homes in the area. But many chose to sell off smaller lots to less wealthy tradespeople who had

recently emigrated from Britain and Ireland. This created an area with close-set houses and narrow streets.

After 1900, the first wave of immigrants were replaced by Jewish (and some Italian) immigrants. Many of these newcomers were fleeing war, poverty, and persecution at home. They introduced the custom of selling wares from carts. Eventually, the carts were abandoned, and people's houses became storefronts. The area became known as the Jewish Market.

Although the area remained mostly Jewish until the 1950s, other immigrants also left their mark on Kensington. Along with Ukrainians, Hungarians, and Italians, large numbers of Portuguese moved in. This last group were the main residents of the area by the 1960s. They opened stores selling fish and other Portuguese foods. Many painted their houses in bright colours, as is the custom in Portugal.

In the late 1960s and 1970s, Americans trying to escape being drafted for the war in Vietnam came to Kensington. Chinese people also moved in, as Toronto's Chinatown expanded westward.

From 1975 on, a huge wave of immigrants from over thirty cultural backgrounds, including South American, South Asian, African, and Caribbean, have found a haven in Kensington Market. These immigrants include people looking for better opportunities as well as some fleeing persecution.

Kensington Market Today
Today, Kensington Market is an **ethnically diverse** neighbourhood—that is, it has residents from an exciting mix of ethnic backgrounds. Walking along the narrow, busy streets of the market, you will likely hear several different languages spoken and run into people from any number of countries.

The market still has specialty stores that sell goods to individual ethnic groups. But nowadays, they also attract Toronto residents who are looking for an interesting shopping experience. You will find all kinds of things to buy here, from fruits and vegetables, to meat and seafood, to dry goods and clothing. At the many restaurants and cafés, you can try foods from different countries and cultures.

1. Make an organizer that shows the different waves of immigrants who arrived in Kensington Market since the 1700s. Include their countries of origin, when they came, and why they came.
2. Which of the pull factors listed on page 108 are present today in Kensington Market? Explain.

▲ **Figure 6.9:** Fruit stores in Kensington Market

Aboriginal Peoples

In the section about Canada's cultural diversity, we treated "Aboriginal" as a single cultural origin because the ancestors of the Aboriginals were the first people to live in North America. The Aboriginal peoples of Canada are actually many distinct peoples who differ greatly—in where they live, their language, culture, government, and way of life.

Why are these groups so different? A big factor is the place where they and their ancestors have lived. The map in Figure 6.10 shows the Aboriginal groups in Canada at the time of contact with Europeans. You can see that the map is divided into six broad cultural areas. For example, groups that lived in the subarctic regions formed one cultural area because most of them relied on hunting for their survival, following caribou and other animals when they migrated south. This way of life affected all aspects of their culture, from the type of houses they built to the stories they told.

In the next section, you will meet three of the many Aboriginal peoples— the Mohawk, the Cree, and the Haida. You will find out how their environment helped form their culture. As you read, pay attention to how these people have maintained their cultures.

▲ **Figure 6.10:** Location of Aboriginal peoples in the 1500s

13. a) Pick one cultural group (other than subarctic) shown on the map.
    b) How do you think the people in this area made their living?
    c) What other features of their location would have affected their way of life?

Mohawk

The Mohawk traditionally lived on the land next to the Mohawk River, in what is now southern Quebec and upper New York State. They settled here so they could make a living by hunting and fishing the rich resources in the area. One way Mohawk culture adapted to the environment was by building longhouses—long wood-framed buildings covered with bark. Families lived together in the longhouse and shared their resources. Open fires provided heat and cooking facilities.

While most Mohawk no longer live in longhouses, the culture of living peacefully together and sharing resources still exists. The Mohawk are members of the Six Nations Confederacy, who refer to themselves as the Haudenosaunee—"people of the longhouse." For over five hundred years they have shared a common government and constitution, just as their ancestors shared the peace and protection of the longhouse. This long tradition of peaceful self-government has allowed the Haudenosaunee to withstand many threats to their culture. For example, the Canadian–American border runs right through the middle of Six Nations territory. The Six Nations do not recognize the border, claiming that they have never given up title to their land.

The Mohawk population today lives mostly on reserves, especially Kahnawake and Akwesasne in Quebec, and the Kahnesatake, Tyendinaga, Wahta, and Six Nations reserves in Ontario. Some Mohawks have become well known for their skill as "skywalkers"—ironworkers who erect steel frames for skyscrapers. You can read about a skywalker in the GeoCareers feature on the next page.

GeoTrivia #3
The Haudenosaunee have the oldest democratic government on the continent. Parts of the US Constitution were borrowed from the Haudenosaunee Constitution.

▲ **Figure 6.11:** A typical scene inside a longhouse during the winter

14. Look at Figure 6.11. Describe what you see. What challenges do you think life in the longhouse might present?

15. How might living in longhouses have helped the Six Nations remain united under one government for so long?

GEO CAREERS IRONWORKER

Name: John N. McComber
High School: Howard S. Billings High School, Montreal, Quebec
Job Title: Ironworker

Geography is about more than the natural environment. It is also about the built environment—the landscape we create when we build cities, towns, and other settlements. Like the workers in the photograph above, John McComber is one of the people who helps construct this human-made environment. He works as an ironworker (or "skywalker"), assembling iron girder structures for skyscrapers.

John's main responsibility is to unhook the girders that are passed up by crane and place them in position. The girders are then bolted in place, and in some cases welded after the bolts have been properly tightened. Ironworkers work high off the ground, often in windy or wet conditions. You will sometimes see them high above, walking effortlessly across girders on a construction site.

John was one year out of high school when he started as an ironworker. His first job was building a hydro line between West Virginia and Washington, DC. There was no formal apprenticeship program at that time, so he learned from the old-timers on the job. All ironworkers licensed in Quebec must pass a safety program, which is forty-eight hours in length. It deals with keeping your workplace clean and safe, and how to lift heavy objects safely.

Some of the tall buildings John has worked on include the Bass Towers in Forth Worth, Texas, which stand at 38 and 42 storeys; and Place Royal Trust in Montreal, which is 32 storeys tall.

To get started in a career related to constructing our built environment, consider getting a Civil Engineering Technician diploma from a community college.

What I like about my work: *"The thing I like most about my work is seeing the finished building on the horizon as I'm leaving the city or return. I can say to family or friends: 'See that building over there? I did the erecting work on that building.' Another thrill is seeing on TV a building that I worked on."*

How a knowledge of geography helps me in my job: *"Geography keeps me in my job by helping me identify the names of the cities and states in the USA that require my services, and when I read maps that help me get to these destinations."*

1. What would you like and dislike about being a skywalker?
2. What skills do you think you would need for this job?
3. What could you do to develop those skills in yourself?

Cree

The Cree nation is one of the largest Aboriginal groupings in Canada. It occupies many reserves in the subarctic, stretching from present-day Quebec to Alberta. The traditional Cree life was **nomadic**. This means that they moved from season to season, following wildlife such as caribou and geese. They used canoes in summer and toboggans and snowshoes in winter. Cree hunters lived in conical or dome-shaped lodges that could be taken down quickly.

The Cree of Oujé-Bougoumou, near James Bay, are an example of how traditional culture can be applied in new ways. Their lands were rich in minerals and forests that attracted mining and logging companies. The Oujé-Bougoumou Cree were forced to move seven times in just fifty years to make way for development. As the lands were clear-cut and mining towns flourished, most of the Cree people lived in poverty.

The government finally agreed to help build a new, permanent home for the Cree. The Oujé-Bougoumou worked with Douglas Cardinal, a famous Aboriginal architect, to design a village that incorporated aspects of their tradition as well as many new ideas. Most of the buildings have skylights or domed ceilings like those on traditional Cree dwellings. The village is circular, with all the community buildings in the centre. This reflects the importance of community in Cree culture.

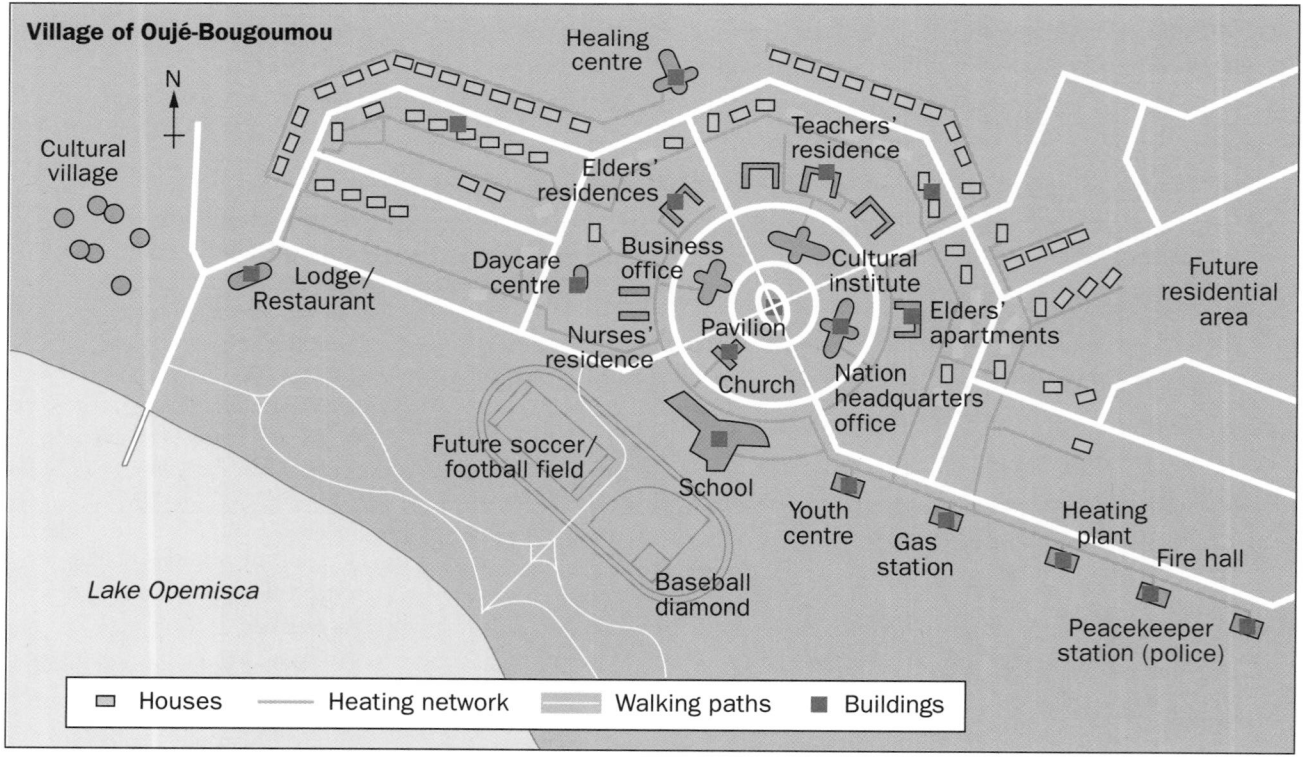

▲ **Figure 6.12:** Layout of the Cree village at Oujé-Bougoumou

The design also expresses the Aboriginal tradition of living in harmony with nature in modern ways. For example, the entire village is heated using sawdust from a local sawmill. The village is now home to about 650 Cree. It attracts visitors from around the world, and has won many awards for its innovative design, including the United Nations' Global Citizen award.

16. In what way did traditional Cree dwellings suit their nomadic lifestyle?

17. How does the new village of the Oujé-Bougoumou Cree reflect aspects of their traditional culture?

Haida

Haida culture has been rooted for thousands of years in the small area of the Queen Charlotte Islands in British Columbia. For centuries, the Haida used the natural resources of the area and were always careful to manage these resources skillfully. But in recent times, they have had to fight hard to preserve their land. During the 1980s, the Haida launched a protest to restrict logging on South Moresby, part of the Queen Charlottes. Their cause attracted worldwide attention, and eventually they were successful. As a result, a large part of the islands is now a national park. The Haida work along with the federal government to manage this area jointly. The United Nations has named the area a World Heritage Site. This means that it is regarded as too important to spoil through over-development.

Because they were separated from the mainland, the Haida had to trade to get supplies that were not available in their area. They became known as superb craftspeople who created high-quality goods, including canoes, bowls, and decorated boxes. They also carved stunning totem poles, like the ones shown in Figure 6.13.

▲ **Figure 6.13:** Haida totem poles

▲ **Figure 6.14:** The Queen Charlotte Islands

18. List several ways that the natural resources in the Queen Charlotte Islands are important to Haida culture.

19. Why did each of the three groups we have looked at—the Mohawk, Cree, and Haida—originally settle in the area where they did?

20. For each group, explain how at least two elements of its culture were influenced by the natural environment.

21. Identify one strategy each group has used to keep its culture strong.

Conclusion

In this chapter, you saw that Canada is culturally diverse. Large urban centres such as Toronto and Vancouver attract most new immigrants. Immigrants with similar backgrounds tend to live close to one another. This often results in neighbourhoods, such as Kensington Market, that have a strong cultural imprint. You also looked at the culture of some of Canada's original inhabitants. You learned that Aboriginal groups vary greatly across the country, although many are facing similar challenges in preserving and maintaining their cultures.

Wrap It Up

1. Identify three ways in which the Canadian population is culturally diverse.

2. Make an organizer to compare information about the Aboriginal groups profiled in this chapter. Fill in each column with point-form notes based on what you learned about their location, traditional culture, and present lifestyle.

3. a) Visit the Statistics Canada Web site to find the latest Census results showing population by ethnic origin. On a blank map of the world, show the number of people coming to your region from the following locations.

Asia	Europe
Africa	West Indies
South America	United States
Other	

   b) Compare your map with the one in Figure 6.3 on page 105. What conclusions can you draw from this comparison?

4. Map the countries of origin of the people in your class. How similar or different are these results from those for the province as a whole? Do you think your class map reflects the ethnic diversity of your city, town, or region? Why or why not?

5. Write a report about an ethnic community in Ontario. Include the following information: (a) background (b) when and why these people came to Canada, (c) where they settled, (d) how they maintain their cultural traditions. Overall, how would you describe the contribution of this ethnic group to Canadian culture?

Chapter 7

OUR CHANGING RURAL ENVIRONMENT

Alone in the Woods

▲ **Figure 7.1:** At one time, the forests of North America seemed to stretch on forever.

Imagine being one of the first European settlers to North America. You would land on the shores of the St. Lawrence River, where you would see a landscape covered in trees. You and the other settlers haven't seen much wilderness in your life, so it might seem that the forest stretches on forever.

Many early newcomers to North America had mistaken ideas about the forest, such as the following.

- The forest is the source of the extreme cold of winter.
- Disease comes from forests and swamps.
- The forest is home to frightening creatures, such as wolves, that make off with little children.

Which of these statements do you think is true?

1. Look closely at Figure 7.1. Imagine that you are about to leave Europe, and will arrive at the above location in North America at the beginning of April in 1650. You must claim a particular plot of land and turn it into a farm.
    a) Make a list of the tools, clothing, and types of food that you will need to set up a farm. Remember that you will not have any crops until August or September. You should list at least 20 items.
    b) List the first 15 things you would do on your land to turn it into a farm.
    c) What problems might you face while working your farm the first year?

2. How are your ideas of the forest different from those of early settlers?

In this chapter, you will

- compare the three major settlement patterns in Canada
- find out about modern rural Canada
- see how rural land is becoming urban land
- find out that there are no easy answers to rural problems

Words to Know

rural
urban
settlement pattern
long lot
township
strassendorf
agribusiness
urbanization
rural–urban fringe
land use
urban sprawl
zoning by-law

Settlement Patterns

The First Nations of North America did not feel a need to divide up the land or cut down forests. They saw the forest as a source of food and protection. European settlers saw the forest differently, as we have seen, and began to cut and burn down the forests as soon as they arrived. They intended to turn the wilderness into rural areas where they would farm and build small settlements.

3. Compare the ways that the First Nations and the Europeans used the land. How did each affect the natural environment?

4. The First Nations lived in the world shown in the photograph in Figure 7.1. How might it have changed their way of life to have this world divided up and given away to foreign settlers?

Farmsteads were the building blocks of early Canada. Although farmsteads are different today, much remains the same. For example, all farmsteads need barns or sheds, even if they might be made of metal now instead of wood.

◀ **Figure 7.2:** A typical Canadian farmstead

5. a) Use Figure 7.2 as a model and draw a small-area map of your own modern farmstead. (See the GeoSkills feature on pages 4–5.) Consider all the necessary features that the farmstead needs (for example, where would the farmer get fuel?). Be sure to label all buildings and roads.
   b) What facilities or services could a farmstead provide for a family?
   c) List five specific items or services that a farmer would have to leave the farmstead to get.

The human imprint on the Canadian land is huge. For example, two hundred years ago, a north–south border was established to divide farmlands just west of downtown York (now Toronto). That border eventually became the major Toronto road you see in the photograph below in Figure 7.3. Borders and roads made centuries ago can still be seen on the land today.

▲ **Figure 7.3:** Looking down University Avenue in Toronto

All the farming areas you are going to look at in this section are part of **rural** Canada. Rural means any area that does not include settlements of 1000 people or more. Areas including cities or towns that have more than 1000 people are called **urban**.

When settlers came to a new region, they came to find a plot of land that had been assigned to them. The land had been divided up in various ways. This created distinctive **settlement patterns**, or arrangements of farms and farmhouses, in different regions. Here are the three patterns of settlement you'll look at in this section:

- the Quebec long-lot system
- the Ontario township system
- the *strassendorf* (in the Case Study on page 123)

Long-Lot System in Quebec

The first Canadian settlement pattern developed in what is now Quebec, along the St. Lawrence River. This river was the major transportation route in the early French settlement, and it provided both water and fish. Naturally, each new settler wanted to have a farm right on the river.

A **long-lot** system developed, with very long farms, or lots, arranged side by side along the St. Lawrence, one end edging the shoreline. These long lots, or *rotures*, varied from one-half kilometre to two kilometres in length. When a farmer died, the farm would be divided among the family's sons. The farm would be split lengthwise, so that each son would still have some portion of the St. Lawrence shoreline. This practice made the farms even more narrow. Eventually there was no room for more farms along the river, so the settlers began to develop a second row, or *rang*, of farms with its own road. Farmers grew wheat, oats, potatoes, peas, and barley.

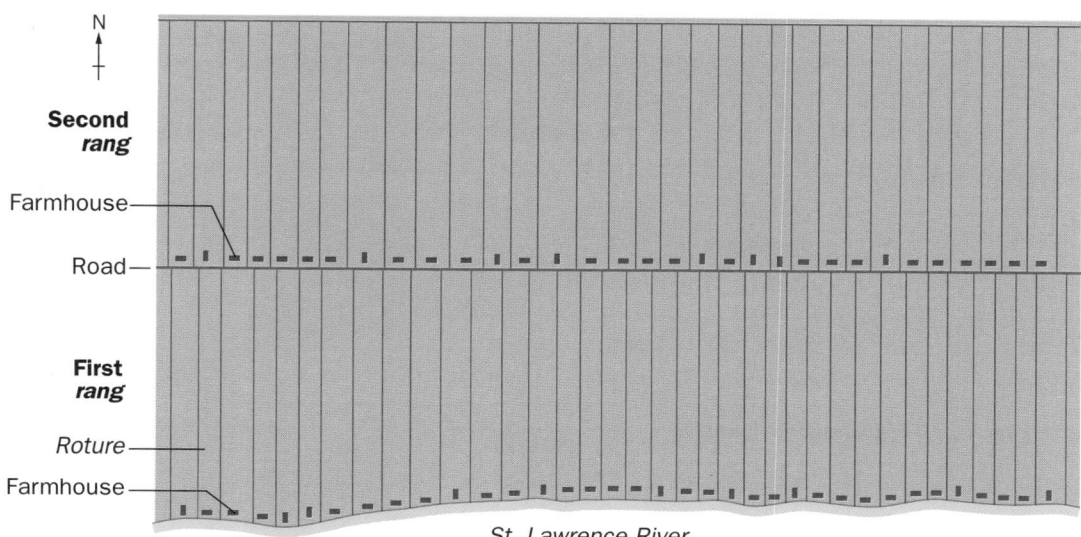

◀ Figure 7.4: The Quebec long-lot system

Notice the shape of the individual farms in Figure 7.4. The farmhouses are all located fairly close to the river or road and close to each other. Take another look at the picture on page 86, which shows the long-lot system as it is today. Many farms are ten times longer than they are wide. You can see the river on which the lots front and the farmhouses along the river's edge.

6. Define the French words *roture* and *rang*.

7. Examine the shape of the average *roture* in Figure 7.4. In settler days, the farmers would use horses to help them plough the fields. Would the shape of the farms be practical for farming? Explain your reasoning.

8. Would farms in the second and third *rang* be more or less desirable than the ones in the first *rang*? Give three reasons to explain your answer.

The Ontario Township System

Settlement began in Ontario after many of Quebec's farms were already well established. The British government controlled the Ontario region at this time. It sent surveyors into the forest to lay out the roads and farms before settlers arrived. They used the St. Lawrence River, Lake Ontario, Lake Erie, and Lake Huron as the foundation for the townships they laid out. **Townships** are areas of land divided up in a grid. The properties tend to be rectangular.

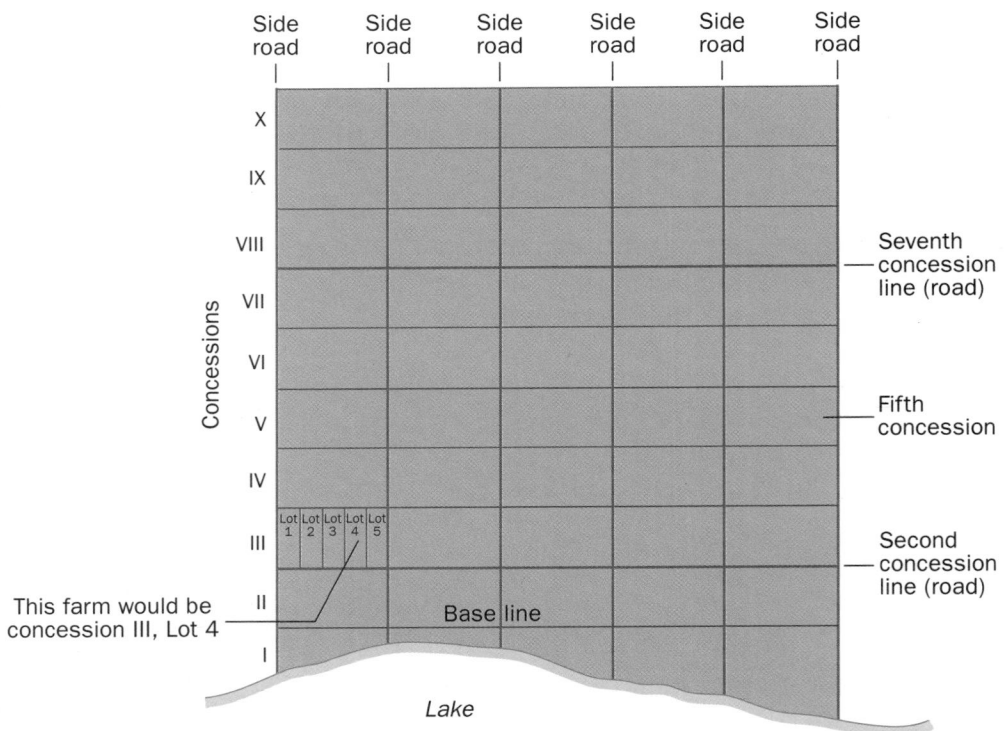

▲ **Figure 7.5:** A typical Ontario township

A base line is a straight line that was drawn parallel to a large body of water, such as Lake Ontario. A base line would provide the base for the whole township. Strips of land, called concessions, were measured off north of the base line and divided by concession lines, which became roads. Side roads were drawn up to run at right angles to each concession line.

Each concession was divided into farms, called lots, that varied in size. The farmhouses would sit back from the road, usually about twenty metres, and were centred along the road about halfway between the two neighbouring farms. If the farm had no stream, there was almost always a well. From the beginning, wheat was by far the most important crop. As in Quebec, the wheat would be sold for much-needed cash. Other crops included peas, barley, and oats (for the horses).

Perhaps you live on a concession line or a side road. In cities such as Sudbury and Hamilton, some of the major streets were originally concession lines. Taunton Road in Oshawa was a concession road. Though it began as a rutted dirt path, it has since become a major commercial street.

9. Describe the size and shape of a) a township, b) a concession, and c) a lot.

10. How far apart were farmhouses in Ontario compared with those in Quebec? How might this factor affect one's sense of community?

11. Examine Figure 7.4 on the previous page and Figure 7.5, above. Compare the pros and cons of the two systems. Keep in mind the point of view of the farmer who had to plant and harvest crops.

CASE STUDY

NEUBERGTHAL:
A DIFFERENT TYPE OF SETTLEMENT

▲ **Figure 7.6:** The village of Neubergthal in southern Manitoba

Prairie settlement featured huge, square farms, with farmhouses scattered far and wide. There were exceptions, however. The case of the Mennonite settlement of Neubergthal shows us a strikingly different pattern, and evidence of a group of people determined to do things their own way.

1. a) Examine Figure 7.6. Name six features, such as types of buildings, that you can see in the photograph.
   b) What signs do you see that this village was planned carefully? Name at least three.

The settlers of Neubergthal were Mennonites, a Christian group. Over the centuries they lived in various areas of Europe and had finally settled in Russia. When the Russian government began to take away their freedom to practise their religion, some Mennonites left and came to Canada. Here they established Neubergthal in 1876. At about the same time, they formed more than 120 other villages in Manitoba.

Rural settlements sometimes reflect the types of housing and road patterns of the area of the world where the settlers came from. Neubergthal was very much like the villages in eastern Europe, where the Mennonites came from. The farmhouses were all built along a main street, so these settlements were called street villages, or **strassendorf**. Some of the original inhabitants built and lived in housebarns, in which the house was attached to the barn. The farmers would travel every day to their farms, which surrounded the town. In the evening they would all travel back to the village. The Mennonites proved to be excellent farmers who showed others how to grow wheat on the Prairies in difficult conditions.

2. a) How was the pattern of settlement in Neubergthal different from the pattern of settlement favoured by other Canadian farmers?
   b) Suggest reasons why the Mennonite settlers may have preferred to live in a *strassendorf*.
3. Parks Canada declared Neubergthal a National Historic Site in 1989. Why might it be important to preserve places such as Neubergthal?

Rural Canada

Early Rural Canada

Until about 1850, Canada was practically all rural. There were no real cities at all—at least no cities as you know them. Even places such as Quebec City and Ottawa were little more than large towns. The land had few large roads, and no cars. Many people farmed enough to feed themselves. In addition, most farmers grew wheat, which they commonly sold to raise the money to pay for needed supplies.

Industries almost all involved the harvesting of the resources of the land or sea. Besides farming, people worked in the forestry and fishing industries. The types of businesspeople that flourished in rural Canada included general-store keepers, blacksmiths (who shoe horses), and millers (who grind grain). All that began to change in the twentieth century.

Rural Canada Today

What is rural Canada like today? Farmers certainly are not ploughing their fields with horses, as they once did. Nor do you attend a one-room school-house. Gradually, the family farm that was passed on from generation to generation is disappearing. In its place, farms are getting very big. These **agribusinesses** are operations that own and farm vast amounts of land. Agribusinesses process products as well. For example, a chicken agribusiness may have huge chicken barns that hold tens of thousands of birds. Not only will the company raise the chickens, it may also butcher and package them, and then transport them to stores.

Other rural activities are changing, too. Natural resources, for example, have been used to develop huge, thriving industries. Tourism is a big source of income in some areas.

GeoTrivia #1
In rural New Brunswick, more than 250 cars crash into moose every year.

12. Compare early rural Canada with rural Canada as it is today.

▲ **Figure 7.7:** A potato farm on Prince Edward Island. Machinery is essential on the modern Canadian farm.

▲ **Figure 7.8:** Small-town Canada

Rural–Urban Migration

A major source of change in rural Canada has been that many people have left the rural areas of Canada and moved to its urban areas. This movement of people has caused **urbanization**, whereby so many people move into rural areas close to existing cities that these areas become urban. What has caused this change?

Many reasons explain this movement of people. One of these is the loss of jobs on farms. As modern machinery has been introduced to Canadian farms, there are fewer and fewer jobs. During the major wars, many young people left the farm to fight overseas or to take jobs in the war industries. Today, some young people leave because they are not so interested in the types of jobs that can be found on farms. Urban Canada (communities of 1000 or more) offers many more jobs in areas such as graphic design, entertainment, and high technology. Some people move to the cities to experience a more exciting way of life, with more things to do and more people to meet.

13. List the reasons people leave rural areas to go to urban areas. Which one do you think is most important? Why?

Year	Rural (%)	Urban (%)	Change in Rural Population Over Previous Decade	Year	Rural (%)	Urban (%)	Change in Rural Population Over Previous Decade
1871	80	20	–	1941	46	54	0%
1881	74	26	-6%	1951	43	57	-3%
1891	68	32	-6%	1961	39	61	-4%
1901	63	37	-5%	1971	35	65	-4%
1911	55	45	-8%	1981	24	76	-11%
1921	50	50	-5%	1991	23	77	-1%
1931	46	54	-4%	2001	20	80	-3%

Sources: Statistics Canada, Series A67-69; *1996 Census of Population, A National Overview* (Catalogue no. 93-357-XPB), Statistics Canada; *Population Counts for Canada*, Census Divisions by Urban and Rural, 2001 Census.

▲ Figure 7.9: Canada's rural and urban population, by percentage, 1871–2001

14. a) Make two bar graphs, one showing the rural population by percentage, and the other showing the urban population by percentage, from 1871 to 2001.
    b) Compare your two bar graphs. What differences do you see?

15. a) In the table in Figure 7.9, look at the columns called "Change in Rural Population Over Previous Decade." During which time period did the rural percentage of Canada's population decrease the most?
    b) What do you think may have led to this decline?

16. Consider what might have happened to Canada if the percentage of people living in rural and urban areas had not changed since 1871. Suggest five ways in which life in Canada would be different today.

A Shrinking World

We saw in the first part of this chapter that cities are growing. This change is having a huge effect on rural communities. To understand why, think about where settlements began in the first place—on fertile land. Only about 10 per cent of Canada's land area is good for farming, and the earliest European settlers chose these areas to settle, for obvious reasons. But the small communities in these areas have grown. Where do they grow? Outward, onto the most fertile land in Canada. About 18 per cent of all Class 1 (the best) farmland is now used for urban purposes. About 50 per cent of all land that is changed to urban uses every year is Canada's very best farmland.

Rural–Urban Fringe

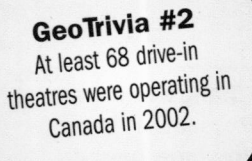

GeoTrivia #2
At least 68 drive-in theatres were operating in Canada in 2002.

The **rural–urban fringe** is where the city and the countryside meet. It surrounds every major city in Canada, and includes a mix of land uses. **Land uses** are the various ways that people use the land. Some land uses are rural land uses, such as farming and campgrounds. Others are urban land uses, such as housing, industry, and businesses. All these can be found in the fringe.

Drive-in theatres and golf driving ranges are good examples of land uses that are usually found only in the fringe. On the one hand, they are not usually located inside the built-up area of a city. On the other hand, they would rarely be found far away from a population centre.

Land uses in the fringe change quickly as the city grows into it. Rural land uses disappear and urban land uses take over. Some buildings and land uses, such as farm buildings and farmland, are abandoned. They lie empty, awaiting development.

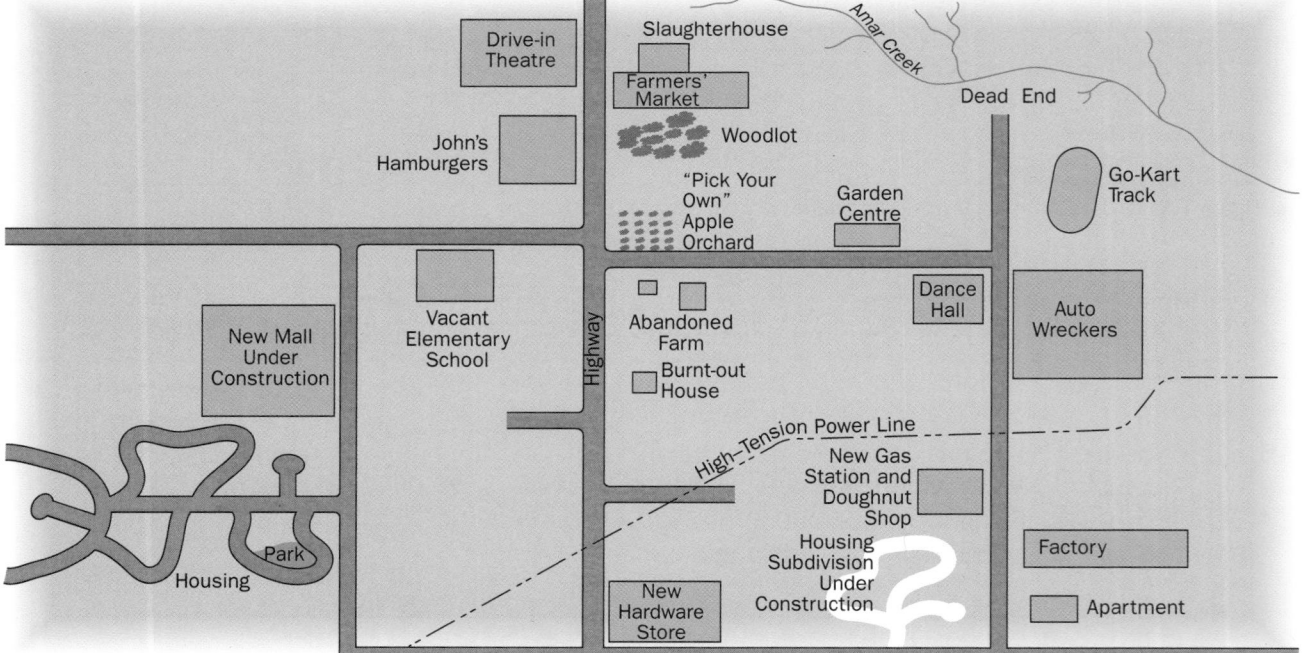

▲ **Figure 7.10:** A typical rural–urban fringe area

17. Examine the diagram in Figure 7.10 on the previous page carefully.
    a) Name six land uses on the diagram: two rural, two fringe, and two urban.
    b) Identify four signs that the nearby city is growing.
    c) In which direction do you think the city is growing? Give two reasons for your answer.

18. a) Are you familiar with or have you seen an area of rural–urban fringe? If not, talk with another student who has. Describe its location as accurately as possible.
    b) Name at least five land uses in this rural–urban fringe area.

19. Imagine that the city in the diagram in Figure 7.10 continues to grow into the area shown on the map. Name four specific changes that you think will probably take place over the next ten years. Give a reason to support each of your answers.

20. Some facilities in the diagram are not in use. Why aren't the owners selling? (*Hint:* Could the owners be waiting for something to happen?)

Loss of Farmland to Cities

As cities grow, the rural–urban fringe moves farther into rural areas. **Urban sprawl** is urban growth that happens quickly. One area seriously threatened with urban sprawl lies about 15 km north of Toronto. This region is called the Oak Ridges Moraine. A moraine is an area of hills that were formed from the debris scooped up and left behind by glaciers. These hills are now the source for the major rivers that run through Toronto. Today this area is mostly forests and farmland, with a few smaller settlements. As Toronto continues to grow, however, the demand for land for housing will increase, especially in beautiful areas like the Oak Ridges Moraine.

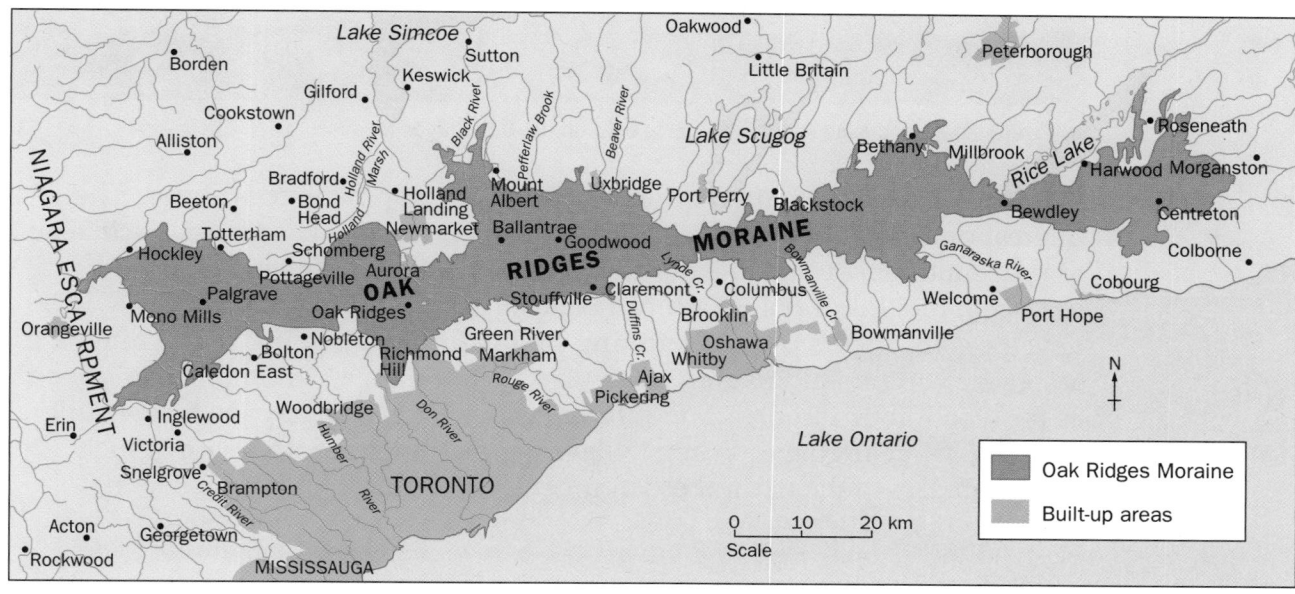

▲ **Figure 7.11:** The Oak Ridges Moraine

21. Examine the map in Figure 7.11 on the previous page. Where do many of the rivers begin that lead south to Lake Ontario and north to Lake Simcoe?

It has been said that if Toronto could be considered to be an eyeball, then the moraine is its eyebrow. Does it look that way to you?

The map of the Oak Ridges Moraine in Figure 7.11 shows the moraine's importance to Toronto as a source of its rivers as well as an area of "green" that people in the city appreciate. As housing spreads into the Oak Ridges Moraine, not only are forests cut down and wildlife numbers reduced, but the rivers become polluted, streams are buried in tunnels underground, and farmland is lost. Many living in the area, as well as residents of Toronto, have become concerned about the future of this beautiful but endangered range of hills. At present, development is continuing in a number of areas, and the debate continues about how to control it.

▲ **Figure 7.12:** A housing subdivision being built on the Oak Ridges Moraine

Many factors can affect whether or not development goes ahead. The interest of developers to develop the land is one factor. The efforts of citizens to prevent or encourage the development is another. Politicians can get involved, too. Local politicians can control where and how much development occurs by using **zoning by-laws**. This planning process involves assigning certain land uses to particular areas, or zones, of land. Areas zoned as parkland, for example, cannot have houses, factories, or even farms built on them. By changing a zoning by-law, a government controls how much change occurs to the natural environment.

22. List the various ways that urban development can affect the environment. Besides the ones given above, think of a few on your own.

23. What might happen if there were no zoning by-laws? Think about the rate of urban sprawl, the organization of communities, and the effect on natural environments.

GeoGames

The Urban Sprawl Struggle

Purpose:

To learn about factors that can influence a pro- and anti-development struggle

Supplies:

- a deck of cards, no jokers
- two playing pieces
- pencil and paper

The Play:

A. Shuffle the deck of cards.

B. Draw up a game board showing 20 spaces from start to finish.

C. Four players divide into two teams.

Two players are in favour of more development in Morelandia Valley, a fictional wilderness area just outside a city:

- a representative of the housing developers
- a person who wants to buy a new home in the area

Two players are opposed to more development in Morelandia Valley:

- a representative of the local residents
- an environmentalist

D. Each team gets one playing piece to share. Your goal is to get your playing piece to the finish before the other team does. Whoever reaches the goal first is the winner—at which point the development is stopped or goes ahead, depending on which side you're on.

E. To move your piece, take turns drawing cards from the deck. The housing developer draws first. You move ahead one space, stay where you are, or move back one space, depending on the card you draw. Find out how you move by checking the chart below.

Card Played	What Happens Next	Pro-development Forces	Anti-development Forces
Ace	A small group of farmers support the development.	move ahead one	move back one
2	You clinch a deal to purchase some marshland.	move ahead one	move ahead one
3	Protesters block the road to the developers' offices.	move back one	move ahead one
4	A television documentary criticizes the developers.	move back one	move ahead one
5	A provincial politician makes part of Morelandia Valley a bird sanctuary.	move back one	move ahead one
6	Banks approve a loan for the housing project.	move ahead one	don't move
7	An Aboriginal burial site is found, but it's not on an area targeted for development.	don't move	don't move
8	A local pro-development mayor pushes through zoning changes that make it legal to build residences.	move ahead one	move back one
9	A protest meeting draws only ten people.	don't move	don't move
10	The provincial government passes legislation to protect habitat in the moraine for an endangered moth.	move back one	move ahead one
Jack	A developer moves in bulldozers to start work.	move ahead one	move back one
Queen	Environmentalists convince a judge to issue an injunction (an order) to stop the building of a road through a forest.	move back one	move ahead one
King	Donations to environmentalist groups fall by 50 per cent.	don't move	move back one

▲ **Figure 7.13:** How you move

Wrap-Up:

1. a) What frustrated you while you were playing the game?
   b) What took place in the game that pleased you? Explain.
   c) Did you agree with the side that you played in the game? Give reasons for your answer.
   d) Suggest three things that you learned about urban sprawl from this game.

2. List as many factors as possible that might cause change in the natural system of Morelandia, according to this game.

Conclusion

In this chapter, you have had the opportunity to learn what rural Canada is like and how it developed. You will have noticed that the rural part of our country is changing very quickly. In some areas, it is even being absorbed into cities. Still, rural Canada remains an important part of our economy, way of life, and future, as you will see in Chapter 9: Gathering Natural Resources.

Wrap It Up

1. Make a chart to compare the three types of settlement pattern you examined in this chapter. (Include the *strassendorf* described in the Case Study.) In your column headings, include General Description, Distance between Farmhouses, Benefits, Drawbacks.

2. Think of two ways that Canadian communities have been influenced by the environment in which they emerge. Think of two ways that Canadian communities have affected the natural environment.

3. Select one rural community and find out the following information by consulting a provincial road map and the Internet. The town's municipal offices will be of great help. Try using such search terms as the town's name, "Ontario," and "town."
   a) Exactly where is the community located?
   b) What roads connect this community to other settlements?
   c) What is the population of the community?
   d) What services does the community provide?
   e) Find out one really interesting fact about this community.

4. What is it like to live in a rural area? Describe the lifestyle of rural residents in areas by looking at the following:
   - types of jobs
   - forms of entertainment
   - where people go to shop
   - why they live where they do

   If you live in a rural area, use some of your own experiences to help you answer this question. If you don't, find out answers by asking someone who has lived in a rural area for some length of time, such as a relative or a student who has recently moved from a rural area.

5. Write a letter to the editor about the issue of urban sprawl. You could write to a newspaper in a small town near Morelandia (the area featured in the GeoGame on pages 129–130) or a newspaper in a region you know of that is experiencing urban sprawl. Predict what will happen to the environment if further development goes ahead. Decide whether or not you support further development. Express your opinion, and include your ideas about the future of this region. Be as specific as you can.

Chapter 8

UNDERSTANDING URBAN PLACES

Life in the City

▲ **Figure 8.1:** Talking about the pros and cons of city life

1. What is the point of this cartoon?
2. Why do people live in cities despite all the problems?

In this chapter, you will
- rank community types according to size
- learn about the various land uses in the city
- conduct a traffic survey
- see how the city is changing and why

Why Cities Are Where They Are

Cities are located where they are for very specific reasons. Someone had to make a decision to establish a community in a particular spot. Why was one spot chosen over another? The usual reasons were access to water and fertile land, but many sites satisfy those requirements. Other factors were involved as well.

- The community had a natural harbour, such as a deep, protected bay on a large lake or ocean. Ships were often used to transport products such as lumber and grain before railways and highways were built.

- The community lay along a river and used running water to power early industries, such as sawmills and flour mills. Water-powered mills were essential before the days of electricity.

- The community developed along a railway as a transfer point for different types of cargo. Wheat, for example, may have been shipped out and manufactured goods shipped in.

- The community developed beside a major highway to serve travellers, offering gasoline, accommodations, restaurants, and tourist attractions.

- The community began at an important road intersection, so people in the surrounding area travelled there for community services.

- The community was close to natural resources, such as fish, forests, and minerals, and may have developed as a centre for related industries, such as fishing, forestry, and mining.

Figure 8.2: ▶
A sawmill in Calgary, Alberta, 1901

3. Examine Figure 8.2. Why did a community grow at this location?

4. Using your atlas, suggest reasons for the location of these cities.
   a) Halifax, NS   c) Prince George, BC   e) Windsor, Ont.
   b) Timmins, Ont.   d) Edmonton, Alta.   f) Chicoutimi–Jonquiere, Que.

5. a) Examine a street map of your community. Identify map symbols that give clues to suggest the origins of your community.
   b) Which of the six factors listed on this page seem to fit your community best? Explain your choice or choices.

Communities Across Canada

You probably live in a town or city. This is a good guess because most Canadians live in urban centres (areas with more than 1000 people). Even the largest cities in Canada began as small centres. As each of these places grew, the nature of the community changed. When Calgary was a town, the roads were made of dirt, and disease was common. This was the case in every early Canadian community. Now Calgary is Alberta's largest city, with all the facilities of a modern Canadian city.

Every major city in Canada progressed through the following **urban hierarchy**, or ranking according to size:

hamlet ⟶ village ⟶ town ⟶ city

The Hamlet

In the early years of Canada's development, most people lived on farms in rural areas. Because they needed goods and services, small centres developed with a few businesses. The **hamlet** is the smallest kind of settlement, with about eight or ten buildings. The services that a hamlet provides are very limited. In the early years, for example, the hamlet might have had a blacksmith. Today a hamlet might have a gas station.

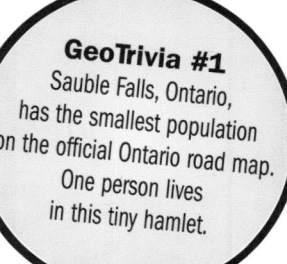

GeoTrivia #1
Sauble Falls, Ontario, has the smallest population on the official Ontario road map. One person lives in this tiny hamlet.

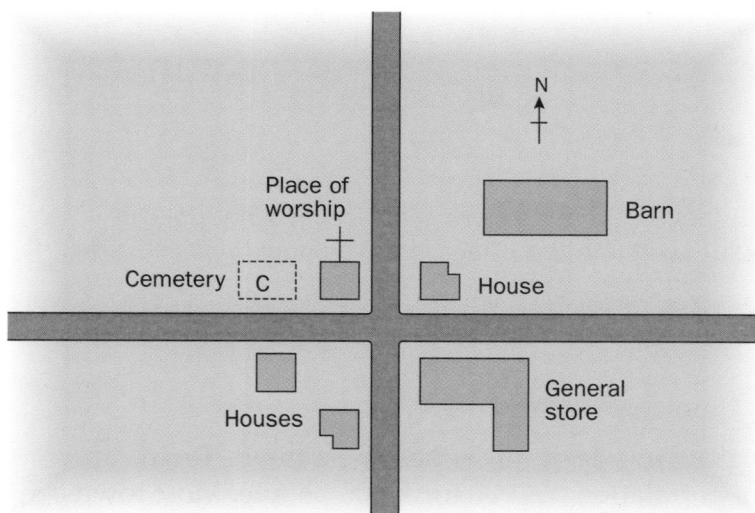

◀ **Figure 8.3:** A typical hamlet in Ontario

All the buildings in Figure 8.3 are clustered around an intersection. This type of settlement is sometimes called a "four-corners community."

6. What services or goods might be provided in this particular hamlet?

Not many people live in hamlets in southern Canada. Some hamlets look much as they did when they were first established. Others have become part of larger settlements. Most Canadian families have cars now, so people tend to travel to larger centres and malls, where they can purchase a wide variety of products. For this reason, the businesses in many hamlets have not survived.

The Village

As more people came to settle in an area, some hamlets grew larger, with more people and more businesses. As they grew, some became **villages**. A village typically has between 200 and 800 people. People travel to villages to buy items that they cannot find in their local hamlet. Hamlets and most villages are considered rural.

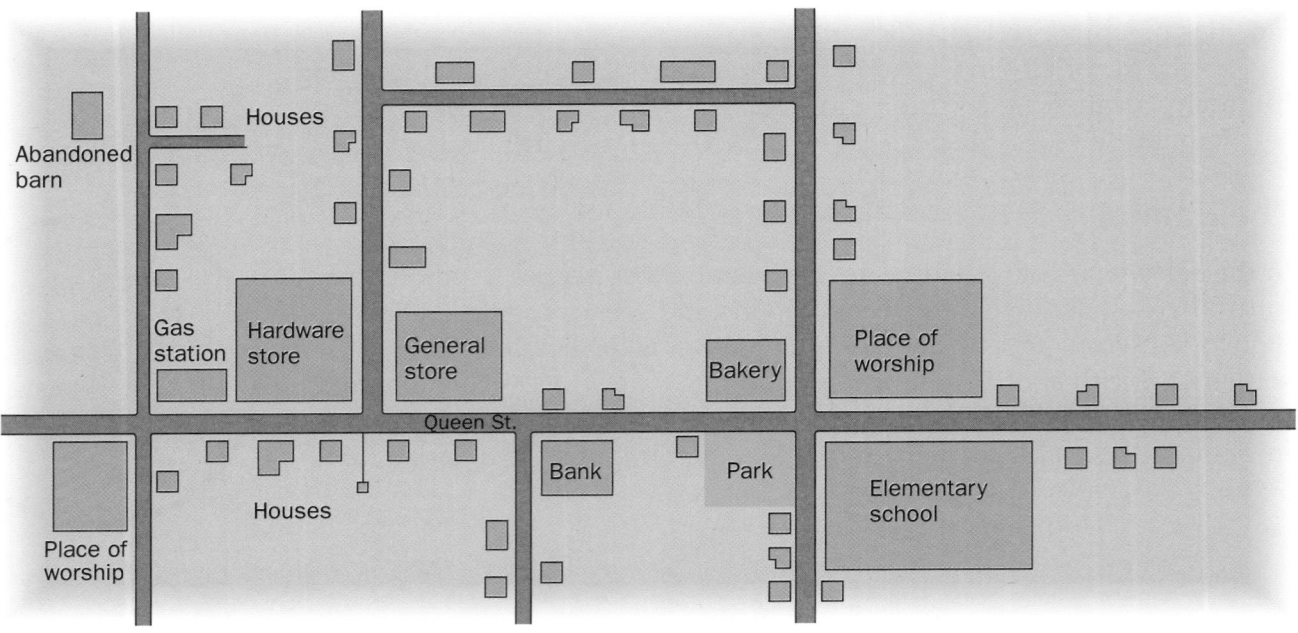

▲ **Figure 8.4:** Centre of a typical village in Ontario

7. Compare Figure 8.3 on page 133 and Figure 8.4, above. What specific services or goods could you get in the village that you could not get in the hamlet?

8. In your opinion, why might someone choose to live in a hamlet?

GeoTrivia #2
The names of a few cities, such as Charlottetown, still have the word "town" in them, even though the community is no longer a town.

The Town

If a village were to grow in size, it might become a town. **Towns** are communities with a population of 1000 to 10 000 people. Most towns have a main shopping area and provide all the main goods and services their residents need.

9. Get a blank sheet of paper to plan your own town with services that can be found in many Canadian towns across the country. Figure 8.4 will give you an idea of the style your map should have. Include the following:
   - a main shopping street with 15 stores including a hardware store, grocery store, video rental store, and bank
   - ten residential streets
   - four places of worship
   - small medical centre
   - four gas stations

- three public parks
- one cemetery
- two small factories
- fire hall

- police station
- bowling alley
- one elementary school
- two fast-food restaurants

On your map, include a title, north arrow, and legend for any symbols that you may have used. (Refer to the GeoSkills feature on page 4 for hints on making a map.)

The City

Towns grow, too, of course. A centre becomes a **city** when it has a population of 10 000 or more people. Most Canadians live in large cities. All cities provide more goods and services than do towns. A town could not support a car dealer for luxury cars such as Rolls-Royce, for example, because there aren't enough potential customers. A large city would have many more potential customers, so virtually every large city has a car dealer that sells luxury cars.

A Rolls Royce is an example of a **high-order good**, a good available only in cities. A specialized health centre is an example of a high-order *service*.

Bread is an example of a **low-order good**, a good sold everywhere. Bread is something most people need, so it is sold even in very small centres. (Specialty breads, however, like hardo bread, are high-order goods.) A hair stylist's shop is an example of a low-order *service*.

10. a) Make a list of ten low-order goods or services that would be sold in almost any size settlement.
    b) Make a list of ten high-order goods or services that would be sold in only very large urban centres.

The industries that are located in a city are important because they bring money into the city. Such industries are part of that city's **economic base**, the industries and businesses that make the community thrive. An automobile plant, for example, can bring millions of dollars into a city because its cars may be sold across the country and even internationally. When the economic base of a city is increasing in size, people go there to work and the city will grow. (The reverse is true when a city's economic base is shrinking.)

Many of Canada's cities have grown so big that there is no rural area between them and neighbouring communities. Such urban areas are referred to as **census metropolitan areas**, or CMAs. A CMA includes all the villages, towns, and smaller cities near the major urban centre. CMAs all have more than 100 000 people.

11. Is your community listed in Figure 8.5 on the next page? What is its ranking?

12. a) Using Figure 8.5, identify the province that has the most cities.
    b) What does the large number of cities tell you about that province in terms of the size of its population?

13. Which province has no cities on this list? Why is this the case?

Census Metropolitan Area	1997 Population	2001 Population	Percentage Change
Toronto, Ont.	4 499 000	4 881 400	+8
Montreal, Que.	3 408 900	3 511 800	+3
Vancouver, BC	1 967 600	2 078 800	+6
Ottawa–Hull, Ont./Que.	1 045 500	1 107 000	+6
Calgary, Alta.	873 200	971 500	+11
Edmonton, Alta.	897 300	956 800	+7
Quebec City, Que.	685 400	693 100	+1
Winnipeg, Man.	677 800	684 800	+1
Hamilton, Ont.	650 400	680 600	+5
London, Ont.	413 100	426 300	+3
Kitchener, Ont.	402 100	431 700	+7
St. Catharines–Niagara, Ont.	385 500	393 100	+2
Halifax, NS	345 300	359 200	+4
Victoria, BC	317 600	318 800	0
Windsor, Ont.	291 600	313 800	+8
Oshawa, Ont.	282 000	305 300	+8
Saskatoon, Sask.	227 600	230 500	+1
Regina, Sask.	199 100	198 100	−1
St. John's, Nfld.	176 500	176 200	0
Chicoutimi-Jonquiere, Que.	162 700	158 700	−3
Sudbury, Ont.	163 900	156 700	−4
Sherbrooke, Que.	151 300	154 900	+2
Trois-Rivieres, Que.	142 200	141 500	−1
Thunder Bay, Ont.	128 500	124 600	−3
Saint John, NB	127 900	128 100	0

Source: Statistics Canada, CANSIM II, table 051-0014, Catalogue no. 91-213-XIB.

Figure 8.5: ▶ Canada's largest CMAs, where just over 64 per cent of all Canadians live. You can see them on the map in Figure 1.16, page 33.

14. a) Calculate the total 2001 population of the six largest cities on the list.
    b) What percentage of the total population of Canada lives in these six largest cities? Use the following formula to work out your answer.

$$\text{Percentage of Canada's 2001 population} = \frac{\text{population of six largest cities}}{31\ 081\ 000\ (\text{Canada's population})} \times 100$$

    c) What does this percentage tell you about where Canadians live?

15. Refer to an atlas to check out maps of industry and natural resources.

    a) How many of the 25 cities have grown between 1997 and 2001? Suggest three reasons why most Canadian cities grew in that five-year period.
    b) How many of the 25 cities lost population between 1997 and 2001? Suggest three reasons why they declined.

16. a) Make a chart to compare life in the city with life in a rural area.
    b) Where would you prefer to live? Why?

Land Uses in the City

In your city, or one you have visited, you have seen homes, stores, offices, factories, roads, schools, and parks, all of which help the city operate. Within each city there are a variety of land uses that meet the needs of the people who live there. As we saw in the previous chapter, governments use zoning by-laws to set aside specific areas for certain land uses. You can guess why it would be wise planning to keep industry far from housing. How would you like it if a slaughterhouse set up shop right across the street from your home?

City land uses include the following:

- residential land uses (homes) (40 per cent)

- commercial land uses (stores and offices) (4 per cent)

- industrial land uses (factories) (6 per cent)

- institutional land uses (schools, libraries, government buildings, and religious centres) (10 per cent)

- recreational land uses (parks and open space) (7 per cent)

- transportation (33 per cent)

GeoTrivia #3
Roads occupy about one-third of all land in the modern Canadian city.

Residential Land Use

The single largest land use in our cities is residential, which uses about 40 per cent of all the land in a typical city. Most cities have housing that suits a variety of income levels and lifestyles, although sometimes low-cost housing is in low supply.

17. Describe the type of city housing in which each of the following people would probably live.
    a) a young college student
    b) an elderly retired couple
    c) a single parent with children
    d) a couple with young children
    e) a wealthy middle-aged family

▲ **Figure 8.6:** In a city, people live in a variety of homes, such as apartments over stores and in towers.

▲ **Figure 8.7:** A new residential area in a suburb of Calgary, Alberta

The type of housing subdivision shown in Figure 8.7 on the previous page is common in the **suburban** areas, or suburbs, of Canadian cities. Suburbs tend to be located around the fringes of cities. They are designed for people who have cars. The long, curving streets of suburban neighbourhoods tend to keep out heavy traffic, but they also discourage walking and keep out buses.

18. a) Examine Figure 8.7. Suggest two reasons why a family with young children might like to live in a subdivision like this as opposed to one with a grid pattern.
    b) In what ways has this area been built with the assumption that every family will own and use a car?

19. Let's assume that you're working at your first full-time job, at the age of 22. You're single with no children. Your task is to find an affordable home for yourself.
    a) In terms of location, what four factors would be important for you?
    b) What four land uses would you not want nearby?
    c) List six features that you would like to have in your home, keeping in mind your level of income.

Commercial Land Use

Commercial land uses include stores and offices and may be found by themselves or in a strip mall or indoor mall. These land uses take up only about 4 per cent of a city's land area. We see them a lot because they tend to be located on busy streets and in areas where there is easy access for cars and public transit.

The **central business district**, or CBD, is the heart of the city: the bustling downtown with many tall office buildings and plenty of stores. For many years, the CBD was the centre where most city dwellers went for both shopping and work, but that situation is changing. Many Canadians now live in the suburbs and shop at suburban retail centres.

▲ **Figure 8.8:** Edmonton's central business district is easy to identify, even from far away.

20. What clues in the photograph in Figure 8.8 tell you that this is a central business district?

21. a) Describe the location of the stores where you and your family do most of your shopping (for example, at a particular mall or the nearest CBD).
    b) Over the last two years or so, what changes have you noticed in the types of stores in your community?

Industrial Land Use

The amount of land occupied by industry is small, usually only about 6 per cent of a city's area. Nonetheless, industrial land is vital to a city because industries employ many people and bring money into the city. Light industry refers to small industrial plants and warehouses. Heavy industry includes large-scale factories, such as steel plants, that produce vast amounts of product and employ a large labour force. Both types of industry tend to locate near transportation routes or railways. Both can be located in an industrial park, which is an area set aside specifically for industries.

▲ **Figure 8.9:** Industrial park in Red Deer, Alberta

22. Why are most industrial parks located on the outskirts of Canadian cities? Think about a) access to highways and airports, b) tax rates, c) access to workforce and markets, and d) noise created by factories.

23. A factory that produces upholstered furniture will need certain things in order to operate. What are they? Think about the supplies it would need, the services it would need (such as electricity), and where the furniture would go after production.

GeoSkills

Doing a Traffic Survey

Purpose

By collecting and analyzing raw data about traffic patterns, we can learn more about land use in a particular area. Planners use traffic data to help them plan for road development, such as whether or not to widen a particular road to accommodate eighteen-wheelers.

As you look at the steps in doing a traffic survey, see how one student, Kareem, did his.

Step 1

Be clear on your assignment. Kareem has been asked to find out how busy the roads are near his school. By counting the number of vehicles that move along the roads nearby, he can determine how dangerous they are to students. His data and analysis can help determine whether or not stoplights, crosswalks, speed bumps, or other traffic measures need to be introduced.

Step 2

Set up a chart in your notebook to record your data. Kareem set up the one in Figure 8.10.

Step 3

Collect your data. First, choose three roads to survey. Choose streets with varying amounts of traffic. Then, over a period of ten minutes for each road, count the number of cars, trucks, and other vehicles that pass the point where you stand. Note the land uses.

	Number of Cars	Number of Trucks	Number of Other Vehicles	Land Uses on the Street
Fifth Street	76	28	6	residential, commercial (with a Wendy's restaurant)
Dora Crescent	2	1	0	residential
Tolloway Road	31	7	1 (tractor)	industrial, commercial

▲ **Figure 8.10:** Kareem's data collection chart

◄ **Figure 8.11:** Choose a nearby intersection to gather your primary data.

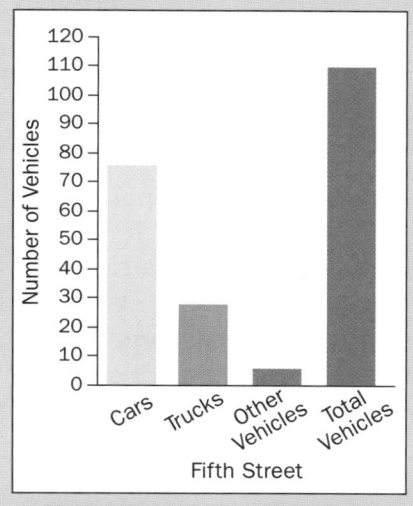

▲ **Figure 8.12a:** Traffic data for Fifth Street

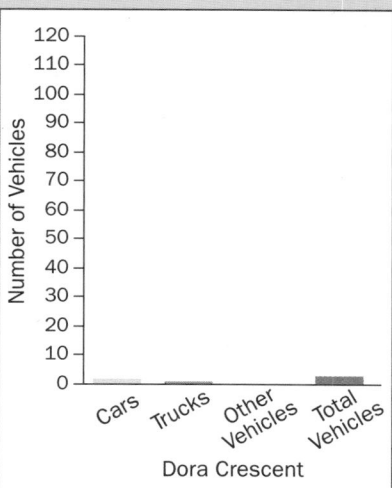

▲ **Figure 8.12b:** Traffic data for Dora Crescent

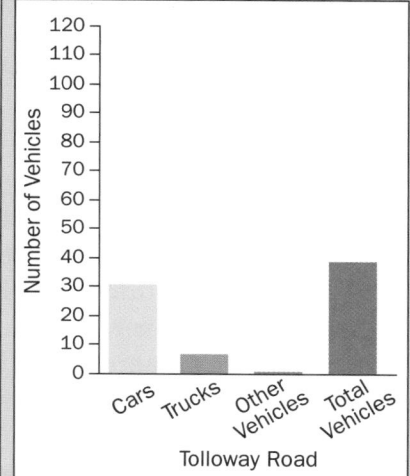

▲ **Figure 8.12c:** Traffic data for Tolloway Road

Step 4

Graph your data. Draw three separate bar graphs, one for each street. Each bar graph will have four bars, one for the number of cars, one for the number of trucks, one for other vehicles, and one for the total number of vehicles. Be sure to label each axis of the graph and give it a suitable title. The scale for each of your graphs should be the same. Kareem made graphs of his data, which you can see in Figure 8.12.

Step 5

Analyze your data. In order to understand the significance of the information you have collected, examine the statistics carefully. Also consider the land uses you observed on the street. Kareem decided that the school should lobby for a crosswalk on Fifth Street, not only because of the higher traffic level, but also because of the fast-food restaurant, which many students visit during lunch hour.

Practise It!

1. Conduct a traffic survey of your own by following Steps 1–5, including data collection and graphing. To aid your analysis (Step 5), answer Questions 2–5.

2. What land uses are located along the busiest street? the least busy street?

3. Which of the land uses along the least busy road would not be suitable for a busy street? Explain your answer.

4. Has the busiest street been built or designed differently than the other streets? Think of factors such as street width. Explain your answer.

To conduct a traffic survey...
- ✔ be clear on your assignment
- ✔ set up a chart for collecting your data
- ✔ collect your data
- ✔ graph your data
- ✔ analyze your data

5. a) Which street has the heaviest volume of truck traffic?
   b) Why do trucks use this street more than the others?

6. a) What vehicles would not be suitable for a residential street?
   b) How could you ensure that these vehicles do not travel along those streets?
   c) How could you slow down the speed of traffic along some of these streets?

Changing Cities

As cities age, they change. Some become more multicultural. Others develop new functions. Perhaps the biggest change of all is size. Most cities grow bigger and bigger, and this isn't always such a good thing.

Bigger and Bigger

How big can cities get? Some cities grow so large that their boundaries touch the boundaries of other cities. When a number of cities grow together like this, they form one huge urban area called a **megalopolis**. Only one megalopolis has emerged in Canada. It swoops around western Lake Ontario from Oshawa to St. Catharines. If you were to drive through this area, you would not be able to see much open space.

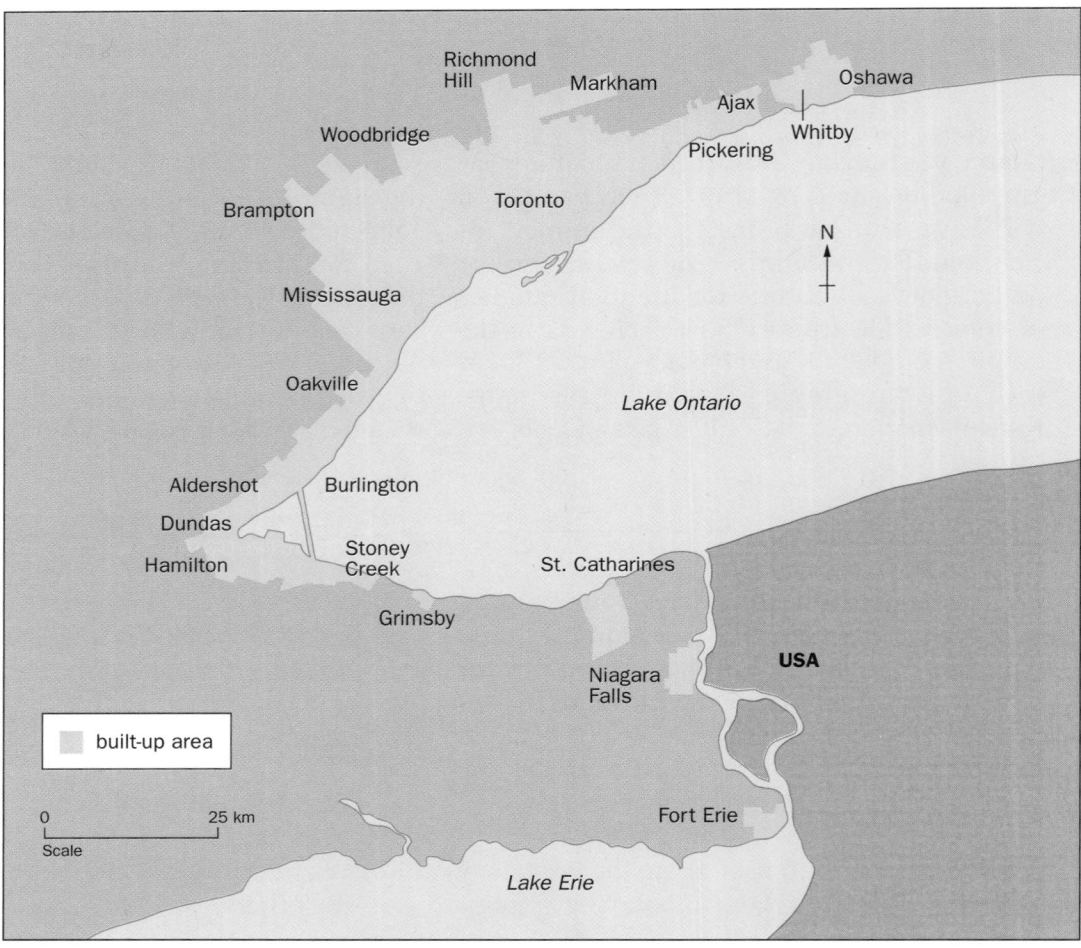

▲ **Figure 8.13:** Canada's only megalopolis

24. Examine Figure 8.13. Assuming that this area will continue to grow in population, name four changes that might occur over the next ten years. For example, more garbage will be going to local landfill sites. These changes can be either positive or negative. Give reasons for each one of your answers.

Modern City Problems

If you live in the city, you probably like it because you have access to things such as sports leagues, movie theatres, and a public transit system. Cities in Canada provide many benefits for their residents, but they also create big problems. As more and more people move to cities, the cities have a hard time coping because of the extra strain on city facilities. Ever been stuck in a traffic jam during rush hour? You probably weren't in a small town. Traffic gridlock wastes a lot of time as people sit in traffic, and also creates air pollution. Building new roads may be part of the solution, but new roads usually become crowded soon after they're built. New public transit projects may help, but they're expensive.

Cities also face problems such as high crime rates, overcrowding in schools, and rundown areas. City governments do what they can, providing services such as recreational facilities and shelters for the homeless. They also make repairs to public transit vehicles, streets, and other city facilities. Canadian cities are presently experiencing a cash crunch. They don't have enough money to fix all the problems. Without new sources of funding, living in or visiting the city may not be as much fun as in the past.

▲ **Figure 8.14:** Hockey star Gary Roberts helps launch the 2002 Reduce Impaired Driving Everywhere (RIDE) program in Scarborough, Ontario.

25. The photograph in Figure 8.14 illustrates a strategy for solving one city problem. Choose another problem faced by modern cities. Explain what causes the problem, how it affects the natural environment, how it makes a community a less pleasant place to live, and suggest potential solutions.

Renewal

If you don't like a report you've been working on, you might choose different approaches for making it better. You might try reorganizing the material, bringing in new material, rewriting material, or even starting again from scratch. Cities with problems can't start from scratch, but they do renew themselves in many ways and on many levels. Here are four types of city renewal:

- renovation
- redevelopment
- land reclamation
- diversifying.

Renovation: On the smallest scale, an individual building is renovated, or altered, to make it useful. In a process called gentrification, an older, rundown house is gutted and completely rebuilt as a nice home. Some renovations alter a building so that it can be used for a different purpose. One example of this would be an older house that is converted into a bookstore. Many large older homes have been modified to become rooming houses in which smaller units or rooms are rented out individually. If you eventually attend university or college, you might live in such a renovated building.

Redevelopment: Another type of renewal is redevelopment, in which one type of building is torn down and another is built in its place. This is most common in older parts of a city when a building has become unsafe and the land has become valuable. In these cases, it makes sense to build a new facility that can generate more money than the old building. A developer can make a lot of money by tearing down an old warehouse, for example, and putting up a new high-rise apartment building. Local governments will change land uses if they believe the redevelopment will benefit the city.

26. a) Imagine you are a low-income individual who used to live in the apartment block that is being blown up in Figure 8.15 on the next page. Explain why you're unhappy about the demolition.
    b) Now imagine you're the buyer of a condominium in the luxury tower that is to be built on the site. Explain why you're happy about the demolition.

Land Reclamation: Another form of renewal, **land reclamation**, involves renewing areas that have become so polluted that they're not being used for anything. For example, plans are in the works to reclaim Toronto's West Don Lands, at the mouth of the Don River. After the zoning by-laws are changed, vacant lots, concrete, and polluted soil will be replaced with parkland and wetlands. This change will improve water quality, restore habitat for wild animals, and provide people with recreational space.

Diversifying: Sometimes renewal is launched on a grand scale. Elliot Lake, for example, is the fifth-largest town in Northern Ontario. It was developed in the 1950s as a uranium-mining town. After the uranium mines

▲ **Figure 8.15:** An old city apartment block coming down to make way for redevelopment

became less profitable, in the 1990s, many people lost their jobs. Elliot Lake faced the possibility of becoming a ghost town. Instead of watching the town run down, the community decided to diversify, or develop new industries. As one of its main efforts, it began to develop facilities for retired people and to market itself as a retirement community. By reducing its dependence on one industry, the community will likely thrive for a long time.

27. Why would it be an advantage for a community to have more than one important industry? Explain your reasoning.

28. Name and explain the four types of renewal.

29. a) Name an area of a city or town that you are familiar with where there has been some change in land use recently.
    b) Describe the types of changes that have taken place.
    c) How will this change affect the community? For example, will it increase traffic or provide new services?

GEO CAREERS   LAND SURVEYOR

Name: Jaro Legat
High School: Stan Staszic, Lublin, Poland
Job Title: Land Surveyor

Jaro Legat works as a registered Ontario land surveyor at Fred G. Cunningham, Inc., a small surveying company he owns with a partner. Much of Jaro's work involves finding and marking the precise location of property boundaries. He also helps determine what can be built on these properties. One project that Jaro worked on recently was a townhouse condominium development. He located and marked the exact dimensions of each property. He then ensured that each townhouse was the proper size and in the right location.

"A lot of people do not understand that when we measure properties, all our measurements are done electronically using laser beams. It is quick and very accurate. After we take the measurements, we go back to the office, where we do all our calculations and drawings on the computer. Things have changed a great deal in the last few years." What hasn't changed is the need for accuracy. People count on Jaro to make sure they build on their own property—and not a neighbour's.

Jaro finds that he must know about city zoning by-laws, construction, law, and architecture. Every day he learns new things that help him become more effective in his job.

Jaro has a Master of Science in surveying. You can get started in this career by getting a certificate in surveying from a community college.

What I like about my work: *What I really enjoy about my work is that every project is different from the one before it. I also have the chance to work with a variety of different people. Sometimes I work outdoors and at times I am inside. My job is anything but boring.*

1. What would you like and dislike about being a land surveyor?

2. What skills do you think you would need for this job?

3. What could you do to develop those skills in yourself?

Conclusion

In this chapter, you have discovered how small communities grow to become larger ones, and why they do so. Most Canadians now live in urban areas that are changing very quickly. We face many challenges as we plan and build our cities. Perhaps the biggest challenge will be to solve city problems without destroying what we love about them.

Wrap It Up

1. a) List the various types of communities in the urban hierarchy.
   b) Besides the four main categories, would you add "megalopolis"? Explain your reasoning.

2. a) Make a chart to investigate land uses in the area where you live.
   - In the first column, list the six land uses on page 137. Add agricultural and wilderness.
   - In the second column, describe what each land use includes.
   - In the third column, give a real local example (e.g., the Singhs' cranberry farm on Twelfth Line).
   - In the fourth and final column, estimate the percentage of the land where you live that is dedicated to that particular land use. Make sure your percentages add up to 100.
   b) Decide if you live in an urban, rural, or fringe area. Justify your opinion by referring to your estimations about land use in the area.

3. About 33 per cent of a city's land area is taken up by roads and 40 per cent by homes. Consider the following developments.
   - a downtown apartment tower built on reclaimed industrial land
   - a dense townhouse subdivision built near a public transit route
   - a new community of large detached homes built on farmland on the outskirts of a city

In a chart, compare the effects of these neighbourhoods on the natural environment.

Consider the land on which the development was built, the amount of land required for roads, and the pollution that will be created by the people living in these neighbourhoods.

4. Select a city. It could be your own or one with which you are familiar.
   a) Name ten different activities that take place in the central business district (CBD) of that city.
   b) Does the CBD appear to be growing or not? Explain how you know.
   c) What does your answer from part (b) tell you about the economy of the city you have chosen? Explain.
   d) Assume you are the mayor of the city you have chosen. What would you propose to make the CBD more welcoming to i) business, ii) tourists, and iii) consumers?

5. Select an urban problem that affects urban areas near you. For the problem that you have selected, research and write notes about the following. You may wish to consult the community's municipal Web site, or search the local papers.
   a) Give four specific examples of this problem.
   b) What specific impact does this problem have on the lives of people?
   c) Can this problem be solved completely or not? Give reasons for your answer.
   d) What three steps would you recommend to reduce the seriousness of this problem now?
   e) Prepare to present your chosen problem and proposed solutions in class.

Unit 2 Performance Task

URBAN CANADA SCRAPBOOK

What is urban Canada like? A hundred years from now, people might wonder what life was like way back at the beginning of the twenty-first century. Your task is to create a scrapbook about urban Canada for your descendents. Your scrapbook will help them see what cities and towns are like today, including problems and potential solutions.

You will need a big, blank scrapbook in which you will paste the information you gather, and then add your analysis. Design a title page for your scrapbook. Be sure to make the page neat. Set aside space for a table of contents.

To begin, let's look at the population of the sixth-largest Canadian city: Mississauga.

Assignment ■: A Population Pyramid of Mississauga

One way to understand a community is to examine its population by age group and gender. Mississauga is a city near the western edge of Toronto's CMA. It has a population of about 610 000. You can see the population by age and gender in Figure 2 on the next page.

1. Examine the population statistics for Mississauga in Figure 2 and draw a population pyramid for the city.

(Refer to the GeoSkills feature on pages 97–98.)

2. a) Using your population pyramid, describe the characteristics of the population in Mississauga.
    b) Which single age group is the largest for the city?
    c) People in this age group have particular needs and concerns. What might these be?

▲ **Figure 1:** These Canadians in Mississauga—like Canadians everywhere—love their doughnuts.

3. a) What will the population pyramid for Mississauga probably look like in fifteen years?
    b) If you were to plan for the future of Mississauga, what types of facilities would you build to meet the needs of the population in fifteen years?

Mississauga, Ont.	Males	Females
0–19 years	89 755	84 575
20–44 years	117 330	125 085
45–64 years	70 170	71 860
65+ years	22 930	29 220
Source: Statistics Canada, 2001 Census.		

▲ **Figure 2:** Population of Mississauga by age and gender, 2001

Assignment ②: Mapping Canada's Growing and Declining Urban Places

Some Canadian towns and cities have been growing quickly while others have been shrinking in size. Examine the lists below of the ten fastest-growing communities and the ten fastest-declining ones.

1. a) Using an atlas, find the locations of each of the towns and cities listed below. Show their location on a blank map of Canada, using one symbol to show communities increasing in size, and another symbol to show communities decreasing in size.
    b) In which province were most of the fastest-growing municipalities? What do you think this shows about that particular province?

2. Select three communities that grew very fast. By referring to thematic maps in an atlas, suggest one reason to explain why each community might have increased so quickly. Try maps that show mining locations, fossil fuel locations, forestry centres, and major cities.

3. a) In general, what do you think might cause a community to decline in size?
    b) Select three communities that declined very fast. By referring to thematic maps in an atlas, suggest one reason to explain why each community might have shrunk so quickly. Try the maps listed in Activity 2, above.

Growing Towns and Cities	1996	2001	Change
Cochrane, Alta.	7 424	11 798	+58.9%
Sylvan Lake, Alta.	5 184	7 493	+44.5%
Strathmore, Alta.	5 314	7 621	+43.4%
Wasaga Beach, Ont.	8 698	12 419	+42.8%
Vaughan, Ont.	132 549	182 022	+37.3%
Okotoks, Alta.	8 528	11 664	+36.8%
Saint-Colomban, Que.	5 569	7 520	+35.0%
Rocky View, Alta.	23 326	30 688	+31.6%
Barrie, Ont.	79 191	103 710	+31.0%
Richmond Hill, Ont.	101 725	132 030	+29.8%
Source: Statistics Canada, 2001 Census.			

▲ **Figure 3:** The ten fastest-growing communities in Canada

Declining Towns and Cities	1996	2001	Change
Greenstone, Ont.	6 530	5 662	−13.3%
Mackenzie, BC	5 997	5 206	−13.2%
Guysborough, NS	5 942	5 165	−13.1%
Kirkland Lake, Ont.	9 905	8 616	−13.0%
Marystown, Nfld.	6 742	5 908	−12.4%
Prince Rupert, BC	17 414	15 302	−12.1%
Elliot Lake, Ont.	13 588	11 956	−12.0%
Comox–Strathcona, BC	8 615	7 584	−12.0%
Gaspe, Que.	16 517	14 932	−9.6%
Baie-Comeau, Que.	31 795	28 940	−9.0%
Source: Statistics Canada, 2001 Census.			

▲ **Figure 4:** The ten fastest-declining communities in Canada

Assignment ③: Analyzing an Article about One Community

Kirkland Lake is a community in decline. Read the following article to better understand what takes place in towns and cities that are struggling with a declining population.

Kirkland Lake—Down But Not Out

by Kate Harries

That's how residents here respond to last week's [2001] census figures that show 1200 people left this once-prosperous mining community since 1996.

That decline of 13 per cent is the fourth-highest in Canada among municipalities of more than 5000 people, and the second-highest in Ontario. Only 8600 people remain.

"Kirkland Lake's not going to become a ghost town," insists Fred Lang, owner of a bowling alley. "Kirkland Lake will bounce back. We are the hub of the North." ...

The signs in store windows along Government Road tell the continuing story of decline, one that started in the 1960s when the population was 20 000 and the mines started to close, the last one shutting down in 1999.

For Rent. For Sale. New Price. Going out of Business. Brodee J's, a popular eatery, has closed. Eight-foot-high snowbanks encroach on potholed streets.

The snow, after several winters of reduced precipitation, is good news. Snowmobiles are lined up outside motels, their drivers coming from as far away as New York, Pennsylvania, and

▲ **Figure 5:** In one plan to provide jobs in Kirkland Lake, garbage from Toronto was to be shipped north to fill the empty Adams Mine. Environmentalists and the First Nations (above) joined forces and stopped the plan.

Michigan to cruise the wide trails that circle down to the Tri-towns area and loop up to Cochrane and Timmins.

"There's huge business in Skidooing," says Bill Enouy, the town's irrepressible and combative mayor. He has been working with the mayor of Rouyn–Noranda, just over the Quebec border, on an interprovincial package: one visit, two cultures.

They hope a joint promotional campaign and a harmonization of permits will bring Quebec's European snowmobilers to

Kirkland Lake and entice this area's US visitors to La Belle Province. ...

Of great symbolic importance is the acquisition of the former Macassa mine and four adjacent mines by a Vancouver company, Foxpoint Resources Ltd.

Foxpoint president Brian Hinchcliffe says the rising price of gold and a non-unionized labour force make it an economic proposition. He expects to have hired 150 to 200 people by the first quarter of next year. ...

continued on the following page

[Finally, there is a controversial] proposal by Vancouver-based Bennett Environmental Inc. for an incinerator that would remove PCBs, dioxins, and other dangerous chemicals from contaminated soils to be shipped here from across North America.

"I'll bet you 90 per cent of Kirkland Lake is in favour of it," says Enouy.

And, indeed, a spirited fight is shaping up over the Bennett project between ... Kirkland Lake's business community, and farmers and environmentalists from the Timiskaming area to the south. ...

People—especially the young—are voting with their feet as northern communities struggle to survive. The exodus that removed 29 000 people

between 1996 and 2000 is playing out almost everywhere, with most—21 000—headed to southern Ontario, according to Statistics Canada's François Nault.

Source: Kate Harries, "Snow, Smoke Are Inspiration for Town Built on Mining," *The Toronto Star*, Saturday, 23 March 2002, p. E4.

1. a) What is the reason that Kirkland Lake has gone into decline?
   b) Give three specific examples of decline in the town.

2. a) Outline three proposals to bring new jobs to the town.
   b) For each one, decide whether or not you believe it is a wise choice. Explain your conclusion.

3. On the basis of this article, what do you think will happen to Kirkland Lake over the next ten years? Explain your prediction.

4. Test your prediction. Use the Internet to research if new businesses or industries have started in Kirkland Lake.

5. Name a community you know that is struggling economically. How do you know? How is the community coping?

Assignment 4: Summarizing Urban Community Issues

As the final section in your scrapbook, you will present newspaper articles about urban Canada, both its character and the problems it faces.

1. Using local and at least some national newspapers, find articles or advertisements about different aspects of town and city life. The articles can focus on one community or Canadian urban communities in general. You may clip the articles from newspapers at home, photocopy articles from newspapers at the library, or print out articles from the Internet. These are the topics that you will research:

   • ethnic groups within the community (3)
   • attractions of the community (3)
   • businesses in the community (5)
   • what people do for recreation and entertainment (5)

   • problems in the community (4)
   • proposed changes for the community (3)

   Beside each one of the topics listed above is a number. This indicates the minimum number of articles or advertisements you need for that particular topic.

2. Organize your articles by topic, and glue them into your scrapbook. Leave space under each article. In this space, write a short summary of four to five lines.

3. At the end of your newspaper clippings, write your summary of urban Canada. For each topic, write about at least one aspect that you feel is important. For example, select one problem that Canadian urban places face and briefly discuss it. Your summary should be at least one-half page long.

ECONOMIC INTERACTIONS

The Somewhere in Canada Contest #3

How have you done in these contests so far? Try your powers of investigation again, this time with the Somewhere in Canada Contest #3. Where in Canada do you think this photograph might have been taken? If you're not sure, look at the clues below.

CLUE 1 The extensive mixed forest tells you this is a rural area. If you look carefully, though, you'll see a city in the distance.

CLUE 2 The city is in Northern Ontario, right on the Canadian Shield. It has a very rocky landscape, with forests surrounding it and 330 lakes inside its boundaries.

CLUE 3 This city has one of the largest nickel deposits in the world.

CLUE 4 Find the largest human-made structure in the photograph. This is the tallest smokestack in the world.

CLUE 5 Inside the city is a park called Big Nickel Park. It features a nine-metre-high copy of a Canadian five-cent coin.

What Will You Study in This Unit?

Can you guess why the city shown in the photograph developed where it did? Two valuable minerals—copper and nickel—were discovered here, and an important mining town took root in the region. A similar story can be told about communities all over Canada. Different industries developed, depending on the natural and human-made advantages found at a particular location.

In this unit, you will learn about the different types of economic activity that are common in the various regions of Canada. You'll encounter everything from Alberta's cattle ranching, to the automobile industry in southern Ontario. You will learn about the high-tech companies in specialized locations, as well as the service businesses that exist in every community. These are all part of Canada's economic systems.

Economic systems may be the most striking example of how Canada's human systems have teamed up with our physical systems. The way that we use natural resources can improve our economic living standard. But if we follow unwise practices, our economic activities can harm the environment and decrease our quality of life.

How does economic activity affect your life? Canada has a healthy economy based on natural resources, ingenuity, skilled workers, and world trade. A country with a healthy economy can provide young people with a real chance to prepare for a career. Get ready, and Canada's economic systems will have a good job for you one day.

In this unit, you will

- examine primary, secondary, tertiary, and high-technology industries

- analyze ways that Canadians use resources in Canada

- explain why different types of economic activity develop where they do

- understand how economic systems are linked by transportation and communication networks

For a challenge, try the Unit 3 GIS activity, "Mineral Mapper," on page 339.

Chapter 9

GATHERING NATURAL RESOURCES

Where's That Burger From?

Imagine you're walking along a street in small-town Ontario. You and your friends get a craving for some fast food, so you drop in at a fast-food outlet. You decide on a hamburger, fries, and pop. As you wait for your order, your mind wanders and you start thinking about what you're about to eat. What goes into a hamburger, anyway, and where does it come from?

There is no simple answer to this question because many ingredients go into a hamburger. Have a look at the photograph in Figure 9.1 below to see where your fast-food meal came from.

Packaging:
• paper from Quebec

Pop:
• sugar from Quebec
• water from Ontario

Hamburger:
• beef from Alberta
• wheat (to make bun) from Saskatchewan
• cheese from Ontario
• tomato from California

Fries:
• potatoes from Prince Edward Island
• canola (to make cooking oil) from Manitoba
• vinegar from New York
• salt from Quebec

Fork:
• oil (to make fork) from Alberta

Ketchup:
• tomatoes (to make ketchup) from California

Mustard:
• mustard seed (to make mustard) from Ontario

▲ **Figure 9.1:** Where does your fast-food meal come from?

1. On a blank map of North America, show where each item in the photograph in Figure 9.1 came from. Draw a line from each source to your community. Which item travelled the farthest?

2. Choose three items, and suggest why each item originated where it did.

Words to Know

primary industry
fishery
aquaculture
location factor
hardwood
softwood
direct employee
indirect employee
selective cutting
clear-cutting
sustainable
mineral

In this chapter, you will

• **identify Canada's primary industries**
• **find out about the jobs they provide**
• **learn how they use raw materials to create wealth**
• **assess location factors using photographs and maps**

Canada's Primary Industries

Most of the raw materials that go into a fast-food meal are products of **primary industries**. These industries produce the raw materials that are eventually processed or manufactured into finished products. The farms that produced the meat for your burger, the potatoes for your fries, and the sugar for your pop are all examples of primary industries. So is the oil well in Alberta that produced the oil that was manufactured into the plastic fork you used.

3. What are primary industries?

4. Besides those mentioned above, identify three other items in the photograph on the previous page that are made by these three primary industries: grain farming, dairy farming, and forestry.

Certain primary industries are suited to Canada because of our natural environment. Rice farming, for example, is not a Canadian primary industry because our climate is not suitable. Look at the pictures below, and decide which Canadian primary industry is being illustrated in each photograph.

▲ Figure 9.2: Canada's four most important primary industries

5. The four primary industries pictured in Figure 9.2 on the previous page took place in New Brunswick, Newfoundland and Labrador, Saskatchewan, and Ontario. List the four primary industries, matching each one to a picture in Figure 9.2 (identify pictures by letter). Then match each industry with the correct location. You may wish to consult a natural resource map of Canada to aid you in your answers.

The Fisheries

You may go fishing in the summertime, and—if you're lucky—catch a big one. Perhaps you're happy you don't have to depend on the fish you catch to make a living. But many Canadians do fish for a living. The fishing industry has supported Canadian communities for many thousands of years, and continues to do so in both Aboriginal and non-Aboriginal communities.

The **fisheries** are commercial fishing operations, not private, recreational fishing. The major Canadian fisheries take place in the Atlantic and Pacific Oceans, and in the fresh waters of the Great Lakes and Lake Winnipeg.

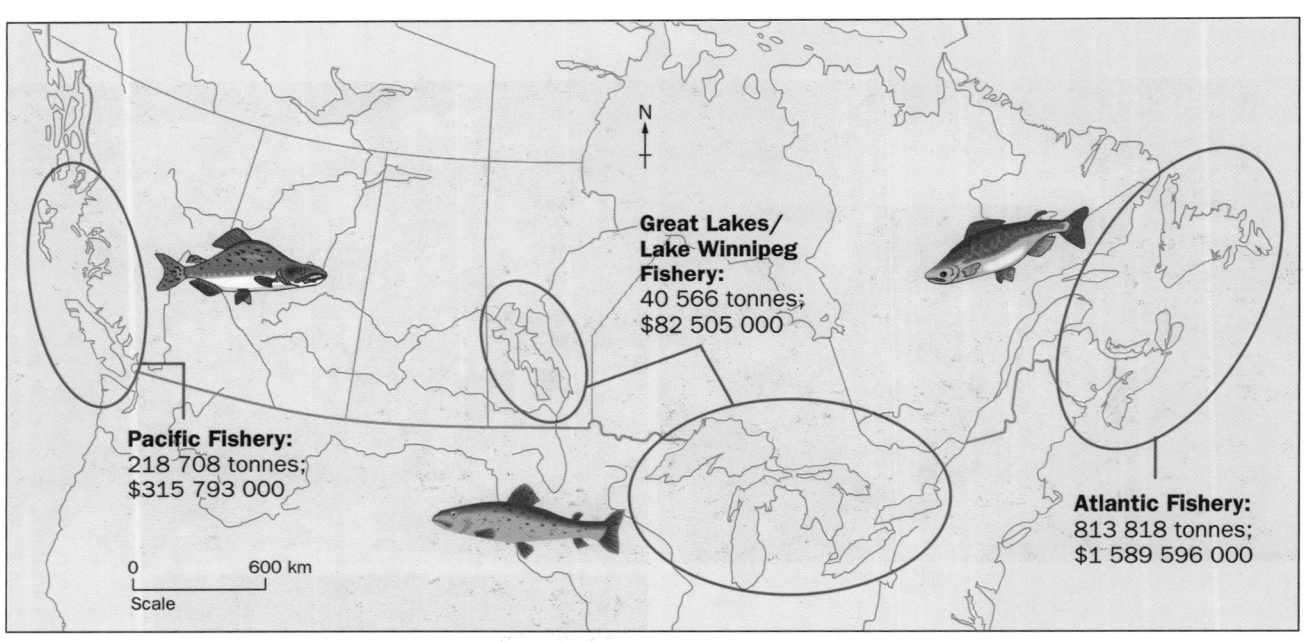

Great Lakes/ Lake Winnipeg Fishery:
40 566 tonnes;
$82 505 000

Pacific Fishery:
218 708 tonnes;
$315 793 000

Atlantic Fishery:
813 818 tonnes;
$1 589 596 000

0   600 km
Scale

▲ **Figure 9.3:** The weight and monetary value of the fish caught in Canada in 1999

6. Which fishery is the largest in Canada? How many times larger is it than each of the other two fisheries? Make your calculations by dividing the value of the largest fishery by the value of each of the other fisheries.

In 1999, about 24 200 commercial fishing vessels were registered in Canada. Some of these were independent fishers, who catch their fish on both big and small boats. They sell their catch to seafood companies for processing and shipping to market. In addition, fishing companies operate fishing fleets and huge fishing ships on the ocean. Some of these are Canadian ships fishing in both Canadian and international waters. Some of them are foreign ships that buy licences to fish in Canadian waters.

For various reasons, the populations of some fish species, particularly cod, have dropped substantially. The possible reasons include overfishing, global warming, and technology that is so effective it has become easier to find and catch fish. Echo sounders for finding fish, and well-designed, massive nets for catching them, are two examples of effective fishing technology. Commercial fishers have shifted from high-volume, lower-priced species of fish (like cod). Now they concentrate more on high-value shellfish, like lobster, scallops, shrimp, and snow crab. Value per tonne fished in 2000 was $2058, compared with $600.53 in 1992.

7. Usually, "more" technology is considered a good thing because it can bring many benefits. In the case of fishing, technology could be considered both good and bad. Explain.

Fish Processing

The fishing industry does not just catch fish. It also processes, ships, and sells seafood products. Canadian seafood companies purchase fish from Canadian fishers to process the fish and bring them to market in central Canada and the United States. In addition, these companies buy fish from foreign-registered vessels. Many ships from Spain, Norway, and Japan regularly sell some of their catch to Canadian processing companies.

▲ **Figure 9.4:** A fish processing plant in Sainte-Marie, Quebec

Over 90 per cent of Canada's fishing industry takes place in rural, coastal areas. Processing operations also cluster along coasts and lakefronts. Although these locations are somewhat remote, they bring the processor close to the source of the fish and other seafood products. Ever smelled a rotten fish? Not a pleasant experience. Fish spoil quickly, so they must be brought into port fast. After being frozen or refrigerated, the fish can then be transported safely by road, rail, or ship all over the world. High-value catches, such as live lobster, are flown to France and other European countries, for sale in stores and restaurants.

8. Fishing captains are not the only people who make a living from the fishing industry. Brainstorm a list of ten careers that exist either directly or indirectly because of the fishing industry. Check the text for hints (for example, the truck driver who transports fish to market).

Aquaculture

Aquaculture is fish farming. Instead of catching fish in the wild, the people who run aquaculture businesses grow fish and other seafood products. In a sense, they are the farmers of the sea. Some grow trout or salmon in fish ponds. Others grow fish, oysters, mussels, or clams in netted-off areas in the salt water of protected bays by the ocean. In 1999, aquaculture production in Canada was 113 083 tonnes, valued at $558 million. Aquaculture provides an alternative to the traditional fishing industry, in which many people have lost their livelihoods as the numbers of fish have decreased.

GeoSkills

ASSESSING LOCATION FACTORS USING PHOTOGRAPHS AND MAPS

▲ **Figure 9.5:** A fish plant in Rose Blanche, Newfoundland

Purpose

Geographers and businesspeople study photographs and maps to identify location factors for businesses. **Location factors** are the reasons why a business locates where it does.

Companies set up businesses in particular places for good reasons. So why do fish processors locate their plants so far away from most of their markets in central Canada and northeastern United States? Take the following steps to assess the photograph in Figure 9.5, which shows a fish plant, and Figure 9.6, which shows a map of the area, to figure out why the company located its plant where it did.

Step 1

Analyze the photograph. You probably spotted the ocean right away. Rose Blanche is on the southwest coast of Newfoundland. You also probably spotted the fishing boat. Rose Blanche clearly provides a protected harbour, making it easy for fishing boats to bring their catch to land even in rough weather. Road access is also available.

Step 2

Analyze a map of the area. As you can see on the map in Figure 9.6, Rose Blanche is close to the Grand Banks. This shallow ocean area provides excellent fishing grounds. From the map, you can also see that Rose Blanche is close to the ferry that runs to the mainland, and has good road access to the central Canadian and northeastern American markets.

Step 3

Relate your findings to your knowledge of the business. Perhaps you remember from the previous page that fish must be brought into port and processed quickly to remain fresh. Access to rich fishing grounds and a safe harbour both contribute to achieving this goal. Perhaps you also recall that the fish industry's main markets are Quebec, Ontario, and the

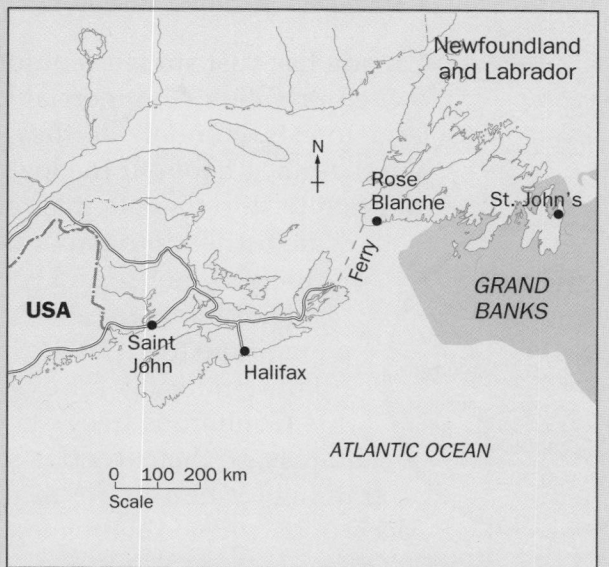

▲ **Figure 9.6:** Location of Rose Blanche in eastern Canada

United States. The ferry and the highways to these locations can be used to transport frozen seafood products to market by truck.

> **To assess location factors using photographs and maps...**
> ✔ analyze information in the photograph
> ✔ analyze information in a map
> ✔ relate what you find out to what you already know

Practise It!

1. Using Steps 1–3, assess the location factors for the aquaculture operation shown in the photograph in Figure 9.7. Refer to a map in your atlas to find Bras d'Or Lake in Nova Scotia, where this photograph was taken.

▲ **Figure 9.7:** A fish-farming operation in the freshwater lake of Bras d'Or, Nova Scotia

Forestry

Canada has vast stretches of forest, some owned by government and some owned privately. Commercial logging companies harvest the trees in these large forests. Not only do they cut down trees, they also build logging roads, assess timber, haul out the logs, ship them to sawmills, cut them into lumber, and finally ship them to market. Depending on the type of trees being cut, they are turned into paper products, like the pages of this book, or wood products for house and commercial construction.

Deciduous trees—broadleaf trees—are called **hardwoods**. They take a long time to grow, so their wood is dense and hard. Hardwood is used to make flooring, for example, and fine furniture.

Coniferous trees—evergreens—are called **softwoods**. They can grow quickly, so their wood is soft, not dense. Softwood is used to make the framing for houses, for example, and roofing shingles. (You read about deciduous and coniferous trees in Chapter 3 on page 60.)

GeoTrivia #1
A small Eastern Canadian Black Spruce tree with a trunk 15 cm wide at chest height can produce 12 500 sheets of computer paper, or 62 500 $20 bills.

9. Explain the difference between hardwoods and softwoods.

10. Which wood—hardwood or softwood—do you think would be used to make a) baseball bats, b) packing crates, c) chopsticks, and d) skateboards? Explain your choices.

Taking Out the Trees

The harvesting and management of forests requires huge machines and lots of money. In 2000, over $57 billion was invested in Canadian forestry companies to pay for the buildings, machines, transportation systems, employees, and licences required to carry on the industry.

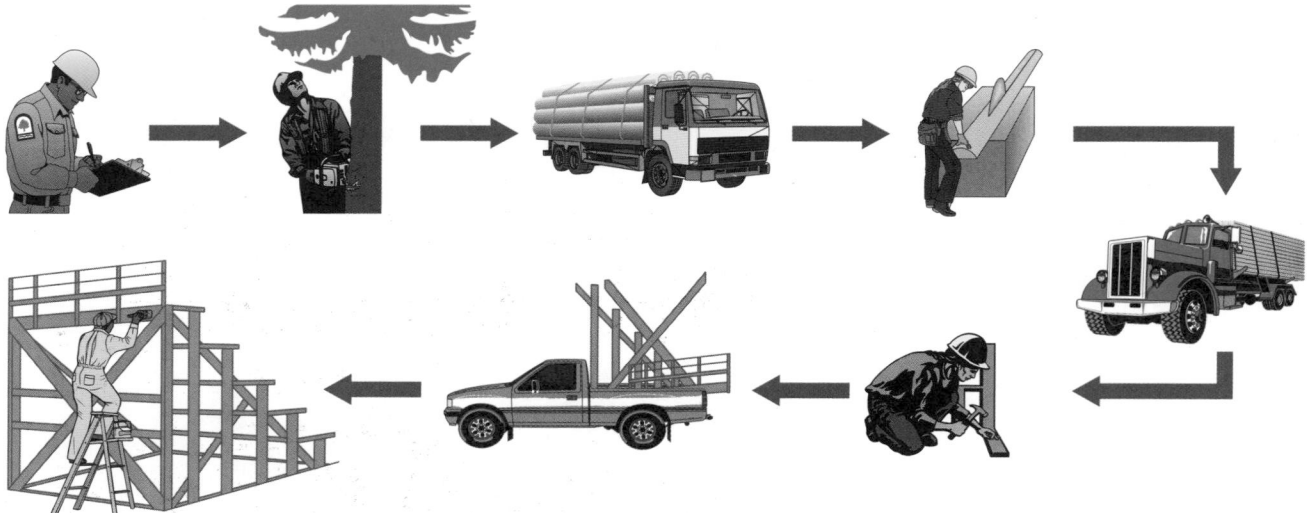

▲ **Figure 9.8:** The route from getting a logging licence to sitting in the bleachers

Harvested trees must be transported over long distances to market. Some travel overseas as rough logs. Others are made into lumber and then sold both in Canada and abroad. Many of British Columbia's largest customers for construction lumber, for example, are the southern United States, California, Arizona, and New Mexico. Large trucks, like the one in Figure 9.2 on page 155, take the tree trunks first to the lumber mill to be cut into wood planks, and then to customers in the final market.

11. Many steps must take place from the time a company purchases the rights to harvest a softwood forest, to the time you sit on the wooden bleachers made from the trees in that forest. Put the following list in order to follow the process shown in Figure 9.8.
    * cut trees; trim branches
    * erect components into bleachers
    * manufacture lumber into bleacher components
    * mill trees into lumber at mill
    * obtain licence to cut forest
    * deliver bleacher components to school
    * truck lumber to bleacher factory
    * truck logs to sawmill

Forestry in Canada

The largest commercial forests in Canada are in New Brunswick, Quebec, Ontario, and British Columbia. The forest industry is of great importance to Canada's economy, as the table in Figure 9.9 shows.

Quick Facts about Forestry in Canada, 2000	
Total sales: $59 billion	Amount exported: $48 billion
Percentage of Canada's total exports: 12%	Number of direct employees: 257 500
Number of indirect employees: 772 500	Total log harvest: 196 million m²
Source: Forest Products Association of Canada, "Quick Facts," <www.fpac.ca/english/facts/index.htm>.	

▲ **Figure 9.9:** The forest industry in Canada, 2000

Direct employees of an industry are people working for companies in that industry. Direct employees in forestry, for example, are those people working for forestry companies. **Indirect employees** of an industry work in support roles. Those who teach the children of families employed in the logging industry, for example, are indirect employees. So are cashiers in the supermarkets where forestry workers shop for groceries.

12. a) Refer to Figure 9.9. How many people worked in the forestry industry in 2000? How many were indirect employees of the forestry industry? In total, how many Canadians owe their employment to the forest industry?
    b) Calculate what percentage of the Canadian population is employed both directly and indirectly by the forestry industry. Divide the total number of employees—your answer to part (a)—by the Canadian population in 1999 (30 491 000) and then multiply by 100.
    c) What conclusions can you reach about the forestry industry in Canada?

13. Compare the total sales from the Canadian forestry industry in 1999 with the total exports. What do these figures tell you about the relative importance of exports in forestry?

Affecting the Environment

Forestry companies use several different methods to harvest wood. One is **selective cutting**, in which foresters identify particular trees to come down. Only these trees are cut down and taken out of the forest. The most common method of forestry is **clear-cutting**, in which a whole section of a forest is taken down, leaving only scrub behind.

Forestry companies prefer clear-cutting because it is both easy and quick. Cutting trees at a low cost is crucial for the industry to be profitable. Clear-cutting has been severely criticized for causing environmental problems, however. For example, without the roots of live trees, erosion takes place. Rain removes the best soil and sometimes causes mudslides on hills. Soil can get into salmon streams, preventing the salmon from breeding. Without older trees producing seeds, new trees will not grow. In addition, tourists don't like the look of clear-cut areas, so the tourism industry suffers.

The forestry industry needs to find a balance between efficiency and protecting the environment. Logging companies have begun to be more careful about where they clear-cut, and how they leave the land. For example, by clear-cutting in strips, forestry companies can avoid some of the harmful effects. Also, companies employ people to plant seedlings in clear-cut areas. Many college students work as tree planters for a summer.

▲ **Figure 9.10:** Although only one in ten seedlings survives, tree planting does pay off with renewed forests.

14. a) Make a chart to compare the pros and cons of clear-cutting.
    b) What can be done to lessen the harmful effects of this method?
    c) What could you do to lessen your impact on the Canadian forest?

15. Consider this statement: "We must find a balance between human needs and the protection of natural systems."
    a) What human needs are satisfied by the forestry industry?
    b) Why is a balance required between these needs and those of the forest?

Farming

One could say that all primary industries "get the food on the table," but none more so than farming. Farming, or agriculture, is a crucial Canadian primary industry. It provides jobs and brings money into the country, just like other industries do. It also provides the food we eat every day, whether it's ice cream from the freezer, chips from the vending machine, or a hot dog from the school cafeteria.

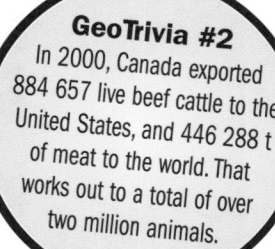

Canada has two main types of farming: animal farming and crop farming. Crop farmers grow plants, including anything from wheat and canola to mushrooms and ginseng. Some animal farmers raise animals for their meat. Dairy farmers raise them for what they produce, such as eggs and milk. Most of the largest farms specialize in just one type of farming, but many smaller farms produce both crops and animals.

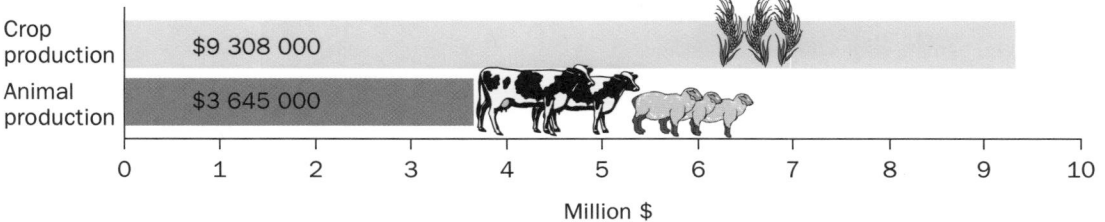

▲ **Figure 9.11:** Value of crop and animal production to Canadian farms, 2001

16. How many times more valuable is crop production than animal production? Find out by dividing crop production by animal production.

Crop Farming

In Canadian crop production, grains are king. Crop farmers devote nearly 11 billion hectares of land to growing wheat. Much of that land is on the vast Prairies, especially in Saskatchewan. Here, the flat prairie land, the short but hot summers, and the plentiful spring rainfall are ideal for wheat farming. The photograph in Figure 9.2b on page 155 shows a combine at work on a Saskatchewan grain farm.

◄ **Figure 9.12:** Saskatchewan grain pours into a freshwater cargo ship in Thunder Bay, Ont. Look at the tugboat and buildings to get an idea about how big this boat is.

Wheat doesn't grow everywhere in Canada. Various regions of the country specialize in particular crops because they have the climate and conditions that especially suit those crops.

17. Take a look at the following lists of Canadian crops and farming areas.
    a) Match the crops with the right locations. (*Hint:* Look at the ideal conditions listed for each crop. Try checking the farming areas in an atlas.)

    b) Write these crops in the correct locations on a map of Canada.

Figure 9.13: ▶
Some Canadian crops and farming areas

Crop/Ideal Conditions	Canadian Farming Areas
1. wheat—most efficiently grown on huge, flat farms	a) red soil of PEI
	b) Prairies
2. grapes for wine—grow well in a climate like France's	c) protected climates of Niagara Peninsula (SW Ontario) and Okanagan Valley (BC)
3. potatoes—grow well in nutrient-rich soils	d) Holland Marsh (north of Toronto) and Okanagan Valley
4. cranberries—best suited to marshlands	
5. ginseng (a medicinal herb)—needs a long growing season and dry climate	e) bogs in the Muskoka region (Ontario) and Newfoundland and Labrador
6. onions—grow well on well-irrigated lands	f) marginal land in BC, Ontario, Nova Scotia
7. Christmas trees—grow well on low-quality farmland	g) warm climates in Annapolis Valley (NS), Niagara Peninsula, and the Okanagan Valley
8. fruit—needs protected, sunny climate	h) old tobacco farms of southwestern Ontario

Animal Farming

While most crops produced in Canada are exported, most animal produce is consumed by Canadians. For example, of all the beef eaten by Canadians, 82 per cent is produced in Canada.

As in crop farming, different areas of Canada specialize in farming different animals. For example, about 40 per cent of cattle and calves are raised in Alberta because it has fertile grasslands and plentiful precipitation. It is relatively cheap to transport meat to market in refrigerated trucks and railcars. So, although a majority of Canadians live in central and eastern Canada, most cattle are raised 3000 km away, in Alberta.

Dairy farming is an important activity in Canada. In 2000, farmers received $4.1 billion from milk sales. This placed dairy farming in third place, with only grains and red meat ahead of it. Dairy farming has quite different location factors to consider than cattle farming. Milk does not keep well, so you cannot transport it over long distances. Dairy cows must be milked twice a day, so they have to be kept fairly close to a milking shed. Further, considerable labour is involved in milking a herd of cows, so herds are smaller. All these factors limit dairy farm size. Local dairy farms tend to be scattered across the country.

18. How are the location factors for beef and dairy farming different? Which one (or both) is well suited to your region of the country? Why?

Affecting the Environment

Farming has a continued effect on the land, largely because we put things on crops to help them grow better. To protect their crops, farmers spray on pesticides. These are chemicals that kill insects, weeds, or fungi. While these chemicals do allow the plants to grow better, they can damage the environment. For example, in Prince Edward Island in 2002, rain washed pesticides off potato fields and into streams, killing large numbers of fish.

Farmers add fertilizers like manure to the soil to enrich it.

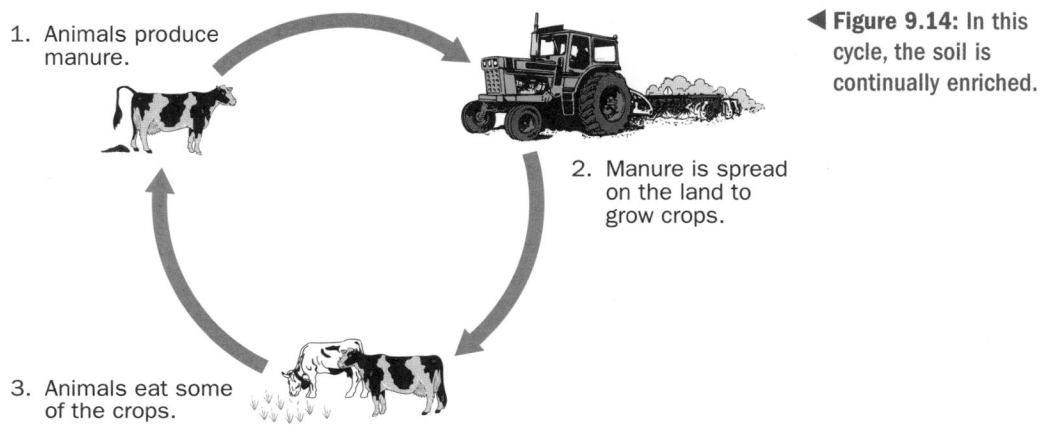

1. Animals produce manure.

2. Manure is spread on the land to grow crops.

3. Animals eat some of the crops.

◄ **Figure 9.14:** In this cycle, the soil is continually enriched.

Untreated manure on land can pollute the environment, however. Rain can wash it into rivers, streams, and wells, polluting human drinking water. This occurred in the town of Walkerton, Ontario, in May 2000. Seven people died and hundreds became seriously ill.

A **sustainable** farm system is one that will flourish into the future without harming the environment. The sustainability of Canadian agriculture depends on our ability to protect the environment from the effects of agriculture. Farmers recognize this need, and farm organizations everywhere place great emphasis on protecting the environment.

19. In what way can animal manure be a) a benefit to farmers and b) a problem?

20. a) Identify how the environment affects farming.
    b) Identify how farming can affect the environment.
    c) How are farming, humans, and the environment interconnected?

Mining

Canada has a hidden treasure: its store of minerals. **Minerals** are natural substances that we value because we can use them for something. They fall into three categories:

- *Metallic minerals* are metals, such as gold, nickel, and iron ore.
- *Structural minerals* are non-metallic minerals, such as cobalt, potash, sand, and gravel.
- *Fuel minerals* are fossil fuels, such as oil, natural gas, and coal.

GeoTrivia #3
The Creighton Deep Mine, in Sudbury, Ontario, will be 2685 m deep by 2019. This could bury Toronto's CN Tower 4.5 times over.

21. Describe each of the three types of mineral. Give one example of each, and explain a way that we use this mineral. For example, we use iron ore to make steel.

Why are minerals a hidden treasure? Unlike forests and agricultural lands, minerals generally do not appear on the surface of the land for all to see. Instead, minerals are normally found only in hidden pockets, sometimes far beneath the surface of the Earth. Prospectors—professionals who search for minerals—may spend years looking for minerals before they hit a "big one."

Where would you look if you hoped to discover gold or oil? Mining geologists have learned that valuable minerals can be found in particular kinds of rock. They understand, for example, that Northern Ontario and Quebec have gold mines, while Alberta has most of Canada's oil and gas.

The map in Figure 9.15 shows that Canada has three main types of rock. Most of the igneous rock (created from molten magma) is found in a wide ring around Hudson Bay. Great expanses of sedimentary rock (rock formed from compressed layers) are found in western Canada and several other regions. Metamorphic rock (rock changed by heat and pressure) occurs in big patches across the igneous rock areas. What is mined in each of these rock zones?

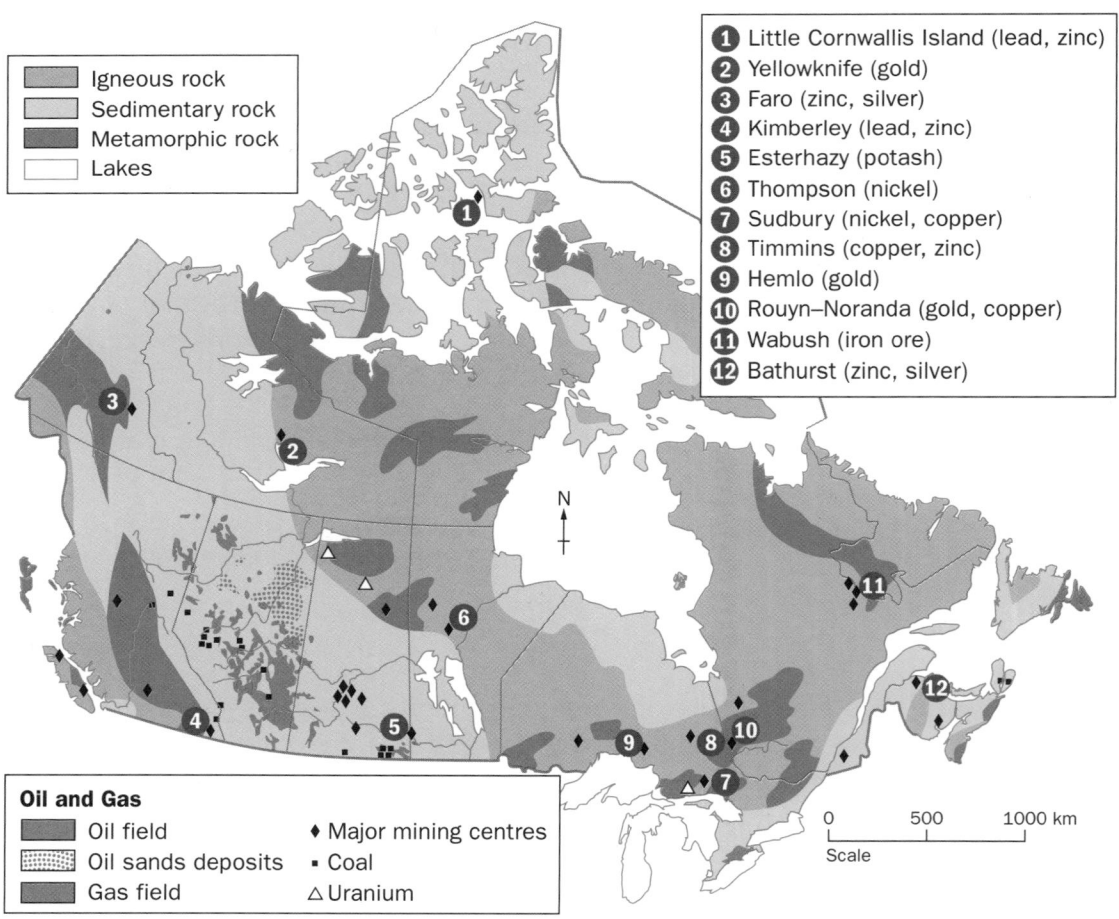

Igneous rock
Sedimentary rock
Metamorphic rock
Lakes

1 Little Cornwallis Island (lead, zinc)
2 Yellowknife (gold)
3 Faro (zinc, silver)
4 Kimberley (lead, zinc)
5 Esterhazy (potash)
6 Thompson (nickel)
7 Sudbury (nickel, copper)
8 Timmins (copper, zinc)
9 Hemlo (gold)
10 Rouyn–Noranda (gold, copper)
11 Wabush (iron ore)
12 Bathurst (zinc, silver)

Oil and Gas
Oil field   ◆ Major mining centres
Oil sands deposits ▪ Coal
Gas field   △ Uranium

0   500   1000 km
Scale

▲ **Figure 9.15:** Mining in Canada

22. Identify different minerals listed in the map legend that are used to make coins.

23. Look at the map in Figure 9.15 on the previous page. In which type of rock are the fuel minerals—coal, oil, and natural gas—found?

24. a) List six different types of metal mined at the numbered locations shown on the map.
    b) In which type of rock are most of these metals mined?

25. Explain in your own words why it is important for mining geologists to know the characteristics of different rocks.

26. a) Describe the pattern of mineral resources in Canada. Which province has most of the fuel minerals? Where are most of the large mines?
    b) Identify the provinces that probably benefit the most from each of the mineral resources.

◀ **Figure 9.16:** The mining industry in Canada

Quick Facts about Mining in Canada

- Number of people industry employs: 350 000
- Number of communities in which mining is the key industry: 150
- Of the total volume of exports loaded onto ships, the percentage that are minerals: 63%

Source: Statistics Canada.

Digging for Minerals

Mines are built in one of two ways. If the minerals lie close to the surface, mechanical diggers just dig a big pit and haul them out. These are called open-pit mines. The Athabasca oil sands project in Alberta uses this technique to get at the oil that lies buried there.

▲ **Figure 9.17:** Open-pit copper mine in Logan Lake, BC

▲ **Figure 9.18:** Driving a big rig 888 m down in the Hemlo gold mine, north of Lake Superior in Ontario

If the mineral lies deep beneath the surface, underground mines are built. Deep shafts, or vertical tunnels, are bored down into the Earth. At varying levels, tunnels called stopes are bored horizontally to gain access to the mineral-bearing rock. Miners go down the shafts and along the stopes to cut out the rock with jackhammers and other digging equipment. It can be dangerous work, and mining accidents are fairly common.

27. Explain the difference between the two basic types of mining. Give examples of the dangers of each type.

GeoGames
The Mining Game

Purpose:

Play this game to learn how difficult it can be to hit gold or other ore in a mine.

Mining is not like shopping for milk. (You're sure to find milk every time you go to the store.) Mining is more like shopping for a rare CD—you may do a lot of searching before you hit "gold." Mining is a hit-and-miss operation that involves digging through masses of rock in the hopes of maybe finding real gold. You give it a try.

Supplies:

- Copy of mineshaft map, Figure 9.19 (see next page)
- One die
- One playing piece per player

Method:

A. Play with two or three other students. Each of you represents a miner trying to win the company's prize for taking the most gold out of the mine in a week.

B. Make up a score sheet with the players listed across the top and the five days of the work week listed in the first column.

C. Place your marker in the frame house (the building at the top of the mine shaft).

D. Each of you takes a series of three rolls to represent Monday's shift, as follows.

  1. Roll the die. Move your marker down the shaft by the number you roll.

  2. Roll the die again. Move your marker sideways into the stope by the number you roll. If you do not land in an area that contains gold, your turn is complete. You blasted through tonnes of rock but found no gold today. Your score for the shift is zero.

  3. If you did land in a place that contains gold, roll the die again. You blast through rock and find the number of ounces of gold that are indicated on your die. Your score for the shift matches your final die roll.

E. After all players have taken a turn, put your markers back in the frame house. Each player, in sequence, takes four more turns to represent Tuesday's to Friday's shifts.

F. Total your week's scores. The player with the highest score at the end of the week has extracted the most gold and is the winner.

Wrap-Up:

1. Did luck play a big role in whether or not you hit gold? Mining is like that, full of risk. Mining companies study the rock carefully before deciding to build an expensive mine. Sometimes mines run out of ore very quickly. Other mines are very profitable.

2. Would you like to be a miner? Think of the advantages and disadvantages.

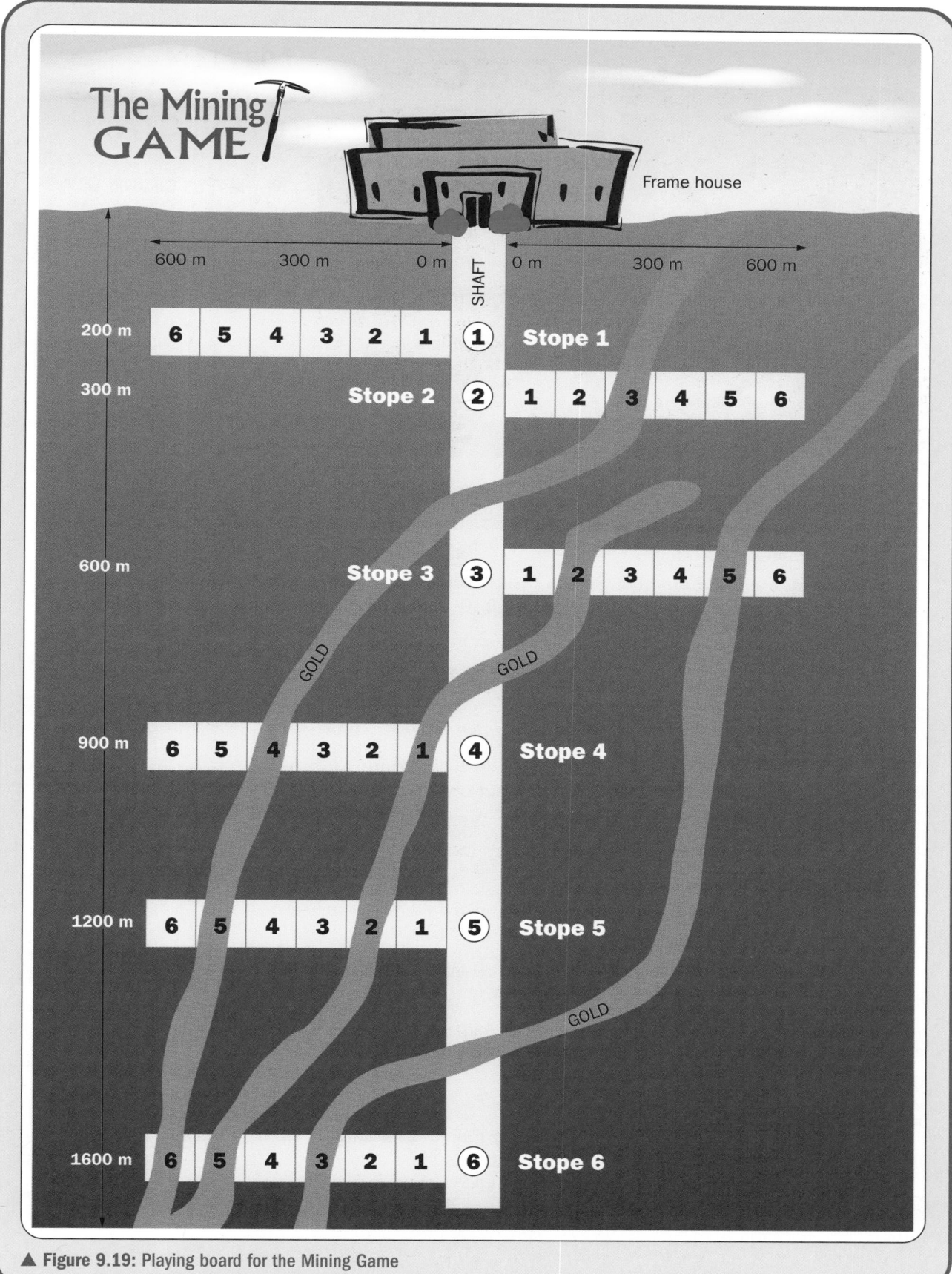

▲ **Figure 9.19:** Playing board for the Mining Game

GEO CAREERS — MINING ENGINEERING TECHNICIAN

Name: Rob DesRivieres
High School: St. Patrick's High School, Sarnia, Ontario
Job Title: Mining Engineering Technician

When Rob DesRivieres was seventeen, a tour of a northern mine sparked his interest in mining. This led him to complete a two-year Mining Engineering Technician diploma at Cambrian College in Sudbury, Ontario. One summer, he worked at an open-pit coal mine, driving gigantic haul trucks. He also worked underground at gold and nickel mines, where he used precise instruments to survey new tunnels. Mine survey methods are similar to those used by land surveyors when they set out property boundaries.

Rob did plenty of camping and canoeing when he was young. That gave him practice reading maps. He also enjoyed working with computers. These skills have come in handy in his career.

According to Rob, Canadian mine technicians are second to none: "Anyone trained in mine technology here can work around the world," he claims. "We have high-tech mines where operators use joysticks and television screens to work rock faces thousands of metres below them."

Postscript: Rob recently graduated as a Mining Engineer from Laurentian University. If you would like to work in this field, you can start by getting a college diploma in Mining Engineering Technology.

What I like about my work: *"Mining is interesting because there is always something new.... When I was up in Red Lake, there was a working area that looked like a jewellery store. The rock face was full of veins with heavy gold concentrations that gleamed under our lamps."*

1. What parts of his career does Rob seem to enjoy?

2. How did Rob's interests and skills help lead to his career?

3. Find out what secondary school courses are required to enter a college program as a Mining Engineering Technician.

How a knowledge of geography helps me in my job: *"You need to be able to read maps well. In fact, now I mostly work with three-dimensional maps on the computer. They show the surface and what's underground, too."*

Conclusion

You have seen in this chapter the variety to be found in Canada's primary industries. These powerhouses produce the food you eat, the materials needed to build your home, and the fuel to heat it. Primary industries provide employment and income for Canadians. They are vital to our economy and the Canadian way of life.

Wrap It Up

1. Make a copy of the following organizer, and complete it with information from this chapter.

Type	Where Located	Types of Product	Important Statistics
Fisheries			
Forestry			
Farming			
Mining			

▲ **Figure 9.20:** Canada's primary industries

2. Write a paragraph in which you state a) what you think is Canada's most important primary industry, b) why you have this opinion, and c) what you think might be the advantages and disadvantages of working in this industry.

3. The raw materials come from the natural system. Fast-food outlets are part of a human system (restaurants). What other human systems will help get your next fast-food meal into your belly?

4. Choose fishing, farming, or mining. Create a diagram with visuals that shows all the processes through which the product goes, and how it is transported along the various stages of its production. Explain to a small group of students what you have shown in your diagram. (See a similar diagram for forestry in Figure 9.8 on page 160.)

5. Investigate a specific primary industry in your province or territory so that you can write a case study about it. Find out three of the following facts:
   a) where it is located
   b) why it is located there
   c) the various stages the product goes through in its preparation for market
   d) how it is transported to market
   e) some figures to show how much of the resource is produced

   Government agencies, which maintain Web sites, are good sources of information. Prepare notes so that you can present your case study to a small group or the class.

Chapter 10

PROCESSING NATURAL RESOURCES

Things People Make

Manufactured products are things that people make. Stop for a moment and think about the many things in your life that have been made. They're in your backpack, in your locker, in your home, and on your body. In fact, even your backpack, locker, and home are manufactured things.

Where do these products come from? Let's check it out. First let's look at a map that shows countries that make many products Canadians like to buy.

Figure 10.1:
Source countries for some manufactured products ▼

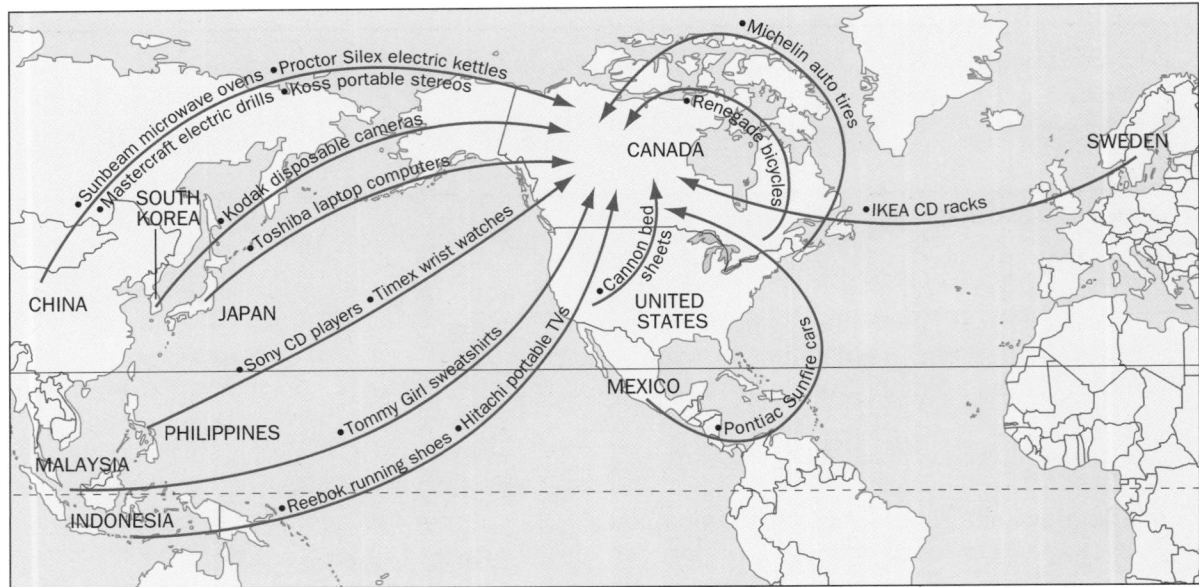

Words to Know

manufactured product

secondary industry

manufacturing

construction

export

import

semi-finished product

molten

component

specialist parts supplier

efficiency

just-in-time delivery

1. a) Check your shoes to see where they were made. Now check your binder, backpack, cell phone, calculator, sweater, or other handy item. Mark all the countries on a class map.
    b) Describe the general pattern of your class map. Describe the general pattern of the map above. Do they match? What can you conclude about where goods are made?

In this chapter, you will

- consider why secondary industries locate where they do
- identify the different types of secondary industry
- focus on a few different secondary industries
- find out how the goal of efficiency has changed how industries operate
- produce a case study of a local business

172

Driving the Canadian Economy

Manufactured items are the products of **secondary industries**. These industries change raw materials into things we can use, like the items on the map on the previous page. The two major kinds of secondary industries are **manufacturing**—the making of goods—and **construction**—the making of buildings and roads. Together, these secondary industries keep a lot of Canadians in jobs.

GeoTrivia #1
In 2000, 125 Canadian workers died because of accidents on the job. A further 285 died as a result of occupation-related illnesses.

▲ **Figure 10.2:** Construction of the Air Canada Centre in Toronto

Industry	Employees in Canada	Employees in Ontario
Manufacturing	2 005 700	922 100
Construction	557 700	196 600
Total (secondary industries)	2 563 400	1 118 700
Total (all industries)	12 199 600	4 791 700
Source: Statistics Canada, CANSIM II, tables 281-0001, 281-0005, and 281-0006 and Catalogue no. 72-002-XPB.		

▲ **Figure 10.3:** Employment in secondary industries, Canada and Ontario, 2000

2. a) Calculate the percentage of workers in Canada who have jobs in secondary industries. Divide the total of secondary industries by the total of all industries, and multiply by 100.
    b) Make the same calculation for Ontario.
    c) Compare the percentages for Canada and Ontario. Are secondary industries more or less important in Ontario than they are in Canada as a whole?

Secondary industries also contribute to the Canadian economy by producing goods for export. **Exports** are things that are sold to people in other countries. They bring money into Canada, which benefits the economy.

Item	Value (in millions)	Percentage of Total Exports
1. Machinery/equipment	$99 732	24%
2. Automotive products	$92 681	22%
3. Industrial goods	$66 797	16%
4. Energy products	$54 743	13%
5. Forestry products	$39 309	9%
6. Agricultural/fishing products	$30 883	7%
7. Other	$30 493	9%
Total exports	$414 638	100%

Source: Statistics Canada, CANSIM II, tables 228-0001, 228-0002, and 228-0003.

▲ **Figure 10.4:** Top six exports from Canada, 2001

3. a) Which of the top six export industries are primary industries? What is their ranking?
   b) Which of the top six export industries are secondary industries? What is their ranking?

4. a) What is the total value of all secondary industry exports?
   b) What is the total value of all primary industry exports?
   c) Which total is larger, and by how much? What does this tell you?

In Canada's early years, most exports were based on agricultural and, later, energy products. These are both primary industries. Today, most exports are automotive products, aircraft, and industrial machinery. Aircraft and other transportation equipment, for example, make up about 6 per cent of Canada's exports. In turn, we **import** (bring into the country) goods like the ones shown on the map in Figure 10.1 on page 172.

5. Think of two or three benefits of a healthy secondary industry sector.

Location Factors

As we learned in the previous chapter, primary industries develop where natural resources are found. Secondary industries in Canada do not follow this pattern. Instead, they usually set up close to their final markets because it is cheaper to transport raw materials than it is to transport finished goods.

6. a) Look at the map in Figure 10.5 on the next page. It shows selected secondary industries. Describe the general pattern you see.
   b) Find a population-density map of the region, and compare the patterns. What do you notice?
   c) Why might secondary industries set up close to populated areas?

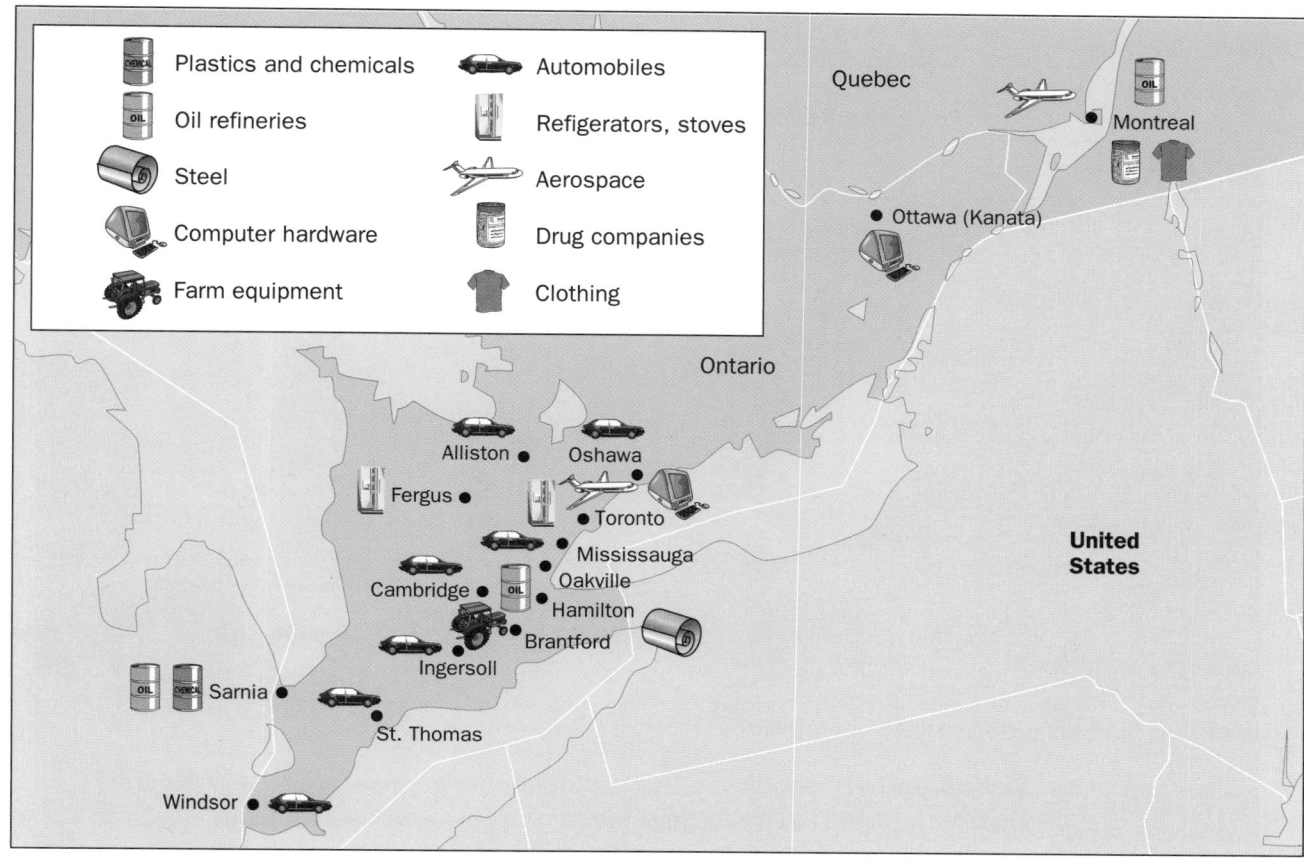

▲ **Figure 10.5:** Location of selected secondary industries in Ontario and Quebec

Secondary industries that set up in Canada consider several factors when deciding where to locate their factories.

- access to skilled employees
- access to supporting industries (such as parts plants)
- access to final market
- access to export markets
- access to well-developed transportation networks

The region shown in the map in Figure 10.5 offers all five types of access, including access to the huge markets of the northeastern United States.

7. Think of a large manufactured item that your family uses, such as a stove or refrigerator. What raw materials went into this item? Find out where it was manufactured. Is this location in or near a populated region? Explain if and how your example illustrates typical location factors for secondary industry.

8. Is your school well situated? Explain your answer.

Types of Secondary Industries

Many types of secondary industries exist, some being more complex than others. As you can imagine, it's more complicated to make a cell phone than it is to make a pencil. Let's look at four different products to see the various stages that they go through in the manufacturing process.

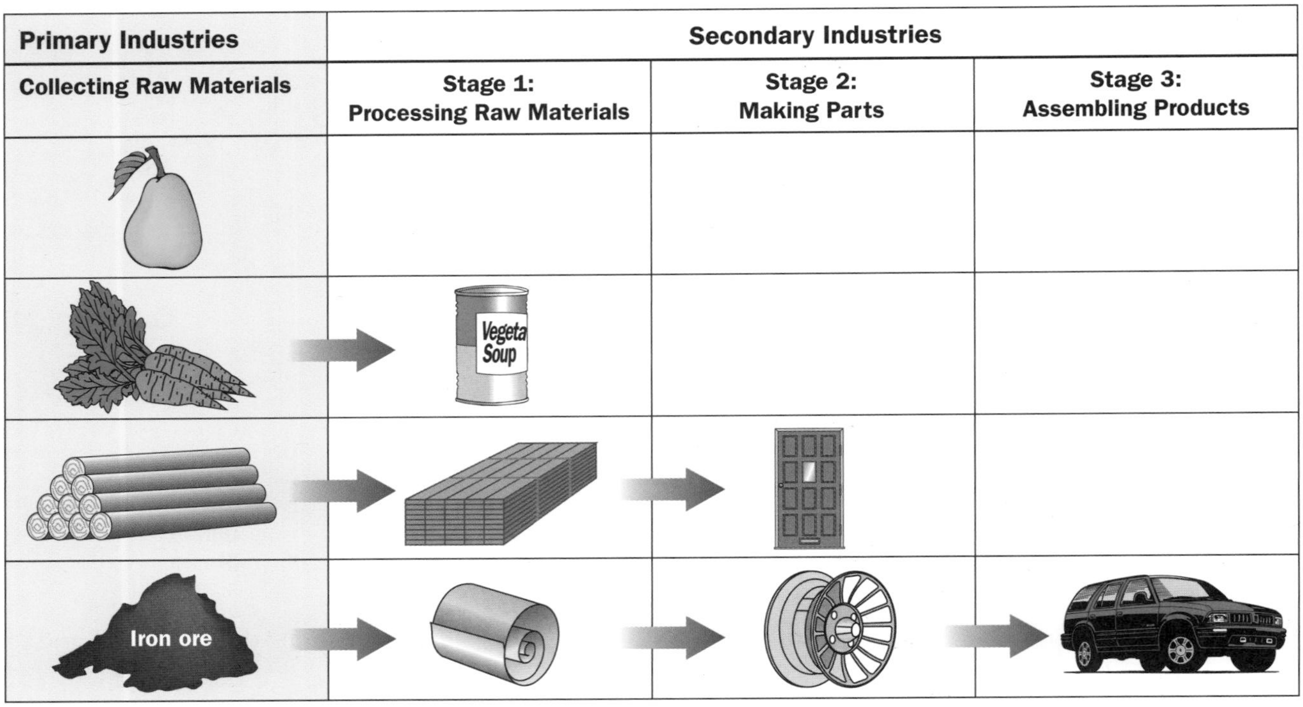

Primary Industries	Secondary Industries		
Collecting Raw Materials	Stage 1: Processing Raw Materials	Stage 2: Making Parts	Stage 3: Assembling Products

▲ Figure 10.6: Stages in primary and secondary industries

9. Describe what happens to the raw materials in each example in Figure 10.6. Use the words "raw materials," "processed," and "assembled."

10. Create a chart like the one in Figure 10.6 using your own examples. Think of industries that create products in one, two, three, and four or more stages.

In the rest of this chapter, you'll be looking at three stages of manufacture:

- processing raw materials
- making parts
- assembling products

Processing Raw Materials

The first type of secondary industry is processing raw materials. Sometimes one stage of processing creates a final product. In Figure 10.6, for example, we saw that vegetable soup involves the processing of raw materials—carrots—into a product. More often, however, raw materials are made into **semi-finished products**, products that are not yet ready for sale to consumers. Individuals don't usually buy semi-finished products. For example, you probably don't have much need for slabs of steel or tubs of artificial flavouring.

Paper is a good example of a semi-finished product. In paper mills, Canadian logs are processed with heat and chemicals to make wood pulp. Have you ever smelled the "rotten eggs" smell near a paper factory? This smell comes from the chemical process used to treat the wood. After the wood fibres break down, the mush is heated, pressed, and formed into long sheets of paper. Most mills make a few grades of paper. The paper is then shipped in giant rolls to factories where it is finished into paper products.

11. What is meant by a "semi-finished product"? Think of four examples.

Steel

The steel industry is a good example of a secondary industry that makes semi-finished products. Iron ore, a raw material dug from the ground, is changed into slabs or sheets of steel in steel mills. These semi-finished products are sold to other plants. Here they are made into bicycle frames, car fenders, electric toaster bodies, or whatever other product the plant makes. Steel factories follow the recipe in Figure 10.7 to make steel.

◄ Figure 10.7: Just like baking a cake, making steel is a step-by-step process.

Recipe for Making Steel

Ingredients:
- coal
- iron ore
- limestone
- oil

1. Inspect the iron ore, coal, and limestone to ensure it is suitable.
2. Burn the gases off the coal, resulting in coke. (Unlike coal, coke is a stable source of heat for furnaces.)
3. Place iron ore and limestone in a blast furnace. Heat with coke and oil. (The limestone will burn off the ore's impurities.)
4. Pour the **molten** (liquid) iron off the top of the blast furnace. Dispose of the remaining liquid.
5. Place a mixture of 70 per cent molten iron and 30 per cent recycled steel into a 300-t oxygen furnace. Heat and pour mixture (molten steel) into a huge ladle with temperature controls.
6. Adjust temperature and chemical mixture of molten steel to particular grade being produced.
7. Pour molten steel into a slab caster. Cool and cut into slabs 9 m long and weighing 20 t.
8. Place in a reheat furnace. Reheat to 1200°C, to ensure proper temperature for rolling.
9. Place in a rougher mill, to trim the slabs down to 20 cm thick and 35 m long.
10. Place in a finishing stand, and further trim to desired thickness, ranging from 10 mm to 1 cm.
11. Roll into a coil and send to shipping department, or send for special treatment, such as rust proofing (if needed).
12. Inspect and ship to customer.

▲ **Figure 10.8:** Steel being processed into coils

▲ **Figure 10.9:** Coiled steel ready for shipment

12. What do you think was the most impressive stage in the steel-making recipe? Explain your answer.

13. What raw materials go into steel? Would you classify steel as a semi-finished or finished product? Why?

Hamilton, Ontario, is the heart of the Canadian steel industry. Here two large Canadian-owned manufacturers, Dofasco and Stelco, produce the bulk of Canada's steel. The steel is made from iron ore shipped through the St. Lawrence Seaway from Quebec and Labrador. Dofasco and Stelco sell more than half their output to the automobile industry. The rest is sold to the construction industry, manufacturers of large appliances, and car producers.

14. Think of three things that you and your family use. Which item contains the most steel? What are the advantages of using steel to make this product?

Most of the steel manufactured in Hamilton is shipped to customers by road. The Hamilton location is crucial because it is no more than about 800 km (a day's truck journey) away from the major automobile plants.

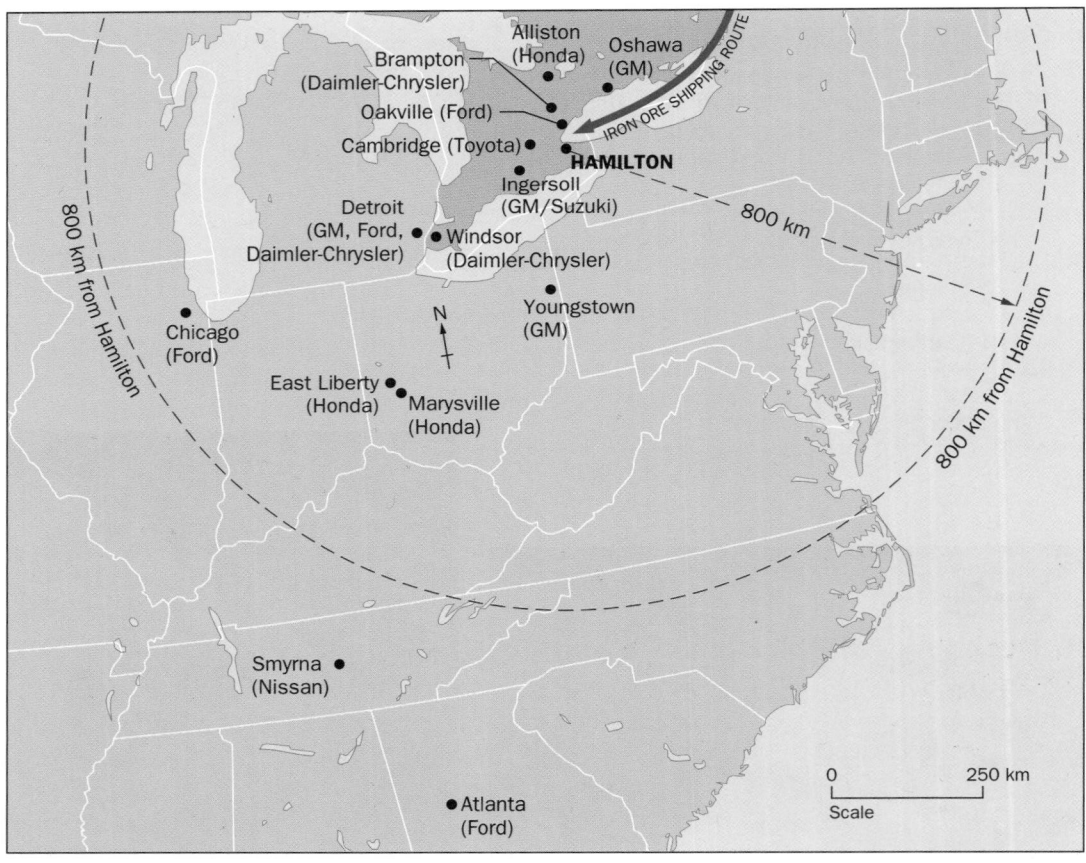

▲ **Figure 10.10:** Hamilton is within one day's truck journey of all the major eastern North American automobile plants.

15. What location factors make Hamilton a good place to make steel? Think of the location of the steel companies' suppliers and customers.

When we drive cars, trucks, or motorcycles, we know that we're polluting the air. We don't always think about how we affect the environment whenever we use *anything* made from steel—even a pair of scissors. Steel production consumes huge amounts of coal, oil, natural gas, and electricity. Historically, the steel industry has been a serious polluter because it lacked advanced pollution-control technology.

Companies such as Dofasco and Stelco have been trying to reduce the pollution they create by installing a range of expensive technology. Specialized equipment filters the smoke in the smokestacks of the furnaces. Old steel is now recycled into new product.

GeoTrivia #3
Canadian businesses get rid of 40 000 t of office equipment every year. Of this, 40% is reused, 15% is recycled, and 35% is dumped.

16. a) What have been the effects of steel production on the environment?
    b) What steps have steel producers taken to improve the situation?
    c) What steps can you take to minimize damage to the environment caused by steel production?

Making Parts

What happens to semi-finished goods? Some go through one more process, and then get sold directly to consumers. For example, a company might purchase huge rolls of paper, and then process the paper further by printing colourful designs on it. The resulting gift-wrap paper is then cut, packaged, and shipped to stores. Many Canadian secondary industries process semi-finished goods into finished goods. Some process yarn into sweaters; butter and flour into cakes and cookies; or leather into baseballs. Many other semi-finished goods are processed into **components**, or parts, which are used to make consumer goods.

17. Some component parts are made from many different semi-finished goods. Think of three semi-finished goods that go into car radios.

Many Canadian companies are **specialist parts suppliers**—they focus on producing one type of component for a particular industry. In this section, we will look at one specialist parts supplier for the Canadian automotive industry to see how it fits in to the car-building process.

Aluminum Wheels

At one time, companies made all the components they needed. An automobile plant would produce car wheels, steering wheels, lights—every part that went into a car. This practice was very expensive. The process for making wheels out of aluminum, for example, requires expensive machinery. So, instead of making wheels themselves, auto manufacturers decided to buy wheels from companies that specialize in making wheels. This is like buying a drinking glass instead of buying glass-blowing equipment and making the glass yourself. By making millions of wheels for many different companies, the specialist parts supplier can keep the price of individual wheels low. In this way, the automobile industry met the goal of **efficiency**—producing as much as possible for the lowest cost.

UBE Automotive is an international company that specializes in manufacturing aluminum wheels. It has two North American plants, one in Sarnia, Ontario, and the other in Mason, Ohio. The Sarnia plant employs 180 people and expects to produce as many as 2 500 000 wheels each year by the year 2005. At four wheels per vehicle, UBE will have the capacity (from its two plants) to provide wheels for 875 000 vehicles.

18. a) UBE Automotive doesn't process raw materials. Refer to Figure 10.6 on page 176. What does the company produce?
    b) Why do automobile companies buy aluminum wheels from specialist parts suppliers, rather than making the wheels themselves?

To make aluminum wheels, UBE and other wheel manufacturers start with the semi-finished product of aluminum. Following the steps outlined in Figure 10.11, they process the aluminum to fit the designs of the various wheels they produce.

19. Look at the recipes for making steel (Figure 10.7, page 177) and aluminum wheels, below. What similarities are there in the methods used?

Recipe for Making Aluminum Wheels

Ingredients:
- coils of aluminum
- special paints

1. Unroll the coils of aluminum.
2. Inspect to ensure aluminum is suitable.
3. Stress-test the aluminum to ensure that there are no weak spots, and that it can withstand impact without shattering.
4. Cut coils into "blanks" of precise size, depending on the diameter and style of wheel being produced.
5. Place blanks in a squeeze-casting machine. Press them into a mould at a force of 1800 t. Remove cast wheels.
6. Heat-treat wheels to ensure consistency of aluminum.
7. Machine the wheels to ensure a high degree of smoothness and polish.
8. Paint wheels with particular designs desired.
9. Inspect final product.

▲ **Figure 10.11:** Although this recipe has only one ingredient, the process is still quite complex.

▲ **Figure 10.12:** Aluminum wheels produced at the UBE production plant

Just-in-Time Delivery

Manufacturers used to keep huge warehouses filled with the parts that they needed. Eventually, they realized that it would be more efficient to order parts from plants just before they need them. That way, the parts don't have to be stored. Using this "**just-in-time**" (JIT) system of delivery, manufacturers order the parts they need every day. They can then expect to have the components delivered within eighteen to twenty-four hours. Workers then immediately put together the parts on the production line to create finished products such as snowmobiles and motorcycles.

▲ **Figure 10.13:** Today, the time from ordering a part to assembling it into a final product is just 18 to 24 h.

The just-in-time delivery system means that no parts supplier can be located more than a few hours away from the assembly plant it services. If a supplier cannot provide the goods within a day, the manufacturer will simply buy parts from another supplier.

The JIT system benefits the environment in two ways. For one, the JIT system requires that suppliers be located close to manufacturers. Therefore, the trucking routes are shorter. The JIT system also reduces the need for warehouses to store components. Warehouses require energy for lighting, heating, and cooling.

20. a) How does the just-in-time (JIT) system work?
    b) What are the benefits? Suggest a possible drawback.

21. Let's assume you have a business selling sports jerseys to other students at school. You have been in the habit of ordering once per month, but you find that the tastes of your customers change frequently. One week they favour the Oilers, the next they favour the Senators. Sometimes you end up with a lot of jerseys you can't sell. Further, you have difficulty coming up with the money for the once-monthly order. Describe a just-in-time system that would help you solve these problems. Explain how it would make your business run better.

Let's examine one specialist parts supplier for the auto industry that has been strongly affected by the just-in-time delivery system: auto glass producers.

Auto Glass

Ever thrown a ball through a window? It probably wasn't a car window. Auto glass is much stronger than regular window glass. Cars require industrial glass because it resists cracking from vibration and is shatter-proof. This is an important quality if you're in a car accident.

Pilkington is one of the world's leading manufacturers of glass products. It has operations in twenty-five countries worldwide. Its Canadian plant is in Collingwood, Ontario, near Georgian Bay. The Collingwood factory supplies many automotive companies. Auto glass is shipped to auto plants on a just-in-time basis.

Let's see if Pilkington's five North American auto glass plants are all located close to auto plants. You can see their locations in Figure 10.14.

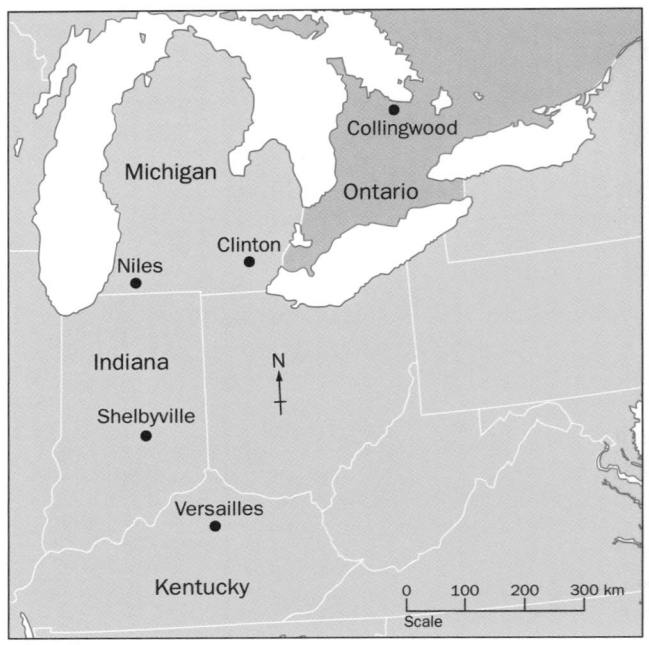

▲ **Figure 10.14:** The five locations of Pilkington's North American auto glass factories

▲ **Figure 10.15:** Windshields making their way through the production process

22. a) Obtain a blank map with the same regions shown as in Figure 10.14. Draw in the locations of all the Pilkington auto glass plants. Using a protractor, draw a circle having a 300-km radius (a 600-km diameter) around each location. (*Note:* it takes about four hours by truck to travel 300 km.)

    b) Place the locations of the eastern North American auto plants (from Figure 10.10, page 178) on your map. How many auto glass factories are fewer than 300 km from at least one auto plant?

23. If you were going to open a new auto glass factory at some location on your map, where would you put it? What are your reasons for your choice?

GeoGames

The Just-in-Time Game

Purpose:

To recognize the importance of speed, efficiency, and location in the just-in-time delivery system

Supplies:

A stop watch, a deck of playing cards, a timing sheet

Method:

A. Work in a group of three. Choose one of the following for your role:
- an assembly manager at an assembly plant that produces sports cars
- a delivery manager at a supplier of car stereo speakers
- the timer

B. Separate out one suit from the deck of cards. Place this suit in a row, in order, face up on a desk. These cards represent the various types of speakers being put into cars in the assembly plant.

C. Divide the rest of the cards into 13 piles, each pile having three matching cards (e.g., three kings). These cards represent the speakers stored at the parts supplier. Place these piles of cards in a row opposite the "assembly plant" cards.

D. Take a few practice turns. The assembly manager removes one of the face-up cards at random. (The assembly plant uses the stereo to assemble a vehicle.) The stereo supplier must, as quickly as possible, take a same-numbered card (the same stereo model) and place it, face up, in the empty spot in the assembly plant.

E. Now start timing. The assembly manager takes away a total of ten cards. After the round is complete, mark the total time on the timing sheet.

F. Return all cards and switch roles for two more rounds so that all players have one chance at each role. The winner is the supplier with the lowest time.

G. For the second round of this game, follow Steps D, E, and F, but set up the speaker supplier's cards about four metres away from the assembly plant cards.

	Time (in seconds)		
	Player 1	**Player 2**	**Player 3**
Round One	20 s	18 s	25 s
Round Two	66 s	56 s	75 s

▲ **Figure 10.16:** Sample timing sheet

Wrap-Up:

1. a) Who had the best time in the second round? Did that time beat any of the times of the players in the first round of the game? Why or why not?

   b) What conclusion can you make about stereo speaker suppliers that locate far away from an assembly plant? What might happen to their business if a competitor set up shop very close to the auto plant?

2. Identify possible weaknesses in the just-in-time delivery system.

Assembling Products

Canada has many companies that assemble products on both a large and a small scale. Consider the case of Rasmussen Log Homes, a small company that Dan and Karen Rasmussen started in 1980. They set up a three-hectare work site in the Okanagan Valley in British Columbia, close to the timber they need to build log homes. They now ship houses to Japan, Europe, and all over North America. Although small, this company provides employment for many people.

Figure 10.17: ▶
A house being constructed by Rasmussen Log Homes

24. Think of another secondary industry that would benefit a small, resource-based community. Identify the industry and the resource that it would need to be near. For example, a community near a gemstone quarry might start a secondary industry that produced jewellery.

CASE STUDY

BUILDING TOYOTAS IN CANADA

Toyota Motor Manufacturing Canada Inc. (TMMC) began production at its assembly plant in Cambridge, Ontario, in November 1988. By 2002, the plant had grown to 253 000 square metres—all under one roof. A $650 million construction project was in progress to expand the plant's plastics and painting capacity.

1. Look at Figures 10.18 and 10.19 on the next page. Use three facts or observations to describe the size of the Cambridge plant.

Toyota's operations are typical of most secondary industries that involve the assembly of components. Note the main features:
- Some parts are manufactured on site. Others are purchased from specialist parts suppliers.
- Off-site parts are brought to the assembly plant quickly, under the JIT system.
- All parts are assembled into finished vehicles, which are immediately shipped to dealers.

▲ **Figure 10.18:** The Toyota plant in Cambridge, Ontario

Quick Facts: Toyota Canada
Number of employees: 3300
Annual payroll: $12 200 000
Products: Corolla sedan, Matrix, Camry Solara coupe, Camry Solara convertible, Matrix crossover vehicle, four-cylinder engines
Export markets: United States, Puerto Rico, Mexico
Operations: stamping, body welding, paint, plastics, assembly, and powertrain
Annual capacity: 200 000 vehicles (2003 projection: 250 000), 150 000 engines
Source: Toyota Canada.

▲ **Figure 10.19:** Toyota Canada statistics, 2002

2. Identify two ways that the goal of efficiency has affected the way that Toyota operates.

Toyota's stamping shop uses steel and related products from suppliers such as Dofasco. The steel is supplied in coils (like the aluminum coils shown in Figure 10.9 on page 177). The coil is unwound like a roll of tape and fed into a blanking machine, where the basic shapes of a vehicle body are cut out. Those parts are then fed into the stamping presses, where body parts such as hoods, roofs, and fenders are stamped. Most of the stamping shop's production goes directly to the welding shop. The remainder is trucked to Toyota assembly plants in Kentucky and Indiana. All painting is done before assembly.

In the assembly shop, employees put together the vehicles in a carefully designed sequence. They add various components, including auto glass and wheels, to the painted bodies. The sequence allows the assembly workers to build the finished vehicles quickly, and helps keep the cost to the consumer down and company profits up.

3. a) In what ways are Toyota's operations typical of most secondary industries today?
   b) Suggest three different ways that the Toyota operations benefit Ontario.

▼ **Figure 10.20:** At the Toyota plant, employees and robots both do a portion of the welding

Conclusion

Canada's secondary industrial capacity greatly benefits Canadians. All along the processing route—from raw material, through semi-finished goods and parts, to finished goods—people have jobs, companies pay taxes, and goods are created to better people's lives. Our flourishing secondary industries do have a drawback—harm to the environment in the form of pollution and waste of resources. You will learn more about these problems in Chapter 15: Pollution: Local and Global and Chapter 16: Reducing Your Ecological Footprint.

Wrap It Up

1. Reorganize the following chart to match up the three stages of manufacture with three steps in making cell phones, putting them all in order.

Stage of Manufacture	Steps
Processing a raw material	assembling all the parts of a cell phone
Making a part	refining oil to make plastic
Assembling a product	moulding a plastic cell-phone case

▲ **Figure 10.21:** Cell-phone manufacture (not in order)

2. What are three main features of Canada's secondary industries? Use the automotive assembly industry as an example.

3. Look at the map in Figure 10.1 on page 172. Many firms do not set up factories close to their markets. Instead, they set up where they can pay very low wages. The payroll savings make up for the additional transportation costs. Speculate on three results of this business strategy.

4. a) Make a chart to compare the pros and cons of increasing the production of Canada's secondary industries. Consider the effects on natural resources, pollution levels, number of jobs, available goods, corporate taxes paid, investment opportunities, and habitat for animals.

   b) Suggest one thing that Canadians could do to keep the cons in check. Explain your suggestion to another student in your class. Improve each other's suggestion. Then present your suggestions together to another pair of students.

5. Select a secondary industry, or a specific business participating in a secondary industry, in your region. Review the section of this chapter that points out the importance of location factors (pages 174–175). Research the company or industry you have chosen. Create a case study about your choice. Show the following topics.
   • the type of activity
   • where the supply materials come from, and how they are transported
   • where the products are sold, and how they are transported
   • why the company or industry you have chosen is located where it is

Present your information in a bulletin-board display with maps, pictures, and text.

Chapter 11

UNDERSTANDING SERVICE NETWORKS

Would You Like Fries with That?

Have you ever considered getting a part-time job? Maybe you already have one. If not, perhaps your friends or older siblings are employed. In any case, you have probably noticed that certain jobs seem to be easier for young people to get when they are just starting out. For example, delivering papers or flyers is a popular first job. It requires very little skill and not much commitment of time or resources.

1. You have been hired as an employment counsellor for your high school. The school board wants you to create a list of jobs that students can do after school, on weekends, or in the summer. See how many job titles you can come up with for your job bank. Identify at least ten. For each job title, list reasons why it is a good job for students.

2. Now, look at your list. How many of these jobs involve providing a service, rather than making something? Chances are, most of them do. That's because service jobs are often the easiest for young workers to get. In this chapter, you will learn more about this fast-growing job sector.

▲ **Figure 11.1:** A young person working in the service industry

In this chapter, you will

- find out why tertiary industry employs more people than primary and secondary industry
- think about the importance of location in retail trade
- consider some of the unique features of government jobs
- look closely at the pros and cons of different forms of transportation

The Growth of Tertiary Industry

The service jobs you listed in your job bank are included in a category of jobs referred to as **tertiary industry**. Tertiary industry workers earn their living in retail trade, service-oriented jobs, and government. Unlike primary and secondary industry, tertiary industries do not produce any raw materials or goods. Instead, they provide services. While many tertiary jobs are unskilled, others, such as doctor, teacher, and lawyer, require training and education.

More people are employed in tertiary industry than in primary and secondary industry combined. This is partly because technology has taken over many jobs in primary and secondary industries. For example, new machinery has meant that fewer workers are needed to work the land or build cars.

GeoTrivia #1
About $40 of every $100 Canadian families spend on food is spent in restaurants.

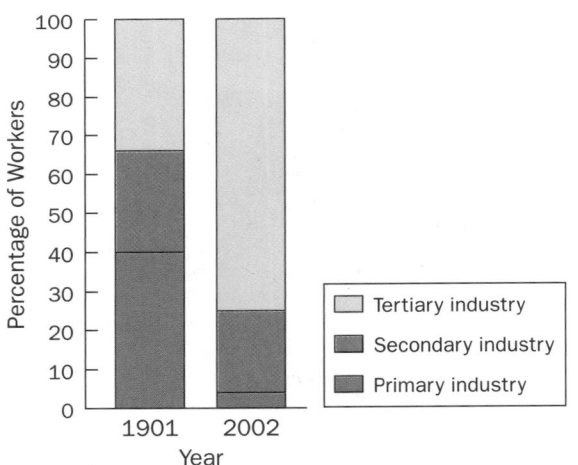

Figure 11.2: Employment in primary, secondary, and tertiary industry in Canada, 1901 and 2002

At the same time, changes in society have led to more demand for services. For example, back in 1960, there were very few fast-food restaurants in Canada. Most mothers stayed at home, and families went out for a meal only on special occasions. Today, most women work, and families with one parent have become more common. These changes have made fast-food restaurants more popular. Today, about 37 per cent of restaurant employees in Toronto work in fast-food outlets. You can read about one example of a successful Canadian fast-food company in the Case Study that follows.

1. a) Look at the graph in Figure 11.2. Compare the figures for 1901 and 2002. What were the major changes in employment between the two years?
    b) In your own words, explain the changes that occurred in primary, secondary, and tertiary industry employment over this time period.

2. List four features or qualities of fast-food restaurants that you feel are important to their success. Briefly explain your choices.

CASE STUDY
TIM HORTONS

Background

Tim Horton was a popular NHL hockey player who spent time with the Toronto Maple Leafs and the Buffalo Sabres. He played in a number of Stanley Cup series, as well as in all-star hockey games. In the early 1960s, he decided to open a coffee and doughnut shop. The very first Tim Hortons store opened in Hamilton, Ontario, in 1964. The owner of the franchise was Ron Joyce. A **franchise** is a licence to operate a business, use the company logo, and sell its products. In return, the company provides advertising and supports the franchisees with help when needed.

The Company Grows

By 1967 Ron Joyce had opened a total of three Tim Hortons franchises. He became a partner in the business. Then, on 21 February 1974, Tim Horton was killed in a car accident on his way to a Buffalo Sabres hockey game. Ron Joyce bought out the business.

Despite the death of its founder, Tim Hortons continued to grow. In 1974, there were forty stores. Twelve years later, the 300th store opened in Calgary, Alberta. Two hundred more stores were added in just four more years.

▲ **Figure 11.3:** A Tim Hortons coffee shop

Another milestone for the company came in 1995, with the merger of Tim Hortons and Wendy's, an American fast-food franchise. A **merger** is a joining of two businesses. When the 1000th store opened in Ancaster, Ontario, that same year, it was one of the first to be built attached to a Wendy's. The merger allowed Wendy's to expand more quickly in Canada and opened up opportunities for Tim Hortons in the United States. Five years after the merger, store number 2000 opened in Toronto, Ontario.

A Community-Minded Business

One of the reasons for the success of Tim Hortons has been its involvement with the communities it serves. Not long after Tim Horton's death, Ron Joyce established the Tim Horton Children's Foundation in his honour. It operates camps for children who come from underprivileged families. Today, there are five such camps. Each one is visited by thousands of children over the course of a summer. On one day each year, Tim Hortons donates all the money spent on coffee in its stores to the camps.

1. a) Based on your personal experience, why do you think that Tim Hortons has been so successful?
   b) Give four factors to explain how Tim Hortons selects the locations of their stores, based on evidence in Figure 11.3 on the previous page and your own knowledge.
2. Both Tim Hortons and Wendy's are restaurants. Explain why the two have been successful even though they are often located next to each other.
3. a) Use the information provided in this Case Study to construct a bar graph that shows the growth in the number of stores since 1964.
   b) What period saw the fastest growth? Suggest a reason for this pattern.
4. What do you think are the main benefits and drawbacks of the franchise system
   a) for the company that owns the business?
   b) for people who buy a franchise?

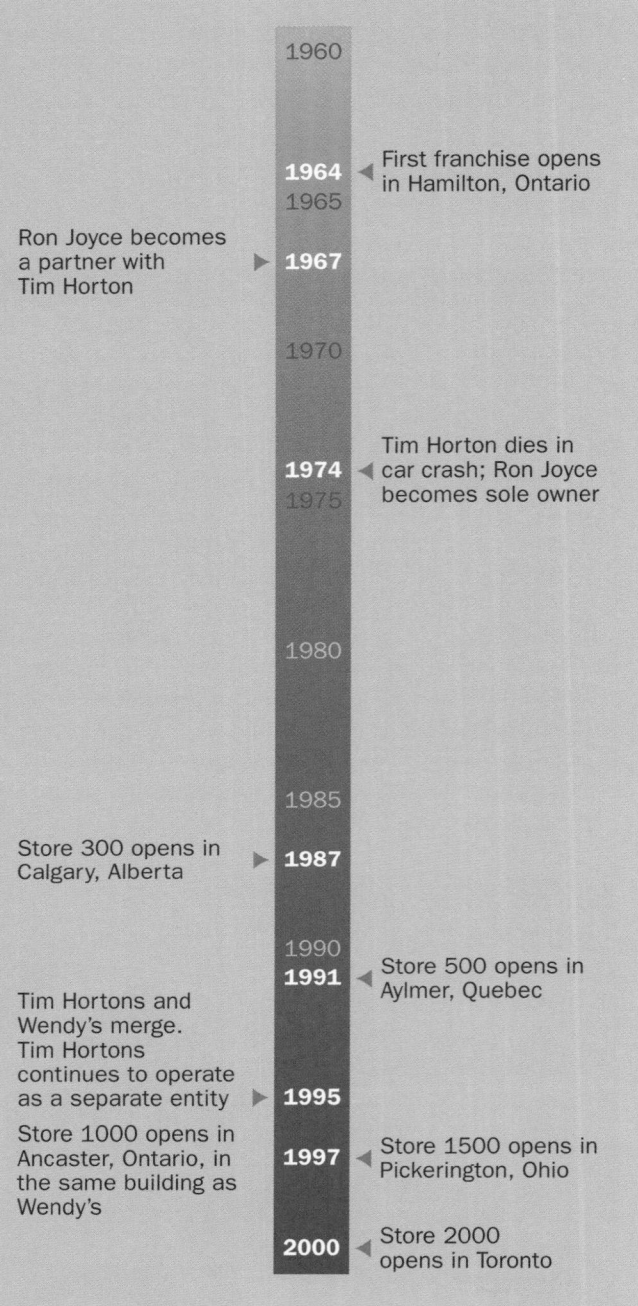

1960	
1964	First franchise opens in Hamilton, Ontario
1965	
Ron Joyce becomes a partner with Tim Horton	**1967**
1970	
1974	Tim Horton dies in car crash; Ron Joyce becomes sole owner
1975	
1980	
1985	
Store 300 opens in Calgary, Alberta	**1987**
1990	
1991	Store 500 opens in Aylmer, Quebec
Tim Hortons and Wendy's merge. Tim Hortons continues to operate as a separate entity	**1995**
Store 1000 opens in Ancaster, Ontario, in the same building as Wendy's	**1997**	Store 1500 opens in Pickerington, Ohio
2000	Store 2000 opens in Toronto

▲ **Figure 11.4:** Timeline of events in the growth of Tim Hortons

The Retail Sector

The **retail sector** provides consumers with a wide variety of goods, from candy to cars. Since we all need to buy things from time to time, we all have some experience of this sector. What's more, more Canadians work in retail than in any other job sector. In older areas of Canadian towns and cities, you often find retail businesses in **ribbon developments**—rows of stores side by side on a main street. These stores usually offer specialty products such as baked goods, unique clothing, or ethnic foods. **Strip malls**, or neighbourhood plazas, are a more recent retail development. These planned shopping areas are found in newer areas and in the suburbs. The advantage of strip malls is that they offer more free parking, and usually provide more space for retailers than ribbon developments.

Figure 11.5: A strip mall (left) and a ribbon development (right)

3. Make a chart to compare a ribbon development and a strip mall that you have visited under these headings:
   a) Location   b) Parking   c) Size of Stores

4. Many small towns in Canada are having trouble attracting shoppers to older, downtown ribbon developments. Larger malls with greater selection and strip malls with more convenient parking have drawn customers away from these areas. What suggestions could you make to a city council to help save these older, downtown ribbon developments and make them more attractive to shoppers? Write your ideas in a letter.

Regional Malls

While ribbon developments and strip malls make shopping convenient because they are close to where people live, other forms of retail attract customers by providing a large selection. **Regional malls** sell a wide variety of goods and serve a very large area. People sometimes drive an hour or more in order to shop at one of these malls. Often a large store, called an **anchor store**, is attached to the mall. Other stores in the mall benefit from the consumer traffic brought in by the anchor store.

Malls also offer a variety of facilities and services such as child care, spas, and blood donor clinics. Restaurants, movie theatres, and entertainment centres often develop nearby, especially in suburbs and rural areas.

▲ **Figure 11.6:** South Centre shopping mall in Calgary, Alberta

5. Use the photograph of the mall in Figure 11.6 to answer these questions.
   a) Approximately what percentage (or fraction) of all the land that the mall occupies is taken up with parking area? What does this estimate tell you about the importance of the automobile to the mall?
   b) From what you can see in the photograph, is this mall well located from the point of view of access to transportation routes? Explain your answer.
   c) Suggest four factors that would explain why this mall was located here. Briefly explain each factor. (Refer to the air photograph as well as your knowledge of malls that you have visited to help you answer.)

Big-Box Stores

Another trend in Canadian retailing is the development of **big-box stores**—large retail stores that offer a huge volume of goods. Some, like Wal-Mart, are giant department stores. Others specialize in a particular area, such as toys, business supplies, or hardware. They are usually located around the edges of cities, in huge one-storey warehouses with very large parking lots.

Because of the size of their operations, these stores can sell products for less than smaller retail outlets. But they have also caused a lot of controversy. Critics point out that many smaller, locally owned stores can't compete with the low prices and huge selection offered by the big boxes. Many small-town downtowns have "died" when people stopped shopping on the town's main street. Since most big-box stores are owned by American companies, some of the money spent in them leaves the country. And big-box stores hold a lot of buying power. Suppliers are often forced to sell their goods to these stores at very low prices—or risk being replaced.

> **GeoTrivia #2**
> Wal-Mart is the largest retailer in the world. One hundred million customers visit Wal-Mart stores every week worldwide.

◀ **Figure 11.7:** A big-box store

6. a) Describe the name and location of a big-box store in your area.
   b) What do you think would appeal to people about shopping in that store?
   c) Why might some people choose not to shop at such a store?

7. Make a chart to show three arguments for and three arguments against big-box stores. Explain which arguments you find most appealing and why.

8. Think of where you and your family shop.
   a) Which types of stores do you shop at most often? Explain why this is so.
   b) Which types of stores do you shop at least often? Explain your answer.
   c) To your knowledge, have you or your family changed where you shop over the last several years? Explain your answer.

The Government Sector

How many government services do you think you have benefited from since you woke up? Let's see: if you are at a publicly funded school, then that's one. If you got to school by driving or walking on roads, that would be another. What about sewage and water? mail? medical services?

Territorial, provincial, and federal governments deliver services to millions of people over huge areas. So, it's not surprising that government services account for about 24 per cent of tertiary industry.

Governments provide services or support programs that affect all areas of our lives. A number of you will likely spend time working for the government at some point in your life. In general, there are three levels of government that serve us. The federal government, based in Ottawa, provides some services, including mail delivery, passports, and national defence. Provincial and territorial governments administer other important services, such as health care, education, and highways. Municipal governments look after local services such as garbage collection, water, and snow removal.

Each province or territory has a capital city, which is the centre of government for the region. But in order to deliver their services, governments must employ people all across the regions they serve. This is one of the things that makes the government sector unique. A retail business can choose where to offer its services, based on what will give it the greatest profits. But government must make sure that all citizens have access to its services, regardless of how difficult it is to deliver them. Canada's low population density can sometimes make reaching this goal a challenge.

▲ **Figure 11.8:** Federal, provincial, and territorial capitals

9. What makes the government sector different from other tertiary industries?

10. How does the size of Canada explain our need for three levels of government?

11. Look at the location of the provincial and territorial capitals in Figure 11.8 on the previous page. What pattern do you notice? What problems might arise in trying to deliver government services in areas that are far from these centres? What can governments do to overcome these problems?

12. Look at Figure 11.8. If the national capital were to be moved, where would you suggest it be moved to? Explain your answer.

The Transportation Sector

Transportation is a key part of our **infrastructure**, the systems that form the skeleton of our economy. Not only do we move large amounts of freight across the country, but we also move millions of passengers as well. The major forms of transportation in Canada are ship, truck, rail, and air. As we will see in this final part of the chapter, each has its advantages and drawbacks. We'll also look at the role of public transit in urban centres.

13. Look at the map in Figure 11.9. Approximately what percentage of Canada's land surface is serviced by a ground transportation system?

14. Why are there so few major roads or rail lines in unserviced areas?

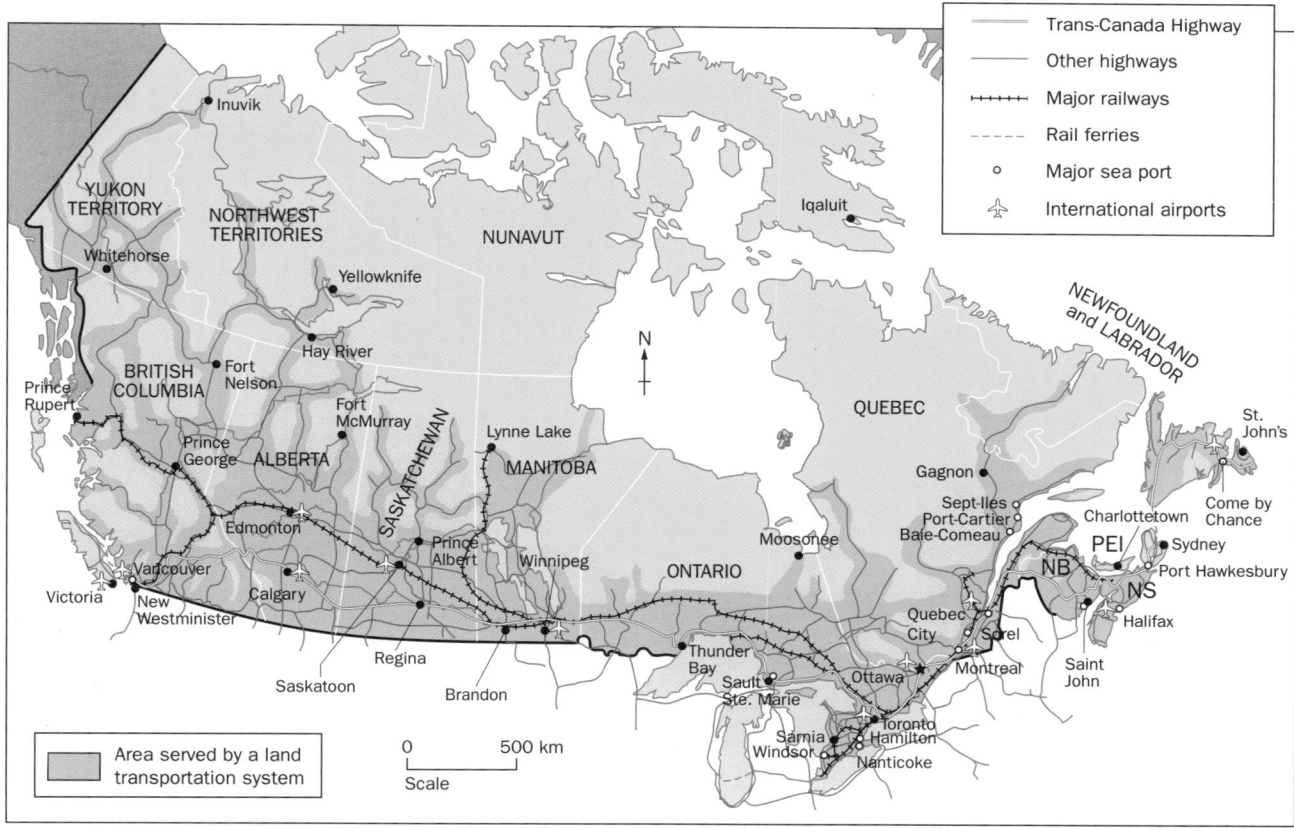

▲ **Figure 11.9:** Transportation routes in Canada

Shipping

Maybe you never thought of shipping as an important form of transportation. But remember, most of the goods that Canada exports to other countries are transported by ship. And we rely on ships to move grain, lumber, and mining and petroleum products within the country. For example, on the West Coast, tugs and barges haul logs from remote forested areas. In eastern Canada, ships deliver goods to and from domestic ports along the Great Lakes–St. Lawrence Seaway. In summer, ships also serve isolated communities in the eastern Arctic, and ferries link island communities with the mainland.

Shipping is often the cheapest way to move heavy goods. But it has some obvious limitations. Ships can go only where there is deep water, and they move slowly. Most of the shipping industry within Canada shuts down during the winter, when waterways are frozen.

Railways

The cheapest way of transporting goods long distances over land is by train. Large, heavy goods such as cars, wheat, or heavy machinery are carried easily on trains. That's why many primary industries, such as the steel companies in Hamilton or mines in northern Ontario, are serviced by railway lines. Trains are also used to transport people over both long and short distances.

Trains are obviously restricted by the fact that tracks don't run everywhere that cargo needs to go. And perishables, such as ice cream or fresh fruit, are not usually sent by rail, since it can be slow.

Figure 11.10: ▶
In Vancouver, ship and rail lines are among the cheapest forms of transport for bulky goods.

15. Western grain headed for markets in eastern Canada is usually moved by rail to Thunder Bay, then transferred to ships that travel the Great Lakes and the St. Lawrence River. Explain the advantages of this system.

Trucking

Trucking is a major industry in Canada. It employs more than 1.5 million people. Unlike trains or ships, trucks are able to move freight almost anywhere there is a road. Trucks can get even small loads to individual factories or stores. In fact, for short distances, truck transport can move goods more quickly than any other form of transport. Trucks can also carry specialized goods such as gasoline, frozen food, and flammable liquids.

Many businesses use a **container system**—a combination of truck, train, and even ship—to get their goods where they need to go. Special "piggyback" containers can be moved directly between rail cars, trucks, and shipping compartments, so the contents don't have to be unloaded.

Air

If you need something moved over a long distance quickly, try air. It's the fastest form of transport for both goods and people—and the most expensive. Goods such as mail bags or urgent medical items are often moved by planes, because the savings in time make up for the extra cost. People often choose to travel by plane for the same reason. Air travel is also important in remote areas of Canada that are not accessible by road or rail.

Airlines can travel only along designated routes, and can't handle very bulky or heavy cargo. And not only are airplanes expensive to buy and operate, but airport facilities are also costly to build and maintain.

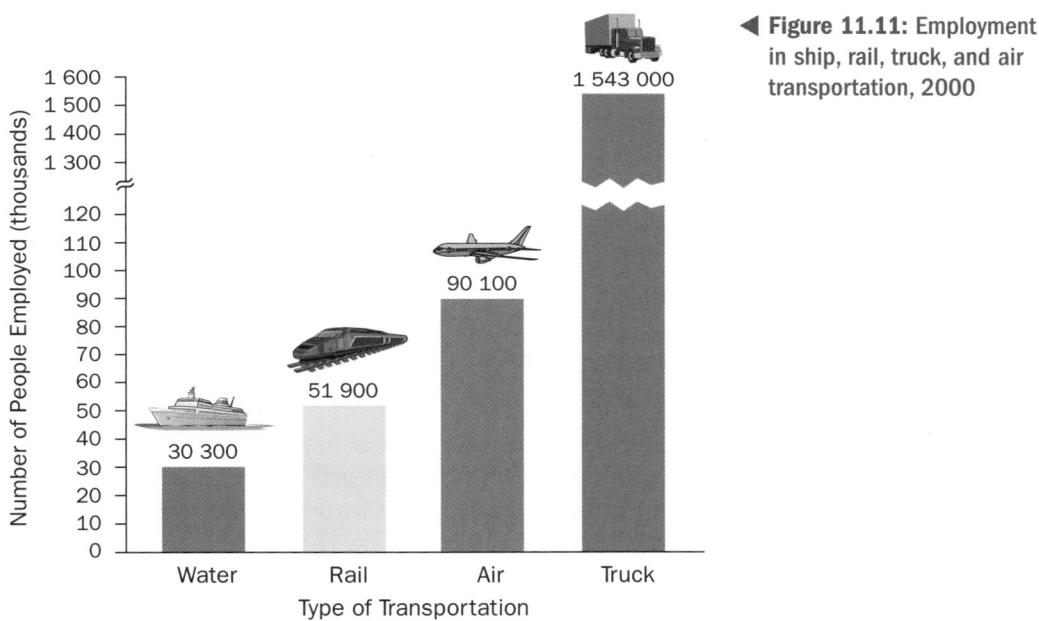

◀ **Figure 11.11:** Employment in ship, rail, truck, and air transportation, 2000

16. a) Look at the bar graph in Figure 11.11. Which form of transport employs the least people? the most?
    b) Explain why trucks are so important for Canada's economy.

Public Transit Systems

Can you imagine a big city like Ottawa or Montreal without a public transit system? The roads would quickly become paralyzed with so many cars, and the air would be almost unbreathable. Transit systems produce less pollution per person than private cars do and reduce the number of vehicles on the road. They also provide a way for people without cars to get around.

What makes a good public transit system? Transit routes have to be as affordable, easy to use, and efficient as possible to compete with cars. In addition to shopping and residential areas, institutions such as hospitals, senior citizens' homes, factories, and sports arenas need to be accessible by transit. Some cities offer special bus services for people with disabilities.

Figure 11.12: Carbon dioxide ▶ emissions of cars and buses. Buses produce less CO_2 per person because they carry so many people at once.

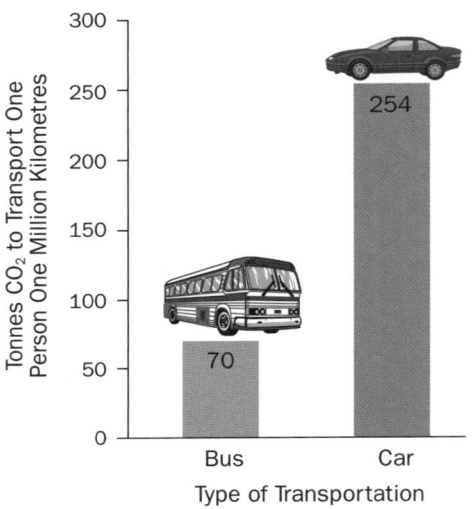

17. a) If you live in or near an area with a public transit system, write a letter to transit officials evaluating the system and suggesting ways to make it serve people better. Consider each of the following factors in your evaluation:
    i) convenience
    ii) frequency of service
    iii) areas covered
    iv) price
    b) If you do not live near public transit, use a road map of a town you are familiar with to plan a transit system with at least two bus routes. Make sure your system covers more heavily populated areas and shopping areas, as well as providing transportation for large institutions in the area.

18. Look at the bar graph in Figure 11.12. About how many buses would it take to equal the CO_2 emissions of one car? Why do you think buses are more fuel-efficient than cars?

GEO CAREERS — CARTOGRAPHER

Name: Sean Severin
High School: Monarch Park Collegiate, Toronto
Job Title: Cartographer

Transportation companies need to deliver goods fast and on time. That's why one trucking company hired DMTI Spatial to create detailed maps for their drivers. The maps they use are accurate down to the speed limits on the streets. Sean Severin, who works at DMTI Spatial, was the person who created these maps.

Sean is a **cartographer**—a person who makes maps for specific purposes. An interest in geography in high school led him to enroll in the Applied Geography Program at Ryerson University. Soon after graduating, he was hired by DMTI Spatial, and he hasn't looked back.

Cartographers like Sean use a wide variety of data to compile geographic information. "All the maps that I make are with the use of computers," says Sean. "I use city maps, air photos, and sometimes even tourist maps to produce what we want." (You can find out more about the software Sean uses in Chapter 12: Canada Goes High-Tech, and try it yourself in Chapter 20: Geography in the Real World.)

Since starting work at DMTI, Sean has worked on many mapping projects. He says he likes the fact that no two projects are ever quite the same. One day he may be compiling detailed maps for transportation companies, the next he may be helping a cell-phone company decide where to place phone towers.

Sean's ability to work with detail, coupled with his love of geography, make this a great career choice for him. What about you? If you would like to get into this line of work, you could start by getting a GIS Technologist diploma from a community college.

What I like about my work: *"I like my job because I am not doing the same thing all the time. DMTI is a young company where people who have other skills teach me, so I have a chance to learn a variety of things. Some of the best advice I got was to pick up as many skills as you can."*

How a knowledge of geography helps me in my job: *"I always liked maps and other things that had to do with geography. I didn't have training in computers in high school, but today I work with them every day. My job today is really geography."*

1. What do you think attracted Sean to take a job like this?
2. What aspects of his job keep him interested?

Conclusion

In this chapter, you took a closer look at some familiar types of businesses: the service and retail jobs that make up most of tertiary industry. You learned that the service industry is the largest and fastest growing of the three sectors of Canada's economy. In the Case Study, you saw how one franchise has become successful in the Canadian and US markets. Finally, you looked at how governments provide services across large areas, and considered the benefits and drawbacks of the major forms of transportation. Each of these is an important element of Canada's economy.

Wrap It Up

1. Give an example of how each of the following tertiary industries tries to deliver its services as efficiently as possible.
   a) fast-food restaurants
   c) governments
   b) retail stores
   d) transit systems

2. In your own words, explain why tertiary industry has grown to become the largest sector of the Canadian economy.

3. Select a college that you are interested in researching. Get information from the Internet or the library to complete the following activities.
   a) Describe the location of the college. Include the name of the city, and where the college is located within the city.
   b) What are the major programs offered at this college? Which of these programs reflect the needs of industries in the city or region?
   c) Does the college have living accommodations? If so, what type?
   d) What connections does the college have with the city or community around it? Think in terms of bus routes, housing nearby, and facilities that college students need off-campus.
   e) Use the information you have gathered to summarize in what ways the college influences the city or region and in what ways the region influences the college.

4. Think of a regional mall that you are familiar with. Prepare a letter or brochure to persuade retail merchants to lease space in the mall. Consider the following questions:
   a) How many stores are in the mall? Classify them according to what they sell.
   b) What anchor store(s) does the mall have?
   c) Where is the next closest mall? Does the mall serve a large or highly populated area?
   d) What other facilities does the mall offer to attract customers?

5. Use a pro and con organizer to compare ship, rail, trucking, and air transport. Use information in the chapter as well as your own ideas to complete your table.

Chapter 12

CANADA GOES HIGH-TECH

You Can Quote Me on That!

My house was the first one in our neighbourhood to have a telephone. It was a big black box that hung on the wall. ... Everyone on the street used to line up to talk on the phone. Even though they had no friends with phones, they would even talk to the operator so they could say they used the phone.

— Jimmy Rogers, actor, recalling 1919

I think there is a world market for maybe five computers.

— Thomas Watson, chairman of IBM, 1943

Computers in the future may weigh no more than 1.5 tons. — *Popular Mechanics* Magazine, 1949

640K [of computer memory] ought to be enough for anybody.

— Bill Gates, President of Microsoft, 1988

It's easy to laugh at these statements. But what they really show is how quickly technology has changed in the last century. What big breakthroughs in technology have happened in your lifetime? Could you have predicted them?

◄ **Figure 12.1:** How does high tech influence your life?

This chapter will take you on a tour of some of the most important areas of high technology being explored in Canada today. You'll find out about the fields of research that are shaping your future. Care to make any predictions?

In this chapter, you will

- **find out what high technology is and which areas of high tech are important in Canada**
- **analyze how high tech has affected our economy and the way we work**
- **locate high-tech centres in Canada**
- **discover some Canadian developments in high tech, especially telecommunications and satellites**
- **find out more about high-tech geographical tools such as GPS and GIS**

Words to Know

high technology
quaternary industry
information technology
telecommunications
aerospace technology
biotechnology
fibre optics
satellite
remote sensing
Global Positioning System (GPS)
bias
Geographic Information Systems (GIS)

What Is the High-Tech Sector?

We all use the term "high tech" when we want to make something sound impressive. But are we really sure what it means? For our purposes, **high technology** is technology that relies on computer power, or the developments in science that have been made possible by computers. Another name for the high-tech sector is **quaternary industry**, meaning all businesses involved in computer technology. Let's look at four areas of high technology that are important in Canada.

Information Technology

The **information technology (IT)** sector deals with ways of storing, retrieving, and sending information. It includes computer and software companies, as well as individuals offering computer services. Companies involved in **telecommunications**—sending messages over long distances—are also part of the IT sector. You'll read more about Canada's role in telecommunications later in this chapter.

Aerospace Technology

Aerospace technology researches and develops new technologies for use in the aircraft and space industries. Canada has made important contributions in this area, including the Canadarm, developed by Spar Aerospace. It has been used successfully to load and unload supplies for the International Space Station, to help build the station, and to launch satellites into orbit. Canada's aerospace industry also includes companies that build or supply equipment for aircraft, such as Bombardier's LearJet and Challenger jets.

Biotechnology

GeoTrivia #1
One example of Canadian research is canola, a crop used to make cooking oil. The c-a-n in its name represents Canada.

Biotechnology uses living plants and animals to make new products. Canadian biotechnologists have created new foods, found treatments for diseases, developed faster-growing crops, and even altered the pig. The "enviropig" shown in Figure 12.2 has been genetically altered so that its waste produces far less pollution!

Figure 12.2: The amazing ▶ enviropig, developed at the University of Guelph

Ocean Research Technology

Ocean research technology is another important area of high tech for Canada. After all, we border on three of the world's oceans. Most of the Canadian research in this field takes place at centres in Victoria and Halifax. Scientists there use modern electronic equipment to analyze fish populations and ocean currents, among other things. Mini-subs are used to explore and even map the ocean floor.

1. What are the four fields of high technology?

2. Name three ways that these high-tech industries affect your life.

Jobs in the Information Age

Figure 12.3 shows that for most of the time you have been alive, high tech has been growing. In the 1980s and 1990s, companies were busy converting to high-tech systems. The world was "getting wired." Then, during the early years of the present millennium, demand for IT products slowed dramatically. But as new technologies are introduced, new types of high-tech jobs will likely be created.

As you can imagine, many jobs in high technology require a lot of training. So an educated workforce has become a precious resource. Oceanographers, physicists, biologists, and computer specialists are among those who work in this sector of the economy.

High tech also provides jobs for people who market, sell, or support high technology. For example, some people are involved in marketing high-tech products or in providing support for customers in call centres. A call centre is an agency that provides telephone support for products. These centres answer phone calls from clients who want to order products or get information on how to use them. If you've ever called a 1-800 number to get help with a new computer program, you're familiar with call centres.

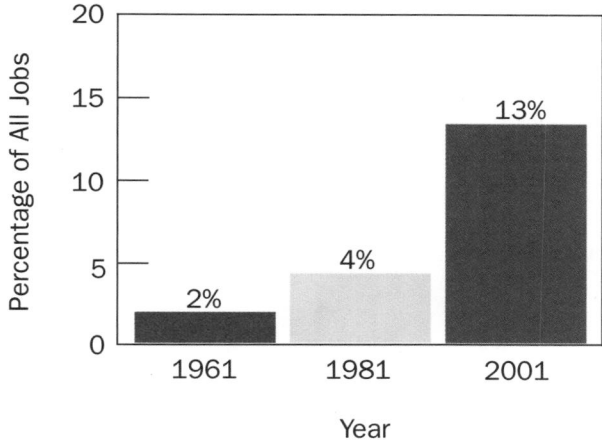

▲ **Figure 12.3:** Jobs in quaternary industry in 1961, 1981, and 2001

3. Look at the bar graph in Figure 12.3. Which period shows the highest growth? What do you think accounts for this trend?

Technology Timeline

Many changes in technology have come from Canada. In fact, Canadians have patented over one million inventions. That's a very high number for a country with such a small population. The timeline in Figure 12.4 shows some important high-tech firsts for Canada. Many of these have had a worldwide impact. The fax machine, for example, is used around the world millions of times every day to send information. And the Java computer language has changed the way that computers operate.

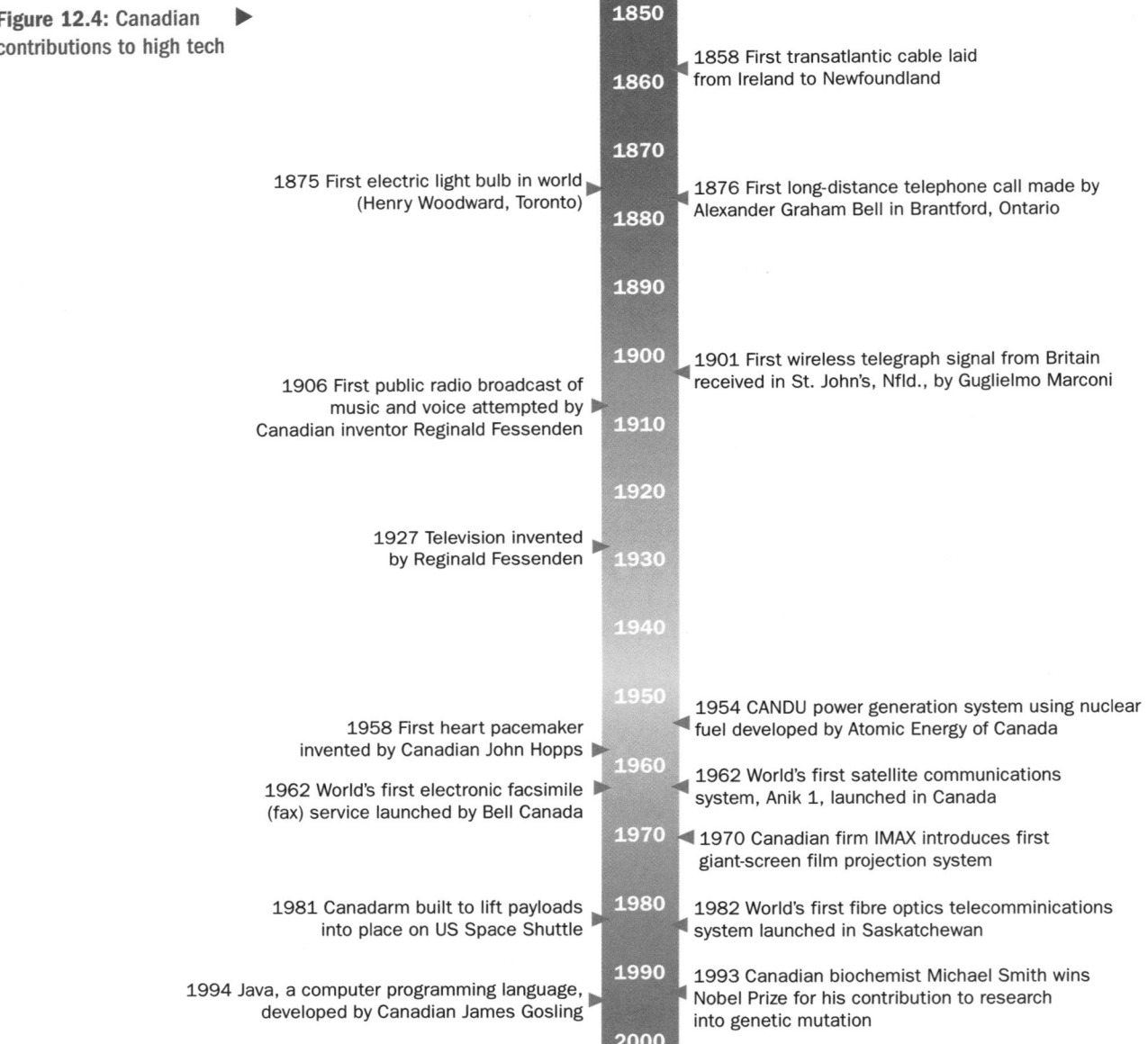

Figure 12.4: Canadian ▶ contributions to high tech

1850

1858 First transatlantic cable laid from Ireland to Newfoundland

1860

1870

1875 First electric light bulb in world (Henry Woodward, Toronto)

1876 First long-distance telephone call made by Alexander Graham Bell in Brantford, Ontario

1880

1890

1900

1901 First wireless telegraph signal from Britain received in St. John's, Nfld., by Guglielmo Marconi

1906 First public radio broadcast of music and voice attempted by Canadian inventor Reginald Fessenden

1910

1920

1927 Television invented by Reginald Fessenden

1930

1940

1950

1954 CANDU power generation system using nuclear fuel developed by Atomic Energy of Canada

1958 First heart pacemaker invented by Canadian John Hopps

1960

1962 World's first satellite communications system, Anik 1, launched in Canada

1962 World's first electronic facsimile (fax) service launched by Bell Canada

1970

1970 Canadian firm IMAX introduces first giant-screen film projection system

1981 Canadarm built to lift payloads into place on US Space Shuttle

1980

1982 World's first fibre optics telecomminications system launched in Saskatchewan

1990

1993 Canadian biochemist Michael Smith wins Nobel Prize for his contribution to research into genetic mutation

1994 Java, a computer programming language, developed by Canadian James Gosling

2000

4. Select three of these Canadian technologies and explain how each has improved your quality of life or that of someone you know.

5. What do you think would motivate someone to work on a new invention like the ones mentioned in Figure 12.4?

Where Are Canada's High-Tech Centres?

You've probably heard of California's Silicon Valley, an area with a high concentration of businesses related to computers. Canada has a number of important centres for high-tech development, too. Let's take a look at some of these centres in and around Ontario.

Kanata, Ontario: Telecommunications

Toronto, Ottawa, Vancouver, and Montreal all have important computer industries. But if anywhere could be called "Silicon Valley north" it's Kanata, Ontario. Kanata is a community west of Ottawa. It is home to many high-tech firms, many of which work in telecommunications. Canada is a world leader in this field. Examples of recent telecommunications technologies are high-speed Internet connections, cell phones, and computer networks. Television and radio are also forms of telecommunication.

Kanata is a good location for this type of industry. It is near two major Ontario universities. Many graduates who study computers find work in Kanata. It is also near the federal government. The government is responsible for making sure all Canadians are connected through telecommunications networks. Locating away from the centre of Ottawa means land is cheaper. It also gives employees a nice area in which to raise a family. And since software companies compete with other firms for employees, it's important to keep the ones they have happy.

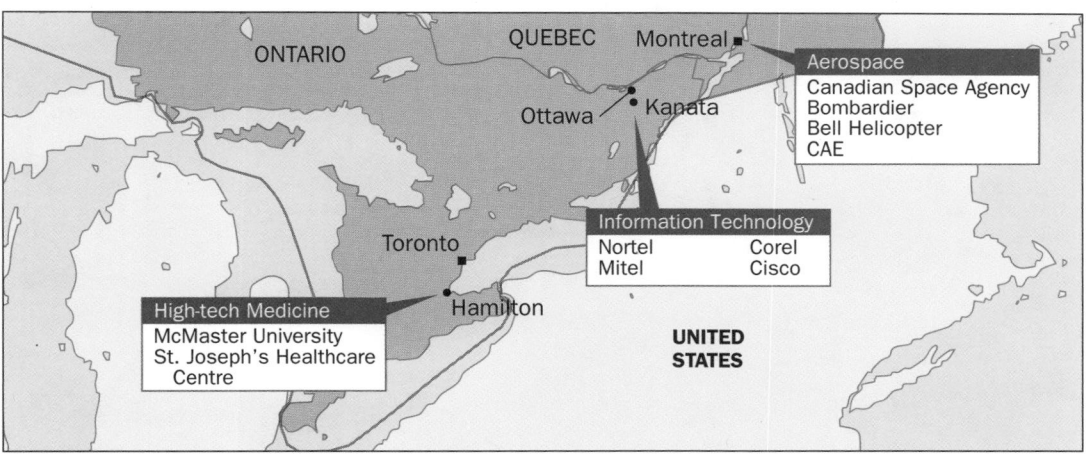

▲ **Figure 12.5:** Canada's high-tech centres for telecommunications, aerospace, and medicine

6. Look at the map in Figure 12.5. Why do you think all these high-tech centres are located in central Canada?

7. What advantages does Kanata have for an industry like software development?

8. Why do you think a high-tech company would prefer to locate in a city like Kanata rather than in a smaller centre by itself?

9. What other related industries do you think might locate in Kanata? Explain your answer.

Montreal, Quebec: Aerospace

The Canadian Space Agency has its headquarters in Montreal. So do several large aviation companies, such as Bombardier, Pratt and Whitney, and Bell Helicopter. Other firms, such as Lockheed Martin and CAE, supply parts and systems for these big firms. About 260 smaller suppliers are also located in the area. Overall, the aerospace industry provides close to 40 000 jobs in or around Montreal.

Why Montreal? Well, Montreal has a long tradition as the aerospace capital of Canada. Even before high tech, Montreal was an important centre for aviation. Pratt and Whitney, for example, has been in the aircraft industry in the city since 1928. Over time, a web of related businesses has grown up in the region. Universities, such as Concordia and McGill, produce graduates who are trained to work in aerospace. And institutes dedicated specifically to aerospace studies have been set up.

Software companies can move their location fairly easily. But aerospace companies such as Bombardier have a huge investment in their plant and machinery. It takes a lot of space and a lot of equipment to build an airplane! So they aren't likely to pick up and move. Governments do their part to keep the industry healthy by giving aerospace companies tax breaks to encourage research and development.

▲ **Figure 12.6:** The Bombardier plant near Montreal

10. Why is an industry such as software development more flexible in terms of location than an aircraft manufacturing firm like Bombardier?

11. What other factors have made Montreal a centre for aerospace?

12. Look at the photograph in Figure 12.6. What evidence do you see that the company has invested a lot in its manufacturing plants?

Hamilton, Ontario: High-Tech Medicine

Hamilton used to be known as Steeltown. The largest employers in the city were the giant steel companies, Stelco and Dofasco. But when these companies began laying people off, another industry was needed.

Today, McMaster University and several health centres in the region have filled the gap. Hamilton has become an important centre for high-tech medicine. This new area of specialty has become a major source of employment in the region.

Hamilton is not the only region to benefit from the expertise of its medical community. Doctors at Hamilton's St. Joseph's Healthcare Centre can now link up with doctors in remote communities in northern Canada through fibre optics. **Fibre optics** uses pulses of laser light to send high-speed signals along a thin glass cable. The doctors in Hamilton can even use robotic instruments to assist in operations on patients thousands of kilometres away!

GeoTrivia #2
A fibre optic cable as thin as a human hair can handle 32 000 telephone conversations at once.

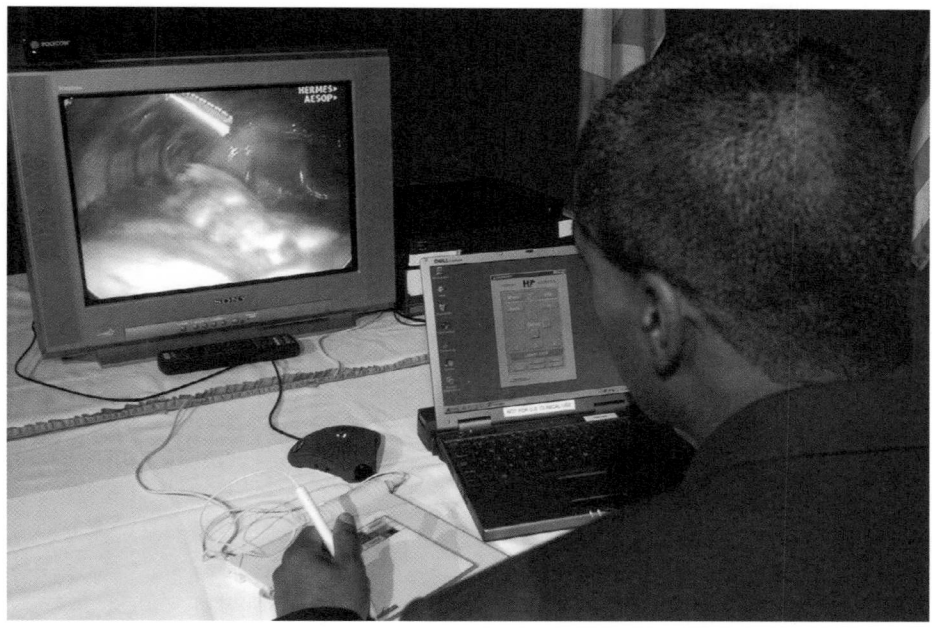

◀ **Figure 12.7:** A doctor assists in long-distance robotic surgery.

13. a) Identify two ways that doctors use fibre optics.
    b) Think of three other ways they could use this communication network to improve rural medicine.

14. Various communications networks can help lessen economic differences in many ways. Explain how each of the following communications networks has improved (or could improve) people's lives in remote areas of the country.
    a) postal network with one price to send a letter anywhere in Canada
    b) a national broadcaster (the CBC) bringing national and local radio and television programming to all areas of the country
    c) telephone networks with access from just about anywhere in the country
    d) building the infrastructure to bring high-speed Internet to rural Canada

15. Explain why each of the cities mentioned on pages 205–207 has become a centre for high technology.

Satellite-Based Technology

Whenever you check the weather forecast, talk on your cell phone, or watch the news on TV, you are relying on satellite-based technology. A **satellite** is a device that is placed in orbit around the Earth. Signals can be sent from the Earth to the satellite and then bounced back to a different part of the Earth almost instantaneously.

Satellite technology affects our everyday life. Not only do we receive satellite weather information, but Internet signals are now being sent through satellites as well. **Remote sensing** technologies allow satellites to take photographs that can penetrate clouds to identify even small objects on the ground. This information can be used to explore for oil and gas, monitor pollution, and track the movement of icebergs to help ships move safely.

An exciting technology that has developed with the use of satellites is the **Global Positioning System (GPS)**. By locating and measuring the signals from three or more satellites, a hand-held GPS unit can determine your location anywhere in the world. GPS can also be used to locate stolen vehicles—or even to open car doors if the owners have locked the keys inside!

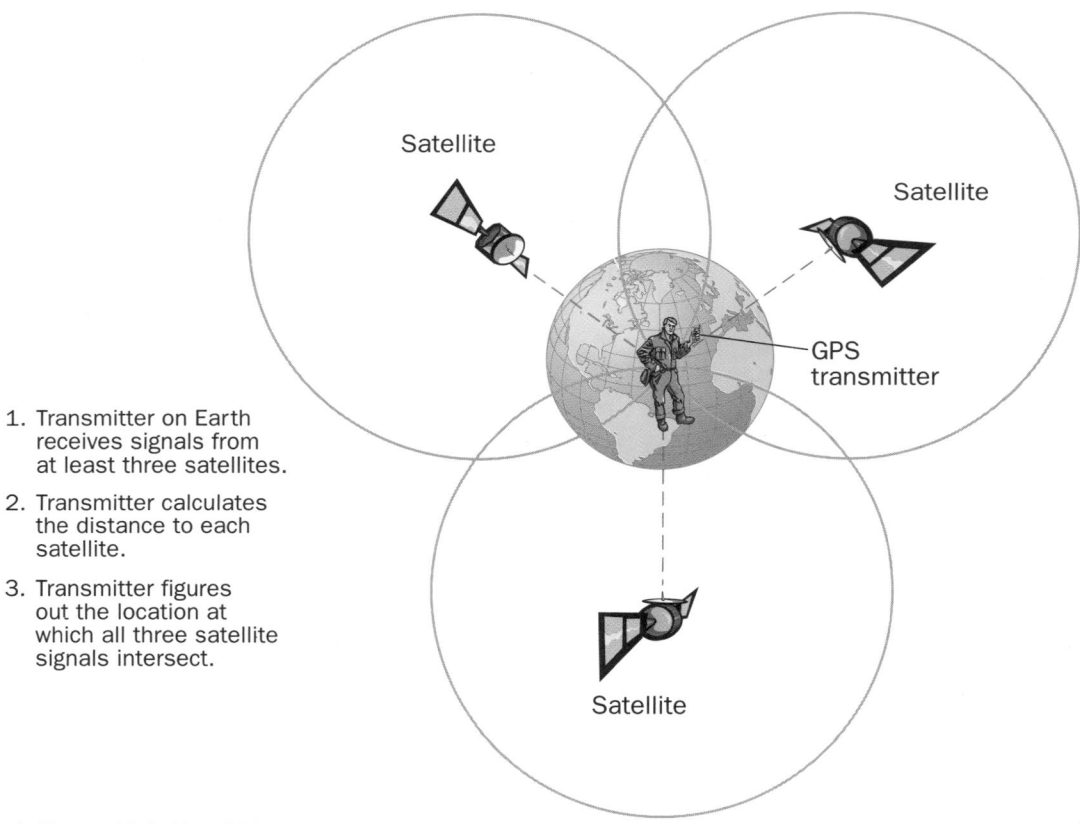

1. Transmitter on Earth receives signals from at least three satellites.

2. Transmitter calculates the distance to each satellite.

3. Transmitter figures out the location at which all three satellite signals intersect.

▲ **Figure 12.8:** How GPS works

16. Suggest how satellite technology might help in the following areas.
    a) police work   b) search and rescue   c) farming

17. Describe the process shown in Figure 12.8 in your own words.

Canada's Role in Satellite Technology

Canada is a big country. And because the surface of the Earth is curved, messages can't be sent directly from one end of the country to the other by direct radio signal. So the use of satellites is of particular importance for us. That's one reason why Canada has been a world leader in satellite technology since 1962. In that year, TelSat Canada launched the world's first satellite dedicated to studying the atmosphere, the Alouette. Canada became the third nation in space, after the Soviet Union and the United States, to launch a satellite.

But unlike these two countries, whose space programs focused on human space flight and exploration, Canada's space industry soon began to focus on telecommunications. With the launch of Anik 1 in 1967, Canada became the first country in the world to have a communications satellite for non-military purposes. Anik 1 allowed Canadians to see live television coast to coast and to talk to others on the telephone via space.

Since then, we have continued our exploration of Earth from space with other, increasingly sophisticated satellites. Today, Canada has some of the most powerful domestic satellites in the world, and one of the most sophisticated telecommunications systems.

GeoTrivia #3
Anik means "little brother" in Inuktitut. The name signifies that these communication satellites unite Canadians into one big family.

Preliminary Artist Rendition

◀ **Figure 12.9:** Canada's Anik F-2 satellite, the most recent generation of Anik communications satellites

18. a) Explain why satellite technology is particularly important in a large country like Canada.
   b) Give three ways that satellite technology has improved life in remote or northern parts of the country.

GEOSKILLS

EVALUATING INTERNET SITES

The Internet is a powerful tool for research. But the volume of information available can make it hard to find exactly what you need. And not all the information on the Net is accurate or reliable. How can you weed out the good from the bad?

Purpose

Knowing how to evaluate Internet sites for accuracy, reliability, and bias allows researchers to find the best sources of information.

Let's try a search to learn more about Canada's involvement in satellite technology. The following steps will help you search efficiently and find the information you need.

Step 1

Enter one to three keywords, joined by "and," into a search engine. A search engine is a program that will produce a list of Web sites containing your keywords. For our search we will enter "Canada and satellite."

Step 2

From the list created by the search engine, choose five sites that seem to contain useful information. Usually, the search engine will display "hits" in order, starting with those that are most likely to be of use.

Step 3

Evaluate each site for accuracy. Is it updated regularly? Does it contain recent information? Always double-check the information you find with at least one other source.

▲ **Figure 12.10:** The Google search engine, one of the most popular ways of searching the Internet

Step 4

Evaluate each site for reliability. Sites with a "~" in the address are usually hosted by individuals and may not be reliable. Better choices are sites sponsored by universities (.edu), governments (.ca), and well-known media publications (.net or .com). Avoid sites that contain sloppy writing or spelling errors.

Step 5

Evaluate each site for bias. **Bias** is a one-sided view of a topic. To recognize bias, ask yourself two questions:

1. Is the site presenting facts—generally agreed-upon information—or opinions? For example, "Canada launched the world's first communications satellite for domestic use" is a fact. But "Canada's satellites are the best" is an opinion, because not everyone would agree. Opinions should be backed up by convincing arguments—supporting facts, examples, or logic. If they are not, the source may be biased. You should usually avoid using such sites.

2. What is the site *not* saying about the topic? For example, the Web site of a company that sells satellite dishes for TV reception will probably tell you only good things about their services. You will have to look elsewhere to find anything negative.

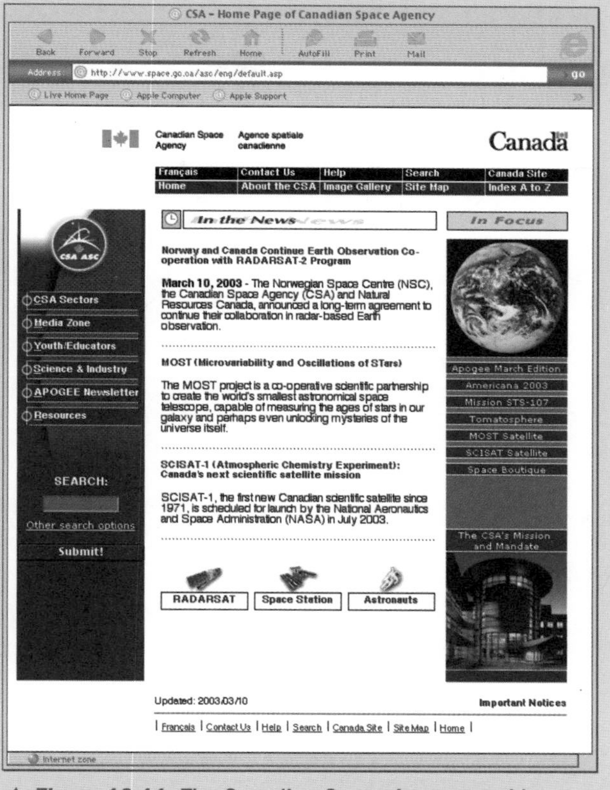

▲ **Figure 12.11:** The Canadian Space Agency would probably be an accurate and reliable source of information.

Step 6

Record the address of each site you use and the date you visited it. Then, write down or print out any useful information from the site.

Practise It!

1. Search the Internet to find out more about one of the Canadian achievements shown on the timeline in Figure 12.4 (page 204). Record your topic and keywords.

2. List five interesting things you learned about your topic.

3. Give the address of two sites that you found to be both accurate and reliable. Explain why you thought so.

4. a) List one example of an opinion backed up by convincing arguments. Explain why you thought the argument was convincing.

   b) Find one example of bias on a Web site. Give specific examples to show the bias.

> **To evaluate a Web site...**
> ✔ enter up to three keywords joined by "and"
> ✔ choose five sites that appear useful
> ✔ make sure site is accurate and up to date
> ✔ decide if site sponsor is reliable
> ✔ evaluate the site for bias
> ✔ record the address, the date, and any useful information

High-Tech Geography: GIS

Many new types of technology are changing the way we look at the world. One of the most powerful of these is **GIS (Geographic Information Systems)**, a new computer-software program that combines different kinds of geographic information.

GIS analyzes data that are input into a computer and produces maps based on this information. Any information that can be put on a map can be part of a GIS image. For example, imagine that you want to find out how quickly wetlands are disappearing from the area where you live. With GIS, you could construct maps showing how wetland areas have changed over the last fifty years, and then determine what is happening to them.

How Does It Work?

Figure 12.12 shows how GIS can be used to create a complex map. In this case, the problem is where to locate an airport around the edge of a city. GIS is able to take four different pieces of geographical information and combine them into one map. By analyzing road patterns, residential housing areas, topographic features such as hills, and the locations of other airports in the region, the computer can suggest the most suitable site for the airport. For the purposes of this diagram, each map uses a separate colour.

When you think about it, this tool has all kinds of uses. Oil and other utility companies, for example, use GIS to co-ordinate their service delivery to customers. Environmentalists use it to monitor changes in environmental conditions and to evaluate the impact of development on ecosystems. And retailers use GIS to decide where to locate their stores in order to serve customers better. It's no wonder GIS technology has become so popular!

You'll read about an example of GIS in the GeoCareers feature on page 214.

19. a) Summarize three different uses for GIS.
     b) With a partner, brainstorm six more uses for GIS technology.

20. a) What four pieces of information have been used to create the complete map in Figure 12.12?
     b) How does the use of GIS represent an improvement over traditional planning methods, in which separate maps or data tables are consulted?

21. Imagine that you have been given the job of finding the best location for a new fire station. What three types of information would you need in order to make your decision?

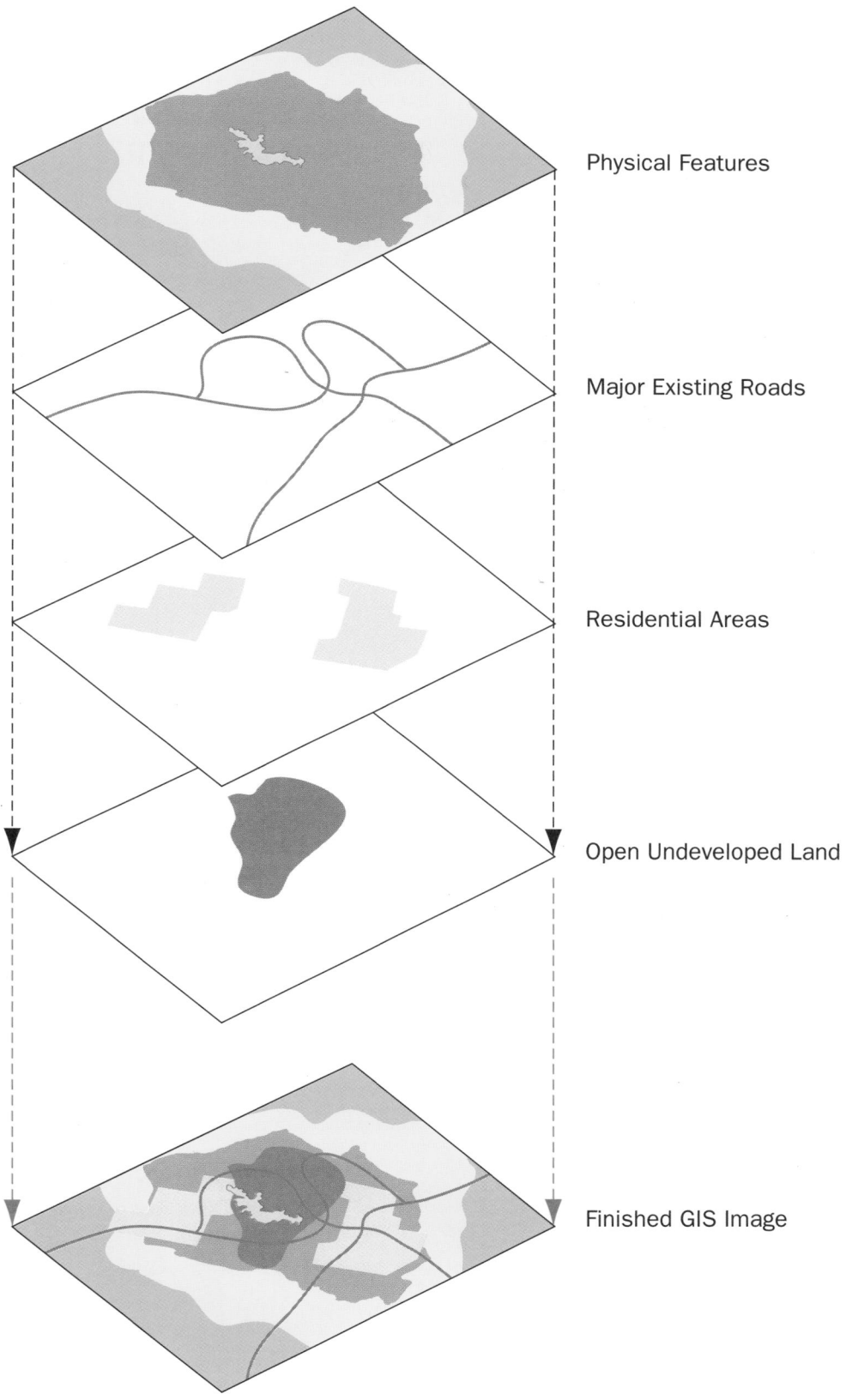

Physical Features

Major Existing Roads

Residential Areas

Open Undeveloped Land

Finished GIS Image

▲ **Figure 12.12:** GIS combines four maps into one

GEO CAREERS   GIS RESEARCH ANALYST

Name: Dina Dellasiepe
High School: Dante Alighieri Academy, Toronto
Job Title: Research Analyst

What does GIS have to do with pizza? Just ask Dina Dellasiepe! Dina is a research analyst for a pizza company. The company sells its products through a series of restaurants located across the city of Toronto and its suburbs. Dina's job is to help the company identify new markets and get the most out of existing ones. She uses GIS technology to do this.

Most of the pizzas sold are delivered to the customer. Part of Dina's job involves using GIS technology to map out routes for the drivers. "The GIS technology was used to set up the delivery areas for each restaurant and to help lay out the routes for the delivery cars to take. Even when there is construction on a street that would slow down delivery, we are able to put that into the computer to make sure our drivers do not waste time. We have little maps for each delivery vehicle to help out."

Another way that GIS is useful for Dina's company is in deciding where to locate their stores. "Before our company opens a store we do market analysis to see where people live and the types of foods that they eat and then we map this information. ... One of the things that I learned about pizza sales is that 70 per cent of the pizzas sold are ordered by males. In addition, the biggest sales night for pizzas is the night of the Super Bowl!"

Dina's education includes a degree in Applied Geography from Ryerson University. But she points out that you can get a job as a GIS technician with a college diploma. It all depends on how you want to apply your skills.

What I like about my work: *"I find that my job is fun. I like to see new stores set up and become successful. I also like to work with maps and people. My job also has lots of variety so that I don't get bored."*

How a knowledge of geography helps me in my job: *"When I was in high school, I did enjoy geography, but I didn't think that there was any future in it. But after high school I realized that there were all sorts of things that I could do with geography—such as the job I am in."*

1. Explain in your own words how Dina uses geography in her job.

2. How does Dina's work help the pizza company earn more money? Give at least two examples.

3. Why do you think she enjoys her job so much?

Conclusion

In this chapter, you learned about some high-tech industries that are shaping the future of Canadians. You analyzed where high-tech companies are located, and considered some of the many high-tech firsts this country has produced. Satellite-based technology has given Canadians a way to overcome the geographic barriers of distance, climate, and low population density that separate Canadians. It's not surprising that Canada has played an important role in satellite communications. Finally, you had a look at GIS, a high-tech mapping tool with many applications.

Wrap It Up

1. In your own words, explain the following statement, and give an example to illustrate. "Information has become our most important commodity, just as iron ore or automobiles once were."

2. a) Describe the four main areas of high technology and give a Canadian example for each.
   b) Given your geographical knowledge of Canada, explain why each of these examples is important for Canada's economy or for the Canadian people.

3. Talk to your parents or an older adult about a technological change that has occurred during their lives. Ask them the following questions:
   a) When did the change happen?
   b) How did they manage before the new technology?
   c) How did the new technology affect their lives in a good way?
   d) What negative effects did it have?

4. Use the Internet or the library to research a new high-tech product or technology that is currently being developed.
   a) Describe the product, including what it does or how it improves on existing technology.

   b) Predict how it might improve the lives of Canadians in the future.

5. Do research to find out more about how high-tech developments have improved the lives of people in remote areas in one of the following ways. Present your findings in an oral report or as a multimedia presentation.
   a) education
   b) communication
   c) health care
   d) economic opportunity

6. With high tech, the location of many industries is flexible because all that's required is a telecommunications infrastructure and an educated population. For example, Moncton, New Brunswick, has become a major location for North American call centres.
   a) How might this new industry affect the migration patterns of people in the Atlantic region who need jobs?
   b) In what other way does high technology allow people in areas with high unemployment to avoid migrating for a job? (*Hint:* How do e-mail, telephone, and courier services change our idea of "the office"?)

Unit 3 Performance Task

PLAN YOUR OWN BUSINESS

Ever thought that you'd like to be your own boss? Millions of Canadians are self-employed, with businesses of their own. These people are entrepreneurs—people with the get-up-and-go to start and run their own companies. Many run small operations from home. A freelance graphic artist or self-employed car mechanic are two good examples. Some entrepreneurs see their small businesses grow into huge companies with many employees. Canadian Tire, for example, began when two brothers opened a small parking garage in east Toronto. Today, the company has more than 400 stores across Canada. Some Canadian entrepreneurs sell products and services around the world.

In this Performance Task, you will choose a type of business that you would like to start. Then, you'll do what every entrepreneur does: prepare a business plan, choose and map a business location, and prepare materials to promote your business.

Assignment 1: Choosing Your Business

In this unit, you learned about the four kinds of economic activity: primary, secondary, tertiary, and quaternary (high-tech). Think of a business in one of these areas that you would like to start one day. For example, your business could be a peach orchard (primary), a woodworking shop (secondary), a CD store (tertiary), or an Internet service provider (quaternary). If you aren't sure what you'd like to do, look back through Chapters 9 to 12 to find examples that might appeal to you. Most new businesses reflect the hobbies, interests, and skills of the entrepreneur. So choose something that takes advantage of your skills, or reflects your hobbies or interests.

Because you want to locate your business in your community or region, choose a business that would be well suited to the area. In other words, be sure that any needed resources would be close by and that you could easily reach a market for your product.

1. In writing, describe the type of business you would like to plan. To which of the four main types of business does it belong? Explain why it fits in this category. Present your idea in writing to your teacher, and get written approval for your business.

◀ **Figure 1:** EBTech is a successful Internet provider started by Bernie Brocklehurst, shown here, and a friend when they were still in high school.

Assignment 2: Preparing Your Business Plan

To find out more about the type of business you are considering, use this textbook, the Internet, and other sources, such as the business-directory section of the telephone book. Before researching on the Internet, review the GeoSkills feature, "Evaluating Internet Sites," on pages 210–211.

You might discover similar businesses right in your community that you can visit for information and ideas. This strategy will help you find out how other people run their businesses. You can learn from their mistakes, copy their best ideas, and come up with better ideas to make sure your business succeeds.

Your goal will be to come up with your own business plan. Look at Figure 2 to see what information a business plan contains.

1. Outline the characteristics of your new business on a copy of the business plan form shown in Figure 2. The hardest part to figure out will be how much money you'll need. Make your best guess of costs in four categories:
   - office or building costs
   - salaries
   - equipment
   - transportation

Then make your best guess about how much money you think your business can make in your first year. Submit the completed business plan to your teacher.

BUSINESS PLAN

1. Type and name of business
2. Classification of business (primary, secondary, tertiary, or quaternary)
3. Product or service provided
4. Local competing companies in this business field
5. Source of customers (local area, province, nation, or world; general public or other companies)
6. Approximate number of employees and their jobs
7. Skills required by employees (e.g., truck driver would need truck licence and good driving skills)
8. Supplies or resources required (e.g., material to make T-shirts)
9. Forms of advertising (e.g., sponsorship of a ball team, or banner ads on Web sites your customers use often)
10. Transportation or communication needed (e.g., e-mail)
11. Money requirements
12. A brief general description of your business

▲ **Figure 2:** The basic information for a business plan

Assignment 3: Choosing and Mapping Your Business Location

In this unit, you learned the importance of location for different types of economic activities. To remind yourself why businesses locate where they do, review the GeoSkills feature, "Assessing Location Factors Using Photographs and Maps" on pages 158–159, or the section called "Location Factors" on pages 174–175. Before you decide on a good location for your business, think about where your competitors are located. Also,

think about the advantages of EBTech's location, as shown in Figure 3 on the next page.

Different types of businesses require different types of locations.
- Primary industries must locate close to a source for the resources they use, such as a fruit orchard or a gravel quarry.

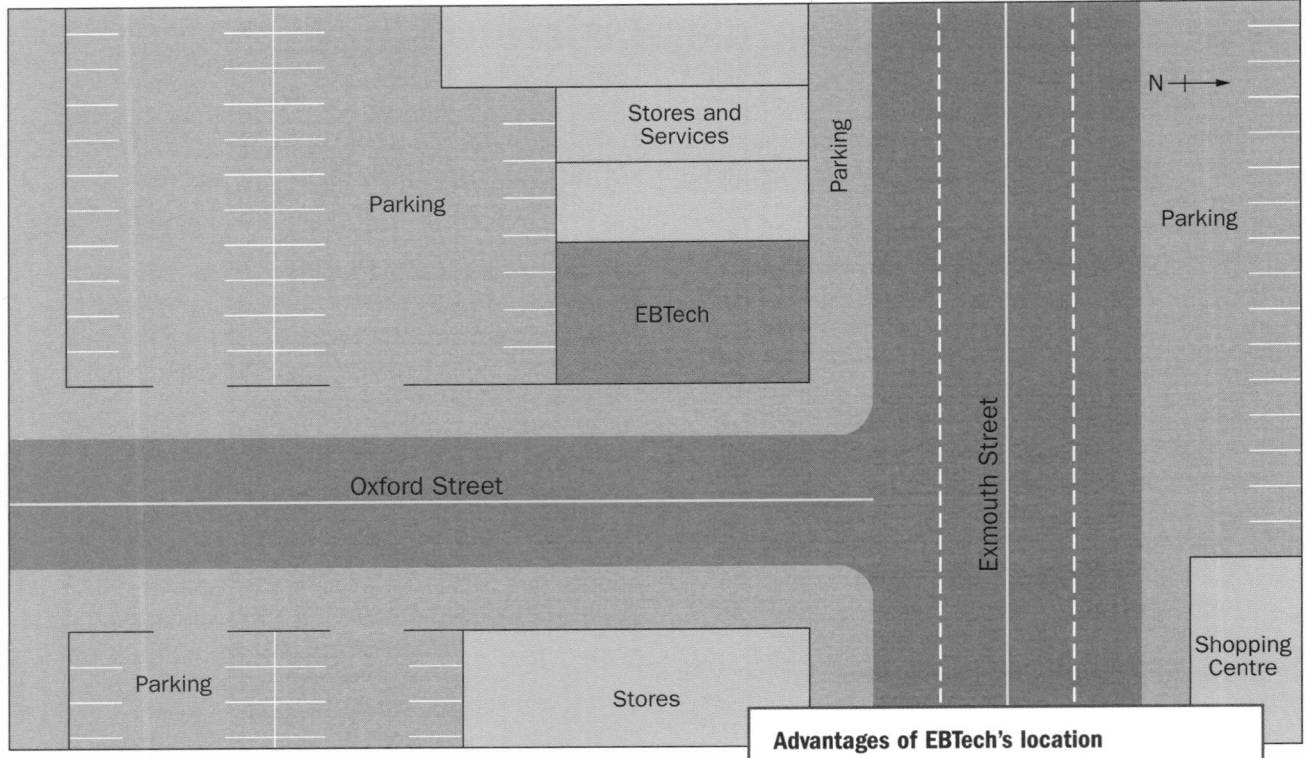

▲ Figure 3: The location of EBTech Internet provider, Sarnia, Ontario

Advantages of EBTech's location

- near the centre of the community
- on a high-traffic street
- at an easy-to-find corner location
- close to many other stores and services
- plenty of off-street parking behind the store

- Secondary businesses, such as a woodworking shop, may locate close to a cheap source of lumber or near their customers. It depends on the amount of the raw material (wood) that is required, and how much it costs to transport it.
- Service businesses, such as a CD store, must locate where customers can find them and get to them easily: a busy mall with a parking lot, for example, or a street location next to a subway station.
- Finally, quaternary industries focused on computers and research can be either close to customers or far away. With e-mail and couriers, business can take place on-line, making location unimportant.

After deciding on the best location for your business, do the following activities to draw a map of your location and explain your choice. If necessary, review the GeoSkills feature, "Drawing a Small-Area Map and Route," on pages 4–5.

1. Prepare a neat close-up map to show the location you picked for your business in your community or region. Show the following information on your map:
   - the business location
   - transportation routes that connect your business with suppliers
   - transportation routes that connect your business with customers
   - parking or public transit access for customers and employees

   Complete your map with the following details:
   - a title, including the name of your business
   - appropriate labels and a legend
   - a north arrow
   - a scale (if known)

2. Why did you pick this location? List three or more reasons why the location you chose is good for this type of business.

Assignment 4: Promoting Your Business

Every type of business has customers, although they are not always the general public. For example, an orchard owner may sell most of the crop to another company that makes juice, jam, or canned fruit. Only a small part of the crop may be sold directly to the public at a roadside stand or a local farmers' market.

Still, every business must keep reminding customers of the quality and reliability of their product or service, even if the customer is a plant manager. This is called good marketing. (Marketing is the act of promoting goods or services for sale.) In this part of the Performance Task, you will prepare a brochure to promote your business with your customers.

1. In your business plan, you stated where your customers are located. Now you need to clarify who your customers are.
   a) Are your customers the public or another company?
   b) If you are selling to the public, are your customers from any particular age, gender, ethnic, or income group? Are they a specific group, such as on-line gamers?
   c) If you're selling to other companies, what individuals are responsible for making purchasing decisions: plant managers? store owners? individuals with small home businesses?
   d) How will your product or service make life easier for your customers? List three or more reasons why your customers should purchase your particular product or service instead of another.

2. Make an illustrated brochure to tell customers about your new business. Be sure to communicate why they should come to you rather than your competitors. Include the following.

▲ **Figure 4:** These businesses put up large street signs to attract customers.

- a logo for your business
- contact information (e.g., telephone number and Web address)
- important product information from your business plan
- a small map of your location
- suitable pictures from the Internet, CD-ROMs, or magazines

ENVIRONMENTAL INTERACTIONS

The Somewhere in Canada Contest #4

Where in Canada do you think this photograph might have been taken? Win the Somewhere in Canada Contest #4 by giving the correct answer before anyone else in your class. If you're not sure what island the photographer is flying over, look at the following clues.

CLUE 1 ▶ This 13-km-long bridge, called Confederation Bridge, opened in 1997.

CLUE 2 ▶ The bridge connects the mainland (in the background) to a large island (in the foreground) where about 140 000 people live.

CLUE 3 ▶ Look at the reddish tinge on the dirt road and in the shallow water. This island is known for red soil, red sand beaches, and red lobsters.

CLUE 4 ▶ Red soil on your potatoes may mean they were grown on the island.

CLUE 5 ▶ The island is the location for a national facility for testing wind energy technology.

CLUE 6 ▶ Lucy Maud Montgomery lived here, and created the world-famous literary character, Anne of Green Gables. The island has developed a thriving tourism industry around Anne.

What Will You Study in This Unit?

Which clues helped you identify the island in the foreground of the photograph? Perhaps it was the products, such as lobsters and potatoes, or the widely recognized red beaches. It may have been the bridge itself, one of the longest in the world. When this island became Canada's seventh province in 1873, it was promised year-round connection with the rest of the nation. Until the bridge was built, government ships and icebreakers did the job.

In this unit, you will learn that this low-lying island and its red beaches are threatened by rising sea levels caused by global climate change. In fact, the changing climate is affecting all of Canada in one way or another. You will learn that dramatic shifts in temperature and precipitation are not accidents of nature. They are caused when we burn coal, oil, and natural gas for energy.

Have you heard the phrase "ecological footprint" before? This refers to the deep tracks modern society leaves across the face of the Earth. We are spoiling our natural places by polluting the air, water, and land. We're using up some resources so quickly that we may run out soon. We are just beginning to realize the enormous impact our way of life has on the planet.

This unit is about environmental problems. But, it also deals with solutions. You will find many ideas in this unit that show how we can enjoy the riches of the Earth without destroying it. We just need to make the right choices.

In this unit, you will

- show that you know some of the important environmental problems and issues affecting Canada

- show that you understand how human choices can affect the environment both negatively and positively

- judge the most sustainable, or lasting, ways in which to use the Earth's resources

For a challenge, try the Unit 4 GIS activity, "Acid Rain Analyst," on page 340.

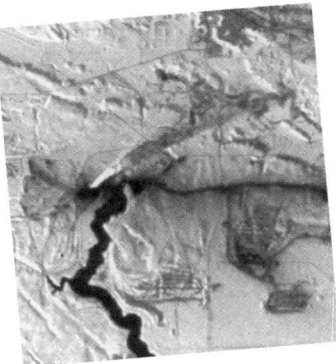

Chapter 13

EVALUATING ENERGY STRATEGIES

Figure 13.1: ▶
Video arcades use a lot of energy to power their flashing lights, loud music, and high-tech games.

Energy Survey

Have you ever played video games or ridden a snowmobile? used the washer for one clothing item? turned up the thermostat instead of putting on a sweater? Take the survey below to find out how you use energy.

Scoring Results

0 to 20 points:
Light energy use

21 to 30:
Moderate energy use

31 to 40:
Above-average energy use

41 or more:
Heavy energy use

1. **Entertainment:** On a daily basis, how long do you spend on each of these activities? Score 1 point per half hour.
   a) watching television/videos/DVDs
   b) listening to recorded music (excluding battery-run units)
   c) playing electronic/video games (excluding battery-run units)
   d) using a computer (excluding electronic/video games)

2. **Personal Care:** On a daily basis, how long do you spend on each of these activities? Score 1 point per 15 minutes.
   a) taking hot showers/baths/washing hair
   b) using the dryer to remove wrinkles/dry one clothing item
   c) using a hair dryer/electric curling iron
   d) using an electric toothbrush/electric razor

3. **Motorized Equipment:** Which of the following energy users does your family own or lease? Score 5 points per item (for example, 2 cars = 10 points).
   a) car/van/SUV/truck
   b) motorcycle(s)/motorbike(s)
   c) all-terrain vehicle/snowmobile
   d) lawn mower/snow blower
   e) boat with motor
   f) motorized recreational vehicle

4. **Home Heating:** Which of the following energy users supply your home's heating needs? Score 5 points per item.
   a) electric heaters
   b) oil furnace
   c) natural gas furnace
   d) wood stove/fireplace insert
   e) steam radiators
   f) other systems or unsure

In this chapter, you will

- analyze the ways Canadians use energy resources
- understand the need to conserve energy resources for the future
- identify benefits and problems of different types of energy systems
- find out how alternative energy resources can improve quality of life

Words to Know

conventional energy
renewable energy
non-renewable energy
fossil fuel
megaproject
bitumen
alternative energy
fuel cell
geothermal energy
energy reserves
hybrid-power vehicle

Energy Use in Canada

Canadians use a lot of energy. In fact, Canada ranks second in the world (after the United States) in energy use per person. Here are some reasons why.

- Long, cold winters require heating. Hot, humid summers (in the Great Lakes region) increase demand for air conditioning.

- The vast size of the country means Canadians must frequently drive or fly in order to get from one place to another.

- Our industries use large amounts of energy to power machines and shape resources into finished products.

- Our high standard of living—what Canadian society thinks is necessary for personal comfort and happiness—means we own many electronic and motorized devices.

- We tend to value comfort and convenience over energy conservation.

◄ **Figure 13.2:** Heavy industry, like this aluminum smelter in BC, uses a lot of energy.

1. Find the class average for the energy survey on the previous page. Then, prepare a bar graph to show the number of students in each score range.

2. Rank the five reasons for Canada's high energy use from "most important" to "least important." Explain your choice for first and last place.

3. List three other countries that would
   a) use a lot of energy per person.   b) use very little energy per person.
   Explain your choices.

Conventional Energy: Renewable Sources

When something is "conventional," it means it is widely used or practised. **Conventional energy** refers to commonly used sources of heat, light, or power, such as water, coal, oil, and natural gas. **Renewable energy** is an energy supply that can reproduce itself fairly quickly. Wood is a good example of a renewable energy resource. It has been used for heat, light, and power since prehistoric times. Today, many northern Canadian communities still rely on wood for heating and cooking. For example, all the homes in the northern Quebec town of Oujé-Bougoumou (see Figure 6.12, page 114) are connected to a large furnace that burns sawdust from the nearby sawmill. Across Canada, wood stoves and fireplace inserts keep homes and cottages warm.

4. Give three reasons why the North often relies on wood for home energy.

Hydroelectric Power

The power of falling water was used by pioneers to saw lumber and grind wheat into flour. Hydroelectricity is power that is generated by water. In 1908, Ontario's first water-powered electric plant was built at Niagara Falls. Since Canada has many large, fast-flowing rivers, about 60 per cent of our electricity today is supplied by hydro. However, the best locations for hydro plants have already been developed.

Look at Figure 13.3 and you will understand how most electricity is produced. Water rushing through narrow tubes, called "penstocks," spins a propeller-like turbine. A shaft from the turbine then spins inside a generator to create electricity. Transformers step up (increase) this power before it is sent through high-voltage power lines to customers.

Figure 13.3: ▶
Hydroelectric generating station

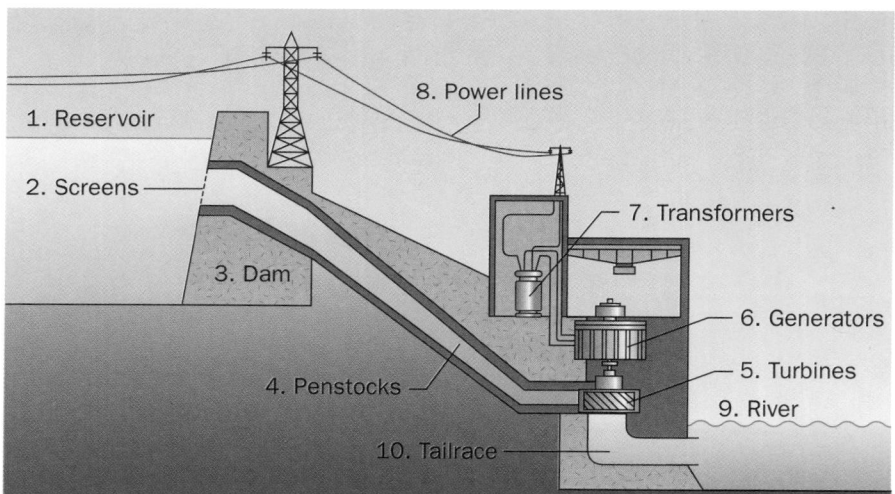

5. Make a simple labelled diagram to show how a hydroelectric power plant works. Number the steps in producing electricity in order (1, 2, 3, 4, 5, and 6).

6. Look at a map that shows the location of Canada's hydroelectric power plants. Name five rivers that have several power stations along them.

The Benefits	The Problems
• running water is a renewable resource	• often must be built far from energy customers
• operating costs are low because no fuel is needed	• because of friction along power lines, the farther the power is carried, the lower the voltage
• no burning fuel means no air pollution	• very expensive to build and repair
• the reservoir provides an agricultural water supply and a site for recreational swimming, boating, and fishing	• flooding the reservoir has many negative effects on human communities and animal habitats

▲ **Figure 13.4:** Benefits and problems of hydroelectric power plants

7. Would flooding to create a reservoir have a good or bad effect on each of the following? Explain your answers, giving an example in each case.
   a) animal habitats
   b) Aboriginal hunters and fishers
   c) recreational boaters
   d) farmers on dry land above the river valley
   e) nearby villages and highways

Conventional Energy: Non-Renewable Sources

An energy resource that cannot reproduce itself is called **non-renewable energy**. This category covers all minerals, and includes uranium and fossil fuels.

Nuclear Power Plant

Have you ever watched or played a game of pool? The cue ball is shot into a cluster of coloured balls, which scatter in all directions, slamming into one another. These actions parallel what happens in a nuclear reactor. Atomic particles called neutrons are fired at large, heavy uranium atoms. As each uranium atom is shattered, heat energy and radioactivity are released. This heat energy is converted to electricity inside the nuclear power plant. Since the process slowly uses up the uranium, uranium is considered a non-renewable energy resource. Nuclear reactors produce only about 15 per cent of Canada's electricity.

GeoTrivia #1
Canada's CANDU nuclear reactors are known for their high-quality construction. They have been sold to countries all over the world.

◀ **Figure 13.5:** Nuclear generating station

3. Steam line
4. Turbine
5. Generator
2. Steam unit
7. Power lines
1. Nuclear reactor
6. Transformers

As Figure 13.5 on the previous page shows, the nuclear power plant uses jets of steam (created by heat from the nuclear reactor) to spin turbines. The rest of the power process is the same as it is for hydroelectricity.

8. a) Which parts of the nuclear power plant are also found in the hydroelectric generating station?
    b) Use Figure 13.5 to explain why nuclear power plants are usually located beside a lake.

9. Use an atlas to identify the Canadian provinces and territories that produce nuclear energy. Which one relies most heavily on nuclear electricity?

The Benefits	The Problems
• Canada has a huge supply of uranium fuel from mines in the Canadian Shield	• scientists are searching for better, safer ways to dispose of nuclear wastes
• very little uranium is used in the reactor, so little storage area is needed	• if the reactor fails, radioactivity can kill plant workers and members of the public
• nothing is burned, so there is no air pollution	• very expensive to build and maintain
• can be located closer to electricity users because it does not require a river system	• because the process is intense, reactors must be rebuilt after a fairly short time

▲ Figure 13.6: Benefits and problems of nuclear power plants

10. Which of the problems listed in Figure 13.6 best explain why Canada has not built any new reactors in recent years?

11. Discuss with a partner each of the following ideas for disposing of nuclear waste. Agree on the best solution. Give reasons for your choice.
    a) shoot it out into deep space
    b) scatter it widely across the oceans
    c) cement it deep into old hard-rock mines

Fossil Fuels

About 25 per cent of Canada's electricity comes from burning non-renewable **fossil fuels**—coal, oil, or natural gas, which contain the stored carbon of once-living things. Canadians rely on fossil fuels more than any other type of energy. They power almost all our transportation systems. They also heat and cool most of our homes, businesses, and industries. Added up, coal, oil, and natural gas provide 85 per cent of our total energy needs!

	Natural Gas	Petroleum	Coal	Hydro-electricity	Nuclear	Steam & Biomass	Other (wind, solar, tidal, etc.)	Total*
1988	3465	3878	1614	1096	281	516	372	11 222
1999	6189	4779	1589	1232	250	609	640	15 288

* in petajoules, a metric measure of energy
Source: Statistics Canada.

▲ Figure 13.7: Energy use in Canada, 1988 versus 1999

12. List eight ways in which you and your family rely on fossil fuels. The energy survey on page 222 will give you some ideas.

13. Create a bar graph to show the information given in Figure 13.7 on the previous page. Record three important conclusions that you can draw from your graph.

Thermal Electric Power

Thermal power plants are the least expensive type of conventional energy system to build because the technology is fairly simple. Large furnaces, fuelled by coal, boil water into steam to spin turbines. This is similar to the nuclear power-plant process. The good news is that Canada has a large supply of both water and coal needed for the process. The bad news is that carbon from burned fossil fuels harms the atmosphere, causing air pollution, global climate change, and acid rain. And pollution-control measures at these power plants are very costly to manufacture and install.

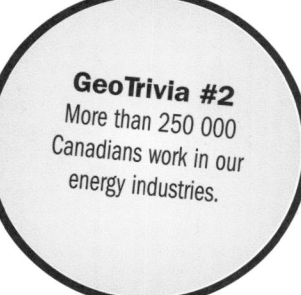

GeoTrivia #2
More than 250 000 Canadians work in our energy industries.

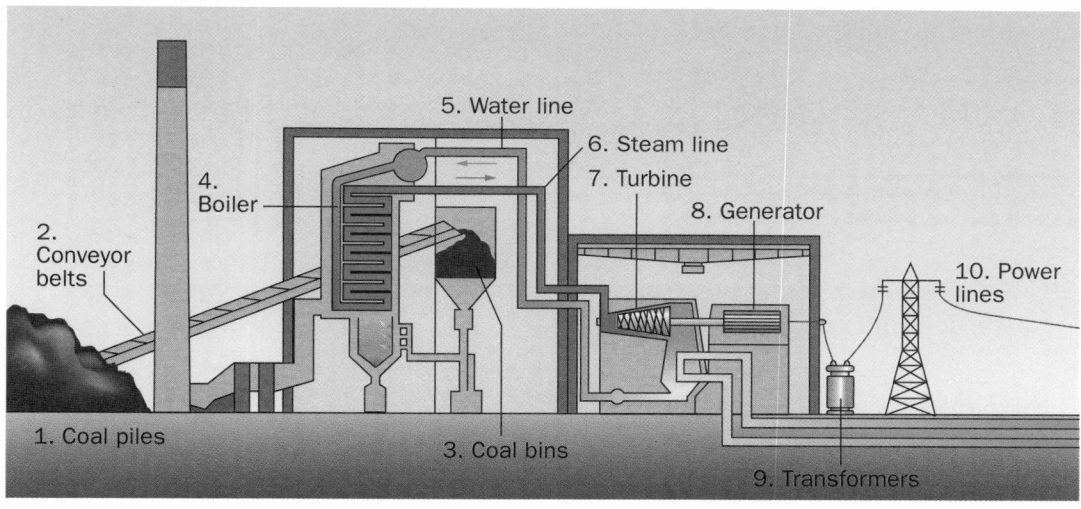

◀ **Figure 13.8:** Thermal generating station

14. Make your own benefits-and-problems chart for thermal electricity.

15. Compare the nuclear power-plant diagram in Figure 13.5 (page 225) with the diagram of the thermal-electric power plant in Figure 13.8, above. How are they the same? How are they different?

16. Use an atlas to identify three regions that make a lot of thermal electricity. Use the benefits in the chart you made in Question 14 to suggest why each of these regions uses thermal power.

17. Which of the three conventional ways of producing electricity will be most important five years from now? Which will be least important? Explain your views.

Flows of Energy

A system is a network of many connected parts. Canada's energy resources are part of a system that brings energy to customers through power lines and pipelines, as the map below shows.

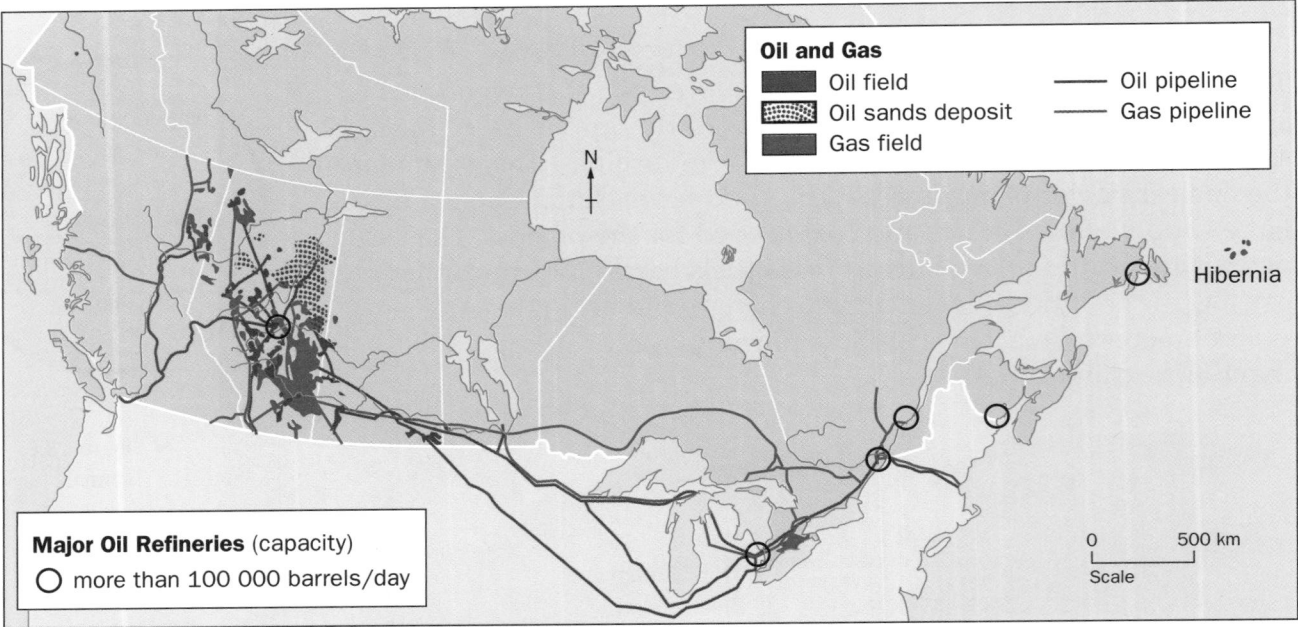

▲ **Figure 13.9:** Canada's oil and natural gas pipeline system

18. Using Figure 13.9, list the top four source provinces of oil and natural gas, starting with number one.

19. Explain why refineries, which make oil and gas products, are often built far from the energy sources.

Thinking Big: Energy Megaprojects

Canadians have a huge appetite for energy, but the current supply cannot satisfy our demands. One solution has been to build big energy **megaprojects**— large-scale, expensive projects for the development of natural resources. Each one promises a new energy feast, but how long will it meet Canada's needs, and at what cost?

Major Petroleum Projects

Since the 1970s, conventional drilled wells have been unable to keep pace with our energy consumption. Canada's petroleum industry has scrambled to find new oil sources. The northern Alberta oil sands and Newfoundland's ocean-floor Hibernia project (see Figure 13.9, above) are two such multibillion-dollar megaprojects intended to solve the problem.

Alberta's oil sands cover an area the size of New Brunswick. The oil sands consist of a resource called **bitumen**—wet sand grains coated by an oily layer, much like an oil spill on a beach. This material is just below the surface of the ground and can be dug out with gigantic bucket-wheel excavators and scoop shovels. Trucks the size of houses haul the sandy mix to a nearby refinery at Fort McMurray. After the separation process, the synthetic crude oil flows south by pipeline, and the sand is returned to the open pit from which it was taken. About 10 per cent of Canada's oil comes from the Alberta oil sands.

There are deposits of oil and natural gas under the ocean floor. The Hibernia oil field, 300 km east of St. John's, Newfoundland, has been supplying oil to the Atlantic region and the northeastern United States since 1998. The Hibernia oil field is mined using the world's largest drilling structure. Like an iceberg, the largest mass of the drilling platform is underwater. An immense, hollow concrete base sits on the ocean floor and is used to store oil that has been recovered. Oil tankers anchor nearby to pump oil out of the platform base. This amazing structure is designed to face hurricanes, 30-m waves, and collisions with icebergs.

GeoTrivia #3
Anchoring the Hibernia drilling platform to the ocean floor are 400 000 t of iron-ore pellets positioned inside its base.

20. What is bitumen? Explain why the oil made from it is called "synthetic," a term meaning human-made.

21. What makes oil megaprojects so expensive? Use examples from Alberta and Hibernia.

Major Hydro Projects

Hydroelectricity is clean and renewable energy. But dams and flooding cause major environmental changes. Two controversial hydro megaprojects are Churchill Falls, in Labrador, and the James Bay Project, in Quebec.

The highland interior of Labrador has produced electricity since 1971. The original Churchill Falls project left the waterfall almost dry and created the Smallwood Reservoir (see Figure 1.6 on page 26). This reservoir is equal in area to Prince Edward Island. A new plan calls for 30 per cent more power by building more dams downstream and reversing the flow of two nearby rivers. The healthy salmon populations in these rivers will be unable to spawn if this happens. Environmentalists and Innu peoples are alarmed about further changes to animal habitats and communities. Neither group had any say about the original project.

There are many similarities between the Churchill Falls and James Bay megaprojects. Built in the 1970s and 1980s at a cost greater than $21 billion, the James Bay Project is one of the world's largest engineering efforts. Six waterways were dammed and redirected along La Grande Riviere, and reservoirs totalling more than 10 000 square kilometres in area were flooded. Other great rivers, such as the Eastmain, are now just small streams. Aboriginal Cree people in the area opposed the project from the first. They were finally compensated in a financial agreement that recognized the damage done to their traditional way of life. They were also successful in stopping a northern hydroelectric megaproject along Quebec's Great Whale River in 1994.

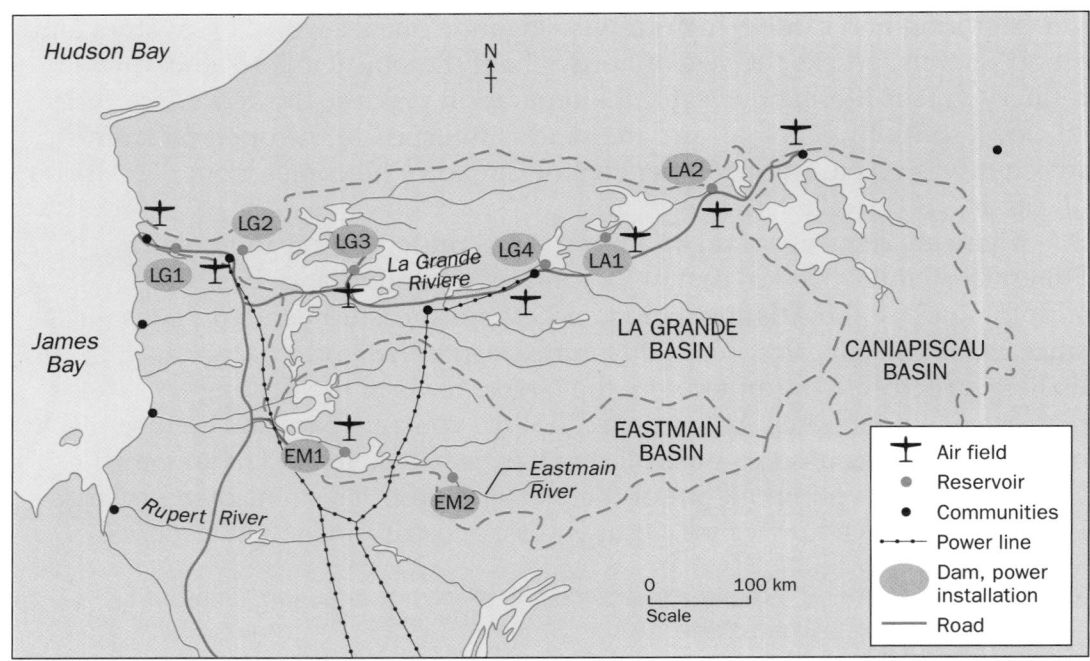

▲ **Figure 13.10:** La Grande Riviere hydroelectric project

22. a) Use Figure 13.10 to identify five ways that $21 billion was spent on the James Bay Project.
    b) How many reservoirs were created?
    c) Describe how river flows at coastal communities would be changed by reservoirs upstream.

23. Why do environmentalists and local citizens believe they must be part of megaproject planning?

24. Work with a group of three other classmates to create and complete an organizer to compare the benefits and problems of the four energy megaprojects described on pages 228 and 229.

Thinking "Green": Alternative Energy

Megaprojects are very expensive and disruptive to ecozones. And, they commit us to conventional energy and the need for more fossil fuels. Meanwhile, a wide range of **alternative energy** sources—new, clean, and renewable ways to produce power—are available. Hydroelectricity is the only renewable energy that has been widely developed in Canada. But all the rivers closest to energy customers have already been harnessed, meaning megaprojects are the only way to harness more. At present, alternative energy sources supply only about 5 per cent of Canada's power needs.

As our desire for a cleaner, "greener" future increases, these alternatives will become much more popular. For example, Vancouver's Ballard Power Systems is a world leader in energy research and development. This company builds and tests fuel cells that can electrically power small vehicles or whole communities. The **fuel cell** chemically converts the element hydrogen into electricity, without any burning. Fuel cells are Earth-friendly alternatives to more megaprojects.

Green Energy

"Green energy" is the popular nickname for alternative energy. It means that the energy source is Earth-friendly: clean, renewable, and non-threatening to natural or human systems.

Energy alternatives—such as solar panels, wind turbines, and tidal power—are already being used by energy-conscious Canadians. Places that have bright sunshine, strong winds, or high daily tides are well suited to green energy.

▲ **Figure 13.11a:** Charlottetown, Prince Edward Island

▲ **Figure 13.11c:** Annapolis, Nova Scotia

▲ **Figure 13.11b:** Pincher Creek, Alberta

▲ **Figure 13.11d:** Vancouver, British Columbia

25. a) Match each of the photographs above to the following green energies: hydrogen fusion, wind power, tidal power, solar power.
    b) Pick two of these systems and briefly explain how each one works.
    c) Why do you think these energies have mostly been overlooked?

26. Create two different drawings to show how a swimming pool could be heated without the use of a conventional water heater.

CASE STUDY

GEOTHERMAL ENERGY: AFFORDABLE HOME ALTERNATIVE

Geothermal energy is a system that uses the even temperature of the Earth itself for both winter heating and summer cooling. Current geothermal systems cost more to install than conventional furnaces and air conditioners. But they can pay for themselves in saved energy costs in a short period of time.

A Simple Geothermal System

Debby DesRivieres operates a small farm in southeast Manitoba. Her aging well, oil furnace, and air conditioner all needed major repairs. Instead of making repairs, Debby went geothermal. Keating Mechanical Services used her old well as the starting point to install a simple geothermal system based on the moderate temperature of ground-water deep beneath the farm.

Follow the operation of this system in Figure 13.12. First, water lying deep in the ground is drawn up through the new well. Then, a heat pump located in the basement of the house uses this water to heat the house in winter and cool it in summer.

A heat pump combines the work of a furnace and an air conditioner. Here's how it works. In winter, the water is warmer than the air outside. The heat pump draws warmth from the well water, concentrates it, then pushes warm air through the house just as a furnace would. In summer, the well water is cooler than the outside air. The cool temperature drawn from this water by the heat pump is used to cool the house, as an air conditioner would.

Summer and winter, the water that has gone through the heat pump is returned underground down the old well (discharge well). The temperature of the water has been changed slightly, but not enough to affect the large groundwater source that it enters. Groundwater will be drawn up through the new well again and again in the endless cycle that heats and cools Ms. DesRivieres's home. This is called an "open-loop" geothermal system, because part of the cycle is not contained in pipes.

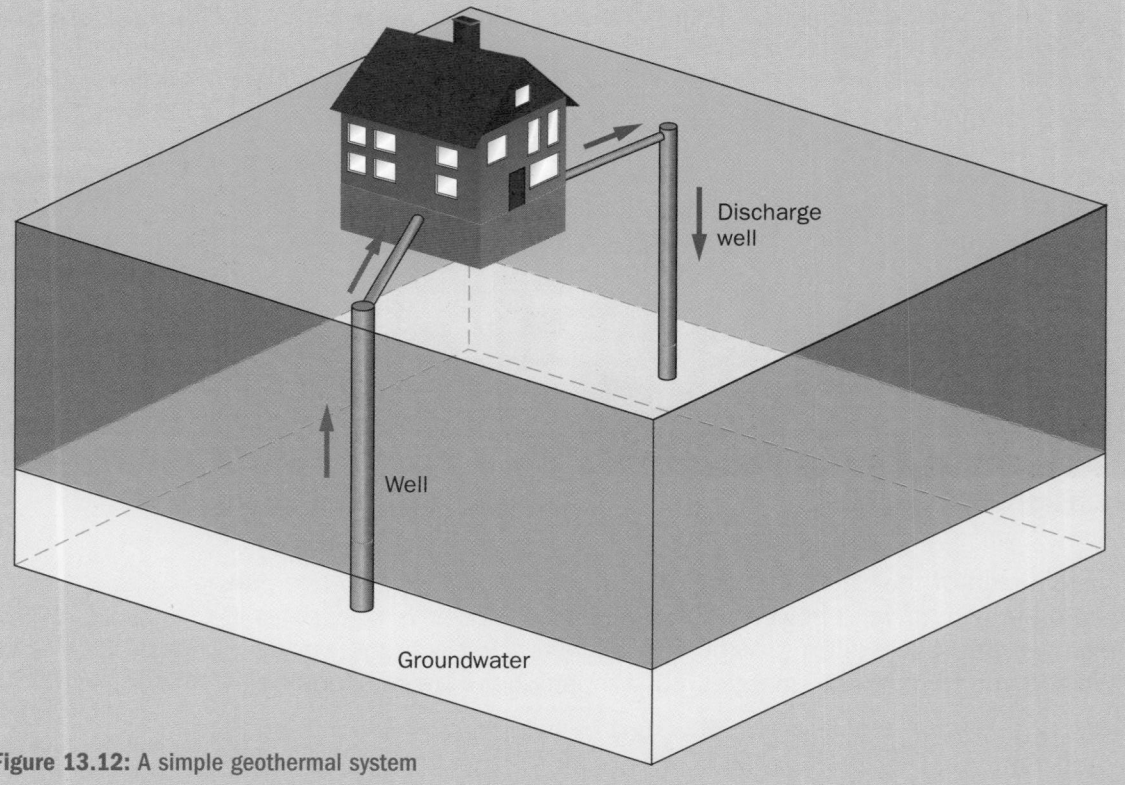

▲ **Figure 13.12:** A simple geothermal system

How effective is a geothermal system? Use the balance sheet in Figure 13.13 to figure it out, and you might be surprised!

A. Direct Cost of New Geothermal System
- geothermal heating/cooling unit $9548
- pump, tank, controls $1711
- pipe, insulation, wiring, all labour $3813
- installation of second well, 50 m deep $2621

B. Financial Benefits of the New System
- avoided cost of new oil furnace/air conditioner $4975
- received a Prairie Farm Rehabilitation grant (for using green energy) $970

C. Direct Annual Geothermal Savings
- no furnace fuel needed $1600
- no furnace or chimney maintenance needed $240
- reduced amount of electricity used to run new system $175

▲ Figure 13.13: Balance sheet: Ms. DesRivieres' geothermal system

1. Is geothermal energy worthwhile? Do the math, using Figure 13.13 to find out.
    a) Add up the amounts in A to find the total direct cost of the system paid to the contractor.
    b) Add up the financial benefits listed in B. This is money either saved or received by using the new geothermal system.
    c) Subtract B from A to find the initial extra cost of going with a geothermal system.
    d) Add up the amounts in C to find the total annual savings of the geothermal system.
    e) Divide the initial extra cost of the geothermal system by C to find how many years of energy savings it will take before the costs are recovered. After that, how much will Ms. DesRivieres save each year?

2. a) Imagine you are building a new home. List the pluses and minuses of including a geothermal system during construction. Which would you use? Why?
    b) Predict how geothermal technology could improve the quality of life for Canadians in the future.

The "Green" Car

Name some cars from Japan and Europe. How do most of them compare in size to vehicles from North American manufacturers? Gasoline has always been much more expensive overseas, and now Canadians need to face the same reality. We need to think "green" when it comes to our homes *and* our cars. Some changes are easy. For example, we can drive smaller cars. We can also convert vehicles from gasoline to cleaner-burning fuels, such as propane and natural gas, at little cost. Canada has much larger **energy reserves**—known future supplies—of natural gas than of petroleum.

New **hybrid-power vehicles**—which use a mix of gasoline and electricity for clean, efficient operation—have been available from Japanese manufacturers since 2000. In comparison, other small cars use twice as much gasoline, while larger cars and sport utility vehicles burn four times more. Honda and Toyota have developed different systems, but this is how they generally work:

- a small gasoline engine powers the car around town
- the motor automatically shuts off and restarts as the car stops for traffic
- speeding up uses both the gas engine and an electric motor
- the action of slowing down and coasting turns a generator that makes and stores electricity
- an on-board computer system controls all parts of the system
- the driver handles the car in the same way as other vehicles

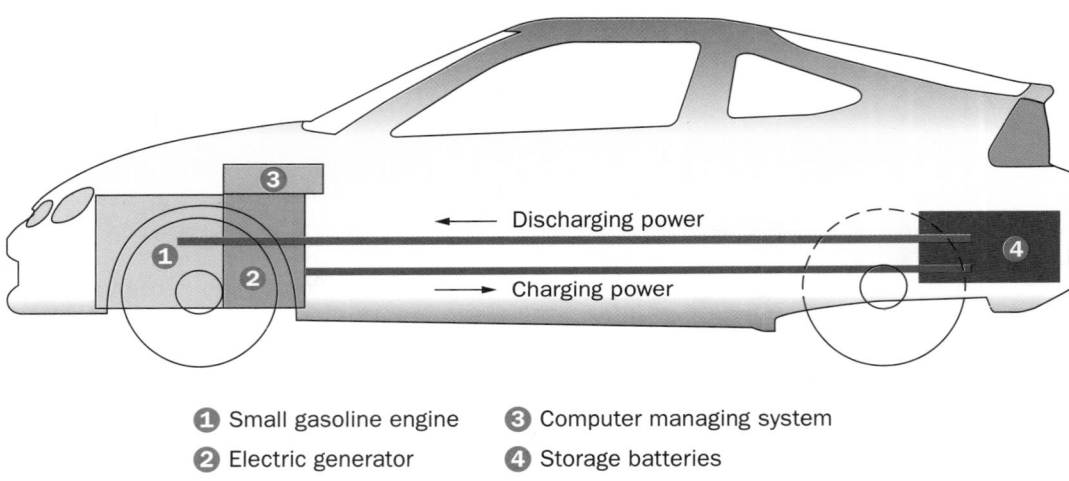

1 Small gasoline engine   3 Computer managing system
2 Electric generator   4 Storage batteries

▲ **Figure 13.14:** Hybrid car components

27. a) Make an organizer that compares a hybrid-power car with a typical North American–made vehicle. Consider size, power source, fuel economy, and effects on the environment.
    b) Would you like a hybrid car or not? Explain your reasons.

28. Use the diagram in Figure 13.14 to explain when each component of the hybrid power system is used (for example, when coasting downhill, when going uphill, and so on).

29. Predict how hybrid cars could improve the quality of life for Canadians in the future.

A green-coloured car may not be in your future. But there's a good chance a "green" car will be.

GEO CAREERS — ENERGY RESEARCH ANALYST

Name: Pauline Chan
High School: Sir Winston Churchill Senior High School, Calgary, Alberta
Job Title: Energy Research Analyst

You may have wondered how energy companies know how much fuel to produce or how much to charge for it. They often use information from a research analyst to make these decisions.

Pauline Chan is a research analyst who works for Canadian Energy Research Institute (CERI) in Calgary, Alberta. This respected research centre, which is funded by government and energy-producing companies, began in 1975. Pauline specializes in researching the North American natural gas industry. She uses a computer to organize vast amounts of information about natural gas supplies, refineries, pipelines, weather patterns, and other factors. Then, she combines past and present data to forecast future natural gas problems and possible solutions.

Although Pauline majored in Applied Energy Economics at the University of Calgary, her work also involves geography: "I draw maps using the computer to show the location and deposit sizes of natural gas resources. These maps also mark the positions of cities, water bodies, and parks that are above the natural gas resource and therefore restrict drilling."

As part of her job at CERI, Pauline prepares a monthly bulletin titled *Natural Gas Market Watch*. Today, businesses and ministries of natural resources and environment rely on this publication to plan projects and policies.

A career as a research analyst can begin with a college diploma in business. Strong computer skills are also necessary for inputting data and running software programs to forecast conditions in one field of business or industry.

What I like about my work:
"This work is interesting and rewarding because I'm constantly learning. I do not know the answers when I begin a project. It is very rewarding to go through the entire research process to come up with answers, or even more questions, at the end. I turn vast amounts of data into something useful for companies and governments trying to make decisions and plan for tomorrow, or ten years from now."

1. Write a newspaper advertisement for a research analyst. Include a description of the work, and the education and skills needed to fill the position.

2. Do any aspects of this career interest you? Explain.

3. Which skills do you now have that would help you in this field? Which skills would you need to work on? List other careers of interest to you that require these same skills.

Conclusion

Canadians have come to take for granted an unlimited supply of energy. In Canada, great distances, extreme climates, and many resource-based industries result in heavy energy demand. So does our high standard of living. Until the 1970s, conventional power plants and fossil fuel deposits supplied all we needed. However, in recent years, we've had to turn to hydroelectric and petroleum megaprojects to meet our energy demand. The impact of some of these projects on both people and the environment has been serious. We must find ways not only to conserve energy but also to develop cleaner, simpler energy sources that are not harmful to us or the planet. "Green" technology is already available. Now Canadians must begin to follow this new direction in energy.

Wrap It Up

1. Work with a partner to make a summary chart comparing the three methods of producing electricity. Include the categories that follow.
   a) percentage of electricity supplied
   b) type of fuel/power used
   c) one major harm or danger
   d) one major strength
   e) another comparison factor that you identify

2. Look at Canada's 1999 energy use (see Figure 13.7 on page 226). How important will each source be in twenty-five years? How important will other alternative energies be then? Explain your views.

3. If we move quickly toward green energy in homes and cars, how will life be different for your children? In what ways will it be better? Express your ideas with a picture, a cartoon, a poem, or a story.

4. a) Cost, comfort, and convenience are three factors that most people consider when evaluating an energy source. Identify one other important factor by which to judge sources of energy.
   b) Use all four factors to judge each of the following energy sources:
   • hydroelectric power
   • geothermal power
   • hybrid power

5. Use magazines or newspapers, CD-ROMs, and the Internet to prepare a one-page report about either a Canadian energy megaproject or an alternative energy source.

Chapter 14

OUR IMPACT ON CLIMATE

▲ **Figure 14.1:** An unseasonably warm day in early March 2000 melted this outdoor Ontario rink.

Top Eight Effects of Climate Change

In each statement below, there are clues to identify how certain regions in Canada will be affected by climate change. Match each statement with a region. Practise with the first statement. The clues are "south" and "cities and towns."

1. In the south, outdoor skating rinks will disappear from cities and towns. [Answer: (d) Ontario and Quebec]
2. Mountain glaciers will melt away even more rapidly than they do now.
3. Warmer oceans will mean fewer Greenland icebergs will interfere with ships.
4. Bitterly cold winter temperatures will be replaced by warmer temperatures.
5. Freshwater lake levels will drop, harming the shipping industry.
6. More severe droughts are expected in this ecozone, which is already dry.
7. Large areas of permafrost will melt, resulting in floods.
8. Warm ocean temperatures may make Canada's rainiest winters even wetter.

Regions
a) The North
b) West Coast
c) Prairies
d) Ontario and Quebec
e) East Coast

Words to Know

global warming
interglacial period
glacial period
shortwave radiation
longwave radiation
greenhouse gases
greenhouse effect
storm surge
conservation

In this chapter, you will
- recognize that climate change is occurring at a rapid rate
- understand that global climate change is largely due to human systems
- understand the impact of climate change on Canada
- assess changes that will protect natural systems

Is Climate Really Changing?

You have probably heard news reports about **global warming.** This is the term used to describe a warming trend caused by unnatural changes in the atmosphere. Many of these reports focus on weather extremes, such as heat waves, hurricanes, droughts, and floods. Some politicians deny that there is any real problem. They want more studies, and often more oil and gas development too. But burning these fossil fuels is a major cause of global warming.

The news report in Figure 14.2 outlines the United Nations' views about global climate change.

Report paints grim environmental scene

UN SAYS WORLD MUST TAKE ACTION SOON OR DEAL WITH CLIMATE-RELATED PROBLEMS

UNITED NATIONS (AP) — A UN report sets the stage for this month's Earth Summit with a sobering assessment of a planet where sea levels are rising, forests are being destroyed and more than two billion people face water shortages.

The report, released Tuesday, reviewed the most authoritative data from UN and international organizations about the use of natural resources.

Fossil fuel consumption and carbon emissions continued to rise in the 1990s, particularly in Asia and North America, according to the study. Signs of climate change linked to global warming were more apparent, including more frequent and intense droughts in parts of Asia and Africa and rising sea levels.

...

UN Undersecretary General Nitin Desai, who will lead the Earth Summit in Johannesburg [South Africa] from August 26 to September 4, said the report underscores that the world is at a crucial crossroads in the new millennium.

"If we do nothing to change our current indiscriminate patterns of development, we will compromise the long-term security of the Earth and its people," he said. ...

— *The Observer* (Sarnia, Ontario), 14 August 2002, p. B10. Reprinted with permission of The Associated Press.

▲ **Figure 14.2:** UN report warns of future disasters resulting from warming trends.

1. a) How seriously does the United Nations take global warming? Find two phrases in the article to prove its point of view.
    b) Describe an opposing point of view to that of the UN. Give reasons why the two opinions differ.

2. Check the news report closely for the information that follows.
    a) where and when the UN Earth Summit took place
    b) two causes of global warming in Asia and North America
    c) two results of global warming

3. Write a four- to six-sentence summary paragraph about the article. In your own words, show the main idea and two supporting points.

Evidence of Climate Change

Most scientists and environmentalists agree that world climates are changing. Look at Figure 14.3, which shows two photographs of the same British Columbia glacier, taken less than twenty years apart. It is difficult to deny that real change has taken place here.

Figure 14.3: British Columbia's shrinking Wedgemont Glacier

4. a) Describe the similarities and the differences between the two photographs in Figure 14.3.
   b) Give reasons why there isn't more ice coming down from the mountains in the 1998 photo.

5. Why are "then" and "now" photos used to show that global warming is a serious issue?

Similar pairs of pictures taken at other locations also show important differences caused by changing climates. Here are some examples:

• Small coastal islands have almost disappeared in Atlantic Canada because of rising sea levels.

• Northern seas are not always covered by ice in Arctic Canada, owing to warmer ocean waters.

• Seasonal wetlands have shrunk or dried up in the Prairies because of hotter, drier conditions.

   Scientists use other methods to prove that global climates are changing. For example, they gather temperature information spanning the past 100 years or more from communities worldwide. This information allows them to make graphs to show trends in the Earth's temperature. By studying the graphs, scientists have found that temperatures rose slowly and steadily for a century. Then, in the 1980s and 1990s, temperatures spiked. For example, Toronto's average temperatures during this period were 2°C higher than they were 100 years earlier.

Today, the Earth is sick. As Figure 14.4 shows, it has developed a temperature that is expected to turn into a fever in the very near future. Many scientists believe that unless drastic steps are taken to help the patient in the next decade, we will be in danger, too!

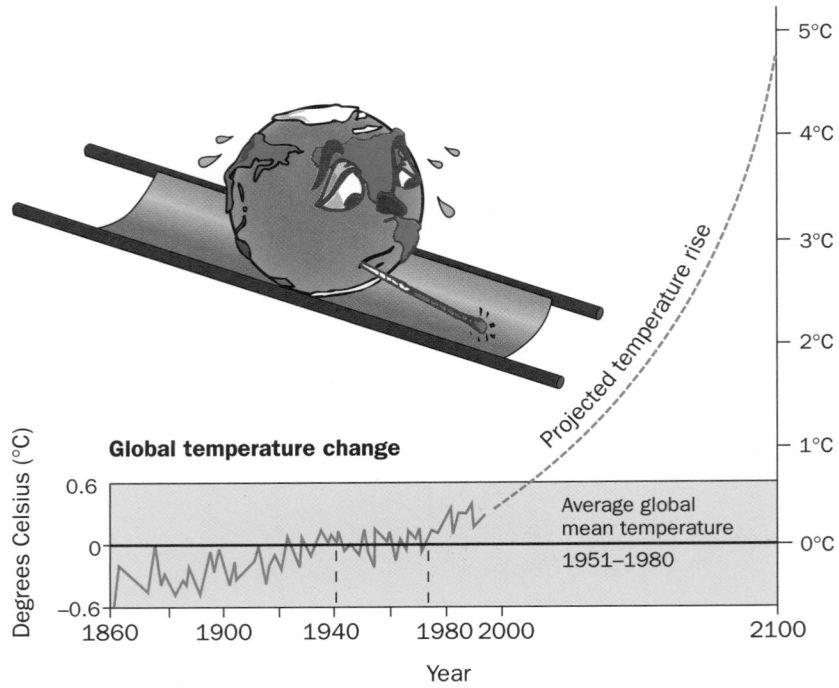

▲ **Figure 14.4:** Global temperature changes, 1860–2000, projected to 2100

6. a) Brainstorm a list of five reasons why Toronto's average temperature is higher now than it was 100 years ago.
   b) Name three inventions that likely contributed to the jump in temperatures during the 1980s and 1990s.

7. How does each of the following also contribute to global warming?
   a) buying cars and trucks with big engines
   b) open burning: leaves, garbage
   c) running central air-conditioning systems
   d) manufacturing consumer products

Understanding Climate Change

It's nice to dream of a warmer Canadian climate, especially on a cold winter day. But unless we are able to reverse warming trends, we may face food shortages as Prairie farms are no longer able to grow wheat and other grains. We may also suffer serious water shortages as the Great Lakes evaporate.

Some people say that we shouldn't worry about global warming, because the Earth's temperature is always going up or down. After all, there have been several ice ages, with a warm period (called **interglacial**) between each one. In fact, at one point in Earth's history, it was so warm on Greenland that the Vikings built farming communities there. This is all true, but past climates changed very slowly, unlike the rapid change in recent years.

GeoTrivia #1
In 1998, Edmonton had its hottest summer on record. Temperatures averaged 3°C higher than the 116-year average.

Researching Past Climates

Scientists gain important information about past climates by examining once-living things, such as fossils and plant pollens. Like geologists, they analyze core samples drilled from ice sheets. They also investigate air pockets between snow layers, and bubbles trapped in Greenland and Canadian Arctic ice sheets. Their research shows that four or more ice ages, or **glacial periods**, occurred in the past one million years. It also shows that the Viking colonies on Greenland lasted for about 300 years. Then, slowly worsening winter conditions, nicknamed the "Little Ice Age," forced people to leave.

Carbon dioxide	54%
Chlorofluorocarbons (CFCs)	21%
Methane	12%
Nitrous oxide	6%
Ozone, other gases	7%

▲ **Figure 14.6:** Gases causing global warming

▲ **Figure 14.5:** Core samples of the Greenland ice sheet are examined for evidence of global warming.

8. Use the example of Greenland to show that climate change was more gradual in the past than it is today.

9. a) How do researchers figure out past climate conditions?
   b) Look at Figure 14.5. Compare the work of ice researchers to the work of geologists or other scientists.

10. What are the benefits of researching present-day glaciers? Make a list of four hazards of this work.

Researching Recent Changes

Studies show that air trapped in snow and ice during the past 200 years is different from older air pockets. During the last two centuries, levels of certain gases in the atmosphere have grown. Several of these gases—especially carbon dioxide, nitrous oxide, and ground-level ozone—result from burning fuels. They are the reason for the sharp short-term rise in world temperature. Another gas trapped in newer snow layers is chlorofluorocarbons (CFCs). This manufactured gas, which has been around for only the past fifty years, is now banned from use in industrialized countries.

11. a) Use Figure 14.6 to create a bar graph showing the gases causing global warming.
    b) Find the sum of the three gases that result from burning fuels.

12. Find out why CFCs have been banned.

The Greenhouse Effect

Have you noticed how hot it becomes inside a car when the sun shines through the windows? Solar energy enters, and then becomes trapped inside. Greenhouses rely on this process during the winter months. Solar energy travels to Earth as light in short wavelengths. This **shortwave radiation** passes through the clear greenhouse ceiling. It heats up the inside, but it cannot escape, because reflected energy travels as heat in *long* wavelengths. This **longwave radiation** can't pass through objects. Plants in the greenhouse grow well in this warm environment.

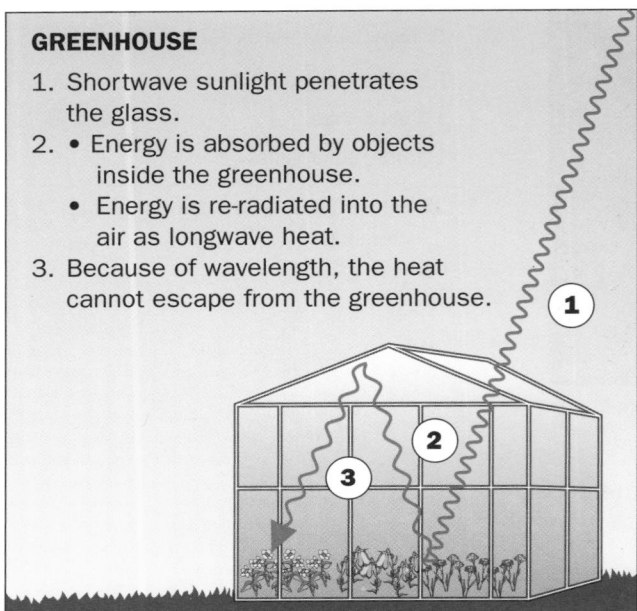
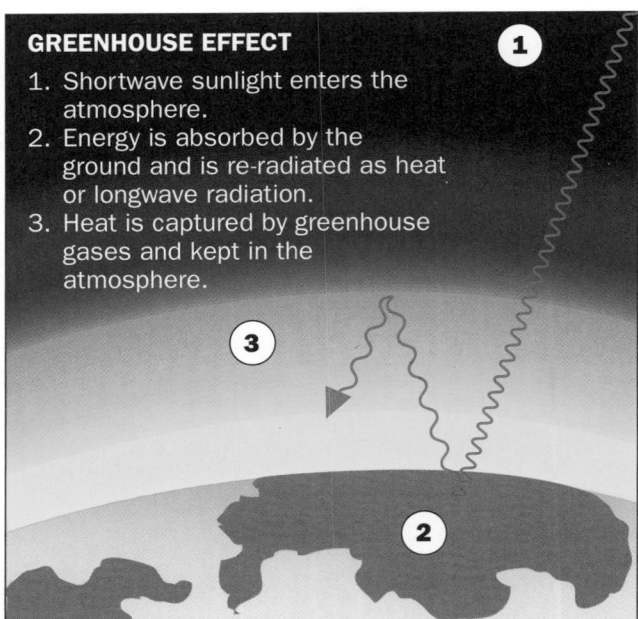

GREENHOUSE
1. Shortwave sunlight penetrates the glass.
2. • Energy is absorbed by objects inside the greenhouse.
   • Energy is re-radiated into the air as longwave heat.
3. Because of wavelength, the heat cannot escape from the greenhouse.

GREENHOUSE EFFECT
1. Shortwave sunlight enters the atmosphere.
2. Energy is absorbed by the ground and is re-radiated as heat or longwave radiation.
3. Heat is captured by greenhouse gases and kept in the atmosphere.

Figure 14.7: How a greenhouse works (left); the greenhouse effect (right)

Humans can live on Earth because of a similar effect. If clouds, water vapour, and gases in the atmosphere didn't absorb and hold the sun's heat energy, Earth would be too hot during the day and very cold at night. The gases that absorb heat are called **greenhouse gases**. Like a greenhouse, they trap and hold energy. This is called the **greenhouse effect**. Unfortunately, all those gases building up for the past 200 years are trapping too much heat close to the Earth. Global climate change is the result.

13. Draw and label a simple diagram to explain how a greenhouse works.

14. Use the terms "shortwave radiation" and "longwave radiation" to explain why pets and young children can die in sealed, parked cars in the summer.

15. How might global warming affect each of these people?
    a) a cattle rancher in the dry lands of southern Alberta
    b) a ski-resort operator in the hills of southern Ontario
    c) a Dene hunter in the Northwest Territories

Impact of Climate Change on Canada

Many different effects of climate change are already upon us, a few of them beneficial. But geographers are especially worried about our ecozones. As climates change, all living things are affected. For example, warmer conditions will mean that forests will be able to survive farther north, replacing large areas of tundra. The result could benefit forest industries, but it is bad news for polar bears and the caribou that live in this ecozone. Their habitats will change quickly, leading to endangerment or extinction.

GeoTrivia #2
Arctic caribou have declined from 24 000 (1960) to 1100 (1997) because warmer temperatures have caused freezing rain, covering the food supply.

Too Hot, Too Cold

Temperatures are expected to rise in most but not all parts of Canada during the twenty-first century. Summer heat waves in the Great Lakes–St. Lawrence region have already led to many pollution episodes and increased health risks for people with breathing problems. Figure 14.8 shows that for the period 1910 to 2040, average temperatures in different parts of Canada will likely increase by 1°C to 5°C. Regions near the Arctic Ocean and Hudson Bay are expected to experience much warmer winters than in the past. But temperatures in the Atlantic region will change very little. In fact, in some Atlantic communities the falling thermometer has led to complaints about the cold.

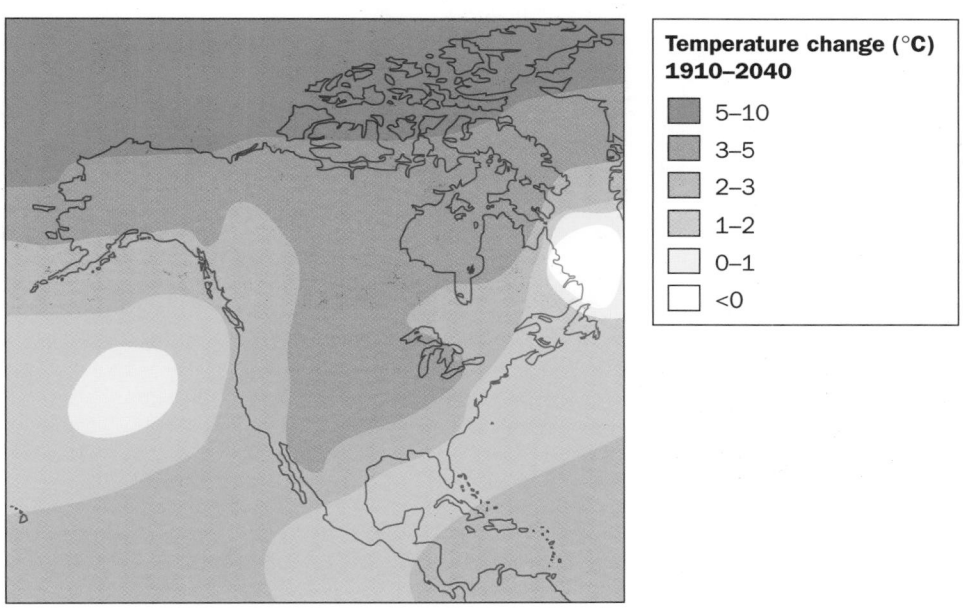

Temperature change (°C) 1910–2040

- 5–10
- 3–5
- 2–3
- 1–2
- 0–1
- <0

▲ **Figure 14.8:** Temperature change in Canada, 1910–2040

16. Describe the overall temperature pattern you see in Figure 14.8 in the regions that follow.
    a) East and West Coasts   b) the interior   c) the North

17. List in table form the benefits and problems of warmer winter conditions in the northern ecozones. Consider growing season, natural vegetation, wildlife, and the permafrost layer.

Too Dry, Too Wet

Climate change has already resulted in weather extremes in many parts of Canada. Overall, precipitation is down across the country, especially in winter. Lower snowfalls are causing water levels to drop in many of Canada's freshwater lakes. In 2002, for example, the Great Lakes were more than one metre below normal levels. During the summer of 2002, parts of Alberta were so dry that emergency trainloads of hay were shipped from across Canada to keep farm animals alive. Many heartbroken farmers had to sell their cattle and horses at extremely low prices because they couldn't afford feed. Before that, the Prairies were much wetter than usual. In 1997, much of southern Manitoba was flooded after very heavy late winter snowfalls. Scientists warn us to expect more weather extremes as part of climate change.

◀ ▲ **Figure 14.9:** The Prairie region—too wet and too dry

18. List in table form the benefits and problems of hotter, drier summers in the Great Lakes region. Consider recreation, health and safety, energy consumption, and livestock farming.

19. How might less winter snow affect each of the following groups of Canadians?
    a) students
    b) boaters and ship captains
    c) crop farmers
    d) travel agents

CASE STUDY

CHANGES IN THE ATLANTIC MARITIME ECOZONE

Global warming is not expected to change the climate of the Atlantic Maritime Ecozone. But changes in the surrounding ocean will have a large impact on the region. Ocean levels are rising rapidly in this region as the ice caps melt. For example, the water in Halifax Harbour rose 36 cm in the past century. A similar increase is expected by 2050. This increase may improve sailing for large ships, but it also increases the risk of storm waves.

Most of Prince Edward Island and many parts of Nova Scotia and New Brunswick's Atlantic shore are threatened by flooding. With sea levels up by 5 mm or more each year, heavy seas can cut back soft sandstone cliffs by 12 m in a single year. The most serious threat is posed by the **storm surge**. This occurs when strong winds blow onshore, raising water levels at least 1 m higher than normal. In January 2000, a storm surge coupled with a very high tide swelled water levels around Prince Edward Island 1.2 m above normal. This caused flooding in Charlottetown and much erosion of the island shores.

Global warming is also heating up the oceans. This should mean that Arctic icebergs melt before they get as far south as ocean shipping lanes and the Hibernia oil field. However, there will be more Atlantic hurricanes to drive waves against the coast. In winter, there will be less sea ice piled along the shoreline, so waves will more easily attack the unprotected coast. Both situations spell more erosion and flooding in the Atlantic Maritime Ecozone.

1. a) Summarize the problems of the Atlantic region under these three headings: Water Levels, Storm Surges, and Shoreline Erosion.
   b) Which problem do you think is most serious? Why?
2. a) Look at the storm-surge map (Figure 14.11). Describe what happens to the ocean surface as the surge gets closer to land.
   b) Why is Prince Edward Island most threatened by storm surges?
3. How does the Atlantic Maritime Ecozone show the importance of worldwide action on global climate change?

▲ **Figure 14.10:** Winter storm waves pound the East Coast.

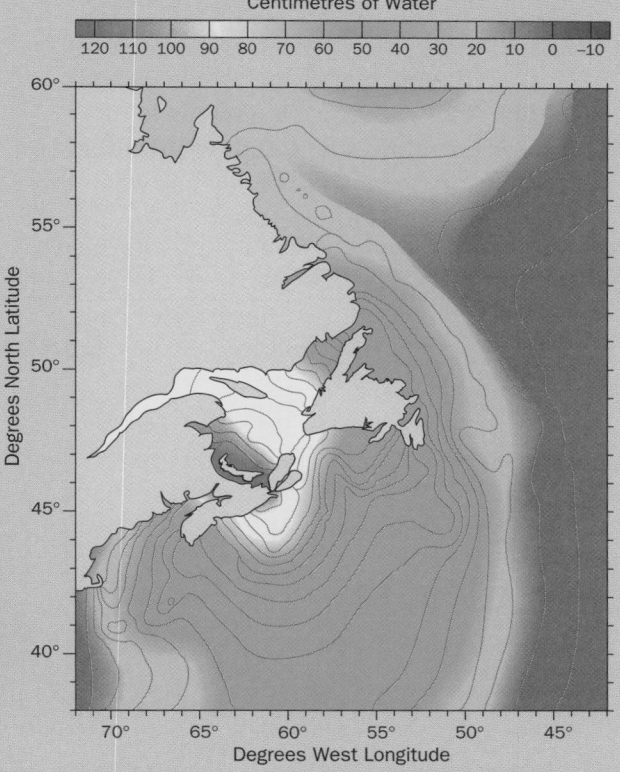

▲ **Figure 14.11:** Storm surge engulfs PEI, January 2000. Record water levels flooded parts of Charlottetown. (High-water levels are shown in red in this computer model.)

GeoGames
Rising Waters!

Play this game of chance and travel around PEI, recording annual sea-level increases. The player whose average score comes closest to the island's actual 5-mm annual rise in sea level is the winner.

Purpose:

To highlight the average amount of annual sea-level rise around Prince Edward Island

Supplies:

- One die per group of players
- Game board (Figure 14.12)
- Individual scoring sheet and pencil

Method:

A. Form groups of three players. The person with the highest roll of the die goes first.

B. Start on the mainland at Confederation Bridge. The object of the game is to move clockwise around the island, visiting the six locations in order. The game ends when one player reaches Charlottetown.

C. Each player rolls the die once per turn. A roll of 5 or 6 is required to move to the next numbered destination. Any number other than 5 or 6 represents the amount of annual sea-level increase (in millimetres) where the player is located. For example, a roll of 1 equals a 1-mm rise, a roll of 2 a 2-mm rise, and so on. Players keep recording the rising water level on their score sheet as they wait to roll a 5 or 6 to move on. (*Note:* Rolls of 5 or 6 must not be recorded on the score sheet.)

D. Each player adds up his or her total rise in sea level and divides by the number of locations visited. The player with an average score closest to the island's actual sea-level rise of 5 mm per year wins the game.

Wrap-Up:

1. Suggest three ways in which governments might prepare for future problems along ocean coastlines as a result of rising sea levels. What issues or problems must be considered for each idea?

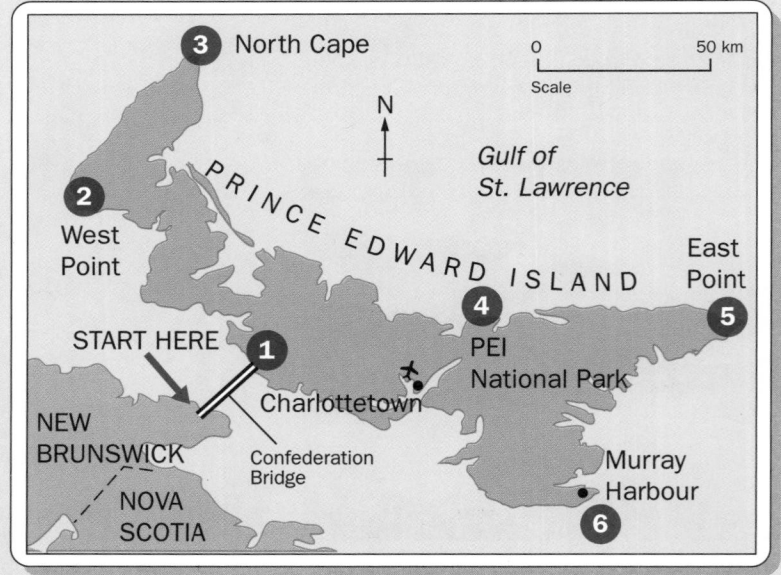

Figure 14.12: Is the water rising?

Taking Responsibility

In 1997, world nations met in Kyoto, Japan, to discuss the problem of global climate change. There, they agreed to reduce greenhouse gas emissions. In 2002, Canada committed to following the Kyoto Protocol (see pages 323–324). But what can we as individuals do about climate change? It's simple. Start by recognizing that our dependence on fossil fuel energy is the major cause of the problem. Then, make wise consumer choices that will preserve the planet.

Suzuki encourages lifestyle changes

PRESERVE NATURE, HE ADVISES

TORONTO (CP) — Acclaimed scientist David Suzuki is challenging Canadians to help preserve nature by making environment-friendly lifestyle changes.

At a news conference to kick off the project—which he calls the Nature Challenge—Suzuki enlisted help from several celebrities as he outlined ways human beings can contribute to a better environment.

"We are inviting all Canadians to sign on to take up our challenge," he said.

The key points of the plan involve "the food that we eat, …

the way we transport ourselves and our heating of our houses," he said.

The veteran conservationist has given his name to the David Suzuki Foundation, which has come up with 10 ways consumers can help the environment.

Among the suggestions are reducing home heating costs, using non-toxic pesticides, walking or biking instead of driving, eating meat-free meals, and buying energy-efficient appliances. …

Suzuki also addressed the Kyoto climate accord, which the federal government has pledged to implement.

In answer to fears expressed by some that adopting Kyoto will harm provincial economies, Suzuki insisted the accord can be controlled by Canada.

"All it is is a target, and how we implement and reach that is up to us in Canada," he said. "We will have a made-in-Canada solution (to limiting greenhouse gas emissions)."

— Canadian Press News Ltd., December 4, 2002.

▲ **Figure 14.13:** The Suzuki Foundation offers solutions to curb greenhouse gas emissions.

20. What do these phrases in the news article mean?
    a) "making environment-friendly lifestyle changes"
    b) "We will have a made-in-Canada solution"

21. a) Five of the Suzuki Foundation's solutions to protect nature are included in the news story. Name them.
    b) Suggest how each one will protect nature.

22. Write a four- to six-sentence summary paragraph of the article. Include the main idea of the news article and supporting information.

Making Wise Choices

One way Canadians can reduce greenhouse gas emissions is by shifting to energy-saving technologies. This is where "green energy" comes into play: wind, solar, and tidal power; geothermal systems; hydrogen fuel cells; and hybrid-electric vehicles.

GeoTrivia #3
It takes only 11 min for a gas lawn mower to emit as much greenhouse gas as a car does in a 100-km trip.

Basic **conservation** measures—controlling and protecting natural resources—are also part of the solution. Sealing cracks around doors and windows can reduce home heating costs and energy use by up to 20 per cent. Fluorescent light bulbs may cost more than regular bulbs, but they more than pay for themselves with long life and low use of electricity. If forty students take the bus to and from school instead of a car, thirty-nine drivers come off the road. This benefits the atmosphere because it saves 70 000 L per year in burned gasoline.

Planting trees also helps. Trees breathe in carbon dioxide and breathe out oxygen. They also shelter homes from chilling winter winds and blazing summer sun, reducing energy needed for heating and cooling. Other landscaping choices can conserve energy too. Using natural materials such as stone, wood chips, and ground-covering plants means less grass to cut, which helps fight global warming.

▲ **Figure 14.14:** Taking a bus conserves energy resources.

▲ **Figure 14.15:** Planting trees reduces energy needs.

23. Does advertising shape our decisions to want things and to buy them? Explain your answer with examples.

24. Explain the energy benefits of each job opportunity below.
    a) raking leaves for seniors
    b) escorting young children to and from their neighbourhoood school
    c) shovelling snow for neighbours

25. List five ways that you could reduce your own consumption of electricity and fossil fuel energy. Then, describe to a partner how this would change your lifestyle.

Conclusion

Ice-core research has taught us a lot about Earth's climate. We know that there have been warm and cold periods in the past. But climate changes are happening much more quickly now. This is because of the high concentrations of greenhouse gases being pumped into the atmosphere by our excessive energy use. There are many simple changes we can make in our own lives to reduce energy use and protect Earth.

Wrap It Up

1. a) Sketch and label a "greenhouse effect" diagram that shows what happens in Earth's atmosphere.
   b) Explain why the atmosphere has become warmer in recent years.

2. a) Use the information in Figure 14.16 to calculate the average city-driving fuel consumption for Canada's five top-selling vehicles.
   b) Compare this average to the average for the sixth to tenth ranked vehicles. What do you notice?

3. Most vehicles are driven about 20 000 km per year. If half of that figure is made up of city driving, chart the annual fuel consumption and cost of fuel for all ten vehicles at current gas prices. Graph the results.

4. As the premier of Prince Edward Island, write a persuasive letter to the United Nations, urging them to act now on the problem of global climate change. Explain your province's problems and why you can't solve them alone.

5. How will climate change make your life different in 2050? List your ideas in a table with these headings: health, transportation, homes, clothing, recreation, and another area that you identify.

Vehicle	Sales Rank	Litres/100 km (highway)	Litres/100 km (city)
Dodge Caravan	1	9.0	13.3
GM Silverado, Sierra	2	10.1	19.0
Ford F-Series	3	10.4	19.2
Honda Civic	4	5.5	8.2
GM Venture, Montana, Silhouette	5	8.3	12.7
Toyota Corolla	6	5.3	7.7
Mazda Protégé	7	6.7	9.9
Chevrolet Cavalier	8	6.8	11.6
Pontiac Sunfire	9	6.8	11.6
Ford Focus	10	6.0	9.3

Source: Natural Resources Canada, DesRosiers Automotive Consultants Inc.; published in *Maclean's*, 12 August 2002, p. 17.

▲ **Figure 14.16:** Fuel efficiency of Canada's top-selling vehicles (2002)

Chapter 15

POLLUTION: LOCAL AND GLOBAL

▲ **Figure 15.1:** A penguin covered in oil from a spill off the coast of South Africa

Great Canadian Garbage Trivia

Pollution: cars make it. Garbage: you toss it, and it's history. Not much to know about these topics, right? Let's find out. Answer these questions to check out what you know about Canadian garbage and pollution.

1. Which country produces the most waste per person?
   a) United States   b) Sweden   c) Japan   d) Canada

2. How many litres of water are used up to produce one litre of gasoline?
   a) none   b) 1   c) 10   d) 20

3. How many plastic grocery bags do Canadians bring home on average every minute?
   a) 10   b) 150   c) 1000   d) 2500   e) more than 5500

4. A poorly maintained car produces as much pollution as how many well-maintained cars?
   a) 2   b) 4   c) 20   d) 40   e) 100

5. Air pollution kills about how many people in Ontario every year?
   a) 150   b) 500   c) 800   d) 1000   e) 1800

6. Recycling one pop can saves enough energy to power a television set for how long?
   a) 10 minutes   b) 3 hours   c) 10 hours   d) 6 days

7. What percentage of Canadians live in municipalities that have no sewage treatment?
   a) 3%   b) 5%   c) 10%   d) 18%   e) 40%

Check your answers against the correct answers, which your teacher will provide. How well did you do?

Words to Know

pollution
landfill site
composting
tailings
Venn diagram
ground-level ozone
chlorofluorocarbons (CFCs)
ozone layer
acid rain
closed system
biomagnification

In this chapter, you will

- see how a number of human activities affect the environment
- learn about land, water, and air pollution
- create and carry out a plan to address a local pollution problem
- debate a pollution issue
- analyze a satellite image

The Challenge of Pollution

Nearly everything we do creates **pollution**. Pollution puts wastes into the environment. These wastes can be garbage or sewage that is not treated. Oil leaking from a damaged tanker is pollution. Cigarette smoke is another example.

We create some pollution in our day-to-day activities, like the fumes pouring from the bus you took to school. Some pollution is created on our behalf by industry, like the smoke generated when the bus was made.

In general, the more material goods we have in life, the more pollution we create. If you buy a new sweater, the quality of your life may improve. (You have a nice, stylish sweater.) However, more waste has been put into the environment. (The sweater factory gave off fumes into the air, and you threw out both the shopping bag and your old sweater.)

The more pollution we create, the greater are the harmful effects to humans. That's why pollution is now a major problem in Canada and around the world. The challenge we face is this: how do we reduce pollution to the lowest possible level without destroying the quality of our lives?

In this chapter, you will learn about three types of pollution:
- air pollution
- water pollution
- land pollution

▲ **Figure 15.2** With pollution, what goes around comes around.

1. Consider the cartoon above. Write down in words what you think the artist was trying to say about pollution.

2. a) Think of two examples of pollution that you cause in your everyday life.
   b) Think of two examples of pollution created indirectly on your behalf.

Land Pollution

Canada's land has also been significantly polluted by human activities. Industries, homes, cities, and individual actions can all pollute land. The most obvious example of land pollution is the litter that we leave behind in the natural environment. Examine Figure 15.3 on the next page to see some of the many sources of land pollution. A *source* is a place where pollution is created.

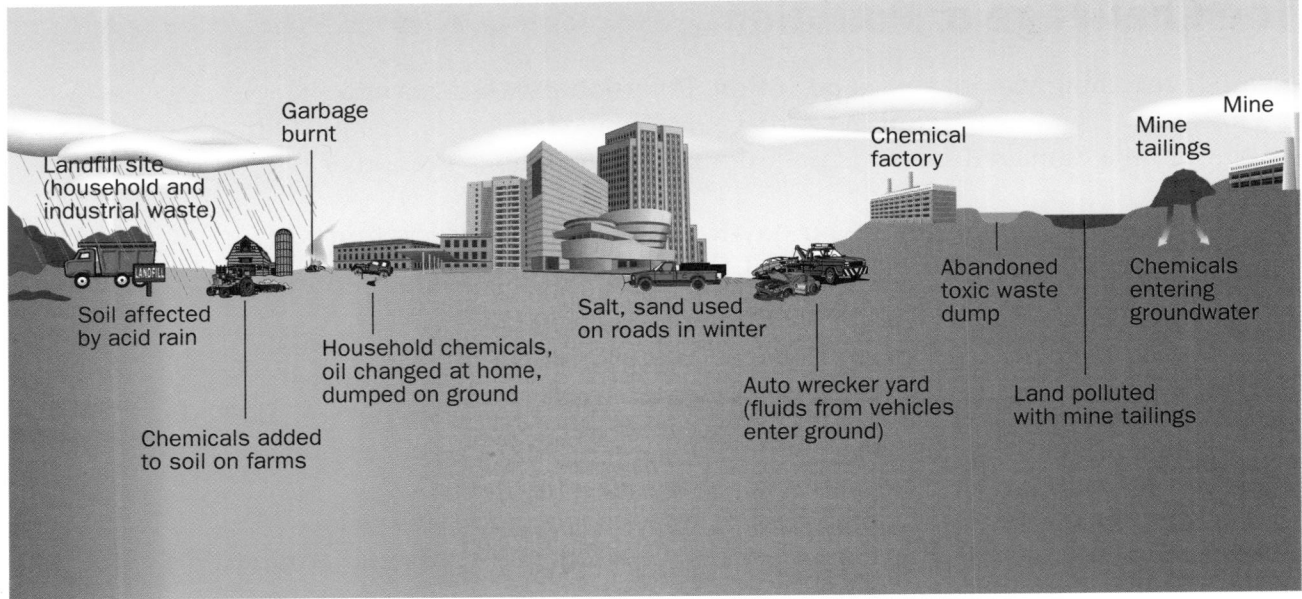

▲ **Figure 15.3:** Sources of land pollution

3. Based on your examination of Figure 15.3, choose the three most serious forms of land pollution.

4. Explain your personal links to three types of land pollution.

Household Garbage

Garbage does not become pollution unless and until we let it escape into the environment. A candy bar wrapper isn't even garbage until you throw it away. And it becomes pollution only if it becomes litter, if it is burned (creating smoke), or if it ends up in a landfill site that leaks. **Landfill sites** are garbage dumps designed to dispose of waste safely between layers of earth. Well-managed landfill sites do not have leaks, and do little harm to the environment outside the site. The problem is that nobody wants a landfill site close to them because of all the noise, smell, truck traffic, and potential danger of leaks. Some local governments choose to export their waste. Large garbage trucks regularly make the trip to other regions and even south to the United States.

Most communities are trying to reduce the amount of garbage they make. For example, Guelph, Ontario, recycles newspapers, bottles, and cans, and composts lawn and garden waste. **Composting** is a method of treating plant or animal wastes. It creates humus, a dark, rich material that enriches the soil.

GeoTrivia #1
Every year, Canadians throw away 1.7 billion disposable diapers.

5. Think of three ways in which transporting trash over long distances affects the environment.

6. What five strategies would help solve the garbage problem? Use the text and your own ideas.

7. Explain, in your own words, how two waste products might be used as a resource. Consider the types of garbage you and your family throw out.

Industrial Waste

Industry creates pollution when it produces goods. For example, in the mining process, the rock dug out of a mine is crushed. It is then treated with harsh chemicals to remove the precious ore. For example, arsenic is used to extract gold. The leftover rock, waste, and chemicals are called **tailings**. Vast fields full of tailings are left beside mines such as lead and zinc mines. The runoff from these tailings goes into huge tailings ponds, which can sometimes be as big as lakes. Lead is easily absorbed into soil, so it can poison the environment even years after a mining operation has closed down.

Canada now has more than 3600 toxic (poisonous) sites. These include old mines and storage sites for poisonous substances. They leak arsenic, cyanide, and other poisons that can kill you. Many of these toxic sites are "orphan sites," which means that we don't know who created them. Other abandoned sites were operated by companies that are no longer in business. Cleaning up these sites is very costly, so governments are reluctant to spend the money. In 2002, the federal government spent about three dollars per Canadian on toxic-site cleanup.

Some waste from industry is not poisonous. It can be used again rather than thrown into the environment. Slag, which is a by-product of making steel, was once considered useless waste. It is now used for a variety of purposes, such as road construction.

◀ **Figure 15.4:** Slag from a steel mill

8. Who should be responsible for cleaning up toxic waste sites?

9. Draw a **Venn diagram** like the one shown in Figure 15.5 to compare the problems posed by a) non-toxic industrial wastes and b) toxic industrial wastes. Your Venn diagram will have two slightly overlapping circles, one for each type of waste. Write common problems in the overlapping space. Write unrelated problems in the part of the circles that doesn't overlap.

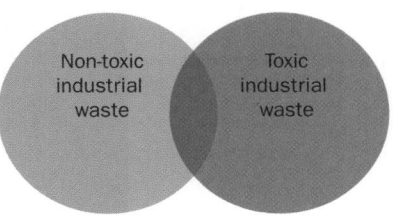

▲ **Figure 15.5:** A Venn diagram

GeoSkills

ANALYZING SATELLITE IMAGES

A satellite image is a picture of an area of the Earth as seen from a satellite. Specialized satellites send harmless radar, or microwaves, toward a particular place on the ground. When the radar bounces back, it carries information that the satellite uses to create a picture. False colours are sometimes added to the images to help us interpret them.

Purpose

By analyzing satellite images, we gain a unique perspective of the surface of the Earth, and learn more about our world.

The satellite image in Figure 15.6 below shows an area near Kimberly, British Columbia, that has been mined for copper. Colour has been added to show the mined area more clearly. Here is your key:
- Orange-brown shows forested areas.
- Mining waste is coloured grey, white, and brown. Little grows here.
- Rivers can be cream, black, or light blue, depending on the background.
- Tailings ponds are green.

North is at the top. Follow the steps below to analyze this satellite image.

Step 1

Identify the theme of the image. The satellite image in Figure 15.6 shows mine tailings from a copper mine.

Step 2

Identify the location. Knowing what area an image shows will help you understand the image. Sometimes the image is labelled. (This image shows a small wilderness area in central British Columbia.) If possible, determine the scale of the image.

Step 3

Identify key geographic features. There may be lakes, rivers, oceans, mountains, or even cities that can be identified in an image. The natural features in this image are as follows.
- A forest covers the left side of the image.
- Streams flow east through the forest toward the tailings, which cover the right half of the image.

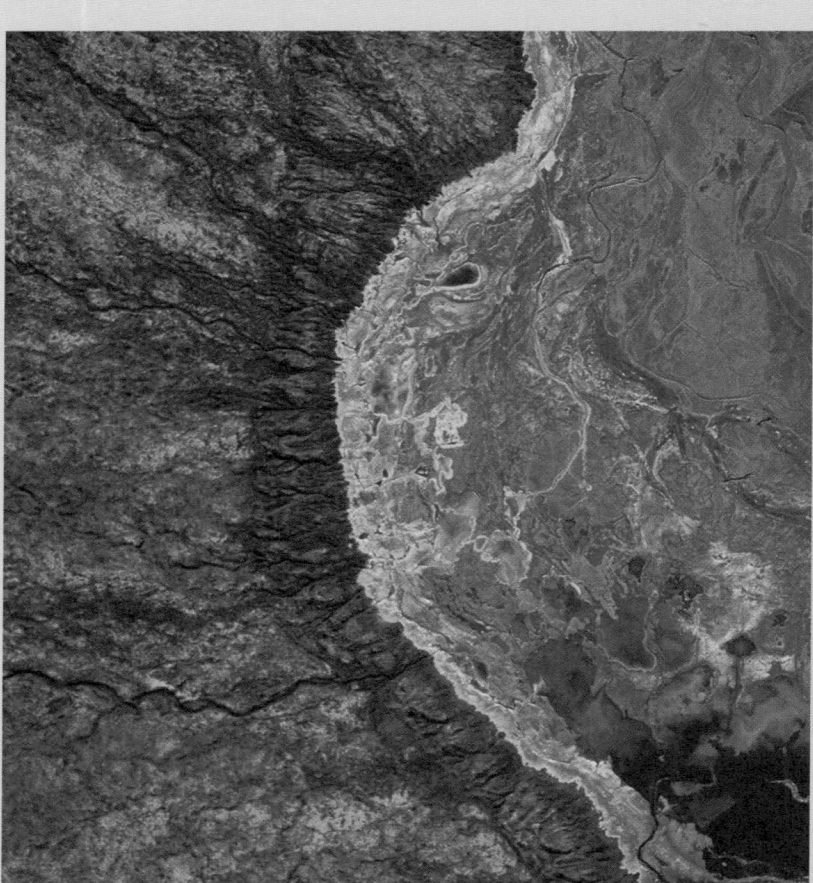

▲ **Figure 15.6:** Satellite image of tailings ponds in Kimberly, British Columbia

- Another stream flows south between the tailings and the forest (a thin grey-blue line near the bottom).
- Tailings ponds are bright green.
- More streams flow to the southeast.

Step 4
Decide on the importance of the image. The image in Figure 15.6 shows a very polluted site left behind by mining. The streams running through the tailings are carrying toxins into the surrounding environment. People could use this image to lobby for a cleanup of the area.

Practise It!

1. Figure 15.7 shows the Estevan coalfield (1500 square kilometres). Follow Steps 1–4 to analyze the image. Here is your key.
   - The image was taken in winter.
   - North is at the top.
   - The Souris River flows from west to east.
   - Each plant has a white plume of smoke.
   - The roads on which the coal trucks drive are dusted black by coal.
   - The active open-pit mine is black.
   - A rough texture shows non-active mines.
   - Estevan is a grey area at the top left.
   - A dam on the Souris River creates a long, thin reservoir (artificial lake) that runs south of one plant. The lake is not frozen.

> **To analyze a satellite image...**
> ✔ identify the theme of the image
> ✔ identify the location
> ✔ identify key geographic features
> ✔ decide on the importance of the image

2. Place a piece of tracing paper over the image and trace the river, lake, roads, city, active mine, non-active mines, power plants, and smoke plumes that you can see. Label all these carefully. You have now created your own map from a satellite image.

3. Suggest steps that could be taken to clean up the pollution shown in the image.

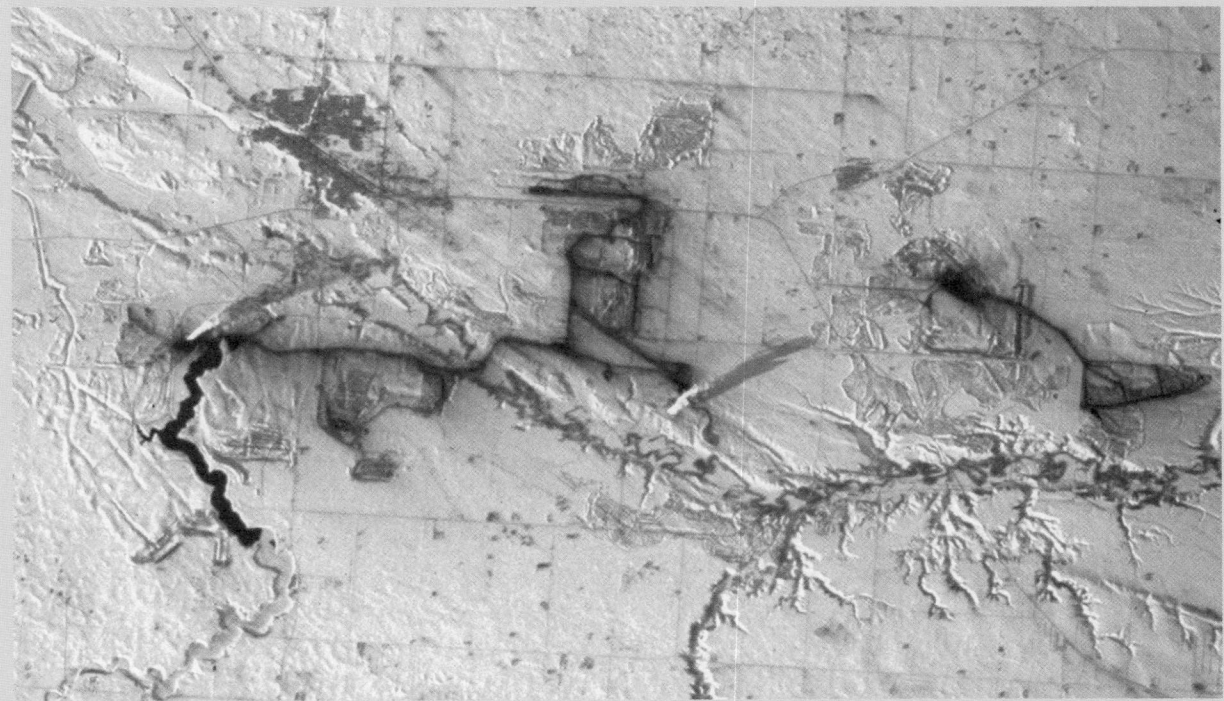

▲ **Figure 15.7:** A satellite image showing the Estevan coalfield in southeast Saskatchewan

Water Pollution

Canadians have more fresh water per person than people in any other country in the world. About 9 per cent of the world's fresh water is located in Canada.

We pollute our water a great deal. As you can see in Figure 15.8, water pollution comes from a variety of sources. About 70 per cent comes from land sources. Some pulp and paper mills, for example, pollute the water with chemicals such as bleach for whitening paper. The better plants treat and reuse their water, so that few or no chemicals are released into the environment.

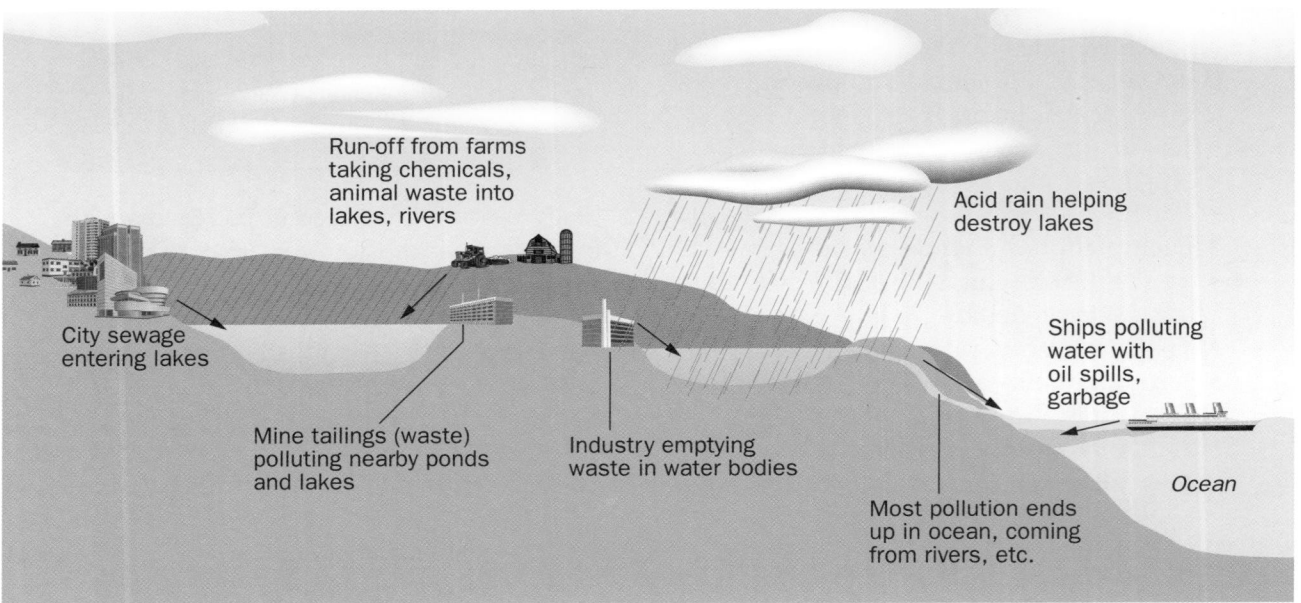

▲ **Figure 15.8:** Sources of water pollution

10. a) Which source of water pollution surprises you most?
    b) Which type of water pollution could you help reduce in some way?

11. Let's say a certain pollutant is found in the middle of a lake or river. Why might it be difficult to identify the exact source of this pollutant?

Polluted waters do not make a healthy place to live. They ruin the habitat for the creatures who live in it. For example, beluga whales in the St. Lawrence Seaway die from cancers caused by pollution. If they float ashore after they die, their bodies are so poisoned that they have to be treated as toxic waste!

Water pollution also affects human health. In one example, the massive English–Wabigoon River system in the Dryden and Kenora area of northern Ontario was poisoned with mercury in the 1970s. The source of the mercury was a mill owned by a large paper company. The fish in the area consumed the mercury. The people of the Whitedog (Wabasseemoong) First Nation and the nearby Grassy Narrows First Nation became ill by eating the fish. Many were permanently disabled. Ball Lake Lodge, a major employer, had to be closed. The commercial fishery ceased operations. The Whitedog and Grassy Narrows people were uprooted and their way of life ruined.

▲ **Figure 15.9:** The English–Wabigoon River

▲ **Figure 15.10:** In 1976, members of the Whitedog Nation protest mercury poisoning of the English–Wabigoon River system.

12. Create a flow chart to show the chain of events that ruined the way of life of the Whitedog and Grassy Narrows First Nations.

Reducing Water Pollution

Many attempts have been made to reduce the amount of water pollution we create in Canada. Solutions include building better sewage treatment facilities. Many people believe that companies should pay to clean up the water they use. Stricter environmental laws and enforcement of those laws would help a great deal. Some governments, however, do not want to spend the money. Through the late 1990s, for example, the Ontario government dramatically reduced the money it spent in enforcing its environmental laws. Education plays an important role in prevention. The more people know about water pollution, the more likely they are to speak up, and the more likely politicians will be to take action.

GeoTrivia #2
Pollution of seven key toxic chemicals in the Great Lakes declined by 71 per cent between 1972 and 2000.

13. Explain why environmental laws are useless unless they are enforced.

14. Where does your community get its fresh water? How does it get rid of its waste water? Could the waste water pollute the fresh water? Explain.

15. Suggest five ways in which you or your neighbours could reduce the amount of water pollution produced in your local area.

GEO CAREERS — POLLUTION MONITOR

Name: Sing Ha
High School: Kiantuschu Kang College, Hong Kong
Job Title: Pollution Monitor

Sing Ha works in a chemistry lab in the large Dofasco steel plant in Hamilton, Ontario. His job is to work with others in the company to lower the amount of air and water pollution that the Dofasco factories produce. He spends much of his day talking with other employees about technical problems that cause pollution.

Dofasco monitors its pollution levels on a regular basis. For example, employees measure the amount of solids suspended in the water every day. Dofasco has done a great deal of research so that it can use waste materials for something useful.

Sing's background is in chemistry, but his first love is the field of geography, especially the environment. While he was at university, Sing took part in a co-op program. This work placement gave him a chance to work at Dofasco. The company liked his work, so when Sing graduated, it offered him a job.

Sing monitors the pollution coming from the plant in several ways. For example, he monitors the cleanliness of water that goes back into Lake Ontario after it has been used in the steel plant. For one test, he puts a rainbow trout into the water. If the trout stays healthy (as it does almost all the time), then Sing knows that the water is clean enough to meet government standards. If the fish dies, then he has a problem to solve!

To get started in this career, you could work toward a diploma as a Chemical Labratory Technician at a community college.

What I like about my work: *"I really enjoy my job because I am able to help people solve the problems they are working on. And I know I'm helping the environment at the same time."*

1. What would you like and dislike about being a pollution monitor?
2. What skills do you think you would need for this job?
3. What could you do to develop those skills in yourself?

Air Pollution

When you think of air pollution, you may think of smoke. Air pollution is made up of both dangerous gases and small particles. Some of these are visible, like smoke, while others are invisible, like ozone or carbon monoxide.

Canada produces air pollution from a number of sources. In Figure 15.11, you can see that much pollution comes from our cities, but there are other sources as well.

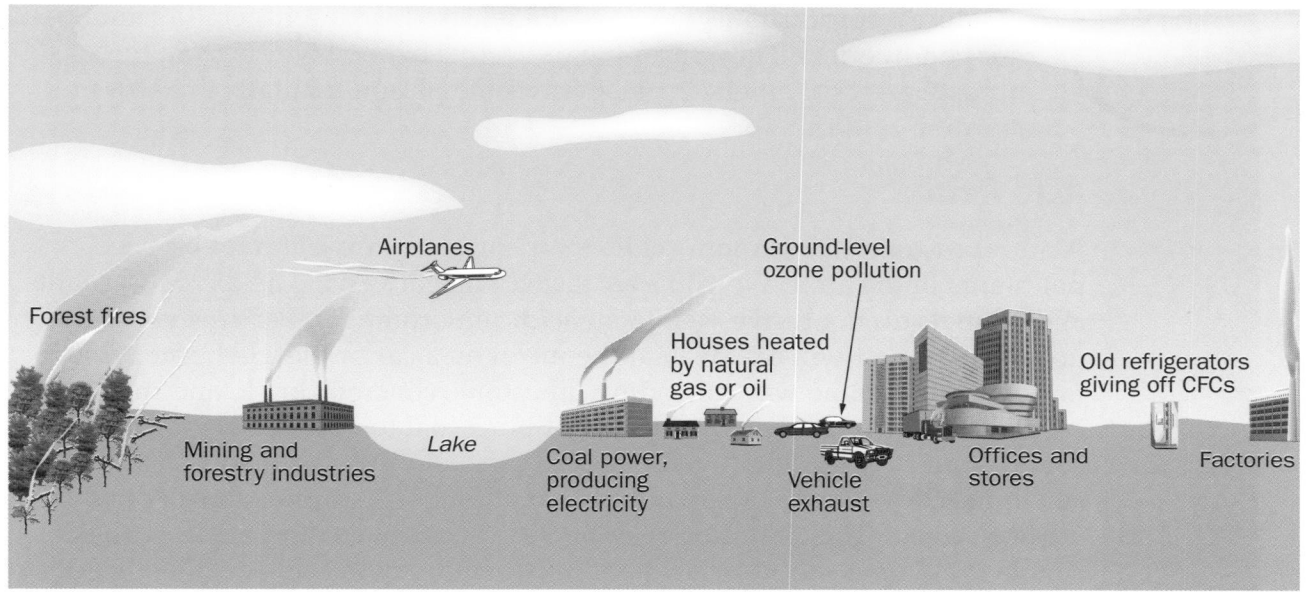

Airplanes

Ground-level ozone pollution

Forest fires

Houses heated by natural gas or oil

Old refrigerators giving off CFCs

Mining and forestry industries

Lake

Coal power, producing electricity

Vehicle exhaust

Offices and stores

Factories

▲ **Figure 15.11:** Sources of air pollution

16. Explain where you have seen at least one source of air pollution.

17. Examine Figure 15.11.
    a) Choose two sources of pollution from the diagram. Explain how they affect you now or may affect you in the future.
    b) In the diagram, what substance that is burned seems to produce the most air pollution?
    c) Why does city air pollution affect the countryside as well?

◀ **Figure 15.12:** Sunlight combines with pollutants to make smog over Toronto.

18. a) In what season was the photograph in Figure 15.12 on the previous page taken?
    b) In what season do you notice air pollution more? Why is this so?

Air pollution comes in several forms. Some gases produce thick, yellow-brown air, called smog, which you can see hovering over Toronto in Figure 15.12 on the previous page. **Ground-level ozone** is a deadly pollutant that hugs the ground. Other gases contribute to global warming, as you learned in Chapter 14: Our Impact on Climate. **Chlorofluorocarbons**, or CFCs, are released from refrigerators and air conditioners. They harm the protective **ozone layer** high in the atmosphere. Still others create an invisible poison that falls to Earth in the form of acid rain (or snow).

Acid Rain

Acid rain is rain that is more acidic than normal because it has absorbed pollutants in the air. Have you ever tasted vinegar? That's acidic. Most plants and animals do not thrive well in an acidic environment. Perhaps you have noticed how rust will eat away at the metal on a car or bicycle frame. Acid rain works the same way, corroding limestone, concrete, brick, and metal.

Acid rain comes from facilities that burn coal to produce electricity. It also comes from transportation vehicles, like cars, and industries such as mine smelting. These sources spew out pollutants such as sulphur dioxide and nitrogen oxide. This pollution rises into the atmosphere and mixes with clouds to become sulphuric acid and nitric acid. These acids eventually fall to Earth again, mixed with rain or snow.

Acid rain is extremely damaging to the environment. It can harm fields, roads, rivers and lakes, and even buildings and outdoor statues. It causes about one billion dollars worth of damage in Canada every year. Acid rain is one of the most damaging environmental problems that Canada faces.

Figure 15.13: ▶
The causes and effects of acid rain

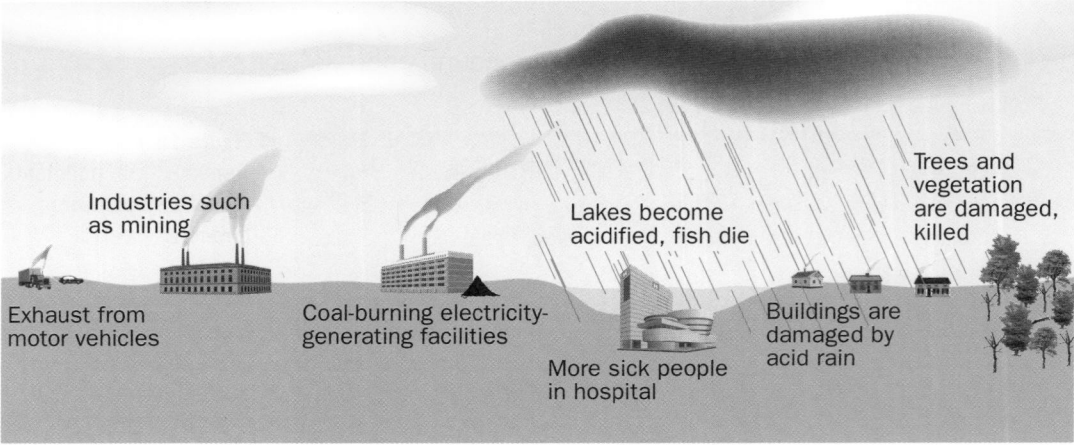

Industries such as mining

Exhaust from motor vehicles

Coal-burning electricity-generating facilities

Lakes become acidified, fish die

More sick people in hospital

Buildings are damaged by acid rain

Trees and vegetation are damaged, killed

19. a) Explain, in your own words, how acid rain is created.
    b) Write a short paragraph to explain how acid rain affects people and the environment.
    c) In what ways is acid rain an invisible threat to our way of life?

Acid rain has killed many forests and more than 14 000 Canadian lakes. These lakes now cannot support fish or plants. Their water looks eerily clear. More than 300 000 Canadian lakes are threatened. Much of Canada's air pollution originates in the Great Lakes region, home to many people and industries, both in Canada and the United States. Half the acid rain that falls in this country comes from the United States. Figure 15.14 shows the prevailing wind (the most common wind) coming in from the southwest. The map also shows the areas in Canada where lakes are suffering most from acid rain.

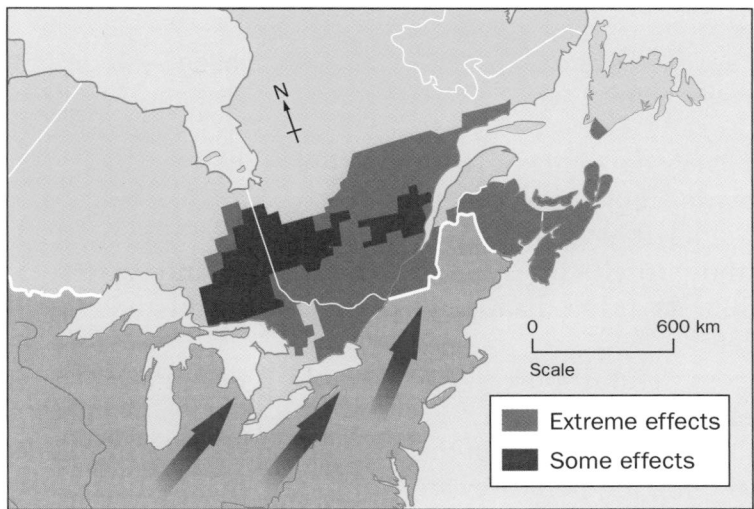

◀ **Figure 15.14:** Areas of Canada with lakes most damaged by acid rain

20. a) What part of the Great Lakes region is most affected by acid rain?
    b) How important is wind in determining where acid rain falls? Explain.

Cleaning Up Air Pollution

There have been many attempts to clean up the air in Canada. The government has passed laws that require car makers to use engines that burn less fuel and burn that fuel cleanly. Lead was removed from gasoline so it would burn cleaner. Some provinces require that cars be tested every year or so to make sure their emissions levels are low. Some industries have installed equipment in their smokestacks to reduce the pollution entering the air. There has been some success. The smog around the Greater Toronto Area and Hamilton, for example, has been reduced by 15 per cent.

Despite these efforts, air pollution remains serious. Part of the problem is that governments do not have the will to enforce current laws and create tougher ones. Another part of the problem is that ordinary Canadians know about air pollution, but still produce a lot of it. For example, as you saw in Chapter 14: Our Impact on Climate, we keep buying large vehicles, which seriously pollute the air. Most people travel by car, too, even though they know bus travel is easier on the environment. If forty urban workers took the bus to work instead of their cars, they would save 70 000 L of gas each year.

21. a) Speculate on why Canadians have not significantly reduced the amount of air pollution they produce since the early 1990s.
    b) List five things that you or your family could do to reduce air pollution.

Earth: A Closed System

Pollution of the land, waters, and air is a major problem for Canada and the whole world. The Earth is a **closed system:** everything produced in the system stays in the system. Pollution in one part of the globe eventually affects all others. A fish tank is a closed system. If you were to accidentally spill one single drop of soda pop into a tank, the fish would probably not even notice. But what would happen if you were to spill a big mug of pop into the tank? Every closed system can handle a certain amount of pollution, and no more.

22. How is each of these a closed system? How is each not a closed system?
    a) a forest   b) the human body   c) the solar system

In Earth's closed system, every small act of pollution contributes to the world's pollution. Ever made a bonfire to get rid of wood scraps? It can be a splendid sight. And all that's left over is a bit of ash in the fire pit. Right?

Not exactly. Smoke and particles fly up from the fire. The wind carries them elsewhere. The pollutants didn't disappear—they just spread and become everyone's problem.

Pollution can come from natural sources. For example, Mount Pinatubo erupted in the Philippines in 1991. It created huge clouds of ash. These clouds, in turn, created higher than normal rainfall in the entire Northern Hemisphere. Clouds blocked the sun, cooling temperatures all over the world for over a year. Canada had a very cold winter. The pollution created by this natural event in one country affected the climate in many other countries.

Figure 15.15: ▶
The eruption of Mount St. Helens, in Washington state, created huge clouds of pollution that gave Canadians red sunsets for six months.

Most pollution comes from artificial sources, not natural sources. Most pollution also comes from more developed countries, whose industries and lifestyles create pollution that affects people all over the world.

23. Explain how air pollution is an international problem. Give an example.

Pesticides in Greenland

Let's look at the example of Greenland, one of the most isolated areas in the world. Greenland has few people and little industry. Still, it has a problem with polluted food supplies. A similar situation exists in Canada's far North.

In 2001, scientists discovered that people living in eastern Greenland had high levels of harmful chemicals in their blood. These chemicals pose a long-term health risk. The source of the chemicals was fat from polar bears and seals, which form part of the traditional diet of people in the area. The chemicals, which include pesticides (chemicals to control weeds), probably entered lakes and rivers in Europe and North America, and spread to the Atlantic Ocean near Greenland. Figure 15.16 shows how the chemicals reached polar bears.

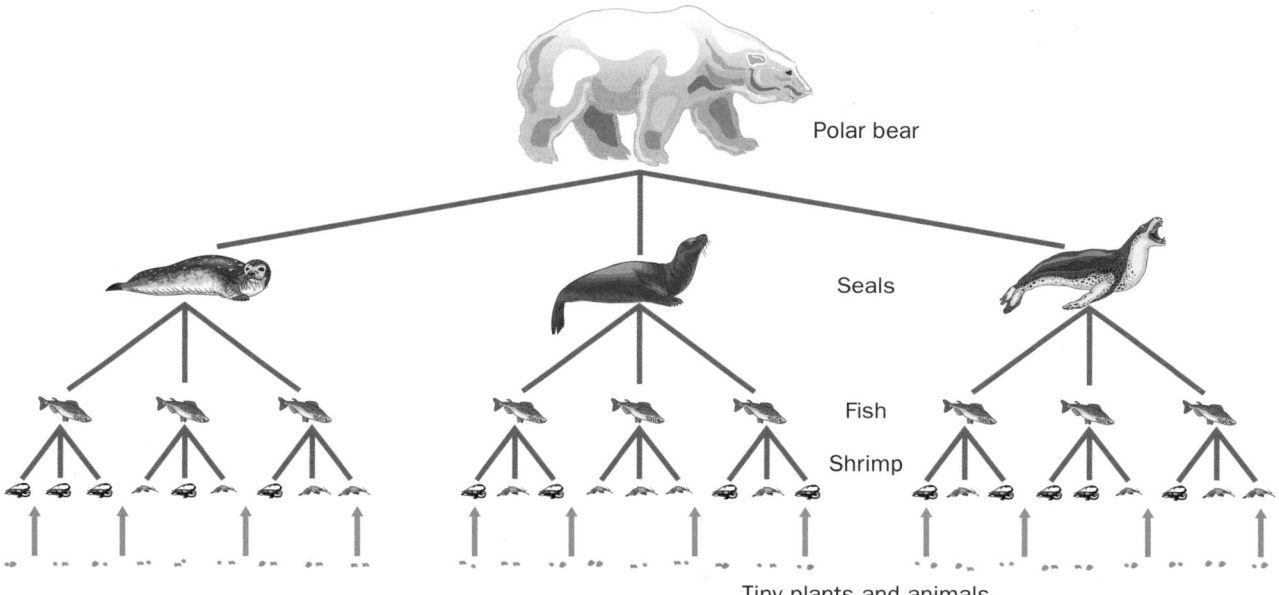

▲ **Figure 15.16:** Chemicals travel through the marine food chain to polar bears and then humans in Greenland.

Biomagnification is the word scientists use to describe how animals at the top of the food chain take in higher levels of chemicals. They absorb all the chemicals consumed by every creature below them on the food chain.

24. Make a diagram like the food chain in Figure 15.16 to illustrate biomagnification. Put one *X* near the bottom of the food chain for each tiny plant and animal. Your *X* represents one unit of poison. For the next level, all the *X*s should go to the shrimp that ate the tiny plants and creatures. Each shrimp should get about two *XX*s. Continue up the food chain to see how many units of poison get into the humans who eat the polar bear.

25. Explain, in your own words, how the situation in Greenland illustrates the international nature of pollution.

Conclusion

Pollution of the land, waters, and air are all international problems. All the world's nations must co-operate to solve these common problems. That is why Canada hosted an International Pollution Prevention Summit in Montreal in October 2000. Canada and other countries have signed many international pollution agreements. Still, much work still needs to be done.

Wrap It Up

1. Make a chart to compare the three major types of pollution listed in this chapter.
   a) List the pollution types across the top.
   b) In the second row, rank them according to their tendency to spread far from their source.
   c) In the third row, list two sources of each type of pollution.
   d) In the fourth row, rank them according to which will have the greatest impact on your life.
   e) Explain your reasons for your choices in part (d).

2. List three specific international situations mentioned in this chapter. Why is it not possible for Canada or any other nation to solve these pollution problems on its own?

3. a) Make a list of ten ways that Canadian drivers could reduce the amount of gasoline they use. Consider the following factors:
   - bad driving habits
   - how often drivers use an air conditioner
   - where drivers travel when they drive
   - the number of people who travel with them
   - how far they live from work or school
   - how often they use public transit
   b) What would be the best way to advertise to your community your suggested methods for reducing gasoline consumption and air pollution? Explain.
   c) Design a newspaper ad that would be part of your advertising program.

4. For this research activity, use your school or local library as well as the Internet.
   a) Name one major source of pollution in your local area.
   b) What type of pollution does it produce?
   c) What has been done over the past five years or so to try to reduce the amount of pollution that this site produces?
   d) Have these attempts to reduce pollution been effective, in your opinion? Explain your answer.
   e) What should be done to help reduce this pollution?

5. Do some research on the Internet to identify one instance in which a Canadian industry or company has successfully changed its business practices or product to do less harm to the environment. You might try forestry companies, auto makers, or agriculture. Summarize your good-news story in one paragraph.

6. Consider the following statement: "Industry is good for Canada, so we shouldn't hinder it with laws to prevent pollution." List three arguments that support this statement. List three that argue against it. Be prepared for an in-class debate, in which half the class will argue "for" and half the class will argue "against." Your teacher will assign you to one side or the other just before the debate.

7. For a challenge, try the "Acid Rain Analyst" GIS activity on page 340.

Chapter 16

REDUCING YOUR ECOLOGICAL FOOTPRINT

Do You Walk Lightly on the Earth?

Every day of our lives, we have an impact on the environment. We use up fuel and other non-renewable resources. We leave waste materials. We breathe carbon dioxide into the air.

Do you walk lightly on the Earth? Find out your environmental impact by answering the following questions about your habits. Write your answers on a separate piece of paper.

1. How much of your travel is by public transit, walking, or bicycle?
   a) Less than 10%   b) 10–50%   c) More than 50%

2. How much of your travel is by car, truck, van, or SUV?
   a) More than 50%   b) 50–10%   c) Less than 10%

3. How many airplane flights have you taken in the past five years?
   a) More than 6   b) 2–6   c) Fewer than 2

4. How big is your home, considering the number of people who live in it?
   a) Plenty of room   b) About right   c) A tight squeeze

5. To what degree is your home air-conditioned in summer?
   a) Too much   b) Just enough   c) Not at all

6. How often do you buy something you don't really need?
   a) All the time   b) Sometimes   c) Rarely

Give yourself three points for every (a) answer, two points for every (b) answer, and one point for every (c) answer. Check your rating in the chart in Figure 16.1.

Score Range	15-18	11-14	7-10	1-6
Your Impact	high	medium	low	very low

Figure 16.1: Rating your score

In this chapter, you will
- learn about the size of Canada's ecological footprint
- understand that deforestation is an international problem
- identify ways that you can shrink your ecological footprint
- create a plan to address a local environmental concern

Words to Know

metaphor
standard of living
consumer
consumer society
ecological footprint
deforestation
desertification
sustainable management

Canada's Ecological Footprint

Imagine that you are walking along a tree-lined beach on a beautiful day. You leave your shoes behind, and you can feel the soft sand under your feet. Every once in a while, you can feel the cool waves of the water. You forget about all your worries. What a great day!

About fifteen minutes after you have walked along the beach, someone else begins to walk exactly the same route. What can this person see of you? Just the footprints that you left behind, and most of those have been washed away.

▲ **Figure 16.2:** Footprints in the sand disappear as soon as the next wave washes in.

Early inhabitants of this planet had an effect on the environment much like the footprints you leave behind when you walk along a beach. Shortly after early humans passed through an area, little evidence of their presence was left behind.

Now imagine that you're walking along the beach again, but this time as the average, modern Canadian. As you walk along the beach, you throw away all kinds of garbage. You toss gum wrappers, pop cans, newspapers, and old clothing. Soon, trailing behind you are buckets of toxic waste, a rusted old washing machine, a huge oil puddle, a car wreck, the bodies of endangered animals, and tree stumps instead of trees. This image of the beach is a **metaphor**, or symbol, of the effect that average Canadians have on the world's environment. We damage it. Badly.

1. Explain in your own words the two metaphors described above. What do they mean?

Canadian Resource Use

We saw on the previous page that Canadians do much more harm to the environment than our distant ancestors did. Canadians also do more harm per person than most other people on our planet today—and not just because of pollution. Our way of life uses up a lot of resources. Most Canadians enjoy a high **standard of living**, which means that we have access to education, health care, and social services. It also means that we have a lot of material goods—we use up a lot of *stuff!* Have a look at the tables in Figures 16.3 and 16.4 to see just a few of the wasteful ways typical of our high standard of living.

Item	Number
Loads of laundry per year, average family	392
Garbage produced per year, average person	500 kg
Sheets of paper average office worker uses per year	10 000
Computers, phones, fax machines replaced per year	41 000 tonnes
Percentage of the above reused/recycled/dumped	40%/15%/35%
Number of birds killed per year, flying into lighted buildings in Toronto	10 000
Number of national parks reporting ecological impact because of high visitor numbers	24 of 36
Number of municipalities that dump raw sewage into waterways	90

▲ **Figure 16.3:** Selected consumption statistics, Canada, 2000

Country	Electricity Used per Person (kW•h)
Canada	15 777
United States	12 410
Australia	9 222
Japan	7 515
Russia	5 090
China	3 970
Brazil	2 017
Egypt	857
Cameroon	202

Source: Geography IQ Web site at <http://www.geographyiq.com>, November 2002.

▲ **Figure 16.4:** Electricity use per person, 2000

2. a) Which data in Figure 16.3 surprised you most? Why were you surprised?
   b) Which data illustrate an excessive use of resources?
   c) For each piece of data, indicate if air, water, or land pollution results.

3. Examine Figure 16.4. Why is Canada's ranking so high? Think of three activities that contribute to electricity use.

Country	Price (Cdn$/L)	Country	Price (Cdn$/L)
United Kingdom	$1.75	Italy	$1.48
Netherlands	$1.61	Canada	**$0.82**
France	$1.49	United States	$0.71

Source: *US News & World Report*, 25 September 2000, Vol. 129, Issue 12, Energy Information Administration.

◀ **Figure 16.5:** Price per litre of premium gasoline, 2000

4. Many Canadians talk about "high" gasoline prices. Consider Figure 16.5.
   a) Do you think Canadians should complain about gas prices? Explain.
   b) Speculate on how gas prices might affect how much gas we use.

You are a **consumer**—you buy goods and services. You live in a **consumer society**. That means that our society depends on people purchasing goods and services. When people purchase a lot of goods, the economy does well and many people have jobs. But is the person with a lot of goods in a big house happier than the person with just enough? And what about the effect on the environment? It's time to consider the real cost of our way of life.

Our Ecological Footprint

The data you've seen so far in this chapter suggest that individual Canadians probably use more resources and create more pollution than many other citizens of the world. We've looked at only a few examples, though. How do we know our total effect on the planet?

William Rees and Mathis Wackernagel, two scientists at the University of British Columbia, thought about this problem. They came up with an idea that would help us get a good picture of a person's overall effect on the planet—our ecological footprint. Your **ecological footprint** is the amount of productive land needed to provide you with the goods you use, and to absorb the wastes you produce. Your footprint includes the types of productive land shown in Figure 16.6.

- *Crop land:* highly fertile farmland
- *Grazing land:* moderately fertile farmland used for grazing animals
- *Fishing ground:* areas of the sea that provide seafood
- *Forest land:* forested areas that are logged
- *Energy land:* forested areas that are needed to clean up the pollution created by burning fossil fuels
- *Built-up land:* productive areas covered by buildings and roads

▲ **Figure 16.6:** Productive land

You will find that almost everything you do uses up land in at least one of these categories. When you take a bus, for example, you use energy land because the bus burns diesel fuel. You also use up a small portion of built-up land because of the roads and the garage where the bus is stored at night.

5. What types of productive land do you use for each of the following activities? You may think of more than one type for each.
   a) eating a burger and fries for lunch
   b) driving to hockey practice
   c) printing out your homework assignment
   d) renting an apartment
   e) eating a shrimp spring roll

A Footprint Too Large

You may suspect that Canadians have a larger ecological footprint than do people in other parts of the world. Find out by looking at Figure 16.7.

Country	Average Ecological Footprint (hectares)	Country	Average Ecological Footprint (hectares)
Australia	9.0 ha	France	4.1 ha
Canada	7.7 ha	India	0.8 ha
China	1.2 ha	United Kingdom	5.2 ha
Egypt	1.2 ha	USA	10.3 ha
Ethiopia	0.8 ha	World	2.8 ha

Source: Earth Council Web site at <http://www.ecouncil.ac.cr/rio/focus/report/english/footprint/ranking.htm>, November 2002.

Figure 16.7: Average ecological footprints of selected countries, 2002

6. a) Rank-order the countries in Figure 16.7 on the previous page from smallest ecological footprint to largest footprint.
   b) What pattern do you notice in your ranking?
   c) Compare Canada's effect on the Earth with that of two other countries.

◄ **Figure 16.8:** Ecological footprint by country

Global hectares per person, 1999
- 5.0 and over
- 3.0 – 5.0
- 1.5 – 3.0
- 1.0 – 1.5
- Less than 1.0
- Insufficient data

7. a) Compare the patterns of the five categories of footprint on this world map.
   b) What does this comparison tell you about the lifestyle of Canadians?

8. Are you and most of your friends aware of this difference between Canada and most of the rest of the world? Why is this the case?

9. If every one of the countries on the map had Canada's ecological footprint, what would happen to pollution levels and the use of resources?

What the Future Holds

Perhaps you're wondering if it really matters that Canadians have a larger ecological footprint. After all, you have everything that you need. In fact, the Earth's environment is currently under great stress, and the situation is getting worse.

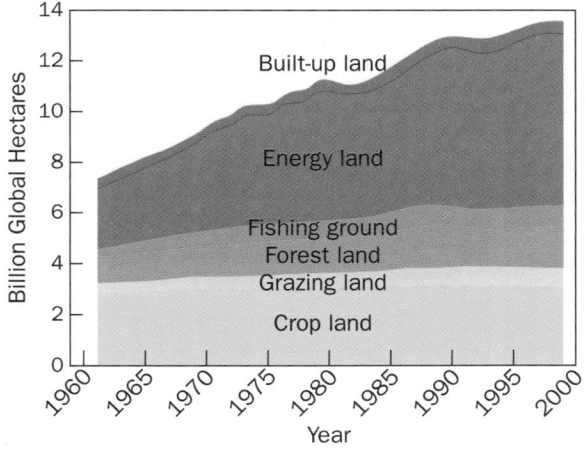

◄ **Figure 16.9:** World ecological footprint, 1961–1999

GeoTrivia #2
By the age of 6 months, a Canadian has used up as many resources as a person in a less developed country uses in a lifetime.

10. Describe the pattern you see in Figure 16.9 on the previous page. What type of land has been increasing most quickly?

11. a) Calculate what the ecological footprint of the world would be if all people on Earth were to have the same quality of life that Canadians have. Multiply the population of Earth (about 6 billion) times the average Canadian's footprint (7.7 ha).
   b) Compare your answer to part (a) with the Earth's total productive land, about 11.4 billion hectares. What conclusion can you reach?

GeoGames

Chasing Your Ecological Footprint

Purpose:
To understand how various actions affect the size of one's ecological footprint.

Supplies:
- one die
- one playing piece per player
- a piece of paper per player
- game board (opposite page)

Method:
A. Up to four players can play this game at one time. Set up your game board with one playing piece for each player. The playing pieces must begin at "START."

B. The goal of this game is to cause less ecological damage than your opponents do. The more points you accumulate, the more damage you are doing to the environment, and the larger your ecological footprint.

C. Roll one die each to determine order of play. The player with the lowest score begins.

D. The players take turns rolling the die and then moving the pieces. Move ahead the number of spaces indicated on the die.

Add or subtract from your score according to the directions in the space where you land. List the points you gain or lose, and write down the reasons given.

E. The game ends when the first person gets to 50 points. The player with the lowest number of points wins.

Wrap-Up:
1. a) What frustrated you as you were playing the game? Explain your answer.
   b) What types of activities added the greatest number of points to your total?
   c) Before you played this game, did you ever think about the damage you do to the environment by doing the types of things shown in this game? Explain your thinking.
   d) What lesson could you learn from this game? Be specific in your answer.

2. a) In this game, did you gain points for harming the environment more quickly than you lost points for avoiding harm?
   b) Considering your answer to part (a), do you think this game accurately reflects real life? Explain.

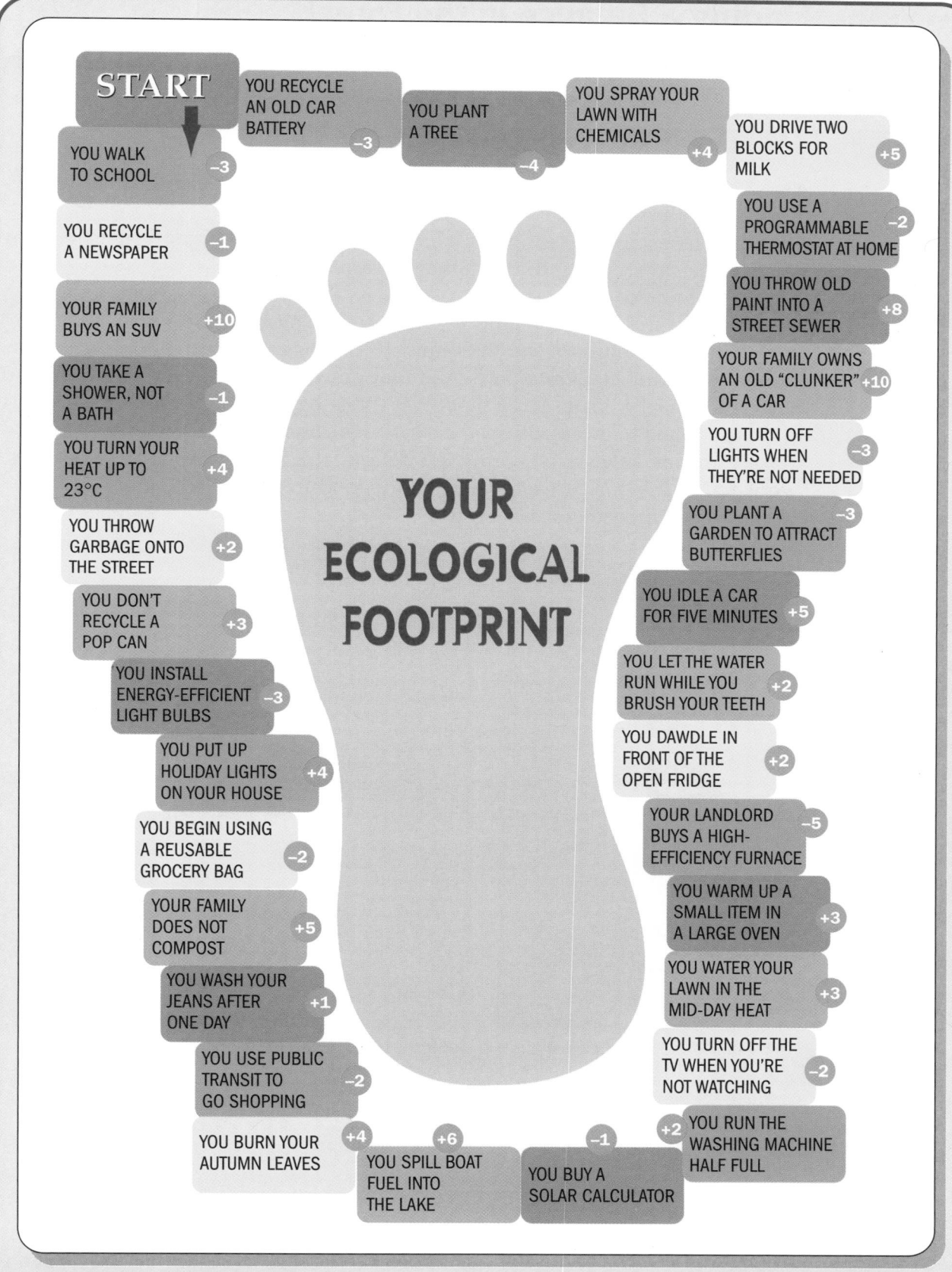

START

YOU WALK TO SCHOOL   –3

YOU RECYCLE AN OLD CAR BATTERY   –3

YOU PLANT A TREE   –4

YOU SPRAY YOUR LAWN WITH CHEMICALS   +4

YOU DRIVE TWO BLOCKS FOR MILK   +5

YOU RECYCLE A NEWSPAPER   –1

YOUR FAMILY BUYS AN SUV   +10

YOU TAKE A SHOWER, NOT A BATH   –1

YOU TURN YOUR HEAT UP TO 23°C   +4

YOU THROW GARBAGE ONTO THE STREET   +2

YOU DON'T RECYCLE A POP CAN   +3

YOU INSTALL ENERGY-EFFICIENT LIGHT BULBS   –3

YOU PUT UP HOLIDAY LIGHTS ON YOUR HOUSE   +4

YOU BEGIN USING A REUSABLE GROCERY BAG   –2

YOUR FAMILY DOES NOT COMPOST   +5

YOU WASH YOUR JEANS AFTER ONE DAY   +1

YOU USE PUBLIC TRANSIT TO GO SHOPPING   –2

YOU BURN YOUR AUTUMN LEAVES   +4

YOU SPILL BOAT FUEL INTO THE LAKE   +6

YOU BUY A SOLAR CALCULATOR   –1

YOU USE A PROGRAMMABLE THERMOSTAT AT HOME   –2

YOU THROW OLD PAINT INTO A STREET SEWER   +8

YOUR FAMILY OWNS AN OLD "CLUNKER" OF A CAR   +10

YOU TURN OFF LIGHTS WHEN THEY'RE NOT NEEDED   –3

YOU PLANT A GARDEN TO ATTRACT BUTTERFLIES   –3

YOU IDLE A CAR FOR FIVE MINUTES   +5

YOU LET THE WATER RUN WHILE YOU BRUSH YOUR TEETH   +2

YOU DAWDLE IN FRONT OF THE OPEN FRIDGE   +2

YOUR LANDLORD BUYS A HIGH-EFFICIENCY FURNACE   –5

YOU WARM UP A SMALL ITEM IN A LARGE OVEN   +3

YOU WATER YOUR LAWN IN THE MID-DAY HEAT   +3

YOU TURN OFF THE TV WHEN YOU'RE NOT WATCHING   –2

YOU RUN THE WASHING MACHINE HALF FULL   +2

YOUR ECOLOGICAL FOOTPRINT

▲ **Figure 16.10:** The playing board

Finding a Balance in the Forest

How do we decrease the size of our ecological footprint? Let's look at forestry to see how changing the way we use resources may be key.

Changing the Footprint on Algonquin Park

Algonquin Park, Ontario, is the largest provincial park in Canada. We value this area on the Canadian Shield for a number of reasons, including its unspoiled lakes and forests, which have been set aside for Canadians to enjoy. You may be surprised to find out that the area the park covers today was once the scene of an ecological disaster.

How did we abuse the land to create such a situation? We used it in an unsustainable fashion. In the 1860s and 1870s, loggers begun chopping down and shipping out the white pine trees that grew throughout the park. Many of these giant trees were so large that even three loggers could not reach around their base. The logs were shipped down rivers and exported to Britain and other countries. Intensive logging left behind almost no trees at all. Forest fires swept across the park area, burning more good trees. By 1890, much of the park area was an ecological disaster.

▲ **Figure 16.11:** Algonquin Park in the 1880s, before it became a park

▲ **Figure 16.12:** Algonquin Park is close to several major Canadian cities.

12. Speculate on why the logging companies were allowed to cause so much destruction to the area that became Algonquin Park.

The general approach of many businesses has been to take from nature whatever it has, without thinking about the consequences. A small group of individuals saw the results of this approach in Algonquin Park. They began to work on the idea of setting up a park that would ban farming, create a wildlife refuge, and protect the sources of five major rivers. In 1893, Algonquin Provincial Park was established. Slowly, the forests returned to Algonquin Park through planting and natural regeneration.

Today, the park is used in a variety of different ways. There are summer camps, outfitters, resorts, lodges, canoe routes, cottages, logging, and hunting and fishing. All these activities provide jobs for the community without devastating the area. The current combination of uses is sustainable.

13. Explain how the Algonquin Park area was once a good example of unsustainable practices, but is now a good example of sustainable practices.

14. In Algonquin Park, logging is kept away from highways, campgrounds, hiking trails, and the water where canoeists pass. Several hundred jobs in nearby communities depend on the logs from the park. Do you believe that logging should continue in this park or not? Give two reasons for your answer. Give at least one reason that supports the other point of view.

Deforestation Today

In Algonquin Park, many people have fought hard to find ways to use the forest resource without destroying it. Trees and forests are enormously important to humans. They give a setting for powerful Aboriginal stories and histories, and many religious stories and experiences. They provide us with places to go for recreation, valuable building materials, and millions of jobs worldwide. In the natural world, too, forests are vital.

But the world's forests are in danger. About 15 million hectares worldwide are destroyed every year. This area is about twice the size of New Brunswick. Forest fires accounted for some of this destruction, but the most significant destroyers are humans. Forests were cut down to provide wood for fuel and construction, and land for farming. This is **deforestation**, the ongoing reduction of the world's forests.

Deforestation has a number of negative effects on Earth.

- The destruction of forests, especially in hot climates, causes **desertification**—the transformation of productive land into desert.

- The livelihoods of some Aboriginal peoples are threatened.

- Climates become more extreme, with more floods and droughts.

- Some species become endangered or extinct.

- Landslides and avalanches become more common.

- Less oxygen is created, without which animals and humans cannot survive.

15. a) List ten ways that trees and forests are vital to the Earth and humans. (*Hint:* Besides looking at the benefits noted in the text, look at the list of things that deforestation takes away.)
    b) List ways that deforestation in one country can harm the international environment.

Every year, the demand for forest products increases. The greatest increase comes from more developed countries in Europe and North America. Is a growing population causing this increase? No. This increased demand is caused by people buying more wood. For example, Canadian houses tend to be larger today than they were thirty years ago, even though families tend to be smaller. Larger houses increase the demand for construction wood.

Figure 16.13: ▶
Many Canadians are not satisfied with anything but a very large house.

16. Larger homes tax the environment in many ways.

   a) From your experience, identify five resources that are needed to build and maintain homes.

   b) Do larger homes use more of each of these resources?

   c) How does the ecological footprint of a person living in a large house compare with that of a person living in a small condominium?

Solutions to Deforestation

Governments and industry have a role to play in halting deforestation. The Canadian International Development Agency (CIDA) is the branch of the federal government that works with less developed countries to increase their level of development. It has been pushing the United Nations to create an International Forest Convention.

The purpose of this convention would be "to ensure that all the world's forests are **sustainably managed**." Forests would be cut down at the same rate that new ones are planted.

In another international development, in August 2002, a World Summit on Sustainable Development was held in Johannesburg, South Africa. Canada announced that it would increase its aid to poorer countries by $1 billion over three years, to promote sustainable development. But the biggest obstacles to sustainability come from rich nations like Canada, where we consume far more than people in poorer nations do.

17. In your own words, explain "managing forests sustainably."

18. Explain why forestry issues are international in nature in terms of a) causes, b) effects, and c) solutions.

Taking Action

We have seen that our federal government is trying to promote sustainability internationally. The harder task will be to change Canadians' habits so that our ecological footprint will shrink. To do this, Canadians must use fewer resources and cause less pollution. All across Canada, people have been working to find ways to reduce our ecological footprint.

Using Energy-Efficient Technologies

Businesses and governments can invest in research to develop new technologies that make better use of our resources. People can use technologies that exist, such as energy-efficient light bulbs. An environmental Education Centre in Airdrie, Alberta, was built using technologies to "minimize the ecological footprint on the environment." Figure 16.14 shows some of the features that were built into the centre to make it eco-friendly.

▲ **Figure 16.14:** The eco-friendly house in Airdrie, Alberta

19. Identify the features of this house that allow the following.
    a) fewer new materials in the construction
    b) reduced heating costs
    c) reduced water use
    d) a lower overall impact on the environment

20. Is this type of house practical for use across the country? Explain.

21. If this type of house were to be built across Canada on a large scale, what impact could it have on our ecological footprint?

Low-Impact Activities

We can change our impact on the environment by engaging in low-impact activities, like canoeing instead of driving a motor boat. We can also give our business to companies that produce environmentally friendly products, such as recycled paper. Companies whose practices don't harm the environment also deserve our business.

GeoTrivia #3
Quaker Oats Company of Canada hopes to save $10 000 every year by switching from single-sided to double-sided photocopying.

▲ **Figure 16.15:** Cree wild rice harvesters do little harm to the environment where wild rice grows.

22. Think of four businesses that do little or no harm to the environment.

Naturalizing Areas

One way to improve the environment is to naturalize an area. In this process, trees, bushes, and wildflowers that occur naturally in an area are planted in an attempt to re-establish a small ecosystem. Sometimes small ponds are dug and marshes are planted. These invite small animals and birds back to the area. Many schools across Canada have naturalized their school grounds.

▲ **Figure 16.16:** A school ground before naturalization

▲ **Figure 16.17:** The same school ground after naturalization

23. a) Examine Figures 16.16 and 16.17 on the previous page. What have students done to naturalize their school ground?
    b) Suggest four types of creatures that might be found in a naturalized school ground.
    c) How would this naturalized school ground benefit the students of the school? Give three suggestions.

24. In your opinion, should the students of the school do the work on a project like this, rather than professionals with heavy equipment? Explain your answer.

From what you have read in this chapter and your own personal knowledge, you have enough background to understand that environmental issues are a significant concern for Canadians. Take the challenge and make up your own plan of action.

25. a) Make a list of ten things you can do personally that would reduce your ecological footprint. Look through this chapter for ideas. Be sure to make the list practical so that you can accomplish your goals without giving up or becoming discouraged.
    b) Taking into consideration the resources you proposed in Question 16 a) on page 274, write a letter to your local newspaper to outline what you are doing to reduce your ecological footprint. Challenge others to do the same.

GeoSkills

USING GEOGRAPHIC INQUIRY TO SOLVE A PROBLEM

One of the most important skills that you can learn is how to solve problems. Sometimes problem solving involves investigating an issue that is of concern or deciding what to do about a situation you face. For example, where should you go to find a part-time job? And, what should you do when you graduate from school?

Purpose
Having the ability to solve problems will help you succeed in geography class, in your career, and in life. This ability is also key to coping with the challenge of our oversized ecological footprint.

Here are the steps for solving a problem.

Step 1
Identify the problem. What problem or issue do you want to work on? Define this as clearly as

you can. The more specific your problem, the easier it will be to work on. Misa, a high school student, noticed that few students were taking part in the recycling program at her high school. She decided to tackle the specific problem of pop cans ending up in the garbage.

Step 2
Divide the problem into parts. Nearly every problem can be divided into parts. Misa decided that her problem had four parts.
• Students were not inspired to recycle their pop cans.
• Recycled pop cans were not always collected.
• More money was needed to purchase containers to hold the pop cans.
• Cafeteria supervisors were not encouraging students to recycle.

▲ **Figure 16.18:** What's wrong with this picture?

Step 3

Plan your research. How will you get information that will help you carry out your plan? Misa decided on the following research strategies.

- Talk to teachers with experience in recycling.
- Search the Internet for successful recycling projects in other schools.
- Search for recycling information in newspapers and magazines.

Step 4

Do your research. Next, you need to carry out the research you have planned. Misa came up with twenty-five pages of information.

Step 5

Identify the valuable information. Much information that we collect is interesting, but not all of it helps us solve the problem. Separate the valuable information from the information that is not useful.

Step 6

Propose a solution. What solution are you going to propose? Misa recommended the following.

- The school should buy five more pop-can recycling bins.
- The student council should hold a student assembly to promote recycling.
- Student volunteers should monitor the cafeteria and encourage people to recycle.

Step 7

Evaluate your solution. Think through your problem again. Will your solution solve the problem, or is there more that can be done? If your solution doesn't work, then go through the process again. Misa decided to talk to the school staff to make sure that the recycled pop cans would be collected more often.

Practise It!

1. a) Now you have a chance to solve a problem yourself. Here are a few questions to help you find a problem to research.
   - Are students in your geography class wasting paper?
   - Are teachers using too much photocopying paper?
   - Are used toner cartridges from the photocopy machine being recycled?

   Follow Steps 1–7 to try to come up with a solution to the problem you choose.

To solve a problem...
- ✔ identify the problem
- ✔ divide the problem into parts
- ✔ plan your research
- ✔ do your research
- ✔ identify the valuable information
- ✔ propose a solution
- ✔ evaluate your solution

b) What obstacles might you face if you try to implement your solution? Explain.

c) Can your solution be applied to another situation? Explain.

Conclusion

In this chapter, you learned that your ecological footprint indicates the impact you have on the environment. You also learned that the average Canadian damages the environment more than most other people in the world do. Can that damage be reduced and reversed? Possibly. Using energy and resources more wisely, and cutting back on waste and pollution, are important steps.

Wrap It Up

1. a) Explain what is meant by the term "ecological footprint."
   b) How does Canada's footprint compare with that of other countries?
   c) Is Canada's ecological footprint too large? Explain your reasoning.

2. List three general ways that Canadians can change their impact on the natural environment. Give an example of each.

3. a) Select a less developed country and find out what kind of lifestyle is typical in that country. Find specific statistics on the following.
   - types of homes
   - percentage of population with electricity, televisions, radios, cars
   - number of people per doctor
   - pollution problems
   - average income per person

   You might try the Web sites for these organizations: Red Cross, World Vision, Inter Pares, the World Bank, CIDA.
   b) Compare the statistics from the country you selected with those of Canada.
   c) What does that comparison show you about our life in Canada and that in a less developed country? Explain your answer.
   d) Do your conclusions agree with what was discussed in this chapter? Explain.

4. Make up ten questions to survey your family about the different ways that you use water. Conduct your survey and identify one bad water-usage habit. Get your family's co-operation to try to fix that habit over the course of one week.

5. Think about what is happening in your community in the areas of water conservation or energy conservation. Choose one topic that interests you.
   a) Write up six questions for a survey. Three should be about the current situation (for example, "Does your shower have a water-conserving spray nozzle?"). Three questions should deal with what could be done to solve the problem. Be specific (for example, "Would you buy a water-conserving spray nozzle?").
   b) Conduct your survey, interviewing ten people, at least four of whom should be adults.
   c) What conclusions can you come to, based on your survey?

6. Consider the topics of ecological restoration of woodlots and schoolyards, river cleanups, and industrial initiatives to reduce pollution. Choose one topic that interests you.
   a) Write out three questions that you can research to discover what is happening in this area. Each one of your questions should clearly relate to your topic. You should also be able to answer it in a straightforward way.
   b) Plan how you are going to answer each question. For example, you might call your municipal government.
   c) Conduct your research, making notes from every source.
   d) Use your research notes to answer your three questions.
   e) Is there any part of your questions that you did not answer fully? If so, explain what part of which question you did not fully answer.

Unit 4 Performance Task

PLANNING A GREEN HOME

In Unit 4, you learned that we have a big problem: the Canadian way of life threatens our natural systems. In this Performance Task, you will plan a "green" home—one that is Earth-friendly because it conserves energy and other resources, and recycles waste. It combines sensible family habits with Earth-friendly technology, such as using alternatives to fossil fuel energy.

You will use the problem-solving method that you learned in Chapter 16 to plan your alternative to the typical Canadian home and its overuse of resources.

Assignment **1**: Focusing on the Challenge

Step 1: Identify the Problem

Imagine that you and your classmates are all home designers who have entered a contest. A home builder will build the dream home of the team that designs the best green home using available technology. Your plans will aim to solve the problem of excessive use of resources in today's typical Canadian home. You will display your completed plans at a display fair. After the fair, the class will vote to decide who has created the most interesting plan.

Step 2: Divide the Problem into Parts

Every home must have several systems in order to function. For example, a home could not operate without a waste system. Figure 1 shows the five different systems that are part of any home. (With one exception: yard landscaping systems do not apply to apartments.)

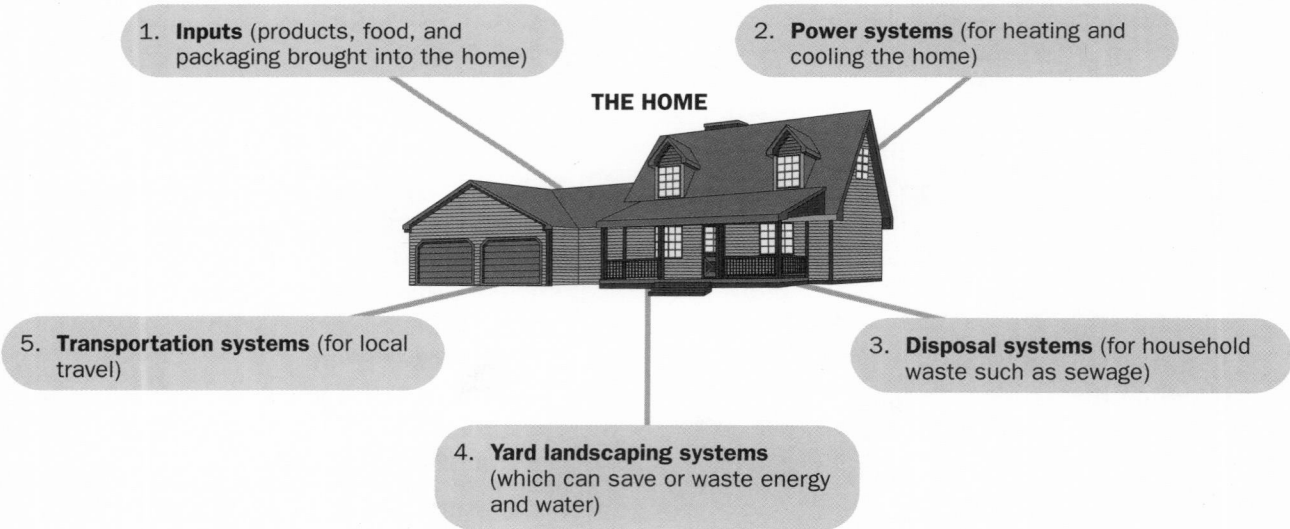

1. **Inputs** (products, food, and packaging brought into the home)

2. **Power systems** (for heating and cooling the home)

THE HOME

5. **Transportation systems** (for local travel)

3. **Disposal systems** (for household waste such as sewage)

4. **Yard landscaping systems** (which can save or waste energy and water)

▲ **Figure 1:** Five systems of any home

Environmental problems exist because we use harmful technologies and because we have bad habits. Focus further on the challenge by identifying common problems found in most Canadian homes. For example, most Canadians use furnaces that burn fossil fuels or electricity created by burning coal as their main energy source. You learned in Chapter 13 that burning coal for electricity creates air pollution and acid rain. Chapter 14 identified fossil fuels as the main cause of global warming and climate change.

1. Working with a partner, put this information into a chart like the one shown in Figure 2. Use your textbook, your notes, and your own general knowledge to fill out the chart. Come up with as many ideas as you can. File your completed chart with the teacher.

	Old Technologies	Bad Habits
Power	• burning fossil fuel for heat, causing pollution and global warming • using electricity made by burning coal • using an out-of-date, inefficient furnace • ...	• leaving lights on • leaving the thermostat high at night • washing clothes in hot water • ...
Inputs	• buying a new microwave oven because the old one isn't designed to be fixed • ...	• purchasing goods with packaging • ...
Disposal		
Yard landscaping		
Transportation		

▲ **Figure 2:** Using resources badly in Canadian homes

Assignment 2: Finding Possible Solutions

Step 3: Plan Your Research

Now you are ready to begin solving the problem of planning a sustainable green home. A useful strategy is to start with what you already know, and then research topics for which you need more information. Chapters 13 through 16 introduce good resource and energy-saving ideas; for example, geothermal systems, hybrid cars, water conservation, and "naturalized" spaces. Use the ideas from these chapters, and your own ideas, to complete a solutions chart for resource problems common in Canadian homes. This will help you plan further research on selected topics.

1. With your partner, fill in a chart of possible solutions. Brainstorm solutions for every point you made in your chart, "Using Resources Badly in Canadian Homes." See the sample in Figure 3 on the next page.

	Green Technologies	Good Habits
Power	• installing a geothermal system to heat the house • installing solar panels for electricity • using a modern, high-efficiency furnace • buying energy-efficient lightbulbs • ...	• turning lights off • buying detergent that washes clothes well in cold water • ...
Inputs	• buying a new microwave oven that you know can be repaired if it breaks • ...	• choosing products with less packaging • ...
Disposal		
Yard landscaping		
Transportation		

▲ **Figure 3:** Using resources wisely in Canadian homes

▲ **Figure 4:** Solar panels can be put on a roof or any other spot with good sun exposure.

◀ **Figure 5:** The plants in this perennial garden come back every year, attracting birds and butterflies.

Step 4: Do Your Research

You may have found some gaps in your solutions chart. These are good places to do some research to locate information. Because you are planning a sustainable home using green technology that currently exists, focus on research about existing products and systems. (In other words, don't make up solutions using imaginary technology!)

2. With your partner, gather information from geographic magazines, CD-ROMs, and keyword searches on the Internet. Organizations such as Pollution Probe, Energy Probe, and World Watch may be of use. Look for pictures and diagrams that can be included in your plans for a green home. You will be making a visual display. After your research is complete, fill in the gaps in your chart, and submit it to your teacher.

Assignment 3: Preparing Your Plans

Step 5: Sort Out What Is Useful

It is time to decide what your plan for your green home will actually include. Keep in mind the aim of this project: to plan a home that conserves resources by using alternative energy sources and reducing waste. Decide how you will answer the following four questions before you start your plans. Your answers will help you choose the most useful information that you have gathered.

- How will you heat and cool this home?
- How will you landscape the property?
- How will you reuse household garbage?
- How will you get around the community?

Step 6: Propose a Solution

The problem posed to you was that the Canadian way of life threatens our natural systems. Your solution to this problem will be expressed in the plans that you prepare.

1. You and your partner will work together to create your plan. One of you will design plans for the home itself (Part A), while the other will design plans for the lawn and gardens, as well as the transportation system (Part B).

Part A

Use a large piece of blank paper or Bristol board to make a plan of the home. You can draw the whole building from overhead, like a floor plan, or from the side, like a cross-section. Add labels and explanations where needed. Include pictures and drawings of the technologies that the sustainable home will use, either on your diagram of the home or in a separate visual display. Instead, you could even create a model.

Part B

Draw or create a model of a landscape plan for the property around the sustainable home. Arrange trees to protect the home from cold winter winds, and to shade the roof from the hot summer sun. Remember: maximum sun exposure is on the south side, while winds generally come from the north and west in Ontario. "Naturalize" the property to reduce grassy areas. Show the transportation methods that you will use to get around the community. Add labels and explanations where needed.

Step 7: Evaluate Your Solution

Display your completed work as a poster or model in a classroom display fair. With your partner, take turns explaining your plans to other students. During your partner's turn, tour the classroom to view other plans. Ask questions. Look at the other plans to see if other students have thought of good ideas that could further improve the Earth-friendliness of your own green-home plan.

After the fair, take a classroom vote to see which dream-green home gets built.

CANADA'S INTERNATIONAL LINKS

The Somewhere in Canada Contest #5

This is your last chance to show how well you can identify parts of Canada. This one is a rural area, with some of the strangest scenery imaginable. Where do you think this picture was taken? If you're not sure, look at these clues.

CLUE 1 ▶ About 75 million years ago, the area was a subtropical rain forest—perfect for dinosaurs.

CLUE 2 ▶ The area now has a semi-desert climate, with very hot, dry summers—perfect for preserving dinosaur skeletons. Joseph Burr Tyrrell discovered dinosaur remains here in 1884.

CLUE 3 ▶ The Royal Tyrrell Museum of Paleontology (the study of fossils) was built here in 1985. It has some of the most stunning dinosaur skeletons in the world—most from the local area. It's a very popular tourist destination, with more than 375 000 visitors a year.

CLUE 4 ▶ European settlers who came here more than a hundred years ago thought the land was so *bad* for farming that they used this word when they named the place.

CLUE 5 ▶ At one time, coal mining was a major industry in the western province where this area is located. Now oil is king.

What Will You Study in This Unit?

You can see from the photograph why European settlers of Western Canada thought this particular area was useless for farming. The area was developed after 1910, when coal was discovered. At one time 120 coal mines were active here. After most of the mines shut down in the 1970s, local and provincial governments began to develop dinosaur tourism to bring in jobs and boost the economy. Today, dinosour tourism brings about $15 million into the area each year. It draws tourists both from within Canada and from other countries.

In the first chapter of this unit, you're going to look at tourism, a major Canadian connection to the world. You'll learn who visits Canada, and where Canadians go when they travel abroad.

When we think about Canada's place in the world, we can examine it in two ways: by looking at Canada's connections—like tourism—and by comparing Canada with other countries. In the second chapter in this unit, you'll see that we can compare countries in many different ways. Why is time different in various countries? What percentage of the population can read? What types of economy do various countries have?

In the final chapter of this unit, you'll look at ways in which Canada is connected to the rest of the world. War in a distant land can require Canadian peacekeepers to go in after peace is reached. Canadian charities work hard to help in cases of drought and famine. And common problems, such as pollution and security, can be tackled only when many nations work together.

In this unit, you will

- analyze international tourism patterns in Canada and other countries

- investigate different methods for comparing quality of life in different countries

- examine various ways in which Canada is connected to other countries

For a challenge, try the Unit 5 GIS activity, "Tourist Attractor," on page 340.

Chapter 17

INVESTIGATING CANADIAN TOURISM

Figure 17.1 ▶
Vancouver's skyline

Plan a Trip Across Canada

Congratulations! You've just won $3000 to spend on a return trip from Toronto to Vancouver! You have up to two weeks, but the length of your stay will depend on how you choose to spend your money. Here are some of the decisions you will have to make. Write your answers in your notebook or on a piece of paper.

1. Will you:
   a) take the car (cost: $400; time: three to five days each way)
   b) take the bus (cost: $300; time: about three days each way)
   c) take the train (cost: $1200; takes about three days each way)
   d) take the plane (cost: about $900, but takes only five hours each way).
   Total transportation cost: _____

2. Will you:
   a) stay at a luxury hotel (cost: $300 a night)
   b) stay at an economy hotel or bed and breakfast (cost: $80 a night)
   c) stay at a youth hostel (cost: $20 a night)
   d) camp out (cost: $18 a night)
   Multiply the cost of accommodation by the number of nights you will stay.
   Total accommodation cost: _____

3. How much of the remaining money will you use for:
   a) eating at restaurants _____
   b) buying souvenirs _____
   c) paying entrance fees at shows, tourist attractions, etc. _____
   d) shopping for clothes and other goods _____

So, are you pleased with your budget choices? Compare your choices with those of a classmate. How do your choices differ? Later in this chapter, you'll find out how other tourists spend their money in Canada.

In this chapter, you will

- find out who visits Canada and why they come
- discover the importance of tourism to Canada's economic development
- look at where Canadians go when they travel abroad
- consider some of the negative and positive impacts of tourism
- find out about the growing trend toward ecotourism

Words to Know

tourist
tourism industry
cultural tourism
sports tourism
adventure tourism
business travel
natural systems
human systems
ecotourism
entrepreneur

Tourism in Canada

The questions you answered when planning your trip to Vancouver are the sorts of questions that all tourists ask themselves as they prepare for a trip. A **tourist** is a visitor who visits a location for more than twenty-four hours but less than a year. Visitors like these come to Canada from all over the world, and for all kinds of reasons.

The **tourism industry** includes all the businesses that cater to these travellers, from travel agents to hotel operators. There are many subcategories of tourism within the industry. For example, **cultural tourism** helps visitors to appreciate the way of life of the people living in an area. This type of tourism includes everything from staying with a local family in a small town to visiting a museum in a large urban centre. **Sports tourism** focuses on the needs of sports enthusiasts. In northern Ontario, sports tourism has been an important source of income for many Aboriginal groups, who act as guides to visitors who want to hunt and fish in the region. **Adventure tourism** offers visitors out-of-the-ordinary experiences, such as polar bear spotting in the Arctic, or hiking through the rainforest.

Business travel is also a form of tourism. Business travellers make up about 18 per cent of the overnight traffic both into and out of Canada. These travellers are often willing to pay much higher prices in exchange for more flexibility and comfort. Airline companies and hotel chains have set up special services for their business customers.

You planned your trip to Vancouver around how much time you had available, and how much it would cost. Visitors to Canada, and Canadians going abroad, plan in a similar way. In this chapter, you will read about what this means for the lives of Canadians and our economy.

1. a) What other forms of tourist activities can you think of in addition to sports tourism, cultural tourism, adventure tourism, and business travel?
   b) Which form of tourism would interest you most? Why?

2. Why do you think business travel is considered part of the tourist industry? What special needs or services might this category of traveller require?

GeoTrivia #1
In 2000, France was the world's most popular tourist destination. Canada was 9th on the list.

Who Comes to Canada?

As you can see from the map in Figure 17.2, the United States is the largest source of tourists to Canada. There are many reasons for this. For one thing, Canada has close economic ties with the United States. Also, it's so close that Americans can just drive their cars over the border. Or, they can come by bus and train. Only about 25 per cent of American visitors arrive by air.

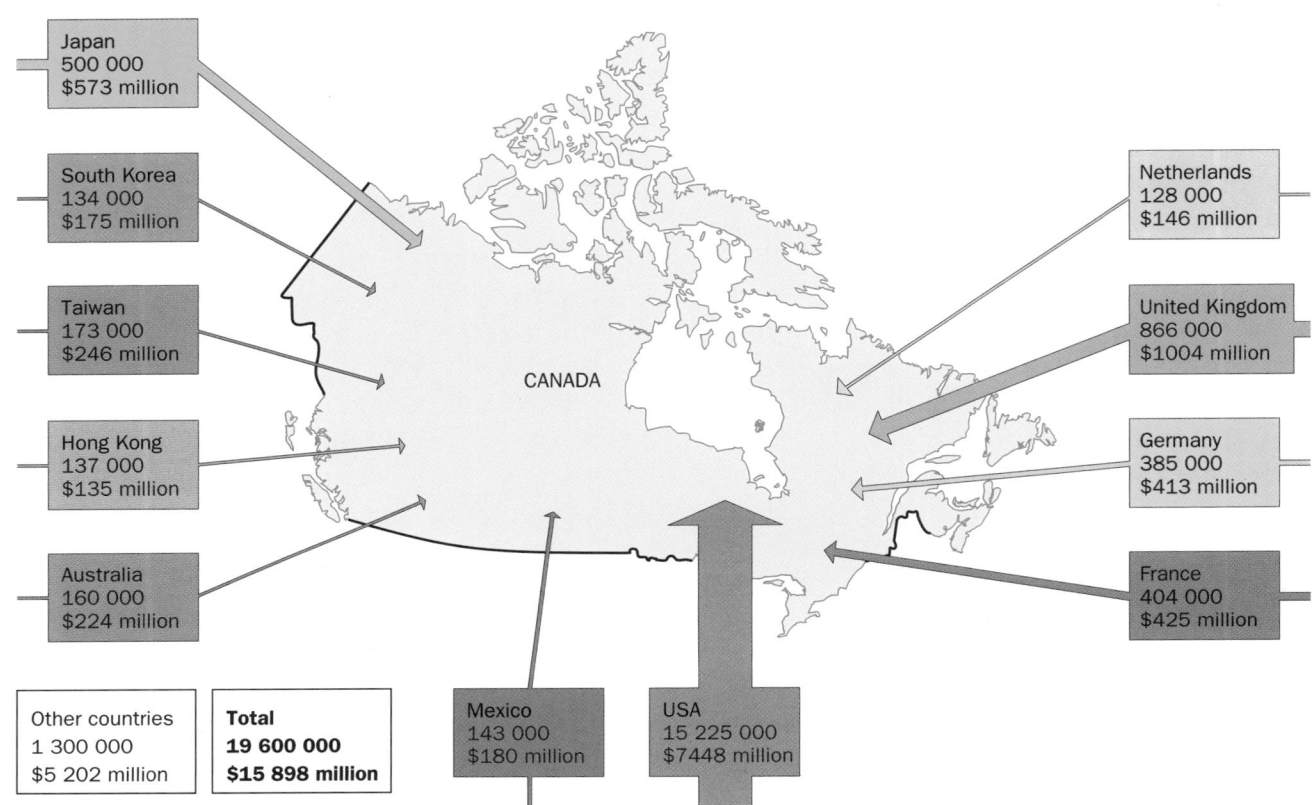

Japan
500 000
$573 million

South Korea
134 000
$175 million

Taiwan
173 000
$246 million

Hong Kong
137 000
$135 million

Australia
160 000
$224 million

Netherlands
128 000
$146 million

United Kingdom
866 000
$1004 million

Germany
385 000
$413 million

France
404 000
$425 million

CANADA

Other countries
1 300 000
$5 202 million

Total
19 600 000
$15 898 million

Mexico
143 000
$180 million

USA
15 225 000
$7448 million

▲ **Figure 17.2:** Major sources of overnight tourist visits to Canada, 2000, shown by number of trips and spending in Canada

3. Look at the map and an atlas.
    a) Which group of travellers has the farthest to go to reach Canada?
    b) What factors do you think might attract this group of visitors to our country?

4. a) Use what you know about Canada's cultural makeup and its history to suggest reasons for the high number of tourists that come here from the United Kingdom.
    b) What do you think might account for the popularity of Canada as a tourist destination for Japanese travellers?

5. List three other reasons why the United States is our biggest source of tourists.

Not surprisingly, tourists who travel long distances to get to their destination are more likely to want to stay longer to make the time, effort, and cost of the journey worthwhile. For example, most visitors from the United States spend on average about four nights in Canada. By contrast, the average German visitor spends almost two weeks here.

Tourism and Canada's Economy

In the year 2000, the tourist industry provided jobs for 546 400 Canadians and generated more than $30 billion in revenue. That makes it a significant part of the nation's economy. Who benefits from all this spending? Airlines, travel agents, tour guides, and hotels all depend on tourism, of course. But visitors also spend money at restaurants, buy souvenirs, and shop in stores. They may go to the theatre to watch a play or movie, attend a concert, or get tickets to sporting events. All this activity is good for the economy.

6. Look at the table in Figure 17.3. Choose three categories from the left-hand column. Think of at least two jobs associated with each of these tourist activities.

7. a) What sector of the economy do most of these jobs fall under?
   b) Do any of these jobs interest you? Why or why not?

8. What three activities would you most recommend to tourists in your area? Use the list in Figure 17.3 as a guide.

	US Visitors (percentage)	Overseas Visitors (percentage)
Total	**100%**	**100%**
Shopping	61%	81%
Sightseeing	54%	76%
Dining at high-quality restaurants	44%	43%
Visiting parks or historic sites	33%	54%
Visiting friends or relatives	30%	54%
Outdoor activities/sports	30%	29%
Visiting zoos, museums, natural displays	20%	40%
Participating in nightlife/entertainment	20%	21%
Attending cultural events	11%	14%
Attending fairs/festivals	8%	13%

Source: Statistics Canada, Canadian Tourism Facts and Figures, brochure from the Canadian Tourism Commission Web site, <http://www.canadatourism.com>.

Figure 17.3: Top activities for tourists to Canada, 2000

The Growth of Tourism

Tourism is a fast-growing industry around the world. Before air travel, it was only the very rich who could afford to travel for leisure. And because of the amount of time it took to travel long distances, business travel was limited, as well. But as travel has become easier and faster, more and more people are taking advantage of cheaper fares to explore parts of their own country or the world at large. In a short period of time, tourism has become an important part of the economies of many countries, including Canada.

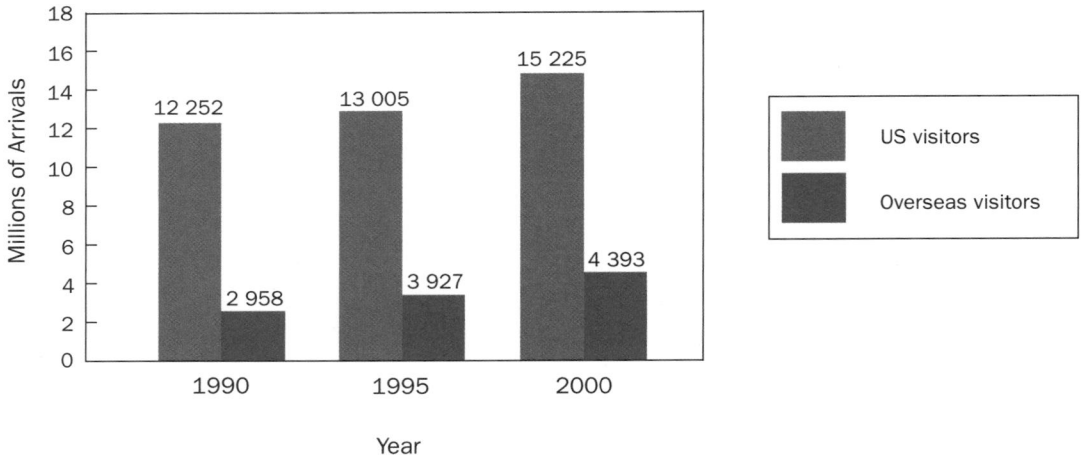

▲ **Figure 17.4:** International tourist arrivals in Canada from USA and overseas, 1990, 1995, and 2000

9. To what extent is international tourism an important industry in Canada? Use some figures from this section to support your conclusion.

Tourist Destinations in Canada

Canada has a lot to offer visitors. Some people come to experience the grandeur of our wilderness. Others come for the excitement of cities like Toronto or Montreal. Still others come to attend special events, such as the Winter Olympics in Calgary or the many carnivals, festivals, and other events that take place across the land. Our **natural systems**, such as climate, landforms, flora, and fauna, are part of the attraction.

But before visitors decide to come here, they want to know that **human systems** are in place to meet their needs. Are there airports and roads to get them where they want to go? Are there places for them to stay? Will they be able to exchange their foreign currency for Canadian dollars? Will there be places to eat and shop? Figure 17.5 on the next page illustrates some of the human and natural systems that have helped create a thriving tourist industry in British Columbia.

In the next section of this chapter, you will read about some Canadian tourist destinations. As you read the descriptions, think about the human and natural systems that support the tourist industry in each case.

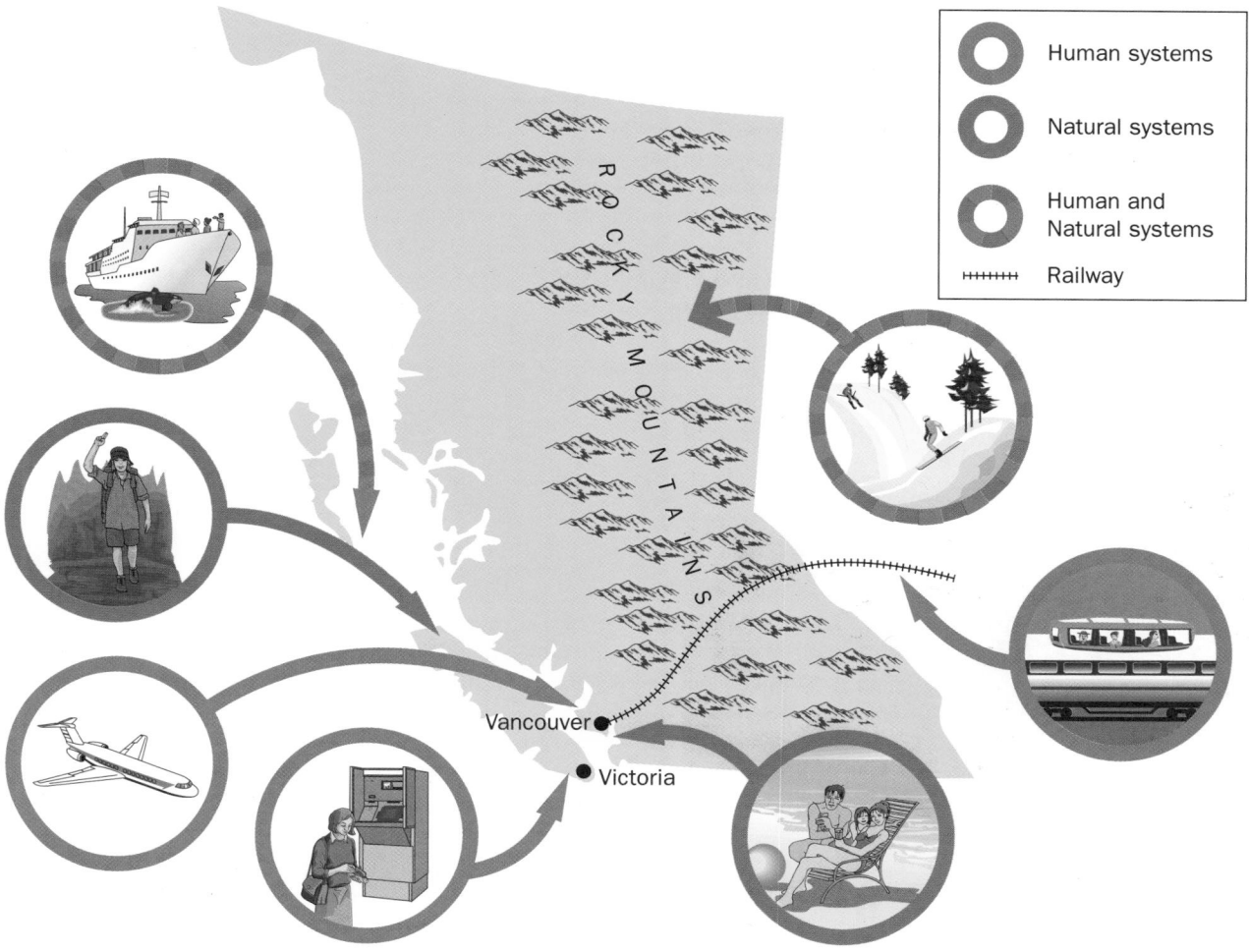

▲ **Figure 17.5:** Examples of human and natural systems in the BC tourist industry

10. Think of three other questions about natural or human systems that foreign travellers might ask before deciding to travel to Canada.

Skiing in Banff National Park

Canada is a premier location for sports tourism, as people come here from all over the world to ski, snowboard, hike, or participate in other sports. Nature has provided us with the perfect requirements for both downhill and Nordic skiing. At Banff, Alberta, high snowfalls combine with steep mountain descents to challenge everyone from beginners to international world-class athletes. The town of Banff is about ninety minutes west of Calgary by road, while the resort area at Lake Louise is closer to Edmonton. Both cater to tourists by offering restaurants, shopping, and a variety of accommodations in different price ranges.

11. What other reasons besides sports might draw tourists to Banff?

Prince Edward Island

Prince Edward Island has the smallest population of any province. Since there is little industry there, its economy relies on agriculture and tourism. In fact, while only 138 500 people call the island home, over one million people visit it every year! Prince Edward Island offers great variety to tourists. Its seaside location and rural setting make it ideal for a relaxing family vacation. Many visitors stay at bed and breakfasts on local farms while visiting some of the best sandy beaches in Canada. The main centre, Charlottetown, offers a variety of activities, from musicals to stock car races. Many Canadian and international visitors come to see Green Gables, the farm where Lucy Maud Montgomery set her novel, *Anne of Green Gables*.

▲ **Figure 17.6:** Moraine Lake and Valley of Ten Peaks, Banff National Park, Alberta

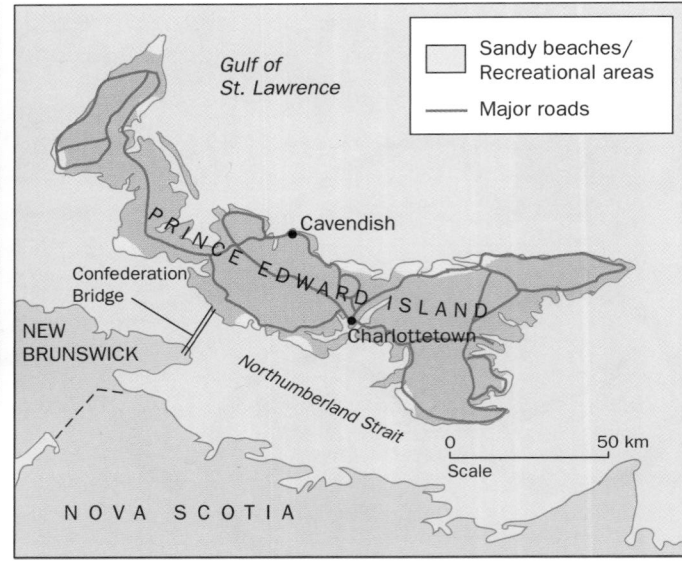

▲ **Figure 17.7:** Prince Edward Island

12. Explain how PEI's small size is an advantage for tourism.

The Polar Bear Express

The Polar Bear Express is one of the last great railway excursions. The 300-km journey runs from Cochrane, Ontario, to Moosonee, on the James Bay coast. It passes through rugged, unspoiled wilderness, crossing huge rivers such as the Abitibi and Moose, which were once important fur-trading routes.

About 14 000 passengers ride the Express in a season—from the last week in June to the first week of September. Almost half of these visitors spend at least one night in Moosonee (population, 3000). To cater to these tourists, a number of businesses have sprung up. The "Polar Princess" takes visitors on whale-spotting cruises on James Bay, while local tour companies offer overland wilderness excursions along the coast, as well as guided trips to Fossil Island to scour for fossils. A boat trip to the island of Moose Factory will show you the site of a Hudson's Bay Company trading post, built in 1673.

13. Explain how the remote location of the Polar Bear Express route is both an obstacle and an attraction to tourists.

14. How might the Polar Bear Express excursion appeal to
    a) cultural tourists   b) adventure tourists   c) sports tourists?

15. Make a chart to show how natural and human systems attract tourists to each of the three tourist destinations described here.

Where Do Canadians Travel?

Tourist traffic between Canada and the United States goes both ways. In fact, Canadians make about 14 million trips to the United States per year, staying an average of seven nights.

Many Canadians go south to avoid the winter. Just over 2 000 000 Canadians visited Florida alone in 2000, most of them during the north's colder months. But other tropical locations are also popular, as you can see on the map in Figure 17.8.

GeoTrivia #3
The September 2001 terrorist attacks against the United States cost the world airline industry an estimated US$18 billion.

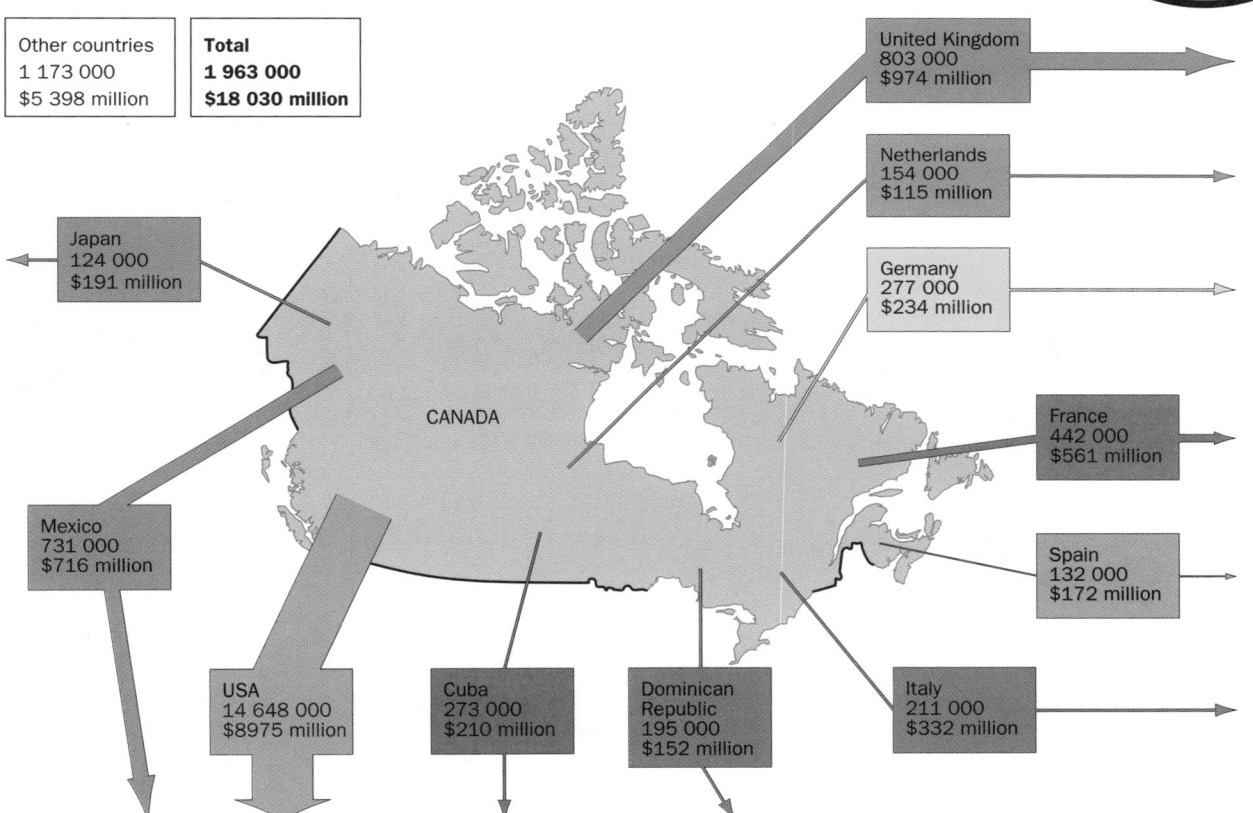

Other countries	Total
1 173 000	**1 963 000**
$5 398 million	**$18 030 million**

United Kingdom
803 000
$974 million

Netherlands
154 000
$115 million

Germany
277 000
$234 million

Japan
124 000
$191 million

France
442 000
$561 million

CANADA

Spain
132 000
$172 million

Mexico
731 000
$716 million

USA
14 648 000
$8975 million

Cuba
273 000
$210 million

Dominican Republic
195 000
$152 million

Italy
211 000
$332 million

▲ **Figure 17.8:** Major destination countries of overnight tourists from Canada, 2000, shown by number of trips and spending by Canadians

16. a) Look at Figure 17.8. Name three countries that received Canadian visitors that are not on the map of visitors to Canada (see Figure 17.2, page 288).
    b) What might account for this difference?

17. Name two reasons why the United States is the most popular destination for Canadian tourists.

Negative Effects of Tourism

We have already seen that a healthy tourist industry can bring great economic benefits. But tourism can have a down side, as well. Too many visitors to exotic locations can destroy the very landscape they have come to see. For example, the Galapagos Islands, off the coast of South America, have had to limit tourist visits. Tourists were coming in such numbers that they were destroying the natural environment. Many National Parks in the United States have had to place a limit on tourists for the same reason.

Another possible down side of tourism is its effect on local economies, especially in developing nations. Most tourists come from the developed countries, where many people have the income necessary to pay the high cost of travel. They may demand the kind of facilities they are used to at home. Often, these services are provided by large hotel chains, owned by companies based in other countries. Most of the jobs that tourism creates tend to be low-skill ones with low wages. Skilled, high-paying jobs are often filled by people from the tourist company's homeland. Local culture may also suffer. Artisans may start to cater to the tourist trade, producing large quantities of cheap crafts, and neglecting traditional forms of art that do not sell as well.

▲ **Figure 17.9:** Identify two ways that local residents are trying to lessen the damage caused by visitors to this beach on the Bruce Peninsula in Ontario.

18. Describe the possible negative effects of tourism. What ways can you think of to avoid each of these problems?

19. Think of a natural area that attracts tourists that is near you or that you have visited. What problems do you think tourists might cause in this area?

CASE STUDY

GAP ADVENTURES

Background

Would you like to stay in a luxury hotel, sit on a beach for a week, and eat five-course deluxe meals every night? If so, GAP Adventures is not the tourism operator for you! This Canadian company is looking for a completely different type of traveller.

GAP books tours for people who want to experience a world completely different from their own. Their clients want to learn about different cultures and eat the food that the local people eat. They are sensitive to the environment and want to have as little negative impact on it as possible. They are what GAP calls "responsible tourists."

GAP won't take you to Florida or Paris. But they will take you to the Andes Mountains of South America, or the plains of southern Africa. You will stay in clean but simple hotels, or on a farm, or in a tent, or with a local family. The hope is that you will meet as many local people as possible and learn about life in your host country. If you can't get ketchup, or even french fries, you should not be upset. You'll eat the local food, and perhaps develop a taste for something you've never tried before.

Ecotourism

In the 2000s, there is a growing market for what is called sustainable tourism or **ecotourism**. Ecotourism is tourism that has a low impact on the environment and is sensitive to local cultures and indigenous peoples. Ecotourists do not usually fly short distances in helicopters, or make short river journeys in speedboats. They probably go by non–air-conditioned bus or dugout canoe, in order to consume less fuel. And they don't insist on luxuries such as clean sheets and towels every day, because this service adds to detergent pollution of waterways. Ecotourism operators design their trips around the idea that tourists should leave as little impact on the environment as possible.

▲ **Figure 17.10:** Canadian tourists on a GAP Adventures trip to North Africa

▲ **Figure 17.11:** GAP Adventures tourists at Machu Picchu, an ancient religious site in Peru

Like other ecotourism operators, GAP has developed a list of standards that guide its tours. Some of these principles include:

- using locally owned transportation when possible
- visiting at least one officially established Protected Area on each tour
- providing employment and business opportunities to local people
- keeping the size of their groups small
- using small, locally owned hotels whenever feasible

Can Tourism Help Save the Environment?

Some believe that ecotourism can do even more than avoid doing harm to the environment. They see it as a way to save ecologically sensitive areas from development. If ecotourists will pay local people to guide them through the rainforest, for example, then they can say no to logging or ranching. That's why the year 2002 was designated the Year of Ecotourism by the United Nations. The UN sees ecotourism as an important tool in preserving the environment.

1. How is a tour with an ecotourism outfit different from a tour with most traditional travel companies?
2. Would you like a tour organized by GAP Adventures? Explain your reasons.

GEO CAREERS — ECOTOURISM ENTREPRENEUR

Name: Bruce Poon Tip
High School: Henry Wisewood High School, Calgary, Alberta
Job Title: Ecotourism Entrepreneur

Being a successful entrepreneur requires a special kind of person. An **entrepreneur** is someone who runs his or her own business. You need to be able to motivate yourself, you need to be willing to work long hours, and you need to be willing to risk everything you have. But the rewards can be great, as Bruce Poon Tip has discovered.

Bruce started to work in the fast-food industry when he left high school. But he soon realized that he did not really want to work for someone else. So after completing a diploma at Mount Royal College in Calgary, he opened his own ecotourism company (GAP Adventures) at the age of twenty-one.

By working with similar companies in other parts of the world, Bruce's company can offer tours virtually anywhere. In turn, other ecotourism companies can send clients to Canada, where Bruce will organize tours to see polar bears in Churchill, Manitoba, or canoe trips in the Northwest Territories.

Bruce believes that originality and creative thinking are vital for the success of any business venture. These qualities have certainly worked for him. In January 2002, Bruce was the only Canadian operator invited to attend the United Nations launch of the Year of Ecotourism in New York. He has won many awards, including the government's Global Traders Leadership award for his groundbreaking ideas in exporting services.

What I like about my work: *"I love the benefits I can bring to local communities by sending tourists there who will respect their culture. I love employing people who support the idea of sustainable tourism. I love having a global impact because of the decisions I make."*

How a knowledge of geography helps me in my job: *"Thinking globally has got me where I am now. Geography has taught me what makes parts of the world unique."*

1. What would you like and dislike about being an entrepreneur?

2. What skills do you think you would need to be an entrepreneur?

3. What steps could you take to develop those skills in yourself?

Conclusion

In this chapter, you have looked at how tourism affects Canada's economy. You learned who comes to Canada, and where Canadians go when they travel abroad. You also thought about the kind of human and natural systems that are necessary for a successful tourist industry. Finally, you considered some of the negative impacts that tourism can have on the environment and local cultures.

Wrap It Up

1. In your own words, explain the importance of tourism to our economy.

2. a) Make a chart to show the possible good and bad effects of tourism.
   b) Write a list of guidelines to be used by people who want to be responsible ecotourists. Include advice on how to interact with the local economy, culture, and environment.

3. The Olympic Games are a major tourist attraction. As a result, cities compete fiercely to host the Games. Prepare a report on a recent or upcoming summer or winter Olympic Games. Include information on
   a) which cities bid for the games, and what advantages and disadvantages each location offered
   b) the number of people (either actual or expected) that attended or are expected to attend the Olympic Games
   c) human systems (for example, accommodations and transportation) that were or are being put in place to deal with the huge number of visitors during the Games

4. Think about what could be done to attract more tourists to your area. Consider existing tourist attractions, the accommodations that are available, travel routes, and other forms of entertainment or shopping. Then either
   a) create a brochure aimed at tourists to persuade them to visit your area, or
   b) write a letter to your local government offering some ideas on why more tourism would be a good idea and how to make your area a more attractive destination.

5. Use the Internet or visit a local tourism office to find some major tourist destinations in each province or territory. Map these destinations on a blank map of Canada. Use a legend to show the kinds of attractions that are available at each destination.

6. For a challenge, try the "Tourism Attractor" GIS activity on page 340.

Chapter 18

MAKING GLOBAL COMPARISONS

Put on the Spot

Imagine that your class has been connected through a video-linkup to a geography class in New Zealand. The New Zealand students want to know what Canada is like. You might identify similarities—you say that Canada and New Zealand are both democracies. You might continue with differences—you say that Canada is a huge country, while New Zealand is small.

Then there is a pause, and you look at the other students in your class. How else can you compare countries? Let's look at a few ways. Write the answers to the following questions in your notes.

1. Which country is largest in area?
   a) Russia   b) China   c) Canada

2. Which country has the largest population?
   a) Russia   b) China   c) Canada

3. Which country has the most time zones?
   a) Canada   b) United States   c) Russia

4. Which country has the most people per square kilometre?
   a) Canada   b) Japan   c) Saudi Arabia

5. Which country is the largest exporter of lamb?
   a) South Africa   b) Canada   c) New Zealand

6. Which country has the most patriotic people (people who love their country)?
   a) United States   b) Canada   c) France

7. Which country's economy is based mainly on the export of oil?
   a) Saudi Arabia   b) India   c) Brazil

▲ **Figure 18.1:** Does this photograph show New Zealand or Canada? Here's a hint: New Zealand has 56 million sheep—16 sheep per person!

When you have answered all the questions, get the correct answers from your teacher. If you did well, congratulations! If you did not, don't feel bad. The point of the quiz is to show you a few of the many ways we can compare countries.

Words to Know

opinion

fact

time zone

diversified economy

gross domestic product (GDP)

GDP per capita

oil-resource
economy

emerging industrial
economy

agricultural economy

human development

life expectancy at birth

adult literacy rate

Human Development Index
(HDI)

In this chapter, you will

- use a time zone map to calculate time differences
- identify four types of economy
- compare Canada's quality of life with that of other countries
- summarize Canada's contributions to telecommunications

A World of Differences

Comparing countries is tricky. We naturally think our country is best. For example, you might think that the pizza that you order on the weekend is the best in the world. People living in Italy might disagree with you, though. Similarly, you might read about "the best beaches in the world" in promotional pamphlets for several different countries. Who is right? It's hard to say.

The above are **opinions**, which are beliefs not backed up with proof. Opinions can vary. They can also be affected by bias, the tendency to favour one view over another. To avoid opinion—and bias—try to stick to the facts. Instead of trying to gauge which country has the "best" beaches, you might investigate which countries have the longest beaches or the highest surfing waves. **Facts** are pieces of information about something that exists or an event that happened. To ensure that our facts are correct, we must always use reliable sources.

1. Which of the following statements show opinion? Which show facts?
   a) "Canada is the best country in the world."
   b) "You can go for an elephant ride in Thailand."
   c) "The elephant rides in Thailand are fabulous."
   d) "New Zealand has summer when Canada has winter."

2. Look over the questions in the quiz on the previous page again.
   a) Which way of comparing countries do you find the most interesting? Why?
   b) Which of the questions require a factual answer? Which ones require an answer based on opinion? Explain.

3. a) Identify another way in which you could compare countries.
   b) Would your suggestion allow you to "stick to the facts," or would it involve opinion?
   c) What sources might you use to find accurate information for your comparison?
   d) Is your comparison more useful or less useful than the questions in the quiz? Why?

In this chapter, you will learn how to compare countries in several ways.

- time differences
- human development
- economic development
- telecommunications

We will try to stick to the facts.

Time Differences

One of the simplest differences between countries is time. Different countries use different times.

On Sunday, 24 February 2002, millions of television sets in Canada were tuned in to live coverage of the men's hockey final at the Winter Olympic Games in Salt Lake City, Utah. Viewers huddled around television sets in Barrie, Ontario, saw the game end just after 10 p.m. The Canadian team won an Olympic gold medal for the first time since 1952. Canadians everywhere went wild!

In Brisbane, Australia, Australians and visiting Canadians also watched the end of the game live. It was just after 1 p.m. The date was Monday, 25 February 2002, and they had just had their lunch.

▲ **Figure 18.2:** Fans in Victoria, BC, cheer after the men's Olympic hockey team wins gold on 24 February 2002.

4. a) What day was it in Canada when the gold-medal game finished? What time was it in Barrie, Ontario?
    b) What day and time was it in Brisbane, Australia?
    c) Why could people in the two places watch the same game live on television, but at different times and on different days?

Longitude and Time

The Earth rotates, or turns, one complete circle every twenty-four hours. A circle has 360 degrees. As you learned in the introductory chapter, Your Geographic Toolbox, there are also 360 degrees of longitude going around the Earth. If we divide 360 degrees by twenty-four hours, we get 15 degrees per hour. The Earth rotates 15 degrees of longitude in one hour. So if you have a friend living 15 degrees of longitude to the east, the time there will be one hour later than your time.

▲ **Figure 18.3:** Calling a friend long-distance? Better check your times.

5. Which of the friends shown in the cartoon above lives farther east? Explain how you know.

6. Why does the time differ by one hour for each 15 degrees of longitude?

Time Zones

As the Earth rotates, the sun is always directly over some point of longitude. At that point, it is noon. In the past, each community set its own time, based on the exact time when the sun was directly over the community. This posed few problems until about 150 years ago. Railways made it possible to travel very quickly from one community to the next. It became impossible to keep track of all the different times in all the different communities.

A Canadian engineer, Sir Sandford Fleming, solved the problem. He proposed a world system of twenty-four one-hour time zones. Every place within a single **time zone** sets its clocks to the same time. The countries of the world began using time zones in 1884.

Ideally, each time zone stretches 15 degrees from east to west, and all the way from the North Pole to the South Pole. In reality, most time zones do not match this shape. Many countries shifted the boundaries somewhat so that the time zone boundaries matched their political boundaries.

In addition, there are a few half-hour time zones. The island of Newfoundland uses one. Clocks there are set one half-hour ahead of the time zone just to the west. This choice was made because the island sits slightly farther east than the other provinces in the Atlantic region of Canada.

7. How many one-hour time zones are there in the world? Why?

8. a) If Canada stretches from about 60°W to about 135°W, how many degrees of longitude does it cover?
    b) Predict how many time zones Canada has. (*Hint:* Divide the degrees of longitude by 15. Then add an extra time zone for Newfoundland.)

GeoSkills

Calculating Time Differences

Purpose

Knowing how to calculate time differences between different places in the world allows us to co-ordinate our activities with people far away.

For this skill feature, let's suppose a hockey game is playing in Ottawa. It will be shown live on television across Canada. Moira, who lives in Hamilton, is planning to watch the 2 p.m. Sunday game. Her friend Pepe calls from Vancouver on Saturday. He says, "I'm going to be out tomorrow, but I'd like to tape the game. What time should I set the VCR to start taping?"

Step 1

Find out your time zone and the other time zone. Look at a time-zone map like the one in Figure 18.4, and find the time zones. What time zones do Moira and Pepe live in? You can see that Hamilton is in the Eastern time

zone, and Vancouver is in the Pacific time zone.

Step 2

Calculate the time zone difference. Count the number of time zone changes between the two places. From Hamilton to Vancouver, there are three time zone changes—from Eastern to Central, Central to Mountain, and Mountain to Pacific. Moira calculates a three-hour time difference between Hamilton and Vancouver. So now she knows that Pepe should set his VCR three hours differently from 2 p.m. But is that before or after 2 p.m.?

Step 3

Find out if the other time zone is ahead or behind yours. The sun rises in the east, so the day begins in eastern Canada before it does in the west. Moira knows that Vancouver is west of Hamilton, so its clocks are set behind (or earlier than) Hamilton time.

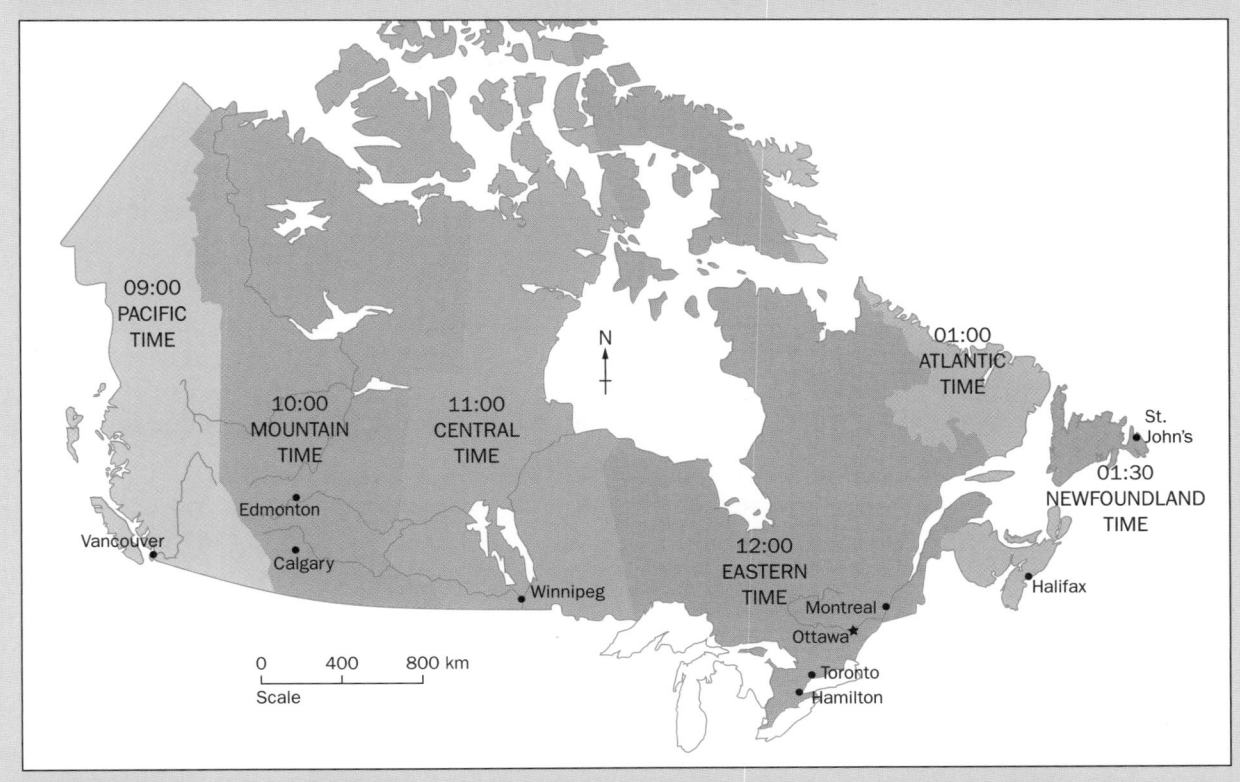

▲ **Figure 18.4:** Canadian time zones

Step 4

Calculate the time in the other time zone. Add or subtract the right number of hours. Moira knows that Vancouver is earlier by three hours, so she subtracts three hours from 2 p.m. That gives her 11 a.m. Moira tells Pepe, "Set the VCR for 11 a.m. Oh, and Pepe—next time, look it up in your TV guide!"

Practise It!

1. Make a copy of the table in Figure 18.5. Follow Steps 1–4 to complete it.

To calculate time differences...

✔ find out your time zone and the other time zone

✔ calculate the time zone difference

✔ find out if the other time zone is ahead or behind yours

✔ calculate the time in the other time zone

Game Time in Host City	Local TV Viewing Time
7:00 p.m. in Calgary	_____ in Montreal
3: 00 p.m. in Winnipeg	_____ in Halifax
1:00 p.m. in Halifax	_____ in Edmonton
2:30 p.m. in Vancouver	_____ in Ottawa
5:30 p.m. in Toronto	_____ in St. John's

▲ **Figure 18.5:** Game times

Different Times, Different Days

Can we explain, now, why two different groups of people can watch the same game at different times and on different days? We know that Brisbane, Australia, is fifteen time zones east of Barrie, Ontario. The time there must be fifteen hours ahead of the time in Barrie. If you add fifteen hours to 10 p.m., the time passes midnight into the next day.

So when viewers in Barrie were cheering madly when Canada's men's hockey team won the gold medal shortly after 10 p.m. on Sunday, 24 February, fans in Brisbane had already finished their lunch on Monday, 25 February. Same game. Different day!

9. Why did the gold-medal game end in Australia a day after it ended in Ontario?

10. Obtain an atlas with a physical and a political map of Canada.
    a) Compare these maps with the time zones map in Figure 18.4 on the previous page. Identify one good example where a time zone boundary does each of the following.
       i. follows a longitude line
       ii. follows a boundary between provinces or territories
       iii. follows bodies of water
       iv. follows a mountain chain
       v. avoids populated areas
    b) For each example in part (a), speculate on why these particular routes were chosen.

Comparing Economic Development

Geographers compare countries in many ways. For example, they compare economies. Geographers have identified four different types of economy:

- diversified economy
- oil-resource economy
- emerging industrial economy
- agricultural economy

Diversified Economies

Countries with **diversified economies** have a wide range of economic activity. Most people work in services such as banking, teaching, and health care. Advanced research occurs in medicine, computers, and telecommunications.

In a diversified economy, the **gross domestic product (GDP)** is always high. GDP is the total value of the goods and services produced in a country in one year. **GDP per capita**, or per person, is also high. Most but not all citizens can afford some consumer luxuries. Canada is a good example of a diversified economy.

Oil-Resource Economies

In countries with **oil-resource economies**, the economy is tied to the export of a single resource: oil. Kuwait, for example, has large deposits of oil. This is extracted from the ground and sold to other nations. The profits from sales are used to import everything people need, including food. The profits help these countries build infrastructure, including transportation networks, government buildings, and an education and health system.

	Countries with Diversified Economies Have...	Countries with Oil-Resource Economies Have...
Activity	• much tertiary activity	• much natural resource industry
Wealth	• high GDP per capita	• moderate GDP per capita
Urban/rural mix	• a highly urban population	• a rapidly urbanizing population
Birth rate	• low birth rates	• high birth rates
Life expectancy	• very long life expectancies	• long life expectancies

▲ Figure 18.6: Diversified versus oil-resource economies

11. Name three important differences between countries with diversified economies and those with oil-resource economies.

12. Speculate on what changes might happen to an oil-resource economy if all the oil ran out.

Emerging Industrial Economies

In countries with **emerging industrial economies**, the industrial sector is growing, and the agricultural sector is declining in importance. More and more people move from country to city in search of work, so these nations are becoming very urbanized. Mexico is a good example of an emerging industrial economy.

Agricultural Economies

Countries with **agricultural economies** do not have a valuable resource that they can export in bulk (such as oil). Nor do they have much industry. The people in these countries make a living as they have for thousands of years, by farming the land. Kenya is a good example of an agricultural economy.

	Countries with Emerging Industrial Economies Have...	Countries with Agricultural Economies Have...
Activity	• rapid industrial growth	• much agricultural activity
Wealth	• extremes of wealth and poverty	• low GDP per capita
Urban/rural mix	• a rapidly urbanizing population	• a largely rural population
Birth rate	• falling birth rates	• high birth rates
Life expectancy	• rising life expectancies	• short life expectancies

▲ Figure 18.7: Emerging industrial versus agricultural economies

13. Name three ways that life in countries with emerging industrial economies is improving compared with countries with agricultural economies.

14. Brainstorm a list of four good reasons that might explain short life expectancies in countries with agricultural economies.

Comparing Economies

Geographers use statistics to decide how to classify economies. They use maps to show their global distribution. Look at Figures 18.8 and 18.9 to compare world economies.

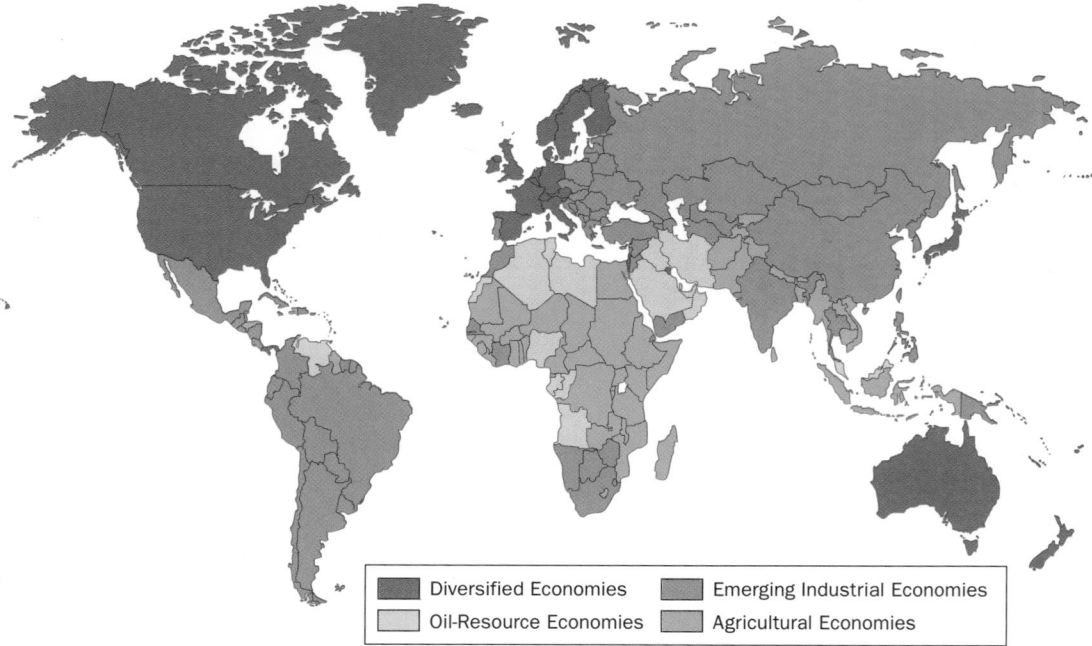

Figure 18.8: ▶ Economies of the world

Legend:
- Diversified Economies
- Oil-Resource Economies
- Emerging Industrial Economies
- Agricultural Economies

15. Using the map, list all the continents of the world. Then list the one or two economic types most common to each continent.

Criteria	Ghana	United States	Saudi Arabia	Brazil
GDP per capita*	$3016	$57 460	$16 667	$10 317
Economic activity in agriculture	36%	2%	6%	9%
Economic activity in industry	25%	18%	47%	29%
Economic activity in services	39%	80%	47%	62%
Unemployment	20%	4%	NA	7%
Industrial growth (annual rate)	4%	6%	1%	7%

*Converted from US$ at a rate of Cdn$1 = US $0.63   *Note:* Oil industries are classified as industrial. NA = not available
Source: Geography IQ Web site at <http://www.geographyiq.com/countries>, November 2002.

Figure 18.9: Examples of the four types of economy

16. a) Which country has the highest GDP per capita, and which has the lowest?
    b) Which country relies most on agriculture? Which relies most on industry? (Industry includes oil.)
    c) Compare the economic activity in the United States and Saudi Arabia.
    d) Which country has the strongest industrial growth?

17. Now decide which country is an example of each of the four types of economy. Support your choices with your answers from Question 16.

Comparing Human Development

At the end of the previous section, we saw how economic activity can affect the level of **human development**, or living standards, in a country. To compare living standards, geographers are interested in the quality of everyday life. Can people purchase adequate food, clothing, and shelter? Does everyone who wants a job have one? Can everyone go to school? Who can see a doctor? The answers to questions like these allow geographers to compare living standards among countries.

GeoTrivia #1
In Canada in 2002, we had 229 doctors for every 100 000 people. Saudi Arabia had 166, Brazil had 127, and Ghana had 6.

The United Nations' HDI

Each year, the United Nations studies the quality of life in all its member countries. It examines three factors that are easy to measure and that give a clear indication of human development.

- **Life expectancy at birth.** This is the average number of years that a person in a given country may expect to live.
- **Adult literacy rate.** This is the percentage of the population, fifteen years and older, who can read and write at a basic level.
- **Gross domestic product per capita.** This factor tells us if there is enough money available to provide the necessities of life.

These three factors make up the **Human Development Index (HDI)**, a system that combines them into a single score, which can then be used to rank countries. The HDI gives us a rough idea of which are the best countries to live in and which are the worst. Similarly, your year's averages in your courses at school allow you to compare how well you do in various subjects.

18. What are the three factors taken into account in the HDI? Give your opinion about why each of these factors was chosen.

The 2002 HDI Index

The 2002 HDI Index listed 173 countries, which it ranked in order from the highest to the lowest in human development. There are three categories.

- *High human development* offers an excellent quality of life (53 countries).

- *Medium human development* offers an adequate quality of life (84 countries).

- *Low human development* offers an inadequate quality of life (36 countries).

The table in Figure 18.10 summarizes the HDI data for three countries.

	Ranking, Country	Life Expectancy at Birth	Adult Literacy	GDP per Capita*
High human development	3. Canada	79 years	99%	$44 190
Medium human development	54. Mexico	73 years	91%	$14 322
Low human development	146. Haiti	53 years	50%	$2 329

* Converted from US$ at a rate of Cdn$1 = US$0.63
Source: United Nations Human Development Index, <http://hdr.undp.org/reports/global/2002/en/indicator/indicator.cfm?File=index.html>.

▲ **Figure 18.10:** United Nations Human Development Index, Canada, Mexico, Haiti, 2002

19. For each of the three factors used to determine HDI, how does Canada compare with a) Mexico and b) Haiti? What is the HDI ranking of each?

20. Use the three factors that determine HDI to identify three main characteristics of the three levels of human development.

21. Look at the three factors that determine HDI for the countries in Figure 18.10. Compare them with the information in Figure 18.11. Which type of human development (high, medium, or low) do you think each one represents? Explain your choices.

Country	Life Expectancy at Birth	Adult Literacy	GDP per Capita*
A	77 years	100%	$38 449
B	52 years	57%	$2 289
C	73 years	86%	$6 838

* Converted from US$ at a rate of Cdn$1 = US$0.63
Source: United Nations Human Development Index, <http://hdr.undp.org/reports/global/2002/en/indicator/indicator.cfm?File=index.html>.

▲ **Figure 18.11:** Miscellaneous statistics

There are poor people in all countries. Nonetheless, many charities, religious groups, and government agencies send assistance to countries with low human development, where the needs are greatest. The HDI helps these organizations identify which countries need their help the most.

◄ **Figure 18.12:** Dr. Shi leaves his village in southern China to attend a free training clinic offered by Doctors Without Borders.

22. a) What do you think are the major needs of countries with low, medium, and high human development?
    b) Which type of country has the greatest needs?

23. Think of one way that each of the following could help a country with low human development meet its needs.
    - the government of the country
    - the Canadian federal government
    - charitable organizations
    - you

Comparing Telecommunications

Sometimes you can learn a lot about a country by looking at just one factor. For example, looking at telecommunications capabilities would tell us a lot about the way people live and what business opportunities they have. Telecommunication is communication over long distances. It includes radio, television, telephone, and the Internet.

Countries with high human development tend to have more telecommunications infrastructure. This refers to human-made systems, such as television-broadcast towers, the cross-country network of telephone lines, and hardwire cabling that people use to hook up to the Internet. The bar graphs in Figure 18.13 provide factors that indicate telecommunications capabilities in three countries.

GeoTrivia #2
For every 1000 people in the USA, 249 had cell phones in 2002. In Cuba, the figure was 0.3 per 1000.

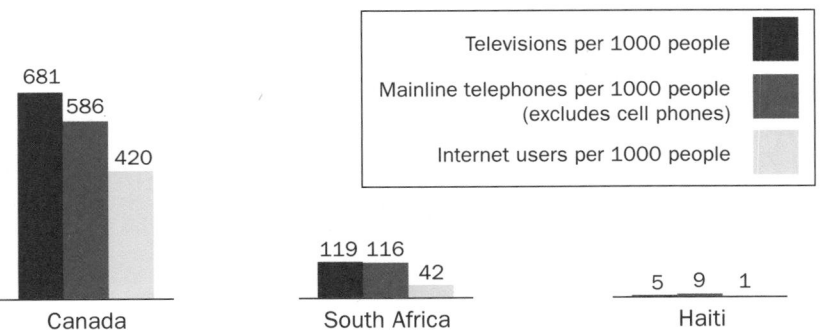

| | Televisions per 1000 people |
| Mainline telephones per 1000 people (excludes cell phones) |
| Internet users per 1000 people |

681 586 420
Canada

119 116 42
South Africa

5 9 1
Haiti

▲ **Figure 18.13:** Communications technology in three countries, 2002

24. Look at the bar graphs in Figure 18.13 on the previous page for Canada, South Africa, and Haiti.
    a) Write down three observations that show how the countries differ in telecommunications capability.
    b) Decide which country is at high, medium, and low human development. Justify your choices.
    c) Which country would be the best place to set up an Internet-based business? Why?

The data in Figure 18.13 tell us two things. First, they tell us about the quality of life of the people living in the three countries. People with telephones, televisions, and Internet access probably live a reasonably comfortable life—they are not struggling to put food on the table.

The data tell us something else, too. They tell us about business opportunity. Which of the countries will most likely have businesses that will succeed locally, nationally, and internationally? While small businesses may get along fine without a telephone, no larger company would have a chance. Obviously, a company setting up a call centre to market products all over the world would be unlikely to consider Haiti, a country with little or no telecommunications infrastructure. Without plenty of telephone lines and computer cabling, it would be unable to meet the company's needs.

Some countries have specialized in providing people and businesses with telecommunications technology. Canada is one such country.

Some Canadian Telecommunications Leaders

By the late 1990s, about 150 Canadian companies were selling communications technology internationally and developing communication networks all over the world. They sell products such as switching systems and fibre optics cabling, and services such as satellite communications and networking. Let's briefly examine two of these companies.

◀ **Figure 18.14:** In Kanata, Ontario, a Nortel employee makes fibre optic components for export.

The Canadian telecommunications giant, Nortel Networks, is headquartered in Brampton, Ontario. It provides network services to customers in more than 150 countries. It specializes in designing computer network systems for companies that have plants and employees spread out over vast distances. It also develops products that allow customers to send and receive e-mail on their portable cell phones. Although much smaller than it was at the height of the technology boom (in 2000), Nortel had about 20 000 employees worldwide in late 2002.

Research in Motion Limited (RIM) is headquartered in Waterloo, Ontario. It has offices in North America, Europe, and Asia. It is most famous for devices that allow customers to send and receive e-mail wherever they go. As well, RIM produces modems for connecting laptop computers to the Internet without a hardwire connection.

25. In what areas of telecommunication do a) Nortel Networks and b) Research in Motion Limited (RIM) specialize?

CASE STUDY

CANADA VERSUS INDIA

In this Case Study, we'll compare two countries, Canada and India, using some of the approaches you've already tried in this chapter.

1. Both Canada and India have major film industries, one of the many similarities between the two countries. In your notebook, mark each of the following as True or False.
   - Both countries were once colonies of Britain.
   - Both have a parliamentary government.
   - Both countries have major computer software industries.
   - Both have constitutions guaranteeing freedom of religion and freedom of speech.
   - English is a recognized language of government in both countries.
   - Both countries have many cricket fans.

Time Zones
If you live in Canada, and you want to telephone a family member in India, you would have to keep in mind that India's time is ahead of Canada's time. It is anywhere from nine hours ahead of St. John's, Newfoundland, to 13.5 hours ahead of Prince Rupert, British Columbia. India is 10.5 hours ahead of all but the westernmost portion of Ontario.

2. When would be the best time to telephone India from Ontario: 6 p.m. or 8 a.m.? (*Hint:* To get the time in India, add 10.5 h.) Explain your choice.

Economic Development
Canada is an example of a diversified economy. India has an emerging industrial economy.

Criteria	Canada	India
GDP per capita*	$39 365	$3492
Economic activity in agriculture	3%	25%
Economic activity in industry	31%	24%
Economic activity in services	66%	51%
Industrial growth	5%	8%

* Converted from US$ at a rate of Cdn$ = US$0.63

▲ Figure 18.15: Comparing the economies of Canada and India

3. Explain what evidence the table in Figure 18.15 provides that Canada has a diversified economy and India has an emerging industrial economy. You may wish to refer to the explanations of these economies on pages 305–306.

▲ **Figure 18.16:** The film industry in India is based in Bombay. Its nickname is "Bollywood."

Human Development

India is classified as a country with a low level of human development. Its people have a moderate life expectancy at birth (63 years). Some 57 per cent of the population are literate. GDP per capita is low ($3743). In 2002, India's HDI ranking was number 124 out of a total of 173 countries.

4. Make an organizer to help you compare the HDI information for Canada and India. (Find the HDI data for Canada in Figure 18.10 on page 308.) Make one overall conclusion from this information.

Telecommunications

Telecommunications tend to be plentiful and efficient in Canada. A large number of telecommunications companies produce a wide range of hardware and software. These products allow Canadian individuals and businesses to communicate effectively.

Telecommunications equipment is less common in India. For every 1000 people, there were 61 televisions, 27 mainline telephones, and four Internet users. As we've seen, a number of software companies in India have a worldwide reputation. But the country itself, with more than a billion people, does not have the infrastructure in place to "connect" the general population.

5. Make an organizer in which you summarize the telecommunications data about India with the similar data for Canada. (See Figure 18.13 on page 309.) Make one overall conclusion from this information.

This comparison shows that life can be easier in Canada than in India. Average incomes are higher, and life expectancies are longer. But Canada has its problems, too. Crime rates tend to be high, and pollution is a major problem. It is important to look at many aspects of daily life before comparing countries.

Conclusion

There are different ways in which we can compare countries. We can focus on economic development. We see that some countries are rich in resources, while others are not. We can compare the quality of life of the average person in various countries. In this way, we see which countries offer their citizens most. In many countries, the average citizen's quality of life is low.

Although many people still live in desperate poverty in Canada, the average citizen lives well. Comparing countries can help us appreciate what we have. It also shows us problems—both in Canada and around the world—that we should have the courage to try to change.

Wrap It Up

1. Make a five-column organizer to compare the four different types of economy. Here are your headings for the left column:
   - Main Characteristics of Economy
   - Example Country
   - GDP per Capita of Example Country

2. List the three levels of human development used by the HDI. Give one example of a country at each level of development. Describe what life is like for the people living in each of these countries.

3. Find a map of the world that shows all the time zones.
   a) Make an organizer that shows the time and date in the following places, when your school is just beginning, at about 8:45 a.m.
   - Honolulu, Hawaii
   - Vancouver, BC
   - Halifax, NS
   - London, England
   - Johannesburg, South Africa
   - Bombay, India
   - Perth, Australia
   - Tokyo, Japan
   - Auckland, New Zealand

   b) What time and date will it be in each place when your school normally finishes, at about 3:00 p.m.?

4. a) Select a country other than those profiled in this chapter. Visit the GeographyIQ Web site (you can get there by searching using the keyword "GeographyIQ"). Select your chosen country by clicking on its first letter and then on the country's name. Click on "Geography," "People," and "Economy" to find statistics. Record statistics for everything listed in Figure 18.9 on page 307. Also, find statistics on population, area, urban population, population below the poverty line, and life expectancy at birth (total population).
   b) Make an organizer with the completed information.
   c) What type of economy do you think your country has? What general statements can you make about your country?
   d) Present your results to the class.
   e) With your class, create four lists of the countries with the four types of economy.

Chapter 19

OUR GLOBAL CONNECTIONS

Adventure in Santo Domingo

Frederic Tardif, a young Canadian, was looking for adventure. He turned to NetCorps Canada International, a Canadian internship program that finds international volunteer placements for 19- to 30-year-olds with skills in information and communication technologies. Read what Frederic had to say about his experiences in the Dominican Republic.

Well, it has already been exactly two months since my arrival in Santo Domingo, Dominican Republic. Although I knew coming in that I would encounter many different things, nothing could have prepared me for what I am experiencing now!

Every day is a new adventure. Back home in Canada, most people I know get caught up in their routines, which is normal. In fact, I was "Mr. Routine" himself! But since my arrival I have had to remove that word and way of life from my habits. So many new things happen to me on a daily basis: some are very subtle and some less so, but either way, I am being bombarded with sensations and feelings like never before.

Has this changed me? Absolutely. I am much more aware of my surroundings and I welcome the differences. It is not always easy, believe me: at least it has not been easy for me. The cultural adaptation classes I took before leaving have really helped me a lot. The noise and pollution in this city is atrocious. At first I didn't think I would be able to handle it for more than two weeks. But I have, and although I still do not like it, I can now manage my feelings toward it. Apart from the city itself, my work is a major challenge. In countries like this, people work and live very differently. ...

My Spanish is improving by leaps and bounds every day. I am already starting to think of my departure because I can't wait to see where this will bring me in terms of my career and destinations. Whatever happens to me, I am now 300 per cent more confident that I could handle living in just about any country, in terms of their people, food, and cultures.

– Frederic Tardif

1. What new experiences does Frederic describe in the Dominican Republic?

2. Why would it be crucial for Frederic to respect cultural differences?

3. What benefits for himself does he see coming from this experience?

4. What skills would you need to join a program like this?

Words to Know

trade surplus
trade deficit
trade balance
tariff
peacekeeping
genocide
refugee

In this chapter, you will

- play a game to discover your own world connections
- learn about Canada's personal, historical, economic, political, and environmental links to the world
- assess a variety of Canada's contributions to the world
- learn how many world problems can be solved through global action

Personal Ties

Have you ever thought of volunteering to work overseas? This is just one way that Canada has connections to the greater world. Here are a few of our ties to the world that you have learned about already:

- physical connections (e.g., the Pacific Ring of Fire; see Chapter 1)
- environmental problems (e.g., acid rain; see Chapter 15)
- economic relations (e.g., exporting lumber; see Chapter 9)
- historical ties (e.g., countries of our ancestors; see Chapter 7)
- cultural ties (e.g., multiculturalism; see Chapter 6)

Today we live in a global world. We can watch live coverage of a sports event taking place in China. We eat international dishes, such as burritos. Our stores are full of goods made in other countries. Our nation includes millions of people who left other countries to make Canada their home.

Not only does the world come to Canada; Canada also goes to the world. Canadians have excelled internationally as musicians, actors, authors, scientists, and political and business leaders.

5. a) In a small group, brainstorm ten examples of the world connecting to Canada, and ten examples of Canada connecting to the world.
    b) For each example, write down one way that this connection affects you.

◀ **Figure 19.1:** Canadian comedian Mike Myers in his wildly popular role as international spy Austin Powers

GeoGames
Personal Ties Bingo

Purpose:

To learn about the many different ties we have with other counties in the world

Supplies:

- a copy of the Personal Ties Bingo card (Figure 19.2)
- a pen or pencil

Method:

A. Your task is to find other students in the class who match the descriptions. You can use each student in only one box.

B. Go around the room and ask your classmates the questions on the bingo sheet. When you find a match, write that person's name in the square, as well as the answer to the accompanying question.

C. The first person to have names in three squares in any direction (up/down, side to side, or diagonally) calls out "Bingo." All students return to their seats.

D. The teacher checks with the people named in the three squares that the information is correct. If the sheet is not correct, repeat steps B, C, and D until you have a winner.

E. Repeat steps B, C, D, and E, but this time the goal is to fill up the complete bingo sheet.

Wrap-Up:

1. a) Which matches were easy to find?
   b) Which matches were hard to find?
   c) What does this tell you about the international ties in your class?

2. What have you learned about international ties from this game?

A student who was born outside Canada: _____ In which country? _____	A student who speaks a language other than English or French: _____ What language is it? _____	A student who has an Internet pen pal in another country: _____ In which country? _____
A student who has travelled in a car made outside North America: _____ In which country was the car made?	A student whose favourite musical performer comes from another country: _____ From which country?	A student who has seen a movie that was set outside North America: _____ Where was the movie set? _____
A student who travelled outside North America in the last year: _____ To which country? _____	A student who has relatives living outside Canada: _____ Where do they live? _____	A student who is wearing a piece of clothing made outside North America: _____ Where was it made? _____

▲ **Figure 19.2:** Personal Ties Bingo sheet

Historical Ties

Historical ties are those connections that link us with other nations and peoples with whom we share a common past.

The Commonwealth

Canada has been a member of the Commonwealth since its formation in 1931. This is an association of fifty-four nations that share a common history. Except for the United Kingdom and Mozambique, all members are former British colonies. Just as you have ties with your brothers and sisters (if you have any) because you share a common history, so do these nations have ties because they were ruled by the same empire. British forms of government, for example, flourish today in many Commonwealth nations. The English language is spoken around the world. Cricket fans, embroiderers, tea drinkers, and soccer players all have connections to the British Empire, which spread these sports and practices the world over. Queen Victoria (1837–1901) has a city in British Columbia, a state in Australia, and Africa's largest lake named after her.

Commonwealth countries are located all over the world because at one time the British Empire covered one-quarter of the world.

Figure 19.3: Wrestler Daniel Igali was the Canadian flag bearer at the 2002 Commonwealth Games. ▼

▲ **Figure 19.4:** Commonwealth nations

6. Where are the Commonwealth nations? Give reasons to explain the pattern.

7. How many countries belong to the Commonwealth? What do they have in common?

Economic Ties

Canada's economic ties involve individuals and companies doing business with the world.

Canada is a major trading nation. Although the country has a small population, we have the fifteenth-largest GDP in the world. (GDP is the value of all goods and services produced in a country in one year.) But no country in the world exports more of the goods and services it produces than Canada does. In 2001, Canada exported nearly 40 per cent of its GDP. As an international trader, Canada is a major player.

Exports and Imports

In 2001, Canada exported more than $415 billion in goods and services. We imported about $350 billion worth. The table in Figure 19.5 shows where these exports went, and where the imports came from.

Destination/Source	Export Value ($millions)	Import Value ($millions)
United States	350 908	255 028
Japan	9 482	10 585
United Kingdom	6 574	11 863
Other European Union countries	15 727	23 255
Other industrialized countries	10 925	18 626
Other non-industrialized countries	21 023	31 295
Total	414 638	350 623

Source: Statistics Canada, CANSIM II, tables 228-0001, 228-0002, and 228-0003.

Figure 19.5: Destinations, sources, and values of Canada's exports and imports, 2001

8. a) Which country received the largest amount of Canadian exports in 2001?
   b) What percentage of all Canadian exports went there? (Take the value of exports that went to that country, divide it by total exports, and multiply by 100.)

9. a) Which country supplied the largest amount of Canadian imports in 2001?
   b) What percentage of all Canadian imports came from there? (Take the value of imports from that country, divide it by total imports, and multiply by 100.)

A **trade surplus** occurs when Canada exports more goods to a country than it imports from it. A **trade deficit** occurs when Canada imports more from a country than it exports to it. We can calculate Canada's **trade balance** by adding up all the trade surpluses and subtracting all the trade deficits. It is the difference between our total imports and exports to all countries. The bottom bar in Figure 19.6 on the next page shows Canada's trade balance.

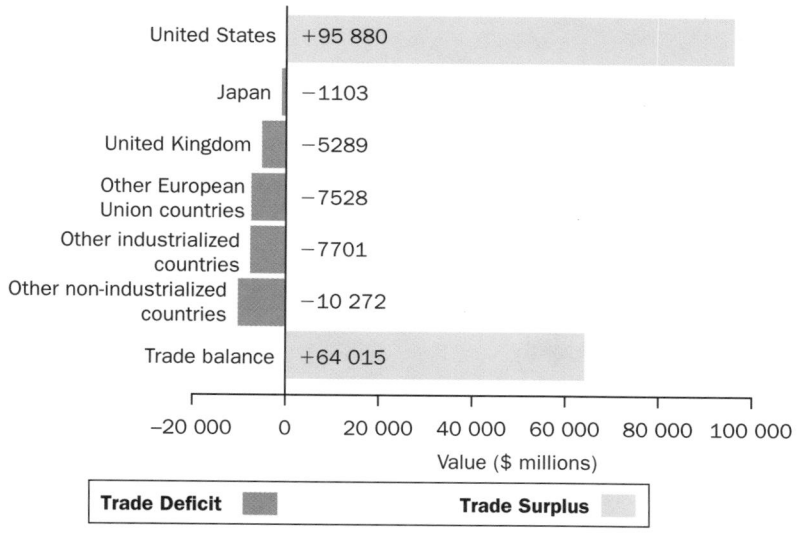

▲ **Figure 19.6:** Canada's trade balance

You will notice that Canada has a large surplus in its trade balance. It was over $64 billion for the whole of 2001. This comes to more than $7 million each hour! Our total trade balance is truly healthy.

10. a) With which countries or areas does Canada have a trade surplus?

    b) With which countries or areas does it have a trade deficit?

11. What conclusion can you make about the value of the United States as a trading partner for Canada?

The NAFTA

Why does Canada do so much trade with the United States? A major reason is location. We are closer to the northern United States than any other nation. Another reason is an agreement we made with our southern neighbour to make trade easier between our two nations. The North American Free Trade Agreement (NAFTA) came into effect in January 1994. Its members (Canada, the United States, and Mexico) agreed that goods made in one of these countries may be sold without **tariffs** (import taxes) in the other member countries.

One of the most visible effects of NAFTA has been the increase in truck traffic along Ontario's Highway 401. Between 1990 and 2001, cross-border truck traffic on Highway 401 tripled. Heavily loaded long-distance trucks speed along, crossing borders with relative ease. More trade flows across the border between Sarnia, Ontario, and Port Huron, Michigan, than at any other international crossing point in the world.

GeoTrivia #1
Two-way trade between Canada and Mexico doubled between 1994 and 2000, largely as a result of the NAFTA.

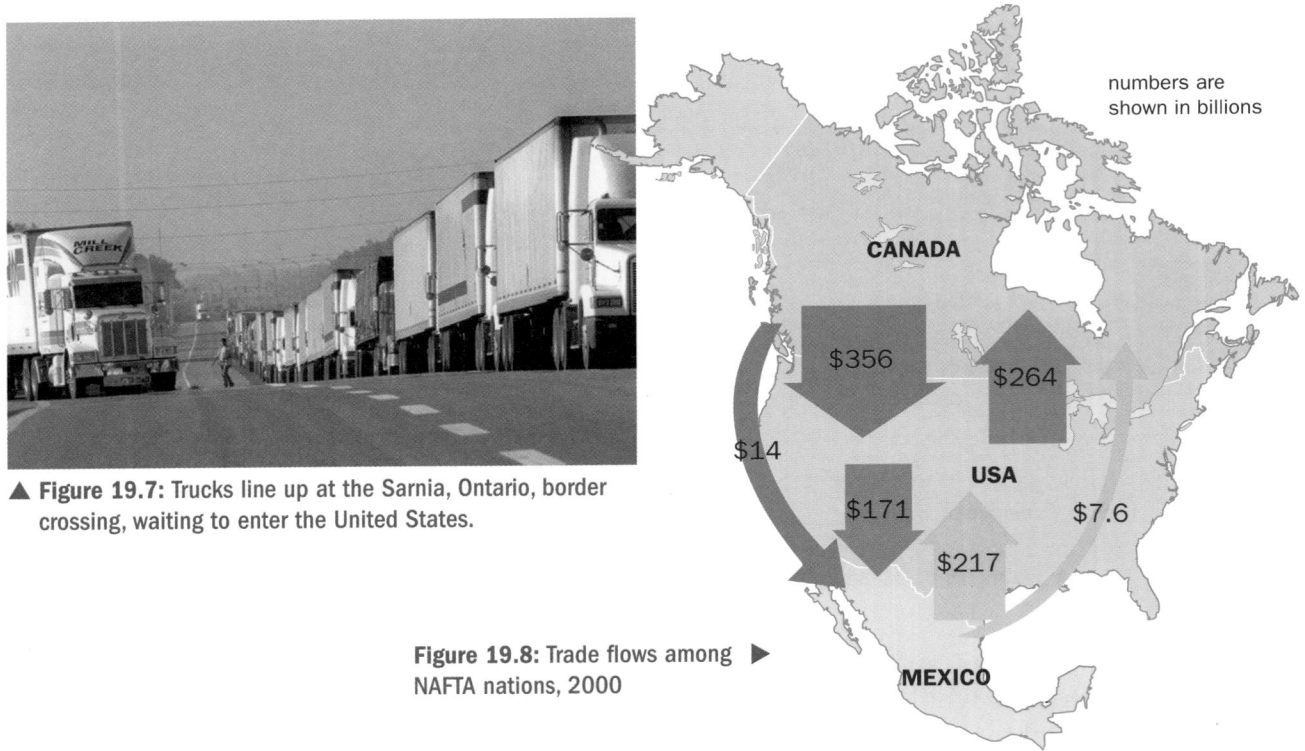

▲ **Figure 19.7:** Trucks line up at the Sarnia, Ontario, border crossing, waiting to enter the United States.

numbers are shown in billions

Figure 19.8: Trade flows among ▶ NAFTA nations, 2000

12. Which is the most valuable trade flow illustrated in the map? Which is the least valuable?

Political Ties

Canada has a relatively small population, yet it is a major player on the international political scene. The country played a prominent role in the First and Second World Wars and other military conflicts. It takes part in most major **peacekeeping** efforts, in which Canadian troops maintain a truce between hostile armies. On the diplomatic front, Canada fights hard to defend the human rights of all people.

The United Nations

Canada participates heavily in the United Nations (UN). This political organization was formed after the Second World War to help prevent future wars. It's an organization in which countries can work out their differences. More countries belong to the United Nations than to any other international organization. The 191 members (2002) include both large and small nations.

Canada was one of the original members of the UN. In 2002, it was the seventh-largest contributor to the UN, giving it more than $40 million for operations. In January 1998, a Canadian, Louise Frechette, was appointed the first-ever UN Deputy Secretary-General.

Today the UN has many goals. It tries to promote international understanding. It helps poor nations increase their wealth. Above all, it tries to reduce international conflict and increase international security.

GeoTrivia #2

Canadian Lester Pearson came up with the term "peacekeeping" in 1956, when he proposed the idea of a UN international peace force.

◀ **Figure 19.9:** Canadian soldiers on parade after a UN peacekeeping mission in Haiti.

13. One of Canada's most important UN roles has been international peacekeeping. It took part in forty-five peacekeeping missions between 1948 and 2002. Do you consider this an important contribution to the world? Explain your opinion.

14. What are some of the goals of the United Nations?

15. Find three pieces of evidence on the previous page that suggest that Canada plays an important role in the UN.

Preserving human rights is a major part of the UN's work. The UN focuses on countries that suffer from war and famine. These efforts include providing emergency aid, making efforts to resolve crises, providing peacekeeping efforts to prevent war, and writing agreements to guarantee basic rights.

By taking part in these efforts, Canada supports human rights around the world. For example, we have participated in creating the Universal Declaration of Human Rights. By encouraging other member nations to sign the declaration—and abide by it—Canada helped improve the conditions of people around the world. Figure 19.10 lists three of the major UN agreements.

UN Agreement	Purpose
Universal Declaration of Human Rights	To establish basic human rights
Convention on the Rights of the Child	To establish the basic rights of children
Convention against Genocide	To ban **genocide** (the destruction of a national ethnic, racial, or religious group)

▲ **Figure 19.10: Three major UN agreements**

16. a) What is the general purpose of UN agreements?
    b) Which agreement would be most important? Justify your choice.

17. Details about the agreements mentioned in Figure 19.10 can be found at the Web site called the Human Rights Web. Choose one of the agreements listed in Figure 19.10, or the Convention against Torture, or the Convention on the Elimination of Discrimination against Women. Research it and write a one-paragraph summary of the agreement, stating its main principles and purpose.

GEO CAREERS

REFUGEE COUNSELLOR

Name: Katie Lynch
High School: Madawaska Valley H.S., Barry's Bay, Ontario
Job Title: Refugee Counsellor

Katie Lynch took a high school course called "Geography: World Issues." The ideas in this course stayed with her. One thing she learned about was the difficult situation of **refugees**—people fleeing their homelands to escape dangerous situations. With this in mind, she applied for a one-year volunteer position as a counsellor at Romero House, a centre for refugees in Toronto.

Romero House provides accommodation and assistance for refugees who have sought safety in Canada. Part of Katie's job is to help new refugees adjust to life in this country. In the photograph above, you can see Katie with Flor Aristizibal and her daughter Laura. Flor came from Colombia as a refugee in 1999.

Katie helps new arrivals apply for refugee status, Social Insurance Numbers, and English as a Second Language (ESL) classes. She helps children get registered at school. With the assistance of some of the supporters and neighbours of Romero House, she helps refugees find work. When residents are ready to leave Romero House (usually after about six months), Katie helps them find housing. Katie does not speak a second language herself, but works closely with interpreters when necessary.

"Many of our residents come from tropical countries. I need to know something about the climate and environment there, so that I can anticipate some of the difficulties they will have adjusting to Canada's winters. Others come from hot, dry climates. They need help in buying clothes for our humid summers."

If you would like to have a career in refugee counselling, you can get started by attending a community college to earn a certificate in Social Service Work.

What I like about my work: *"I love building a relationship with our residents and learning about different cultures. I like building a community with shared goals. I've learned how people are different. But I've also learned how all humans have the same basic needs for safety, security, spirituality, family, and friends. All humans have a need … to survive and prosper."*

1. What would you like and dislike about the job described above?
2. What skills do you think you would need for this job?
3. What things could you do to develop these skills in yourself?

Environmental Ties

Through our human relations, Canada has many ties to the world. All these positive connections are nothing, however, if the Earth is ruined. In this section, we will look at two international environmental problems. We will see how all the ties we have to the world must be enlisted to help us solve these pressing problems. No nation can solve these problems alone.

Global Warming

Scientists around the world are alarmed about increasing world temperatures. Examples of "weird" weather are becoming more common all over the world.

▲ **Figure 19.11:** Unusually warm weather melts the sea ice that seals need to give birth and nurse their young.

As we learned in Chapter 14: Our Impact on Climate, global warming is caused by burning carbon-based products such as oil, coal, and gas. As these products burn, they give off greenhouse gases, which stay in the atmosphere and prevent heat from escaping into space (see Figure 14.7 on page 242).

Industrialized nations have produced most of the greenhouse gases now in the atmosphere. Global warming is an international problem, however, because it doesn't matter who produced the greenhouse gases. All people in the world are affected by the results. For example, island countries in the South Pacific and Indian Ocean may eventually be completely covered with ocean water.

18. Make a cause-and-effect organizer showing the connections between a) you running a lawn mower and b) the forced relocation of a family living on islands in the South Pacific.

How do you solve an international problem? Working together is essential. In 1997 many nations met in Kyoto, Japan, to discuss the problem of increasing greenhouse gases. One hundred sixty nations came to an agreement known as the Kyoto Protocol on Climate Change. In December 2002, the Canadian government became the ninety-ninth to commit to the agreement.

All countries that signed the Kyoto agreement have promised to reduce their greenhouse gas emissions to 6 per cent below 1990 levels by 2012. Because of economic growth since 1990, this figure means that Canadian emissions will have to fall by about 25 per cent from their 2002 levels. Businesses as well as consumers will have to do their part to reduce emissions.

Figure 19.12 shows a few of the actions that businesses and governments in Canada and other countries can take to meet their Kyoto targets.

Strategies for reducing greenhouse gases
- improve the efficiency of automobiles
- make vehicles lighter
- improve public transit systems so people use their cars less
- give tax rebates for energy-efficient appliances, such as gas furnaces
- improve the insulation of all buildings
- phase out coal-fired electricity plants in favour of gas-fired ones
- improve filtering systems on industrial chimneys
- encourage the use of cleaner fuels
- finance alternative energy research
- give consumers the option of purchasing more expensive "green" electricity

▲ **Figure 19.12:** What other strategies can you think of?

19. What target does the Kyoto Protocol on Climate Change set for Canada?

20. Each of the strategies in Figure 19.12 suggests an action that government or business can take. For each item, suggest one action that individual consumers can take to make the strategy work. You can suggest anything from writing a letter to a politician, to making wise purchases.

The United States is the largest producer of greenhouse gases in the world. In 2002, however, it refused to enforce its Kyoto targets. The general feeling was that it would harm the American economy too much.

In Canada, the federal and provincial governments agree that we must reduce greenhouse gas emissions. But the provincial governments of Ontario and Alberta—the biggest greenhouse gas producers—disagree with the federal government on several matters. They disagree about how the targets should be met and how fast. They worry that their businesses will be harmed because they will have to compete with businesses in the United States that are not bound by the Kyoto Protocol.

21. Create a pro-and-con organizer to evaluate Canada's participation in the Kyoto Protocol.

22. Write a one-page reasoned argument to support or oppose Canada's participation in the Kyoto Protocol.

23. Think of one way that each of the following ties could help the world solve the problem of global warming: personal ties, historical ties, economic ties, and political ties.

Global Biodiversity

The variety of plants, fungi, birds, animals, insects, and fish in our world make it a wonderful place. This variety in species is called biodiversity (or biological diversity). Having a wide variety of creatures on Earth keeps the environment healthy and supports a variety of ecozones.

Scientists have become concerned that the number of species on Earth is declining. As humans use up more of the land, even in remote areas, less land is available for other species.

Why are scientists worried about losing species? The loss of any species shrinks our world. In addition, plants are the source of most of our medicines. Many universities are trying to save the seeds of endangered plants. Others are trying to clone tissues from threatened species. But wouldn't it be easier, and far less costly, to save the habitat of these species now?

> **GeoTrivia #3**
> Members of Canada's Seed Heritage Program have saved 675 varieties of tomatoes and 45 varieties of potatoes.

24. a) In your own words, explain the meaning of biodiversity.
    b) Why is the loss of plant or animal species an important topic for Canadians? Give an example.

The problem of lost biodiversity is larger than losing one plant or animal. We are threatening whole ecozones. Let's look at the Great Lakes as an example. Think of this system of lakes as a giant aquarium. You know that an aquarium is a carefully balanced system of plants, animals, water, air, and food. The living things are interdependent on one another. Introduce one piranha, and soon enough you won't have any other fish species.

A similar imbalance has occurred in the Great Lakes. This water system is under great stress from overfishing, pollution, and the introduction of foreign species. The lamprey eel (not a true eel) was introduced into the Great Lakes in the 1970s. It severely damaged stocks of lake trout. In recent years, two more foreign species, zebra mussels and gobies, have ruined much Great Lakes fish habitat. Only three of the original 13 species of lake trout in Lake Superior remain.

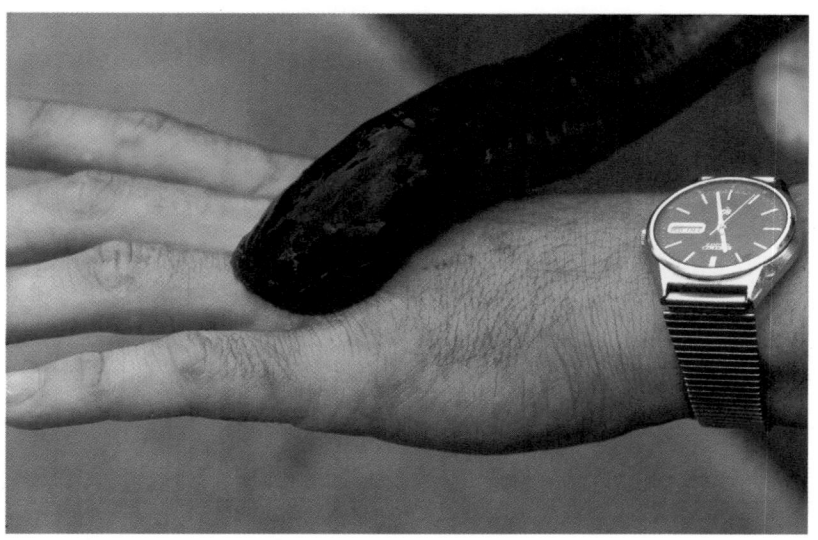

◀ **Figure 19.13:** Lamprey eels attach to fish and feed on the fishes' blood and flesh as they are carried along.

25. a) Make a chart or a drawing to show how an aquarium is a balanced system.
    b) List three species that threaten the Great Lakes system.

Protecting Biodiversity

If natural systems are to remain in balance, we must think about the future. Canada has a mixed record of success and failure in protecting biodiversity. In 1992, the Convention on Biological Diversity was drawn up. Canada was the first of 150 countries to sign this important part of international law. It aims to

- recognize the importance of biodiversity
- use Earth's resources in a way that will protect the variety of living things

Unfortunately, Canada has been slow to pass laws to support these two ideas. The federal government did finally pass its Threatened and Endangered Species Act in 2002. However, critics believe that this law is not as strong as it should be.

▲ **Figure 19.14:** To save our biodiversity, we must change the way we see the relationship between our human systems and natural systems.

Many scientists believe that to promote biodiversity, we must step back and see the big picture. If building a new community threatens a natural system, they say, we must stop the construction. Until we have made a shift in the way in which we see the relationship between human systems and natural systems, biodiversity will always be under threat.

26. What has Canada done to preserve biodiversity? What shift do we have to make in our thinking before we can preserve the Earth's biodiversity?

27. What do groups such as Greenpeace and the World Wildlife Fund do to protect species? Research these organizations and evaluate their strategies.

Conclusion

You and other Canadians are increasingly connected with the rest of the world. As communications technology improves, it becomes impossible for any country to live in isolation. As we have seen in this chapter, Canadians are linked with the rest of the world in numerous ways. Our personal ties give us connections to individual friends and family. Our historical ties keep us close to countries with which we share a common past. Our economic ties bind us to the countries with which we buy and sell goods and services. Our political ties give us a way to participate in the world to make it a better place for all. And the solutions to the most pressing environmental problems we face will be found only if we all work together.

Wrap It Up

1. What are the five kinds of ties that Canada has with the world? For each, give an example.

2. Make a list of five different contributions that Canada has made to the world. Identify what you consider to be the most important contribution and your reason for choosing it.

3. Think about the international agreements you have read about in this chapter. Decide which one allows Canada to play the most useful international role. In a paragraph, explain what this role is and why you chose it.

4. Research the international organization La Francophonie, whose members are nations and states with French-speaking peoples. Begin by searching "international Francophonie" on the Internet. Find the answers to the following questions.
   a) How many members are there in La Francophonie?
   b) When was the organization founded?
   c) How is the membership different from membership in the Commonwealth?
   d) How does La Francophonie assist its less developed member nations?

5. Research and summarize Canada's world contributions in one of the following areas. A federal government Web site would be a good place to start.

- peace and security
- global assistance
- environment/sustainable development
- foreign policy/international relations
- world economy
- research, science, and technology

6. Make a visual display, such as a poster or a collage, to promote a strategy in support of either a) climate change control or b) protection of international biodiversity. (Examples of strategies: leaving the car at home, fully insulating your home, preventing urban sprawl, and protecting endangered species). Be sure to include an interesting slogan. On the back, explain the ideas that you are trying to communicate in your display. Show your work to three other class members. Discuss with them what you think has been done well—and any improvements that could be made—to the four displays.

7. Think about the ideas in this chapter, particularly those about Canada's many connections to the world. Think about the connections that Frederic Tardif and Katie Lynch have made for themselves. (See the chapter opener on page 314 and the GeoCareers feature on page 322.) What kind of connection could you make with the world? Write a story set five years from today. The story features you. It shows you operating on a different level—as a citizen of the world.

Unit 5 Performance Task

A GEOGRAPHY OF YOUR COMMUNITY

In this Performance Task, you and your classmates will apply what you learned in this course. You will create a report about one aspect of your community's geography. You and your classmates will then put these reports together to produce a geographic profile of your community. You may even

work with your teacher to create a Web site for your report. Students in other schools are posting similar information by making Web sites at the Canadian Communities Atlas Project. This site lets you compare your community to others across Canada.

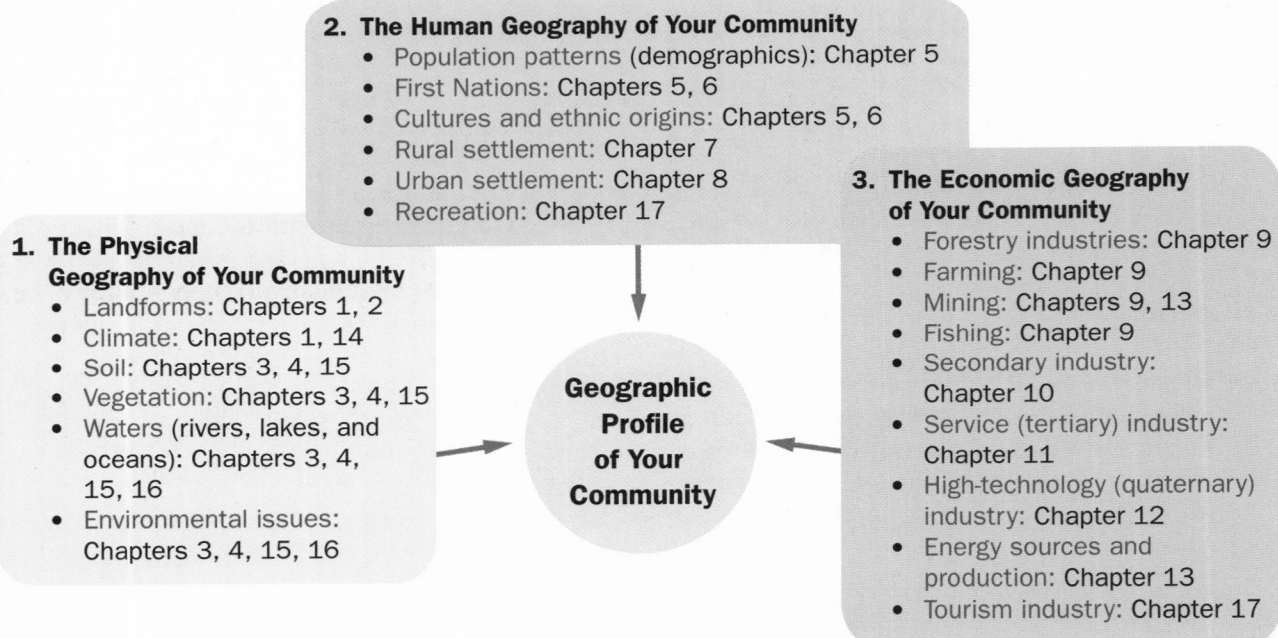

2. The Human Geography of Your Community
- Population patterns (demographics): Chapter 5
- First Nations: Chapters 5, 6
- Cultures and ethnic origins: Chapters 5, 6
- Rural settlement: Chapter 7
- Urban settlement: Chapter 8
- Recreation: Chapter 17

3. The Economic Geography of Your Community
- Forestry industries: Chapter 9
- Farming: Chapter 9
- Mining: Chapters 9, 13
- Fishing: Chapter 9
- Secondary industry: Chapter 10
- Service (tertiary) industry: Chapter 11
- High-technology (quaternary) industry: Chapter 12
- Energy sources and production: Chapter 13
- Tourism industry: Chapter 17

1. The Physical Geography of Your Community
- Landforms: Chapters 1, 2
- Climate: Chapters 1, 14
- Soil: Chapters 3, 4, 15
- Vegetation: Chapters 3, 4, 15
- Waters (rivers, lakes, and oceans): Chapters 3, 4, 15, 16
- Environmental issues: Chapters 3, 4, 15, 16

Geographic Profile of Your Community

▲ **Figure 1:** Topics for a geographic study

Assignment **1**: Choosing Your Topic

Look at the list of topics in Figure 1. Which ones interest you? Your teacher will help you get started by giving you the following information:
- whether you will be doing this activity by yourself or as part of a small group
- the size and limits of the area you will be researching as part of your community. It may be the large city you are in or near, your rural county, or even a region in your province.

- the topics in Figure 1 that are not part of the geography of your community, and which you cannot choose

1. Pick one of the topics from Figure 1, and have your teacher approve it.

2. Go to the chapters of the textbook listed for your topic in Figure 1. Use these pages to complete the following, and give it to your teacher.

a) Make a list of five important geographic terms that are a part of your topic. Define each of them. This will help you use these terms correctly in your report.

b) Make a list of three important geographic ideas that you would like to find out more about for your community. These ideas must relate to your topic. For example, if your topic is farming, you might research which crops are grown in your region.

c) Write down one important question that you would like to find out about your community. It must be based on the topic you are investigating. For example, how important is farming in your region?

Assignment 2: Researching Your Topic

Gathering Information

It is always best to begin your research with general sources. These are books such as atlases, encyclopedias, almanacs, and other texts. General sources will introduce you to some of the main geographic characteristics of your community.

Next, move to more detailed sources. To find articles on local tourism, for example, watch for geographic information in the local newspapers. To find out which types of businesses are found in the community, consult the advertising pages of the telephone book. You may want to review the GeoSkills feature, "Evaluating Internet Sites" (pages 210–211), before starting a keyword search for your topic.

As you research, think about how your topic affects your community and the natural environment. For example, if you're researching mining, you might want to find information about how many people are employed in mining in your community. You could also find out about any pollution problems that have resulted from the mines.

As you gather information, keep a list of each source, including the author, title, publisher, date, and page for each book you use. Look for this information near the front. Carefully record good Web site addresses or bookmark them.

1. When you find a good source, make notes about the information that relates to your topic. Gather data and visuals. Find supporting evidence for the key features of your community. Use note paper or cue cards, as in Figure 2.

2. When you have made good progress on your research, supply your teacher with the information you have found. Include an organized list of print and electronic sources you have used.

Key Feature	Supporting Evidence
Vancouver's population is growing	• 1996 population = 1 967 600 • 2001 population = 2 078 800
Just over 22 per cent of BC's Aboriginal population lives in Vancouver.	• Vancouver: Aboriginal population (2001) = 31 140 • BC: Aboriginal population (2001) = 139 655 • 31 140 ÷ 136 655 × 100 = 23%

▲ **Figure 2:** Cue cards make great note-taking tools

Researching Visuals

Geographers are especially interested in visual information. So, as you research, watch for maps, graphs, photographs, and diagrams related to your topic. Also watch out for information you might turn into visuals. For example, a table of figures might work very effectively as a circle graph or bar graph.

Talk to your school's teacher-librarian or your teacher to get hints on where to locate this important information.

3. Find or prepare at least one of each of the following three types of visuals for your topic. Add any necessary labels or captions to explain each visual, and hand them in to your teacher.

- Prepare a detailed map related to your topic. It should show the location of the major features in the community. For example, if your topic is demographics, draw and label a map that shows the population distribution in your area.

Use the GeoSkills feature, "Drawing a Small-Area Map and Route" (pages 4–5) to review how to make a good map.

- Find number tables of geographic information. Use one of these to make a detailed graph about your community. For example, you could make a population pyramid of the local population. Use the GeoSkills feature "Making Population Pyramids" (pages 97–98) to review this skill.

- Find photographs or diagrams in books or on the Internet to show certain characteristics of your community's geography. You might choose to take your own photographs, or draw your own diagrams. For example, an aerial photograph or a satellite image might show the population growth of your area. Use the GeoSkills feature, "Analyzing Satellite Images" (pages 254–255) to review image interpretation clues.

▲ **Figure 3:** Winnipeg, Manitoba. What characteristics of your community could a photograph illustrate well?

Assignment 3: Writing Your Report

It is important to organize your notes and visuals before you write your report. First, review all the information you have collected, and cross off anything that seems to be off topic. Check with your teacher or group members if you are unsure. Next, identify from three to six subtopics in your information. For example, if your topic is energy, you may have collected information and visuals about four different kinds of locally produced energy. These could be shaped into four paragraphs in your report.

1. Follow the plan in Figure 4 to write your community geography report. When you complete the report, give it to your teacher.

2. After all the class reports are finished, you can put together the class's geographic profile of your community. Here are a few suggestions of ways your class could do this.
   - bulletin board display
   - booklet to go in the school or local library
   - video or class presentations
   - the school Web site, if you have one
   - a Web site to be created at the Canadian Communities Atlas Web site

Part	Purpose/Method
1. Title page	• Tell the reader your title (your topic and community), name, class, and date.
2. Introduction (1 paragraph)	• Tell the reader what your topic is, and some of the key ideas that you investigated.
3. Main body (3–4 paragraphs)	• Write one paragraph for each key idea.
	• In each paragraph, state the key idea and provide supporting evidence.
	• Include your tables, graphs, maps, or other visuals.
4. Conclusion (1 paragraph)	• Summarize your findings about your topic and its effect on your community.
5. Bibliography	• List your general and detailed sources.

▲ **Figure 4:** Parts of a geographic report

Assignment 4: Comparing Communities

Check out the Canadian Communities Atlas Web site, where other students have posted geographic profiles of their own communities. Alternatively, your teacher may provide you with the e-mail address of a class in another Canadian community that would like to trade community information with you.

1. Sticking to your topic, compare one other community with yours, as directed by your teacher. All students will consider the same comparison community but will focus on their own topic. On an organizer with the headings listed below, fill in the information about the topic you worked on.
   - community for comparison
   - province or territory it's in
   - my topic
   - major similarities between this community and mine (in my topic)
   - major differences between this community and mine (in my topic)
   - my overall impression of this community

2. As a class, or in small groups, discuss the comparisons you made with another community. Use the summary that you created in the previous activity. What features of your comparison community do you find the most interesting? Would you like to visit this community? Why or why not?

Chapter 20

GEOGRAPHY IN THE REAL WORLD

▲ **Figure 20.1:** Did GPS help us figure out the exact height of Mt. Logan?

The Gee-Whiz Quiz

Sometimes, the real world is almost stranger than science fiction. See if you can tell the difference between what's possible today and what's not, in the following quiz. Answer each one of the questions as either True or False.

1. Core samples of glaciers can show what the climate was like long ago.

2. Geographers can study infrared satellite photos to see inside any building.

3. Volcanologists can actually explore and do research inside active volcanoes.

4. Police can use satellite images of a crime scene to establish that a suspect's car was at the scene when a crime was committed. This evidence can help convict the suspect.

5. The height of Mt. Logan, the highest mountain in Canada, was accurately determined only recently, by climbers using a GPS unit at the peak.

Perhaps you get the hint: geographers have many more powerful tools today than they had even ten years ago. And we need the best tools geography can offer to better understand our ever-changing world—your world.

> ### In this chapter, you will
> - **look at how GPS and GIS technology have improved our ability to answer questions about geography**
> - **try out some GIS activities related to each of the units in this book**
> - **consider how what you have learned in this course affects your daily life**

A Fresh Look at Geography

Back in the introductory chapter, Your Geographic Toolbox, we talked about the three questions that geographers try to answer:

- Where are things located on Earth?
- What are the connections between people and the Earth?
- How can we illustrate this information to understand it better?

In the following sections, we'll look at how these questions are being answered today with much greater precision and power.

The introductory chapter also explained that geography works not only on the global level, but at the local and regional levels as well. You've seen examples of this throughout the book. Here, we'll take a final look at just how your knowledge of geography can affect your daily life.

Science Fiction Becomes Reality: GPS

When the early European explorers sailed toward the New World, they had only a very general idea of where they were heading. They had only basic navigating tools, the stars, and perhaps a few maps or charts. They must have longed for some sure way of knowing where they were and where they were going.

Geography has come a long way since then. Not only have we explored and mapped the whole Earth, we now have Global Positioning System (GPS) technology that can pinpoint a location anywhere on the planet in a matter of seconds, regardless of the weather or the time of day.

GeoTrivia #1
In the hot new sport called geocaching, players hide small treasures and then post the GPS locations. The first player there gets the treasure and leaves another.

▲ **Figure 20.2:** Statue of Samuel de Champlain, holding a navigational device called an astrolabe

1. Imagine you were able to go back in time to show the early explorers a GPS instrument and the satellite technology that goes with it. How do you think the explorers would have reacted? Give at least three possible responses.

You don't have to be a world explorer to find a use for GPS. GPS is a geographic tool that can help us answer "Where…?" with amazing accuracy at the local, regional, and global levels. Consider the examples below.

Sonya sets out on a one-day wilderness trek near Sudbury. She uses her GPS unit to keep track of where she is and the route that she is following. At about three o'clock in the afternoon she notices a violent thunderstorm heading toward her. She checks her GPS location and finds the nearest settlement. Quickly, she leaves her planned route and heads for shelter in the closest village. She arrives at the general store just minutes before the storm hits.

Imran and his family have been planning a car trip across the country from Vancouver to Halifax for about a year. Before setting out, they purchased a GPS unit. It helps them find their location and the sights they want to see along the way. Imran and his family are able to find the fastest route through every province, and even avoid roads that are under construction.

Helen is a geologist who works for a large mining company. She treks through wilderness all over the world in search of possible mine sites. One week she might be in Indonesia, and the next week she could be in South Africa. At the end of each trip, she relays her location to the helicopter that will pick her up. She also uses GPS to find the next location where she needs to be dropped off in her search for mineral deposits. GPS is an essential part of her survival gear.

▲ **Figure 20.3:** An elephant stands with the GPS monitor collar

2. In what ways does GPS technology help make the world "smaller"?

3. a) Look at the photograph in Figure 20.3 on the previous page. What use of GPS does it show?

   b) What other ways can you think of that GPS technology might be used to help the environment?

GIS: Mapping and Making Connections

Satellites and GPS have created a new flood of data that has to be managed. One of the ways of dealing with all these data is by using a Geographical Information System (GIS). We saw in Chapter 12: Canada Goes High-Tech that a GIS can create maps with any type or amount of data, at any scale, for any part of the world. Just as GIS helps us answer "Where are things located on Earth?" with more precision, it also gives us a powerful tool for answering the other two geography questions, "What are the connections between people and the Earth?" and "How can we illustrate this information to understand it better?"

In the GeoSkills feature and the GIS activities that follow, you'll get a chance to try your hand at this new technology, and revisit some of the themes raised in each of the five units of this textbook.

GeoTrivia #2
Roger Tomlinson, a Canadian geographer, created the very first GIS in the 1960s. It was used to monitor land use.

GEOSKILLS

APPLYING GIS TECHNOLOGY

Using computers today in geography makes it easier to organize and display maps with vast amounts of data. With a GIS, you can quickly add, modify, and edit map features and data. GIS also allows you to save many versions of a map to see how it changes over time. Many GIS systems share common features. This skills activity provides an introduction to some of these shared features, using ArcView GIS software.

Purpose
Geographers use GIS to help them compare various features of an area. For example, they can easily compare population patterns with natural resource locations.

Step 1
Start the ArcView computer program. In the **Project Window**, click on the **Views** Icon, and then click the **New** button. (Or, from the **File** menu, select **Open Project**... to continue working on an existing project.) Notice that the menus and buttons along the top have

changed. The **View1** window will appear. Maximize it so it fills the screen.

Step 2
Add a map theme to the view by clicking on the **Add Theme** button (the "+" button) and locating the file you want on the disk drive and directory. Then click **OK**. In this case, let's add the theme **cd96.shp**. Click on the file name and then click **OK**. To make the map visible, click on the small box to the left of the theme name in the legend.

Step 3
Add a data theme to the view by clicking the **Add Theme** button (the "+" button) and locating the file you want on the disk drive and directory. Then click **OK**. To practise, try adding the data theme **cities.shp** to your map. Click on the small box to the left of the theme name in the legend to make the data visible. What two pieces of information are displayed on the screen?

Step 4
Save your work. From the **File** menu, select **Save Project**. Locate the disk drive and directory where you want to save the work. Give the project a file name, then click **OK**. In this case, we'll call our file **skills1.apr**.

Step 5
Use ArcView's tools to examine the data. Figure 20.4 shows some of the most commonly

used tools and what they do. You can try them out in the Practise It! activities that follow. (Note that the name of the button appears when the mouse pointer is placed over that button.)

Step 6
Make sure you have saved your work. Then, select **Exit** from the **File** menu.

 Identify – Get all the available information about an item or theme when you click on the item using the **Identify** tool.

 Pointer – Select objects to edit or move by left-clicking on them.

 Zoom In – Left-click and drag to box an area on the map that you want to make bigger.

 Zoom Out – Left-click on any area of a map to zoom out a little at a time.

 Zoom to Full Extent – Click to zoom out to the full map.

 Measure – Left-click once to start measuring. Left-click twice to stop measuring. The distance will show at the bottom left.

 Label – To label features or areas on your map, left-click and hold on the **Label** button to choose a type of label. Then, hold the mouse over the map feature you want to label, and drag the mouse until its name appears.

 Text – Left-click and hold on the **Text** button to choose a type font. Left-click on a map area and type the text to be placed there. To edit the text, use the **Pointer** tool and press Ctrl + P.

▲ **Figure 20.4:** Some of the main tools and buttons used in ArcView

Practise It!
Try these GIS skills on some real Canadian data. Follow the instructions below and refer to Steps 1–6 for help. Your completed map should look similar to Figure 20.5 on the next page.

Click on **cities.shp** in the legend to make it active. It should look raised.

1. Use the **Identify** tool (see Step 5) to click on some of the grey dots (cities). What do you think determines the size of the dot?

2. a) Use the **Zoom In** tool to zoom in on Ontario (see Step 5). If you zoom in too

To work on any GIS program...
✔ create a new view by clicking the **View** icon and then **New**
✔ return to a file started before by choosing **Open Project** from the **File** menu
✔ add map themes and data themes by clicking the **Add Theme** button
✔ use the tools to find information or make connections
✔ remember to save your work regularly

far, use the **Zoom Out** tool or **Zoom to Full Extent** tool. Find the city where you live (or a city near where you live).

b) Use the **Measure** tool to find the straight-line distance from the city to the nearest of the Great Lakes. What is the name of the lake and the distance travelled?

Now click on **cd96.shp** in the legend to make it active. It should look raised.

3. Use the **Identify** tool (see Step 5) and click on the county that you live in. What is the name, area in kilometres, and population of that county?

4. Use the **Label** tool (see Step 5) and select the **Callout Label** to label the county.

5. a) Use the **Text** tool button (see Step 5) to label Ontario.
   b) Use the **Pointer** (see Step 5) to enlarge the text and move it to an appropriate location.

6. **Zoom to Full Extent** (see Step 5), **Save** your work (see Step 4), and **Exit** the project.

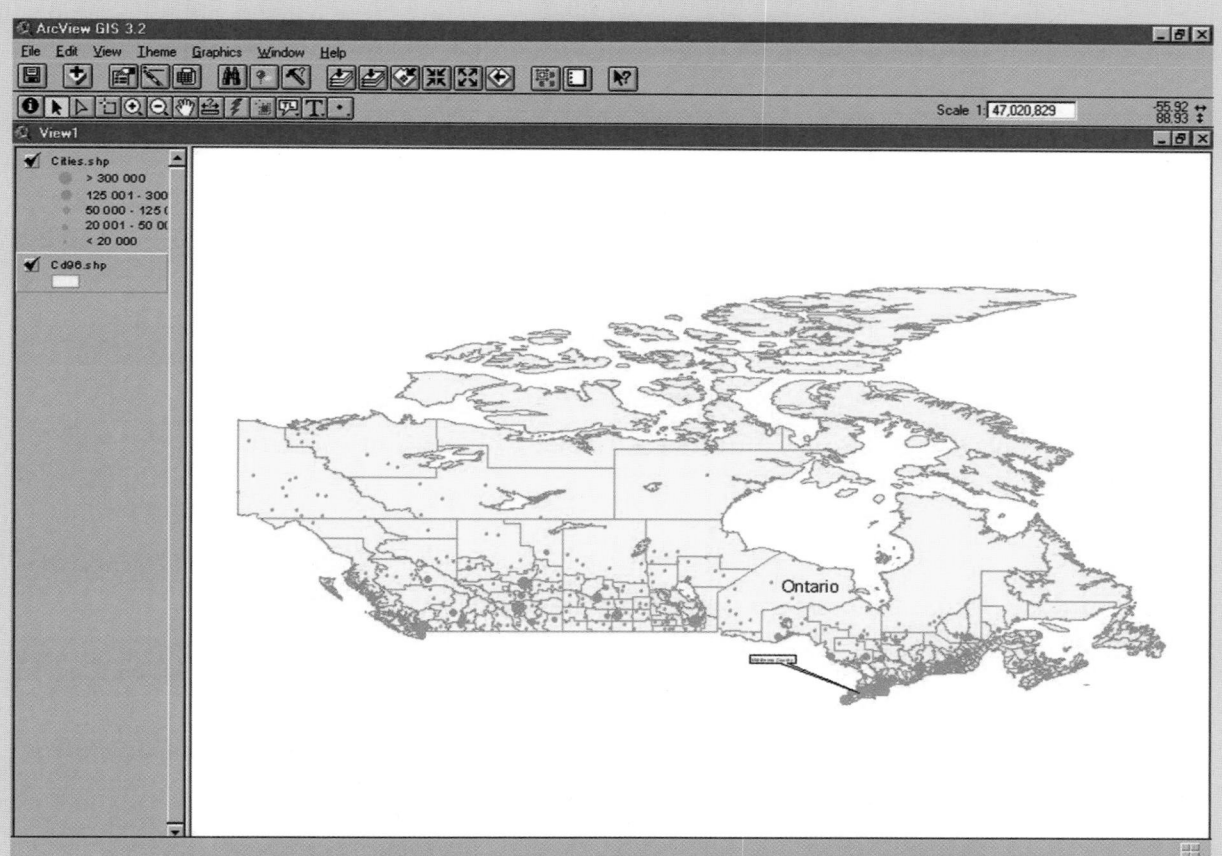

▲ **Figure 20.5:** Here is what your finished map should look like.

GIS Activities

GIS is a useful tool for all sorts of geographical issues. Each of the following activities, using the ArcView software program, relates to issues raised in one of the five units of this textbook. Try your hand at each of them, and see what it is like to be a geographer! To access the Lesson Packs referred to below, go to the Esri Canada Web site at http://k12.esricanada.com/teachingmaterials/lessons/english/all.html.

Unit 1: Volcano Investigator

As you learned in Unit 1: Canada's Natural Systems, Canada still has potentially active volcanoes. The Canadian government plans and prepares for possible volcanic eruptions. It needs to know where Canada's potentially active volcanoes are, their size, and how close they are to people. In this ArcView activity, you will find out about one potentially active Canadian volcano of your choice.

To get started, follow the student instructions on pages 6–12 of "Volcanoes of the World: The Lesson Pack." Do *Part I: "Finding Active Volcanoes"* and *Part II: "People and Places,"* following the steps outlined in the GeoSkills feature on pages 335–337 of this text. If the computer you're using is able to print, then you may try *Part III: "The Finished Product,"* and create a map to print out. To focus on a Canadian volcano, adjust the activity as follows.

- In Part I, Step C, Number 7, page 9: Instead of using "Active," use "Potentially Active."
- In Part I, Step D, Number 1, page 10, zoom in on Canada.
- In Part II, Step B, Number 4, page 11: Instead of using 500 000 for the population, use 10 000.

4. Which province has the most potentially active volcanoes?

5. Name some of the Canadian cities shown on your map.

6. a) How many potentially active volcanoes are located within 100 km of your selected volcano? How many are within 250 km? within 500 km? (*Hint:* Use the Measure tool in ArcView to answer this question.)
   b) Are these volcanoes located on or near plate boundaries? Why is this so?

7. Write a brief report about your findings for the government. Include the name, type, and status of your volcano. Also include how close the nearest cities are, and what other potentially active volcanoes are within 500 km. State whether or not the cities are in danger, and why. Be sure to support your conclusions with specific evidence.

Unit 2: Settlement Sleuth

In Unit 2: Canada's Human Systems, you learned about Canada's population patterns. Knowing where people settled in the past helps determine where people like to settle and live today. The Canadian government uses information like this to know where to build new roads, railways, and airports. In this ArcView activity, you will find out about three of the many factors that determine where early Canadian settlers chose to live.

Follow the student instructions on pages 4–13 of "Settlement in Canada: The Lesson Pack." Do Parts A to J, following the steps outlined in the GeoSkills feature on pages 335–337 of this text. If the computer you're using is able to print, then you may try *Part K: "Map Layout: Show Off Your Work!"* and create a map to print out.

▲ **Figure 20.6:** Early advertisements for immigration to Canada

8. Why has most of British Columbia still not been settled?

9. Why do few people settle in northern Alberta? northern Saskatchewan?

10. Look at the posters in Figure 20.6. What other factors may have influenced where the early settlers chose to live?

Unit 3: Mineral Mapper

In Unit 3: Economic Interactions, you found out that Canada is a country rich in minerals. Mining companies look for new deposits by examining information about where existing minerals are located. In this ArcView activity, you will locate a site for a new mining town in Ontario. You can choose the type of mine based on local rock types.

Follow the student instructions on pages 4–13 of "Mining: The Lesson Pack." Do Parts A to G, following the steps outlined in the GeoSkills feature on pages 335–337 of this text. If the computer you're using is able to print, then you may try *Part H: "Map Layout: The Final Frontier"* and create a map to print out. For *Part F: "Ontario: Yours to Discover!,"* locate Sudbury, Timmins, Kirkland Lake, and Thunder Bay on an atlas map before you start the ArcView activity. For Part G, Step 3, you can locate just one mine, then label and explain it in the steps that follow.

11. What other factors will determine whether a mine becomes active?

12. Do you think the mine you located will become active? Why or why not?

Unit 4: Acid Rain Analyst

In Unit 4: Environmental Interactions, you looked at how human activities affect the natural environment. Scientists in Canada look for patterns showing how acid rain and population size are related. In this ArcView activity, you will create maps showing the amount of acid rain in Canada and its relation to Canada's population.

Follow the instructions on pages 1–7 of "Acid Rain: An Introduction." Do Parts A and B, following the steps outlined in the GeoSkills feature on pages 335–337 of this text. If the computer you're using is able to print, then you may try *Part C: "Analyze the Results,"* and create a map to print out. Afterwards, save your work by clicking on the **Save** icon, or by going to the **File** menu and clicking on **Save**. Finally, answer each of the questions at the end of Part C, Step 4, using the two maps displayed on the screen.

GeoTrivia #3
The Canada–US agreement to reduce acid rain should save Canada $1 billion in health costs by 2010.

13. Does the amount of acid rain change with time? Explain why or why not.

14. Since Canada's population density is increasing, why will the amount of acid rain keep getting worse? Is there any way it might get better?

15. How can you decrease the amount of acid rain that you create? Suggest three different ways.

Unit 5: Tourism Attractor

In Unit 5: Canada's International Links, you found out that tourism is an important part of our economy. Knowing what tourists want to do helps people working in the tourism industry make decisions about what to offer. Some homeowners turn their houses into bed and breakfasts, offering room and board to travellers. In this ArcView computer activity, you will locate a new bed and breakfast in Newfoundland. You can choose its location based on tourism patterns in the area.

Follow the student instructions on pages 4–13 of "Tourism in Newfoundland and Labrador: The Lesson Pack." Do *Part I: "Getting Started"* and *Part II: "Transportation Factors,"* following the steps outlined in the GeoSkills feature on pages 335–337 of this text. When you save the file at the end of Part II, Step 8, give it the name "Tourism." Now try *Part III: "People and Places."* Remember to save the file when you are done. Do *Part IV: "For the Naturalist"* and *Part VI: "The Finishing Touches,"* but skip *Part V: "Cultural Factors: Creating Your Own Data."* Also leave out the extension section on National Historic Sites.

16. What other factors might attract tourists to an area?

17. What else needs to be considered to attract more tourists to your bed and breakfast?

18. Make a brochure advertising the attractions close to your bed and breakfast.

Geography in Your World

You may not be investigating volcanoes, mineral deposits, or acid rain in real life. But this is not to say that geography doesn't touch your world already. In fact, the knowledge you've gained in this course could give you a whole new perspective on your daily routine! Let's track the events in one day that bring geography into your life.

Perhaps you start your day with a shower to help you wake up. You've probably always taken it for granted that when you turn on the tap, water comes out. Now you know how lucky you are. In Unit 1, you learned that climate and the ice ages have given Canada a vast system of lakes and rivers. Some of the water flowing through your taps could be coming from glacial lakes, formed thousands of years ago. You also know that much of our fresh water is threatened by pollution.

19. Explain how a) our climate and b) the ice ages have contributed to Canada's reserves of fresh water.

20. Where does your community's fresh water come from? Where is its wastewater treated? Who operates these local water systems?

After your shower, you head to the kitchen for a healthy breakfast including cereal, toast, or other grains. As you eat, you gaze out the window at the new subdivision being built across the street, and the fields beyond. In Unit 2, you saw that some of Canada's best farmland is threatened by urban growth. Suddenly, you are able to make a connection between your piece of toast and the construction going on outside your door.

▲ **Figure 20.7:** Making connections between geography and your life

21. Identify some negative effects of the loss of farmland.

At school, you use pencils, books, and paper in just about every class. You doodle on a piece of paper, then crumple it up and throw it away. But then you remember reading in Unit 3 that large areas of Canada are used by the forest industry. You think about the importance of primary resources like forests, and about the manufacturing and transportation systems that have to be in place to get that paper to you. Next time, you may think twice about wasting those resources.

22. What ecozone did the wood used to make the paper most likely come from?

23. What forms of transportation do you think were most likely used
     a) to get the logs to the mill?   b) to get the paper to markets near you?

On your way to and from school, perhaps you take a school bus or public transit. With what you now know from Unit 4 about our reliance on fossil fuels, you feel good that you are using a much more efficient means of transportation than the car.

24. What alternatives to gasoline-powered cars are currently being developed?

Back home, you relax in a world of music, television, or computers. Unit 5 showed how closely Canadians are tied to the rest of the planet. You start to think about how global telecommunications bring a world of information and entertainment to your home. Then, you notice some of the many objects in your home that come from other countries, and wonder about the global networks and systems that got them there.

▲ **Figure 20.8:** Geography helps us understand our world.

25. Make a list of the food and drink that you have consumed today. Beside each item, record whether or not it could have been grown or raised in Canada.

26. Examine Figure 20.8. What topics discussed in each of the five units of this book are shown in this illustration?

GeoGames

The Career Game

Geography could end up a part of your career, as it has for the people profiled in this book. Take a few minutes to review the ten GeoCareers features and think about which might interest you!

Purpose:

To review some geography-related careers

Supplies:

One die; pencil and paper; copy of game board; one playing piece each (2–3 players can play)

Method:

- On your turn, roll the die and move your playing piece. Read the question on the space where you land, which describes one of the GeoCareers. If you know whom the statement is describing, score 10 points. Check your answer using the textbook. You get only one guess per roll.

- The winner is the player with the most points after all questions are answered.

Wrap-Up:

Of all the careers listed here, which two interest you the most? Why?

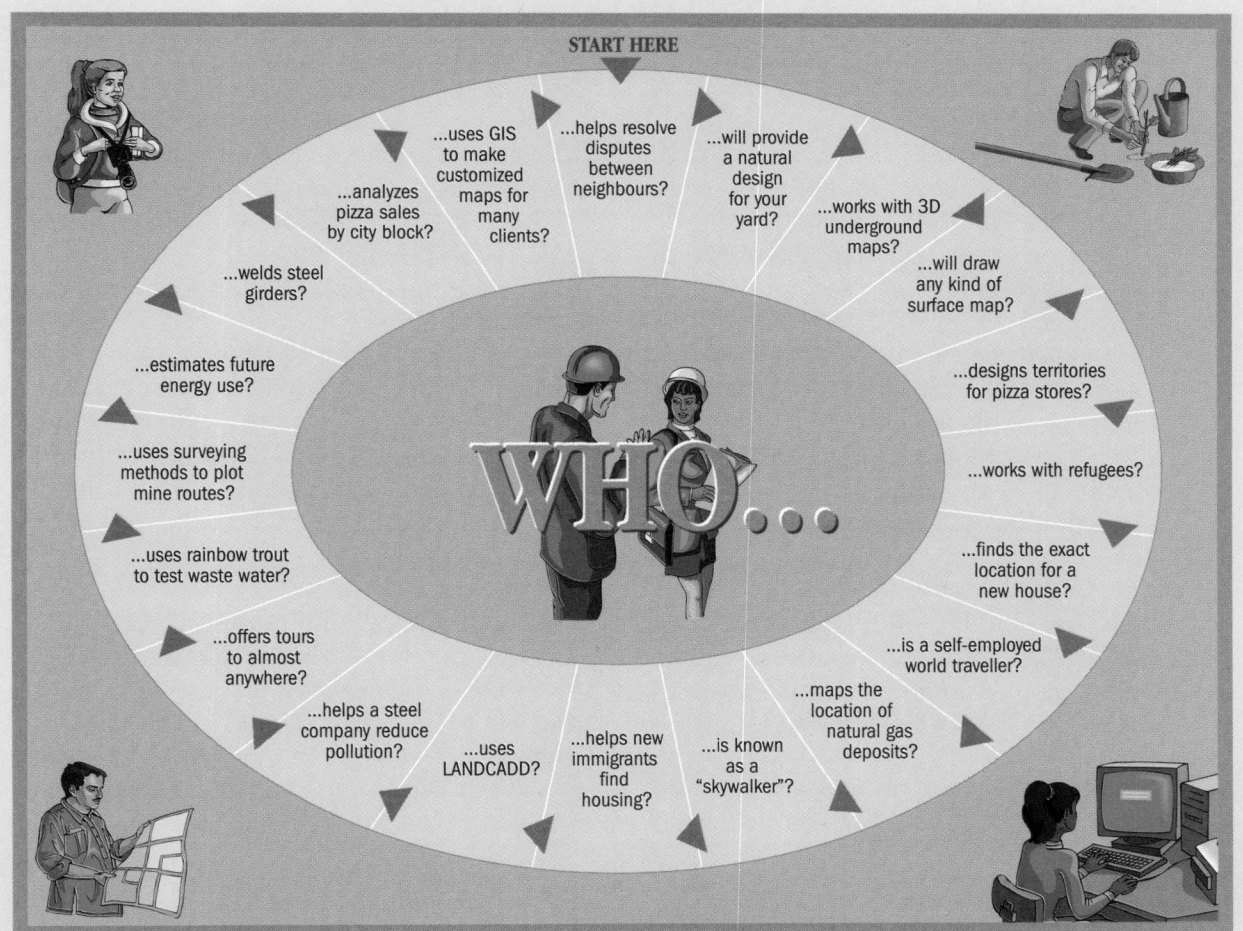

START HERE

...uses GIS to make customized maps for many clients?

...helps resolve disputes between neighbours?

...will provide a natural design for your yard?

...analyzes pizza sales by city block?

...works with 3D underground maps?

...welds steel girders?

...will draw any kind of surface map?

...estimates future energy use?

...designs territories for pizza stores?

...uses surveying methods to plot mine routes?

...works with refugees?

...uses rainbow trout to test waste water?

...finds the exact location for a new house?

...offers tours to almost anywhere?

...is a self-employed world traveller?

...helps a steel company reduce pollution?

...uses LANDCADD?

...helps new immigrants find housing?

...is known as a "skywalker"?

...maps the location of natural gas deposits?

WHO...

▲ Figure 20.9: The Career Game board

Conclusion

As you worked through this book, you discovered that the question, "Where are things located on Earth?" can be asked about everything, including landforms, people, industry, and pollution. This question can focus on the smallest of ecosystems, or on the planet as a whole. "Where…?" is where geography starts.

But you soon discovered that the question does not end there. Geography looks at connections—between living and non-living things, between people and their physical environment, and among people in neighbourhoods, across regions, and around the globe. As new technology and communications systems continue to make the world a smaller place, these global connections will become ever more important in our lives.

Finally, you saw how map-making tools have changed and improved, and how this has changed our understanding of the world we live in. You also saw how geographers use bar graphs, pie charts, tables, climate graphs, population pyramids, and more, to see and understand systems, patterns, and connections. By showing the world more clearly, geography may also help us find our way to a better future.

Wrap It Up

1. Canada's way of life is built around many different physical and human systems. Brainstorm a list of the physical and human systems covered in this book.

   a) Select one of these systems that is present in your region and collect at least seven articles or pieces of information about it.

   b) Glue your articles into a scrapbook. At the bottom of each page, write a short summary of the article.

   c) End your scrapbook with a half-page conclusion explaining what you have learned about this local system.

2. Imagine some ways that GPS technology might be used in the future. Feel free to be creative, and "invent" other future technologies that could be used along with GPS.

3. Find out about a major industry (other than the automobile industry) and complete the following activities.

   a) Explain its impact on the lives of ordinary Canadians.

   b) Make a web diagram to show other industries this industry is related to.

   c) Describe specific ways that this industry affects the environment.

   d) Explore the jobs that people who work in this industry have.

4. Write your own geographic "day in the life" of a Canadian high school student like the one on pages 341–342, but with different examples. Link your description to at least one topic covered in *each* of the five units of this book.

5. Research a geography-related career other than the ones described in the GeoCareers features. Explain what the job is, how it relates to geography, and what kind of training it requires. Tell why you would or would not like to pursue this career.

Glossary

Key Term	Definition	Example/Explanation
acid rain	rain that is more acidic than normal rain because of pollutants or natural causes	Acid rain has damaged millions of trees in Ontario and Quebec.
adult literacy rate	the percentage of the population, 15 years and older, who can read and write at a basic level	The adult literacy rate of Canada is over 99 per cent.
adventure tourism	tourism that allows people to have challenging or unusual experiences	Adventure tourism companies can arrange for you to go camel riding in Africa.
aerospace technology	technology that involves research and development for use in the aircraft and space industry	Montreal—with Bombardier and other aerospace companies—is one of Canada's aerospace-technology centres.
age distribution	the percentage of a country's population in various age groups, such as 0–19, 20–44, 45–64, and 65+	To show the age distribution of countries' populations, geographers use population pyramids.
agribusiness	operations that own and farm vast amounts of land, often using advanced technology	Factory farms that raise and process turkeys is one type of agribusiness in Ontario.
agricultural economy	a country in which the majority of people make a living by farming the land	Agricultural economies, like Ghana, tend to have a lower standard of living than industrialized countries do.
alpha-numeric grid	a location-finding method in which two sets of lines cross a map, dividing it into squares. Each square has a unique letter-number identification.	On a particular map, Montreal might be located in alpha-numeric grid square C5. For an example, see page 8.
alternative energy	clean and renewable forms of energy used instead of conventional energy	The many types of alternative energy include solar energy, tidal power, wind energy, geothermal energy, and fuel cells.
alvar	an area of flat limestone bedrock with the soil removed by erosion	Alvars are common in several parts of southern Ontario, such as the Bruce Peninsula and Manitoulin Island. For locations, see page 63.
anchor store	a large, well-known store attached to a mall	Department stores such as The Bay often serve as anchor stores.
aquaculture	the commercial farming of fish in specially created fish ponds or in netted areas in open water	Companies specializing in aquaculture raise either freshwater or saltwater fish.
bias	a one-sided view of a topic	Some people have a strong bias against rap music.
big-box store	a large retail store that offers a huge volume of goods	Many big-box stores in Canada—such as Home Depot—are owned by US-based companies.
biodiversity	the biological variety of living things found in an area	A forest has broad biodiversity. Cutting natural vegetation and then replanting the area with only one type of tree reduces biodiversity.

Key Term	Definition	Example/Explanation
biomagnification	the process by which pesticides accumulate as they travel up the food chain	Owing to biomagnification, sharks, which are high on the food chain, have a greater concentration of chemicals than most other fish.
biome	a very large area with a community of plants and animals common throughout the region	The coniferous forest region is sometimes called the "spruce–moose" biome. For biomes in the Northern Hemisphere, see page 70.
bioregion	a part of the Earth's surface, large or small, identified by its combination of natural and human characteristics	Tundra, wetlands, and woodlots are three examples of the many different types of bioregions.
biotechnology	technology that uses plants and animals to make new products	Canola is an example of a Canadian product developed using biotechnology.
bitumen	the material mined in the Alberta oil sands project, consisting of wet sand grains coated by an oily layer	The oil from bitumen is called synthetic crude oil because refining is required to separate the sand and water from the oil.
boundary	an imaginary line on the Earth's surface, or on a map, that divides one area from another	The line of latitude numbered 49°N marks the boundary between western Canada and the United States.
business travel	travel as part of one's job, often involving more expensive hotels and plane fares than tourism	A Canadian entrepreneur who flies to Peru to make a deal to import organic coffee beans to Canada is a business traveller.
cartographer	a person who makes maps for specific purposes	A cartographer would be a valuable employee for a tourist bureau that produces its own travel brochures.
census	a survey of population figures taken by a country's national government, normally every five or ten years	A recent census of Canada was carried out in 2001.
census metropolitan area (CMA)	an urban area including all villages, towns, and smaller cities near a major urban centre, with no rural area between them	Halifax, Vancouver, and Edmonton are each the centre of a CMA.
central business district (CBD)	the downtown area of a city	Calgary's CBD has most of its offices and tallest buildings.
chain migration	the pattern of migration whereby one wave of immigrants settles in a region or city, thereby encouraging a second wave to come, and so on	Italians have come to Canada in a series of chain-migration waves.
chernozem	the thick, dark soil under natural grasslands	Large areas of the Prairie region of Alberta, Saskatchewan, and Manitoba are covered by chernozem soil.
chinook	a warm, dry wind that descends east from the Rocky Mountains and suddenly warms winter temperatures in southwestern Alberta	In January 1966, a chinook raised the temperature of Pincher Creek, Alberta, by 21°C in just four minutes!
chlorofluorocarbons (CFCs)	chemicals released into the air that destroy the protective ozone layer in the upper atmosphere	CFCs are released by manufactured items such as aerosol cans, refrigerators, and air conditioners.

Key Term	Definition	Example/Explanation
city	an urban centre with 10 000 or more people	Charlottetown, Prince Edward Island, is a city.
clay belt	a pocket of farmland where glacial lakes once existed over rocky ground	Farmers grow hay and raise livestock on large clay-belt regions in Northern Ontario and Quebec.
clear-cutting	forest logging in which every tree is cut down, leaving only scrub behind	Some Canadian logging firms have used clear-cutting, which ruins habitat for animals.
climate	weather conditions at a certain place or region averaged over a long period of time	Edmonton has an extreme climate, with average temperatures that range from −14°C in January to +16°C in July.
climate graph	a standard graph that uses bars to show the precipitation for each month and a line to show monthly temperature	A climate graph clearly shows that Iqaluit's climate is very different from Ottawa's. For examples, see pages 34 and 56.
closed system	a system that occurs when everything produced by it stays within that system	Several pulp-and-paper plants have been built as closed systems; they produce almost no pollution.
compass bearing	one of the numerical divisions of a directional compass, measured in degrees; each compass bearing represents a different direction	A compass bearing of 90 degrees points east.
component	parts that are made into products	Moulded plastic, wire, and computer chips are all components that are made into a telephone.
composting	allowing plant or animal waste to decompose, producing humus	Many Canadians compost kitchen and garden waste in containers in their backyards.
conservation	protecting natural resources by using them wisely	Conservation practices range from saving energy by turning down the thermostat in winter to planting trees and shrubs to encourage wildlife.
construction	a type of secondary industry that makes buildings and roads	The construction industry built Highway 407.
consumer	in the food chain, an animal that eats either producers or other consumers to feed itself	Humans are consumers that eat both producers, such as corn, and other consumers, such as cattle.
consumer	any person who buys a product or service	Teenagers love to be consumers of music CDs.
consumer society	an economy that depends on people spending money	The United States is the wealthiest consumer society in the world.
container system	a transportation system that transfers goods in containers that can be carried on ships, trains, or trucks	A container of steel girders can be transferred from truck onto rail, and then onto ship.
continental drift	Alfred Wegener's theory that the continents were once joined together and are gradually moving apart	The matching coastlines of South America and Africa strongly suggest that these two continents were once connected.

Key Term	Definition	Example/Explanation
continental shelf	a large area of shallow water that stretches offshore before the ocean deepens	The shallow Grand Banks, which extends off the coast of the island of Newfoundland, is part of a continental shelf.
contour interval	the amount of elevation from one contour line on a map to the next	If two neighbouring contour lines are marked 20 and 30, the contour interval is 10 metres.
contour line	thin, brown lines used to show surface elevation on topographic maps. The brown numbers on contour lines give the elevation above sea level.	Circular contour lines show rounded hills. The more circular contour lines there are, the higher the hills (see page 47).
conventional energy	commonly used sources of heat, light, or power	Examples of conventional energy forms include wood, water, coal oil, natural gas, and nuclear power.
core	the dense nuclear furnace found at the centre of the Earth	Scientists believe that the intense heat of the Earth's core melts rocks in the mantle zone above it.
cultural diversity	a quality that describes a population drawn from many cultural backgrounds, illustrating a wide range of practices and beliefs	The cultural diversity of Canada increases as people of different cultures immigrate here.
cultural imprint	the effect an ethnic group has on the characteristics of a neighbourhood	Haitian immigrants have left a cultural imprint on Montreal.
cultural tourism	tourism geared to learning about the history, culture, and lifestyle of a country	On a cultural tourism vacation to Egypt, you might visit the pyramids to learn about the nation's history.
deforestation	the ongoing reduction of the size of the world's forests	The entire province of New Brunswick has gone through the process of deforestation at least once.
dependency load	the percentage of a country's population aged 0–15 years and over 65	Countries with a high proportion of children, such as Mexico, have a high dependency load.
desertification	the transformation of productive land into desert	Some areas of sub-Saharan Africa are experiencing desertification.
direct employee	a person employed in a particular industry is a direct employee of that industry	A teacher is a direct employee of the school system.
diversified economy	a country with a wide range of economic activity and a high standard of living	Canada is an example of a diversified economy.
drainage basin	an area of land drained by a river system	The smallest drainage basin in Canada is the southern edge of Alberta and Saskatchewan. The waters of this region flow south into the Gulf of Mexico. For Canada's drainage basins, see page 79.
ecological footprint	the amount of productive land needed to provide you with the goods you use and absorb the wastes you produce	The ecological footprint of a person in central Africa is small; that of a North American is large.
economic base	the industry and businesses that make a community thrive	The economic base of Sudbury is mining.

Key Term	Definition	Example/Explanation
ecotourism	tourism that has a low impact on the environment and is sensitive to local cultures and Aboriginal peoples	An ecotourist guide takes a tour group on public transit to the city market in Scarborough, Tobago.
ecozone	a large geographical area in which human activities interact with the natural world	There are fifteen terrestrial (land) ecozones in Canada, each of them more than 200 000 square kilometres in area. For Canada's ecozones, see pages 74–75.
efficiency	producing as much as possible for the lowest possible cost	A company's efficiency could be increased by using the latest production technology.
emerging industrial economy	a country whose industrial sector is growing, and whose agricultural sector is declining in importance	Brazil is an emerging industrial economy, with some high-technology industry but many people still employed in agriculture.
emigrant	a person who moves away from a country permanently	Many doctors from Canada emigrate to the United States.
energy reserves	the known future supply of an energy resource	Canada's energy reserves of natural gas are much larger than our reserves of oil.
entrepreneur	someone who starts and builds a business	A high school student who starts a small business selling pop to other students is an entrepreneur.
erosion	the weathering, or wearing down, of the Earth's surface by water, ice, wind, plant roots, animals, and people	Erosion has worn away the ancient mountains that once covered the Canadian Shield.
escarpment	a sharp change in elevation caused by the rapid erosion of soft sedimentary rock	The Niagara Escarpment, which crosses southern Ontario, shows the cliffs found along this type of feature (see page 42).
ethnic origin	the racial or cultural background a person comes from	In Canada, British and French are the two most common ethnic origins.
ethnically diverse	a characteristic describing an area or country where people of many backgrounds and cultures live side by side	Canada is an ethically diverse country; according to the 2001 Census, 37 per cent of the population had been born in another country.
export	a product or service (such as insurance) that is sold to people in other countries	Automobiles are a major Canadian export to the United States.
fact	a piece of information about something that exists or an event that happened	It is a fact that Ottawa is the capital of Canada.
fibre optics	a thin glass cable along which pulses of laser light move, carrying high-speed signals	The fibre optics network in Saskatchewan was the first large system of its kind in the world.
fishery	commercial fishing operations, as opposed to private, recreational fishing	The Atlantic fishery is the largest fishery in Canada.
fossil fuel	an energy source, including coal, natural gas, and oil, that formed from the ancient remains of once-living things	At present, fossil fuels supply about 85 per cent of Canada's total energy for transportation, industry, and all other uses.
fragmentation	the human process of dividing the natural environment into smaller and smaller areas, threatening the survival and diversity of plant and animal species	Small woodlots are often all that remain of once-large forested areas cleared for farming. For illustration, see page 65.

Key Term	Definition	Example/Explanation
franchise	a licence to operate a business, use the company's logo, and sell its products	Franchises for well-established businesses such as McDonald's are very expensive.
fuel cell	a device that chemically converts hydrogen into electricity without any burning	Vancouver's Ballard Power Systems builds a variety of different fuel cells, including the hydrogen fuel cell.
gazetteer	an alphabetical listing of places and their locations; these are found in atlases	An atlas gazetteer would list the location of Winnipeg, Manitoba, as 50°N, 97°W.
genocide	the destruction (killing) of a national ethnic, racial, or religious group	In Rwanda, in central Africa, one group of people tried to commit genocide on another in 1998, by killing 800 000 people in one month.
geographic information system (GIS)	computer software that combines different kinds of geographic information	Town planners use GIS to better understand the characteristics of their community and the needs of the residents.
geographic inquiry	a step-by-step method used by geographers to research a topic or an issue	Geographic inquiry is a useful approach for finding good solutions to local transportation problems. For examples, see pages 14 and 277–278.
geography	the study of the Earth that describes the distribution of natural and human features	The study of Canada's geography tells us that most of its population lives along the southern edge of the country.
geothermal energy	an alternative energy system that uses the even internal temperature of the Earth for heating and cooling buildings	In summer, the geothermal system in a house uses the relatively cooler temperature of the Earth below to cool the house. In winter, it uses the relatively warmer temperatures below to warm the house.
glacial period	a period of cold temperatures during which glaciers and ice caps advance and grow larger; also called an ice age	During the last glacial period, thick ice sheets covered almost all of Canada.
global positioning system (GPS)	a method of determining a location on the Earth based on signals from three or more satellites	Back-country skiers and hikers use GPS units to check their locations.
global warming	a long-term warming trend caused by unnatural changes in the atmosphere	Across the Northern Hemisphere, global warming has caused glaciers and ice caps to melt as temperatures rise.
greenhouse effect	the process by which the temperature of the lower atmosphere increases when invisible gases trap heat	The greenhouse effect parallels the trapping of heat within the glass of a greenhouse (see page 242).
greenhouse gases	the invisible gases of the atmosphere that absorb and hold heat	Carbon dioxide, CFCs, methane, nitrous oxide, and ozone are the most common greenhouse gases in the Earth's atmosphere.
gross domestic product (GDP)	the value of all the goods and services produced in one country in one year	In 2002, Canada's GDP was $1.07 trillion.

Key Term	Definition	Example/Explanation
gross domestic product per capita	a country's gross domestic product divided by its population	In 2002, the United States' GDP per capita was $57 460 (Cdn), which gave many people rich lifestyles.
ground-level ozone	deadly air pollutant that hugs the ground and comes from the burning of fossil fuels	Ground-level ozone is common in Vancouver in the summer.
growing season	the average period of the year during which temperatures are higher than 6°C (the temperature at which plants grow)	Vancouver has a nine-month growing season, from March to November. For an example on a climate graph, see page 34.
habitat	the surroundings in which an animal lives and feeds itself	In populated areas, deer habitat often includes small woodlots, which provide protection, and nearby fields, which provide food.
hamlet	the smallest kind of settlement, with about eight to ten buildings	Many hamlets across Canada have been abandoned. For a map of a typical hamlet, see page 133.
hardwood	slow-growing, deciduous trees that produce dense and hard wood, often used for flooring and fine furniture	Maple is a hardwood used to make flooring.
high-order good	a product available only in cities	A Jaguar sedan is a high-order good.
high technology	technology that relies on computer power or scientific developments made possible by computers	Canada's aerospace industry is a high-technology industry.
human development	the degree to which people can live healthy, educated, and prosperous lives	A nation's level of human development gives us some idea of the people's quality of life. Haiti has a low level of human development.
Human Development Index (HDI)	the United Nations' system to estimate the human development of people in a given country	For many years, Canada has been listed near the top of the Human Development Index.
human geography	the distribution of human features on the surface of the Earth	Human geography examines population and communities, industries and jobs, recreation, transportation, and communication.
human systems	the systems built by humans, making up a network of roads, houses, railways, factories, and so on	Your school is part of the human system because it was planned and built by people.
humus	the dark, organically rich top layer of a soil profile, composed of the remains of once-living plant and animal matter	The material produced by composting is humus.
hybrid-power vehicle	a car or truck that uses the combined power of gasoline and electricity for clean, efficient operation	The Honda Insight and Civic, as well as the Toyota Prius, are examples of hybrid-power vehicles for sale in 2003.
immigrant	a person who comes to a new country to live there permanently	Canada allows approximately 250 000 immigrants into the country each year.
import	a product or service (such as insurance) that is brought into Canada from another country	Oranges are a major Canadian import because they cannot be grown in cold climates.

Key Term	Definition	Example/Explanation
indirect employee	a person who supplies or supports someone employed in a specific industry is an indirect employee of that industry	An editor working for a company that produces educational textbooks is an indirect employee of the school system.
information technology	technology that deals with ways of storing, retrieving, and sending information	IBM, Microsoft, and Research in Motion are all companies in the information-technology sector.
infrastructure	systems that form the basis of the economy	Southern Ontario has a highly developed infrastructure, including transportation and electricity networks.
interglacial period	a period of warm temperatures that occurs between successive ice ages	The last ice age ended about 10 000 years ago, and we have been in an interglacial period ever since.
internal migrant	a person who moves from one region of a country to another	People who have moved from Saskatchewan to Alberta to find work are internal migrants.
just-in-time delivery (JIT)	the industrial system of delivery in which manufacturers order the components they need every day and immediately use them in finished products	Under the JIT system, when windshields are delivered to automobile plants, they are not stored but instead are immediately put into finished vehicles.
land reclamation	renewal of areas that have become so polluted that they are not being used	Land reclamation is often needed on the sites of old factories.
land use	various ways people use the land	Urban parks are a land use often surrounded by housing, another land use.
landfill site	garbage dumps designed to dispose of waste safely between layers of earth	Every city in Canada has at least one major landfill site. One such site was converted into a small ski hill called Centennial Hill, in western Toronto, Ontario.
landform region	an area of the Earth's surface with certain physical landforms that set it apart from other areas	The Canadian Shield is a landform region of ancient rock that encircles Hudson Bay. For Canada's landform regions, see page 37.
large-scale map	a "close-up" map that shows a small part of the Earth with a high level of detail	The store-finder maps posted in shopping malls are large-scale maps (see page 5).
latitude	an imaginary line that circles the Earth, parallel to the Equator	Winnipeg, Manitoba, is located at about 50°N latitude, that is, about 50 degrees north of the Equator. For an example, see page 15.
life expectancy at birth	the average number of years that a person in a given country may expect to live	For a country to have a high life expectancy at birth, it must have good medical facilities and an adequate diet for its people. Japan's people have a high life expectancy.
lithosphere	the thin, brittle outer crust of the Earth	North America is one of the large pieces, or plates, that make up the lithosphere.

Key Term	Definition	Example/Explanation
location factor	a reason—such as closeness to a major highway or availability of skilled labour—that explains why a business locates where it does	An important location factor for fish processing plants is closeness to a safe harbour where fishing boats can unload, even in rough weather.
long lot	a long, narrow farm property	Long lots are typical of the settlement pattern in early Quebec. For an illustration, see page 121.
longitude	an imaginary line that runs from pole to pole, either east or west of the Prime Meridian (which passes through Greenwich, England)	Winnipeg, Manitoba, is located at about 97°W longitude, which is about 97 degrees west of Greenwich, England. For example, see page 15.
longwave radiation	the re-radiated energy of the sun travelling in long wavelengths from the heated surface of the Earth	The heat that radiates from a wood stove is a form of longwave radiation.
low-order good	a product sold almost everywhere	Candy bars are low-order goods.
mantle	the thick zone of molten material beneath the Earth's lithosphere	Scientists believe that slow currents in the mantle gradually move the Earth's plates.
manufactured product	something that people make	Cars, furniture, and the desks in your classroom are all manufactured products.
manufacturing	a type of secondary industry that creates either components or finished products	Manufacturing industries take rolls of steel and stamp them into finished car-body parts.
mean	another word for average	Edmonton's mean January temperature is –14°C.
median	the number, in a series of numbers, that is larger than half the other numbers and smaller than the other half	The median age is the age at which half the people are younger and half are older. In 2001, the median age of all Canadians was 37.6 years old.
megalopolis	a group of cities that have expanded until they touch one another	Canada's only megalopolis is located around the western edge of Lake Ontario.
megaproject	a large-scale, expensive project for the development of natural resources, particularly energy	Two examples of Canadian energy megaprojects are the development of the Alberta oil sands and the construction of La Grande Riviere hydroelectric power dams.
merger	a joining of two businesses	In 2002, Clarica Life and Sun Life Financial merged to form one larger life insurance company.
metaphor	a figure of speech that uses one thing to represent another to make a comparison	A metaphor to express a runner's speed might read: "He was a bolt of lightning."
migrant	a person who moves from one country or region to another	Refugees from overseas and people moving from Montreal to Ottawa are migrants.
migration	the movement of people from one region or country to another region or country	The movement of people from rural Quebec to Montreal is part of a migration pattern.
military grid	two sets of parallel lines that cross at right angles that are used to give the precise location of map features	The military grid location of the place of worship in Figure 2.14 on page 47 is 541817.

Key Term	Definition	Example/Explanation
mineral	a natural substance from the ground, such as oil or nickel, that we value because we can use it for something	Gold mines are among Canada's most valuable mineral producers.
molten	a characteristic of ore or metal that is so hot that it is liquid	Molten steel is poured into moulds and then cooled to form steel bars.
mother tongue	the language that a person first spoke and still understands	English and French are the most common mother tongues in Canada.
multiculturalism	a government policy by which people are encouraged to keep their cultural heritage while also being committed Canadians	Multicultural nations such as Canada hold festivals to celebrate many different cultural traditions.
natural corridor	wide, connected passageways of trees, grassland, or water that allow animals to travel safely, without human contact, from one natural area to another	Planting a row of trees and shrubs through a field can provide a natural corridor for birds and small mammals. For an illustration, see page 67.
natural systems	naturally occurring things, such as climate, landforms, plants, and animals	Today's weather is part of the natural system.
nomadic	a lifestyle in which people move according to the season, to find wildlife such as caribou and geese	Because they were a nomadic people, the Cree built portable lodges that they could move easily.
non-renewable energy	an energy supply that cannot replace itself quickly	Coal, natural gas, and oil have each taken millions of years to form from the ancient remains of once-living things.
oil-resource economy	a country whose economy is tied to the export of a single raw resource, namely oil	Saudi Arabia is an oil-resource economy and the largest oil exporter in the world.
old-growth forest	the remaining population of original trees that grow in an area that has never been logged	The old-growth forest areas of Northern Ontario are mostly tall white pines. Many are several metres in diameter at the base.
opinion	a belief not backed up with proof	It's my opinion that hockey is a more interesting game than baseball.
outcrop	a rock layer that can be seen because it projects above the soil on the Earth's surface	Glacial erosion has created many rock outcrops in northern Canada.
ozone layer	a layer of ozone gases high in the atmosphere that protects life on Earth from harmful solar radiation such as ultra-violet rays	Although we cannot see the ozone layer, it protects our skin and eyes from much damage.
Pacific Ring of Fire	a global system of active volcanoes that circles the Pacific Ocean	The volcanic Coastal Mountain Range of British Columbia is part of the Pacific Ring of Fire. For an example, see page 25.
peacekeeping	maintaining a truce between hostile forces in a foreign country	Canadian soldiers were among the United Nations peacekeeping troops sent to Afghanistan in 2002.
permafrost	areas of permanently frozen ground in climates close to the North and South Poles	Large areas of northern Canada have permafrost, resulting in many wetlands, since water cannot drain through the soil.

Key Term	Definition	Example/Explanation
physical geography	the distribution of natural features on the surface of the Earth	Physical geography examines landforms; oceans, lakes, and rivers; weather and climate; plants and animals; and natural resources.
plate tectonics	the study of plate movement to understand the formation of mountains, volcanoes, and earthquakes	When two of Earth's plates move together, the section of the Earth's crust between them gets squeezed together and becomes shorter, forming fold mountains. For an example, see page 24.
plateau	an area of elevated land that is mainly level	Lava flows have built up a large plateau in the interior of British Columbia.
podzol	the type of soil under areas covered by (or once covered by) trees	Forests once covered southern Ontario; therefore, podzol soil is found in this region.
pollution	wastes that are put into the environment	Toxic wastes, such as mining tailings, are a serious pollution problem.
population density	a nation's area in square kilometres divided by its population	Canada has a low population density because of its large size and relatively small population.
population pyramid	a horizontal bar graph that illustrates the age distribution of a country's population	For the population pyramid of Canada's population, see page 95.
precipitation	the various forms by which moisture in the atmosphere reaches the Earth's surface	Rain, freezing rain, snow, sleet, and hail are all examples of precipitation.
primary industry	an industry producing the raw materials that are eventually processed or manufactured into finished products	Oil, forestry, and agriculture are all primary industries.
primary source	information from a person who originates that information	Field research, surveys, interviews, and photographs are all primary sources.
producer	in the food chain, a green plant that makes its own food—in the form of plant sugar—through photosynthesis	Producers are at the base of the food chain because most other living things eat either the producers or another creature that did. Examples include grasses, vegetables, and trees.
pull factors	the factors that attract, or pull, immigrants to move to a country or region	Job opportunities are a major pull factor to Vancouver.
quaternary industry	high-technology sector of the economy	Computer-software development is part of the quaternary industry.
ratio scale	a map scale that uses a number ratio to compare map measurement to actual distance on the Earth	A ratio scale of 1:100 000 means that 1 cm on the map represents 1 km on the Earth.
refugee	a person fleeing to another country to escape a dangerous situation	Many refugees fleeing to Canada would be in danger for their lives if they were to remain in their home country.
region	an area of the Earth's surface that has certain characteristics that set it apart from other areas	The Prairie region is an area that covers southern Alberta, Saskatchewan, and Manitoba. It is fairly flat, with a dry climate and few trees.

Key Term	Definition	Example/Explanation
regional mall	a large indoor collection of stores that sell a wide variety of goods and serve a very large area	The West Edmonton Mall is a regional mall.
relief profile	a side view or cross-section of the land, showing its height	The process for creating a relief profile across Quebec and Labrador can be found on page 27.
remote sensing	technologies that allow satellites to take photographs of the Earth's surface	An image taken using remote sensing can be seen on page 254.
renewable energy	an energy supply that can replace itself fairly quickly	Wood is a renewable energy supply because trees can reproduce themselves in about 20 to 50 years through natural regeneration.
reserve	an area of land owned and controlled by an Aboriginal people	The Six Nations Reserve near Brantford, Ontario, is one of the richest reserves in Canada.
retail sector	businesses that sell consumers a wide variety of goods	Shopping at a store, on the Internet, and over the phone are all examples of people participating in the retail sector.
ribbon development	rows of stores side by side on a main street	Ribbon developments often appear in the older sections of major Canadian cities and along the original main street in small towns. For a photograph, see page 191.
road distance	the actual distance by road between two places	Curves and hills make actual road distances across the Rocky Mountains longer than the distance a plane would travel between the two places.
rural	an area that does not include settlements of 1000 people or more	Prince Edward County, on the shores of eastern Lake Ontario, is largely rural.
rural–urban fringe	the zone where the city and the surrounding countryside meet	Many major Canadian cities have a rural–urban fringe, where old farms await development and new subdivisions emerge.
satellite	a device in orbit around the Earth	Canadians watch television signals sent by satellite every day.
satellite image	a picture taken from space, using reflected light; many images are colourized to help identify features	Satellite images can be used for many purposes, including the location of forest fires in remote sections of Canada's wilderness. For an example, see page 50.
scale	a comparison of measurement on a map to the actual distance on the Earth's surface	A scale of 1 cm: 5 km means that 1 cm on the map represents 5 km of distance on the ground.
secondary industry	an industry that takes raw materials and changes them into things that we can use	A refinery that processes crude oil into gasoline and diesel fuel is an example of a secondary industry.
secondary source	a summary of primary information	Articles, encyclopedias, video documentaries, and a wide variety of maps are all secondary sources.

Key Term	Definition	Example/Explanation
selective cutting	forest logging in which only identified, mature trees are cut	Many forestry companies in Canada today use selective cutting because this method allows partially grown trees to survive until they mature and does not ruin the habitat of animals.
semi-finished product	a partially manufactured product that is not yet ready for sale to consumers; most are further processed into other products	Steel companies supply semi-finished sheets of steel to companies for manufacturing into finished refrigerators.
settlement pattern	the arrangement of farms and farmhouses in a region	Quebec's settlement pattern features long, narrow farm lots running perpendicular to a river or a road.
shortwave radiation	solar radiation that travels to the Earth in short wavelengths	Shortwave radiation carries both light and heat from the sun, making life on the Earth possible.
small-scale map	a "big-picture" map that shows a large part of the Earth in broad detail	A small-scale map of North America shows the Great Lakes but not small lakes (see page 18).
smog	air pollution caused by the mixture of industrial and automotive smoke with fog or humidity in the atmosphere	Smog has become very common in the heavily populated and industrialized regions of southern Ontario and Quebec. For a photograph, see page 259.
softwood	fast-growing, coniferous trees that produce soft (not dense) wood, often used to make the framing for houses and roofing shingles	Cedar is a softwood used to make roofing shingles for houses.
soil profile	a side view, or cross-section, of soil layers, from the surface down to the rock or gravel material below	Trees that have large, deep root systems are found only where the soil profile is at least a metre or two deep. For an example, see page 58.
specialist parts supplier	a manufacturer that specializes in producing one type of component for an industry	Specialist parts suppliers make wheels for automobile manufacturers.
sports tourism	tourism that allows people to participate in sports (such as skiing) or to watch sports (such as professional basketball)	Some people enjoy sports tourism vacations, such as rock climbing in British Columbia.
standard of living	the level of material wealth; a measure of people's access to goods and services	Canadians have access to education, health care, and social services, giving them one of the highest standards of living in the world.
storm surge	a higher than normal push of ocean water against a shore, driven by high winds	In January 2000, a storm surge along the coast of Prince Edward Island caused flooding in Charlottetown.
strassendorf	a "street village" where the houses are all built along one main street	Only a few villages in Canada are true *strassendorfs*. See a photograph of Neubergthal on page 123.
strip mall	a planned neighbourhood plaza, usually with free parking	Convenience stores are common in strip malls. For a photograph, see page 191.

Key Term	Definition	Example/Explanation
suburban	generally newer areas found around the fringes of established cities	Many people live in suburban areas surrounding Ottawa and commute to work in the city.
sustainable	a system, such as farming or tourism, that can flourish into the future without harming the environment	In order to make them sustainable, many US national parks have limited the number of tourists that can visit every year.
sustainable management	an approach that ensures a renewable resource is replaced as quickly as it is used up	A forest is sustainably managed if, for every one chopped down, one tree is planted and grown to maturity.
tailings	rock, waste, and chemicals left over from the mining and processing of ore	Tailings can be found as small, unnatural hills at many Canadian mines. See page 254 for an example of a tailings pond.
tariff	a tax on imported goods	If you buy a television manufactured in Thailand, included in the sale price is a tariff that goes to the federal government.
telecommunications	sending messages over long distances	Bell Canada is in the telecommunications business.
tertiary industry	businesses in retail trade, services, and government	A downhill ski instructor works in a tertiary industry—tourism and recreation.
time zone	a part of the world in which every location sets its clocks to the same time	Barrie, Ontario, is in the Eastern time zone, which is three hours ahead of Vancouver, BC, which is in the Pacific time zone.
topographic map	a detailed, large-scale map that shows both physical and human features	The topographic map on page 46 shows flat land and many oil wells.
tourism industry	the businesses that cater to tourists by providing travel, lodging, and entertainment services	Canada's tourism industry is seasonal because people who visit in the summer and those who visit in winter expect different types of vacations.
tourist	a person who visits a region or country for more than 24 hours but less than one year	Many tourists from Japan spend about one week in Canada.
town	a community of more than 1000 and less than 10 000	Springford, Ontario, is a town in Norwich County.
township	an area of land divided up in a grid	All of southern Ontario is divided into townships. Norwich Township lies just outside London, Ontario. For an example, see page 122.
trade balance	the difference between what a country imports and what it exports	Canada had a positive trade balance in 2001 of $64 billion, meaning that, overall, it exported more than it imported.
trade deficit	the situation that occurs when a country imports more than it exports	In 2001, Canada had a trade deficit of $1.1 billion with Japan, meaning that it exported less than it imported.
trade surplus	the situation that occurs when a country exports more goods than it imports	In 2001, Canada had a trade surplus with the United States of almost $96 billion, meaning that it exported more than it imported.

Key Term	Definition	Example/Explanation
transition zone	an area between two different regions, in which the characteristics of one region gradually blend into those of the other	The taiga region of the Northwest Territories is a transition zone between the coniferous forests to the south and the tundra to the north.
urban	areas including cities or towns that have more than 1000 people	Most Canadians live in urban centres. Sudbury, for example, is urban.
urban hierarchy	a ranking of communities from largest to smallest	Cities such as Halifax, Nova Scotia, are near the top of the urban hierarchy.
urban sprawl	urban growth that happens quickly and is sometimes out of control	A lot of urban sprawl surrounds Calgary, Alberta.
urbanization	a process by which so many people move into rural areas close to existing cities that these areas become urban	Urbanization has transformed the area of Richmond Hill from a largely rural area to a largely urban area.
Venn diagram	a graphic with two or more intersecting circles to show how certain factors overlap	See page 253 for an example of a Venn diagram.
village	a small settlement of about 200 to 800 people	Many Canadians have left villages to move to cities. For map of a typical village, see page 134.
visible minority	people who look different from the majority of the population because of their physical characteristics	Asians are a visible minority in Canada.
weather	the daily conditions of temperature, precipitation, wind, humidity, and cloud in the atmosphere	Blizzards and heat waves are unusual examples of weather.
wetland	an area of swamp, marsh, or bog; these usually exist in low-lying locations, which collect plenty of water	The Holland Marsh, north of Toronto, is a wetland area that has been drained for agriculture.
zoning by-law	a law that controls where, how much, or what kind of development takes place	Zoning by-laws help keep noisy factories away from housing.

Index

Photo Credits

t=top; b=bottom; c=centre; l=left; r=right

2 PhotoDisc; **6 r** PhotoDisc, **l** Eyewire; **20** Al Harvey/The Slide Farm; **21 l** S. Irwin/Natural Resources Canada, **c** CORBIS Royalty Free/MAGMA, **r** Courtesy of Dennis DesRivieres; **28 both** Al Harvey/The Slide Farm; **30 l** PhotoDisc, **r** Eyewire; **31** CP/Ottawa Citizen/Paul Latour; **38 l** Al Harvey/The Slide Farm, **r** © Johan Adlercreutz/Viewpoints West Photofile Ltd.; **39** Al Harvey/The Slide Farm; **42** Ron Layton Photography; **45** Ron Garnett/AirScapes; **50 l** Gunter Marx Photography/CORBIS/MAGMA, **r** Spatial Mapping Ltd., Victoria, BC; **52** Victor Last/Geographical Visual Aids; **54 t** © Mark & Leslie Degner, **c** Stephen J. Krasemann/Valan Photos, **b** © Kennan Ward/CORBIS/MAGMA; **56** © James L. Amos/CORBIS/MAGMA; **57** © Gunter Marx Photography/CORBIS/MAGMA; **58** © Barrett & MacKay Photography Inc.; **62** Photographer: Phil Kor, Ministry of Natural Resources, Taken at Queen Elizabeth The Queen Mother M'Nidoo M'Nissing Provincial Park, Belanger Bay/Manitoulin Island; **63** Courtesy of Dennis DesRivieres; **64** © Bev McMullen/Lone Pine Photo; **69** Ivy Images; **73** © Dan Guravich/CORBIS/MAGMA; **74 t** National Archives of Canada/C-093017, **b** Daphne Odjig, "Meares Island," 1985, acrylic on canvas, 166.3 × 121.8 cm; **75 t** "Laurentian Hills" by Jacques de Tonnancour, Gallery Lambton, Sarnia, Ontario, **b** "Spring, Lower Canada (Maples, Early Spring)" by AY Jackson, Gallery Lambton, Sarnia, Ontario, Permission granted by the Estate of AY Jackson; **78** Al Harvey/The Slide Farm; **80** Courtesy of Ida Karelsen, Photo: Dennis DesRivieres; **82** CORBIS Royalty Free/MAGMA; **84** © Barrett & MacKay Photography Inc.; **86** Ron Garnett/AirScapes; **87 l and c** PhotoDisc, **r** Courtesy of Jaro Legat, Photo: Rob Harshman; **88** CP/Toronto Star/Vince Talotta; **89 l** Dick Hemingway, **r** CP/Kevin Frayer; **96** PhotoDisc; **99 l** Eyewire, **tr** Karen Beard/Stone/Getty Images, **br** CP/Toronto Sun/Mark O'Neill; **104** Al Harvey/The Slide Farm; **107 t** Al Harvey/The Slide Farm, **b** C.I.S./Ivy Images; **110** CP/Toronto Star/Boris Spremo; **112** © Canadian Museum of Civilization from *Canada's Visual History*, Quebec Prehistory, volume 79, image # 24; **113** Eyewire; **115** Halle Flygare/Valan Photos; **116** Ivy Images; **118** Jean du Boisberranger/The Image Bank/Getty Images; **119** Dick Hemingway; **120** William Lowry/Ivy Images; **123** © Robert Tinker 2000; **124 l** © Barrett & MacKay Photography Inc., **r** Dick Hemingway; **128** Victor Last/Geographical Visual Aids; **131** Theo Moudakis/Toronto Star Syndicate; **132** Glenbow Archives, Calgary, Alberta/NC-32-3; **137 l** Victor Last/Geographical Visual Aids, **r** Ron Garnett/AirScapes; **138** Ian Biggar/Take Stock Inc.; **139** Ron Garnett/AirScapes; **140** Andy Caulfield/The Image Bank/Getty Images; **143** Andrew Palamarchuk/Scarborough Mirror; **145** Fred Charles/The Image Bank/Getty Images; **146** Courtesy of Jaro Legat, Photo: Rob Harshman; **148** CP/Toronto Star/Tony Bock; **150** CP/Fred Chartrand; **152** D. Johnston/Ivy Images; **153 l** Courtesy of UBE Automotive, **c** Courtesy of Dan and Karen Rasmussen, Rasmussen Log Homes, British Columbia, Canada, **r** Courtesy of Sean Severin, Photo: Rob Harshman; **154** Rick Souders/Foodpix/Getty Images; **155 a)** B & C Alexander/firstlight.ca, **b)** © Paul A. Souders/CORBIS/MAGMA, **c)** © Barrett & MacKay Photography Inc., **d)** © Paul A. Souders/CORBIS/MAGMA; **157** CP/L'Acadie Nouvelle/Sylvie Pauline; **158-159** Victor Last/Geographical Visual Aids; **162** Eyewire; **163** © Paul A. Souders/CORBIS/MAGMA; **167 l** © Brian Stablyk/Take Stock Inc., **r** © Paul A. Souders/CORBIS/MAGMA; **170** Courtesy of Rob DesRivieres; **173** CP/Frank Gunn; **177 l** © Paul A. Souders/CORBIS/MAGMA, **r** © AFP/CORBIS/MAGMA; **180** Courtesy of UBE Automotive; **182** Courtesy of Pilkington Glass; **184** Courtesy of Dan and Karen Rasmussen, Rasmussen Log Homes, British Columbia, Canada; **185 tl** Courtesy of Toyota Canada, **bl** © Keith Dannemiller/CORBIS SABA/MAGMA, **br** © Charles O'Rear/CORBIS/MAGMA; **187** Victor Last/Geographical Visual Aids; **189** © Clarence W. Norris/Lone Pine Photo; **191 l** Peter Saunders/Mach 2 Stock Photography Ltd., **r** Dick Hemingway; **192** Ron Garnett/AirScapes; **193** Clarence W. Norris/Lone Pine Photo; **196** Victor Last/Geographical Visual Aids; **199** Courtesy of Sean Severin, Photo: Rob Harshman; **201** PhotoDisc; **202** CP/The Globe & Mail/Fred Lum; **206** CP/Ryan Remiorz; **207** CP/Toronto Sun/David Lucas; **209** Canadian Space Agency; **214** Courtesy of Dina DellaSiepe; **216** Courtesy of Bernie Brocklehurst, EBTech, Sarnia, Ontario; **219** William Lowry/Ivy Images; **220** Ron Garnett/AirScapes; **221 l** Eyewire, **c** STS 098-715B-84, Earth Sciences and Image Analysis Laboratory, Johnson Space Center, NASA, **r** PhotoDisc; **222** Dick Hemingway; **223** © Paul A. Souders/CORBIS/MAGMA; **231 a)** V. Wilkinson/Valan Photos, **b)** CP/Jeff McIntosh, **c)** Stephen J. Krasemann/Valan Photos, **d)** © Ballard/Spence/Visuals Unlimited; **235** Courtesy of Pauline Chan; **237** CP/Frank Gunn;

Text and Figure Credits

Every possible effort has been made to trace the original source of the text material contained in this book. Where the attempt has been unsuccessful, the publisher would be pleased to hear from the copyright holders to rectify any omissions.

t=top; b=bottom; c=centre; l=left; r=right

8 *Southwestern Ontario Map Guide*, 1991/92 ed., MapArt Corp., p.57; **10-11** *Ontario: Official Road Map, 2001*, Ontario Ministry of Transportation, © 2001 Queen's Printer for Ontario; **13** *Map of London, Ontario*, Copyright Mapmedia Corp. 2003 Edition, Published by Peter Heiler Ltd.; **18** *Canadian Oxford School Atlas* 8/e, 2003, p.59, © Oxford University Press; **25 t** Sourced from Ron Chasmer, *Earth Matters: Studies in Physical Geography* (Toronto: Oxford University Press, 2001), p.69; **34** Environment Canada Web, http://www.msc-smc.ec.gc.ca/climate, May 2002; **39 l** Adapted from Dennis DesRivieres et al: *The Land: Canada's Physical Diversity*, Toronto: Prentice-Hall, 1996, p.12, reprinted with permission by Pearson Education Canada; **40** *Ontario: Official Road Map*, 2001, Ontario Ministry of Transportation, © 2001 Queen's Printer for Ontario; **43** Adapted from Dennis DesRivieres et al: *The Land: Canada's Physical Diversity*, Toronto: Prentice-Hall, 1996, p.12, reprinted with permission by Pearson Education Canada; **46** © Produced under licence from Her Majesty the Queen in Right of Canada, with permission of Natural Resources Canada; **49 both** Adapted from Dennis DesRivieres et al: *The Land: Canada's Physical Diversity*, Toronto: Prentice-Hall, 1996, p.13, reprinted with permission by Pearson Education Canada; **63** Adapted from Federation of Ontario Naturalists: *Great Lakes Alvars*, Toronto; **67** Adapted from Brian Byrne: *Saving the Countryside: Conserving Rural Character in the Countryside of Southern Ontario*, Toronto: Conservation Council of Ontario, p.17; **73** © Produced under licence from Her Majesty the Queen in Right of Canada, with permission of Natural Resources Canada; **74-75** Sourced from Quentin H. Stanford, *Canadian Oxford School Atlas*, 7th ed. (Toronto: Oxford University Press, 1998), p.17 and Canadian Council on Ecological Areas, http://www.ccea.org; **76-77** Environment Canada, Canadian Council on Ecological Areas, http://www.ccea.org/ecozones/index.html; **83** *Ontario: Official Road Map*, 2001, Ontario Ministry of Transportation, © 2001 Queen's Printer for Ontario; **85** Copyright © 1995 Her Majesty the Queen in Right of Canada. Department of Energy, Mines and Resources; **91** Data from Statistics Canada, Census of Canada, 2001; **92** Statistics Canada, Population by provinces and territories, http://www.statcan.ca/English/Pgdb/People/Population/demo02.htm; **93** Statistics Canada, Census of Canada, 2001; **94** Statistics Canada, http://www.statcan.ca/English/Pgdb/People/Population/demo03.htm, http://www.statcan.ca/English/Pgdb/People/Population/demo23a.htm, http://www.statcan.ca/English/Pgdb/People/Population/demo23c.htm; **95** Statistics Canada, http://www.statcan.ca/English/Pgdb/People/Population/demo31b.htm; **96** Statistics Canada, http://www.statcan.ca/English/Pgdb/People/Population/demo23c.htm; **97** Statistics Canada, CANSIM II, table 051-0001, http://www.statcan.ca/English/Pgdb/People/Population/Page.cfm; **98** Statistics Canada, *Census of Canada 2001*, Catalogue no. 97F0011XCB01003; **99** Statistics Canada, CANSIM II, table 051-0004; **100** Statistics Canada, *Census of Canada 2001*, Catalogue 97F0008XCB01002; **105 tr** Statistics Canada, Census of Canada 2001, Catalogue no. 97F00010XCB01001, **bl** Data from Statistics Canada, Census of Canada, 2001; **106 t** Statistics Canada, Visible minority population, *1996 Census*, census metropolitan areas, http://www.statcan.ca/English/Pgdb/People/Population/demo08.htm; **106 b** Statistics Canada, Population by mother tongue, 2001 Census, Catalogue 97F0007XCB1001; **109** *Toronto*, 2002, © MapArt Corp.; **114** www.ouje.ca; **125** Statistics Canada, Series A67-69; *1996 Census of Population, A National Overview* (Catalogue 93-357-XPB), Statistics Canada, *Population Counts for Canada*, Census Divisions by Urban and Rural, 2001 Census.; **127** Adapted from *Canadian Geographic*, November/December 2001, pp.50-51, Sources: Geological Survey of Canada, Ontario Ministry of Natural Resources; **136** Statistics Canada, CANSIM II, table 051-0014, cat. No. 91-213-XIB, http://statcan.ca/English/Pgdb/People/Population/deom05.htm; **149 both** Statistics Canada, 2001 Census; **150-151** Reprinted with permission—*Torstar Syndication Services*. From an article originally appearing in the *Toronto Star*, March 2002; **156** Data from Statistics Canada, http://www.statcan.ca/english/Pgdb/Economy/Primary/prim45.htm; **163** Data from Statistics Canada, http://www.statcan.ca/english/Pgdb/Economy/Primary/prim03.htm; **173** Statistics Canada, CANSIM II, tables 281-0001, 281-0005 and 281-0006 and Catalogue no. 72-002-XPB,

http://www.statcan.ca/English/Pgdb/Economy/Manufacturing/manuf17b.htm; **174** Statistics Canada, CANSIM II, tables 228-0001, 228-0002 and 228-0003, http://www.statcan.ca/English/Pgdb/Economy/International/gblec04.htm; **188** Statistics Canada, CANSIM II, table 282-0008, http://www.statcan.ca/English/Pgdb/labour10a.htm; **190** Sourced from http://www.timhortons.com; **197** Statistics Canada, "Employment in the trade, transportation, storage, communications and other utilities industries," CANSIM II, tables 281-0001 and 281-0005, Catalogue No. 72-002-XPB, http://www.statcan.ca/English/Pgdb/trade03.htm; **198** Data from Canadian Urban Transit Association, http://www.cutaactu.on.ca; **210** www.google.ca, reprinted with permission of www.google.com; **211** Canadian Space Agency; **230** Adapted from Dennis DesRivieres et al: *The Land: Canada's Physical Diversity*, Toronto: Prentice-Hall, 1996, p.36, reprinted with permission by Pearson Education Canada; **238** Reprinted with permission of The Associated Press; **240** Adapted from Natural Resources Canada, http://adaptation.nrcan.ca/posters, *Atlantic Climate Change* poster; **242 both** Adapted from: Bruce Clark and John Wallace: *Making Connections*, Pearson Education Canada, p.458, reprinted with permission by Pearson Education Canada; **243** Adapted from Natural Resources Canada, http://adaptation.nrcan.ca/posters, *Atlantic Climate Change* poster; **245 r** Adapted from Natural Resources Canada, http://adaptation.nrcan.ca/posters, *Atlantic Climate Change* poster; **247** Canadian Press News Ltd., December 4, 2002; **249** *Maclean's*, 12 August 2002, p.17; **261** Sourced from Environment Canada, *Acid Rain: The Effects of Acid Rain*, http://www.msc.ec.gc.ca; **267** *US News & World Report*, 25 September 2000, Vol. 129, Issue 12, Energy Information Administration; **269 both** *Living Planet Report 2002*. Reproduced with permission from WWF. © 2003 WWF—World Wide Fund For Nature (Formerly World Wildlife Fund). All rights reserved;

288 Statistics Canada, Top 15 countries of origin for visitors to Canada, 2000, http://www.statcan.ca/English/Pgdb/arts37b.htm; **289** Statistics Canada, Canadian Tourism Facts and Figures, Brochure downloaded in PDF from The Canadian Tourism Commission web site, http://www.canadatourism.com; **290** Statistics Canada, International Survey, found at The Canadian Tourism Commission web site, http://www.canadatourism.com; **293** Statistics Canada, Top 15 countries visited by Canadians, 2000, http://www.statcan.ca/English/Pgdb/arts37a.htm; **306** Adapted from *Canadian Oxford School Atlas 6/e*, 1992, p.140, © Oxford University Press; **309** Data from Geography IQ, http://www.geographyiq.com; **314** http://www.netcorps-cyberjeunes.org/English/stories/tardif_e.html; **317** Data from Commonwealth Institute, http://www.commonwealth.org.uk; **318** Statistics Canada, CANSIM II, tables 228-0001, 228-0002, and 228-0003, http://www.statcan.ca/English/Pgdb/gblec02a.htm; **319** Statistics Canada, CANSIM II, tables 228-0001, 228-0002, and 228-0003, http://www.statcan.ca/English/Pgdb/gblec02a.htm; **320** http://www.freetradeat10.com/trade.html, http://www.census.gov/foreign-trade/balance/c005.html, http://www.bts.gov/publications/nattt/figures/figure_1.html; **337** Copyright © ESRI ArcView GIS 3.2

Maps on the following pages referenced Quentin H. Stanford, *Canadian Oxford Student Atlas*, 7th ed. (Toronto: Oxford University Press, 1998): 24, 26, 33, 37, 42, 44, 56 r, 59, 60, 70, 74-75, 79, 166, 228, 303.

Statistics Canada information is used with the permission of Statistics Canada. Users are forbidden to copy the data and redisseminate them, in an original or modified form, for commercial purposes, without the expressed permission of Statistics Canada. Information on the availability of the wide range of data from Statistics Canada can be obtained from Statistics Canada's Regional Offices, its World Wide Web site at http://www.statcan.ca, and its toll-free access number 1-800-263-1136.